THE

Goo
Gu

THE

Good Food Guide 1996

Edited by Jim Ainsworth

Which? Limited

Which? Books are commissioned and researched by
Consumers' Association and published by
Which? Ltd,
2 Marylebone Road, London NW1 4DF

Cover photograph by Johanna Fernihough
Cover design by Paul Saunders
Typographic design by Tim Higgins
Base mapping © Map Marketing Ltd/
European Map Graphics 1995
Map information © Which? Ltd 1995

British Library Cataloguing in Publication Data
A catalogue record for this book is available
from the British Library

ISBN 0 85202 585 8

Photoset in Linotron Meridien Medium
by Tradespools Ltd, Frome, Somerset
Printed and bound in the Netherlands
by Rotatie Boekendruk B.V., Krommenie

Distributed by The Penguin Group:
Penguin Books Ltd, 27 Wrights Lane,
London W8 5TZ

Contents

Features:

Main entries:

Lists, index, report forms and maps:

To all readers

The Good Food Guide is your guide. It is independent, takes no free meals, inducements or advertising, and reflects the experience of thousands of consumers in restaurants throughout the land. It is not a self-appointed arbiter of hide-bound gastronomic taste. It reports on real experiences by real people in search of nourishment, pleasure or celebration.

As a purchaser of this *Guide,* you are part of a huge network of correspondents, and you are a member of the Good Food Club. Please help other readers by recounting your own experiences to us.

There is a form at the back of this book (just before the maps); you can ask for more report forms from the *Guide* office; the address is FREEPOST, so you do not have to use a stamp. Or if you are on the Internet, send your report by electronic mail to: *guide-reports@which.co.uk*. Every letter or e-mail received is one more brick in the edifice of next year's *Guide.*

A service to keep readers up to date

From December 1995 readers with a touch-tone telephone will be able to use a 24-hour information service giving details of restaurant sales, closures, chef changes and so on, since this edition of *The Good Food Guide* was published. Telephone 0171-830 7575 to hear the latest information, or to leave a message.

How to use this *Guide*

All the entries in this year's *Guide* have been rewritten between April and July 1995. The information on which they are based is from reports sent in by readers over the past year and confirmed where necessary by anonymous inspection. No entry is based on a single nomination. In every case, readers and inspectors have been prepared to endorse the quality of the cooking, the dining-room and the value for money.

The rating system grades restaurants, on the basis of their cooking, from 1 to 5. Grading is not based on elegance, ambience, service and value but on food and cooking. The marks reflect the perception of the *Guide* and its reporters, and signify the following:

1 **Competent cooking** Restaurants that achieve a satisfactory standard, endorsed by readers as worthy of the *Guide*.

2 **Good cooking** Restaurants that produce good food in most departments, though some inconsistencies may have been noted. They please most readers much of the time.

3 **Very good cooking** The kitchen achieves consistent quality, rarely disappointing in any department. Seldom faulted by *Guide* reporters.

4 **Excellent cooking** Restaurants with a high level of ambition and achievement. Generally, they delight.

5 **The best** These may excite debate, not as to whether the cooking is good, but whether it is better than their peers'.

* An asterisk next to a mark signifies that the *Guide* and its readers are of the opinion that the restaurant is a particularly fine example within its numeric classification.

The *Guide* office is reliant on proprietors for price information. Each year owners are asked to mark on a questionnaire the cost, for autumn of that year, of any set meals, and also the lowest and highest à la carte prices for each course. We then calculate the lowest and highest prices for a three-course meal per person, including the cost of coffee, service and half a bottle of house wine (or corkage in the case of unlicensed establishments where you can 'bring your own'). The lowest price forms the first figure that you see in the cost line above an entry. In practice, some people may have drinks before the meal and drink a more expensive wine; also, prices are likely to rise during the currency of the *Guide*. To reflect this, the second price in the cost line is the highest price we have calculated for a three-course meal (sometimes four or five courses if it is a set meal) inflated by 20 per cent to bring some realism to bear on the likely upper limit. In essence, the cost line shows the least and the most you are likely to pay, with most meals falling somewhere in-between.

How to read a *Guide* entry

CANTERBURY Kent [1] map 3 [2]

▲ *Mary's Kitchen* [3] 🍷 🍾 [4] [chef's hat] [5] [symbol] [6] £ [7] **NEW ENTRY** [8]

16 Elwood Avenue, Canterbury CT41 4RX [9]
TEL: (01227) 770666 FAX: (01227) 770555 [10] COOKING 2* [12]
on B2068, 2m S of Canterbury [11] COST £19–£24 [13]

(main text) [14] CELLARMAN'S CHOICE [15]

CHEF: Mary Smith PROPRIETORS: Mary and David Smith [16] OPEN: Mon to Sat L12 to 2, Tue to Sun D 7 to 9 [17] CLOSED: Aug [18] MEALS: alc (main courses £6 to £12). Set L £12, Set D £15 (2 courses) to £25. Cover £1. Minimum £5 L [19] Unlicensed, but bring your own: corkage £1 [20] SERVICE: net prices, card slips closed [21] CARDS: Access, Amex, Delta, Diners, Switch, Visa [22] DETAILS: 72 seats. 4 tables outside. Private parties: 26 main room, 10 private room. [23] Car park. Vegetarian meals. [24] Children's helpings. No children under 10. [25] Jacket and tie. [26] No smoking in dining-room. [27] Wheelchair access (2 steps; also WC). [28] No music. [29] Air-conditioned ACCOMMODATION: 14 rooms, all with bath/shower. TV. Phone. Air-conditioned. B&B £20 to £40. [30] Deposit: £50. [31] Rooms for disabled. [32] Children welcome. [33] Baby facilities. [34] Pets welcome. [35] Afternoon teas. [36] Garden. Swimming-pool. [37] (*The Which? Hotel Guide*) [38]

1 The town and county. The *Guide*'s main entries are divided into eight sections: London, England, Scotland, Wales, Isle of Man, Channel Islands, Northern Ireland and Republic of Ireland. In the London section, restaurants are listed alphabetically by name; in all other sections, they are listed under town. The maps (at the back of the book) can be used as a starting point to locate areas of interest; then look up the entries under the town name. The London maps locate restaurants by name.

2 The map number. The maps are at the end of the *Guide*.

3 The name of the restaurant. ▲ in front of the name denotes that it offers accommodation too.

4 🍷 denotes a wine list that is good, well above the ordinary. The symbol 🍾 indicates a truly outstanding wine list.

5 [chef's hat] indicates that the chef has changed since last year's entry. It does not apply to every minor change or promotion, and is used with discretion – i.e. only in cases where the change of chef seems to have made a significant

difference, and where we have either inspected the new regime or have received enough reports to award a cooking score.

6 ✱ indicates that smoking (cigarettes, pipes and cigars) is either banned altogether or that one dining-room is maintained for non-smokers. The symbol does not appear if a restaurant simply has a no-smoking area, or bans smoking at one mealtime only, although these features will be mentioned in the details at the end of an entry. Establishments that do not allow smoking in a dining-room may allow it elsewhere on the premises, such as in the bar or lounge. If you are a smoker, it is always worth checking beforehand.

7 £ indicates that it is possible to have a three-course meal, including coffee, a half-bottle of house wine and service, at *any* time the restaurant is open (i.e. at dinner as well as at lunch, unless a place is only open for dinner), for £20 or less per person. Meals may often cost much more than this, but, by choosing carefully, you should find £20 achievable.

8 If a restaurant is new to the *Guide* this year (it did not appear as a main entry in the last edition), NEW ENTRY appears opposite its name.

9 The restaurant's address and post code.

10 The restaurant's telephone number and, if it has one, fax number, including STD codes.

11 Any special directions in case the restaurant is difficult to find.

12 The *Guide*'s mark, out of five, for cooking quality, ranging from 1 for competent cooking to 5 for the best. See page 7 or the inside front cover for a full explanation. NEW CHEF is indicated instead of a cooking mark for restaurants which had a change of chef as we went to press. These are not the only places (listed) that have new chefs, but are those where the change was too late for our inspection. (See also point 5.)

13 This is the price range for three-course meals (lunch and/or dinner) for one person, including coffee, wine (or corkage in the case of 'bring-your-own') and service, according to minimum and maximum prices provided by the proprietor for set meals and à la carte dishes. The first figure shows what is probably the least you would have to pay for a three-course meal (often at lunch only), while the second figure indicates a likely maximum amount (sometimes for a set meal of more than three courses). The second figure has been inflated by 20 per cent to reflect (i) that some readers will order extra drinks and some top-range dishes, and (ii) likely price rises that will come into play during the life of the *Guide*.

14 The text is based on reports sent in by readers during the last *Guide* year, confirmed where necessary by commissioned, anonymous inspections.

15 Some entries conclude with a CELLARMAN'S CHOICE. These are wines, usually more expensive than the house wine, that the restaurant assures us will be in stock during 1996, and recommends as suitable for the kind of food served.

16 The names of the chef(s) and owner(s).

17 The days of the week the restaurant is open, and the times of first and last orders for meals. It is always advisable to book before going to a restaurant. If you book and then cannot go, please remember to telephone the restaurant to cancel.

18 Annual closures.

19 The types of meals that are available, with any variations for lunch (L) or dinner (D). The letters alc denote an à la carte menu. This is followed by a range of main course prices (rounded up to the nearest 50p). Set L and/or Set D denote set lunches and set dinners, and include the basic charge for those meals. Set meals consist usually of three courses, but can cover anything from two to seven courses. If a set meal has only two courses, this is stated. Coffee is often included in set meals, wine very occasionally. The meal information will be followed by details of any cover charge and minimum charge. (Note that set meals or special menus may not be available at all times – it is always best to check.)

20 A restaurant is unlicensed but customers may bring their own alcoholic drinks on to the premises. Any corkage charge is indicated.

21 The restaurant's policy on service charges. Net prices indicates that prices of dishes and wine include service, and this fact is clearly stated on menu and bill; not inc, that service is not included and is left up to the discretion of the customer; 10%, that there is a fixed service charge of 10 per cent automatically added to the bill; 10% (optional), that 10 per cent is automatically added to the bill along with the word 'optional'; and none, that no service charge is made or expected and that money offered is refused. Card slips closed indicates that the total on the slips of credit cards is closed when handed over for signature.

22 The credit cards accepted by the restaurant. If no cards are accepted we state none.

23 Not all restaurants will take private parties. The maximum number of people in a party is given for both main and private rooms.

24 The restaurant has its own car park. Vegetarian meals means that the establishment always lists on the menu at least one vegetarian dish as a first course and one as a main course. Many restaurants which do not have non-meat or non-fish options on their menus may be able to provide a vegetarian meal with prior notice: best to phone ahead and check.

25 Some restaurants, pubs and hotels are not keen on children in the dining-room. Where it says children welcome, this indicates that they don't mind, although children must be well behaved. Any limitations on age are specified. Children's helpings means that smaller portions at a reduced price are available for children.

26 Jackets and ties are compulsory in very few restaurants and this is specified; otherwise, it is indicated if smart dress is preferred.

27 Any no-smoking arrangements as given to us by the restaurants. See also point 6.

28 Wheelchair access means that the proprietor has confirmed that the entrance is at least 80cm wide and passages at least 120cm across – The Royal Association for Disability and Rehabilitation (RADAR) recommendations. This does not guarantee access to all areas of an establishment. Where there are steps, it will say so. If there are more than three steps, wheelchair access is not stated. If it says 'also WC', then the owner has told us that the toilet facilities are suitable for disabled people. The *Guide* relies on proprietors giving accurate information on wheelchair access. If you find the details in the *Guide* are inaccurate, please tell us. It is always important to ring first and inform the restaurant of any special requirements.

29 Dining-rooms where live or recorded music is never played. Where a restaurant has told us that music may be played, we indicate this.

30 Room details and the price for rooms and breakfast as given to us by hotels, rounded up to the nearest 50p. The first price is for one person in a single room or single occupancy of a double, the second is the upper price for two people in a double room or suite. When a price is for dinner, bed and breakfast, it is indicated as D,B&B.

31 The deposit required to secure accommodation. It may sometimes be expressed as a percentage.

32 The establishment has informed us it has bedrooms suitable for wheelchair users.

33 Children are welcome in the accommodation. Any age limitations are specified.

34 At least some facilities, such as cots and high chairs, are available for those guests with babies. It is important to inform the proprietors of any special requirements.

35 Pets are welcome in the hotel, although they may be restricted to certain rooms.

36 Teas are served to non-residents.

37 Other general details about the establishment.

38 (*The Which? Hotel Guide*) denotes that this establishment is also listed in the 1996 edition of our sister guide to over 1,000 hotels in Britain.

The top-rated restaurants

Mark 5 for cooking

London
Chez Nico at
Ninety Park Lane, W1
La Tante Claire, SW3

England
Le Manoir aux Quat'Saisons, Great Milton

Scotland
Altnaharrie Inn, Ullapool

Mark 4* for cooking

London
Le Gavroche, W1
Hyde Park Hotel,
The Restaurant, SW1

England
Gidleigh Park, Chagford
L'Ortolan, Shinfield
Waterside Inn, Bray
Winteringham Fields,
Winteringham

Mark 4 for cooking

London
Aubergine, SW10
The Capital, SW3
Connaught, W1
Interlude de Chavot, W1
Les Saveurs, W1
Turner's, SW3

England
Adlard's, Norwich
Carved Angel, Dartmouth
Castle Hotel, Taunton
Chester Grosvenor Hotel, Arkle,
Chester
Croque-en-Bouche, Malvern
Wells
Fischer's Baslow Hall, Baslow
Gordleton Mill Hotel, Provence,
Lymington
Hambleton Hall, Hambleton
Lettonie, Bristol
Mr Underhill's, Stonham
Paul Heathcote's, Longridge

Scotland
Airds Hotel, Port Appin
Braeval Old Mill, Aberfoyle
Kinnaird, Dunkeld
Peat Inn, Peat Inn
La Potinière, Gullane

Wales
Plas Bodegroes, Pwllheli
Walnut Tree Inn, Llandewi
Skirrid

Northern Ireland
Roscoff, Belfast

Restaurants with outstanding wine cellars

marked in the text with a 🍷

London
Au Jardin des Gourmets, W1
Bibendum, SW3
Clarke's, W8
Fifth Floor, SW1
Leith's, W11
Mijanou, SW1
Odette's, NW1
Le Pont de la Tour, SE1
RSJ, SE1

England
Adlard's, Norwich
Angel Inn, Hetton
Beetle & Wedge, Moulsford
Buckland Manor, Buckland
Carved Angel, Dartmouth
Cherwell Boathouse, Oxford
Chewton Glen, Marryat Restaurant, New Milton
Cobwebs, Leck
Corse Lawn House Hotel, Corse Lawn
Croque-en-Bouche, Malvern Wells
The Crown, Southwold
Epworth Tap, Epworth
Fountain House, Dedham
Fox and Goose, Fressingfield
French Partridge, Horton
George of Stamford, Stamford
Gidleigh Park, Chagford
Gravetye Manor, East Grinstead
Hambleton Hall, Hambleton
Harveys, Bristol
Hollington House, Woolton Hill
Hotel du Vin & Bistro, Winchester
Le Manoir aux Quat'Saisons, Great Milton
Markwicks, Bristol
Normandie, Birtle
Old Beams, Waterhouses
Old Manor House, Romsey
Old Vicarage, Ridgeway
Old Vicarage, Witherslack
Pheasants, Ross-on-Wye
Porthole Eating House, Bowness-on-Windermere
Priory Hotel, Wareham
Read's, Faversham
Riverside, Helford
Rösers, Hastings
Seafood Restaurant, Padstow
Sir Charles Napier, Chinnor
Sous le Nez en Ville, Leeds
Summer Lodge, Evershot
Le Talbooth, Dedham
Village Restaurant, Ramsbottom
White Horse Inn, Chilgrove
White House Hotel, Williton
White Moss House, Grasmere

Scotland
Airds Hotel, Port Appin
Altnaharrie Inn, Ullapool
Braeval Old Mill, Aberfoyle
Cellar, Anstruther
Champany Inn, Linlithgow
Clifton House, Nairn
The Cross, Kingussie
Inverlochy Castle, Fort William
Knipoch Hotel, Oban
Peat Inn, Peat Inn
La Potinière, Gullane
Summer Isles, Achiltibuie
Ubiquitous Chip Glasgow

Wales
Old Rectory, Llansanffraid Glan Conwy
Penhelig Arms Hotel, Aberdovey
Plas Bodegroes, Pwllheli
Walnut Tree Inn, Llandewi Skirrid

Restaurants of the year

This award does not necessarily go to the restaurants with the highest mark for cooking, but rather to ones which have shown particular merit or achievement during the year, whether as all-rounders or in some particular field. It may go to an old favourite or to a new entry, but in either case the places listed below are worth visiting in their own right, and have enhanced the eating-out experience in some way.

London

Harbour City, W1
Interlude de Chavot, W1
Turner's, SW3

England

Barwick Little Barwick House
Baslow Fischer's Baslow Hall
Brighton Black Chapati
Bristol Rocinantes
Broadhembury Drewe Arms
Chagford Gidleigh Park
Chinnor Sir Charles Napier
Coln St Aldwyns New Inn
Crosthwaite Punch Bowl Inn
Great Gonerby Harry's Place
Halifax Design House
Hambleton Hambleton Hall
Haslemere Fleur de Sel
Keyston Pheasant
Kingston upon Thames Ayudyha
Leeds Pool Court
Long Melford Scutcher's Bistro
Ludlow Merchant House
Mary Tavy Stannary
Masham Floodlite
Mawnan Smith Nansidwell
Newark Gannets Bistrot
Ponteland Café 21
Preston Heathcote's Brasserie
Romsey Old Manor House
Sandiway Nunsmere Hall
Wells Ritcher's
Wethersfield Dickens
Whitby Magpie Café
Whitstable Whitstable Oyster Fishery Co
Winchester Hotel du Vin & Bistro
Yarm D.P. Chadwick's
York Middlethorpe Hall

Scotland

Aberfeldy Farleyer House
Edinburgh Martin's
Eriska Isle of Eriska
Kingussie The Cross

Wales

Dolgellau Dylanwad Da
Eglwysfach Ynshir Hall
Fishguard Three Main Street
Llanfihangel nant Melan Red Lion Inn

The *Guide's* longest-serving restaurants

The *Guide* has seen many restaurants come and go. Some, however, have stayed the course with tenacity. (Qualification for this list is that the restaurant has been in each edition of the *Guide* subsequent to its first entry.)

Connaught, W1	43 years
Gay Hussar, W1	39 years
Porth Tocyn Hotel, Abersoch, Gwynedd	39 years
Gravetye Manor, East Grinstead, West Sussex	35 years
Sharrow Bay, Ullswater, Cumbria	35 years
Dundas Arms, Kintbury, Berkshire	33 years
French Partridge, Horton, Northamptonshire	31 years
Walnut Tree Inn, Llandewi Skirrid, Gwent	31 years
Black Bull Inn, Moulton, North Yorkshire	29 years
Rothay Manor, Ambleside, Cumbria	27 years
Sundial, Herstmonceux, East Sussex	27 years
Chez Moi, W11	25 years
Le Gavroche, W1	25 years
Summer Isles Hotel, Achiltibuie, Highland	25 years
The Capital, SW3	24 years
Miller Howe, Windermere, Cumbria	24 years
Cringletie House, Peebles, Borders	23 years
Old Fire Engine House, Ely, Cambridgeshire	23 years
Ubiquitous Chip, Glasgow, Strathclyde	23 years
White Moss House, Grasmere, Cumbria	23 years

Introduction

During the course of the past year the media made a momentous discovery: that *The Good Food Guide* does not charge restaurants for an entry, while some other guide books do. Quite why it took them so long to spot the difference is anybody's guess.

The *Guide* has never wavered in its independence, nor in its belief that only a restaurant's cooking, not its financial resources, should determine whether or not we recommend it to readers. No payment is ever made by establishments, under any circumstances, for inclusion in the *Guide*. It would be an absurd situation if, for example, there were two restaurants in the same town with an equally good standard of cooking, and only one of them ended up appearing in a guide because it could afford the fee. Such a publication would, in effect, be a book full of restaurant ads, and who wants one of those?

Mind you, it is easy to feel sorry for the publishers of such books. They do not have the one enormous asset that this *Guide* does, namely you, the reader, the reporter, the person who eats out and feels strongly enough, one way or the other, to write to us about your meal. Use the freepost address and there's no need for a stamp. Or, if you are on the Internet, e-mail us on *guidereports@which.co.uk*.

Without the letters and reports you send, we would be much the poorer. Please don't stop. We cannot thank you enough for all the feedback you've given us over the past 12 months.

Drop us a line

The reasons you write to us are many and varied, but the core motive is doubtless a desire to share your finds and pleasures with others, and to steer them away from places you would never again touch with a bargepole. The passion is evident. Some reporters write regularly, others occasionally, perhaps with a sorry tale about how the booking was mislaid, how they had to wait in a cold, cavernous hall while a grumpy and uncommunicative proprietor brought them a glass of warm white wine, and how it all cost a fortune and they had a puncture on the way back home. And the food? In all the hurly-burly they forgot to mention it.

Such a report, as it stands, is helpful to us. If it turns out that a significant number of other reporters experience something similar, then it gives us the confidence to warn readers what is likely to happen. If, on the other hand, a disastrous meal turns out to be a one-off, caused by a unique set of circumstances in which, say, the proprietors were stranded miles from their restaurant thanks to a puncture, and were dependent on a visiting relative, just arrived from overseas and with little English, to look after guests (none of this is as unlikely as it may sound), then we need reports from other diners to tell us that the couple who run the place are really quite delightful, and would never forget to turn on the heating, nor to chill the white wine. In other words, every single time you eat in a restaurant, every experience you have, no matter how normal and ordinary, is valuable to us. Your words give us a more complete picture of the restaurant, and enable us to render a more accurate account in the *Guide*, which in turn means that the *Guide* is more useful to you.

The hypothetical report above could have been even more useful, though. It would have been helpful, first, to know more about the look of the dining-room and the feel of the place. When a restaurant has been in the *Guide* for years, reporters assume there is no need to tell us yet again about the old beams, the green paint, the teddy bears on display, and so on. But since we re-write the *Guide* every year from scratch, we are always pleased to receive new words, new ways of describing familiar places: a new perspective, if you will. A thumbnail sketch is all we are after, and in any case your perception may well differ from other people's. To quote just one example: 'Our entry in the '95 *Guide* describes our upstairs dining-room as having a bare wooden floor,' wrote one restaurateur. 'In fact, it is fitted with a good-quality Axminster carpet, and has been for many years to our certain knowledge.' You see. Another pair of eyes would have helped.

Second, it is helpful to know what you ate and what you thought about it. 'The beef was very tasty.' Fine. But was it roasted, carved from a trolley or pan-fried, was it fillet or sirloin, and had it been cooked in a casserole until it fell apart, or briefly chargrilled? Did it come with a sauce that was made from stock, laced with cream or full of exotic mushrooms? And so on. If it was really good, what made it stand out, why did you like it? This information helps us to understand the level of skill in the kitchen, and thus contributes to the cooking score awarded to each restaurant in the *Guide*. Once again we can't get enough of it. If you can do the same for all three (or seven) courses, brilliant.

A few words about the service are helpful too: when you asked a question about the food, did you get a straight answer, or did somebody rush off to the kitchen to find out just what a mille-feuille of aubergine was when it was at home? (And come back, as some do, none the wiser.) How did the staff look after you? Were they earnest youngsters concentrating intently on the job, or detached professionals, were they reasonably courteous and attentive, or just so fed-up that they couldn't be bothered to bring your glass of wine no matter how many times you had to remind them?

And finally, did you think it was good value? Would you happily spend money there again, would you recommend it to friends, and by implication other *Guide* readers?

All change

There is a good reason why we need all this information. The décor might stay the same for years, but performance in the kitchen may not. It can change in small and subtle ways, perhaps when a chef just gets tired of churning out the same food year after year, or more dramatically as chefs move about, get promoted or set up on their own.

This year we list an extra dozen or so pubs, for example, thanks partly to chefs who want to be their own boss but don't have the backing for a plush hotel in the country or a smart address in the West End, or who just want to cook simple and inexpensive food. Ideally they would all move on 1 January, so that we can get lots of feedback in time for the next edition. Reports are valuable throughout the year, no question of that, but those in springtime have a particular edge because they are bang up to date: February to May is ideal.

In practice, most chefs seem to move at that particularly awkward moment, 'as we go to press'. In the past the *Guide* automatically dropped any restaurant where this happened, because we could not judge the food, and did not have the confidence to recommend it or award a score. The trouble was, readers did not know the reason for a restaurant's disappearance: it may have closed, just gone downhill, changed hands, got a new chef, or whatever. Last year, in response to readers' requests, we introduced a new idea. Where a new chef arrived at the last minute, but we had reason to believe the restaurant would continue along roughly similar lines as before, we gave it a NEW CHEF flash. This meant that we knew who the chef was, but had insufficient feedback to score the cooking.

Readers were thus aware that the restaurant still existed, and were encouraged to report on the new kitchen regime. Of the seven restaurants to which this applied, six remain in the *Guide* this year with full entries, which would seem to justify the action. As a result, we have continued the practice in this edition, and there are a dozen restaurants to which it applies.

For some reason, the past year seems to have witnessed more movement among chefs than usual, so we have signalled another kind of change in this edition, which is really no more than a bit of fun for regular readers. In those cases where a change was made early enough for us to produce a regular main entry (from reports and, where necessary, inspection), we have added a 'change of chef' symbol. We have not dished out a hat in every single instance, only when a significant change appears to have occurred. We felt it unnecessary, for example, to make the point where a sous-chef has taken over a kitchen and is carrying on in more or less the same vein as before. This symbol merely makes it easier for readers to keep track, at a glance, of changes since the previous edition that would normally have required close comparison to bring to light. We hope the curiosity factor will provide even more incentive to drop us a line about these places.

Meanwhile, the NEW ENTRY flash applies, as before, to restaurants that are completely new main entries this time round, although some may have been in the round-up section before.

One thing that keeping close track of all these changes has done is to highlight the amount of movement that occurs from one year to the next. Taking the *NEW CHEF*, and NEW ENTRY restaurants all together, and adding in restaurants that have closed, been dropped or simply disappeared since last year, there are some 260 significant changes in total: enough, I'm sure you will agree, to prove the worth of an up-to-date copy of the *Guide*.

Even so, changes were taking place almost daily as we went to press, and several more are imminent, planned or likely to take place during the early currency of the *Guide*. So if you want to know the latest, don't forget that whenever you send in a report between December and May, you automatically receive an updated list of changes. Alternatively, readers with a touch-tone phone can now ring 0171-830 7575 and select the information they want to hear. And you can leave a brief message too: it is a 24-hour line.

A regular meal

It is not that we are obsessed with change. The *Guide* has always applauded that most difficult yet essential attribute of a kitchen: consistency. The most consistent of all are listed on page 15. It is important that we all get a good meal in any restaurant that appears in the *Guide*, and it is of little use to know that friends enjoyed themselves wonderfully, but that it was chef's night off when we went, so we had second-rate food yet had to pay the normal price. Circumstances like these help to explain a few anomalies that readers will have noticed. You send in a glowing report, only to find the restaurant has been marked a whole point lower than you expected; or you insist that the restaurant be dropped from the *Guide* after your experience, only to find it still there when the next edition comes out. It doesn't seem fair.

What the *Guide* does is to balance reports and give as fair a picture as possible. In some cases, however, inconsistency seems built into the system, perhaps where a hotel is open seven days a week and has difficulty covering for the chef's day off. It is not our intention to campaign on behalf of Sunday lunch particularly, but we can't help noticing, in report after report, that this meal is often not typical of the rest of the week. One otherwise very good restaurant (we scored it 3* last year) in the north of England was criticised by a fan for its Sunday lunch: 'dried-out ravioli, missing ingredients, catastrophic roast beef, poor vegetables, barely warm food, bottled horseradish.' Even the dessert of 'exotic fruits' only managed to rustle up grapefruit, orange and pineapple. 'We hope for better next time' was the forgiving conclusion.

There is no simple way of identifying restaurants that perform particularly well or poorly at any given mealtime, although restaurants that score 3 or more in the *Guide* should have a high degree of consistency. Just in case it is the chef's day off, one suggestion is to ask, when booking, whether the chef named in the restaurant's entry details will be in the kitchen that day. Restaurants often ask us for a phone number; it seems reasonable to ask them for a small item of information in return.

Best food forward

Consistency in a kitchen, however, does not mean just doing the same old thing over and over again. One restaurateur wrote during the year to say that he had been doing the same thing for many years, and wanted to know why his restaurant had not scored as highly in the latest edition of the *Guide*. Nothing in his kitchen or dining-room had changed, so why should our assessment change? The answer is that what was good 20 years ago is not necessarily so good now. In the context of an earlier time a restaurant that didn't use tinned or processed food, or that made its own bread, stood out like a beacon. Now that these are commonplace – at least for restaurants that appear in the *Guide* – and standards are rising, it is no longer good enough to stand still and expect the same recognition.

In any case, anybody who produces the same food for 20 years must get just a little bit tired of it. Sanity alone demands some refreshment of ideas; if these become stale, then the cooking itself loses the appeal of freshness. A bored cook produces boring food. (And if you ever wondered where top chefs get their ideas from, to keep themselves and their customers unbored, turn to ex-Bibendum chef Simon Hopkinson's musings on creativity in the kitchen, on page 32.)

A desire for change does not mean that fashionable food is best. Fresh food is best, and many restaurants go to considerable lengths to procure it. A country restaurant's vegetable and herb garden, along with its close links with local farmers, provides ideal material for the kitchen. It is still possible to make a hash of the cooking, but restaurateurs who go to that amount of trouble usually have a keen enough sense of what to do with the broad beans and raspberries once they have picked them.

Many restaurants claim to use fresh and seasonal produce, though in practice they may also use out-of-season items: hands up, any reader who has not seen a strawberry in a restaurant in February. I spent a week in the Lake District in April trying to avoid them, and failed miserably. The idea of parsnips being sent from Australia to the UK to appear on our tables out of season is one of the more bizarre examples of food-miles. Tim Lang, like the *Guide,* is a supporter of fresh, local (and therefore seasonal) produce, and delivers much common sense about them in his article on page 25.

A bit of a tonic

The inertia that can affect some kitchens also applies to wine lists. There are still scrappy little lists with a humdrum choice bereft of producers' names or vintage dates, as well as big fat tomes with every wine you can think of, at hugely inflated prices. But by far the great majority of wine lists are now, at long last, catching up with developments in the wine world, as well as their customers' preferences. Wines in restaurants are getting better. This is turn means that what might have been an unusually good list five years ago – one to which we would have awarded a glass or a bottle symbol – may now seem more ordinary. Restaurateurs continually have to run faster to catch up with their neighbours and competitors. We review the lists for each edition, and there are always one or two changes to the awards that reflect this. The hurdle is raised higher every year, otherwise the symbols would become meaningless.

A good wine list need not be lengthy, of course. In fact, many shorter lists appeal precisely because they are a manageable size, carefully chosen and appropriate to the circumstances.

The small print

Restaurants and customers constitute a partnership: it is in the interests of each that the other survives. I would like to thank all the restaurants in the *Guide* for their co-operation in filling in our rather long questionnaire, and for keeping us up to date with changes in their organisation, kitchen, menus and so on. We rely on them for the accuracy of the information in the details presented beneath the main entries.

We have tried to be particularly careful about two items this year. Ask a restaurant if it serves vegetarian food, and they pretty well all say, 'Yes, of course.' Go along and eat, however, and you may find you should have ordered it when you booked, though they didn't mention that at the time. If you are lucky you might get an omelette, or a plate of vegetables that would normally accompany a meat-eater's main course. This state of affairs would not be tolerated if it were the other way round, so why should vegetarians put up with it? This time we have made as sure as we can that in every case where the details at the bottom of an entry say vegetarian meals are available, it means that there is always at least one first-course and one main-course vegetarian option on the menu at all times. If your experience is any different, please let us know.

Second, a number of cases of difficult wheelchair access were brought to our attention. Some restaurants that claimed on the questionnaire to provide wheelchair access were not always as accurate about this as they could have been. Extra steps, narrow doors, immovable furniture sometimes confronted the wheelchair user upon arrival. This time we have asked restaurants to answer a truthful 'I don't know' if they are at all unsure about whether access is really in accordance with the recommendations of RADAR (Royal Association for Disability and Rehabilitation). We hope that we have now cracked it, but, once again, please report your experiences and tell us of any problems. See also page 35.

At your service

Most meals are enjoyed in a fairly happy atmosphere. Occasionally, though, and sadly, it can turn into an 'us' and 'them' confrontation, as when a 'stroppy customer' takes issue with a perfectly reasonable request to arrive on time (the restaurant's view), or perfectly reasonable customers (ourselves) happen to be delayed by a few minutes and are treated to sullen, morose and irritable service from a dragon of a proprietor who ruins the whole evening for us.

This is not the place for a detailed legal treatise, but as a rule of thumb it is always best to make any dissatisfaction known on the spot. It may be difficult to do this in some circumstances, but it is worth trying to root out the most senior person you can find, and telling him or her, in matter-of-fact terms, what the problem is. It may be possible to resolve it there and then; but if not, at least the groundwork has been laid.

One of the *Guide*'s functions in all this is to present as accurate a picture as we can of what lies in store, so that readers have an idea of whether to expect an informal and noisy pub with Muzak, bare tables, and cheap and cheerful food, or a large and elegant country house with formal service, impeccably cooked food and high prices. Forewarned is forearmed.

Bearing in mind that one of the common themes of complaint in our postbag has to do with service charges, we have this year adopted a slightly different way of representing these. Details are given on page 10, but in essence 'net prices' and 'none' indicate that there is no need for any further payment, regardless of whether or not credit card slips are left open. 'Not inc' means it is left entirely up to you: leave more money if you wish, not if you don't, there is no obligation. Another possibility is that either a straight or an 'optional' charge (say 10 per cent) is added to the bill. It is the latter, so-called optional charge that seems to cause most confusion. How optional is it?

One restaurateur put it this way: 'If service is included, we have to deduct 17.5 per cent VAT before distributing the charge to the staff. If it is "optional", then VAT is not applicable.' So in other words, the 'optional' is not so much for our benefit as a wheeze on the part of restaurants to duck out of a spot of VAT. This might explain why they get shirty if we try to opt out of it, though it does not explain why the loophole apparently exists.

Some reporters object to any service charge at all, believing that we should simply pay the printed price – a view the logic of which is difficult to refute. Many more object when service charges rise above 10 per cent. We are pleased to note that the number of restaurants charging 15 per cent has reduced slightly since last year, but there are still a lot which consider 12.5 per cent to be acceptable, especially in London.

The issue is another source of potential confrontation between restaurant and customer, which is a pity. The reason the *Guide* bangs on about it is that there is no point in customers coming out of a restaurant feeling antagonistic, swearing never to return. Such restaurants are cutting their own throats, and spoiling it for others. The enormous benefits to be reaped from a proper understanding of how customers feel has been ably demonstrated by many restaurants that participated in the *Financial Times* Lunch for a Fiver scheme, the brainchild of Nick Lander, whose sensible words concerning the cost of eating out appear between pages 29 and 31. Those restaurants which went on to retain an inexpensive midweek lunch throughout the year found themselves very busy, and with much healthier finances than before.

The message is simple: if customers get a fair deal, they will come back. Restaurateurs can encourage the feel-good factor by offering good value, sometimes by offering spectacularly good value, even if it is only for three or four lunch-times a week. Eating out must be about feeling good, or it has lost its way. We believe that the restaurants in this book will make you feel better than the ones that aren't in. Please help us to keep it that way.

Food of the future

Tim Lang, Professor of Food Policy at Thames Valley University, on the challenges to food in Britain, and to British food culture

Since Raymond Postgate launched *The Good Food Guide* in 1951, British food has undergone a remarkable transformation. New foods, cuisines and tastes have erupted on to the restaurant scene, and into retail, at a truly extraordinary speed. Although the *Guide* still bears witness to the tussles consumers can have over standards and value for money, there is much to celebrate.

But what of the future? The optimists argue that progress moves in straight lines. There can be no turning back: food will never be drab again. Optimist though I am by nature, I am not so sure. A number of key trends appear to be going in the wrong direction. The good news is that movements have sprung up, led by cooks and consumers alike, alerting us to the dangers of what might lie ahead.

Three challenges in particular face the British consumer on the food front: the erosion of cooking skills among the general population, the tussle between bland globo-food and distinctive local foods and, most worrisome of all, the fragmentation of food culture.

The disappearing art of cookery

Good Food Guide readers will be the first to acknowledge the formidable skills required to deliver a first-class meal. Such a meal is a miracle of timing, planning, taste, imagination, experience and so forth. In a restaurant, these skills, to which those of teamwork and leadership must often be added, are pushed to the limit. Many chefs acknowledge that they first learned to cook and to be discriminating about food from their family – usually their mother or grandmother. Yet this tradition, reinforced by the removal of cookery from school curricula, is wasting away.

Traditional meal-times are becoming extinct, while grazing and snacking have become the order of the day. According to some estimates, about a quarter of food and drink in the UK is taken between meals. At home, people often don't eat together, and it is common not to eat at table, but in front of the TV, at the expense of such eating-related pleasures as conviviality and conversation. Increasingly, the food comes pre-prepared. Ready-meal sales continue to climb. Government figures suggest that over four-fifths of food sold in the UK is now pre-processed.

There is nothing wrong with having others cook for you. How many people *really* want to make their own fresh pasta? But the emerging non-cooking culture is producing a generation of young people who may be street-wise and computer-literate, but who have no idea of how to turn raw ingredients into a meal and who cannot tell good food from bad. A recent survey of nearly 300 young people aged 7-16 by Get Cooking!, a project set up by the National Food Alliance and funded by the Department of Health, found that nearly every child knew how to play computer games, two-thirds could program a video-recorder to record from the TV, but only half could boil an egg or bake a cake. And only a third could cook a jacket potato in the oven.

It is foolish to allow the ability to cook to disappear within one generation, not least because it creates a new dependency culture. Many caterers regret this development. Those running catering management courses report that they are now getting students who have never seen unsliced bread or washed a raw potato.

The good news, however, is that three out of four young people say they want to learn more about cooking. Girls, who according to a MORI survey learn earlier than boys and generally know more about the subject, want to increase their knowledge; and two-thirds of boys surveyed aged 7 to 11 (and over 50 per cent aged 12 to 15) also wanted to know more. About half of the children wanted to learn at school and two-thirds at home.

It is also cheering that a vast range of interested parties, from top chefs to health professionals, as well as the teachers who used to be called home economists but who now teach consumer studies or design and technology, have come together to promote good basic skills. One initiative, from the Académie Culinaire de France (the British branch, launched in 1980, of France's Académie Culinaire), encourages chefs to link up with local primary schools to teach the different tastes of food (hot, sweet, sour, acid, for example), while the Get Cooking! project, with the backing of 180 voluntary groups and health bodies, urges the creation of local food clubs in schools and youth organisations.

Good Food Guide readers – who were, after all, dubbed by Postgate the Society for the Prevention of Cruelty to Food – can do their bit to help, perhaps by introducing children and grandchildren to the joys of good food at an early age and encouraging them to cook. The return of cookery to the school curriculum would be another change for the better, well worth campaigning for.

Food from the locality

The second challenge to the food of the future is environmental. The use of fresh ingredients in cooking is good for the environment. It means less packaging, less energy and greater use of local and therefore fresh foods. But just how often is the food offered in your neighbourhood restaurants truly local?

Modern food culture dazzles us with choice. Supermarket buyers roam the globe in search of items that will titillate our taste buds. A fruit salad in any above-humble establishment will tend to come complete with star fruit or mangoes, and strawberries can appear at any time of year. But is this sensible? While some British fruit-growers have gone bust, producers elsewhere in the world are increasingly competing with each other to supply British needs. A similar pattern applies to other crops, even when it is humanly and climatically possible to grow them on our doorstep. Britain now imports cabbages. Green beans are flown in to Britain and elsewhere in the West from Africa in mid-winter, while people in nearby areas face starvation. Supermarkets in late spring are full of Spanish asparagus, while, in some areas, British asparagus beds rot. Whatever happened to seasonality, let alone 'locality'?

One of the paradoxes of the post-war food revolution is that food now travels further. For the sake of a bargain, distance is no drawback. The average European weekend shopping trolley contains goods that have already travelled 4,000km before we take them home. The food industries account for a third of all the growth in UK freight miles in recent years despite being one-tenth of the economy. The same amount of foodstuffs is being hauled over longer distances. No wonder there is less diversity of produce growing in the fields but apparently greater diversity in shops and restaurants. We all pay for this as consumers. Perhaps, as consumers, we should endeavour to stimulate home-grown production by our actions, attitudes and choices when we shop for food or eat out.

Roll on the day when every restaurateur celebrates not only home cooking, but also as much home-grown or home-made produce as possible. Just as some menus now sprout a 'V' to indicate vegetarian dishes, perhaps an 'L' could indicate local ingredients, grown within, say, a ten-mile radius. Menus could briefly explain the establishment's sourcing policy. Using our purchasing power to help relocalise produce would do nothing but good both for the local economy and for bio-diversity, which the UK government, together with more than a hundred other countries, is now pledged to support. There is scope, surely, for groups of chefs in a particular locality to join together to ask farmers to grow for them. In this mad world of 'set-aside', loathed by farmers and townies alike, why not encourage diverse crops to be grown? British gardens have demonstrated, on a small scale, what can be achieved. In the US a colloquium of big-name chefs is spearheading just such a movement.

The fragmentation of our food culture

As this *Guide* proves, this country has much to celebrate. Given the money, time and inclination, we can eat brilliantly in Britain (it was not ever thus, as Raymond Postgate would remind us were he here today). But the positive post-war trends, driven by consumers' rising living standards, experience of foreign travel and general willingness to try food previously shunned as foreign, could be in jeopardy. The pace of life, and the increasing informality of our lifestyles, has not only put paid to structured eating patterns but has also nurtured a fast-food culture based on fatty foods – 'heart disease specials' – and a belief that we don't have time to cook our own meals. This, and a sense that cooking is just another 'labour' to be saved, is destroying our interest in food, and hence, our food culture.

Perhaps we don't believe we have a food culture at all, so we can hardly claim that it is coming under threat. Yet no one would dispute that the French and the Italians do, and it is significant that they too have been alarmed by the seemingly unstoppable takeover of fast food. In response, the French government formally endorsed a 'Day of Taste', while a group of Italians has launched a 'Slow Food' movement.

Such initiatives point the way forward. So too will demands for the return of locally grown food to our tables, and teaching young people both to cook and to realise that there is more to food than the fatty burgers and sweet mush peddled by the fast-food joints.

A good food culture is one at ease with itself. It should celebrate diversity, reflect the output of local producers, and ensure that culinary skills are passed on from generation to generation, not cut off in childhood. And it should promote the pleasures of eating together. Good food, after all, is to be shared and enjoyed.

Filling the empty tables

Nicholas Lander, restaurant correspondent for the *Financial Times*, on some exciting new pricing schemes and strategies restaurateurs are using to lure the customers

There has never been a better time to be a restaurant-goer in Great Britain.

What! you exclaim, with dinner at £50 a head or more – without wine or service – at many a top restaurant? You must be joking.

I'm not, and I will try to explain just what good value is to be had. What is more, I'll do it virtually without referring to the rise of the British chef and the vast improvement in the range and quality of British produce – both of which are additional reasons for enjoying the better restaurants in Great Britain today.

My argument will be based on simple economics: no, please don't turn the page. I spent nine hectic but happy years as a restaurateur and the fact that I can now appreciate these economic facts of life means they must be simple indeed.

Going to lunch

It all started with the recession of the early 1990s. This and the Gulf War severely hurt restaurants, and not just in Britain. Empty tables led to lower prices and to competition among chefs and restaurateurs to deliver value for money. For anyone visiting London today, the best advice on how to maximise gastronomic pleasure while minimising financial cost is simple: eat out at the best places you can afford *at lunch-time*. As a result of the cutbacks in personal spending and corporate entertaining, lunch at places such as La Tante Claire, Le Gavroche, The Restaurant, Bibendum or Clarke's will cost you 40-50 per cent less than dinner. With what you have 'saved' over lunch you can buy a theatre ticket and supper in Chinatown.

The early '90s also saw an increase in the number of large restaurants or brasseries around Britain – venues such as Brasserie Forty Four and Leodis in Leeds, the Atrium in Edinburgh and, in London, the Gastrodrome on Butler's Wharf, Belgo (now Belgo Noord), Wagamama, St John and the People's Palace – all devoted to the idea of affordable and approachable food. Falling property prices, another consequence of the recession, were the initial cause of the rise of the brasserie-style establishment, but the trend was accelerated by the eagerness of the consumer to abandon what he or she had hitherto always thought were the *sine qua non* of a good restaurant – tablecloths, silver service and several pages of expensive claret in the wine list. (Interestingly, one of the first items the Savoy Hotel sold off in its reorganisation in May 1995 was its cellar of 100,000 bottles of fine wine and port.) Instead, there was a growing awareness of the importance of what was on the plate and how it was served, the range of New World wines, the desirability of having more wines available by the glass, and – not least – the size of the bill.

In today's economy, restaurants must hold not one but several cards to survive and succeed: substantial investment and working capital, patience, good management and caring staff. Above all, they need customers – all the year round.

Filling those quiet hours

This is the difficult part. For any city-centre restaurant there are six good trading months a year – April, May, June, September, October and December (these vary slightly for country/seaside restaurants) – and four good sessions a week – Tuesday, Wednesday, Thursday, Friday lunch and Saturday night. Profits disappear in January and February, during Easter and school half-terms, and Mondays are invariably quiet.

Even the most popular restaurants suffer flat periods. Early in the year, I asked Grahame Edwards from Kensington Place, one of London's busiest restaurants, how business was. 'Fine,' he said, 'but we could do with a few more customers for dinner at the beginning of the week.' And because Kensington Place is not quite in the West End, there are usually tables to be had in the early evening.

The Fifth Floor restaurant at Harvey Nichols faced the same problem, but its management came up with an incentive. Now on a Monday night you can buy your wine in the Harvey Nichols wine shop at retail prices and drink it in the restaurant or café without any additional mark-up.

Such incentives to the consumer to go out and spend leisure time at a restaurant are likely to become increasingly prevalent in the second half of the '90s, and will make eating out even better value.

Signs and portents

An advertisement for Belgo in the London *Evening Standard* was, perhaps, an indication of things to come. This restaurant is so popular from 8pm onwards that it had introduced what some people might consider the user-unfriendly policy of placing time limits on their bookings. But, because it was quiet in the early evening, in came 'Beat the Clock'. Listing dishes normally priced between £10.20 and £12, the advertisement said that if you ordered one of these between Monday and Friday at 6.05pm you would pay £6.05 instead; at 7.45pm you would pay £7.45, and so forth (the last cut-price orders were £8 at 8pm).

The need to keep busy continually pertains not just to large, less expensive restaurants like Belgo. In January 1995 I organised the second *Financial Times* 'Lunch for a Fiver' promotion, which involved 310 restaurants around the country offering two-course menus at £5, £7.50 and £10.

The restaurateurs participated because they needed to fill empty tables – and not just in January. Paul Henderson, proprietor of the widely lauded Gidleigh Park in Chagford, Devon, filled his restaurant for the initial fortnight and then extended it by a week. He also realised that there was such demand to eat at the restaurant once the right price was established that he kept a list of over 200 customers whom he could not accommodate; these he mailed in early March 1995 with the details of his new lunch menu and pricing. Instead of a £40 menu for largely empty tables, a two-course lunch at £15 was introduced from Monday to Thursday, £20 for Friday and Saturday, and £25 for Sunday and holiday weekends. These prices, together with Gidleigh Park's offer of wine tastings, a garden tour, cooking demonstrations and a croquet day, are enticing the customers, keeping the staff busy and happy, and satisfying even the bank manager.

Several American restaurateurs have devised pricing schemes which their British counterparts may decide to copy as the number of large restaurants increases. In Manhattan, the restaurateur Allan Stillman found business at Cité slow once the theatres opened. Having made a few deals with his wine suppliers, he was able to include for bookings after 8pm good wines, both American and French, in the price. His advertising slogan showing the wines' labels was unforgettable: 'Hail a cab to the great wine regions of the world. You pay for the cab, we'll buy the wine.' In 1994 Stillman's staff poured 36,484 bottles of wine to keep the restaurant busy and their customers happy.

As the *Guide* was going to press, several new large restaurants had just opened or were getting ready to open in London: Conran's new Wardour Street site (Mezzo); the second Wagamama in Soho; Oliver Peyton's second venture in Albemarle Street (The Coast); a second Blue Elephant in Marble Arch called Porte des Indes; Bruno Loubet's new place, L'Odeon; and, only a stone's throw away, the reborn Criterion under Marco Pierre White. They will all have to find ways of persuading you, the consumer, to cross their threshold again and again. The omens are good – British restaurants need you!

Onwards and upwards

Simon Hopkinson, founding chef and co-proprietor of Bibendum (London), on what puts a top chef on top

Having recently emerged from the heat of the kitchen, I have been pondering whether this stressful, emotional, adrenaline-injected environment really is the nucleus of creativity. It is of course easy to be inspired by three kilos of beautiful ceps, and challenging to have to do something very interesting with a halibut at short notice, and flattering to be told that you have to cook the same dish over and over and over again because people love it and you can't take it off the menu. But, like a fly crawling over an elephant, it is only when you step back from it that you get a glimpse of the big picture. Hence my musings. Where do the good chefs get their creative energies from?

Copying is not enough

All chefs copy, at least once. Even the best do it. A few years ago Raymond Blanc became inspired to incorporate Thai flavours into his repertoire at Le Manoir aux Quat'Saisons. I noticed on one menu the inclusion of a – no doubt suitably refined – version of Gaeng Dom Yam Gai, that delicious coconut-cream-rich chicken and galanga soup that I, for one, can never resist ordering in Thai restaurants. The reason for wishing to put this sort of dish on the menu of a super-flash restaurant is quite simple: it just tastes so damn good.

But I worry that the world is full of copyists just now. I clearly remember, on a cook's tour of France some years ago, the extraordinary influence of one particular dish on a whole nation of chefs: the great Troisgros dish, salmon with sorrel sauce. It was everywhere, and not just in France. The whole world had embraced it. In Britain today, with similarly influential chefs, entire chunks of a chef's 'style' (for want of a better description) are being plundered. And, inevitably, without the soul of that particular chef. Individual characteristics may be visible – menuspeak, ingredients, use of the word 'jus' a lot – but one cannot hope to mimic individual 'character'.

Fashion is not enough

Just getting excited about a few sticks of lemon grass and a couple of lime leaves does not, how shall one say, indicate that here is a chef with verve, style and charisma. Today's aspirant chefs may think that flinging a few sliced-up sun-dried tomatoes over a salad, dousing it with balsamic vinegar and garnishing it with wildly unsuitable clumps of coriander constitutes intelligent and noteworthy cooking. It doesn't quite work like that. Chefs also need common sense and good taste.

All around one sees chargrilling (from the ubiquitous peppers to madly inappropriate carrots), all manner of mashed potatoes (some of them so revolting I would rather eat the packet stuff), a quite irresponsible flood of balsamic vinegar, and endless raw fish and meat 'carpaccios' buried under a rocket salad or showered with unwanted flakes of Parmesan. One could argue, 'Ah, but that is a matter of opinion, and who says one cannot play around with a classic?' Call me old-fashioned, but I say go back to the classic first, and then you will understand why there are certain things you can and can't do to it.

Eat your own words

Where, then, should inspiration come from? Of a keen young cook coming into the kitchen at Bibendum, one of the first questions I would ask is 'What do you like eating?' Not 'What do you like to cook?' and certainly not 'What do you like cooking best?' because they all say 'Fish'. Heaven knows why. I ask them because, if getting stuck into a great plate of good food – be it steak and chips or the most ethereal mousseline of sole – does not come high on their list of priorities, it would be like a budding concert pianist not wishing to listen to Chopin. So for me eating – ergo tasting – food, at whatever venue, is the greatest inspiration for a fanatical cook. Techniques naturally develop through interest.

Young chefs should be sent into the dining-room to see whether they might like to eat their salad of grilled salmon (farmed), tomatoes (sun-dried), oil (extra virgin, naturally), vinegar (aged balsamic), chervil fronds (purely for decoration) and various out-of-season salad leaves. And then send them out a slice of perfect jambon persillé and see whether a sparkle of recognition lights up their fashionable faces.

Follow your own nose

I have been blessed with the opportunity to cook and create exactly what I please for the past 20-odd years, which is a luxury not bestowed on many. I have always strived to cook what I like to eat: it is down to greed really, together with a longing to impress the eater with my craft and pass on my love of good food. I don't think there is any other way to cook. Of course I have been influenced by others – Franco Taruschio of the Walnut Tree Inn, Llandewi Skirrid, as well as Michel Guérard, Elizabeth David, Yves Champeau, Richard Olney and (from Australia) Anders Ousbäck.

I have learned the importance of the seasons, and a respect for tradition and correctness, as all cooks must. But for any aspiring young chef there must also be a strong element of individuality or 'self' that shines through, without which there would not be a great deal of point in customers going to chef/proprietor restaurants. Technique and training are important, but the interest in developing one's own style has to come from a driven mind endowed with wit and personality. I am thrilled when I go to a restaurant where a protége of mine is the cook and has adapted one of my ideas into something even more special. That is progress, and it is thrilling to see.

A note on restaurants and disabled customers

There are more than six and a half million disabled people in the UK, many of whom enjoy – or would enjoy, if access were easier – eating out. While it may not be reasonable to expect all restaurants to provide access for wheelchair users, owing to space and other constraints, establishments that do should surely try to ensure that, once inside, the customer in a wheelchair does not feel too conspicuous or uncomfortable. Basic access means that the establishment has an entrance that is at least 120cm across in accordance with the standards set by the Royal Association for Disability and Rehabilitation (RADAR), as well a ramp or negotiable steps.

Once through the front door of establishments that do claim to welcome wheelchair users, however, some customers in wheelchairs find that furniture has to be moved and other diners disrupted before they can reach their table – an uncomfortable experience for everyone. Here at *The Good Food Guide,* we have also been told of one customer's embarrassment on arriving at a pale-carpeted establishment in her chair on a rainy night: as her companion put it, 'Wheelchairs cannot wipe their feet.' Car parks too can be a problem: in one instance, a customer was asked to leave her car in a car park up a gravelled road that would have been extremely difficult to negotiate in her wheelchair, and it was only grudgingly that staff allowed her to park in a paved area close to the entrance. Finally, although many establishments do provide basic access to lavatories for those in wheelchairs, in some cases neither taps nor towels are within reach.

In future, *The Good Food Guide* would like to present fuller information for disabled customers. We would therefore welcome more feedback from disabled readers on their eating-out experiences, both pro and con. We will also be looking more closely at what restaurants tell us about the facilities they offer wheelchair-users.

A final note: as we say above, not all restaurants can be expected to have access for wheelchairs (for example, many small eateries and pubs, those with limited resources, those located upstairs or downstairs with no lifts, and so on). However, restaurateurs who do have the space and wherewithal to provide reasonable facilities for disabled consumers should check whether they are really doing so, or whether the wheelchair-bound customer is in fact a second-class customer.

Vintage Chart

In order to retain the very good vintages of 1961 and 1962, it has been necessary to omit the poorer vintages of 1965 and 1968.

SYMBOLS:

- △ = immature
- ● = mature
- ▽ = drink up
- □ = wines unlikely to be found in Britain, or undeclared vintages for port and champagne, which come from regions where only certain years are 'declared' or marketed as vintage wines.
- ★ = vintages not yet 'declared' or marketed (port, champagne)

All figures and symbols apply to the best wines of each vintage in each region.

Vintages have been rated on a 1 to 20 point scale (20 being the best).

	1	2	3	4	5	6	7	8	9	10	11
1994	14△	13△	15△	10△	13△	15△	17△	12●	18△	15△	13△
1993	11△	12△	12△	8△	14△	14△	14△	13●	13●	14△	13△
1992	12△	12△	13△	8△	15△	15△	14△	14●	18△	16△	15△
1991	14△	12△	13△	12△	14△	14△	13△	12●	14●	16△	13●
1990	17△	18△	14●	19△	19△	19●	19△	19●	19△	18△	18△
1989	19△	19△	17●	19●	17●	19●	20△	18●	18△	16△	18●
1988	18△	19△	16●	18△	18△	15●	16△	17●	19●	18△	17●
1987	14●	13●	15●	10●	13●	15●	8●	12▽	12●	14●	11▽
1986	19△	18△	14●	17△	14●	18●	16●	18▽	16●	15●	16●
1985	18●	18●	18●	15●	19●	16●	18●	16▽	17●	18●	19●
1984	13●	10●	12●	13●	11▽	12▽	8●	10▽	12▽	14●	13●
1983	18△	17●	18●	18△	14▽	17●	16●	14▽	18●	19●	17●
1982	19●	19●	16●	14●	13▽	15▽	13●	13▽	13▽	16●	15●
1981	16●	15●	15●	13●	11▽	8▽	16●	17▽	16●	13▽	12▽
1980	11▽	10▽	11▽	12●	13▽	11▽	13●	12▽	8▽	14▽	14▽
1979	16●	18●	17●	14●	14▽	16▽	14●	14▽	10▽	15●	14●
1978	17●	17●	17●	12●	18●	17●	15●	18▽	12▽	19●	18●
1977	9▽	9▽	7▽	6▽	7▽	10▽	5▽	8▽	7▽	8▽	7▽
1976	16▽	14▽	16▽	17●	14▽	14▽	18●	16▽	18●	18●	14▽
1975	16●	17●	17▽	18●	4▽	6▽	16●	15▽	14▽	10▽	9▽
1974	12▽	10▽	9▽	8▽	11▽	10▽	8▽	11▽	10▽	9▽	11▽
1973	13▽	12▽	11▽	12▽	10▽	14▽	13▽	16▽	14▽	12▽	13▽
1972	8▽	8▽	6▽	9▽	12▽	10▽	8▽	6▽	5▽	14▽	15▽
1971	15●	16●	18●	16●	18●	17▽	16●	18▽	19●	17●	17▽
1970	18●	17●	16●	14●	13▽	13▽	16●	16▽	11▽	16●	18●
1969	11▽	9▽	8▽	13▽	16▽	17▽	18●	16▽	13▽	18●	17▽
1967	12▽	12▽	11▽	17●	13▽	14▽	13▽	12▽	17▽	16●	18▽
1966	17●	18●	16▽	14▽	16▽	17▽	15●	18▽	16▽	17●	18▽
1964	14▽	16▽	11▽	6▽	14▽	14▽	18●	14▽	15▽	17▽	16▽
1963	5▽	5▽	3▽	□	11▽	14▽	□	□	8▽	7▽	8▽
1962	14▽	15▽	16▽	17●	16▽	18▽	15●	14▽	14▽	17▽	16▽
1961	20●	20●	18▽	16▽	14▽	16▽	14●	16▽	18▽	20●	19●

1 = Red Bordeaux: Médoc & Graves
2 = Red Bordeaux: St-Emilion & Pomerol
3 = Dry white Bordeaux
4 = Sweet white Bordeaux: Sauternes & Barsac
5 = Red Burgundy
6 = White Burgundy
7 = Loire (sweet)
8 = Loire (dry)
9 = Alsace
10 = Northern Rhône
11 = Southern Rhône
12 = Midi
13 = Champagne
14 = Rioja
15 = Vintage port
16 = Red Portuguese
17 = Barolo & Barbaresco
18 = Tuscany
19 = Mosel–Saar–Ruwer
20 = Rhinelands
21 = Australia (red wines)
22 = New Zealand (white wines)
23 = California (red wines)

12	13	14	15	16	17	18	19	20	21	22	23	
17△	★	17△	★	16△	14△	13△	15△	15△	15△	19●	16△	**1994**
13△	★	14△	★	13△	17△	14△	19△	14△	13△	14●	15△	**1993**
15△	★	16●	19△	16●	14△	13△	18●	17●	16△	15●	19△	**1992**
16△	★	16●	18△	16●	13△	14△	13●	14●	18△	18●	19△	**1991**
19●	17△	18●	□	17●	18△	20△	20●	20△	17●	15●	18△	**1990**
18●	16△	18●	□	17●	18△	13●	19●	18●	10●	19●	14●	**1989**
19●	19△	17●	□	11●	17△	19△	17●	17●	16●	14●	15●	**1988**
14●	□	16●	17△	15●	14●	14●	6▽	7▽	18●	16●	12●	**1987**
16●	15●	17●	□	9▽	15●	17●	11▽	13▽	19●	18▽	14●	**1986**
18●	19●	19●	19△	19●	20●	19●	15▽	15▽	17●	□	19●	**1985**
13●	□	13●	□	14▽	8▽	9▽	3▽	5▽	18●	□	13●	**1984**
18●	16●	15●	18△	18●	13▽	15▽	16▽	14▽	14●	□	12▽	**1983**
17▽	17●	16●	13●	15▽	19●	17●	7▽	8▽	19●	□	15●	**1982**
17▽	16●	17●	□	10▽	13▽	14▽	8▽	10▽	13▽	□	14▽	**1981**
15▽	10▽	16▽	16●	17●	11▽	13▽	3▽	4▽	18●	□	17●	**1980**
15▽	17●	14▽	□	14▽	14▽	17●	11▽	12▽	16●	□	14▽	**1979**
18▽	12▽	19●	□	15▽	18●	16▽	9▽	9▽	18●	□	16●	**1978**
□	□	6▽	20△	16▽	11▽	16▽	5▽	8▽	14▽	□	12▽	**1977**
□	18●	13▽	□	12▽	14▽	13▽	19●	17●	17●	□	14▽	**1976**
□	14▽	15▽	13▽	13▽	12▽	17▽	17●	18●	19●	□	14▽	**1975**
□	9▽	14▽	□	10▽	16▽	14▽	3▽	4▽	11▽	□	18●	**1974**
□	14▽	17▽	□	6▽	13▽	16▽	11▽	10▽	14▽	□	17●	**1973**
□	□	7▽	□	12▽	10▽	9▽	6▽	7▽	13▽	□	15▽	**1972**
□	17▽	9▽	□	9▽	18▽	18▽	20●	19●	20●	□	14▽	**1971**
□	16▽	19●	18●	17▽	17▽	16▽	12▽	11▽	14▽	□	17●	**1970**
□	14▽	12▽	□	9▽	14▽	14▽	16▽	13▽	□	□	16▽	**1969**
□	13▽	12▽	16●	14▽	16▽	18▽	17●	17●	15▽	□	14▽	**1967**
□	16▽	15▽	18●	19▽	15▽	16▽	16▽	16▽	19●	□	16▽	**1966**
□	17▽	20●	□	□	19▽	18▽	17●	15▽	□	□	16▽	**1964**
□	□	12▽	20●	16▽	□	□	12▽	12▽	17▽	□	16▽	**1963**
□	15▽	13▽	□	□	13▽	16▽	14▽	16▽	18●	□	13▽	**1962**
□	16▽	10▽	□	□	18▽	15▽	10▽	12▽	□	□	15▽	**1961**

London

Adams Café £

map 12

77 Askew Road, W12 9AH — COOKING 1*
TEL/FAX: 0181-743 0572 — COST £17–£25

Frances and Abdel Boukraa's sole aim in the evening is to serve a trencherman's version of native Tunisian and Mediterranean cooking in the western enclaves of Shepherd's Bush and Acton. Their prices are low, their menu is short. Couscous holds centre-stage and it comes four ways. The royal version is bolstered by merguez sausages, skewered lamb and chicken: 'the couscous was light and fluffy, the vegetables still had some bite and meat was so tender it was falling off the bone.' Starters include various 'briks' – 'crispy fans of filo pastry' – holding anything from eggs to seafood, and salads including one composed of grilled pepper purée, tomatoes and tuna. Pâtisseries tunisiennes round things off, or go for cassis sorbet or hot lemon crêpes. The cover charge pays for French bread, harissa sauce, meatballs and marinated olives. An extra 55p will allow you to bring your own wine and drink it as well, but a short list includes some Tunisian representatives that are, says the wine list, 'unique to Adams Café' and house French is £6.95.

CHEF: Abdel Boukraa PROPRIETORS: Frances and Abdel Boukraa OPEN: all week D only 7 to 11 CLOSED: 25 and 26 Dec MEALS: alc (main courses £6 to £8). Cover 95p SERVICE: not inc CARDS: none DETAILS: 60 seats. Private parties: 36 main room, 24 private room. Vegetarian meals. Children welcome. Wheelchair access (1 step). Music

Ajimura

map 15

51–53 Shelton Street, WC2H 9HE — COOKING 1*
TEL: 0171-240 0178 FAX: 0171-497 2240 — COST £14–£53

'The longest-established Japanese restaurant in Britain,' proclaims the menu at this Far Eastern fixture of the Covent Garden scene. Susumu and Harumi Okada set up in 1972 with the aim of providing Londoners with an accessible version of their cuisine and culture. Since then, they have deliberately shied away from dignified ceremony. Their style has been described as 'bohemian'; casual friendliness rather than kimonos and bowing are the order of the day. Miso soup is rich and tangy ('a nice, warm beginning on a midwinter night'), and the full menu spans sushi, sashimi, tempura and a host of omelettes, hotpots and peasant-style dishes based on udon and soba noodles. Ajimura has always had a reputation for its vegetarian dishes, and reporters of that persuasion have been satisfied by ositashi (spinach rolled in nori seaweed) and grilled tofu 'steak' with teriyaki sauce. Set lunches and pre-theatre dinners are great value. Drink green tea, Sapporo beer, plum wine or saké. Otherwise, there is a minimal wine list, with house wine at £7.

CHEFS: Susumu Okada and Tasuo Tanizawa PROPRIETORS: Susumu and Harumi Okada OPEN: Mon to Fri L 12 to 3, Mon to Sat D 6 to 11 CLOSED: bank hols MEALS: alc (main courses £8 to £15.50). Set L £8 to £8.90, Set pre- theatre D Mon to Fri 6 to 7.30 £13 to £14.50, Set D £19.50 to £35 CARDS: Access, Amex, Diners, Visa DETAILS: 58 seats. Private parties: 25 main room, 18 private room. Vegetarian meals. Children welcome. No smoking in 1 dining-room. Music. Air-conditioned

Alastair Little

map 15

49 Frith Street, W1V 5TE — COOKING 3*
TEL: 0171-734 5183 — COST £35–£72

Few London restaurants produce such widely differing assessments among reporters. Some swear never to return, while others compare it favourably with restaurants that achieve higher scores in the *Guide*. Alastair Little is no stranger to controversy, having been a pioneer of a kind of cooking that is now taken for granted. He is self-taught, insists on no frills for either décor or staff, and produces simple food that is proudly British yet happy to borrow from any gastronomic culture that takes his fancy, on a menu that changes twice daily to cope with all the permutations and combinations of ingredients and ideas that pass through the kitchen.

Thus the menu might offer chickpea soup, 'sensational' black pasta with scallops, squid, tomato and garlic, or tempura of courgette flowers with a soy dip, followed by sea bass with roasted tomato salsa, or haunch of rabbit with wild mushrooms. The virtues of simplicity are evident in a Caesar salad with crisp leaves, grated Gruyère and a light dressing, or in bortsch with sausage and horseradish deriving 'great depth of flavour from good stock'. Stocks are the foundation of other successes, from fish stew to a sauce served with 'brilliantly roast Tuscan pigeon, a whole bird, the legs cooked through, the breast pink and moist', that came with 'lovely fatty' sarladaise potatoes. Puddings demonstrate baking skills of a high order, including a light Sauternes sponge cake and 'meltingly fragile' shortcake with raspberries and thick cream, while others – from bread-and-butter pudding to a rhubarb and pistachio trifle – have also drawn praise.

In all this, though, 'I don't think you can ignore the prices'. Clearly some reporters expect linen cloths and penguin-suited service for their money, or even a diverting view of some sort, but none is on offer here, so all eyes are on the food to see if it can carry the cost by itself. 'Our verdict was that it was good, but not as good as it should have been' was one opinion. Perhaps in recognition of the price problem, Alastair Little is planning to open an additional and less expensive restaurant in W11 towards the end of 1995. Reporters' experience of service in Frith Street, meanwhile, has ranged from 'offhand' to 'laid back, confident, competent and warm'. The short wine list concentrates its energy on a wide variety of flavours in the £20 to £35 range. House wine is £12.

The Guide *always appreciates hearing about changes of chef or owner.*

CHEFS: Alastair Little and Andy Parle PROPRIETORS: Alastair Little, Mercedes André-Vega and Kirsten Pedersen OPEN: Mon to Fri L 12 to 3, Mon to Sat D 6 to 11.30 CLOSED: bank hols MEALS: alc (main courses £15 to £22). Set L £25, Set bar L £12.50 (2 courses) SERVICE: not inc CARDS: Access, Amex, Switch, Visa DETAILS: restaurant 35 seats, bar 16 seats. Private parties: 16 private room. Children's helpings. Wheelchair access (2 steps). No music. Air-conditioned

Alba

map 13

107 Whitecross Street, EC1Y 8JH COOKING 1
TEL: 0171-588 1798 COST £25–£41

Alba has expanded into the shop next door, enlarging both the kitchen and dining-room. It is a short stroll from the Barbican, and open early and late enough in the evening to take advantage of the proximity. Northern Italy is the inspiration for much of the food, including gnocchetti with fontina cheese, and osso buco alla milanese, complete with gremolada sprinkled over the saffron risotto. However, a risotto of spinach in honour of St Patrick's Day shows the menu is not hidebound.

The *carte* has produced good minestrone soup, and a plate of spaghetti with scallops, clams and mussels in a creamy sauce, while the fixed-price menu offers four courses: on one occasion a salad of pheasant and p[illegible] mushrooms followed by risotto of artichokes and salmon, then marinated hare cooked in red wine and served with polenta, and (another Alban speciality) nougat pudding. Or there may be exotic fruit to finish. 'It is one of our favourite restaurants in London,' write one couple who also rate the friendly and helpful staff highly. Wines comes from Veneto, Tuscany and Umbria as well as Piedmont. The list is a bit short on detail, but includes Barbera and Grignolino as well as the more prestigious Barolo. House Dolcetto is £10.90, house white £8.90.

CHEFS: Armando Liboi and Andrea Martino PROPRIETOR: Rudi Venerandi OPEN: Mon to Fri 12 to 3, 6 to 11 CLOSED: bank hols MEALS: alc (main courses £9 to £13). Set D £16.90 SERVICE: 12½%, card slips closed CARDS: Access, Amex, Delta, Diners, Switch, Visa DETAILS: 60 seats. Private parties: 80 main room, 20 and 40 private rooms. Vegetarian meals. Children's helpings. No-smoking area. Wheelchair access (1 step). Music. Air-conditioned

Al Bustan

map 14

27 Motcomb Street, SW1X 8JU COOKING 2
TEL: 0171-235 8277 and 1668 FAX: 0171-245 0056 COST £32–£49

Set in one of Belgravia's more opulent streets, much favoured by lovers of antiques, Al Bustan is not your average ethnic café. Inside there are elegantly laid tables, and the tone is set by masses of greenery, trellises and *faux* stone walls. Service is correct, formal and well informed. The menu covers most of the classic Middle Eastern repertoire, with a few carnivorous exotica, such as brains, sweetbreads and raw meat, added for good measure. Regulars get hooked on the Lebanese meze: highlights from one feast of a lunch included moussaka bizeit (a cold dish of fried aubergines with tomatoes and chickpeas), spicy little sausages made from finely minced meat 'innocent of cereal', superb ungreasy sambousek (mini-pastries filled with minced lamb and pine-kernels) and a special of casseroled stuffed courgettes. What impresses is the quality and authenticity of the cooking. The list of main courses relies heavily on the chargrill. Puddings and pastries are impeccable, breads come fresh from the oven, and Turkish coffee is the real thing. The cover charge pays for a harvest festival of raw vegetables, cracked green olives, and a ferocious garlic and chilli dip. French wines dominate the short list, but look for the white Ch. Musar, which is 'remarkably steely and robust for a hot-country wine'. House wine is £12.

CHEF: Mrs Ina'am Atalla PROPRIETORS: Mr and Mrs R. Atalla OPEN: all week 12 to 11 (10 Sun and bank hols) CLOSED: 25 and 26 Dec, 1 Jan MEALS: alc (main courses £8.50 to £10). Set L £21, Set D £25. Cover £2.50. Minimum £12 SERVICE: not inc CARDS: Access, Amex, Diners, Switch, Visa DETAILS: 65 seats. Private parties: 20 main room, 8 private rooms. Vegetarian meals. Children's helpings. Smart dress preferred. Music. Air- conditioned

Alexandra

map 12

507 Kingston Road, SW20 8SF — COOKING 1
TEL: 0181-542 4838 — COST £17–£31

Eric Lecras has devised a neat scheme to attract locals to his converted house near Raynes Park Station: he has had thousands of leaflets delivered throughout the neighbourhood, offering a 25 per cent discount on midweek meals. The strategy seems to have worked, and he reckons that things are looking up. In addition, he has teamed up with five other restaurateurs to obtain twice-weekly deliveries of fresh fish and seafood direct from France.

His daily blackboard menu varies depending on what is available, and the result is French provincial cooking with a big heart and plenty of flavour. 'First-class' fish soup with rouille, warm salad of boudin noir (each piece of pudding on a croûton) with well-dressed salad leaves, fillet of pork with a grain mustard sauce, and tender, grilled pigeon breast in a rich winey sauce laced with armagnac have all been endorsed. The food is generally consistent, although sweets seem the least reliable aspect of the set-up: on the one hand, excellent meringue with pear and chocolate sauce; on the other, a passable tarte Tatin, and a crème brûlée that 'failed dismally'. Front-of-house man Phillipe Barre is the genial host who keeps things running smoothly, and has even been known to show off his talents in the kitchen. The wine list is short and wholly French, a movable feast that depends on what has been purchased in France or what food is on the day's menu. House wine is £8.45.

CHEF/PROPRIETOR: Eric Lecras OPEN: Sun L 12 to 1.30, Mon to Sat D 7 to 9.30 MEALS: Set L Sun £9.90, Set D Mon to Thur £15.80, Set D Fri and Sat £17.95 SERVICE: not inc CARDS: Access, Visa DETAILS: 55 seats. 5 tables outside. Private parties: 30 main room, 30 private room. Children welcome. Smart dress preferred. No cigars/pipes in dining-room. Music

Alfred

NEW ENTRY map 15

245 Shaftesbury Avenue, WC2H 8EH — COOKING 1*
TEL: 0171-240 2566 FAX: 0171-497 0672 — COST £24–£43

'A jolly place for the young and hungry', Alfred sits on a site previously occupied by other cheerful cafés. Before that 'it was owned by Cat Stevens's father'. It is Spartan, 'like a post-war boarding school', with close-packed Formica tables and '50s-style café chairs made in Czechoslovakia, and is 'full of happy people scoffing, chatting and quaffing'. The enthusiasm of Fred Taylor and Robert Gutteridge for British food is evident in toad-in-the-hole, calf's liver with bubble and squeak, faggots, fish-cakes and treacle tart.

A seat-of-the-pants appeal comes across in rough, gutsy, tasty boar sausages with colcannon potatoes, outsize guinea-fowl served 'in its entirety', and ham hock with a crunchy topping of mustard and demerara sugar served with mounds of pease pudding, pickled cabbage and a chutney-ish apple compote. Sauces can be buttery-rich, and one reporter found the all-purpose 'kitchen gravy' went better with some dishes than others. Puddings vary in their appeal, but mango ice-cream in a brandy-snap chalice, and gingerbread with lavender custard have both been endorsed. Friendly, cheerful, attentive service is laid on by 'staff in short white jackets which reminded me of the one I wore as a medical student'. It is all helped along by 'masses of marvellous beers and ciders', including bottle-conditioned Shepherd Neame Spitfire ale, some English wines (by the glass too) and a few malt whiskies. House French red and English white are £10.50.

CHEF: Robert Gutteridge PROPRIETOR: Fred Taylor OPEN: Mon to Sat 12 to 3.30, 6 to 11.30 CLOSED: bank hols MEALS: alc (main courses £8 to £11.50). Set L £11.95 (2 courses) to £15.90 SERVICE: not inc CARDS: Access, Amex, Diners, Visa DETAILS: 61 seats. 9 tables outside. Private parties: 10 main room. Vegetarian meals. Children's helpings. Smart dress preferred. Wheelchair access. No music. Air-conditioned

Al Hamra

map 15

31–33 Shepherd Market, W1Y 7RJ
TEL: 0171-493 1954 and 6934

COOKING 2
COST £31–£48

Most of the Mediterranean ingredients and ideas that currently find their way on to fashionable British restaurant tables hail from the northern and western end of the sea, around France, Spain and Italy. Few other restaurants bother with Middle Eastern offerings of fresh raw lambs' liver or fried lambs' testicles, and there is a rich vein of bits and bobs here that, but for Al Hamra, would remain untapped. No part of a lamb, it seems, is wasted, and anything not identifiable as brain (tossed in eggs), tongue (served in salads), or sweetbread (in lemon juice) is either mixed with cracked wheat to make kibbeh, or minced and chargrilled.

The food is equally strong on vegetables and pulses, using aubergines, rice, chickpeas, lemon juice, garlic, olive oil, herbs and spices in traditionally ingenious fashion. A meatless meal can offer a varied mix of halloumi cheese grilled on pastry, falafel (spiced and deep-fried ground chickpeas), stuffed vine leaves, foul medames (broad beans cooked in lemon juice and olive oil), or a Lebanese pizza. With nearly 100 dishes on offer there is no excuse for not finding something to suit. Sops to Western taste include smoked salmon, prawn cocktail and the wine list. Service has been wanting on occasion. A cover charge of £2.50 goes towards the colourful display of olives, carrots, radishes, lettuce and chilli peppers on each table. French house wine is £11.

CHEFS: Mahir Abboud and A. Rafiey Batah PROPRIETORS: Hassan Fansa and Riad Nabulsi OPEN: all week noon to 11.30 CLOSED: 25 Dec, 1 Jan MEALS: alc (main courses £9 to £12). Cover £2.50 SERVICE: not inc CARDS: Access, Amex, Diners, Visa DETAILS: 75 seats. 4 tables outside. Private parties: 80 main room. Vegetarian meals. Children welcome. Smart dress preferred. Wheelchair access. Music. Air-conditioned

All Saints

map 13

12 All Saints Road, W11 1HH — COOKING 1
TEL: 0171-243 2808 — COST £21–£45

All Saints wears its street cred on its sleeve, catering (like its near neighbour, Mas Café; see entry) for a diverse population, with an easy charm that encompasses avant-garde flavour combinations, low prices and a multiracial atmosphere. Shortcomings in comfort have to be seen in this context, but customers are mostly young and don't seem to mind. Decoration is all in the food, which is broadly Pacific Rim: the chefs are New Zealanders who range as far as Mexico for some of their ideas.

As might be expected, some of the cross-cultural combinations work better than others. Salmon with coconut rice, wilted spinach and a banana and mango chutney was '90 per cent there', on account of the quality and timing of the fish and judicious spicing, and a similar success rating applied to a chargrilled vegetable salad with coriander dressing and two thick triangles of toast topped with goats' cheese. Few lilies are left ungilded, though, and some of the cooking seems to be 'two ideas trying unsuccessfully to combine'. Puddings are simpler and more limited in scope, including pecan pie and good chocolate brownies. Service is pleasant and chatty, although not entirely clued up about the menu, and 14 wines begin at £8.50.

CHEFS: Dean Keddell and Carl Kopenhagen PROPRIETOR: Rupert Smith OPEN: Tue to Sun breakfast 10 to 12.30, L 12.30 to 3 (Sat brunch 10.30 to 3.30, Sun brunch 11 to 4), Mon to Sat D 7.30 to 11.30 CLOSED: Christmas, bank hol Mons MEALS: alc (main courses £5 to £14) SERVICE: not inc, card slips closed CARDS: Access, Delta, Switch, Visa DETAILS: 60 seats. Private parties: 20 main room, 20 private room. Vegetarian meals. Children welcome. Wheelchair access (2 steps). Music

Al San Vincenzo

map 13

30 Connaught Street, W2 2AF — COOKING 2*
TEL: 0171-262 9623 — COST £31–£57

The compact dining-room, 'like a small converted shop', is tastefully decorated yet unpretentious, with a few prints and black and white pictures of Italy on the walls. This is a traditional restaurant in the Italian sense, which is to say it serves simple food very well, and the menu is blessedly free from the usual 'new Italian' clichés. 'The food is refreshingly itself, authentic and untrendy,' writes an inspector. The relatively straightforward and often rustic assemblies of hot tongue with salsa verde, or octopus and potato stew may look easy, but they don't work unless really good ingredients are used.

Quality is evident in such dishes as baked sea bass, 'beautifully moist and fresh tasting', stuffed with herbs and a traditional Italian trio of celery, carrot and onion. To one side, 'a fragrant puddle of olive oil made a simple and perfect sauce'. At the same meal a risotto al vino Rubesco was simplicity itself and 'perfectly executed'. Quibbles about vegetables and timing have surfaced this year, pasta seems to have been more mundane of late, and bread has been variable in quality. Puddings go beyond tiramisù to a semifreddo di zabaglione with Amaretto – two slices of marsala-rich mousse surrounded by crushed amaretto biscuits and a sparse syrup – which is 'light in texture, heavy on flavour', while an almondy, rich cheesecake on coffee sauce is 'far removed from the usual stodge which the word cheesecake evokes'.

Although there is not a lot wrong with the food, reporters do not always come away with the sense of well-being they feel they should, partly thanks to 'grumpy', 'inhospitable and charmless' service experienced on occasion by some. Any restaurant that is deemed (in the words of one reporter) to 'suit its own convenience rather than that of its customers' might do well to sit down and take stock. The short wine list is well put together and not greedily priced, with house wine at £11, and four good pudding wines by the glass.

CHEF: Vincenzo Borgonzolo PROPRIETORS: Vincenzo and Elaine Borgonzolo OPEN: Mon to Fri L 12.30 to 1.45, Mon to Sat D 7 to 10 CLOSED: 2 weeks Christmas MEALS: alc (main courses £11.50 to £21) SERVICE: not inc; 12.5% on parties of 5 or more CARDS: Access, Visa DETAILS: 22 seats. Private parties: 6 main room. Smart dress preferred. No cigars/pipes in dining-room. Music

L'Altro

map 13

210 Kensington Park Road, W11 1NR — COOKING 1
TEL: 0171-792 1066 FAX: 0171-792 1077 — COST £19–£57

The setting is rustic, with 'aged' plaster, wrought ironwork, wooden tables and chairs (a couple of them outside in hot weather), and the feeling for one reporter that it is 'rather like eating in the back streets of Rome'. The style is casual, full of young people enjoying themselves, and 'can get noisy and smoke-filled'. Part of the reason for enjoyment is the lunchtime spread of antipasto dishes at bargain prices: from gratin of baby artichokes to sweetbreads with wild mushrooms, from gnocchi and ravioli to various salads, as well as chunks of grilled ciabatta covered with smoked pancetta and mozzarella, or with tomato and basil. Some of these selections increase in size and price to become first courses at dinner. Menus change often enough to stay lively, and fish plays a starring role, taking in grilled squid with chilli and lemon, spaghetti with lobster, or whole fresh sea bass with fresh herbs. 'Lots of healthy eating', concluded one regular, who adds that 'generally speaking all the pasta dishes are worth having'. Vegetarians might take these pasta starters as main courses, or the restaurant will prepare something specially with advance notice. Wines on the short Italian list are well chosen and fairly priced, with house wine at £8.90.

CHEF: Massimo Bianchi PROPRIETOR: Raymond Butler OPEN: all week L 12 to 3, Mon to Sat D 7 to 11 MEALS: alc (main courses L £7 to £12.50, D £12.50 to £19.50). Set L £10 (2 courses) to £12.50 SERVICE: not inc; 12½% for parties of 5 or more CARDS: Access, Amex, Delta, Diners, Switch, Visa DETAILS: 45 seats. 3 tables outside. Private parties: 40 main room. Children's helpings. Wheelchair access. Music. Air-conditioned

Anna's Place

map 13

90 Mildmay Park, N1 4PR — COOKING 2
TEL: 0171-249 9379 — COST £24–£38

This is as much a neighbourhood restaurant as a Swedish one. Tables are set close, adding to the already strong feeling of friendliness the place generates, and staff are young and enthusiastic. Pictures, ornaments and *objets trouvés* have been added over the years but stop short of clutter, while the small garden has been made weather-resistant in conservatory style. The essentials of Swedish food seem to be salmon and herrings, or beef, variously cured or smoked, a small compass that nevertheless provides variety. In case it doesn't there may well be pasta, a fresh fish and vegetarian dish of the day, and perhaps an apple pie or ice-cream for those not tempted by dark rich chocolate cake or blueberry waffles.

Cured fish is meaty and moist, and the well-tried partnership with mustard and dill sauce as successful as anywhere: the restaurant has been here for 20 years and counts as a pioneer of gravad lax. Dumplings, and potatoes – boiled, in pancakes, or cooked in dauphinois style – add bulk, and temper the sometimes concentrated flavours. Biff Strindberg is not the playwright's brother but diced fillet of high-quality beef marinated in mustard and sauté. The short wine list is sensibly priced, with four wines available by the glass from £2.

CHEFS: Beth Diadone and Peter Abrahamsson PROPRIETOR: Anna Hegarty OPEN: Tue to Sat 12.15 to 2.15, 7.15 to 10.30 CLOSED: 2 weeks Christmas, 2 weeks Easter, 3 weeks Aug, first week Sept MEALS: alc (main courses £8 to £11.50) SERVICE: 10% CARDS: none DETAILS: 42 seats. 5 tables outside. Private parties: 12 main room. Vegetarian meals. Children's helpings. Wheelchair access. Music

Arisugawa map 15

27 Percy Street, W1P 9FF COOKING 3
TEL: 0171-636 8913 FAX: 0171-323 4236 COST £27–£64

This is the serious face of Japanese food in London, a restaurant of myriad parts devoted to public and private eating, tradition and ceremony. Go through the door and you are in the teppan room, but the most interesting space is downstairs, where there is a sushi bar, a triangular counter containing a miniature stone garden and several separated rooms (including one with a hanging sculpture incorporating a lantern and a cooking pot). Most amazing of all is a remarkably designed platform eating area with sliding partitions so that tables can be combined or separated. This is a shoe-free zone: slippers are apparently provided for anyone visiting the lavatory. Japanese waitresses in kimonos drift around, serving with other-worldly charm.

The understated minimalist elegance of the décor is matched by cooking of a high order. Mr Takeuchi is one of the few Japanese chefs with a licence to prepare and cook fugu fish, although diners are unlikely to find this potentially life-threatening species on the menu. Instead, there are various set dinners built around teriyaki, sashimi and the like, plus a more challenging *carte* and a separate list of specialities inscribed on a fan in untranslated Japanese. Lunch is a simpler and cheaper assortment of good-value dishes. Ingredients are as fresh as can be; flavours are finely tuned and delicate rather than strikingly intensive. The quality of the sushi is outstanding, and the kitchen can also deliver an exquisite assortment of appetisers, including namaune-ponzu (chilled sea urchin with a vinegar sauce and a garnish of seaweed and cucumber). Yakimono (grilled dishes) include a version with quail's eggs, which you can order either salted or with soya sauce. Elsewhere there are faultless sunomono and tempura specialities, and the kitchen has full mastery of the art of tsukemono (salting and pickling vegetables). Six different kinds come with rice as the signal that a meal is drawing to its close: amazingly crisp and crunchy turnips and astringent

plums have been singled out for praise. Most people drink tea, Japanese beer or saké. House wine is £10.

CHEF: Akira Takeuchi PROPRIETOR: Masako Yamamoto OPEN: Mon to Fri L 12.30 to 2.30, Mon to Sat D 6 to 10.30 (10 in winter) CLOSED: bank hols MEALS: alc (main courses £7 to £16). Set L £7 to £12, Set D £25 to £40. Cover £1 SERVICE: 15%, card slips closed CARDS: Access, Amex, Diners, Switch, Visa DETAILS: 100 seats. Private parties: 100 main room. Vegetarian meals. Children welcome. No music. Air-conditioned

Les Associés map 12

172 Park Road, N8 8JY COOKING 1
TEL: 0181-348 8944 COST £26–£45

The setting is a two-storey terraced house, opposite the public baths, on a traffic-clogged road between Crouch End and Alexandra Palace, but Les Associés makes the best of it and continues as a useful neighbourhood eating place. The artwork on the walls may not be to everyone's taste, but the décor is generally pleasing and there are a few 'highbrow' touches in the huge plates and the untranslated French menu. Chef and co-proprietor Gilles Charvet has moved on, and his place in the kitchen has been taken by Marc Spindler. Lunch has been abandoned, but the thrust of the cooking is much as before, although some details still need to be sharpened up. The short *carte* is bolstered by a few daily specials, including Barbary duck with garlic sauce, and nicely cooked skate served on a pile of braised chicory surrounded by stalks of white asparagus. Fish also shows up well in salad of grilled red mullet, and gratiné fillet of lemon sole in a sabayon sauce laced with citrus juice. Choices on the carnivorous front could range from lamb cutlets in fennel sauce to fillet of beef with tomato béarnaise. The special selection of desserts is a competently handled assortment including nougat glacé, tarte Tatin ('a good one') and strawberry mousse. Service is friendly. The wine list is short and Gallic, with a few bottles from out-of-the-way regions. House wine is £9.80.

CHEF: Marc Spindler PROPRIETORS: Didier Bertran and Dominique Chéhere OPEN: Tue to Sun D only 7.30 to 10 MEALS: alc (main courses £10 to £14) SERVICE: not inc, card slips closed CARDS: Access, Switch, Visa DETAILS: 38 seats. Private parties: 20 main room. Children's helpings. Wheelchair access. Music

Atelier NEW ENTRY map 15

41 Beak Street, W1R 3LE COOKING 2*
TEL: 0171-287 2057 COST £26–£48

Gone are the days of cooking quietly and waiting for success to arrive in its own good time. Stephen Bulmer worked with Raymond Blanc, the one-man training academy for some of Britain's brightest culinary hopes. There he met Joanna Shannon, who had escaped from advertising (although not entirely, to judge by Atelier's press releases). Together they threw architects and designers at the premises near Carnaby Street where Canaletto once lived – hence the name. To emphasise the point, canvas has been stretched across metal frames and the results parked down one side of the long, thin, terracotta-coloured dining-room 'as if waiting until somebody decides what to do with them'. The cutlery is stylish steel, stamped, a little disconcertingly, with 'David Mellor'.

The point is, Atelier comes impressively packaged in all departments, promising good things, and much of the time it delivers. 'This is seriously good food,' writes one who compliments the kitchen on not being afraid to keep the menu short – there are five choices at each course of the *carte*, one or two on the fixed-price menu – and on keeping prices at a manageable level. Successes have included 'an intense and deeply satisfying spinach soup with nutmeg cream', and a daube of beef with horseradish mash and a red wine sauce that rated as 'one of the best-conceived and executed casseroles' the reporter had eaten. Where it needs to be, the food is light, helped by an attractively varied array of sauces, from basil-scented oil, which is served with a tomato and olive tart, to a herb purée, a lemon sabayon and a mustard-seed sauce, all served on the same plate as a monkfish tail. The reporter who ate it, though, wondered if just one sauce might not have sufficed. 'Service is willing, human and mostly male.' The short but varied wine list includes seven or eight by the glass, and house Vin de Pays des Côtes du Tarn is £9.95.

CHEF: Stephen Bulmer PROPRIETORS: Stephen Bulmer and Joanna Shannon OPEN: Mon to Fri L 12 to 2.30, Mon to Sat D 6 to 10.45 CLOSED: 2 weeks Christmas, 2 weeks Aug, bank hols MEALS: alc (main courses £14 to £16). Set L £14.50 (2 courses) to £17, Set D £14.50 (2 courses) and £17 SERVICE: 10% (optional) CARDS: Access, Amex, Delta, Diners, Switch, Visa DETAILS: 45 seats. Private parties: 60 main room, 16 private room. Vegetarian meals. Children's helpings. Wheelchair access. Music

Atlantic Bar and Grill

NEW ENTRY map 15

20 Glasshouse Street, W1 5RQ — COOKING 1*
TEL: 0171-734 4888 FAX: 0171-734 3609 — COST £24–£55

'If you can get past the intimidating roped-off entrance, the cacophonous racket that has you yelling all through dinner, and the mind-blowingly pretentious menu-writing, there is quite a good restaurant at the heart of it all.' Greeting is done by 'a bloke in an Andy Pandy suit and a girl in a swishy linen trouser ensemble', one of whom unhooks the rope (provided you have enough glamour or a booking) and, 'brimful of corporate well-wishing', sweeps you downstairs to the bar and restaurant. The space is huge, 'like an Art Deco air-raid shelter', with mighty marble pillars, and lazy propellers on the ceiling, while music blasts out at nightclub intensity all around.

The outsize menu is 'just the right size to send glasses flying', and reads like a pastiche of Californian menu-speak. Provenance, variety and colour are given priority, as in Azura tomatoes, Meyer lemons, black fig ratatouille (really a chutney), or spiny blue crab soup. Behind all the bluster, slowly roasted belly-pork is sweetly fatty, with a lush pile of salad leaves heavily dressed with an assertive mustard vinaigrette, and rare duck breast is 'as tender as red meat gets', served with 'smoked sweet-potato pancakes' that turn out to be ordinary rösti. 'Suddenly bananas are respectable,' noted a close follower of fashion between mouthfuls of a baked one sitting on brioche toast with a scoop of toffee ice-cream. The cooking is prone to 'significant fluctuations' in execution, but reporters are prepared to give it the benefit of the doubt, and at least the ideas are bold and lively. Staff are quick on the uptake, and wines are sharp, running all the way from La Serre Sauvignon Blanc and Syrah to first-growth claret, by way of two dozen from the New World. Good drinking under £20 includes a house selection of 16 wines all available by the glass from £2.10.

CHEF: Richard Sawyer PROPRIETORS: Oliver and Siobhan Peyton OPEN: Mon to Sat L 12 to 3, all week D 6 to 12 (7 to 11.30 Sun) CLOSED: 25 Dec, 1 Jan MEALS: alc (main courses £6.50 to £15.50). Set L £11.90 (2 courses) SERVICE: not inc; 12.5% on parties of 8 or more CARDS: Access, Amex, Delta, Switch, Visa DETAILS: 160 seats. Private parties: 10 main room, 60 private room. Vegetarian meals. Wheelchair access (also WC). Music. Air-conditioned

Aubergine

map 14

11 Park Walk, SW10 0AJ — COOKING **4**
TEL: 0171-352 3449 FAX: 0171-351 1770 — COST £33–£72

'It is very difficult to get in,' wrote one reporter. Having failed once, 'the following day I tried it in French and got a table'. Although the chef was born in Scotland, Aubergine is really a modern French restaurant, whose popularity may seem surprising, given that brasseries seem to hold all the fashionable aces at the moment. But 'the food is complex, looks sensational, and flavour is paramount'. Prices may have crept up since last year, but that was only to be expected of a restaurant with a waiting-list for every meal-time. Renovation at the beginning of 1995 improved its attraction: warm colours, discreet lighting, wooden floors, screens and mirrors produce a feeling of both space and privacy.

Despite its popularity, this is not just a place where all the year's fads fetch up, although it does go into frothy cappuccino mode quite a bit, whether using the brew as a sort of non-alcoholic aperitif or as a way of making sauces appear ultra-light. 'In my opinion his cappuccino of roasted langoustines will become famous for its intensity and lightness,' predicted one. Intensity and lightness are certainly hallmarks of the style, and are particularly apparent in fish. Ravioli of lobster is served with baby spinach and a ginger cream, fillet of roasted John Dory comes with a cream of peas, while choucroute of fish is a vehicle for presenting the day's trawl from the market, and for showing off accurate cooking. Other successes have included mackerel with lime and coriander, and 'well-balanced and subtle' roasted sea bass with vanilla sauce.

Some may wonder about such fine points as whether the repertoire is developing, or whether the food has acquired its own confident identity, but there is no doubt that it pleases a large number of reporters. Wonderful fish, oils, salads and vegetables are offset off with just enough luxury from foie gras, lobster and wild mushrooms, and the cooking works equally well with a plain, understated dish of pigeon, the breasts in a light stock, the legs on a roundel of spinach, as with a tortellini of ratatouille in a buttery tomato sauce. Flavours can be bold, but are well controlled. Among puddings, pistachio soufflé has been 'brilliant', prune and armagnac ice-cream is exemplary, and the same process of slow roasting that brings out intense flavours in, say, tomatoes, also works for strawberries, slices of which at one meal added a vivid edge to a crème brûlée.

Food of this quality deserves a no-smoking area, and some may find it surprising that women are handed menus without prices. The three-course lunch is considered 'terrific value for money'. Staff can get carried away with their own enthusiasm, but this is the acceptable face of Gallic service: 'charming, helpful and informative'. The same wine waiter who will treat you to a rapturous account of the exotic fruit flavours in a New Zealand Sauvignon Blanc will also point out that the vintage has changed and recommend 'an improbably good Pinot Noir to accompany our awkward range of main courses'. France naturally dominates the list, and there are some good vintages in the right places, but mark-ups are on the high side. House French is £15, and ten wines are available by the glass from £4 to £8

CHEF/PROPRIETOR: Gordon Ramsay OPEN: Mon to Fri L 12.15 to 2.30, Mon to Sat D 7 to 11 CLOSED: 2 weeks Christmas, Easter, 2 weeks Aug, bank hols MEALS: Set L £19.50, Set D £34 to £44 SERVICE: not inc CARDS: Access, Amex, Delta, Diners, Switch, Visa DETAILS: 50 seats. Private parties: 6 main room. Children welcome. Smart dress preferred. No cigars/pipes in dining-room. No music. Air-conditioned

Au Jardin des Gourmets  map 15

5 Greek Street, W1V 6NA — COOKING 2
TEL: 0171-437 1816 FAX: 0171-437 0043 — COST £37–£55

There has been plenty going on in the Jardin in recent years, the uprooting and replanting involving a change of ownership in 1993, followed a year later by a new chef. Since Vincent Hiss took over at the stoves, there seems to have been a shift of emphasis from the ground-floor brasserie, where recessionary crowds once flocked, to the smartly formal first-floor restaurant. This is an idiosyncratic room, both in shape and in the mildly incongruous figurines of bears that take up much of the table surface.

The Jardin has long been one of Soho's bastions of culinary tradition. The restaurant *carte*, supported by a set-price menu of two courses, is as classically French as it ever was. A starter of salad of foie gras, prawns, scallops and smoked salmon, followed by breast of duck with redcurrants, and then strawberry sablé bear witness to time standing reassuringly still. When it works, the cooking is powerfully satisfying. An inspection meal began winningly with grilled sliced scallops on potato croustillant, and an earthy fricassee of forest mushrooms in an intensely reduced, but not syrupy, red wine and meat stock sauce. Main courses were similarly well sauced – girolles, port and cream for a breast of corn-fed chicken, textbook bordelaise for a fillet steak – although the meats themselves on this occasion were dry and thus undermined the success of both dishes. Vegetables might arrive on the plate, on a separate side-dish, or both. Tarte Tatin – 'more a puff pastry pie' – comes with honey ice-cream, but a triumph among puddings is a red fruit sabayon, served by one waiter who douses the berries in kirsch, followed by another who arrives with the flames. Coffee arrives with more petits fours than you may be able to eat.

'Lovely' would be to damn the wine list with faint praise. The principal focus is France, with clarets especially offering a majestic run back to 1945 Calon-Ségur, but genuine effort has been made to find pedigree wines across a range of prices from all over the world, and there's a good spread of halves. House wines start with Duboeuf at £9.50. CELLARMAN'S CHOICE: Bourgogne Chardonnay 'La Vigne' 1993, Bouchard £14.50; Chorey-lès-Beaune 1991, Tollot-Beaut £25.50.

See inside the front cover for an explanation of the symbols used at the tops of entries.

CHEF: Vincent Hiss PROPRIETOR: Novoport Group Ltd OPEN: Mon to Fri L 12.15 to 2.30, Mon to Sat D 6.30 to 11.15 CLOSED: Christmas, Easter, bank hol L MEALS: alc (main courses £12.50 to £16.50). Set L and D £16.75 (2 courses). Cover £1.50 SERVICE: 15%, card slips closed CARDS: Access, Amex, Delta, Diners, Switch, Visa DETAILS: 75 seats. Private parties: 55 main room, 12 to 55 private rooms. Vegetarian meals. Children's helpings. Smart dress preferred. No smoking in 1 dining room. No music. Air-conditioned

L'Aventure

map 13

3 Blenheim Terrace, NW8 0EH — COOKING 1
TEL: 0171-624 6232 FAX: 0171-625 5548 — COST £28–£44

Discreetly tucked away in a sheltered cul-de-sac not far from Lords cricket ground, L'Aventure is a crowd-pleaser for the locals, and a useful spot for those who want to eat away from the centre of town. You can sit in the dining-room with its abundance of brown wood, natural brick walls and flowers, or make for the glassed-in terrace (which gives the impression of eating al fresco when the doors are thrown open). Daily fixed-price menus are augmented by a few specials, and the cooking is true to its French roots. Fish lovers might be tempted by scallops with basil, sea bass with ratatouille, or turbot with a leek fondue, while those with more red- blooded affections could go for magret of duck with pears and ginger or garlicky rack of lamb 'en chemise'. Snails appear in puff pastry with oyster mushrooms, while smoked salmon can be found in crêpes. Desserts are well-tried offerings, such as tarte Tatin, chocolate mousse and îles flottantes. The wine list is wholeheartedly French, although prices are far from bistro. House wine starts the ball rolling at £14.25.

CHEF: Alain Perdrix PROPRIETOR: L'Aventure Ltd OPEN: Mon to Fri L 12.30 to 2.30, Mon to Sat D 7.30 to 11 MEALS: Set L £18.50, Set D £25 SERVICE: not inc CARDS: Access, Amex, Delta, Visa DETAILS: 40 seats. 6 tables outside. Private parties: 50 main room. Vegetarian meals. Children's helpings. No cigars/pipes in dining-room. Music

Bahn Thai

map 15

21A Frith Street, W1V 5TS — COOKING 2
TEL: 0171-437 8504 — COST £25–£41

Philip Harris's Soho restaurant remains one of the premier-league Thai addresses in central London, and it is capable of delivering authentic food from a long menu peppered with interesting ingredients. Lunch on the ground floor can become a boisterous, bistro-style occasion. Order a handful of starters or have a stab at the whole menu.

This is not a kitchen that goes in for flamboyant garnishes or arty presentation. Dishes are served unfussily on plain stone-coloured plates, bowls and pots, and portions are restrained. The results are, for the most part, impressive: khanom jeep (dim-sum dumplings) with a 'sexily good' warm soy and garlic sauce, ferocious hot-and-sour scallop salad, superbly fresh king prawns stir-fried with chillies and Thai basil, and al dente asparagus bathed in a garlicky oyster sauce have all hit the button. Occasionally a dish falls flat: fried pomfret appeared to be dried out rather than crispy, with a tamarind sauce that seemed to be composed largely of sieved tomatoes. But one senior reporter concluded that kaeng kiew wan was unquestionably the best Thai curry he had ever eaten: pieces of chicken and baby aubergines were cooked in an exact broth that was hot and creamily soothing at the same time, 'with loads of fragrance and freshness zinging around'. If Bahn Thai has an Achilles' heel it is the service, which seems increasingly variable. At times the waitresses cannot be more helpful or charming, but they have also been described as slow and off-hand, a state of affairs not helped by severe language difficulties from time to time. Singha Thai beer and chrysanthemum tea suit the food, as does the thoughtfully assembled wine list. House wine is £7.95.

CHEF: Penn Squires PROPRIETOR: Philip Harris OPEN: Mon to Sat L 12 to 2.45, Sun L 12.30 to 2.30, Mon to Sat D 6 to 11.15, Sun D 6.30 to 10.30 CLOSED: Christmas, Easter, bank hols MEALS: alc (main courses £7 to £20) SERVICE: 12.5% (optional), card slips closed CARDS: Access, Amex, Diners, Switch, Visa DETAILS: 100 seats. 4 tables outside. Private parties: 50 main room, 20 and 30 private rooms. Vegetarian meals. Children welcome. Smart dress preferred. No cigars/pipes in dining-room. Wheelchair access (1 step; also WC). Music. Air-conditioned

Belgo Noord

map 13

72 Chalk Farm Road, NW1 8AN — COOKING 1

TEL: 0171-267 0718 FAX: 0171-267 7508 — COST £24–£47

Three of Belgium's greatest gifts to the world are mussels, chips and beer. Debate rages over the fourth. As far as Belgo Noord is concerned, the first three will do fine, thank you very much. It is really good at those, and although other dishes appear on the menu, the general opinion is that such a simple order is not only a good buy – a kilo of mussels with chips for £8.95 – but will also save valuable time ploughing through the various set-meal and *carte* options, since tables are usually rented for about two hours. However, the options are worth considering: a lunchtime pot of mussels, chips and a Hoegaarden beer for £5, or the early-evening 'beat-the-clock' formula when you pay (for selected dishes) according to the time you order – hence an order at 6.05pm costs £6.05, and so on until £8.00pm.

'Mussels good, sausage good, salad superb, beer good, bread very good' ran one cryptic endorsement from a reporter who resisted the temptations of a waterzooi of North Sea fish, carbonade flamande, choucroute, and lobster. The noise level is high when the place is full, beery talk bouncing off the grey walls decorated with the names of obscure fish. There are Hoegaarden and Jupiler beers on tap, Trappist Chimay, and ales as strong as wine. Service might be 'patchy', but the service charge is 15 per cent anyway. Belgo has now opened another branch called Belgo Centraal (see entry, London round-ups).

CHEFS: Philippe Blaise and Poul Jensen PROPRIETORS: Denis Blais and André Plisnier OPEN: Mon to Fri 12 to 3, 6 to 11.30, Sat noon to 11, Sun noon to 10.30 CLOSED: 25 and 26 Dec MEALS: alc (main courses £8 to £16). Set L £5 (1 course, inc beer) to £10 (2 courses, inc beer), Set D £8.95 to £10 (both 2 courses, £10 inc beer) SERVICE: 15% (optional), card slips closed CARDS: Access, Amex, Delta, Diners, Switch, Visa DETAILS: 110 seats. Private parties: 10 main room. Vegetarian meals. Children's helpings. Smart dress preferred. Wheelchair access (2 steps; also WC). No music. Air-conditioned

Bertorelli's 🍷 map 15

44A Floral Street, WC2E 9DA COOKING 1
TEL: 0171-836 3969 FAX: 0171-836 1868 COST £23–£50

Bertorelli's lays claim to being one of London's oldest Italian restaurants, established before the First World War, and relocated in Covent Garden in 1981. It faces the stage door of the Royal Opera House, so diners may encounter corpulent tenors flushed with post-operatic triumph taking refuge here after the last curtain call. Maddalena Bonino brought with her a formidable breadth of culinary knowledge when she arrived in 1992.

Eating is on two levels: simple café fare in the basement, modern Italian cooking on the ground floor. A salad of marinated smoked eel and monkfish with roasted red peppers, deep-fried caperberries and bruschetta might get the taste-buds going to start, followed by fried pork cutlet on agrodolce peppers with a sauce flavoured with Sardinian myrtle liqueur, and there are also stimulating pasta sauces. A 'rather patchy' winter meal began with roast artichoke with smoked tuna strips of curious texture, but progressed to considerably better roasted monkfish with salsa verde. Apricot flan with maraschino cream, and cappuccino roll with caramel sauce add interest to a dessert menu centred on the Italian standards and lots of ice-cream. Friendly service contributes to a warm atmosphere. The wine list marshals many of the best Italian growers and offers plenty of its wares by the glass. Prices start at £8.50. CELLARMAN'S CHOICE: Regaleali Bianco 1993, Sicily, £14.50; Le Volte 1993, Antinori, £21.

CHEF: Maddalena Bonino PROPRIETOR: Groupe Chez Gérard Restaurants Ltd OPEN: Mon to Sat 12 to 3, 5.30 to 11.30 CLOSED: 25 and 26 Dec MEALS: alc (main courses £7.50 to £16). Cover £1.50 SERVICE: 12.5% (optional), card slips closed CARDS: Access, Amex, Delta, Diners, Switch, Visa DETAILS: 85 seats. Private parties: 36 main room. Car park at D. Vegetarian meals. Children's helpings. Wheelchair access (1 step). No music. Air-conditioned

Bibendum  map 14

Michelin House, 81 Fulham Road, SW3 6RD COOKING 3*
TEL: 0171-581 5817 FAX: 0171-823 7925 COST £37–£81

The Art Deco building is wonderful. How could it ever have been a garage? It was surely wasted on cars. Light shines in through a mixture of stained-and clear-glass windows, bringing to life one of London's most individual, distinctive and attractive dining-rooms. It looks good whatever the hour of day, or time of year – seat covers change colour to match the season – and feels comfortable without being given over to luxury. 'As ever, I found the whole experience spot-on in terms of ambience and service.' After eight successful years, Simon Hopkinson has exchanged his chef's hat for a word processor, and his sous chef of two years has taken over.

Inevitably, there have been comparisons with the Hopkinson regime, with some reporters happy to endorse Matthew Harris as a worthy and comparable successor (his brother Henry cooks at Fifth Floor; see entry, London). He has maintained some dishes in the repertoire, such as deep-fried cod and chips with tartare sauce, and punchy flavours still rule the roost in Baltic herrings, lightly textured salt-cod fish-cakes with a pungent tomato and coriander sauce, or salt-duck with beetroot chutney. At one meal, 'beautifully judged and creamy' risotto primavera came with broad beans, asparagus, peas and globe artichokes, among others, while a first-rate prosciutto, fontina and truffle tart looked a bit like a pizza but was made from buttery puff pastry. In both these dishes, and in several more, there is a richness that can build up over the course of a meal.

A few doubts have surfaced from inspectors' meals, such as an excellent calf's kidney, cooked delightfully pink, but seared so viciously that it tasted burnt and bitter, or a dry pithiviers of chocolate. And the chips, as one reporter put it, 'used to be some of the best in London'. Such things are easily remedied, and Bibendum stays mostly on track, including the dessert department, with its blackcurrant custard tart, and an acclaimed iced honey parfait with poached pears and a light caramel sauce. Olives and bread are as good as ever. 'Service is efficient and competent yet human', while lack of provision for non-smokers is regretted. 'Smoking has no place in a high-class restaurant,' maintained one reporter. The oyster bar downstairs offers simple, tasty, light meals that work well given the constraints of the small room, and deals in first-class fish, shellfish (a huge platter for two is £45), meat, salads, oils and vinegars.

The restaurant's wine list can appear daunting given the very high prices and the virtual blanket world coverage, in which case the 15 or so house wines come to the rescue, some of them available by the glass or in a 45cl pot. But if time and pocket permit, the list is well worth exploring: it is full of gems, has just about every style in the book, with long runs from Burgundy villages, and ancient vintages in Bordeaux and among sweet wines. CELLARMAN'S CHOICE: Bourgogne Blanc 1992, Coche-Dury, £32.50; Savigny-lès-Beaune, Pavelot, £31.50.

CHEF: Matthew Harris PROPRIETORS: Sir Terence Conran, Paul Hamlyn, Simon Hopkinson and Graham Williams OPEN: all week 12.30 to 2.30 (3 Sat and Sun), 7 to 11.30 MEALS: alc D (main courses £12.50 to £22). Set L £27 SERVICE: 12.5% (optional), card slips closed CARDS: Access, Amex, Delta, Switch, Visa DETAILS: 72 seats. Vegetarian meals. Children's helpings. Wheelchair access (1 step). No music. Air-conditioned

Billboard Café £

map 13

222 Kilburn High Road, NW6 4JP — COOKING 1
TEL: 0171-328 1374 FAX: 0171-625 1550 — COST £15–£40

It's best to know what to expect if you are planning a first-time visit here. The location is a less-than-salubrious part of Kilburn High Road, and the building itself has been described as a 'bleak echoey barn'. Rock music is loud enough to drown out the traffic noise, there are large abstract paintings on the walls, and the high-ceilinged room has air ducts above the glass frontage. Oddly, it seems to appeal to more than just a young crowd. The menu is 'straight-up modern Italian' with a few faint echoes of 'California dreaming' along the way. Pasta is made on the premises, but has not always pleased; soups were found at inspection to be 'lacking pizazz'. Much better are the fish choices: 'excellent' squid (the bodies grilled, the tentacles marinated in lemon juice) is piled on to a colourful salad assemblage; grilled shark steak is paired with grilled vegetables and roasted new potatoes. Elsewhere, the menu woos the carnivorous. Desserts are in the mould of dark chocolate rum mousse and tiramisù. Coffee appears in all its fashionable guises, including latte. The Billboard is also a useful Sunday

daytime spot with flexible brunch and lunch menus. Around 20 fairly priced wines are gleaned mostly from Italy and the New World. House wine is £7.45.

CHEF: Nasser Nateghi PROPRIETORS: Nasser Nateghi and Lindsay Smith OPEN: Sat and Sun L 12 to 2.45, Mon to Sat D 6.30 to 12 (12.30 Fri and Sat) MEALS: alc (main courses £5 to £12.50). Set brunch Sat and Sun £6.50, Set D £10 to £15 SERVICE: 10%, card slips closed CARDS: Access, Delta, Switch, Visa DETAILS: 65 seats. Private parties: 65 main room. Vegetarian meals. Children's helpings. Smart dress preferred. Wheelchair access. Music. Air-conditioned

Bistrot Bruno

map 15

63 Frith Street, W1V 5TA COOKING 3
TEL: 0171-734 4545 FAX: 0171-287 1027 COST £25–£44

Not all reporters come here for the décor. The blank walls and minimal design feel 'like a camouflaged air-raid shelter with 1950s coffee-house furniture' for one. Close-set tables, hard seats and a usually crowded room generate a good-humoured, bistro-like atmosphere – 'lively and cramped' in one estimation – although some wonder why it is not called a restaurant since the hearty French food points in that direction, offering grilled quail with liver crostini, beef paupiette in juniper sauce with gnocchi, or roast rack of lamb with merguez sausage and saffron mash. 'One always feels well nourished,' summed up one regular on his way out.

It is the informality and exuberance of the cooking that delight, from a version of rabbit rillettes served with home-made piccalilli to black pudding with mashed potato cake, from roast mackerel with Indian spices to woodpigeon cooked rare and served with mash and a rhubarb and onion marmalade. Flavours are as direct as a curried salt-cod brandade, or sauces of Roquefort or strong mustard for duck, while mashed potatoes are typically on hand to soak up any liquid. 'Each dish we ordered was packed with flavour, accurately cooked and beautifully presented.' Meals finish with bread-and-butter pudding, strawberries and ice-cream, or rice pudding with orange and cardamom. The only cloud on the horizon has been that while plans are taking shape for Bruno Loubet's new venture, L'Odéon in Regent Street, where he is scheduled to do the cooking, he may have let his attention wander slightly from the kitchen here, which brings in a slightly uneven performance, and inevitably under such circumstances some reporters question the value. Three dozen flavoursome wines, including Dom. Virginie Syrah and South African Mulderbosch Sauvignon Blanc, are mostly under £20 and do their bit to keep the final tally in perspective.

CHEFS: Bruno Loubet and Jason Hornbuchle PROPRIETORS: Kathleen and Pierre Condou OPEN: Mon to Fri L 12.30 to 2.30, Mon to Sat D 6.15 to 11.30 CLOSED: Christmas to New Year MEALS: alc (main courses £10.50 to £16.50) SERVICE: not inc CARDS: Access, Amex, Diners, Switch, Visa DETAILS: 42 seats. Private parties: 12 main room. Children's helpings. No cigars/pipes in dining-room. Wheelchair access (2 steps). Music. Air-conditioned

The text of entries is based on unsolicited reports sent in by readers, backed up by inspections conducted anonymously. The factual details under the text are from questionnaires the* Guide *sends to all restaurants that feature in the book.

Bistrot 190

map 14

190 Queen's Gate, SW7 5EU — COOKING 1*
TEL: 0171-581 5666 FAX: 0171-581 8172 — COST £22–£41

This is where the Worrall-Thompson phenomenon began, just around the corner from the Albert Hall, and 190 still functions on two levels: the ground-floor Bistrot, where only membership entitles you to make a reservation, and the smarter Downstairs. The Bistrot can turn out some more than competent renditions of AW-T signature dishes. A correspondent who considers he ate very well enjoyed stewed mussels in a hot-and-sour broth ('a pleasant change from marinière'), Barnsley chop with ratatouille vegetables, and 'notably good' Valencia orange cake served with yoghurt and honey. One reporter thought his Caesar salad 'lovely', while another found the mayonnaise dressing made it 'unnecessarily heavy'. Who knows what he would make of a starter of smoked salmon with caponata toast and anchovy ice-cream?

There seems to be a tendency to cook meats for slightly too long, but the accompaniments are spot-on, from good thin frites to a 'large, succulent field mushroom coated with melted Taleggio' served with rump steak. Vibrant desserts include chocolate cake with mascarpone and coffee sauce, and lemon and lime tart with blackberry coulis. As at other AW-T places, the wine list offers individual merchants the chance to make a selection from their current lists on a quarterly basis. The house wines from France, Italy and Chile are £8.50 and £10.50. Downstairs offers the same kind of cooking in a more opulent room; service on both floors has had its ups and downs.

CHEF: Antony Worrall-Thompson PROPRIETOR: 190 Queen's Gate plc OPEN: all week noon to midnight CLOSED: 25 Dec MEALS: alc (main courses £7 to £13). Set L Sun £14.50 SERVICE: not inc, card slips closed; 10% for parties of 6 or more CARDS: Access, Amex, Diners, Switch, Visa DETAILS: 60 seats. Private parties: 150 main room, 27 private room. Vegetarian meals. Children welcome. Smart dress preferred. Wheelchair access. Music

▲ *Blakes*

map 14

33 Roland Gardens, SW7 3PF — COOKING 2*
TEL: 0171-370 6701 FAX: 0171-373 0442 — COST £48–£111

Lady Weinberg's sleek South Kensington hotel is an unfading snapshot of '80s opulence. Monochrome minimalism was the way then, so Blakes is black. Off the lobby a flight of stairs leads down to one of the most heavily designer restaurants in town, a room without a view, partitioned in glass and discreetly lit with ceiling spots. Walls are adorned with framed clothing of the mountain people of Thailand. Patrons in Versace and with diamonds as big as the Ritz mingle with summer diners dressed for the beach in sunglasses, T-shirts and shorts.

The food is a resourceful agglomeration of world cookery, with Italian and French modes probably outshouted by oriental influences: Chinese roasts, Indian marinades, Japanese fingerfood. As the *Guide* went to press last year, Neville Campbell was promoted to head chef, and the style-conscious approach continues. At a July dinner, for example, first courses were preceded by the arrival of a glass box containing a dozen quails' eggs on a layer of crisps. When a langoustine salad came, the minimalism began to pall: six delicately cooked shellfish garnished with one tiny leaf and no dressing: £18.25, if you please. Making a better impression was a main- course fillet of baked sea bass, 'the skin singed black and imbued with fennel', on a fennel underlay with 'well-executed' hollandaise. Visual conceits abound: more langoustines came sitting on chilli noodles sitting in a little lidded box of sesame-seeded filo, a pair of cheese straws on top like chopsticks. For all the fiddle-faddle, the tastes in this case worked well, a side-dish of chilli sauce aiding and abetting them. Chicken and crabmeat are worked into ovular form, tied with a string of nori, sauced with lime and ginger and baptised 'chicken Fabergé'.

Another box, this time of chocolate and holding an intense passion-fruit mousse, may turn up at dessert stage – 'the whole effect genuinely pleasing' – or there is much-praised cinder toffee parfait under barley brittle. Finish with high-roast Chagga coffee or gunpowder tea. The substantial outlay such artistry is thought to command is augmented by a top-whack 15 per cent service levy. In that context, it comes as no surprise to find the wine list preoccupied with champagne, white burgundy and claret. Whoever wrote it needs to know that the names of premier cru vineyards in Chablis need the names of the growers, especially if you are going to charge £70 per bottle. House wines are £18.

CHEF: Neville Campbell PROPRIETOR: Anouska Hempel (Lady Weinberg) OPEN: all week 12.30 to 3, 7.30 to 12 CLOSED: L 25 and 26 Dec MEALS: alc (main courses £22.50 to £24.50). Set L £26 (2 courses) to £32, Set post-theatre D £36 SERVICE: 15%, card slips closed CARDS: Access, Amex, Diners, Switch, Visa DETAILS: 40 seats. Private parties: 60 main room, 15 and 22 private rooms. Children welcome. Smart dress preferred. Music. Air-conditioned ACCOMMODATION: 52 rooms, all with bath/shower. TV. Phone. Some rooms air-conditioned. B&B £137 to £620. Children welcome. Baby facilities. Afternoon teas. Garden (*The Which? Hotel Guide*)

Blue Elephant

map 12

4–6 Fulham Broadway, SW6 1AA — COOKING 1*

TEL: 0171-385 6595 FAX: 0171-386 7665 — COST £28–£58

Designed to resemble a Thai village as seen though the eyes of a tour operator, complete with lush plants, waterfall and carp swimming in a pond, the Blue Elephant goes in for glamour in a big way – which isn't surprising since it is part of an international chain with branches in several European cities. The owners tell us that more than 500 kilograms of fresh vegetables, herbs and spices are flown in from Thailand each week, and that their chefs keep their hands off the MSG. The menu is as lavish as the décor, with deliberately evocative names and even more florid dish descriptions: sarika is 'a crisp golden cake from which prawns and juicy sweetcorn burst forth in a cascade of flavours, named after the famous waterfall in central Thailand'; sunburst pomelo salad is 'an awakening of citrus fruits from Nakornchaisri – the orchard province'; while floating market is the title of a 'seafood soup flavoured with lemon grass, makrude leaves and nam prik pao served in a beaten brass bowl'.

In more prosaic territory, the 70-dish menu also promises satays, fish-cakes, fiery stir-fried beef with baby aubergines, and Thai chicken soufflé steamed in a banana leaf, backed up by the usual rice and noodles. Prices are 'high', and not helped by the 15 per cent fixed service charge tacked on – although as the *Guide* went to press we were told that this was to be dropped. The wine list favours the

New World, although there is not much below £15, apart from the house wine at £10.30. A second branch, La Porte des Indes, is due to open in the winter of 1995 at 32 Bryanston Street, W1H 7AE, Tel: 0171-224 0055.

CHEF: Rungsan Mulijan PROPRIETOR: Blue Elephant International plc OPEN: Mon to Fri and Sun L 12 to 2.30, all week D 7 to 12.30 (10.30 Sun) MEALS: Set L and D £29 to £34 (min 2 for both). Cover £1.50 SERVICE: 15% CARDS: Access, Amex, Delta, Diners, Visa DETAILS: 250 seats. Private parties: 100 main room. Vegetarian meals. Children welcome. Smart dress preferred. Wheelchair access (2 steps; also WC). Music. Air-conditioned

Blue Print Café map 13

Design Museum, 22 Shad Thames,
Butlers Wharf, SE1 2YD COOKING 1
TEL: 0171-378 7031 FAX: 0171-378 6540 COST £28–£47

'An up-market works canteen' with 'a splendid view of the river and floodlit Tower Bridge' is one opinion, and a handy reminder to book a table by the window. The place has a busy hum and is likely to be 'filled with forty-somethings, mostly doing business...possibly arts rather than City'. The minimalism and plastic-topped tables may seem a bit dated now, but the food is still in the swim, with sun-dried tomatoes, red onion tart, Caesar salad, pasta, and lots of olive oil giving it an Italifornian thrust. Daniel Leberman has come up through the ranks to head the kitchen, and the repertoire remains virtually unchanged, dealing in pan-fried sweetbreads with confit potatoes and salsa verde, and baked salmon with saffron and a knob of butter made from sun-dried tomatoes and capers. A dozen or so desserts may include banana croustade with chocolate sauce or prune and almond tart. Service is not always on top form. The short wine list is a bit pricey. House Italian red and South African white are £10.50.

CHEF: Daniel Leberman PROPRIETORS: Sir Terence Conran and Joel Kissin OPEN: all week L 12 to 3 (3.30 Sun), Mon to Sat D 6 to 11 MEALS: alc (main courses £7.50 to £13.50). Minimum £10 SERVICE: 12½%, card slips closed CARDS: Access, Amex, Diners, Visa DETAILS: 86 seats. 20 tables outside. Private parties: 15 main room. Vegetarian meals. Children welcome. No pipes in dining-room. Wheelchair access (also WC) at lunch only. No music

Bombay Brasserie map 14

Courtfield Close, Courtfield Road, SW7 4UH
TEL: 0171-370 4040 and 373 0254 COOKING 1
FAX: 0171-835 1669 COST £22–£50

'London for a long weekend is not complete without Sunday lunch in Bombay,' writes a traveller from North Wales whose family relishes the prospect of tucking into the fixed-price ten-dish buffet that is one of the major attractions at this sumptuously appointed brasserie. The décor is a luxuriant re-creation of Raj splendour – complete with a plant-filled conservatory – and the menu is a cook's tour through the regional cuisines of the Subcontinent. You will find Goan fish dishes laced with red chillies and fresh coconut, tandoori specialities from the north-west frontier, Kashmiri kormas and blisteringly hot South Indian chicken pepper fry. Added to this are Bombay roadside and seaside snacks and

appetisers: aloo tuk (crisply fried baby potatoes in their skins topped with sweet yoghurt, tamarind chutney and cumin), vegetable samosa chaat, and biscuit-like sev bateta puri loaded with cubed potatoes, lentils and a trio of chutneys, for example. Three thalis provide some of the best value. If you want to venture beyond lassi and lager, there is a short, mainly French wine list with prices to match those of the food. House wine is £10.50.

CHEF: Udit Sarkhel PROPRIETOR: Taj International Hotels OPEN: all week 12.30 to 3, 7.30 to 12 (11.30 Sun) CLOSED: 25 and 26 Dec MEALS: alc D (main courses £11.50 to £18). Buffet L £14.95. Minimum £25 D SERVICE: not inc CARDS: Access, Diners, Visa DETAILS: 180 seats. Private parties: 100 main room, 100 private room. Vegetarian meals. Children's helpings L. Smart dress preferred. Wheelchair access (3 steps; also WC). Music. Air-conditioned

Boyd's 🍷 map 13

135 Kensington Church Street, W8 7LP COOKING **2***
TEL: 0171-727 5452 FAX: 0171-221 0615 COST **£25–£55**

As London restaurant style moved away from quiet formality towards a more free-and-easy approach, Boyd's moved surreptitiously with it. This narrow, bright, glass-roofed dining-room is too small and intimate ever to go headlong into the full-throated clamour found in places such as Kensington Place up the road (see entry), but its tone loosened up a little and the food evolved in parallel.

Boyd Gilmour is still fond of the chargrill, but its use seems moderated. It comes into its own in a first course of seared scallops with charred vegetables provençale marinated in basil, a summer dish of sunny flavours, the shellfish themselves sensitively cooked to retain moistness. Warm salad of boned quail in a sesame oil, soy sauce and raspberry marinade is a bold enough conception, but there is no hesitation in offering a tried-and-tested combination such as avocado salad with crab mayonnaise and pink grapefruit. Fish dishes of the day are worth enquiring about. Other main courses centre on interesting but apposite preparations: lambs' sweetbreads are roasted in puff pastry, and roast pigeon breast comes on a potato rösti with sweet-and-sour cabbage and a black truffle sauce. A reporter has singled out a 'lovely' quintet of lemon – five variations on a theme – and there may be hot cherry pancake with vanilla ice-cream, or chocolate parfait. Service is amiable enough, and drinkers are very well looked after here. Not only is there a distinguished collection of malt whiskies and digestifs, but an impeccably chosen wine list to boot. France is accorded its place after a careful run through the New World. The list is not the longest one in the *Guide*, but it is well-constructed. Clarets are a particular strength, and bin-ends are always worth considering. House wines from Spain, France and California start at £10. CELLARMAN'S CHOICE: Muskateller 1993, Weingut Walter Scoff, £16.25; Shafer Merlot 1991, Napa, California, £24.

CHEF/PROPRIETOR: Boyd Gilmour OPEN: Mon to Sat 12.30 to 2.30, 7 to 11 CLOSED: 2 weeks Christmas to New Year MEALS: alc (main courses £10 to £17). Set L £15 SERVICE: not inc CARDS: Access, Amex, Diners, Visa DETAILS: 40 seats. Private parties: 40 main room. Children welcome. Smart dress preferred. Wheelchair access (3 steps). Music. Air-conditioned

See the inside of the front cover for an explanation of the 1 to 5 rating system for cooking standards.

Brackenbury £ map 12

129–131 Brackenbury Road, W6 0BQ COOKING 2*
TEL: 0181-748 0107 FAX: 0181-741 0905 COST £17–£32

At the far end of a residential street off Goldhawk Road, with a few tables outside in summer, the Brackenbury adopts an admirably low-key approach. It thinks of itself as a wine bar/restaurant, mainly serving the local community, and the plain and functional furnishings don't go out of their way to be comfortable. The Brackenbury deserves credit for its part in pioneering enterprising, imaginative and inexpensive contemporary food with a British bias. Typical dishes might be potato and wild garlic soup, deep-fried salt cod-cakes with aïoli, raw scallops with black-bean dressing and coriander, roast widgeon with salsify, or lamb sweetbreads and tongues with button onions and mint. The results may occasionally fall short of expectation, but supporters get round this by lowering their expectations to match what is on offer. It is simple food with good intentions, and doesn't take refinement too seriously – an approach that works perfectly well with dishes ranging from rib of beef with enormous chips through seafood grill of sea bass, salmon and squid, to apple and blackberry crumble with freshly made custard. The menu changes at every meal and service is invariably praised. The perceived good value is helped by the wines – around 30 – most of which are under £20 and available by the glass. House French is £8.50.

CHEF: Adam Robinson PROPRIETORS: Adam and Katie Robinson OPEN: Tue to Fri and Sun L 12.30 to 2.45, Mon to Sat D 7 to 10.45 CLOSED: Christmas and New Year, bank hols MEALS: alc (main courses £4.50 to £10) SERVICE: not inc CARDS: Access, Amex, Delta, Diners, Switch, Visa DETAILS: 55 seats. 5 tables outside. Private parties: 8 main room. Vegetarian meals. Children's helpings. Wheelchair access. No music

Brady's £ map 12

513 Old York Road, SW18 1TF COOKING 1
TEL: 0181-877 9599 COST £14–£21

Just about everyone agrees that Brady's is a pleasant, cheery little place and a godsend for the inhabitants of Wandsworth. A few fishy motifs and identification charts on the walls are reminders of the main business here – although most reporters think it is nearer to a neighbourhood restaurant than high-street chippie. Luke and Amelia Brady don't compromise on freshness, and ring the changes with blackboard dishes that could promise anything from haddock to tuna. Their batter is top-quality and grease-free, chips are excellent and details such as home-made mayonnaise and tartare sauce give the whole set-up a touch of class. Additional items, including potted shrimps, smoked salmon, and salmon fish-cakes, have also been favourably received – although puddings have disappointed. Another branch is at 696 Fulham Road, London SW6. The wine list is a modest affair, with house wine at £6.75.

CHEF: Luke Brady PROPRIETORS: Luke and Amelia Brady OPEN: Mon to Sat D only 7 to 10.45 CLOSED: Christmas, bank hols MEALS: alc (main courses £4 to £6) SERVICE: 10% (optional) CARDS: none DETAILS: 38 seats. Children's helpings. Music

Brasserie St Quentin

map 14

243 Brompton Road, SW3 2EP
TEL: 0171-581 5131 and 589 8005 — COOKING 2
FAX: 0171-584 6064 — COST £23–£48

'Very French in a timeless way,' noted a visitor who lunched at this Kensington brasserie with closely packed tables and waiting staff who are thoroughly professional in their duties. Like its sister establishment Grill St Quentin in Yeoman's Row (see entry, London), this place specialises in authentic bourgeois cooking, and prices are reckoned to be very reasonable for the area.

English chef Nigel Davis, who oversees both kitchens, delivers some very accomplished dishes, including a 'distinctive' velouté de coquillages (fish soup, to you and me), tripe 'à la mode de Caen', roast guinea-fowl, and sea bass stuffed with oyster mushrooms in a well-balanced cream sauce with lots of extra fungi dotted around it. The presence of sausages with onions pleased a visitor from Sheffield, while another with vegetarian tendencies decided that a request for asparagus risotto was well worth a 20-minute wait (St Quentin still adheres to the rather antiquated policy of expecting vegetarians to inform them of their requirements in advance). Desserts get the thumbs-up: tarte au citron, crème brûlée, and St Quentin's bitter chocolate and orange pavé have all been pleasantly received. Copious quantities of decent French bread accompany the meal. The wine list is totally French, prices are fair and there is a good bunch of halves to choose from. House burgundy is £8.90.

CHEF: Nigel Davis PROPRIETOR: Savoy Group plc OPEN: all week L 12 to 3 (3.30 Sun), Mon to Sat D 7 to 11.30, Sun D 6.30 to 11 MEALS: alc (main courses £7 to £15.50). Set L £9 (2 courses), Set D 7 to 7.30 £9 (2 courses) SERVICE: 12.5% (optional), card slips closed CARDS: Access, Amex, Delta, Diners, Switch, Visa DETAILS: 80 seats. Private parties: 8 main room, 25 private room. Children welcome. Smart dress preferred. No music. Air- conditioned

▲ *Brown's Hotel*

NEW ENTRY map 15

Albemarle Street, W1A 4SW — COOKING 2
TEL: 0171-493 6020 FAX: 0171-493 9381 — COST £35–£72

Brown's is one of those Mayfair hotels that seems untouched by time: despite having undergone a multi-million-pound refurbishment, its charm remains intact. The hotel would be instantly familiar today to the Evelyn Waugh characters who once breezed through it, the chintzy sofas and chandeliers impeccably maintained, a pair of samovars guarding the entrance to the spacious dining-room. Forte's acquisition of Brown's has brought John King to the stoves, and if all else is preserved in amber, the cooking hearteningly isn't.

An Italian influence is evident in a starter of linguine with morels, chervil and parmigiano reggiano, and oriental notes exist in another first course of crab beignets with bean sprouts and lemon grass. Calf's liver with bacon and mash won't startle anybody, but roast duck breast with figs and a strawberry jus strikes a more inventive note. An inspection meal tested dishes from the main *carte*, as well as the fixed-price menu of three courses plus coffee, and found much to admire. A salad of Parma ham with roasted tomato and shaved Parmesan was agreeably presented, the tomato making an 'intense and juicy' variant on the usual fruit-and-Parma combination. Loin of venison was lightly cooked and sauced with a good clear stock, accompanied by a red cabbage and mushroom timbale, while grilled medallions of beef on ratatouille – 'a lesson in simplicity' – impressed for the quality and timing of the meat and the strong flavours of the vegetables.

Just to show that time really has stood still, desserts come on a trolley. A slice of apricot mousse tart decorated with chocolate was well-made and delicately flavoured. Cheeses are properly looked after, and good petits fours come with coffee. Both for the ambience and the vibrancy of much of the cooking, this is a place that could well achieve cult status. Afternoon teas are also served. Four wines are available by the glass; house French is £15.50 a bottle.

CHEF: John King PROPRIETOR: Forte Hotels (UK) Ltd OPEN: Mon to Fri and Sun L 12.30 to 2.30, all week D 6 to 10 (6.30 to 9.30 Sun) MEALS: alc (main courses £16 to £22.50). Set L £24.50, Set D £29 SERVICE: not inc CARDS: Access, Amex, Delta, Diners, Switch, Visa DETAILS: 90 seats. Private parties: 24 main room, 80 private rooms. Children's helpings. No children under 8. Smart dress preferred. No-smoking areas. Wheelchair access (also WC). Music. Air-conditioned ACCOMMODATION: 116 rooms, all with bath/shower. TV. Phone. Air-conditioned. D,B&B £185 to £425. Children welcome. Baby facilities. Afternoon teas

Buchan's

map 12

62–64 Battersea Bridge Road, SW11 3AG — COOKING 1
TEL: 0171-228 0888 FAX: 0171-924 1718 — COST £18–£39

Buchan's aims to be a little Caledonian outpost in fashionable north Battersea, a wee step away from the bridge. The author of *The Thirty-nine Steps* is invoked as a kind of household god, and prints of Highland scenes bedeck the walls. In fact, the Scottishness is by no means all-pervading, nor could it be when the chef's name is Alain Jeannon and he does such things as Sicilian tagliatelle, lamb casserole basquaise and Toulouse sausages with sauté potatoes and onions. That said, there are also Loch Fyne oysters in season, Oban crab soufflé, or haggis with neeps and tatties served with a jug of Scotch to start, and maybe salmon fish-cakes to follow. Red mullet comes in a fine bouillabaisse sauce, wild boar with a good red wine sauce: 'moist, tender and not overdone'. Whisky crops up again in flambé Scottish fillet steak. Enthusiasm seems to grow fainter at dessert stage, with a white and dark chocolate terrine noted as 'perfectly adequate', though bread-and-butter pudding is 'unduly elegant'. The functional wine list wanders hither and yon, keeping prices on a tight rein, and takes in Moniack Castle birch-sap wine from Inverness. House Italian is £8.95.

CHEF: Alain Jeannon PROPRIETOR: Jeremy Bolam OPEN: all week 12 to 2.45, 6 to 10.45 (7 to 10 Sun) CLOSED: 26 Dec MEALS: alc (main courses £7 to £14). Set L £7.50 (2 courses), Set L Sun £10.95, Set D Sun and Mon £5.95 (2 courses); bar meals available SERVICE: 10% (optional), card slips closed CARDS: Access, Amex, Delta, Diners, Switch, Visa DETAILS: 75 seats. 4 tables outside. Private parties: 55 main room. Vegetarian meals. Children's helpings. Wheelchair access (1 step). Music. Air-conditioned

The 1997 Guide *will be published before Christmas 1996. Reports on meals are most welcome at any time of the year, but are particularly valuable in the spring (no later than June). Send them to* The Good Food Guide, *FREEPOST, 2 Marylebone Road, London NW1 1YN. Or e-mail your report to guidereports@which. co. uk.*

Bu San £

map 13

43 Holloway Road, N7 8JP — COOKING 1
TEL: 0171-607 8264 — COST £15–£47

First impressions can be deceptive. Bu San (named after Korea's second-largest city) is housed in an unprepossessing converted shop that 'seems to be constructed of cement as a fill-in after wartime bombing'. Inside, it is functional, with stone-coloured walls and tables that are 'too close for comfort'. The mood is informal, and the food shows some skilful touches: owner Mr Lee cooks, his wife generally works front-of-house, and young children scamper around.

The menu is mostly Korean, seafood is the major focus and there are occasional forays into Japan for sashimi, sukiyaki and sunomono. Appetisers are especially good: look for superb kim-chee (chilli-laden pickled cabbage served ice-cold), ho bak bok um (fried pumpkin with sesame seeds), and ka gi cho riem (thick sticks of aubergine in a 'sticky', sweetish soy sauce). The kitchen also delivers authentic versions of yuk hoe (Korean-style steak tartare flavoured with pears), pa jean (a kind of omelette packed with seafood) and jap chae (Korea's answer to chop suey). Visual artistry counts for a great deal here: dishes are attractively served in Japanese-style bowls of many colours, and the restaurant is renowned for its flamboyantly carved vegetables. Bargain-price one-dish lunches are a good deal. Drink green tea, Korean ginseng tea or beer; otherwise, delve into the 'short but surprisingly advanced' wine list. House wine is £7.80.

CHEF: Young Hyung Lee PROPRIETORS: Young Hyung Lee and K. Lee OPEN: Mon to Fri L 12 to 2.30, all week D 6 to 11 CLOSED: 25 and 26 Dec, 1 and 2 Jan, Easter Sun MEALS: alc (main courses £5 to £25). Set L (1 course) £4.20 to £6.50, Set D £13.95 to £17.25. Minimum £6.50 SERVICE: 10%, card slips closed CARDS: Access, Visa DETAILS: 46 seats. Private parties: 46 main room. Vegetarian meals. Children's helpings. Smart dress preferred. Wheelchair access (also WC). Music. Air-conditioned

Butlers Wharf Chop House 🍷

map 13

36E Shad Thames, Butlers Wharf, SE1 2YE — COOKING 2
TEL: 0171-403 3403 FAX: 0171-403 3414 — COST £26–£54

'I do love the view from Mr Conran's gastrodrome.' It is much the same from neighbouring Pont de la Tour and Cantina del Ponte (see entries) – of Tower Bridge and the Thames – but the food here is more matey and down to earth, with a distinctly British stamp. The cooking is a smart, modern interpretation of the nineteenth-century chop house idea, with stainless-steel baggage racks above the new wood of tables, floors and benches, and it significantly captures the spirit, rather than the letter, of this kind of eating. The noise from fellow diners helps, and the no-nonsense British food brings a surge of national pride to the breast – the gastronomic equivalent of the Last Night of the Proms.

Just look at the line-up: Lincolnshire chine with mustard leeks, cold roast beef with pickled vegetable relish, sausage and mash, beef stew with dumplings, not to mention steak and kidney pudding with oysters, deep-fried cod and chips, and a list of puddings from bread-and-butter through apple fritters and Cambridge burnt cream to rice pud and a plate of British cheeses. The standard may go up and down a bit, like the service, but as a shop window for some of our best-loved old-fashioned dishes it works a treat. The wine list is a subset of the superior version at Pont de la Tour, with fine claret and ace Burgundy, good Italians and an impressive showing from the New World. Nine house wines start at £10.50, and all are available by the glass. CELLARMAN'S CHOICE: Capel Vale Reserve Chardonnay 1992, Margaret River, W. Australia, £19.75; Auxey-Duresses 1991, Maréchal Jacquet, £27.50.

CHEF: Rod Eggleston PROPRIETORS: Sir Terence Conran and Joel Kissin OPEN: Sun to Mon L 12 to 3, Mon to Sat D 6 to 11 CLOSED: 1 Jan, Good Friday MEALS: alc D (main courses £11 to £15.50). Set L £22.75. Bar meals available SERVICE: 12.5%, card slips closed CARDS: Access, Amex, Diners, Visa DETAILS: 115 seats. 12 tables outside. Private parties: 12 main room. Children welcome. Wheelchair access (also WC). No music

Le Cadre map 12

10 Priory Road, Priory Park, N8 7RD COOKING 1*
TEL: 0181-348 0606 COST £18–£40

If you are looking for 'hidden talents in North London', one local resident heartily recommends this discreet French restaurant between Muswell Hill and Crouch End. All kinds of options are available and the food is reckoned to be 'extremely good value for money'. Three-course fixed-price menus are alternatives to the *carte*, and there is even the prospect of special events. 'The Best of Britain & France', served for two weeks in March, advertised such dishes as mussel and saffron soup; steamed Scotch salmon with lime and ginger sauce; wild boar, pheasant and venison pie; as well as roast leg of lamb stuffed with mushrooms, herbs and foie gras sauced with black olives and port. Otherwise, the kitchen holds on firmly to its Gallic roots with sauté Burgundy snails in champagne and garlic butter, breast of duck with a provençale herb crust and Beaujolais sauce, and pan-fried veal kidneys with a trio of mustards (Dijon, Meaux and Bordeaux) and green peppercorn sauce. To round things off there are classic confections such as tarte Tatin, îles flottantes and crème brûlée. Service is brisk and attentive, and sometimes one of the proprietors lends a hand. The wine list is short, French and regional; also look for the Calvados and Alsatian Schutz Jubilator beer. House wine is £9.

CHEF: Yannick Chuat PROPRIETORS: David Misselbrook and Marie Fedyk OPEN: Mon to Fri L 12 to 2.30, Mon to Sat D 7 to 11 CLOSED: 25 to 30 Dec, bank hols MEALS: alc (main courses £9.50 to £12.50). Set L £10.50, Set D Mon to Thur £13.50, Fri and Sat £15.50. Minimum as per the set price menu SERVICE: 10%, card slips closed CARDS: Access, Amex, Delta, Diners, Switch, Visa DETAILS: 50 seats. 8 tables outside. Private parties: 50 main room. Vegetarian meals. Children welcome. No cigars in dining-room. Wheelchair access. Music

Café dell'Ugo NEW ENTRY map 13

56–58 Tooley Street, SE1 2SZ COOKING 1*
TEL: 0171-407 6001 FAX: 0171-357 8806 COST £23–£46

For those who are still counting the sequels, we must be up to about Antony Worrall-Thompson XII by now. This time the intrepid explorer has found a niche in a railway arch under London Bridge, which doubles as a watering-hole for thirsty workers on their way home. The location naturally attracts City types 'who are used to screaming at each other across vast dealing rooms', so when it gets busy the noise can be deafening. Tables in the upstairs open-plan dining-room are laid with cloths tied in such a way that it may be necessary to eat sitting side-saddle.

The pattern is eight or nine choices per course, and simple, clean flavours show to good effect in a menu that runs from chilled cucumber and fennel soup with lemon balm, through a beef and chickpea tagine with raita and tabbouleh, to steamed cinnamon sponge with banana ice-cream. Roasting (of lobster or suckling pig), steaming (of mussels), pan-frying (of sweetbreads) and braising (of veal shank) supplement the chargrill's inevitable sway with corn-fed chicken, or with sweet-tasting squid partnered by good olive oil, tomatoes and bitter aubergine tahini. Dishes are subject to modern garnish in the form of spinach-under-everything and aubergine (or yam) crisps on top. To begin, ciabatta comes with a saucer of olive oil and balsamic vinegar for dipping, and to finish there may be blueberry and cherry gratin or banana and toffee crumble. Sharper service would help with both food and wine, although the varied list of 40-odd bottles suits the circumstances well. House wines start with Italian at £7.95.

CHEF: Matthew Fanthorpe PROPRIETOR: Simpsons of Cornhill plc OPEN: Mon to Fri L 12 to 3, Mon to Sat D 7 to 11 CLOSED: bank hols MEALS: alc (main courses £8 to £15) SERVICE: not inc CARDS: Access, Amex, Delta, Diners, Switch, Visa DETAILS: 80 seats. Private parties: 100 main room. Vegetarian meals. Children welcome. No pipes in dining-room. Music

Le Café du Jardin

NEW ENTRY map 15

28 Wellington Street, WC2E 7BD COOKING 1*
TEL: 0171-836 8769 FAX: 0171-836 4123 COST £20–£51

Situated on two levels in the heart of Covent Garden's theatreland, Café du Jardin has found a new lease of life with the arrival of Tony Howorth (who did a spell at Soho Soho – see entry, London). There are tables outside, although traffic fumes and pedestrian bustle may be a deterrent for anyone seeking relaxation; it might be better to retreat to the light, air-conditioned atmosphere of the conservatory-style basement. Tony Howorth's menu changes with the seasons, and specials vary from day to day. His style is hard to pigeon-hole: the menu is in a mix of languages, ingredients are often culled from the trendy Italian larder, and there are a few wayward items such as New England clam chowder, deep-fried dim-sum, and blackened tuna with sweet pepper and corn salsa to confuse matters even more.

The results, however, are creditable, although prices are on the high side, with vegetables charged extra, and a 15 per cent service charge added to the bill. Bruschetta is exactly what you might expect, although omelette japonaise bears little relation to rolled-up sushi. Instead it is a thin, flat omelette piled with marinated duck breast, shiitake mushrooms, nori seaweed and toasted sesame seeds. Pasta and risottos can be had as starters or main courses. Filet aux dix secondes has appeared as three medallions of judiciously seared meat ('I'm sure it took more than ten seconds to cook,' noted the recipient); and monkfish tails were wrapped in Bayonne ham and served with a compote of garlic and mixed beans. To finish, assiette of fruits with tropical fruit sorbet was just the job on a sweltering June evening; on another occasion, white and dark chocolate mousse might fit the bill. Service copes well even when the pressure is on. The wine list covers a lot of territory, from the French regions to New Zealand, and there is plenty of drinking by the glass. House wine is £8.95.

CHEF: Tony Howorth PROPRIETORS: Robert Seigler and Tony Howorth OPEN: Mon to Sat 12 to 3, 5.30 to 12, Sun noon to 11 CLOSED: 25 Dec MEALS: alc (main courses £8 to £16). Set L £9.95 (2 courses) to £13.50, Set D £9.95 (2 courses) SERVICE: 15% (optional), card slips closed CARDS: Access, Amex, Delta, Diners, Visa DETAILS: 110 seats. 8 tables outside. Private parties: 60 main room. Vegetarian meals. Children's helpings. Smart dress preferred. Wheelchair access. Music. Air-conditioned (downstairs only)

Café Fish

map 15

39 Panton Street, SW1Y 4EA — COOKING 1
TEL: 0171-930 3999 FAX: 0171-839 4880 — COST £21–£33

Brisk, busy, sometimes frenetic, but always on the ball, this 'good fish restaurant' copes valiantly with the crowds and does a great job serving the needs of visitors heading for the nearby theatres and cinemas. The kitchen turns out big helpings of fish and chips, full-flavoured *soupe de poisson*, first-rate grilled Dover sole, and more modern offerings such as grilled red mullet (three baby fish cooked to perfection) with roasted Mediterranean vegetables, and scallops with Chinese vegetables and coriander dressing. Vegetarians are wooed with the likes of grilled aubergine sausages with spinach and creamed turnips. The cover charge is fair, given the fact that you do actually get something for your money – namely fish pâté, French bread and butter that are 'just right, quell the hunger pangs and titillate the appetite'. Below stairs is a wine bar that provides a lively meeting place for drinks and light meals. The cappuccino is 'excellent' and the wine list provides a fair choice, especially among the whites. House wines start at £8.50, although the cheapest red is £10.75.

CHEF: Andrew Magson PROPRIETOR: Groupe Chez Gérard Ltd OPEN: Mon to Sat 12 to 3, 5.45 to 11.30 MEALS: alc (main courses £7 to £15.50). Cover £1.25 SERVICE: 12.5% (optional), card slips closed CARDS: Access, Amex, Delta, Diners, Switch, Visa DETAILS: 94 seats. 3 tables outside. Private parties: 50 main room. Vegetarian meals. Children welcome. No cigars/pipes in dining-room. Music

Café Royal 🍷

map 15

Regent Street, W1R 6EL — COOKING 2
TEL: 0171-437 9090 FAX: 0171-439 7672 — COST £26–£85

'A step back into another and perhaps more gracious time than our own' was the rather wistful impression of one visitor. 'Service is as solicitous as it is unobtrusive,' he added, after being moved out of earshot of a bunch of lads talking serious football. The Grill Room is indeed a majestic setting, and were Oscar Wilde himself to sweep back in tomorrow he would readily recognise the place. Herbert Berger's food, however, makes little concession to century-old habits.

Berger is an accomplished chef whose culinary flourishes deserve the sort of background the Grill Room can provide. One dinner began with escalope of foie gras in a truffled madeira sauce with caramelised apple, before medallions of veal with saffron risotto and spinach, and concluded with marinated berries with pastry leaves, a sorbet and a drop of raspberry coulis. It left the reporter overwhelmed. Others have enjoyed escalope of salmon – 'moist and just right' – with a compote of peppers, as well as pear poached in red wine with amaretto sabayon and vanilla ice-cream. Incidentals like the tomato and basil bread and the friandises with coffee add to the general satisfaction.

The Brasserie offers simpler fare in more modest characterful surroundings. Smoked rabbit salad with asparagus and mustard dressing, grilled calf's liver with bacon and onions and crème brûlée are the order of the day. The wine list spans the globe, its roll-call of illustrious clarets supplemented by sure-footed selections from Italy and California. Half-bottles alone provide a cosmopolitan choice. House French is £14.95. CELLARMAN'S CHOICE: Montagny 1992, Louis Latour, £26.50; Pomerol, Ch. Plince 1986, £27.

CHEF: Herbert Berger PROPRIETOR: Forte Restaurants OPEN: Grill Room Mon to Fri L 12 to 2.30, Mon to Sat D 6 to 10.45, Brasserie all week L 12 to 2.30, Mon to Sat D 6 to 10.30 CLOSED: bank hols MEALS: Grill Room alc (main courses £18.50 to £24); Set L £24, Set D £39. Brasserie alc (main courses £8 to £16); Set L and D £13.50 (2 courses) to £16.50 SERVICE: not inc CARDS: Access, Amex, Diners, Visa DETAILS: Grill Room 45 seats, Brasserie 90 seats. No children under 12. Jacket and tie Grill Room. No pipes Grill Room. No-smoking area Brasserie. No music Grill Room. Music Brasserie. Air-conditioned

Caffé Italia

NEW ENTRY map 12

107 Humber Road, SE3 7LW — COOKING 1
TEL: 0181-858 7577 — COST £29–£39

This gas-lit Italian restaurant in thinly served Blackheath has a number of attractions, not least a patio garden with tables outside in the summer, access to which is gained through the kitchen. Even more of a pull may be the uncommonly personal front-of-house approach. 'The manager has the best bedside manner in town,' wrote one in need of solace, who was gratified by everything from the 'tongue-in-cheek brio' with which the menu is presented to the goodnight kiss on departure.

Caffé Italia does food as well, not necessarily the most trend-conscious version, but soundly based peasant cooking that makes all the right 'rustic' noises. Home-made sausages come with new potatoes seasoned with mint and chilli; beef rolls are chargrilled on a skewer. 'Comfortingly creamy' tagliatelle carbonara uses fine home-made pasta, but one reporter thought that a little more of it wouldn't go amiss. Calf's liver is slivered and fried, finished with balsamic vinegar and raisins and accompanied by polenta. The extra charge for a portion of lightly cooked and oiled spinach seems well worth it. Poached pears have made a pleasingly authentic dessert. Coffee is as good as it should be. A basic list of 11 Italian wines, including Prosecco, starts with house wine at £9 a bottle.

CHEF: Sarah Lovecchio PROPRIETORS: Domenico and Sarah Lovecchio OPEN: Tue to Sat D only 6.30 to 9.30 CLOSED: Christmas MEALS: alc (main courses £8.50 to £10.50) SERVICE: 10%, card slips closed CARDS: Access, Switch, Visa DETAILS: 56 seats. 10 tables outside. Private parties: 12 main room. Vegetarian meals. Children's helpings. Smart dress preferred. Music

All main entries are fully indexed at the back of the Guide.

Canteen

map 12

Unit G4, Harbour Yard, Chelsea Harbour, SW10 0XD — NEW CHEF

TEL: 0171-351 7330 and 7440 FAX: 0171-351 6189 COST £38–£47

Chelsea Harbour is a flagship of 1980s property development that combines residential and retail use, offices, and hotels and restaurants. Not all of these have been equally successful, as a wander around the empty shops demonstrates, but even when the rest of the complex feels like a ghost town, the Canteen is buzzing and jumping. Michael Collins (architect of Tante Claire, among others) has achieved a welcome level of cheeriness that makes the most of natural daylight streaming in above the idle yachts in the harbour. Diamond and harlequin motifs extend from the small bar through to the banquettes and curtains that run around the dining-room, encircling as wide a variety of customers as you are likely to clap eyes on.

They have come for a largely unchanging menu of generous choice that has delivered good quality for a fair price. Given Marco Pierre White's part-ownership, it should be no surprise that the food has relied on the standard French repertoire plus a flash of Mediterranean modernism. The style will very likely continue under Tim Powell, who has worked at Pont de la Tour, Tante Claire and in France. His appointment was announced as we went to press, part of the reorganisation that is scheduled to transfer the Canteen's previous chefs – Tim Payne and Peter Reffell – to the Criterion in Piccadilly.

CHEF: Tim Powell PROPRIETORS: Michael Caine, Claudio Pulze and Marco Pierre White OPEN: all week 12 to 3 (3.30 Sun), 6.30 to 12 (7 to 10.30 Sun) MEALS: alc (main courses £12). Cover £1 SERVICE: not inc CARDS: Access, Visa DETAILS: 140 seats. Private parties: 200 main room. Children welcome. Smart dress preferred. No pipes in dining-room. Wheelchair access (3 steps; also WC). No music. Air-conditioned

Cantina del Ponte

map 13

36C Shad Thames, Butlers Wharf, SE1 2YE COOKING 2

TEL: 0171-403 5403 FAX: 0171-403 0267 COST £25–£49

The Cantina does more than most to celebrate the rediscovered cooking of Italy, and what London has made of it. It is a large, bustling, noisy place, and whether you enjoy it will depend on whether you can enter the rough-and-ready spirit of ripping up bread on the scratched wooden table-top and whether you like your pizzas good and oily and your quantities huge.

At inspection a bowl of fish broth rang true with its acidulated shellfish taste and shreds of sharp sorrel, while the utter simplicity of a salad of peppery rocket with thin peelings of Parmesan and good olive oil succeeded. Main courses may include prosciutto with asparagus, or ribeye steak. 'Fish is treated with respect', as in a firm-fleshed monkfish steak of great succulence cocooned in a jacket of polenta. Vibrant chocolate truffle cake offers intriguing textural contrasts all the way through the slice, while crema cotta with baked pears will appeal to the sweet of tooth. When firing on all cylinders, the Cantina is capable of delivering some great food. Service gets into a groove as the place fills up, and brings you what you want when you want it with the sunniest of smiles. The Italian wines offer a reasonable spread of prices and good names, although there are no half-bottles. Prices open at £9.95 for a Pinot Grigio and a Montepulciano d'Abruzzo.

CHEF: Louis Loizia PROPRIETORS: Sir Terence Conran, Joel Kissin and David Burke OPEN: all week L 12 to 3, Mon to Sat D 6 to 11 CLOSED: 5 days Christmas, Good Fri MEALS: alc (main courses £7 to £14.50). Minimum £10 SERVICE: 12.5%, card slips closed CARDS: Access, Amex, Diners, Visa DETAILS: 90 seats. 13 tables outside. Vegetarian meals. Wheelchair access. Music

▲ *The Capital* 🍷 map 14

Basil Street, SW3 1AT COOKING 4
TEL: 0171-589 5171 FAX: 0171-225 0011 COST £31–£73

'Very little changes at the Capital, thank goodness, other than the décor.' The dining-room's refurbishment has hardly wowed reporters. It has gone from pink to buff-beige and amassed a 'half-surrealist collection' of wooden objects, globes and vases, reflected in the tall mirrors at one end of the room. But it is an improvement, and the Capital remains 'probably the friendliest, most humanly scaled grand hotel in London' according to one familiar with the genre. For another, 'service and food are exemplary from the moment the doorman greets you until departure; the whole operation exudes quality'. Not only that, it is 'a real oasis after some serious shopping', and shopping doesn't come much more serious than around this part of Knightsbridge.

Aperitifs, nibbles and ordering are taken care of in the bar, and by the time you are bidden to table you may already have eaten a big candyfloss blob of smoked haddock mousse, and a wun-tun-type piece of deep-fried battered sole, soon to be followed by a tiny brochette of marinated tuna and pepper. 'Haute cuisine comfort food' is how a seasoned reporter described the rich, classically based French style that comes 'in vibrant colours on crazy square plates'. No luxury is left unused, and of the three or four dishes that can be taken either as a first or main course, one consists of three hunks of lobster in a bright saffron-coloured fish stock with fronds of hair-fine root ginger, sugar-snap peas and a dollop of caviare.

What matters, though, is that ingredients are used to good effect, as when slices of boudin of foie gras are 'scattered sublimely with crystals of coarse salt', and served with tiny oil-marinated chunks of artichoke, or when a pot-roast saddle of rabbit with cep and morel mushrooms comes in a rib-stickingly thick cream sauce. If there is a fault, it may be a lack of textural variation – 'everything has that softish, get-your-teeth-in-Gladys quality that big hotels seem to go in for' – although flavours are deep and distinctive, and timing is perfect, including a risotto of Bresse chicken that is 'full of buttery chickeny flavour.' Among puddings, an inspector was impressed by an assiette of vanilla consisting of crème brûlée in a tartlet case with a brittle, wafer-thin top, a spoonful of oeufs à la neige, an excellent speckly fast-melting ice-cream, and a sablé sandwich of luxuriously rich vanilla cream, all providing a much lighter finish than an assiette of chocolate might have done.

British and Irish cheeses might include Milleens, Welsh goats' and creamy Jersey Blue, which come with big slices of walnut bread. Service is faultless throughout, and the sommelier is a hero, presiding over an appropriately stylish list of good claret from decent vintages at what for London hotels are fair prices –

and service is included, which helps. Little comes in for less than £20, though house wine is £12.50. CELLARMAN'S CHOICE: Evans Family Chardonnay 1993, Hunter Valley, New South Wales, £18.50; Beaujolais Villages 1992, Drouhin, £13.50.

CHEF: Philip Britten PROPRIETOR: David Levin OPEN: all week 12 to 2.30, 7 to 11.15 (10.30 Sun) MEALS: alc (main courses £21.50 to £24). Set L £25, Set D £40. Minimum £30 D SERVICE: none, card slips closed CARDS: Access, Amex, Delta, Diners, Switch, Visa DETAILS: 40 seats. Private parties: 8 main room, 12 and 24 private rooms. Car park. Vegetarian meals. Children's helpings. Jacket and tie. No cigars/pipes in dining-room. No music. Air-conditioned ACCOMMODATION: 48 rooms, all with bath/shower. TV. Phone. Air-conditioned. Room only £197 to £341. Children welcome. Baby facilities. Pets by arrangement. Afternoon teas (*The Which? Hotel Guide*)

Le Caprice

map 15

Arlington House, Arlington Street, SW1A 1RT — COOKING 2*
TEL: 0171-629 2239 FAX: 0171-493 9040 — COST £26–£63

At the end of one of St James's less characterful thoroughfares, behind the Ritz, lurks the Caprice. Clamorously popular at both lunch and in the evening, it has been, over the past decade and more, one of the mainstays of modern London eating. You are not advised to come for peace and quiet, and the space does feel slightly more cramped than at its equally well-supported sister restaurant the Ivy (see entry), but the combination of minimalist monochrome style, voluble professionalism and dynamic cooking is a persuasive one. Surrounded by suits you may be, but if you turn up in jeans and T-shirt, nobody bats an eyelid. The starry atmosphere can be heady, though if you don't spot anyone famous you may feel a bit let-down.

Tim Hughes cooks on, the central menu changing little over the years, but well enough supplemented by specials on most days to allow regulars an impression of variety. Many dishes are models of simplicity – chilled avocado and herb soup at a summer lunch, for example, or tomato and basil galette – while others are renderings of classic dishes such as eggs Benedict or steak tartare, which resist the temptation to give them an extraneous twist. The style may be characterised as mid-Atlantic, for among the salmon fish-cakes and Lincolnshire sausages are chargrilled squid with bacon, rocket and a pimento salsa, and Mexican griddled chicken salad with avocado, piquillo peppers and chorizo. Potatoes may be matchstick chips or fried hash browns. Puddings bring on pear Tatin, cappuccino brûlée, honey-roasted tamarillos and – if you've a mind – chocolate ripple and popcorn ice-cream with hot fudge sauce. Such is the press of business that first-timers may find the pace of service unexpectedly brisk, though most enjoy the vivacity of it all, including the maître d's apparently uncanny ability to recognise everybody. The wine list offers a good cosmopolitan spread at manageable prices, with a healthy range available by the glass. The list opens at £8.75.

CHEF: Tim Hughes PROPRIETORS: Jeremy King and Christopher Corbin OPEN: all week 12 to 3, 6 to 12 CLOSED: Christmas to New Year MEALS: alc (main courses £8.50 to £19.50). Cover £1.50 SERVICE: not inc CARDS: Access, Amex, Delta, Diners, Switch, Visa DETAILS: 85 seats. Vegetarian meals. Children's helpings. Wheelchair access. No music. Air-conditioned

Charco's

NEW ENTRY map 14

1 Bray Place, SW3 3LL — COOKING 2
TEL: 0171-584 0765 — COST £22–£38

Time was when the keen gastronaut touching down in Sloane Square was hard-pressed to find anywhere in the immediate vicinity worth a second look. Suddenly Chelsea has caught up, the options are multiplying, and not least of the attractions is Charco's. A wine bar and eatery since the 1950s, it was transformed last year by the arrival of Jon Bentham, formerly at Stephen Bull in Blandford Street (see entry), to cook in the basement restaurant. It is a stark enough space, with a tiled floor, whitewashed brick walls and tormenting chairs, but the cooking has created quite a *frisson*.

Much of the menu is eloquent testimony to the chef's CV. That happy mixture of refinement and earthiness brought together in challenging but apposite combinations is the textbook Blandford Street idiom. A meal might begin with a terrine of fried duck, potato and foie gras with shallot vinaigrette, and proceed to fillets of John Dory with peas, pancetta and braised celery. Crab cannelloni with a gazpacho sauce, a culinary mixed metaphor if ever there was, came with spinach and red peppers. Main courses achieved lift-off for one reporter: 'an excellent piece of tender veal with a version of dauphinois done in blue cheese' could scarcely be faulted. Rabbit came as 'a tasty bit of saddle' and two pieces of ballottine, one with the liver, the other with a herb stuffing, garnished with vegetables and accompanied by a bowl of tapénade topped with roasted garlic bread. Chocolate desserts have received good reports – a chocolate and orange mousse 'the lightest, fluffiest ever' – while lightness also distinguishes coffee mascarpone cheesecake with poached pear and crème fraîche.

This is thoroughly modern and eminently successful food, served 'courteously and competently', with the canniest eye on what is stirring London imaginations these days. A fairly safe wine list is offered, France forming its backbone, with a cursory smattering from southern Europe and the New World. House French starts at £8.25.

CHEFS: Jon Bentham and Gary Pavitt PROPRIETOR: Vinemark Ltd OPEN: Mon to Sat 12 to 2.30, 6.30 to 10.30 CLOSED: bank hols MEALS: alc (main courses £7.50 to £12). Set D £18 (2 courses) to £21.50 SERVICE: not inc CARDS: Access, Amex, Diners, Switch, Visa DETAILS: 55 seats. 3 tables outside. Private parties: 35 main room. Vegetarian meals. Children welcome. Smart dress preferred. No pipes in dining-room. Music. Air-conditioned

Cheng-Du

map 13

9 Parkway, NW1 7PG — COOKING 1
TEL: 0171-485 8058 — COST £19–£48

The name is Chinese – and so is the food – but there is something curiously Westernised about this restaurant on the edge of Primrose Hill. It feels almost like a brasserie, with its long bar, tiled floor, green woodwork and cool background Muzak. The menu focuses on Peking and Szechuan specialities, although it makes occasional fishy forays into the Cantonese repertoire. The substantial list of starters includes such things as breast of chicken dusted with crushed walnuts, deep-fried crispy veal sticks, and 'cold, tossed prawn slices in Szechuan marinade'. Even more intriguing is the list of specials, which reads like a global interpretation of 'nouvelle chinoise': sizzle-grilled sesame steak with teriyaki sauce; steamed chicken with red dates, black fungi and golden lilies; braised spare-ribs with star anise and rock sugar. The rest is mostly familiar provincial stuff, such as double-cooked pork, crispy aromatic duck, baked lobster with ginger and spring onions, and home-style bean curd.

CHEF: Mr Lam PROPRIETOR: Redfern Enterprises Ltd OPEN: all week 12 to 2.30, 6.30 to 11.30 MEALS: alc (main courses £4.50 to £18), Set L and D £17.20 (min 2) SERVICE: net prices CARDS: Access, Amex, Visa DETAILS: 75 seats. Private parties: 75 main room. Vegetarian meals. Children welcome. Smart dress preferred. Wheelchair access (also WC). Music

Chez Bruce

NEW ENTRY map 12

2 Bellevue Road SW17 7EG — COOKING 2*
TEL: 0181-672 0114 FAX: 0181-767 6648 — COST £24–£42

'The last time we ate in this restaurant was when Marco Pierre White was beginning his upward spiral.' Bruce Poole has come to the former Harvey's from Chez Max in Ifield Road (see entry), bringing much of his repertoire with him. The room now has a couple more tables, and has developed a rustic air that makes it feel more like a bistro than before. The atmosphere is relaxed, even when the place is buzzing, and service is warm and welcoming. 'We had one of the most charming young French waiters I have ever met,' enthused one. 'The head waiter doesn't miss a trick,' added another.

A set menu is priced according to the number of courses, and the restrained inventiveness and generally precise technique are 'perfectly French, and impervious to fashion'. Jambon persillé, ballottine of rabbit with onion confit, and chicken liver and foie gras terrine 'just like in France' confirm the thrust. The range of techniques and treatments runs from pan-fried calf's liver or braised rabbit ('the meat just fell off the bones') to sauté chicken breast full of flavour, poached wild salmon, roasted cod, and grilled sea bass. Chargrilling can be enthusiastically rather than carefully done, though when it works, as it did for one reporter's calves' kidneys, it produces excellent results.

Among other successes have been creamy-textured deep-fried brains with sauce gribiche, smooth brandade de morue with the sweetness of braised tomatoes providing a welcome foil to the salt and garlic, and imam bayaldi 'not quite for fainting but very good'. Huge platefuls and good ingredients help things along. Peppered fillet steak comes with 'five-star frites', and most desserts are praised, including tarte Tatin and tarte fine aux pommes, the former 'deliciously caramelised', the latter with 'tissue-paper-thin pastry' and 'impossibly fine slices of apple'. All the wines on the short and canny list are available by the glass, beginning with house Syrah and Chenin Blanc at £1.75.

CHEFS: Bruce Poole and Graham Grafton PROPRIETOR: Larkbrace Ltd OPEN: Tue to Fri L 12 to 2, Sun L 12.30 to 3, Mon to Sat D 7 to 10.30 CLOSED: bank hols MEALS: Set L Tue to Fri £12 (2 courses) to £15, Set L Sun £15 (2 courses) to £18.50, Set D £18.50 (2 courses) to £25 SERVICE: 12.5% (optional), card slips closed CARDS: Access, Amex, Delta, Diners, Switch, Visa DETAILS: 65 seats. Private parties: 8 main room, 18 private room. Smart dress preferred. Wheelchair access. No music. Air-conditioned

Chez Liline

map 12

101 Stroud Green Road, N4 3PX — COOKING 1
TEL: 0171-263 6550 and 272 9719 — COST £21–£49

In a 'bland' area between Finsbury Park and Holloway Road, Chez Liline provides the local crowd with an injection of colour, exoticism and noisy exuberance. Go through the door, past a tank full of live parrot-fish and lobsters to reach the dining-room – an informal hotch-potch of jam-packed tables, prints and posters. Service is friendly, although there may be a wait for the food (a note on the menu says that dishes are prepared to order 'to maintain the freshness of the food'). The kitchen's stock in trade is fish and shellfish – most of which comes from faraway waters, especially the Seychelles. Much of the cooking owes a debt to Mauritius, with some French/Creole overtones and colourful use of tomatoes, saffron, chillies, coriander and garlic. What you get are dishes such as king prawn curry, parrot-fish in mustard sauce, sea bream with fennel and thyme, 'excellent' provençale bouillabaisse, and whole crab with ginger and spring onion. Bourgeois fish might be cooked with a 'delightful' creamy garlic sauce or grilled with sweet potatoes, tomatoes and chillies. Basmati rice and accompaniments are fine, although vegetables have occasionally let the side down. Reasonably priced whites dominate the wine list, which dips into the Old and New Worlds for ideas. House wine is £9.25.

CHEFS: Mario Ho Wing Cheong and Pascal Doudrich PROPRIETOR: Mario Ho Wing Cheong OPEN: Mon to Sat L 12.30 to 2.30, all week D 6.30 to 10.30 CLOSED: bank hols MEALS: alc (main courses £9.50 to £17). Set L £7.25 (2 courses) to £12.75, Set D Mon to Sat £12.75, Set D Sun £15. Minimum £9.25 SERVICE: not inc CARDS: Access, Amex, Switch, Visa DETAILS: 48 seats. Private parties: 35 main room. Children's helpings. Music

Chez Max

map 13

168 Ifield Road, SW10 9AF — COOKING 2*
TEL: 0171-835 0874 — COST £27–£48

Most of the eating at this 'little piece of France' within shouting distance of Earl's Court takes place in the basement, down a steep spiral staircase that 'requires crampons'. Walls are covered in menus from French restaurants, and tables are so close that 'you appear to be eating off your neighbour's plate', although some refurbishment is anticipated before the *Guide* appears. It could all so easily misfire if the cooking weren't so good. Apart from its 'stone age' antipathy to young children, Chez Max turns out to be a quintessential French restaurant.

What is unarguable is that the soul of this restaurant is firmly rooted in the great cuisine bourgeoise tradition, as evidenced by terrine maison, salade lyonnaise, boeuf à la ficelle, and pot-au-feu. The view is that you come here to eat simple food, but executed with tremendous panache. Fish, usually the fleshier kind, takes up a large slice of the menu, and ranges from rare grilled tuna served cold with a salad to start, to 'sweet and fresh' roast Cornish sea bass with a crisp skin for main course, though deep-fried cod and chips with tartare sauce reveals the other side of the Renzland coin. An inspector rated a dish of 'startlingly fresh' Scottish langoustines with a tub of mayonnaise as 'one of the best dishes of the year', partly because of the kitchen's restraint in serving them so simply.

That approach was also evident in a round of grilled goats' cheese on a bed of bitter salad leaves. Vegetables are not merely for decoration but serve a useful purpose too: mashed potatoes mop up sauces such as the 'deep rich gravy' served with pink calf's liver. The overall effect was 'totally memorable and extremely convincing' for one seasoned reporter who finished a May meal with a tarte fine aux pommes of feather-light pastry and lightly caramelised apple slices. The almost exclusively French wine list has expanded to around 40 bins, with the balance over £20, and there are few halves. One reporter was unpleasantly surprised to discover that corkage for taking his own wine had leapt to £7.50 a bottle. House Côtes du Ventoux is £9.50.

CHEFS: Max Renzland and Christopher Eve PROPRIETORS: Max, Marc and Joanna Renzland OPEN: Sun to Fri L 12.30 to 2.30, all week D 7 to 11 (10.30 Sun) MEALS: Set L Mon to Fri £15 (2 courses) to £17.50, Set L Sun £17.50, Set D £25.50 to £29, Set post-theatre D 10.30 to 11 £20 (2 courses, inc wine). Licensed, but you may also bring your own: corkage £7.50 SERVICE: 12.5% (optional), card slips closed CARDS: Access, Delta, Switch, Visa DETAILS: 65 seats. Private parties: 14 main room. No children under 8. No cigars/pipes in dining-room. No music. Air-conditioned

Chez Moi

map 12

1 Addison Avenue, W11 4QS COOKING 3
TEL: 0171-603 8267 COST £22–£49

With this year's edition, Chez Moi clocks up a quarter-century of *Guide* appearances, an achievement that owes much to the professionalism of Richard Walton. He is not just an accomplished chef, but also has a keen sense of the expectations of his clientele. We tend to forget in these days of daily-changing menus that sometimes people return to a restaurant hoping to relive precisely past experiences. Thus do customers become regulars. On the other hand, a regular who occupies the same table whenever he lunches here remarks that 'the menu changes enough to keep familiarity at bay'.

Eating takes place in a warmly enveloping room of reddish-gold within a framework of punctilious hospitality. The fixed-price lunch menus are where most of the new ideas receive an airing. In recent years there has been a fondness for oriental, especially Thai, treatments. Deep-fried stuffed chicken wing with sweet chilli sauce was a bold innovation, but there have also been Japanese and Chinese borrowings. In the evenings the accent is predominantly French. Commended dishes have been warm goats' cheese on a garlic croûton with pesto, quenelles of salmon in a lobster sauce as a main course, and rare sauté saddle of hare with a 'tasty' honey and vinegar sauce. French cheeses 'in prime condition' as well as satisfying puddings, such as 'deep and intense' coffee ice-cream or a slice of lemon tart with crème anglaise and strawberry coulis, maintain the momentum. 'Very good' chocolates accompany only 'OK' coffee. 'Only in Holland Park could this be a neighbourhood restaurant,' sighed one reporter.

If the budget for wine is £20, you may have to repair to the Loire, Alsace and Rhône sections of the list, which are small but serviceable. Clarets and both red and white burgundies are good but expensive. The rest of the world receives pretty short shrift. Halves offer a generously wide choice.

CHEF: Richard Walton PROPRIETORS: Richard Walton and Colin Smith OPEN: Mon to Sat (exc Sat L) 12.30 to 2, 7 to 11 CLOSED: bank hols MEALS: alc (main courses £11 to £16). Set L £14 SERVICE: not inc CARDS: Access, Amex, Diners, Visa DETAILS: 45 seats. Private parties: 16 main room. Vegetarian meals. Children's helpings. Smart dress preferred. No pipes in dining-room. Wheelchair access. No music. Air-conditioned

Chez Nico at Ninety Park Lane map 15

90 Park Lane, W1A 3AA COOKING 5
TEL: 0171-409 1290 FAX: 0171-355 4877 COST £42–£94

'Still my favourite London venue for top food,' writes a well-travelled supporter. The designers have done a good job on what is really just another hotel dining-room, using mirrors to give it interest and depth. Tables are arranged down either side, leaving the centre free for comings and goings, mostly by the team of black-coated waiters. Service is never snooty or pretentious, always smooth yet personable and friendly, adding to a feeling of rock-solid quality and dependability that is shared by very few other restaurants in Britain. Consummate skill, assurance and confidence are hallmarks of the Ladenis style.

Much is made, rightly, of the good value afforded by the fixed-price lunch, which might include a fat boudin blanc made with chicken and foie gras in a buttery sauce with apple, or a confit of duck that really is a confit, not the merely well-cooked leg that so often masquerades under this label. But the gastronomic menu of ten mini-courses also 'has to be one of the great bargains of eating out', according to one of many who find this impossible to resist. It is available only to multiples of two diners, and changes over time, but many elements remain constant. Highlights have included the 'perfect little cup of langoustine soup' served first, which is 'intensely flavoured in a way I have never experienced elsewhere', and a salad of haricot beans flavoured with truffle oil and its accompanying boudin of foie gras.

Cep risotto is a classic Ladenis dish. 'Having tried to cook this myself on several occasions, it brings home to me just how wonderful this version is.' Fishy triumphs have included 'perfectly grilled scallops' on a delicate chive velouté with 'a little bundle of stunning vermicelli', and red mullet on a purée of basil with a delicate red wine sauce, while an inspector was taken with a beautifully prepared medallion of beef with a few wild mushrooms, sitting on a pool of 'stunning demi-glace sauce whose intensity and complexity was a real delight'. An excellent range of French cheeses arrives 'in the peak of condition', while among desserts praise has been heaped on passion-fruit sorbet, on a small crisp disc of apple tart in a toffee sauce containing chunks of chopped nuts, accompanied by a brandy-snap of ice-cream, and most of all on the lemon tart, distinguished by 'the sheer perfection of the pastry and the balance of the filling', an apparently simple dish, yet 'a reminder of just how good the cooking really is'. Indeed, one of the defining characteristics of Nico Ladenis's food is that apparently straightforward dishes taste about as good as they can ever get.

Quibbles about the temperature and cost of the food have arisen, but are usually drowned out by those who find the whole experience untoppable. The joys of the predominantly French wine list – and there are many – are tempered by high prices, although as a consolation they include service charge. The cheapest bottles on the list are house Bergerac white and red, £18 and £19

respectively. As we go to press we learn that the Pavilion restaurant, also part of Grosvenor House, is due to be revamped, and will have a Nico-trained chef at the helm.

CHEFS: Paul Rhodes and Nico Ladenis PROPRIETORS: Nico and Dinah Jane Ladenis OPEN: Mon to Fri L 12 to 2, Mon to Sat D 7 to 11 CLOSED: 10 days Christmas, 4 days Easter, bank hol Mons MEALS: Set L £29 to £50, Set D £51 to £65 SERVICE: net prices, card slips closed CARDS: Access, Amex, Diners, Visa DETAILS: 70 seats. Private parties: 12 main room, 20 private room. No children under 5. Smart dress preferred. No pipes in dining-room. Wheelchair access. No music. Air-conditioned

Chiaroscuro

NEW ENTRY map 15

24 Coptic Street, WC1A 1NT — COOKING 2
TEL: 0171-636 2731 FAX: 0171-580 9160 — COST £26–£47

After making a name for herself at the Café des Arts in Hampstead, Sally James moved to Bloomsbury to run her own show in partnership with husband Carl. Their premises are a town house on three floors (the top is for private parties) within trekking distance of the British Museum. True to the artistic derivation of the restaurant name, the décor is all about light and shade. The ground floor is modern and minimalist, with a vibrant 'mussel blue' mural and paintings derived from old Italian masters. Bell-shaped frosted-glass lights hang over the wooden-topped tables.

Sally cooks to a short menu that is based on bold assemblages of pasta, beans, pesto, capers and rocket, bolstered by a few Cajun ideas such as blackened fillets of grey mullet with a multi-coloured relish of sweet pickled vegetables. The vegetarian antipasto is a bright, lively assortment of seared courgettes, black olive purée, spiced lentils, baked tomato and other morsels that 'resound on the palate', while tiny pungent capers balance out the innate richness of saffron risotto. Chargrilling also works well: squid with a chilli dressing, and lamb cutlets (with a 'clean, spring flavour') have been endorsed.

Puddings might include apple soufflé with cinnamon or frozen lemon parfait. The two-course lunch and the early-evening set dinner are bargains, as is Sunday brunch, when every child with an adult eats for free from a special kids' menu. Service tries hard, although some nervousness and inattentiveness occasionally surface. The short wine list is an ever-changing slate dictated by customer requests and the owners' own experimentation; prices start at around £10.

CHEF: Sally James PROPRIETORS: Carl and Sally James OPEN: Mon to Fri L 12 to 3.30, Sun L 11.30 to 5, Mon to Sat D 6 to 11.45 CLOSED: 24 to 30 Dec, last week Aug MEALS: alc (main courses £7 to £13). Set L and Sun brunch £10 (2 courses), Set D before 8pm £10 (2 courses) SERVICE: not inc CARDS: Access, Amex, Delta, Switch, Visa DETAILS: 65 seats. 2 tables outside. Private parties: 30 main room, 14 and 30 private rooms. Vegetarian meals. Children's helpings. Smart dress preferred. Wheelchair access (1 step). No music

Restaurateurs justifiably resent no-shows. If you quote a credit card number when booking, you may be liable for the restaurant's lost profit margin if you don't turn up. Always phone to cancel.

Chinon

map 12

23 Richmond Way, W14 0AS — COOKING 3
TEL: 0171-602 4082 and 5968 — COST £28–£50

The ground-floor restaurant is a shop conversion in a small parade behind Shepherd's Bush Green, with a blue neon sign in the window, abstract pictures, hanging baskets, and a picture window overlooking the balcony at the back. The modern French food can be as straightforward as a salad of leaves and cresses, or a platter of oysters, mussels, prawns and crab, but flourishes of roast saddle of rabbit with black pudding and morel mushrooms, or roasted cod with a fondant of tomato and olive oil mash demonstrate the kitchen's fondness for fish and game.

Steamed mussels, and crab bisque of 'beautifully intense flavour' have impressed, and at one meal a plate of squid, 'faintly resistant outside, deliciously soft and creamy within', was stuffed with both pesto and a tomato and onion purée: 'Full marks for quality of ingredients and sensitive cooking,' concluded an inspector. Equally, breast of duck with a crisp skin, and pheasant 'in a wonderful gamey sauce' have been highly rated, while a dish unusually combining hare and venison, both cooked pink, was judged extremely successful. Vegetables are tailor-made for the main dish.

The menu is a *carte* of around six items per course, with a daily special or two, and what stands out from reports is that flavours are 'pure' and 'intense' – good cooking of outstanding ingredients is the general view – although there is a slight tendency to over-garnish, and towards richness. Chocolate tart has been a winner, and even the sorbet flavours are strong and distinct, including one of grapefruit and one of cinnamon. Bread is £1.80, and not even given away to mop up soup or moules marinière; there are no nibbles to begin, or petits fours with coffee, chairs might be more comfortable, and there are grumbles about the 12½ per cent service charge. 'The wine list fell to pieces in my hands, so I have little sense of the whole, save that it was French dominated and fairly mainstream', and the restaurant has not supplied us with one, nor a menu, nor filled in the questionnaire, so we cannot confirm the details below.

CHEF: Jonathan Hayes PROPRIETORS: Barbara Deane and Jonathan Hayes OPEN: Mon to Fri L 12.30 to 2, Mon to Sat D 6.30 to 10.30 (11 Fri and Sat) SERVICE: 12.5% (optional) card slips closed CARDS: Access, Amex, Visa DETAILS: 50 seats. 4 tables outside. Private parties: 35 main room. No children under 10. No cigars/pipes in dining-room. Music. Air-conditioned

Chiswick

NEW ENTRY map 12

131 Chiswick High Road, W4 2ED — COOKING 1*
TEL: 0181-994 6887 FAX: 0181-747 8708 — COST £21–£42

It may sound like a pub, or a pub conversion, but what we have here is a big lavender-painted restaurant on the High Road that opens up at the front in summer, and is owned by the same pair who own the Brackenbury (see entry, above). The Chiswick opened in October 1994 with an ex-Bibendum chef, Ian Bates, and seems to have hit the ground running, establishing a tone that is 'youthful but quite civilised and not at all arrogant'.

The menu is a pretty vigorous exercise in the kind of rustic peasant food that city-dwellers have taken to their hearts. Fish is left to speak for itself in a dish of grilled mackerel with olives and parsley, and another of halibut with an intense aïoli, while earthier appetites get to grips with a ragoût of snails, chorizo and chickpeas. Among meatless dishes a version of baked Piemontese pepper was a sensual triumph, a bright orange slithery object glossed with olive oil, next to a heap of couscous 'highly charged' with harissa. Dessert jellies have awaited their renaissance longer than most, but here in June was a blackcurrant version served with Jersey cream. More seasonal fruits are given the simple treatments that once made their arrival a cause for rejoicing: gooseberry tart, cherry clafoutis, peach fool. For those in search of a bargain, two-course set lunches are available, and there is an early evening menu of two courses and coffee for £8.50.

Wines have been chosen with supreme confidence, the list tripping lightly from Rolly-Gassmann Sylvaner through Dumazet's Condrieu to Argiano's authoritative Brunello. Pricing is agreeable, and there is a good choice by the glass. House French is £9 for white and £9.50 for red.

CHEF: Ian Bates PROPRIETORS: Adam and Kate Robinson OPEN: Mon to Fri and Sun L 12.30 to 2.45, Mon to Sat D 7 to 11.30 CLOSED: 1 week Christmas to New Year MEALS: alc (main courses £6.50 to £14). Set L Mon to Fri £8.50 (2 courses), Set L Sun £13.50 (2 courses), Set D before 8pm £8.50 (2 courses) SERVICE: not inc CARDS: Access, Amex, Delta, Switch, Visa DETAILS: 75 seats. 10 tables outside. Private parties: 14 main room. Vegetarian meals. Children's helpings. No pipes/cigars in dining-room. Wheelchair access (also WC). No music. Air-conditioned

Christopher's map 15

18 Wellington Street, WC2E 7DD COOKING 1
TEL: 0171-240 4222 FAX: 0171-240 3357 COST £30–£58

The architecture thrills. Housed in an ornate old bank building just off the Strand, Christopher's is a ground-floor bar that positively buzzes, and a sepulchrally lit upstairs dining-room (with magisterial ceiling) reached by an echoing spiral staircase. The cooking is American-style, not low-cal Cal-Ital, but shameless demotic: crisp-fried oysters with mash, smoked tomato soup, half-pound burgers and fries, and New York strip steak with maybe spinach on the side (creamed or regular). That said, there are splashes of the Mediterranean too, in a sauté of chicken livers with polenta, balsamic vinegar and sage, or penne with smoked chicken, spinach and fontina cream. Pâté de foie gras topped with 'bubbles' of melon, and grilled tuna with rocket salad in walnut oil have been praised, though one reporter was unimpressed with a plain-grilled steak, especially as 'no sauce was offered other than a jar of tomato ketchup'. Chocolate, toffee and cream are the components of authentic State-side desserts. Service sets to with a will, but final bills can cause regret: 'The price seems high, however grand the ceiling.' The wine list offers a surprisingly wide choice of Old World classics as well as soundly chosen bottles from the USA and the southern hemisphere. The house selection is all good, and opens with California Chardonnay and Cabernet at £13.

CHEF: Adrian Searing PROPRIETOR: Christopher Gilmour OPEN: all week L 12 to 3, Mon to Sat D 6 to 11.45 MEALS: alc (main courses £8 to £16) SERVICE: not inc CARDS: Access, Amex, Diners, Switch, Visa DETAILS: 120 seats. Private parties: 100 main room, 32 private room. Vegetarian meals. Children welcome. Smart dress preferred. No music

▲ *Claridge's* 🍷 ✱ map 15

Brook Street, W1A 2JQ NEW CHEF
TEL: 0171-629 8860 FAX: 0171-499 2210 COST £37–£89

You are likely to be in good company if your put on your tie and cross the line into that other world known as Claridge's. The royals are often here, famous faces celebrate weddings, dignitaries of all persuasions are courted and cosseted by legions of uncommonly pleasant staff who also seem to know their true place in the hierarchy of things. If you go for Sunday lunch you might find the dining-room peppered with young bloods and parents with children dressed in designer gear. If you want to sample the full works, you can expect much lifting of domes and mannered swaying from waiters who are past masters at balancing plates and proffering solicitous comments. 'The restaurant can provide anything a guest wishes to eat,' says the management.

After a long and celebrated run, Marjan Lesnik departed as we went to press and John Williams took over the kitchen. The style may not change much. It has always been haute cuisine without apologies, but laced with abundant supplies of foie gras and fresh truffles. The kitchen has delivered lobster and artichoke salad, baked Dover sole with champagne sauce, and chateaubriand, while at lunch-time the carving trolley has held pride of place. The whole experience has varied from immensely seductive to merely 'predictable', depending on reporters' views of gastronomy and social graces. Wines are all you might expect, and rather more besides, including a smattering from the New World, magnums of claret for celebrations and a decent spread of half-bottles. House wine is £16. CELLARMAN'S CHOICE: Macon-Lugny 1993, Louis Latour, £20; Beaujolais Villages 1993, Brac de la Perrière, £20.

CHEF: John Williams PROPRIETOR: Savoy Group plc OPEN: all week 12.30 to 2.30, 7 to 11 (11.30 Fri and Sat) MEALS: alc (main courses £23 to £36). Set L £29, Set D £36 to £45 SERVICE: net prices, card slips closed CARDS: Access, Amex, Diners, Visa DETAILS: 110 seats. Private parties: 240 main room, 14 to 240 private rooms. Vegetarian meals. Children's helpings. Jacket and tie. No smoking in 1 dining-room. Wheelchair access (also WC). Music. Air-conditioned ACCOMMODATION: 189 rooms, all with bath/shower. TV. Phone. Air-conditioned. B&B £217 to £347. Rooms for disabled. Children welcome. Baby facilities. Afternoon teas

Clarke's 🍾 map 13

124 Kensington Church Street, W8 4BH COOKING 3*
TEL: 0171-221 9225 FAX: 0171-229 4564 COST £31–£50

'"Simple" would be the word I would use, in a complimentary sense,' begins a typical report. Another adds that 'once you come to terms with the fact that Clarke's is about super-fresh Mediterranean and Californian salads, quick charcoal grilling, simple desserts, fine British cheeses and great bread, then it is hard to find much fault in the beautifully balanced clean-tasting no-choice meals'. Lightness remains a characteristic, and chargrilling is applied to everything, from leg of lamb through corn-fed chicken to breast of guinea-fowl. Entering the ground-floor dining-room is just like walking into a shop, while the downstairs one is pine-floored and decorated with abstract paintings and flowers in green ceramic pots.

It is, maintains Sally Clarke, her private army of vegetable, salad and fruit growers who plan her menu. If so, they seem to be a remarkably well- organised bunch. 'Menus are posted at the beginning of the week, dispelling any notion that our Sally is at the market at five every morning picking the freshest ingredients and shaping the menu around them.' A Wednesday meal gives the flavour, beginning with sweet and tender pigeon, lightly grilled, with watercress, raisins, and 'the tiniest wetting of pan juices and a squeeze of blood orange', then sweet, firmly textured grilled fillet of brill served with tarragon, chives and a rösti-like potato pancake. Two British cheeses follow, with 'wonderful, thin oatmeal biscuits', and finally 'a rich hemisphere of white, creamy and very vanilla-ish pannacotta with stoned cherries and two superb almond biscuits'.

In these circumstances chargrilling naturally gets put under the microscope, and when two scallops and a fillet of salmon are barbecued on the same skewer, each needing slightly different cooking times, then 'this can be cause for concern'. Although simplicity is at the heart of Sally Clarke's cooking, there is a view that 'I don't go out to an expensive restaurant to have a grilled chicken breast'. As one reporter puts it, 'The niggle comes from knowing that the chefs have not slaved for hours over turbot carcasses or veal bones, nor made labour-intensive purées.' The chargrilling may be of the best, but it explores a limited range of the repertoire, and reporters are aware of other restaurants' wider range of flavours and textures, brought about by additional cooking methods. 'The deliberately uncomplicated formula should reflect a little better in the pricing.'

Wines, however, are well thought out and not greedily marked up, with good bottles from Italy and particularly California, including some from Bonny Doon. Although vintages are recent, the wines are ready to drink and cover a broad spectrum of flavours. Ten or twelve interesting ones are usually available by the glass from £2.50. CELLARMAN'S CHOICE: Bonny Doon Roussanne 1993, California, £19.50; Il Podere dell'Olivos Nebbiolo 1992, California, £19.

CHEFS: Sally Clarke and Elizabeth Payne PROPRIETOR: Sally Clarke OPEN: Mon to Fri 12.30 to 2, 7 to 10 CLOSED: 10 days Christmas, 4 days Easter, 3 weeks Aug MEALS: Set L £22 (2 courses) to £26, Set D £37 SERVICE: net prices, card slips closed CARDS: Access, Switch, Visa DETAILS: 90 seats. Private parties: 10 main room. Vegetarian meals. Children welcome. No smoking in 1 dining-room D. Wheelchair access. No music. Air-conditioned

Como Lario

NEW ENTRY map 14

22 Holbein Place, SW1W 8NL — COOKING 1

TEL: 0171-730 2954 FAX: 0171-244 8387 — COST £25–£48

This old-stager underwent a thorough transformation when its current owners acquired it two years ago. Occupying a trio of converted shops round the corner from Sloane Square tube station, it has been ably designed to give a feeling of spaciousness within, an impression that may be belied as you lock elbows genteelly with those sitting at the neighbouring table. The food is regional Italian, not drop-dead trendy, but not stuck in the trattoria time-warp either. Spicy-fried baby squid with peas and polenta, tagliolini with spider-crab, and breaded John Dory with artichokes strike contemporary chords. Meats are more traditional. At one meal monkfish calf's liver veneziana was 'excellent – very tender strips with plenty of caramelised onion and two slices of polenta'. Vegetables are priced separately, but might include 'succulent and powerful' fennel roasted with garlic.

Textbook desserts run to 'light and smooth' pannacotta with 'twin lakes of cream and strawberry sauce', pale chocolate mousse topped with crumbled amaretti biscuits, and the usual ices and sorbets. Service is 'very friendly and capable'. In nostalgic Italian fashion, most of the wines are listed without benefit of producer or vintage, making them impossible to assess. House wines are £8.25.

CHEF: Giancarlo Moeri PROPRIETORS: Guido Campigotto, Giancarlo Moeri and Roberto Colussi OPEN: Mon to Sat 12.30 to 2.45, 6.30 to 11.30 MEALS: alc (main courses £7 to £14). Cover £1.25 SERVICE: not inc CARDS: Access, Amex, Delta, Switch, Visa DETAILS: 80 seats. 6 tables outside. Private parties: 80 main room, 20 private room. Vegetarian meals. Children welcome. Smart dress preferred. Wheelchair access. Music. Air-conditioned

▲ *Connaught* map 15

Carlos Place, Mayfair, W1Y 6AL COOKING 4
TEL: 0171-499 7070 FAX: 0171-495 3262 COST £44–£128

For those who want to pack a meal and the theatre into a single evening, the Connaught might fit the bill. The floor show is all male, and performs a well-choreographed dance hovering round tables to carve and slice, flame and pour, with special effects provided by carts, domes, trolleys and trays. The set is a gentlemen's club, *circa* 1910, and as in some theatres the cast can outnumber the audience. 'It was everything we had been led to expect from the report in the *Guide,*' began one couple who enjoyed the 'grandness' of the occasion. The friendly and courteous service was, for one, 'the Connaught's greatest attraction', although he also enjoyed the food enormously.

That the *Guide*'s longest-serving restaurant can maintain such traditional dining in grand-hotel style without becoming a museum piece is a tribute to the kitchen's unceasing vigilance. 'We have only one kitchen, under the supervision of one chef,' maintains the management, cocking a snook at some other grand London hotels, although there are two rooms for eating. Both serve the *grande carte*, as it is called, and differ only in detail, with the Grill Room offering a set-price dinner as well. The choice is vast, from omelette Arnold Bennett to 'superb' croustade d'oeufs de caille Maintenon, to steak, kidney and mushroom pie. Seafood has ranged from oysters that were 'the largest and best-tasting I have ever had', spiced up with pepper and Tabasco, to lobster in jelly that 'looked and tasted spectacular'.

Today, when ingredients from all over the world are mixed together without a qualm, combining, say, Thai spices with black pudding and gravad lax on a pizza base (let's hope that nobody actually does that), the Edwardian habit of keeping British and French strands largely separate may seem strange. But this approach, which the Connaught embodies, respects the identity of the two cultures. Hence we get cold ox tongue, roast beef with Yorkshire pudding, and sherry trifle on the one hand, and fresh foie gras, oeufs pochés Bénédictine, and crêpes soufflés Belle Epoque on the other. Then there are fowl and game dishes. Not many places serve teal these days, but a roast breast was 'beautifully cooked with a real gamey flavour', while for one visitor pheasant was 'a bit dry but full of flavour and plenty of it'.

One reporter felt that 'there is nothing wrong with this wonderful restaurant at all except for the prices', which can grate when the food disappoints. In these circumstances the 15 per cent service charge doesn't help either. Another visitor was 'very disappointed to see two young men light up large cigars in the dining-room. They stank the place out.' Wines are predominantly French, indisputably aristocratic, and prices make a night at the opera look cheap, though house wine is £16.50 per carafe.

CHEF: Michel Bourdin PROPRIETOR: Savoy Group plc OPEN: restaurant all week 12.30 to 2.30, 6.30 to 10.45; Grill Room Mon to Fri L 12.30 to 2.30, all week D 6 to 10.45. CLOSED: Grill Room bank hols (but open 25 Dec and New Year's eve) MEALS: alc (main courses £10 to £40). Set L £25, Set Sun L £30, Set D £35. Minimum £25. SERVICE: 15%, card slips closed CARDS: Access, Amex, Diners, Visa DETAILS: 75 seats restaurant, 35 seats Grill Room. Private parties: 12 and 22 private rooms. Car park. Vegetarian meals. Children welcome. Jacket and tie. Wheelchair access (also male WC). No music. Air-conditioned ACCOMMODATION: 90 rooms, all with bath/shower. TV. Phone. Room prices on application. Air-conditioned. Rooms for disabled. Children welcome. Baby facilities. Afternoon teas (*The Which? Hotel Guide*)

▲ *Conrad London, Brasserie* map 12

Chelsea Harbour, SW10 0XG COOKING 2
TEL: 0171-823 3000 FAX: 0171-351 6525 COST £29–£66

This is 'the other restaurant' in Chelsea Harbour, slightly overshadowed for reporters by the Canteen (see entry), but delivering its own brand of modernism with conviction. The thick carpets, comfortable chairs and a slightly nautical air ('a bit like 1930s ocean liner architecture') are on a big scale, with large and well-spaced tables lending a sense of extravagance that is picked up by the menu prices. Of the two fixed-price offerings, dinner is by far the simpler: at one July meal a choice between salads of warm shredded duck or shrimp, then tomato and basil soup, before grilled breast of chicken or pan-fried cod, finishing with a mixed berry assiette. Lunch, meanwhile, like the *carte*, runs to seven or eight more ambitious items per course, with additions of Dover sole, fillet steak or rack of lamb from the grill.

Peter Brennan enjoys paddling in the Mediterranean as much as the next man, out of which he pulls prawns for a risotto, and makes cannelloni of ceps and potato, or pairs Parma ham with a fig compote. He throws himself into salads, along with the likes of baby globe artichokes, pine- and cashew-nuts, sun-dried tomatoes, beetroot crisps and spiced cheese biscuits – and, yes, that is all one salad. Just as welcome is the gutsy Britishness of Cumberland sausages with mashed potato and onion gravy, or cod in a Guinness batter with chips, mushy peas and tartare sauce. Prices on the globe-trotting annotated wine list are high, though the house selection brings a few bottles within reach, beginning in the South of France at £14.50. Half a dozen wines are available by the glass from £3.

The Guide *relies on feedback from its readers. Especially welcome are reports on new restaurants appearing in the book for the first time. All letters to the* Guide *are acknowledged.*

CHEF: Peter Brennan PROPRIETOR: Conrad International London OPEN: all week 12 to 2.30 (4 Sun), 6.30 to 10.30 MEALS: alc (main courses £8.50 to £22.50). Set L £17 (2 courses) to £19, Set Sun brunch £31.50 (inc champagne), Set D £22 (2 courses) to £24 SERVICE: 10%, card slips closed CARDS: Access, Amex, Delta, Diners, Switch, Visa DETAILS: 60 seats. 19 tables outside. Private parties: 160 main room, 8 to 160 private rooms. Car park. Vegetarian meals. Children's helpings. Smart dress preferred. No cigars/pipes in dining-room. Wheelchair access (also WC). Music. Air-conditioned ACCOMMODATION: 160 rooms, all with bath/shower. TV. Phone. Air- conditioned. B&B £204 to £300. Rooms for disabled. Children welcome. Baby facilities. Pets by arrangement. Afternoon teas. Swimming-pool

Cork & Bottle 🍷 £

map 15

44–46 Cranbourn Street, WC2H 7AN — COOKING 1

TEL: 0171-734 7807 FAX: 0171-483 2230 — COST £19–£31

'The feel-good factor is definitely with us,' writes Don Hewitson, Cork & Bottle's director, who noticed during 1995 that 'the Dom Pérignon has started flowing again'. The basement wine bar is often a scrum of lively, cheerful, talkative people who consider themselves fortunate to have found standing room. If it gets too crowded, take a regular's tip and go after 8pm. It may be difficult to believe that wine bars were once as trendy as brasseries now are; many fell by the wayside, but Don Hewitson's single-mindedness has ensured a long run. Food suits the casual mood, from an open sirloin sandwich through various grills to raised ham and cheese pie, or braised lamb shank in Zinfandel sauce. A two-course lunch might consist of pea soup followed by pan-fried kidneys. Service may get off to a grumpy start but soon hots up with more arrivals.

Don Hewitson is a tireless promoter of wine in general and Australian wine in particular – Barossa Valley can give Bordeaux a run for its money on the list – although the French are given every chance to fight back. Twenty wines by the glass for around £3 might offer the chance to compare a French Syrah with an Australian Shiraz. CELLARMAN'S CHOICE: Brancott Estate Sauvignon Blanc 1993, Marlborough, New Zealand, £19.95; McDonald Winery Cabernet Sauvignon 1992, Hawkes Bay, New Zealand, £14.95.

Another Don Hewitson operation, the Hanover Square Wine Bar & Grill at 25 Hanover Square, W1, has pleased a couple of reporters with its grilled steak, and smoked salmon and scrambled eggs.

CHEF: Louis Eghan PROPRIETOR: Cork & Bottle Wines 1991 Ltd OPEN: Mon to Sat 11am to midnight, Sun 12 to 10.30 CLOSED: 25 and 26 Dec, 1 Jan MEALS: alc (main courses £4 to £9). Set L (2 courses) £9.50 SERVICE: not inc CARDS: Access, Amex, Diners, Switch, Visa DETAILS: 85 seats. 4 tables outside. Private parties: 20 main room, 10 and 12 private rooms. Vegetarian meals. No pipes in dining-room. Music. Air-conditioned

---

'The anachronistic policy of insisting on a jacket and tie resulted in an exchange with a fellow guest, who was told (since it was extremely hot) that they would relax the rule on ties, but that he would still need to wear a jacket, though he could take it off when he sat down. At this point the man suggested that he might borrow my jacket and walk into the dining-room, then take it off and return it, and after that we could take turns to go to the bathroom.' (On eating in Wiltshire)

The Cow

NEW ENTRY map 13

89 Westbourne Park Road, W2 5QH — COOKING 1
TEL: 0171-221 0021 and 5400 — COST £17–£30

Just when you thought the idea of taking over a pub, filling it with young folk and feeding them superior grub had fizzled out (after the Eagle's and Lansdowne's pioneering efforts, see entries, London), up pops another to prove you wrong. This spacious and much-frequented old pub owes its renaissance to Tom Conran (son of Sir Terence) and is all the buzz, though it is not glamorous and the food is not refined. The ground-floor bar opens early in the evening and runs on beer and shellfish, while the upstairs dining-room offers simple décor and three courses of not much choice for a fixed price (although half a litre of house wine is thrown in). It also has two sittings per evening – which, although an inconvenience to some, is at least a sign of health in the restaurant trade. Anglo-French-Italian dishes are the mainstay, along the lines of pissaladière, Ligurian fish stew, ox tongue with salsa, roast leg of lamb, and (one lunch-time) four curvy chunks of immaculately fresh sole fried in golden breadcrumbs, on a pile of rocket leaves with a mustard dressing. Puddings are missable, but there is always cheese. A dozen wines meet most requirements, starting with house wine at £9 bottle.

CHEF/PROPRIETOR: Tom Conran OPEN: restaurant Sat and Sun L 1 to 2.30, Tue to Sat D 7.30 and 9.30 (two sittings); bar Tue to Sun L 12 to 3, all week D 5.30 to 11 CLOSED: restaurant Aug MEALS: restaurant Set L £16.50, Set D £16.50; bar alc (main courses £4.50 to £7.50) SERVICE: 12.5% (optional), card slips closed CARDS: Access, Switch, Visa DETAILS: 30 seats. Private parties: 30 main room. Vegetarian meals. Children welcome. Smart dress preferred. No cigars/pipes in restaurant early evening. Music. Air-conditioned

Crowthers

map 12

481 Upper Richmond Road West, SW14 7PU — COOKING 2
TEL: 0181-876 6372 — COST £27–£37

We are 'still hanging in there', affirm the Crowthers, who have been wooing the citizens of East Sheen and beyond for more than 13 years. 'Dependable' and 'solidly competent' are the kind of comments that the cooking generates from a band of loyal followers who continue to patronise the place with reassuring regularity. The food has moved on a bit from classic French, and it is currently flirting with the Mediterranean and Britain, in response to customers' requests. Reporters have particularly enjoyed filo parcels of wild mushrooms, grilled salmon on green noodles with saffron and Noilly Prat, and pink chump of lamb in a herb crust sliced on to a pile of vegetables with a rosemary sauce. Elsewhere, the menu could embrace seafood tortellini; ribeye steak with rösti potato and shallot sauce; and boned, stuffed quails with flageolet beans. As a finale, sticky toffee pudding has been 'magnificent', while grilled fruits glazed with a light sabayon and mango sorbet made a refreshing end to one 'skilfully balanced meal'. Service can be 'a bit nervous' but, as one reporter proclaimed, 'the price is right'. Thirty wines constitute a thoughtfully chosen selection matching quality with value for money. House wine is £8.50.

CHEF: Philip Crowther PROPRIETORS: Philip and Shirley Crowther OPEN: Tue to Fri L 12 to 2, Tue to Sat D 7 to 10 (early or late bookings by prior arrangement) CLOSED: 1 week Christmas, 2 weeks August MEALS: Set L £16 (2 courses) to £18.50, Set D £18 (2 courses) to £22 SERVICE: not inc CARDS: Access, Visa DETAILS: 32 seats. Private parties: 47 main room. Children's helpings. Smart dress preferred. Wheelchair access (1 step). No music. Air-conditioned

Daphne £

map 13

83 Bayham Street, NW1 0AG COOKING 1
TEL: 0171-267 7322 COST £12–£31

This 'family' restaurant pleases the neighbourhood with its combination of friendliness and regular Greek-Cypriot dishes. Low prices (the set lunch is a particularly good deal) and a consistent standard of cooking bring regulars back for more. 'A favourite local,' writes one supporter, happy with a menu that stays with hummus, tsatziki, loukanika sausages and grilled haloumi cheese, along with kleftiko, stifado and afelia. A blackboard goes through the motions of presenting daily fish specials – although since they rarely change they might as well join the ordinary menu. Never mind, they focus attention on charcoal grilling of bream, mullet, octopus, or skewers of swordfish, cuttlefish and shellfish. Aubergines, artichokes, broad beans and pulses generally come with olive oil and lemon juice; and sticky pastries finish things off. The short list includes a handful of Greek and Cypriot wines under £10. House wine is £8.50.

CHEF: Lambros Georgiou PROPRIETORS: Panikos and Anna Lymbouri OPEN: Mon to Sat 12 to 2.30, 6 to 11.30 CLOSED: 25 Dec and 1 Jan MEALS: alc (main courses £5.50 to £9.50). Set L £6.50 SERVICE: not inc CARDS: Access, Visa DETAILS: 85 seats. 10 tables outside. Private parties: 30 main room. Vegetarian meals. Children's helpings. Wheelchair access (also WC). Music

Daphne's

map 14

112 Draycott Avenue, SW3 3AE
TEL: 0171-589 4257 and 584 6883 COOKING 2
FAX: 0171-581 2232 COST £23–£58

Largely because of its location, Daphne's has become some sort of Mecca for the style-hungry beau monde who trip in, clothed head to foot in Versace, to do lunch. When busy, the place may feel like a set from *Absolutely Fabulous*. Décor, by contrast, is self-consciously understated, with tiled floor, walls of artfully exposed brick, and climbing plants in the garden room at the rear. At one stage the food was occasioning a few dissatisfied mutterings, but the arrival of new chef Kamel Benamar in January 1995 seems to have restored equilibrium. The emphasis is still contemporary Italian, with classic risotto dishes, inventive pastas, such as tortelloni with crab and aubergine, tagliata (beef fillet grilled rare in thin slices) and plenty of polenta. An inspector was suitably impressed by a colourful and smartly dressed starter of goats' cheese on red and yellow peppers with olives, pine-nuts and shredded radicchio. Tiger prawns came with a grade-A sweet red salsa dip. A main course of tagliatelle with porcini proved to be a generous serving but tasted disappointingly mild, while sliced chicken breast was scattered with thick twigs of rosemary and 'absolutely delicious' caramelised onions. Vegetables add to the bill and deep-fried courgettes on one occasion proved more successful than the rather diminutive 'selection' of vegetables. Pastry-work in a prune and almond tart was 'perfect', the mild mascarpone cream that came with it was jazzed up with armagnac, and the pot au chocolat managed to deliver both the density and strength required. As fashion moves on, this sort of food 'may not be at the cutting edge, but when it works, it works well'.

Italy is the leading country on the wine list. The choices are sound and backed by assured selections from the South of France and the New World. Prices are reasonable for Chelsea, and there is a good clutch of halves, though hardly any of those are Italian. House Italian is £9.50.

CHEF: Kamel Benamar PROPRIETOR: Mogens Tholstrup OPEN: all week 12 to 3 (4 Sun), 7 to 11.30 MEALS: alc (main courses £5.50 to £18.50) SERVICE: 15%, card slips closed CARDS: Access, Amex, Delta, Diners, Switch, Visa DETAILS: 110 seats. 10 tables outside. Private parties: 8 main room. Vegetarian meals. Children welcome. Smart dress preferred. Wheelchair access (1 step). No music. Air-conditioned

Del Buongustaio

map 12

283 Putney Bridge Road, SW15 2PT — COOKING 1
TEL: 0181-780 9361 FAX: 0181-789 9659 — COST £23–£44

Behind its discreet frosted windows, Del Buongustaio specialises in the cooking of northern Italy. The Putney location, among some fairly dilapidated shops, may not inspire, but the culinary intentions are serious enough. The fare is not the Californian version of Italian food found so often elsewhere, but the unashamedly fortifying stuff of Piedmont, Emilia-Romagna and the Veneto. Sformatino (a kind of savoury egg pudding) of broccoli is served with a sauce of tomatoes and pistachios, while another starter of carpione is a variant of the escabèche technique of marinating after cooking – in this case a chicken breast with celery, onion, sage, garlic and rosemary served with grilled courgettes. The meatier sorts of fish receive bold treatments in main courses – grilled tuna with tomatoes and chicory has a sauce infused with lemon, oregano and garlic – while stuffings feature in many of the meat dishes: prosciutto, rosemary and marjoram in roasted goat, for instance.

Puddings too are intriguingly authentic, and are by no means dominated by ice-cream. Chocolate and almond flan arrives with a glass of Recioto della Valpolicella, whle an April menu yielded Neapolitan Easter cake of ricotta and grana cheeses, dried fruits and lemon zest. The dual orientation of the wine list, Italy and Australia, ensures that the choice is sharply focused and that halves are thin on the ground. House wines from the Veneto, a Tocai and a Merlot, are £8.50.

CHEFS: Antonio Strillozzi and Aurelio Spagnuolo PROPRIETORS: Rochelle Porteous and Aurelio Spagnuolo OPEN: Sun to Fri L 12 to 2.45 (12.30 to 3.15 Sun), all week D 6 to 11.15 (6.30 to 10.15 Sun) CLOSED: 10 days Christmas and New Year MEALS: alc (main courses £6.50 to £11). Set L £9.50 (2 courses), Set D £19.50. Cover 90p. Minimum £15 D SERVICE: not inc, card slips closed; 10% for parties of 5 or more CARDS: Access, Amex, Visa DETAILS: 60 seats. Private parties: 60 main room. Vegetarian meals. Children's helpings. Smart dress preferred. No cigars/pipes in dining-room. Wheelchair access (1 step). Music. Air-conditioned

dell'Ugo

map 15

56 Frith Street, W1V 5TA — COOKING 1

TEL: 0171-734 8300 FAX: 0171-734 8784 — COST £25–£47

It gets less noisy as you ascend the three floors, from frenetic café through bustling bistro to slightly more formal restaurant. The same food is served throughout, its relative importance increasing the higher you go. The large menu – 35 savoury items, 10 puddings – seems to have been produced using a big Mediterranean cocktail shaker. Out falls a stream of bruschetta with a trio of plum, sun-dried and roast tomatoes; smoked eel and potato salad with mustard dressing; steamed mussels with harissa, pickled lemons and garlic leaves; goats' cheese tart; and deep-fried ricotta and spinach dumplings.

Some of the cutting-edge ideas may now seem blunted by overuse, but strong and clearly distinguishable flavours predominate. Cooking on this scale, however, almost inevitably brings approximate results, even though there are really only two speeds: fast chargrilling or slow roasting, the latter producing more than its share of dishes that have dried out. 'Wonderful sweet puddings' include Tunisian orange cake with yoghurt and honey, and bananas cooked in their skins and served with ice-cream. Service tends to be slow and very casual. Three dozen wines are arranged in price bands, beginning at around £10, and are usually sharp enough for the food. Over a dozen are available in a 25-centilitre pichet from £3.45.

CHEF: Mark Emberton PROPRIETOR: Simpsons of Cornhill plc OPEN: ground floor Mon to Sat 11am to 11.30pm, first and second floor Mon to Fri L 12 to 3, Mon to Sat D 5.30 to 12.15am CLOSED: bank hols MEALS: alc (main courses £8 to £12) SERVICE: not inc CARDS: Access, Amex, Delta, Diners, Switch, Visa DETAILS: 180 seats. 5 tables outside. Private parties: 75 first floor, 60 second floor, 14 private room. Vegetarian meals. Children welcome. No cigars/pipes in dining-room. Music. Air-conditioned

▲ *Dorchester, Grill Room* 🍷

map 15

Park Lane, W1A 2HJ — COOKING 2

TEL: 0171-629 8888 FAX: 0171-495 7351 — COST £33–£79

All the restaurants at the Dorchester are overseen by Willi Elsener, and all have their own independent kitchens. The Terrace is for dinner-dances on Friday and Saturday nights – foxtrot to duck consommé with gnocchi made from confit, waltz to an escalope of salmon with a potato crust – while the Bar menu offers Italian items along the lines of artichoke risotto, a daily pasta dish on top of the listed ones, and Amaretto parfait with prickly pear sauce. Of the two main restaurants, the Grill Room is British and the Oriental (see entry, opposite) majors on Cantonese food.

Thanks to predominantly red fabrics and upholstery, the Spanish-style Grill Room 'feels a bit tarty'. It dates from 1931 and was refurbished in original style when the entire hotel had a face-lift in 1990. The food is hardly more recent, trawling through timeless British dishes of deep-fried battered cod, boiled leg of lamb with caper sauce, and puddings from one of the many trolleys: presentation is very old-school. The food has its appeal, especially in dishes where timing is not critical. A trolley of roast Aberdeen Angus beef (with Yorkshire pudding, of course) cannot be at its best throughout a whole meal-time, whereas braised beef in Guinness or steak and kidney pudding is less likely to suffer. While other chefs bring British food up to date, here it remains as the tourists always imagine it.

The wine list is a good one, providing money is no object. It is the same for all restaurants (apart from the Bar), and consists of mainstream French wines backed up by good Italian and New World bottles. Wines under £20 are in the minority, but they do exist. Wines by the glass start at around £4.50. CELLERMAN'S CHOICE: Matua Valley Sauvignon 1994, Hawkes Bay, New Zealand, £26; Chiroubles 'Dom. du Clos Verdy' 1993, Georges Boulon, £24.

CHEF: Willi Elsener PROPRIETOR: Dorchester Hotel Ltd OPEN: all week 12.30 to 2.30, 6 to 11 (7 to 10.30 Sun and bank hols) MEALS: alc (main courses £14.50 to £32). Set L £24.50, Set D £32 SERVICE: net prices, card slips closed CARDS: Access, Amex, Diners, Switch, Visa DETAILS: 81 seats. Vegetarian meals. Children's helpings. Smart dress preferred. Wheelchair access (also WC). Music. Air-conditioned ACCOMMODATION: 244 rooms, all with bath/shower. TV. Phone. Air-conditioned. B&B £247 to £311. Rooms for disabled. Children welcome. Baby facilities. Afternoon teas

▲ *Dorchester, Oriental* 🍷 map 15

Park Lane, W1A 2HJ — COOKING 3
TEL: 0171-317 6328 FAX: 0171-495 7351 — COST £33–£95

The Oriental is expensive but worth it, according to an inspector. 'The cooking equals many of the best in Hong Kong, and the chef is really special.' Although Simon Yung brings in abalone and shark's fin, much of the menu reads like any other Cantonese, except for the prices. There are also set dinner menus from £32 to £70, and all menus specify that MSG is not used in the cooking. This makes a big difference. Tastes may seem restrained, even timid, to those used to MSG, but in fact they are true to the ingredients, finely balanced and refined. Seemingly ordinary ingredients are turned out exquisitely, and presentation is of the highest order.

The star dish at inspection consisted of seven pieces of crab claw, the meat mixed with mushroom and prawn and returned to the shell: 'refined flavours, wonderfully fresh ingredients'. Deep-fried crispy pigeon is served with pickled vegetables. Seasonings are sensitively and skilfully handled, chilli saucing is delicate, 'adding just enough excitement but never overwhelming', and textures given due care and attention. Chilled mango pudding is quite possibly 'the best of its genre in London', and the restaurant itself is among the best of its kind in the country. 'Every dish tastes different from every other. How many people can say that in a Chinese restaurant in the UK?'

The setting and service are 'grand hotel' and rather lacking in warmth. Silver domes are lifted, and some dishes assembled at table. Wines are fine for French haute cuisine, but might do more to adapt themselves to the Oriental's food in particular. Great Wall and Dynasty are merely tokens. For other details of the wine list, including CELLARMAN'S CHOICE, see previous entry.

Several sharp operators have tried to extort money from restaurateurs on the promise of an entry in a guidebook that has never appeared. The Good Food Guide *makes no charge for inclusion.*

CHEFS: Willi Elsener and Simon Yung PROPRIETOR: Dorchester Hotel Ltd OPEN: Mon to Fri L 12 to 2.30, Mon to Sat D 7 to 11 MEALS: alc (main courses £9.50 to £32). Set L £22.50 (2 courses) to £24.50, Set D £32 to £70 SERVICE: net prices, card slips closed CARDS: Access, Amex, Diners, Switch, Visa DETAILS: 81 seats. Private parties: 51 main room, 6 to 14 private rooms. Vegetarian meals. Children's helpings. Smart dress preferred. Wheelchair access (also WC). Music. Air-conditioned ACCOMMODATION: see entry above for details

La Dordogne

map 12

5 Devonshire Road, W4 2EU — COOKING 1
TEL: 0181-747 1836 FAX: 0181-994 9144 — COST £26–£45

This two-roomed neighbourhood restaurant aims to be as French as the French management and staff can make it. Oddly though, given the name, specialities are not truffles and foie gras. There is a bit of duck breast about, and one dish of foie gras, but the main thrust is seafood, particularly Irish rock oysters and lobster, the latter cold in a salad, or grilled with butter sauce, for example. Among other fishy offerings are hot crab meat topped with hollandaise sauce and grilled, and turbot on a bed of vegetables with a champagne sauce. Meat dishes include well-flavoured fillet steak, served with delicate little potato pancakes and a red wine sauce. Desserts, however, are the glory of La Dordogne, including intensely flavoured apple tart on thin pastry, superior profiteroles, and crème brûlée, with six of them gathered together as a 'sumptuous' assiette gourmande. Service, sadly, has been described as 'cold' and 'indifferent'. The entirely French wine list includes a handful from the south-west, including house Pécharmant red and Bergerac white at £9.50.

CHEF: Jean-Luc Morcellet PROPRIETOR: La Dordogne Ltd OPEN: Mon to Fri L 12 to 2.30, all week D 7 to 11 CLOSED: bank hols MEALS: alc (main courses £8.50 to £12). Cover £1 SERVICE: 10% CARDS: Access, Amex, Delta, Diners, Switch, Visa DETAILS: 80 seats. 6 tables outside. Private parties: 30 main room, 20 to 50 private rooms. Children welcome. Smart dress preferred. Wheelchair access (1 step; also WC). Music

Eagle £

map 13

159 Farringdon Road, EC1R 3AL — COOKING 1*
TEL: 0171-837 1353 — COST £19–£28

It's crowded, it's noisy, it's smokey and it's a pub. There are handpumps on the bar, you are not obliged to eat and no bookings are taken. The scenario can be a tricky one: 'Trying to get a table brings out the predatory worst in some people. Seeing all this tempting food, knowing what you want to order and waiting for a couple to smoke 20 cigarettes before vacating a table must be the most frustrating eating-out experience in London,' commented one long-suffering visitor. But patience was repaid on that occasion with really interesting food and a bill that represented superb value for money.

The cooking has strong Portuguese overtones (chef David Eyre spent his childhood in colonial Mozambique), although the menu (changed at every meal) loots the entire Mediterranean for inspiration and ingredients. Salads are regularly endorsed, as for example roast green 'pachino' tomatoes with grilled sweet green chillies, olives, coriander and goats' cheese. Fans also praise Italian sausages with sweet roast onions and rocket, 'huge but still delicious' pork chops, scallops and much more besides. Portuguese-style dishes such as salt cod baked with potatoes, green peppers and olives, or bife Ana (a marinated rump steak sandwich), are also recommended. As an alternative to pints of Charles Wells Bombardier or bottles of Pilsner Urquell, there is a fistful of gutsy wines that seldom break the £10 price barrier; all are served by the glass.

CHEF: David Eyre PROPRIETORS: Michael Belben and David Eyre OPEN: Mon to Fri 12.30 to 2.30, 6.30 to 10.30 CLOSED: 2/3 weeks Christmas, bank hols MEALS: alc (main courses £7.50 to £10) SERVICE: not inc CARDS: none DETAILS: 55 seats. 4 tables outside. Private parties: 100 main room. Vegetarian meals. Children's helpings. Wheelchair access (1 step). Music

Efes Kebab House £ — map 15

80 Great Titchfield Street, W1P 7AF — COOKING 1
TEL: 0171-636 1953 FAX: 0171-323 5082 — COST £18–£31

Opened in 1975 by Kazim Akkus and Ibrahim Akbas, this remains one of the most reliable and best-loved Turkish restaurants in the capital. Customers can build a whole meal from the assortment of hot and cold meze: hummus, cacik and taramasalata, arnavut cigeri (deep-fried, diced lambs' liver), cerkez tavugu (chicken with walnut sauce), and peynir salata ('white cheese' with chilli and parsley), to name but a few. If you want something more red-blooded there are also skilfully chargrilled kebabs, lamb cutlets, offal and minced lamb. Sweets include the inevitable sticky pastries, but reporters have also praised the 'first-class' selection of fresh fruit. Set meals (min two people) are great value. Vegetarian and fish dishes are available, although not actually listed on the menu, and lots of the starters are also vegetarian. Service is attentive, unless the place is full to bursting. Efespilsen Turkish beer is an appropriate tipple; otherwise, the short wine list features a few punchy Turkish bottles. Efes II at 175–177 Great Portland Street, W1, 0171-436 0600, has floor shows and belly-dancing seven nights a week.

CHEFS/PROPRIETORS: Kazim Akkus and Ibrahim Akbas OPEN: Mon to Sat noon to 11.30 CLOSED: 25 Dec, 1 Jan MEALS: alc (main courses £5.50 to £9). Set L (minimum 2) £15 to £16, Set D (minimum 2) £15 to £16. Cover 75p SERVICE: not inc CARDS: Access, Amex, Delta, Diners, Switch, Visa DETAILS: 190 seats. 20 tables outside. Private parties: 150 main room, 40 private room. Children welcome. Smart dress preferred. No smoking in 1 dining-room. Wheelchair access. Music. Air-conditioned

English Garden — map 14

10 Lincoln Street, SW3 2TS — COOKING 2
TEL: 0171-584 7272 FAX: 0171-581 2848 — COST £21–£55

In a well-heeled residential backwater just off the Kings Road, this Chelsea town house makes much of its setting and its horticultural theme. Pride of place goes to the lofty Gothic-style conservatory at the back of the restaurant, with its domed roof, luxuriant greenery and rattan chairs, although the whole place has style and vibrancy. As befits the name, the cooking is English, but the menu is unlikely to generate much flag-waving from the diehard bubble-and-squeak brigade. Chef Brian Turner takes a more modern view of things, creating up-to-the minute realisations of old favourites and grafting on a few original ideas that can't be pigeonholed. Lunch is fixed-price for three courses and coffee, dinner is a *carte*.

A lot of marinating must go on behind the scenes to keep the essential ingredients so tender, reckoned one reporter: witness wonderfully succulent skewered scallops with rich, slightly minty hollandaise, and duck breast 'cooked English pink' with onion marmalade and a powerful jus. Elsewhere, praises have been heaped upon a leek and goat's cheese tart with 'out-of-this-world' pastry and an 'oh-so-delicate' filling, and a rack of lamb perked up with 'lovely' roasted garlic. The kitchen also gets to grips with saddle of hare and raisin salad, cured salmon with coriander salsa, and steamed breast of guinea-fowl with a green peppercorn sauce. Old-school English cookery has the final say in the shape of orange flummery and poached pears in sloe gin syrup, although one contented soul reckoned that white chocolate mousse layered in a glass with fresh raspberries and crushed meringue was the perfect finale to a first-class meal. The enviable setting and impeccable service set everything off to a tee. The wine list hangs its hat on stylish Bordeaux and Burgundy from a good run of vintages, and manages a balanced selection with a fair range of prices. House Bordeaux red and white is £9.50.

CHEF: Brian Turner PROPRIETOR: Roger Wren OPEN: all week 12.30 to 2.30 (2 Sun), 7.30 to 11.30 (10 Sun) CLOSED: 25 and 26 Dec MEALS: alc (main courses £8.50 to £17), Set L Mon to Sat £14.75, Sun £18.75 SERVICE: not inc CARDS: Access, Amex, Delta, Diners, Switch, Visa DETAILS: 70 seats. Private parties: 20 main room, 10 and 20 private rooms. Vegetarian meals. Music. Air-conditioned

L'Escargot map 15

48 Greek Street, W1V 5LQ COOKING 2*
TEL: 0171-437 6828 and 2679 FAX: 0171-437 0790 COST £32–£58

In its new incarnation, L'Escargot is a great crowd-pleaser: 'Can't wait to go back!' enthused a visitor from Hampshire; 'Eminently appealing...without pandering fawningly to fashion,' commented another. Most reports focus on the ground-floor 'brasserie' – although you won't see much in the way of brass rails and mirrors. Instead, it is a large, cavernous sort of place that can feel empty even when 'the cream of Soho' is out on the town. Around the perimeter of the room is 'an endless squidgy sofa' done out in red, exquisite bouquets adorn the tables, chandeliers sparkle from the ceiling, and the whole set-up is run impeccably by 'suited and booted' overlords and a brigade of staff kitted out in long aprons and trendy waistcoats. The mood manages to be both cool and colourful.

David Cavalier has left, and Garry Hollihead (joined, as we went to press, by Anand Sastry, formerly of Argyll and L'Esprit de L'Escalier) works to a menu that eschews high art in favour of gutsy, French-inspired dishes cooked and presented with care and deliberation. Salad of rich, gluey pig's trotters with fried potatoes and sauce gribiche, 'incredibly thin' carpaccio with Parmesan and chives, and a delicate little mound of risotto with truffles are typical starters. To follow that, you might opt for a crab ravioli with Puy lentils and saffron sauce, glorious daube of beef from 'a wonderful ancient animal, stewed for hours' and served with a pile of purée of potato and parsnip, or confit of duck with orange salad. As a finale, it's hard to beat the quintessential tarte Tatin, caramelised to perfection, or a wedge of chocolate tart served with vanilla ice-cream visibly studded with seeds. Business on the upper level, in the rather private first-floor dining-room, is altogether more modernist: abstract prints line the walls, the plates have designs created by students at the Royal College of Art, and the menu inhabits the realms of roast foie gras with mango and ginger, escabèche of brill with tapénade, and loin of venison with celeriac purée. The wine list takes France seriously, although it ventures without trepidation into the New World; you need to look seriously to find much below £15. House wines start at £10.50 and move up to £25.

CHEF: Garry Hollihead and Anand Sastry PROPRIETOR: Jimmy Lahoud OPEN: brasserie Mon to Fri L 12 to 2.15, Mon to Sat D 6 to 11.15; dining-room Tue to Fri L 12 to 2.15, Tue to Sat D 6 to 11.15 CLOSED: 24 and 25 Dec MEALS: alc brasserie (main courses £10.50 to £12.50). Set L brasserie £17 (2 courses) to £21.50, dining-room £21.50 (2 courses) to £25, Set D brasserie £19 (2 courses) to £23.50, dining-room £27 (2 courses) to £36.50 SERVICE: 12.5%, card slips closed CARDS: Access, Amex, Diners, Visa DETAILS: brasserie 90 seats, dining-room 50 seats. Private parties: 12 main room, 30 and 60 private rooms. Children welcome. Smart dress preferred. Music. Air-conditioned

L'Estaminet

map 15

14 Garrick Street, WC2E 9BJ — COOKING 1*
TEL: 0171-379 1432 FAX: 0171-409 2414 — COST £21–£42

'We would have been delighted to come across it in many a provincial town in France, and head over heels to find it in [our home town of] Cambridge,' noted a couple who lunched pleasantly at this family-run restaurant. The setting is a converted Victorian glassworks factory opposite the Garrick Club on the fringes of Covent Garden. Everyone agrees the atmosphere and service are unfailingly cheery, despite the crowds, and the kitchen is generally on the ball. Simple, confident cooking is the order of the day and the menu is in the classic mould of fish soup with rouille, lyonnaise sausage, 'over-generous' chateaubriand in 'superb condition', confit of duck with lentils, crème caramel and chocolate mousse. There is also an excellent-value pre-theatre menu (served 5.45pm to 7pm), although one satisfied reporter warned that you may need to ask for it, as it was read to them 'out of a notebook'. The short wine list is strongly Gallic, prices are fair and half-bottles show up well. House wine is £8.50.

CHEF: Philippe Tamet PROPRIETORS: Christian Bellone and Maria Echevarria OPEN: Mon to Sat 12 to 2.30, 5.45 to 11.30 CLOSED: Christmas, Easter, bank hols MEALS: alc (main courses £7.50 to £14). Set pre-theatre D £10.99. Cover £1.50 SERVICE: 12.5% (optional), card slips closed CARDS: Access, Amex, Switch, Visa DETAILS: 70 seats. Private parties: 25 private room. Children welcome. Smart dress preferred. No smoking in 1 dining-room. Wheelchair access (1 step). Music

Fifth Floor

map 14

Harvey Nichols, 109–125 Knightsbridge, SW1X 7RJ — COOKING 2
TEL: 0171-235 5250 FAX: 0171-235 5020 — COST £32–£75

The fifth floor is given over entirely to food and drink, with a café, well-stocked food and wine shops, and a restaurant that feels like 'an outsize café: Sloaney, noisy and restless'. The cooking is a bit restless too. Henry Harris combines a rich vein of hearty British food with lots of Mediterranean borrowings. Alongside staunchly British poached ox-tongue with parsley mash is a plate of grilled veal kidneys, North Africanised with an aubergine and couscous salad with harissa dressing and minted yoghurt. Even though the menu may also take in zampone fritters, and scrambled eggs with shaved 'botarga' (smoked fish roe), the cooking nevertheless seems to have a sense of direction.

Vegetarian menus, both à la carte and fixed price, offer stir-fried noodles with chilli and coriander, or a colourful red pepper and aubergine roll with scoops of herby goats' cheese and triangles of toast with tapénade. Fish runs from smoked haddock fish-cakes with tartare sauce and thick-cut chips, to lobster with coriander, ginger and noodles. Puddings are listed with a recommended glass of wine: a pear pithiviers, for example, with a Tuscan vin santo at £6, marginally more than the pud itself costs. One reporter managed to enjoy a brittle-topped tourron glacé stuffed with crystallised fruits, with a sweet fresh apricot sauce, without a glass of anything.

Incidentals, from olives to varied breads, are good. 'Coffee was so weak it was unlikely to keep anyone awake', although one party nearly fell asleep by the time main courses arrived, nearly two hours after they had sat down. That, and the gung-ho approach to the basics of table spacing and arrangement ('the waiter had to pass our table and the next one in order to serve the table behind'), suggests that front-of-house needs tightening up. It is now possible to buy wine on Monday evenings at shop prices to drink in the restaurant, a small but welcome initiative. The wine list itself is staggeringly good and fairly priced, a rare combination for London. House recommendations are a good place to start, with a generous 15 or so by the glass from £2.50, while the body of the list is packed with interesting producers, epic vintages, mainstream bottles, odd curiosities – in short, everything you could ask for, even if some individual countries (South Africa, for instance) are rather light. CELLARMAN'S CHOICE: Arbois, Savagnin 1989, Puffeney, £24,50; Ornellaia 1991, Antinori, £32.50.

CHEF: Henry Harris PROPRIETOR: Harvey Nichols & Co Ltd OPEN: Mon to Sat 12 to 3 (3.30 Sat), 6.30 to 11.30 CLOSED: 25 and 26 Dec, D bank hols MEALS: alc (main courses £10 to £29). Set L and D £17.50 (2 courses) to £21.50 SERVICE: 12.5% (optional), card slips closed CARDS: Access, Amex, Delta, Diners, Switch, Visa DETAILS: 110 seats. Private parties: 6 main room. Car park. Vegetarian meals. Children's helpings. Smart dress preferred. No pipes in dining-room. Wheelchair access (also WC). No music. Air-conditioned

Fire Station £ — map 13

150 Waterloo Road, SE1 8SB
TEL: 0171-620 2226 and 401 3267 — COOKING 1*
FAX: 0171-633 9161 — COST £20–£30

The bright neon sign tells you this is certainly not a fire station any more. It still looks like one inside, though, with its red-painted girders, black ventilation pipes, tiled floor and some sepia pictures of fire-engines. The junk-shop furniture is in varying stages of decrepitude. There is no booking and no menu: dishes of the day are chalked on a blackboard and are erased as they sell out. Have a drink at the bar and wait for a table.

The food is good, and there is lots of it, so starters may be sustenance enough if your appetite is less than Rabelaisian. Chargrilled mackerel with Greek meze offers 'lusciously juicy' blackened fish, accompanied by feta cubes, aubergine purée with coriander seeds and lemon. Gravad lax was subtly flavoured, while a main course of roast chicken with mashed potato and green beans came on a 'deliciously rich cream sauce with big, earthy morels'. 'Perfectly executed' bavette steak was served rare – take it or leave it. Desserts may include a 'huge quantity' of apricots poached in a tart liquor of honey and lemon juice, sprinkled with toasted nuts and served with a blob of mascarpone. 'Espresso,' wrote one reader, 'was among the best I've ever had in London.' Service can be casual, but invariably cheerful. The hubbub shows that London loves the place. The wine list, too, could stand as an emblem of the times: fifteen wines from seven countries – all under £20 – plus weekly-changing bin-ends. House French is £7.95.

CHEF: Eugene Fadil PROPRIETOR: Regent Inns plc OPEN: Mon to Sat 12.30 to 2.30, 6.30 to 10.45 CLOSED: bank hols MEALS: alc (main courses £7 to £9.50) SERVICE: not inc CARDS: Access, Amex, Delta, Diners, Switch, Visa DETAILS: 90 seats. Private parties: 120 main room, 70 private room. Vegetarian meals. Children's helpings. Wheelchair access (also WC). Music. Air-conditioned

First Floor

map 13

186 Portobello Road, W11 ILA — COOKING 1

TEL: 0171-243 0072 FAX: 0171-221 9440 — COST £23–£49

The restaurant, naturally, is on the middle floor of this three-storey building, its quirkiness apparent from the entrance – Japanese stepping stones set in a gravel path – right through to the mis-matching mix of antique and modern furniture and the faintly Bohemian atmosphere. The food is styled along Mediterranean lines with input from the Caribbean and Australia; this means not just baked kangaroo sausage with potato galette and mustard sauce, but also a good smattering of fish and vegetable dishes including pastas and risottos, breads and cheeses, grilled yellowfin tuna and sauté softshell crab.

The simple cooking is often no more than an assembly of ingredients, such as a three-tier stack of corn pancake, avocado and palm heart, or a plate of onion foccacia with artichoke heart, rocket leaves and sun-dried tomato rémoulade. But rather this than misplaced ambition, the downfall of many cooks. The food has a restless feel of 'so many ingredients, so little time' about it, and flings some unlikely platefellows together, but if you want novelty here it is, from sauté mushrooms and spinach with fried plantain, to baked salmon fillet with a roast garlic tabbouleh. After all that travelling there is a sense of 'coming home' to steamed coconut pudding with lemon caramel, and sticky toffee pudding. Forty-odd good-value wines for explorers include Italians, South Africans, Australians and Chileans, with house wine at £9.50.

CHEFS: Nilton Campos and Walter Andriollo PROPRIETOR: Esprit Properties Ltd OPEN: all week 10.30 to 4.30, 7.30 to 11 (noon to 10 Sun) CLOSED: 25 Dec, 1 Jan, Aug bank hol Mon MEALS: alc (main courses L £5 to £7.50, D £11.50 to £17). Cover £1.50 SERVICE: not inc; 12½% for parties of 6 or more CARDS: Access, Amex, Delta, Diners, Switch, Visa DETAILS: 130 seats. Private parties: 50 main room, 30 and 50 private rooms. Vegetarian meals. Children welcome. No cigars/pipes in dining-room. Music

▲ *This symbol means accommodation is available.*

▲ *Four Seasons Hotel* 🍷 map 15

Hamilton Place, Park Lane, W1A 1AZ COOKING 3*
TEL: 0171-499 0888 FAX: 0171-493 6629 COST £33–£70

The hotel has all the usual West End accoutrements, from doormen and footmen and men who park your car, to two restaurants (Lanes offers various breakfasts, a buffet, daily specials and a dessert trolley) and a pianist in the bar. The typically functional hotel dining room runs on a number of set-price options plus a generously furnished *carte* of ten first and 16 main courses as well as desserts. It changes, unsurprisingly, four times a year, and a spring version demonstrates the intricacy of Jean-Christophe Novelli's style, which often takes its starting-point from the standard repertoire but turns a dish into something individual. A mild element of surprise is often a characteristic, as in turbot poached in coconut milk, or spit-roasted pigeon stuffed with wild mushrooms and sprinkled with liquorice, while orange zest and cardamom are favourite flavourings for fish.

The food is often built up on the plate in layers, like a tower of filo pastry discs interleaved with scallops and thin strips of chicory, and there is no question about the high level of skill and accomplished techniques. Reporters have enjoyed wild mushroom cake with pistachios and a port wine sauce – 'cooking at its very best' – as well as 'beautiful fillet steak, beautifully cooked', served with beef marrow in a rich, strong wine reduction 'that stopped short of being syrupy'. Much of the best cooking has an economy about it, and this food is just so full of enthusiasm that it can't resist playing around, as it does, for example, with braised saddle and leg of rabbit with a risotto of the liver, or fillet of venison served on an apple Tatin with a maple syrup sauce.

The pick of desserts is a small, steamed chocolate pudding, rich yet light – 'as you broke into it, it oozed a rich bitter chocolate sauce' – that comes with white chocolate ice-cream. Coffee arrives with 'some of the best brandy-snaps we have eaten'. Service is polite, friendly and efficient. Wines are mostly French, high in quality, with specialist pockets in Burgundy (Louis Jadot) and Bordeaux (Ch. Latour). Prices are high – even Spain manages to muster only one wine under £20 – in which context the few house wines from £15 (£3.80 a glass) are especially welcome. CELLARMAN'S CHOICE: Rully 1992, Bouchard Père et Fils, £38; Lussac St-Emilion, Ch. Lyonnat 1989, £29.

CHEF: Jean-Christophe Novelli PROPRIETOR: Four Seasons, Regent Hotels & Resorts OPEN: all week 12.30 to 3, 7 to 10.30 MEALS: alc (main courses £19 to £27). Set L £19 (2 courses) to £28, Set D £45 SERVICE: net prices CARDS: Access, Amex, Diners, Switch, Visa DETAILS: 60 seats. Car park. Vegetarian meals. Children's helpings. Jacket and tie. Wheelchair access (also WC). Music. Air-conditioned ACCOMMODATION: 227 rooms, all with bath/shower. TV. Phone. Air-conditioned. Room only £235 to £288. Rooms for disabled. Children welcome. Baby facilities. Small dogs welcome. Afternoon teas. Garden

The Guide *office can quickly spot when a restaurateur is encouraging customers to write recommending inclusion – and sadly, several restaurants have been doing this in 1995. Such reports do not further a restaurant's cause. Please tell us if a restaurateur invites you to write to the* Guide.

The French House Dining Room

map 15

49 Dean Street, W1V 5HL COOKING 2
TEL: 0171-437 2477 FAX: 0171-287 9109 COST £28–£43

The big change since last year is that Fergus Henderson has left to open St John (see entry, London), leaving his partner Margot Clayton to continue at this Soho landmark. The small dining-room is over the pub, one floor removed from the pavement hubbub, with open windows on bright days to let in some street atmosphere. Neither the room nor the food suffers from embellishment. Plainness is a virtue, from parsnip soup or leek vinaigrette through Welsh rarebit to steamed plum pudding. The short menu may change frequently, but revolves around a core of items that will probably include at least one offal dish – lamb sweetbreads, perhaps, with oil-dressed watercress and fried onions on a round of bread – as well as fish, and something gamey at the right time of year.

'Hearty British food with a French influence' is a fair description of faggots and haricot beans, fish stew with toast and aïoli, or 'straightforward' roast poussin flavoured with tarragon. Another put it thus: 'Despite not being outstanding in any single area, the overall impression is of good food for a reasonable price.' To finish, Lancashire cheese is served with Eccles cakes, and sponges and crumbles abound. It is the sort of food that gives simple British cooking a good name: enough care is taken over essentials, and energy is not wasted on fripperies. The 25 or so wines are entirely French and well chosen, although house wine (at £8.95) could be improved.

CHEF: Margot Clayton PROPRIETORS: Margot Clayton, Fergus Henderson, Jon Spiteri and Melanie Arnold OPEN: Mon to Sat 12.30 to 3, 6.30 to 11.15 CLOSED: 10 days Christmas and New Year, bank hols MEALS: alc (main courses £7.50 to £12) SERVICE: not inc CARDS: Access, Amex, Delta, Diners, Switch, Visa DETAILS: 30 seats. Private parties: 30 main room. Vegetarian meals. Children welcome. No music

Fulham Road 🍷

map 14

257–259 Fulham Road, SW3 6HY COOKING 3
TEL: 0171-351 7823 FAX: 0171-376 4971 COST £30–£70

Enthusiasm is undimmed for the Kensington and Chelsea branch of Stephen Bull's operation, two rooms separated by no more than an archway, kitted out in David Collins's 'strange elephantine upholstery', and full of chatter. To the extent that British food is inventive and relies on the unashamed borrowing of ideas, the Bull-Corrigan team is very British. What it provides is nothing like the sluggish stroll through a few Mediterranean clichés that is sometimes expected to pass for enlightened cooking, but genuinely imaginative and playful, as strong on technique as on popular appeal.

Ravioli and risotto are favoured and successful devices, and fish is worked a little harder than is customary: cured sea bass and herrings come with a beetroot bavarois and a mustard and dill sauce, while monkfish may be wrapped in cured ham and served with spinach, artichokes and crab juices. But the results hit the mark. 'Ingredients are of the highest quality and sauces are delicate and delicious.' Humble items – hearty oxtail risotto, or eels in red wine sauce – rub shoulders easily with more extravagant foie gras, perhaps in a terrine with guinea-fowl and celeriac, served with madeira jelly and toasted brioche.

Standards of the repertoire and simpler dishes, such as omelette Arnold Bennett, roast venison, crab or lobster salad, are not forgotten. The bacon and cheese bread is a hit, as are puddings of poached pears with an almond biscuit and vanilla cream with Marsala, or a hot caramel soufflé, 'not too sweet, really light and just the thing to finish'. Service has struck reporters differently, from 'an unsmiling regiment of sixth-form schoolgirls' to 'warm, friendly, efficient, helpful, thoroughly professional and *happy*'. The 100-strong wine list is varied, bang-on for quality and fairly priced, with particular interest in regional France, Italy and California. House wine is £10.50, and over a dozen wines are available by the glass. CELLARMAN'S CHOICE: Touraine, Azay-le-Rideau 1992, Pibaleau Père et Fils, £14.95; Madiran, Ch. Montus 1989, Brumont, £38.

CHEF: Richard Corrigan PROPRIETOR: Stephen Bull OPEN: Mon to Fri L 12.15 to 2.15, Mon to Sat D 7 to 11 CLOSED: bank hols, 1 week Christmas MEALS: alc (main courses £14 to £22). Set L £18 (2 courses) to £22 SERVICE: not inc, card slips closed CARDS: Access, Amex, Visa DETAILS: 80 seats. Private parties: 12 private room. Children's helpings. No cigars/pipes in dining-room. Wheelchair access (1 step). No music. Air-conditioned

Fung Shing £

map 15

15 Lisle Street, WC2H 7BE — COOKING 2*

TEL: 0171-437 1539 FAX: 0171-734 0284 — COST £20–£51

Lisle Street is not the tidiest or cleanest thoroughfare in Chinatown, but once you are through the doors 'Fung Shing is like another world, sedate, with lots of greenery and heavy linen cloths'. The main thrust of the cooking is Cantonese, which shows up best in the list of specials: eel and coriander, chicken with preserved clam sauce, or grilled minced pork with salted fish. Seafood is the strong suit, and sweets are virtually non- existent. Fire temporarily closed the restaurant shortly after our inspection, but it is scheduled to reopen before the *Guide* appears, under the same management and with the same chef.

The Fung Shing Special appetiser is not the usual mound of sesame toasts on crispy 'seaweed', but a well-judged mix of different ingredients, cooking techniques and flavours: sweet, smooth, silkily tender deep-fried squid; crispy spring rolls; two monster Pacific prawns grilled; and marinated spare ribs 'of real subtlety'. Among seafood successes have been 'divinely tender' scallops served in their shells with black-bean sauce, high-class spicy prawns theatrically sizzled at table, and soft-shell crab with chilli and salt. Stewed duck with preserved plum sauce is a winner too – the meat soft and full of gamey flavour – served straight from the oven in its lidded pot, in a sauce with just a hint of sourness: real earthy Cantonese peasant food. Vegetables are the usual pak choi greens, but classier than at most other places, Singapore noodles are good, and plain boiled rice has just the right amount of glutinous stickiness. Service has been variable, and wines are better than average for a Chinese restaurant, with house French at £9.

CHEF: Kwun Fu PROPRIETOR: Forum Restaurant Ltd OPEN: all week 12 to 11.15 CLOSED: 24, 25 and 26 Dec MEALS: alc (main courses £6.50 to £55). Set L and D £12.50 to £13.50. Minimum £8.50 SERVICE: not inc CARDS: Access, Amex, Delta, Diners, Switch, Visa DETAILS: 85 seats. Private parties: 50 main room, 28 private room. Vegetarian meals. Children welcome. Jacket and tie. Music. Air-conditioned

Le Gavroche 🍷 map 15

43 Upper Brook Street, W1Y 1PF
TEL: 0171-408 0881 and 499 1826 COOKING 4*
FAX: 0171-491 4387 and 409 0939 COST £37–£114

Le Gavroche sails on like a grand ocean liner. Tradition is upheld, service is exemplary, and the cooking is more or less consistent from year to year. Since Michel Roux took over from his father, changes have been slight: lighter sauces perhaps, and desserts that now seem rather heavy-handed and over-sugary. The basement dining-room, under a nondescript Mayfair mansion block, is 'essentially a gentleman's library without the books', but with French flourishes. Olive greens, reds and dark wood dominate the room, and the artwork runs from Picasso and Chagall downwards.

Dishes are a triumph of technique over fashion. The menu is full of mousseline de homard, terrine de foie gras, medallion of veal with sage butter, and so on, all pretty standard stuff repertoire-wise, but the execution is near to faultless. A mix of meat and shellfish, for example, so often an empty gesture, here works a treat: plump, sweet, juicy shelled crayfish with small chunks of delicate pig's trotter 'were held together by a wonderful cream sauce made with Meaux mustard, providing just enough acidity to sharpen the sweetness of the crayfish'. First courses tend to have a lot of shellfish in them. At one meal half a roasted baby lobster was accompanied by an al dente risotto cooked in squid ink that 'steals the show with a lovely depth of flavour.'

Given that the three-course lunch at £37 offers a choice of three dishes at each stage, doesn't stint on luxuries, and includes half a bottle of good house wine, excellent canapés, coffee and service, it can fairly be considered a bargain in the context. Even at this humble level the French tradition of dining-room service lives on; staff have to do more than just fetch and carry plates. A fat pigeon, partially deboned, is carved at table – luscious pink breast meat, moist and deeply flavoured – and served in a sauce that is almost a soup: a light gravy given extra depth by an injection of foie gras sauce, also added at table, and 'which tasted like an elixir'. For the inspector 'it was undoubtedly the best dish of the year'. Desserts (and bread) are the Achilles' heel, although one reporter who registered disappointment felt that this 'hardly matters when the petits fours are as plentiful and good as these'.

'Orchestrated, immaculate, correct and calm' is how one reporter saw the service. Not only is the balance of friendliness and formality perfectly mastered, but the choreography of the army of waiters and waitresses is astutely managed. 'All the expected flourishes were there, like the dome lifting, and the presentation of almost a truckload of cognac, but somehow nothing appeared gimmicky or unnecessary, everything seemed so natural.' Any wine list that opens with over 60 bottles of champagne, most of them vintage, is going to be for big spenders, and so it proves. But if the wine is French, and any good at all, it is probably here, and you can bet they have at least eight vintages of it. There are many prices in treble figures, just one or two under £20, and discreet service comes to the rescue of the bewildered. CELLARMAN'S CHOICE: Chablis St Martin 'Cuvée Albert Roux' 1993, Dom. Laroche, £29 50; St-Emilion, Ch. Vieux Sarpe 1985, £29.50.

CHEF: Michel Roux PROPRIETOR: Le Gavroche Ltd OPEN: Mon to Fri 12 to 2, 7 to 11 MEALS: alc (main courses £25 to £34). Set L £37 (inc wine) to £75, Set D £55 to £75. Minimum £50 D SERVICE: net prices CARDS: Access, Amex, Diners, Switch, Visa DETAILS: 60 seats. Private parties: 80 main room, 20 private room. Children welcome. Jacket and tie. No cigars/pipes in dining-room. No music. Air-conditioned

Gay Hussar

map 15

2 Greek Street, W1V 6NB COOKING 2
TEL: 0171-437 0973 FAX: 0171-437 4631 COST £25–£54

The owners reckon that the Gay Hussar is now the only Hungarian restaurant in London. If it had opened this year, it would probably have found itself championed as part of the current vogue for recherché ethnicity. As it is, it remains one of Soho's more venerable and revered institutions, a 'Transylvanian railway carriage' of a place where Labour Party grandees and curious tourists flock for Laszlo Holecz's Magyar fare.

Chilled wild cherry soup is mentioned in reports every year, as befits an old stalwart. It is a hearteningly unsubtle melange of fruit, soured cream and wine. Pressed boar's head – 'reminiscent of corned beef but more sophisticated', according to one reporter – is chunky pieces set in aspic. Fish dumplings are almost delicate in comparison, made of very light white river fish, served with a mushroom cream sauce, strongly flavoured with dill, and rice. Smoked goose breast comes with scholet, a fortifying bean dish seasoned with paprika. Veal goulash with egg dumplings is 'very hearty and rich' and is served, as are most things, in a portion that 'would have fed two or more hungry people'. Pancakes are a good bet for dessert, either with walnuts or sweet cheese, and 'wonderfully textured' chestnut purée will plug whatever gap you may feel you still have. Service makes everyone feel at home. Some up-to-the-minute Hungarian wines by Hugh Ryman mean the choice isn't entirely confined to Bull's Blood and Tokai. For those determined not to enter into the spirit, there are French bottles too. House wine is £9.50.

CHEF: Laszlo Holecz PROPRIETOR: Restaurant Partnership plc OPEN: Mon to Sat 12.30 to 2.30, 5.30 to 10.45 CLOSED: bank hols MEALS: alc (main courses £11.50 to £15.50). Set L £16 SERVICE: 12.5% (optional), card slips closed CARDS: Access, Amex, Diners, Switch, Visa DETAILS: 70 seats. Private parties: 10 main room, 12 and 22 private rooms. Vegetarian meals. Children's helpings. Smart dress preferred. Wheelchair access (1 step). No music. Air-conditioned

Gopal's of Soho

map 15

12 Bateman St, W1V 5TD COOKING 1
TEL: 0171-434 1621 and 0840 COST £21–£44

There are more palatial curry houses in central London, but the considered view is that Gopal's is 'the best Indian establishment in Soho'. It is often 'busy, noisy and smoky', but there's no doubting the quality of the food. Ingredients are first-rate, 'essentially brilliant' herbs and spices are used in subtle ways and the balanced flavours shine through. The menu covers a lot of territory, taking in specialities from Hyderabad, Malabar and Karnataka in the south, although the 'unparalleled taste of Goa' was the highpoint for one reporter. Familiar items such as aloo chana chat 'draped in fresh coriander', murgh jalfrezi and bhindi bhaji are well up to the mark, and the kitchen also scores with dishes such as meenu fish curry and dum ka murg (chicken steamed in a pot sealed with a flour and water pastry lid). Rice and breads are a cut above average. The wine list, put together by consultant David Wolfe, is reckoned to be varied and 'entertaining', although big 650ml bottles of Cobra beer also suit the food admirably. House wine is £7.90.

CHEF/PROPRIETOR: N.P. Pittal OPEN: all week; 12 to 3, 6 to 11.15 (11 Sun) CLOSED: 25 and 26 Dec MEALS: alc (main courses £6 to £12). Cover £1 SERVICE: not inc CARDS: Access, Amex, Delta, Switch, Visa DETAILS: 50 seats. Vegetarian meals. Children's helpings. Smart dress preferred. Music. Air-conditioned

Granita

map 13

127 Upper Street, Islington, N1 1QP — COOKING 2
TEL: 0171-226 3222 — COST £21–£33

The décor may be all Islington minimalism – bare wooden tables, trendy chairs, plain flooring – and it may not be to everyone's taste, but there's no doubt that Granita is delivering the goods. 'A really excellent meal on my first visit here,' noted a well-travelled London reporter. Like the interior, the short menu is pared down to the bone, but it hits you in the eye with its staccato descriptions written in big, bold capitals. For example, 'warm basil, shredded zucchini, toasted pine-nut, garlic, feta, in wafer pastry, salad of winter greens' may read like a disjointed shopping list but is actually a starter. The style might be modern British, but the inspiration is global, with a serious dip into the Mediterranean.

Ahmed Kharshoum cooks with vigour and his dishes are as confident and full-blooded as the menu itself: scallops are served on a heap of spiced lentils with rocket salad; fine-textured linguine is paired with wild mushrooms (excellent seasoning here); chargrilled fillet of tuna has been presented with avocado and red onion relish, roasted potatoes and mange-tout, or – equally colourfully – with aubergine purée, roasted red pepper, shredded potato cake and green beans. Elaborate salads are perked up with vivid balsamic dressings, the home-made breads are enticing (although slicing them so thin is rather a waste) and cheeses from Neals Yard are kept 'in good nick'. Crème brûlée or chocolate marquise with vanilla cream are typical ways of rounding off a meal. Granita generally pleases, although a few niggles have crept into reports of late: delays and disorganisation out front, and undistinguished flavours, for instance. The short wine list fits on to one page but it is a sharp, keenly chosen selection with some promising choices from the New World. Prices are kept in check: house wine, for example, is £8.50.

CHEF: Ahmed Kharshoum PROPRIETORS: Ahmed Kharshoum and Vicky Leffman OPEN: Wed to Sun L 12.30 to 2.30, Tue to Sun D 6.30 to 10.30 (10 Sun) CLOSED: 10 days Christmas, 1 week Easter, 2 weeks Aug MEALS: alc (main courses £7 to £10.50). Set L £11.95 (2 courses) to £13.95. Minimum L £11.50, D £7 SERVICE: not inc CARDS: Access, Visa DETAILS: 62 seats. Private parties: 60 main room. Vegetarian meals. Children welcome. Wheelchair access (1 step). No music. Air-conditioned

Great Nepalese £

map 13

48 Eversholt Street, NW1 1DA — COOKING 1*
TEL: 0171-388 6737 and 5935 — COST £15–£31

'One of the enduring strengths of this place is the fact that it can shift into top gear from the moment it opens,' observed a staunch supporter who arrived at seven o'clock and found the restaurant 'already three-quarters full'. All comers pack into the dining-room to enjoy superb-value food in a laid-back setting of mystical prints, Ghurka artefacts and photographs of the Himalayas. There is a 'marvellous empathy' between staff and customers.

The menu has its quota of curry-house stalwarts, but the restaurant lives up to its name by offering some of the most authentic Nepalese food in the capital. Starters such as kalezo ra chyau (chicken livers with mushrooms and onions), and mamocha (steamed pastries) warrant exploration, and it is worth noting the presence of pork and duck among the main dishes. The Nepalese mixed grill is a 'huge mound' of tandooried and barbecued morsels, 'all distinct, all subtly different', but the real stars are the vegetables, pulses and accompaniments: toriko sag is 'still arguably the best in the business, quite simply because it is made with fresh, roughly chopped spinach leaf and stem', noted an aficionado. Otherwise, look for aloo bodi tama (potatoes, bamboo shoots and beans), black dhal and aloo kerauko achar (potatoes, peas, green chilli and powdered sesame seeds, served cold). Cobra and Kingfisher lager, spicy masala tea and potent Nepalese rum are the favoured drinks. House wine is £6.55.

CHEF: M. Miah PROPRIETOR: Gopal Manandhar OPEN: all week 12 to 2.30, 6 to 11.30 MEALS: alc (main courses £4 to £8.50). Minimum £5 SERVICE: 10% CARDS: Access, Amex, Diners, Visa DETAILS: 48 seats. Private parties: 34 main room. Vegetarian meals. Children's helpings. Smart dress preferred. Wheelchair access. No music

Greek Valley

map 13

130 Boundary Road, NW8 0HR — COOKING 1
TEL: 0171-624 3217 and 4717 — COST £15–£27

'This is a wonderful place (except for the car parking),' enthuses an out-of-town reporter about Peter and Effie Bosnic's restaurant just off Abbey Road. Saturday-night crowds can occasionally put the service and organisation under pressure, but the mood is generally cheerful, and live piano music helps to ease any stress. The cooking is robustly in the Greek-Cypriot mould and the kitchen makes good use of decent raw materials: dips and two kinds of sausages are home-produced and the Bosnics tell us that they buy 'only small kalamaria'. According to satisfied customers, you could make a meal of the meze, although 'it would be a shame to miss the souvlakia' (skewered lamb or chicken). Otherwise, the repertoire is a familiar run through dolmades, grilled salty halloumi cheese, kleftiko and baklava. Special weekday menus (Monday to Thursday) are eminently affordable. Gutsy Greek-Cypriot wines are the main contenders on the short list. House Cambas is £6.50.

CHEF: Peter Bosnic PROPRIETORS: Peter and Effie Bosnic OPEN: Mon to Sat D only 6 to 12 MEALS: alc (main courses £5.50 to £8.50). Set D Mon to Thur £7.95 SERVICE: not inc CARDS: Access, Visa DETAILS: 62 seats. Private parties: 42 main room, 30 private room. Vegetarian meals. Children welcome. Smart dress preferred. Wheelchair access (1 step). Music

Greenhouse map 15

27A Hays Mews, W1X 7RJ COOKING 3
TEL: 0171-499 3331 FAX: 0171-225 0011 COST £30–£63

The Greenhouse is truly a restaurant for all seasons. A couple who arrived on a Monday night in January were amazed to find it bursting at the seams. Indeed, it seemingly never stops. Nothing about the designerish approach through canopied walkway, past extravagant spotlit topiary, quite prepares the first-timer for the hue and cry within. To find the reason for the immense popularity of the place, look at the menu. Or turn on the telly. Gary Rhodes has become probably *the* media chef of the 1990s. The ubiquitous visage innocent of condescension grins out from page and screen, a prime mover in the campaign to return us to a sense of pride in our culinary culture, whether it be salmon fish-cakes, braised oxtail or rice-pudding blobbed with jam.

In fact, the food at the Greenhouse was always more broadly based than that, at least for first and main courses. Seared tuna glazed with garlic and almond cream, and leek tart with red wine vinaigrette and a poached egg are not exactly echoes of an English yesteryear. But the genius – for there is plenty in evidence – is to add those demotic elements to dishes in a way which would once have aroused a cloth-cap guffaw: piccalilli is spooned on to smoked eel salad, crisp-fried black pudding adorns a red wine risotto. Now everyone's doing such things, of course, but Rhodes deserves acknowledgement for his galvanising role in all this. The risk is that dishes such as calf's liver and bacon with mashed potato and onion gravy can sometimes seem banal, though when it's on form the cooking delivers all that it promises from griddled scallops with a green salad, to duck confit with peas and onions, to bread-and-butter pudding 'so light as to be out of this world'. Pear sorbet and marmalade ice-cream are even lighter ways to finish. Note that vegetables are charged extra, and that there is also a cover charge. Service has occasioned both complaint and praise, and the habit of opening wine before it comes to the table has drawn particular criticism.

The wine list is provocatively brief for a smart Mayfair restaurant, and doesn't betray an excess of imagination. With one exception, every white is either Sauvignon or Chardonnay. Prices, however, are restrained enough for the context, and there is a hidden list of half-bottles and fine wines 'available on request' that the *Guide* has not been privileged to see. House Sauvignon and Gamay from Touraine are £10.50.

CHEF: Gary Rhodes PROPRIETOR: David Levin OPEN: Sun to Fri L 12 to 2.30 (3 Sun), all week D 7 to 11 (10 Sun) CLOSED: Christmas, bank hols MEALS: alc (main courses £7.50 to £19). Set L Sun £19.50. Cover £1. Minimum £10.50 SERVICE: not inc CARDS: Access, Amex, Delta, Diners, Switch, Visa DETAILS: 105 seats. Private parties: 10 main room. Vegetarian meals. Children's helpings. Smart dress preferred. No pipes in dining-room. No music. Air-conditioned

The Guide *always appreciates hearing about changes of chef or owner.*

Grill St Quentin

map 14

3 Yeoman's Row, SW3 2AL — COOKING 1
TEL: 0171-581 8377 FAX: 0171-584 6064 — COST £22–£54

To find this spacious, airy basement just off the Brompton Road, 'look for the sign high up on the west wall at the end of Yeoman's Row', advises a reporter. The room is bedecked with vases of flowers and run by a team of waiters who are noticeably attentive, 'as befits Knightsbridge'. The cooking is traditional French-brasserie, and quite a lot of grilling goes on: steaks, poussin, calf's liver, lambs' kidneys, veal chops, tuna and halibut all receive the treatment, and results are generally pleasing. Accompanying chips are reckoned to be exemplary. Other choices might range from fine coq au vin and choucroute to roasts carved from 'le chariot'. Again, most things succeed, although one reporter found the fish soup 'harmless' but virtually unidentifiable and was underwhelmed by duck with olives. To start, there are soups and terrines, plus a wide selection of shellfish, including oysters, while desserts are such things as lemon tart and sorbets. The wine list is patriotically French, with some well-aged clarets as well as plenty of youthful drinking at realistic prices. House wine is £8.90.

CHEF: Nigel Davis PROPRIETOR: Savoy Group plc OPEN: all week 12 to 3 (3.30 Sun), 6.30 to 11.30 (10.30 Sun) MEALS: alc (main courses £6.50 to £17.50). Set L £9 (2 courses), Set D 6.30 to 7.30 £9 (2 courses) SERVICE: 12.5% (optional), card slips closed CARDS: Access, Amex, Delta, Diners, Switch, Visa DETAILS: 140 seats. Private parties: 30 main room. Vegetarian meals. Children welcome. Smart dress preferred. No music. Air-conditioned

▲ *Halcyon Hotel*

map 12

129 Holland Park Avenue, W11 3UT — COOKING 1
TEL: 0171-221 5411 FAX: 0171-229 8516 — COST £37–£53

This is a small luxury hotel with all the trappings, including *trompe-l'oeil* paintings and oriental carpets, pinstripe upholstery and expensive mirrors in mahogany frames. The food is also steeped in luxury – steamed lobster ravioli with truffle sauce, for instance – and charges reflect this. The menu aims at a modern style that is not all chargrilling and idle tossing of chic ingredients on to smart plates, but one that takes some skill to put together, as in steamed sea bass with scallop mousse and confit of fennel, or roast squab pigeon with morel mushroom sausage.

Although one senior reporter found some items overcooked and pastry 'below par', others have endorsed a plate of calves' sweetbreads, properly crisp outside, soft within, with mustard sauce; shin of veal 'soft enough to cut with a spoon'; and desserts such as a gratin of red fruits, or a glazed lemon tart with raspberry sorbet. Service is 'relaxed but not lax', and although the short wine list scales some impressive heights it also has a fair selection up to and around £20 to £25, with house Spanish red and French white at £9.50.

Report forms are at the back of the book; write a letter if you prefer; or if you are on the Internet, e-mail us at guidereports@which. co. uk.

CHEF: Martin Hadden PROPRIETOR: Halycon Hotel Corporation Ltd OPEN: Sun to Fri L 12 to 2.30 (3 Sun), all week D 7 to 10.30 (11 Fri and Sat) MEALS: alc (main courses £14 to £18). Set L £21 (2 courses), Set D £26 SERVICE: not inc CARDS: Access, Amex, Diners, Visa DETAILS: 70 seats. 12 tables outside. Private parties: 80 main room, 12 private room. Vegetarian meals. Children welcome. Smart dress preferred. Music. Air-conditioned ACCOMMODATION: 43 rooms, all with bath/shower. TV. Phone. Air-conditioned. D,B&B £165 to £550. Children welcome. Afternoon teas

▲ *The Halkin*

map 14

5–6 Halkin Street, SW1X 7DJ — COOKING 1*

TEL: 0171-333 1000 FAX: 0171-333 1100 — COST £40–£73

This smallish hotel, part of a terrace in Belgravia, boasts cool, modern, Italian design, with marble floors, arched windows, bright arrangements of sunflowers, and simple seating. The food is more authentic than that found in many Britalian restaurants, with a bias towards northern Italy, hence more elegant than rustic. Luxury ingredients are not skimped, and a dish of 'impeccably fresh' and accurately grilled scallops on a salad of young spinach, dressed with good olive oil and scattered with chopped black truffles shows the sort of refinement on offer.

Some dishes appear to get very tied up with themselves; only the kitchen sink appears to be missing from a plate of cod mixed with mashed potato and olive oil, roasted quail, braised radicchio (don't go yet, we haven't finished) with ham and broccoli sauce. One late-August luncher enjoyed a similarly complex dish of grouse: two breasts cooked pink, boned out, sitting on a disc of crisp turnip, accompanied by a lobe of tender foie gras and a sticky stock reduction; two quenelles of intense carrot purée completed the rich and tasty ensemble. Despite all, clear flavours are achieved much of the time. Á la carte prices are high, but the two-course lunch affords some relief, and all prices are net. Service is assiduous, somewhat formal but still pleasant, and only rarely falls apart. Italian wines are mostly from the north and centre, very fine indeed, and, of course, there is no service charge to add. House wine is good too, at £3.50 a glass or from £15.50 a bottle.

CHEF: Stefano Cavallini PROPRIETOR: Kuo International OPEN: Mon to Fri L 12.30 to 2.30, all week D 7.30 to 11 (10 Sun) MEALS: alc (main courses £18 to £25). Set L £18 to £32, Set D £32.50 SERVICE: net prices, card slips closed CARDS: Access, Amex, Delta, Diners, Switch, Visa DETAILS: 55 seats. Private parties: 55 main room, 30 private room. Vegetarian meals. Children's helpings. Smart dress preferred. No cigars/pipes in dining-room. Wheelchair access (also WC). Music. Air-conditioned ACCOMMODATION: 41 rooms, all with bath/shower. TV. Phone. Air-conditioned. B&B £245 to £313.50. Children welcome. Baby facilities. Guide dogs only. Afternoon teas (*The Which? Hotel Guide*)

The Guide *is totally independent, accepts no free hospitality, and survives on the number of copies sold each year.*

indicates that smoking is either banned altogether or that a dining-room is maintained for non-smokers. The symbol does not apply to restaurants that simply have no-smoking areas.

Harbour City NEW ENTRY map 15

46 Gerrard Street, W1V 7LP COOKING 1*
TEL/FAX: 0171-439 7859 COST £16–£44

Turn into Gerrard Street from Gerrard Place and you cannot fail to notice the curved, cream-painted frontage of Harbour City, a restaurant that is drawing a favourable response from those who spend their time trawling Chinatown for culinary action. The dining area is on three floors, pink is the favoured colour, and framed black-and-white drawings are discreetly arranged on the walls. A legion of hyper-attentive staff bustles around, opening doors and checking the level of tea in your pot.

The considered view is that this is currently the hot spot for dim-sum in Soho; the list runs to more than 80 items, ranging from steamed prawn dumplings, slithery chueng fun, Vietnamese spring rolls, and char siu buns to anatomically challenging stuff including cold chicken claws in wine sauce, pig skin and turnip in soup, and beef intestines in spicy bean sauce. Dishes are served straight from the kitchen, rather than from heated trolleys, and are all the fresher for that. The full menu is vigorously Cantonese: steamed scallops come with a separate bowl of soy sauce laced with red chillies, threads of ginger and bunches of coriander (a 'wonderfully assertive brew', noted one reporter). Dishes such as baked prawns with salt and chilli, braised bean curd with vegetables, and mixed meat with fried noodles are emphatically flavoured, but the restaurant's trump card is its separate list of specialities. Here you will find curious mixtures involving fish lips and a contingent of sizzlers, although the real treasures are the hotpots. Finest of all, and a dish already verging on cult status in foodie circles, is lamb 'goulas' – 'meltingly rich' and tender, potently laced with star anise and bound together in a stew with bean paste. 'Dazzling, comforting and unnerving, by virtue of its sheer immediacy' was one reporter's verdict. Drink tea, Tsingtao beer or the house wine at £7.50

CHEF: Hing Lee PROPRIETOR: Mr Cheung OPEN: all week noon (11 Sun) to 11.30pm; dim-sum all week 12 (11 Sun) to 5 MEALS: alc (main courses from around £5). Set D £10.50 to £20 SERVICE: 10%, card slips closed CARDS: Access, Amex, Diners, Visa DETAILS: 160 seats. Private parties: 80 main room, 60 and 90 private rooms. Vegetarian meals. Children welcome. Smart dress preferred. No smoking in 1 dining-room. Music. Air-conditioned

Hilaire map 14

68 Old Brompton Road, SW7 3LQ COOKING 3*
TEL: 0171-584 8993 FAX: 0171-581 2949 COST £31–£67

Hilaire has had a face-lift, and the yellow weatherboarding of the ground-floor dining-room helps to keep it bright and cheerful, a pleasant and welcoming contrast to the busy street of cafés, bars and fast-food joints. Book the ground floor if you can, since the basement can feel removed from the action. The food is modern, but not experimental. It is as happy with refined parfait of foie gras as with gutsy oxtail faggot with mashed potato, and dips into sharp flavours with care rather than abandon, producing horseradish cream, a Thai dip, lime butter, or an olive relish very much in contemporary British mode as accompaniments to the likes of deep-fried oysters or calves' kidneys.

It is the judgement which impresses, as in a dish of large griddled scallops, well timed, arranged around a pile of rocket leaves and separated by small mounds of micro-diced vegetables in a sharp dressing. A herb crust on a rack of lamb is common enough these days, but here 'the skin was thin enough to eat', and incidentally added necessary flavouring to the spring lamb, so the idea worked better than it usually does. It came with roast garlic and a dish of rich potatoes in cream.

Bryan Webb's salute to his native Welsh flag takes in Lady Llanover's salt-duck (on the menu at the Walnut Tree Inn; see entry, Llandewi Skirrid, Wales), and usually slots in laverbread at some point: at one May meal it came in a beurre blanc with sea bass, the fish half-skinned, barely roasted, wonderfully moist, with a few salt crystals sprinkled over. The simplicity of this food works very much in its favour. Ingredients are generally first-rate, the timing accurate, and the result balanced. If there is a shortage of 'oohs' and 'aahs' about the cooking, then that is because it pleases in a gentle way rather than trying to grab attention with loud flavours.

'We were well looked after,' wrote one reporter who found the service all it needs to be. A two-course supper is available before 7.30 and after 10. The arrangement of wines by style is helpful, as is the lively house selection of bottles under £20. Mulderbosch South Africans indicate a finger on the pulse, and although mark-ups are about average there is a serious attempt to find attractive bottles in the mid-price range. CELLARMAN'S CHOICE: Gavi di Gavi 1993, Vigneti Lugarara, £18; Graves, Dom. de Gaillat 1986, £23.

CHEF: Bryan Webb PROPRIETORS: Bryan Webb and Dick Pyle OPEN: Mon to Fri L 12.15 to 2.30, Mon to Sat D 6.30 to 11.30 CLOSED: bank hols MEALS: alc (main courses £14 to £19.50). Set L £16.50 (2 courses) to £20.50, Set D 6.30 to 7.30 and 10 to 11.30 £16.50 (2 courses) to £32.50 SERVICE: not inc CARDS: Access, Amex, Diners, Switch, Visa DETAILS: 60 seats. Private parties: 50 main room, 30 and 50 private rooms. Children's helpings. No cigars/pipes in dining-room. No music. Air-conditioned

▲ *Hyde Park Hotel, The Restaurant* map 14

The Restaurant, 66 Knightsbridge, SW1X 7LA COOKING 4*
TEL: 0171-259 5380 FAX: 0171-235 4552 COST £45–£141

'Marco is a genius!' writes a fellow restaurateur, one member of a large fan club. The approach through a 'dismal entrance hall' elicits no superlatives from reporters, who are able to reserve their enthusiasm for the food. The dining-room is pretty and well arranged, with impressive flower displays, 'better paintings than last year', and smart-looking tables. The food is French-inspired (many would say French *and* inspired), and generous with langoustines, lobsters, truffles and foie gras. Indeed, it can be difficult to find a first course without at least one of them. There is no Thai spicing, no Great British flag-waving, and (big improvement, this) no longer any date-stamping of a dish's first performance.

Lunch offers two choices per course, includes both an appetiser and coffee with petits fours, and is well worth having. At dinner, coffee and chocolates alone cost £6 and a bottle of water £4. But even £100 a head 'for the best meal I have ever had' can fairly be considered good value. Dishes that have excited reporters include enormous chargrilled scallops with crunchy calamari tentacles on top, and dabs of squid ink around the plate, 'so simple, and yet so fresh and full of flavour'. A square of rich, dark pink parfait – made from foie gras and chicken livers flavoured with truffle – on a light brown jelly was 'knockout stuff, a perfect amalgam, beautifully tasty'. Fish can be sublime, an example of which is roasted John Dory with lentils: absolutely first-rate fish, ultra-fresh, 'as good as I have ever tasted', according to an inspector.

Other dishes divide reporters. Cod with a baked herb top has been dubbed 'one of the most exceptional dishes I have ever eaten'. Another's carpet square of herb crust 'looking like Astroturf' on a fillet of brill was a major disappointment. Occasional errors in timing, textural shortcomings, poor bread, and flavours lacking the expected impact all contribute to the general feeling that a more even performance would be welcome. Brilliance is fine, but consistency matters just as much. Disappointments are all the more poignant when people have saved up and looked forward to a visit as a treat, sometimes for years. Others have travelled half-way across the world, many from Japan: the customers are a very cosmopolitan mix. But when the high points come, they are terrific.

The pre-dessert crème brûlée is 'superb, with a sublime texture'. Chocolate soufflé with chocolate sauce is 'gorgeous', though the pyramid construction of caramel and nougat ice-cream surrounded by a sauce of grapefruit and passion-fruit must take the biscuit. Alternatively, a selection of cheese comes already plated. Service has improved out of all recognition since the early days. Unless you are finely attuned to Franglais you may miss some of the exchanges, and conversations may be interrupted by the breadcrumb disposal squad, but at least service is willing, and there is now a real sense that the customer matters. Wines are solidly French, with burgundy predominating, although 'laughably priced, not for real people'. We are told that the Criterion in Piccadilly is due to re-open under Marco Pierre White's tutelage as the *Guide* comes out.

CHEF: Marco Pierre White PROPRIETOR: Marco Pierre White (The Restaurant), Forte plc (Hyde Park Hotel) OPEN: Mon to Fri L 12 to 2.15, Mon to Sat D 7 to 11.15 CLOSED: 2 weeks Christmas, 2 weeks Aug, bank hols MEALS: Set L £29.50, Set D £70 SERVICE: not inc CARDS: Access, Amex, Diners, Visa DETAILS: 70 seats. Private parties: 80 main room. Vegetarian meals. Children welcome. Smart dress preferred. Wheelchair access (also WC). No music. Air-conditioned ACCOMMODATION: 186 rooms, all with bath/shower. TV. Phone. Air-conditioned. Room only £241 to £300. Rooms for disabled. Children welcome. Baby facilities. Pets welcome in bedrooms only. Afternoon teas

Inaho

map 13

4 Hereford Road W2 4AA — COOKING 1*

TEL: 0171-221 8495 — COST £14–£41

It may be 'uncomfortably cramped', but this 20-seater restaurant is 'much more endearing than the functional cafeterias which are the usual source for reasonably priced Japanese food'. No wonder the place is popular. There are few trappings, the set-up is first and foremost a neighbourhood bolt-hole, and the cooking takes its inspiration from the traditions of the domestic kitchen rather than expense-account gastronomy.

The menu is a familiar run through high-quality sashimi, well-prepared appetisers such as age-dofu (crisp deep-fried bean curd with ginger), creditable miso soup, seaweed salad ('a visually delightful assembly of colours and textures'), yakitori and tempura, plus bowls of soba and udon noodles. Specials are listed on little strips of wood pegged to a board on each table: a dish of tuna with ginger was the memorable high-point of one favourably reported meal. Sushi is available only from Wednesday to Saturday evenings. The cooking generally pleases, although there have been occasional criticisms relating to timing and the quality of the raw materials. While some reporters have found the service 'peremptory', others have found it extremely helpful. There is saké or Japanese beer as well as a fistful of workaday wines, including house French at £7.

CHEF: S. Otsuka PROPRIETOR: H. Nakamura OPEN: Mon to Fri L 12 to 2.30, Mon to Sat D 7 to 11 CLOSED: 2 weeks Christmas and New Year, 4 days Easter MEALS: alc (main courses £6.50 to £13). Set L £8 to £10, Set D £20 to £22 SERVICE: 10% CARDS: Access, Visa DETAILS: 20 seats. Private parties: 22 main room. Vegetarian meals. No children under 10. No cigars/pipes in dining-room. Music

L'Incontro

map 14

87 Pimlico Road, SW1W 8PH — COOKING 2
TEL: 0171-730 6327 and 3663 FAX: 0171-730 5062 — COST £30–£76

High-class antiques are the principal business of this section of the Pimlico Road. L'Incontro deals in *la cucina veneziana* in a bright white room where the mirrored panels and hard-edged acoustics contribute to a sense of dynamism. The Venetian style is uncomplicated and relies inevitably on the quality of raw materials. The standard *carte* menu is bolstered by weekly specialities such as a salad of scampi, king prawns and cannellini beans, spaghetti with lobster, or grilled swordfish. Pasta is produced in-house, and may include bigoli (the thicker version of spaghetti) with a sauce of anchovy and onions, or maltagliati ribbons with artichoke. Polenta is naturally a favourite accompaniment, whether it be alongside cuttlefish in ink sauce, or roast quail with wild mushrooms.

Torta di pinoli, a tart filled with pine-nuts and lemon, is a traditional dessert, and there are the usual ice-creams, sorbets and, of course, tiramisù. It all comes at quite a price, which may in turn occasion grumblings about portion control. Fixed-price menus at lunch offer better value. Plentiful service is enthusiastic, but has been known to get a bit mixed up. The predominantly Italian wine list has some fine bottles at powerfully dissuasive prices. House wines, a Chardonnay and a Cabernet Franc from Grave del Friuli, are £16.50.

CHEF: Danilo Minuzzo PROPRIETOR: Gino Santin OPEN: Mon to Fri L 12.30 to 2.30, all week D 7 to 11.30 (10.30 Sun) CLOSED: 25 and 26 Dec MEALS: alc (main courses £16 to £23.50). Set L £13.50 (2 courses) to £17.50. Cover £1.50 SERVICE: not inc CARDS: Access, Amex, Diners, Switch, Visa DETAILS: 55 seats. Private parties: 65 main room, 35 private room. Vegetarian meals. Children's helpings. Smart dress preferred. No pipes in dining-room. Wheelchair access. Music. Air-conditioned

'The French waiters and waitresses were interspersed with a few desultory British who looked as if they wished they were in Bournemouth having a good time.'
(On eating in Hampshire)

▲ *Inter-Continental, Le Soufflé* 🍷 map 14

1 Hamilton Place, W1V 0QY COOKING 3*
TEL: 0171-409 3131 FAX: 0171-491 0926 COST £39–£77

'A grand location overlooking Hyde Park Corner and Green Park, although perhaps not such a grand building' is one opinion of this West End fixture. The public spaces are in predictable international hotel mould, 'like a business convention stopover'. In the dining-room, indoor trees and 'witty wire sculptures' do their best to offset the feeling. The Kromberg style remains classic French, hardly knocked off-course by gestures of aubergine tempura here, or a squab pigeon baked in filo pastry there. It stays largely with goose liver, mousses, lobster in tarragon jelly, and navarin of lamb, with useful diversions of ravioli or 'a deliciously sticky risotto'.

Reporters have enjoyed 'plump, juicy grilled scallops' whose sweetness contrasted well with slightly bitter endive, and a gamey-tasting duck breast given a lift from a sauce of honey and thyme. The three-course fixed-price lunch menu, which includes a soufflé of the day 'to which we were steered firmly', is described as 'remarkable value for money' since it included a Kir royale, good bread from an organic brown loaf, a canapé, coffee and excellent have-as-many-as-you-like petits fours. 'Everything was characterised by a purity and intensity of flavour that we have rarely encountered elsewhere,' concluded one couple.

The tendency towards intricacy and elaboration, however, at the expense of structure, seems to be getting the upper hand. An inspector who has visited the hotel on a regular basis felt a recent performance to be the least convincing: 'Fussy handiwork served to detract from the main item of a dish and contributed to its demise.' It is as if 'the cooking has been stuck in a time warp, so common in chain hotels, and has lost direction'. Cheeses 'in superb condition' have included Reblochon and Brie de Meaux. Impeccable service is 'formal and correct' from a 'large, friendly and highly skilled team', and dome-lifting is standard. The wine list is serious about claret and burgundy, with a few showy vintages and prices among the former. Wines under £20 are the exception, although the sommelier's selection and wines by the glass are much more realistic. House vin de pays d'Oc is £14.50. CELLARMAN'S CHOICE: Graves, Ch. du Seuil 1990, £24; Jurançon 1992, Dom. Bellegarde, £20.

CHEF: Peter Kromberg PROPRIETOR: Inter-Continental Hotels and Resorts OPEN: Mon to Fri and Sun L 12.30 to 3 (12 to 4 Sun), Tue to Sat D 7 to 10.30 (11.15 Sat) CLOSED: 2 weeks after Christmas, Aug MEALS: alc (main courses £13.50 to £23). Set L £27.50, Set D £37.50 to £43 SERVICE: not inc CARDS: Access, Amex, Delta, Diners, Switch, Visa DETAILS: 80 seats. Private parties: on application. Car park. Vegetarian meals. Children welcome. Smart dress preferred. No pipes in dining-room. Music. Air-conditioned ACCOMMODATION: 460 rooms, all with bath/shower. TV. Phone. Air- conditioned. B&B £210 to £270. Rooms for disabled. Children welcome. Afternoon teas

Prices quoted in the Guide *are based on information supplied by restaurateurs. The prices quoted at the top of each entry represent a range, from the lowest meal price to the highest; the latter is inflated by 20 per cent to take account of likely price rises during the year of the* Guide.

Interlude de Chavot

LONDON 1996 NEWCOMER

NEW ENTRY map 15

5 Charlotte Street, W1P 1HD — COOKING **4**
TEL: 0171-637 0222 FAX: 0171-637 0224 — COST £32–£38

The site used to be Walsh's fish restaurant, and before that Rue St Jacques. It has a solid air and a slightly provincial feel that seem well suited to serious French food. The front dining-room is discreet and elegant, with dark wooden chairs, rectangular mirrors, and pistachio-coloured walls, while the back one is apricot with horsey prints. Eric Chavot has worked with a number of eminent chefs, including Nico Ladenis and, most important for this venture, Marco Pierre White, who helped him set it up. What pleased early reporters was the value for money: all half-dozen dishes at each course are the same price, and 'you feel you're eating in a place which should be much more expensive'. No doubt if we wait long enough they will oblige, but in the meantime there is a zest about the food that is unusual at these prices.

'The cooking is extremely secure,' sums up one reporter, and the large number of endorsements bears that out, from scallops on a warm tomato and shallot vinaigrette, to brill in a mustard grain sauce with 'fine buttered noodles', to a quail pithiviers – 'like a quail pork pie' – with good pastry, and an intriguing and slightly gamey sauce. Throughout, flavours are three-dimensional and invariably intriguing: 'they shift as you eat', from one component of a dish to another, yet always remain firmly anchored by the main ingredient. Staples of the French repertoire, such as foie gras and chicken liver parfait, are brilliantly done, and the small blob of dense jam that comes with the parfait, 'tasting as if made from figs or dates, and spiced with cloves', is so good that 'every mouthful has you guessing about what might be in it'.

Flavours command attention throughout the meal, without resorting to sheer power, and the food doesn't rely on luxury for impact: it can be as simple as pink slices of rump of lamb, or roast chicken stuffed with a herb-flecked eggy mixture, served with a tarragon jus, or pan-fried cod with a 'terrifically good' lentil salad. While there have been small ups and downs in the quality of savoury courses, desserts are particularly reliable, including a lemon tart to rival the best in London, and anything with chocolate. 'Here is someone who knows precisely what an enemy sugar can be to really fine chocolate', and the expertise shows in chocolate soufflé, chocolate tart and chocolate soup, the last served with a scoop of liquorice ice-cream.

Amuse-gueules outshine the bread, but service has been the weak link for most reporters: keen to look after regular customers and friends, 'lacklustre' for others, and if it is knowledgeable about the food, then it doesn't show. Wines are mostly French, many of them aristocratic with mark-ups to match, although there are a few bottles below £20.

CHEF/PROPRIETOR: Eric Crouillere-Chavot OPEN: Mon to Fri L 12 to 2.30, Mon to Sat D 7 to 11 CLOSED: bank hols MEALS: alc (main courses £14) SERVICE: not inc CARDS: Access, Amex, Delta, Diners, Switch, Visa DETAILS: 60 seats. Private parties: 8 main room, 10 and 16 private rooms. Children's helpings. Smart dress preferred. No pipes in dining-room. Wheelchair access (1 step). No music. Air-conditioned

All main entries are fully indexed at the back of the Guide.

Isohama

map 13

312 Vauxhall Bridge Road, SW1V 1AA COOKING 2
TEL: 0171-834 2145 FAX: 0171-233 7743 COST £14–£44

The location – not far from Victoria Station and opposite the Apollo Theatre – makes Isohama a very useful address, but it is much more than a simple neighbourhood restaurant. Through the entrance lobby is a dining-room, with watercolours on the walls and a metal-covered serving counter at one end, which looks like something out of a futuristic 1930s film set. This is a very affordable lunch spot, with excellent-value set menus that vary from week to week. Specials such as maguro don (raw tuna with soy sauce and 'green mustard') or nishin shioyaki (grilled herring with salt) are alternatives to the more familiar tempura prawns and chicken teriyaki; the usual back-up of appetisers, rice, pickles, miso soup and fruit is included in the price.

In the evening choose between a variety of set dinners, or delve into the long *carte*. There is plenty of interesting stuff among the selection of appetisers: ohitashi (spinach with grated bonito), nameko oroshi (a pile of little mushrooms piled on to grated mooli) and wakame su (seaweed and cucumber in seasoned rice vinegar), for example. Sushi, sashimi and grills are all represented, although it's worth noting the long list of udon noodle dishes, either served hot in soup or cold with dipping sauce; there are also unusual chazuke ('tea soups') based on rice, with accompaniments ranging from pickled plums to salmon roe. Brown tea and saké, Japanese beer and a few familiar wines provide liquid nourishment. House wine is £10.

CHEF: Yukio Saito PROPRIETOR: Senko (UK) Ltd OPEN: Mon to Fri 12 to 2.30, 6 to 10.30, Sat D only 5 to 9.30 MEALS: alc (main courses £5 to £12). Set L £6.50 to £18, Set D £20 to £23 SERVICE: 10%, card slips closed CARDS: Access, Amex, Diners, Visa DETAILS: 36 seats. Private parties: 36 main room. Children welcome. Music. Air-conditioned

Ivy

map 15

1 West Street, WC2H 9NE COOKING 2
TEL: 0171-836 4751 FAX: 0171-497 3644 COST £27–£64

Here is a place fully geared to Theatreland. Whether you have 45 minutes to get down a bowl of fettuccine ai due formaggi before curtain-up or prefer post-performance late eating, the Ivy can make it happen. The volume of business is such that it is essential to book, and yet service is consistently 'quick and careful, confident without being pompous, knowledgeable without being superior'.

The large 'elegant' dining-room still feels aptly theatrical. Heads discreetly swivel as semi-familiar figures sashay past, the stained-glass windows in harlequin colours an effective backdrop for an entrance. Menus open out to A3 size, and lo, the contemporary brasserie stage-set is complete: potted shrimps, sevruga caviare with blinis, deep-fried lambs' brains rémoulade, ricotta tortelloni with artichokes, hamburger, thyme-roasted baby beets with balsamico on the side, and sticky toffee pudding to finish. And it works. A bowl of morel truffle soup had 'just amazing flavour'. Roast cod, its surfaces crisped and succulent, sat on cloves of roasted garlic that were 'sweet and strong and lingering'. Duck confit on lentils with garlic mash restored a jaded palate to life, while griddled chicken salad with chillies set another's tastebuds smouldering gently.

The show-stopping – 'attention-seeker's,' admitted one – dessert is baked Alaska for two, with griottes and kirsch, full of 'excellent light meringue' and fired at the table for maximum impact. Otherwise, finish with 'heavily indulgent' cappuccino brûlée or rice pudding with brandied apricots. Extra charges for vegetables and a cover charge tweak up the bill, but don't seemingly dent the popularity of the place. The Ivy operates the same wine list as its sister restaurant Le Caprice (see entry, London). Choices are imaginative and broadly spread, and there is a good range on offer by the glass. Prices open at £8.50.

CHEF: Des McDonald PROPRIETORS: Jeremy King and Christopher Corbin OPEN: all week 12 to 3, 6 to 12 MEALS: alc (main courses £7 to £19). Set brunch Sat and Sun £14.50. Cover £1.50 SERVICE: not inc CARDS: Access, Amex, Delta, Diners, Switch, Visa DETAILS: 100 seats. Private parties: 8 main room, 60 private room. Vegetarian meals. Children's helpings. No music. Air-conditioned

Iznik £ map 13

19 Highbury Park, N5 1QJ COOKING 1*
TEL: 0171-354 5697 COST £17–£25

This Turkish restaurant is a café by day, dishing up sausage and beans, egg and chips, omelettes and cups of tea, as well as 30-odd Turkish dishes from taramasalata or smooth hummus with fresh pitta bread to börek and stuffed peppers. 'Eccentric, but warm and welcoming' is how one reporter saw it. Turkish rugs are strewn around, a soft glow comes from lamps and candles, and the food is 'way ahead of the pack of similar Mediterranean places'.

Meatless dishes abound, although it is not self-consciously vegetarian – that is just the way things are with Turkish food. Hence cracked wheat with tomatoes and peppers, grilled aubergine in various guises (including imam bayaldi), courgette and feta cheese fritters, falafel, and stuffed vine leaves that impressed a seasoned reporter as one of the best examples of their kind. Chicken breast, ground beef and diced or cubed lamb are the main meat ingredients – usually grilled or cooked with vegetables – although diced liver is fried in paprika, and lamb knuckle is baked in a spicy sauce. Yoghurt features in many sauces, and rice and salad accompany. To follow, baklava is good, and English bramble mousse crops up among the more syrupy Turkish specialities. A short list of international wines bulks out the few Turkish drinks.

CHEF: Ahmet Poyraz PROPRIETORS: Adem and Pirlanta Oner OPEN: all week 10 (9 Sat and Sun) to 4, 6.30 to 11 (7 to 12 Sat and Sun) CLOSED: 25 to 28 Dec MEALS: alc (main courses £6 to £9.50) SERVICE: 10% CARDS: none DETAILS: 54 seats. Vegetarian meals. Children welcome. Music

All details are as accurate as possible at the time of going to press, but chefs and owners often change, and it is wise to check by telephone before making a special journey. Many readers have been disappointed when set-price bargain meals are no longer available. Ask when booking.

Jade Garden £ map 15

15 Wardour Street, W1V 3HA — COOKING 2
TEL: 0171-437 5065 FAX: 0171-439 7851 — COST £15–£40

'I get the feeling that this place has moved up a gear,' observed a reporter who regularly frequents this reliable Wardour Street establishment. The décor is fairly functional, although its outstanding feature is the curving staircase leading to a galleried eating area above the dining-room. Service is sharp and speedy. The list of first-rate dim-sum now runs to more than 60 items brought direct from the kitchens, rather than ferried around on trolleys. A few maverick ideas have crept in of late: minced meat and quail's egg dumplings ('Cantonese Scotch eggs?'), curried whelks, cold chicken feet in wine sauce, prawn and seaweed roll (a hot parody of sushi), not to mention some sweet items such as steamed egg yolk buns.

Highlights have included chiu-chow dumplings (two mighty morsels that 'looked for all the world like mini Cornish pasties ready for the oven') and deep-fried squid-cake flecked with red chilli and green coriander. Portions are huge: 'Main dishes seem to be based on the traditional table of ten,' observed an evening visitor who delved into the full menu. The cooking is dyed-in-the-wool Cantonese, with no stinting on duck feet and intestines. This is roughly hewn stuff, full of strong flavours and based on good-quality ingredients, with little sign of MSG on the tongue. Crispy fried scallops, steamed duck with Chinese mushrooms, and fried beef with preserved vegetables have all been up to standard. Steamed whole fish with ginger and spring onion has also impressed with its succulence. The short wine list comes from a better-than-average source as far as Chinatown is concerned, and it promises some very reasonable drinking. House wine is £7.50.

CHEF: Lee Man PROPRIETORS: L.S. and P.W. Man OPEN: all week noon (11.30 Sat and Sun) to 11.30pm (10.30 Sun) MEALS: alc (main courses £5.50 to £12). Set L and D £9.50 (2 courses) to £17 SERVICE: not inc CARDS: Access, Amex, Delta, Visa DETAILS: 130 seats. Private parties: 80 main room. Children welcome. Smart dress preferred. No music. Air-conditioned

Joe's map 14

126 Draycott Avenue, SW3 3AH — COOKING 1
TEL: 0171-225 2217 — COST £32–£52

In the chic world of Joe's, it pays to move with the times. Have fun, but don't look dated; keep ahead or bow out – that's the message. One regular visitor quickly spotted that this smart venue has had a subtle revamp: it is now done out in unobtrusive neutral colours 'without being insipid', classic fashion photographs adorn the walls and crisp white linen graces the tables. The suffix 'Café' has been dropped and the place seems to be moving into 'serious restaurant mode', with a formally structured menu rather than a take-your-pick brasserie assortment. Coming in for one or two courses, however, still seems to be the pattern.

Jane Rawson now heads the kitchen and the food is getting better. The components of one highly enjoyable lunch indicate what the style is all about: a 'lovely mushy' goats' cheese risotto with pine-nuts and herbs, stuffed inside two 'fritters' topped with Parmesan shavings; Bayonne ham with asparagus and artichoke hearts; crab and smoked salmon with mustard mayonnaise; and a 'vibrantly sunny' dish of grilled tuna with a tomato salsa, baked chillies, caper berries and couscous. Those wanting a dessert could choose, say, soaked prunes in Sauternes with pink grapefruit, or chocolate mocha pots with macaroons. Staff are typically efficient, well turned out and friendly, which is a good thing since the 'optional' service charge tacked on to the bill has gone up to 15 per cent. The short wine lists casts its net wide for some good bottles, although prices are decidedly SW3. House wine is £10 for white and £11 for red.

CHEF: Jane Rawson PROPRIETOR: Joseph Ltd OPEN: all week L 12 (11.30 Sun) to 3 (4 Sat, 4.30 Sun), Mon to Sat D 7 to 11 MEALS: alc (main courses £12 to £14). Cover £1. Minimum £12 SERVICE: 15% (optional), card slips closed CARDS: Access, Amex, Delta, Diners, Switch, Visa DETAILS: 75 seats. 2 tables outside. Children welcome. Smart dress preferred. Wheelchair access. Music. Air-conditioned

Jones Restaurant and Bar

NEW ENTRY map 15

35 Earlham Street, WC2H 9LD — COOKING 1

TEL: 0171-240 2662 FAX: 0171-240 8084 — COST £21–£45

'Conceptually bizarre' is how Jones struck one reporter, momentarily fazed by the 'scarlet illegible logo outside' and barely reassured by the heaps and heaps of 'design' inside. 'I wonder how many more places like this London can take,' queried one, 'and what they'll do when the bandwagon moves on?' Stuccoed sandy-grey walls merge curvaceously into the ceiling 'in a kind of 1960s womb-like effect', and the ceiling is covered in overlapping lighting panels like lily-pads. Everything else is steel and wood: the menu is metal bound, chairs are 'not for the large of bum', and tables are graced with bottles of fruity Tuscan olive oil. The kitchen is open-plan, as well as open to offers from Italy to Thailand, from the Middle East and North Africa to Japan, 'with puddings by Mrs Beeton'.

To give an idea, bubble and squeak is made with sweet potatoes flavoured with ginger, chilli and coriander, and served with duck breast, while beef sirloin may come with wind-dried sausage. At inspection a confidently rendered dish of three thin but 'wonderfully oily' merguez sausages sat on a small pile of couscous, with mint leaves and purée apricot for company. Some intended flavours may be shy, but cooking is generally accurate: lightly smoked, deep-fried quail, and lamb cutlets grilled pink with spinach and green lentils have pleased. Some organic ingredients are used, and vegetables are ordered separately and charged extra. A crispy wun-tun pudding served with coconut custard and mango is clearly one that Mrs Beeton missed, though steamed ginger pudding was considered 'a triumph of the genre', substantial but not stodgy, and studded with 'heavenly clods' of crystallised ginger. The short wine list is not as trendy as the rest of the operation, but does have a few good bottles around £15 to £20. House vin de pays is £9.95, and ten wines are available by the glass from £2.10.

CHEF: Daniel McDowell PROPRIETORS: Caroline Stirling and Stuart Malloy OPEN: Mon to Sat 12 to 3, 6 to 11.30 (bar 5.30 to 11) MEALS: alc (main courses £8.50 to £14). Set L £9.50 (2 courses) to £12.50, Set D 6 to 7 £10.50 (2 courses) to £13.50 SERVICE: not inc CARDS: Access, Amex, Delta, Diners, Switch, Visa DETAILS: restaurant 70 seats, bar 60 seats. Private parties: 9 main room, 10 private room. Vegetarian meals. Children's helpings. Music. Air-conditioned

Kalamaras £

map 13

76–78 Inverness Mews W2 3JQ — COOKING 2
TEL: 0171-727 9122 — COST £17–£28

'A fine ambassador for Greek food,' reports an aficionado. After many years as figurehead of this much-loved establishment, Stelios Platonos bowed out in 1995. The changeover has been effortless, and it is business as usual: the fact that the new chef was trained by Stelios has obviously helped matters considerably. Mega-Kalamaras is reached down a 'dingy alley', and the dark, unglamorous basement looks as if it is 'firmly stuck in the Nana Mouskouri era'. The walls are 'yellowed with age', the carpet is 'industrial grey' and the music is 'bouzouki gone bonkers', but no one seems to care.

What matters is the food – a genuine version of peasant Greek, as opposed to the ubiquitous plate-smashing Greek-Cypriot stuff peddled in most similar places. This is one of the few restaurants where you can sample horta (vitamin-loaded wild greens that are simply steamed and served with a squeeze of lemon juice). Other starters could include fasolia pilaki (beans cooked with tomato, olive oil, parsley and onions) and grilled octopus perked up with oregano. Even that much-abused cliché, the Greek salad, is the real thing with all the right ingredients. Many dishes are given highly involved Romanised Greek names, but the results are fine: baked aubergine topped with mincemeat and béchamel sauce, and courgettes stuffed with a mixture of chicken and herbs both earn approval. To finish it's worth having a go at one of the intriguing daily specials, such as bouzatsa – a cylinder of pastry filled with creamy semolina spiked with cloves. One reporter thought the predictable wine list was out of touch with Greek trends and needed a shake-up. House wine is £7.60. Micro-Kalamaras, at 66 Inverness Mews, uses the same kitchen, has a touch more liveliness and is unlicensed (bring your own wine).

CHEF: Mr Karim PROPRIETOR: Mr F. Ridha OPEN: Mon to Fri L 12 to 2.30, Mon to Sat D 6.30 to 12 MEALS: alc (main courses £7 to £10). Set D £16 SERVICE: 10%, card slips closed CARDS: Access, Amex, Diners, Switch, Visa DETAILS: 86 seats. Private parties: 28 private room. Vegetarian meals. Children welcome. Smart dress preferred. Wheelchair access. Music

Kastoori

map 12

188 Upper Tooting Road, Tooting, SW17 7EJ — COOKING 1
TEL: 0181-767 7027 — COST £13–£22

A Surrey reporter notes that Kastoori emanates 'cleanliness and purity' with its plain white walls, pink woodwork and halogen 'eyeballs' in the ceiling. Service is generally charming and the Thanki family offers a menu that centres on 'Indo-African' and 'pan-Indian' vegetarian recipes from Kathia Wadi (a region of Gujarat where tomatoes grow profusely). Most unusual are the special family recipes: 'unforgettably delicious' stuffed chilli banana, karela bharela (stuffed bitter cucumber), 'drumstick' curry made with a curious foot-long vegetable that is eaten in the manner of globe artichoke leaves, and kasodi (sweetcorn in coconut milk with peanut sauce) – 'you could imagine a recipe for this in a women's magazine,' observed one reporter. In more familiar territory there are first-rate samosas, sev puri and bhajias (including a version made with cassava) that are the perfect foil to brilliant home-made chutneys. Thalis are good value, rice and breads are generally up to the mark and desserts include 'excellent' ras malai. Drink lassi, Kingfisher beer or milky masala tea. House wine is £6.95.

CHEFS: Dinash Thanki and Manoj Thanki PROPRIETOR: Dinesh Thanki OPEN: Wed to Sun L 12.30 to 2.30, all week D 6 to 10.30 CLOSED: 25 Dec MEALS: alc (main courses £3 to £4.50). Set L and D £7.25 to £11.25 Minimum £4 SERVICE: not inc, card slips closed CARDS: Access, Visa DETAILS: 84 seats. Private parties: 20 main room. Vegetarian meals. Children's helpings. Wheelchair access. Music. Air-conditioned

Kensington Place 🍷 map 13

201 Kensington Church Street, W8 7LX COOKING 3
TEL: 0171-727 3184 FAX: 0171-229 2025 COST £21–£57

Kensington Place opened in late 1987, at a defining moment in London restaurant style. Along with Simon Hopkinson at Bibendum (see entry), Rowley Leigh was among the first to forsake the solecisms of late nouvelle cuisine and plunge headlong into earthier, seemingly more honest, rustic cookery. At the time, it was received as manna from heaven: Kensington Place's first *Guide* entry referred to a dish of rabbit wrapped in pancetta on a bed of lentils that represented 'a good example of peasant cooking'. The rest is happy history, as the crowds that flood through its 14 sessions a week still noisily attest.

Rowley Leigh cooks on, and still wraps his rabbit in pancetta. In fact, there is a will these days to make more of British produce, and the restaurant now has a fruit and vegetable grower exclusively contracted to it. Certainly, there is a solid British backbone to the menus, evidenced in black pudding with turnips and mustard, cod with parsley sauce, honey-glazed duck, and even oyster fritters with tartare sauce. Other dishes are difficult to pin down, but then devotees are not much exercised by the problem. The man who ate swordfish with lentils on salsa verde and a side order of chips pronounced it 'absolutely delicious', and his partner similarly enjoyed chicken with leeks and a poached egg in red wine sauce – 'a well-balanced dish, the leek especially good, crunchy but not bitter'. Another poached egg cropped up in a winter salad with artichoke (presumably not from the British grower), rocket and Parmesan, dressed with truffle oil and looking 'so good that the lady on the next table leaned over to ask what I'd ordered'. Sometimes dishes can topple into imbalance, as reported at a summer dinner where a charlotte of smoked eel was overwhelmed by cream cheese, and a heavily saffroned mash did little for roasted bream. 'Puddings appear to be better in the summer,' opines a reporter, but a February couple who shared the grand selection would tend not to agree: highlights were baked tamarillo, passion-fruit sorbet and lemon tart, but the rest – tarte Tatin, poached pear and a chocolate creation – were all up to scratch. 'The chairs remain bum-numbing,' comments an undeterred regular, but the service is 'friendly'.

Wines match the intentions of the cooking with a brightly modern selection strong on personality. St Hallett Chardonnay from the Barossa Valley, Viognier from Rhône grower Pierre Dumazet, Villa di Vetrice Chianti Rufina and Weinert Merlot from Argentina indicate the catholicity. Prices do a gentle cruise up to £50, and a good handful can be had by the glass. House French starts at £9.25. CELLARMAN'S CHOICE: Crozes-Hermitage Blanc 1993, Graillot, £17.50; Lirac 1993, Dom. de la Mordorée, £13.50.

CHEF: Rowley Leigh PROPRIETORS: Nick Smallwood and Simon Slater OPEN: all week, 12 to 3 (3.30 Sat and Sun), 6.30 to 11.45 (10.15 Sun) MEALS: alc (main courses £8.50 to £15). Set L Mon to Fri £13.50 SERVICE: not inc CARDS: Access, Switch, Visa DETAILS: 140 seats. Private parties: 26 main room. Vegetarian meals. Children's helpings. Wheelchair access (also WC). Music. Air-conditioned

Lahore Kebab House £

map 13

2 Umberston Street, E1 1PY — COOKING 1
TEL: 0171-488 2551 — COST £10–£17

The décor is about as basic as you can get and the whole place is built for speed rather than comfort, but it's worth putting up with the surroundings because the food here is 'ace'. As you come in from the street you will see a counter where curries are held in large dishes; a board indicates the availability of daily specials. Sit on bare benches downstairs or enjoy the air-conditioning and the relative luxury of chairs on the first floor. Service begins with solemn signals and gestures, but soon settles into familiarity. The kitchen is known for its vibrant spicing and clear, distinctive flavours; a rapid turnover ensures up-to-the-minute freshness. Chicken tikka and nan served hot from the tandoor set the tone; dhal is handled with respect for the pulses themselves. Other curries and vegetables are of a similar standard. Finish with rice pudding or kulfi, if it hasn't run out. The Lahore is unlicensed, but you can always arrive armed with a bottle of wine or cans of lager.

CHEFS: M. Din and M. Azeem PROPRIETOR: M. Siddique OPEN: all week noon to midnight MEALS: alc (main courses £3 to £4). Set L and D £6 to £10. Unlicensed, but bring your own: no corkage SERVICE: not inc DETAILS: 80 seats. 6 tables outside. Private parties: 60 main room. Car park. Vegetarian meals. Children welcome. Wheelchair access. No music. Air-conditioned

▲ *Lanesborough*

map 14

1 Lanesborough Place, SW1X 7TA — COOKING 2
TEL: 0171-259 5599 FAX: 0171-259 5606 — COST £30–£81

'I was so taken by the decorations that I (forcibly) took my husband there to admire them.' The Conservatory is a glass-roofed take-off of the Brighton Pavilion, 'done with such jollity'. Trickling fountains and potted palms combine into 'a scholarly evocation of the Regency period' for one reporter. Another found that the colour scheme – 'pistachio green and sugar pink, with white icing curlicues' – made a good venue for 'a glitzy, ritzy lunch on a grey day'. Menus are plentiful and wide-ranging, 'with every protein known to man' as well as a strong line in vegetarian dishes. Paul Gayler's long-standing commitment to meatless meals is not only undimmed, but has seemed less quirky as every year goes by and others hasten to catch up with him.

A Eurasian theme is another recognisable trademark – lettuce spring rolls with crab, soy and ginger, for example – but there is also a rich and classic vein, represented by terrine of foie gras with a parfait of morels, or braised lobster. British touches of onion marmalade, swede purée and the cheeseboard mingle with numerous pasta dishes and grilled vegetables as well as pesto, tapénade and other Mediterranean gestures. There is, in other words, and rather like the

décor, a bit of everything. Among the highlights have been first-class grilled codling with minted bean purée, chunks of tender pink lamb tasting of the grill, and a gratin of citrus fruits with honey and pistachio ice-cream. Service is willing, charming and professional, and 'if you leave for the loo in mid-meal your napkin is taken up and re-folded'. Wines are undeniably out of the top drawer, but prices are high: a glass of house wine costs £4, or from £15 a bottle.

CHEF: Paul Gayler PROPRIETOR: Goodwill Nominees OPEN: all week 12 to 2.30, 6.30 to 12 MEALS: alc (main courses £7.50 to £29.50). Set L £19 (2 courses) to £22.50, Set D £28.50 SERVICE: net prices, card slips closed CARDS: Access, Amex, Diners, Visa DETAILS: 100 seats. Private parties: 120 main room, 12 to 60 private rooms. Car park. Vegetarian meals. Children's helpings. Jacket and tie at D. Smart dress preferred other times. Wheelchair access (also WC). Music. Air-conditioned ACCOMMODATION: 95 rooms, all with bath/shower. TV. Phone. Air-conditioned. Room only £206 to £911. Rooms for disabled. Children welcome. Baby facilities. Pets welcome. Afternoon teas

Langan's Brasserie

map 15

Stratton Street, W1X 5FD COOKING 1
TEL: 0171-491 8822 COST £29–£50

Langan's is a repository for 'an extraordinary collection of people, ranging from young city dealers in braces and shirtsleeves to wrinklies in pinstripes to ad agency executives on the make with assorted bimbos'. There is probably no truth in the rumour that glamour or a well-known face gets a table on the bright ground floor (mind the flashbulbs), while the rest are shown upstairs to the Venetian Room. The menu is on a true brasserie scale (nearly 20 puddings, for example) and flies the British flag, as it has for a generation, with bangers and mash, cod and chips, and roast rib of beef with Yorkshire pudding.

The assembly jobs – prawns with avocado and mayonnaise, for example – are 'very ordinary', but other dishes rise to a more convincing level, including a first course of puff pastry with chopped mushrooms, four soft-boiled quail's eggs and a well-made hollandaise sauce. As a rule of thumb, main courses are better than puddings – try a hunk of steak or braised duck – and portions are generous. Some things can annoy, like the charges for 'a selection of vegetables' and for house wine by the glass at £3, the ever-present smoke and so on, but service is plentiful and professional. Wines are hardly serious, and most of them sell for under £20.

The details below may not be entirely accurate because Langan's has not returned the questionnaire the *Guide* sends restaurants to confirm information.

CHEFS: Richard Shepherd, Dennis Mynott and Roy Smith PROPRIETORS: Michael Caine and Richard Shepherd OPEN: Mon to Fri L 12.15 to 2.45, Mon to Sat D 7 to 11.45 (12.45 Sat) CLOSED: bank hols MEALS: alc (main courses £10 to £14). Cover £1 SERVICE: 12.5% CARDS: Access, Amex, Diners, Visa DETAILS: 200 seats. Private parties: 12 main room. Music. Air-conditioned

London round-ups listing additional restaurants that may be worth a visit can be found after the main London section.

'The summing-up from four ladies behind us, now well into the Cointreau, was "I'm not feeling sickeningly stuffed – just stuffed".' (On eating in Hampshire)

Lansdowne £

map 13

90 Gloucester Avenue, NW1 8HX — COOKING 1
TEL: 0171-483 0409 — COST £16–£25

The Lansdowne is a converted pub that makes a virtue of cheap grub, and is 'extremely popular with Camden locals who graze there in their masses'. All ages, sizes and shapes come here, which is part of the appeal. Also on the plus side, the food is simple, wholesome, unrefined and served in generous portions: a soup of lamb with beans and barley, 'an admirable rare rump-burger with giant fries', whole crab with celeriac rémoulade, or 'home-made' pork sausages served with oven potatoes and canned (nice of them to admit it) peas. Garlic, herbs, chilli and other aromatics give the food a lift. A meal-time might start with ten dishes of one sort or another on the blackboard, but choice soon diminishes, as latecomers have found to their regret. Some food, especially pasta, can be stodgy. Everything has to be paid for, in cash, when an order is placed, which can be irritating: bills were invented for a good reason. The wine list is short, mostly Franco-Spanish, and includes a good Corbières from Ch. de Lastours. House wine is £8, and nine are available by the glass. Bass Best and Hopwood beers are on draught and Burrowhill cider is also on offer.

CHEFS: Amanda Pritchett, Simon Green and Byron Wheeler PROPRIETOR: Amanda Pritchett OPEN: Tue to Sun L 12.30 to 2.30 (1 to 3 Sun), all week D 7 to 10 MEALS: alc (main courses £3 to £9) SERVICE: not inc DETAILS: 80 seats. 5 tables outside. Vegetarian meals. No children under 14. Music

Launceston Place 🍷

map 14

1A Launceston Place, W8 5RL — COOKING 2*
TEL: 0171-937 6912 FAX: 0171-938 2412 — COST £25–£58

Hidden discreetly in a leafy Kensington backwater, Launceston Place sounds cool and sedate. On the surface it could not be more of a contrast to the cosmopolitan bullishness of its sister restaurant, Kensington Place (see entry). But Launceston Place charms as it bustles along. As the *Guide* was going to press, we learned that Cathy Gradwell is taking a well-earned rest and Derek Francis, who has worked alongside her for many years, has taken over for the time being, thus assuring continuity.

The menu is fiercely modern and the kitchen delivers ingredient-led cooking with a vengeance, taking a backward glance for brawn with Oxfordshire sauce and pickled walnuts, or poached smoked haddock with parsley sauce, and looking to far-away cuisines for stir-fried squid with lemon, garlic, ginger and coriander. The litany of dishes continues with seared foie gras with grilled sour-dough bread, chutney and rocket salad; pan-fried calf's liver with cotechino, lentils and salsa verdi; and daube of lamb with carrot and pontswede mash. Roast lobster comes with chips, roast poussin with ceps. Desserts take in the likes of plum and almond tart, and rhubarb and raisin bread-and-butter pudding. Any wrinkles in the service seem to have been ironed out. The pocket-sized wine list is predominantly French, and makes a successful job of talent-scouting good wines at under £20; whites are particularly varied. Six wines are available by the glass. CELLARMAN'S CHOICE: Mâcon-Chaintré 1993,

Dom. Valette, £17.50; Thelema Mountain Vineyards Merlot 1992, Stellenbosch, South Africa, £13.50.

CHEF: Derek Francis PROPRIETORS: Nick Smallwood and Simon Slater OPEN: Sun to Fri L 12.30 to 2.30 (3 Sun), Mon to Sat D 7 to 11.30 CLOSED: Christmas and Easter MEALS: alc (main courses £9.50 to £18.50). Set L and D £13.50 (2 courses) to £16.50 SERVICE: not inc, card slips closed CARDS: Access, Amex, Switch, Visa DETAILS: 70 seats. Private parties: 85 main room, 14 and 30 private rooms. Vegetarian meals. Children's helpings. Smart dress preferred. Wheelchair access. No music. Air-conditioned

Laurent £ map 13

428 Finchley Road, NW2 2HY COOKING 1
TEL: 0171-794 3603 COST £17–£27

If couscous counts as fast food, then Laurent is a quirky fast-food restaurant – according to a regular who relishes the sheer pace of eating here. This modest family eating-house isn't built for long, lingering repasts, and perusing the menu takes no more than a minute or two. The only real decision is which of the five versions of couscous to plump for: the 'complet' gets its share of votes, or you might go for vegetarian, fish, chicken or the full royal (complete with a mixed grill that includes merguez sausages). The quality is high, helpings are dauntingly large, and prices are low. To start there is brique à l'oeuf, to finish there are ice-creams, sorbets and crêpes. Mint tea refreshes the palate, and house wine, from North Africa, is £8

CHEF/PROPRIETOR: Laurent Farrugia OPEN: Mon to Sat 12 to 2, 6 to 11 CLOSED: first 3 weeks Aug MEALS: alc (main courses £6.50 to £10). Minimum £6.50 SERVICE: not inc CARDS: Access, Amex, Delta, Visa DETAILS: 36 seats. Private parties: 45 main room. Vegetarian meals. Children's helpings. Smart dress preferred. No cigars/pipes in dining-room. Wheelchair access (1 step). No music

Leith's map 13

92 Kensington Park Road, W11 2PN COOKING 3
TEL: 0171-229 4481 COST £34–£78

Leith's has passed its first quarter of a century in the combined ground floors of three Victorian terraced houses, 500 yards north of Notting Hill Gate. During that time it has weathered ups and downs in the economy, and picked its way steadily through wholesale changes in the way we eat without becoming a follower of fashion. It has also experienced changes of its own recently. A buy-out by Leith's School of Food and Wine has prompted refurbishment (due to be completed before the *Guide* appears) and added some lunchtime openings. Alex Floyd remains at the stoves, and the same conservative style is expected to continue, from roast salmon with scrambled eggs and anchovy sauce, to charcoal-grilled rib of beef with béarnaise sauce (for two people).

The antiquated hors d'oeuvre trolley, however, is to be scrapped in favour of a plated selection of four or five regularly changing items straight from the kitchen. Alternatively there might be a warm salad of veal tongue with gherkins and grain mustard, or of foie gras with artichoke parfait and truffle oil.

Desserts are generous, and a highlight. Certainly, the extra effort that goes into them appears worth while, producing rhubarb and frangipane tart on a spring menu, or pineapple tarte Tatin with coconut ice-cream, and a 'fantastic' chocolate soufflé. Service has been an odd mix, varying from 'verging on the obsequious' to 'professional but unfriendly', all in the course of one evening. Wines put quality first, and prices follow where that leads, sometimes below £20, more often above. Mark-ups can be high, and are more justified on some of the venerable vintages – mostly from Burgundy and Bordeaux, but also including California – than on bottles you can buy in any branch of Majestic. The list is full of interest at every turn, a delight to browse through. A greater choice of ever-changing wines by the glass is promised, and the 'optional gratuity' will be reduced to 12.5%. CELLARMAN'S CHOICE: Albarino Vald Amor 1992, Rias Baixas, Galicia, £23.50; Elyse Zinfandel 1992, Morisoli, California, £24.50.

CHEF: Alex Floyd PROPRIETOR: Leith's School of Food and Wine OPEN: Tue to Fri L 12.15 to 2.15, Mon to Sat D 7 to 11.30 CLOSED: 4 days Christmas, 2 days Aug bank hol MEALS: alc (main courses £17.50 to £23.50). Set L £16.50 (2 courses) to £19.50, Set D £26.50 (2 courses) to £33 SERVICE: 12.5% (optional), card slips closed CARDS: Access, Amex, Diners, Switch, Visa DETAILS: 80 seats. Private parties: 24 main room, 40 private rooms. Vegetarian meals. Children's helpings. No children under 7. Smart dress preferred. Wheelchair access (3 steps). No music. Air-conditioned

Lobster Pot

map 13

3 Kennington Lane, SE11 4RG — COOKING 1*
TEL: 0171-582 5556 FAX: 0171-582 9751 — COST £27–£64

It is something of a challenge to invoke a maritime air in landlocked Kennington, but Hervé Régent remains undaunted in the attempt. You will need your sea legs to eat here. Ring the bell and 'a cacophony of seagulls' cries' is heard. The stairs are heaped with seashells, the dining-room done out as a boat, with a row of portholes looking on to a tank of drifting fish. Sea shanties fill the air. If all these pointers hadn't already made it clear, the theme is fish, from simple marinated salmon to fully fledged Breton specialities. Begin with a selection of smoked items or an 'unfailingly excellent' seafood platter. The eponymous lobster may be chosen live as you wish.

One meal began in fine style with 'a huge portion' of mussels cornouaillaise, steamed with tomatoes, garlic and cream, pepped up with cayenne. The mixed grill of sardines, huss, monkfish and red mullet scored highly, although monkfish with wild mushrooms in a cream sauce was less successful. Recommendations too, have come in for highly spiced fish couscous and the grilled tuna with a Creole sauce. There is also a small range of meat dishes. A slug of vodka poured over a grapefruit sorbet adorned with passion-fruit provided a 'perfectly bittersweet' dessert, or you may wish to opt for a crêpe. The Lobster Pot is a modest but good family-run restaurant, and first-timers should note that M. Régent is a tireless advocate of his special dishes (and so he should be), but remember to ask how much the supplement is. The entirely French wine list is short and to the point, majoring in Sauvignon Blanc and Chardonnay, but mark-ups are heavy. House wines are £9.50.

CHEF: Hervé Régent PROPRIETORS: Hervé and Natalie Régent OPEN: Tue to Sat 12 to 2.30, 7 to 10.45 CLOSED: 25 Dec to first week Jan, Easter MEALS: alc (main courses £14 to £30). Set L £14.50 (exc Sat), Set D £20.50. Minimum £15.50 L, £23 D SERVICE: net prices, card slips closed CARDS: Access, Amex, Delta, Diners, Switch, Visa DETAILS: 24 seats. Private parties: 30 main room. Children welcome (no babies). Smart dress preferred. No pipes in dining-room. Wheelchair access (1 step). Music. Air-conditioned

▲ *London Hilton, Windows Rooftop Restaurant* 🍷 map 15

22 Park Lane, W1Y 4BE
TEL: 0171-493 8000 and 208 4021 COOKING 2*
FAX: 0171-208 4136 COST £41–£96

'Surreal' is how one reporter described this twenty-eighth-floor restaurant with magnificent views over London. It has a faintly raffish air about it, given the dance-floor in the middle of the room, the ceiling mirrors, and an ambience that doesn't appear to put food centre-stage. 'The bimbo coefficient here is high,' observed one. So also is the count of luxury items on the menu, together with such rarities as roast zander with artichoke and shallots. Fish is obviously one of Jacques Rolancy's favourites, and is correspondingly well handled, from a tiny amuse-gueule of red mullet fillet, grilled and dribbled with balsamic vinegar, to a terrine of smoked salmon and eel, nicely balanced by a sharp beurre blanc.

Contemporary credentials are established with a cappuccino of white beans flavoured with truffles, or a jellied seafood consommé with crab, and the range of ingredients and techniques is satisfyingly broad, from poached egg in a fondant of red peppers and a tomato coulis, to hearty beef cheek and veal tongue with a gribiche sauce. Mild invention characterises some dishes, such as the mixture of mango, apples and celery served with pan-fried goose liver, but for the most part there is little to ripple the smoothly reassuring surface. With first-course prices on the *carte* at dinner ranging from £12 to £24, you can easily tell this is not going to be a cheap evening. At lunch there is a choice of four set menus: one a trolley of meats for carving, and all offering an hors d'oeuvre buffet as a first-course choice and including a half-bottle of wine. Cheese is a dozen choices in good condition, while desserts of vanilla ice-cream in a tulip biscuit, and pistachio tart have been endorsed. Silly wine prices continue to bedevil what is quite a good list. House vin de table is £14, or £4.50 a glass.

CHEF: Jacques Rolancy PROPRIETOR: Hilton International OPEN: Sun to Fri L 12.30 to 2.30, Mon to Sat D 7 to 11.30 (12.30 Fri and Sat) MEALS: alc (main courses £15.50 to £29.50). Set L £30 to £38.95 (inc wine), Set D £39 to £44. Cover £5 Fri and Sat D SERVICE: not inc CARDS: Access, Amex, Delta, Diners, Switch, Visa DETAILS: 120 seats. Private parties: 20 main room. Vegetarian meals. Children's helpings. No young children. Jacket and tie. No smoking in 1 dining-room. Wheelchair access (also WC). Music. Air-conditioned ACCOMMODATION: 450 rooms, all with bath/shower. TV. Phone. Air-conditioned. Room only £195. Children welcome. Baby facilities. Pets by arrangment. Afternoon teas

An asterisk (*) after the 1 to 5 cooking mark at the top of an entry signifies that the Guide *and its readers think that the restaurant is a particularly fine example within its rating.*

Lou Pescadou

map 13

241 Old Brompton Road, SW5 9HP — COOKING 1
TEL: 0171-370 1057 FAX: 0171-244 7545 — COST £21–£44

Catch Lou Pescadou on a good night and you could easily imagine that you were in a quayside bistro somewhere in the South of France. The atmosphere is colourful, the conversation animated, the décor is a happy-go-lucky mix of beams, big round window, curved arches and prints of yachts and fish on white Artex walls. A loud chatter emanates from the closely packed tables, and staff join in the fun. Seafood is the main business, although at inspection a pan-fried salmon with shallots did not quite come up to scratch. Plates of oysters, langoustines, squid and mussels are the backbone of the menu, but there are also daily specials and more elaborate creations, such as scallops with tagliatelle and saffron sauce, monkfish with mustard sauce, and turbot with tomato and basil. Pizzas, pissaladière (overdosed with anchovies on one occasion), salads and steaks flesh out the repertoire, while desserts get a mixed reception – enjoyable oeufs à la neige, but disappointing tarte aux pommes. The style may be bistro, but prices are not, and an obligatory cover charge plus an 'optional' 15 per cent service charge automatically tacked on to the bill do not help matters. House wine is £9.80.

CHEF: Laurent David PROPRIETORS: Daniel Chobert and Laurent David OPEN: all week 12.15 to 2.30, 7 to 12 CLOSED: Sun in July and Aug MEALS: alc (main courses £6 to £12.50). Set L Mon to Fri £8, cover £1 SERVICE: 15% (optional), card slips closed CARDS: Access, Amex, Delta, Diners, Switch, Visa DETAILS: 60 seats. 9 tables outside. Private parties: 40 main room, 40 private room. Children welcome. Wheelchair access (1 step). No music

Magno's

map 15

65A Long Acre, WC2E 9JH — COOKING 1
TEL: 0171-836 6077 FAX: 0171-379 6184 — COST £25–£50

The opera may not be over until the fat lady sings, but when it is, those who have had the foresight to book will find a welcome awaiting them around the corner at Magno's. Service is efficiently geared to pre- and post-theatre dining, and the deal is all the more appreciated for the value of what's on offer, especially on the set-price menus (not available after 7.15pm). The style is bistro French, as in moules marinière and marinated anchovies with grilled peppers. New ideas – including a smattering of Italian dishes – have been tried out in recent times, so dinner might take in potato galette with creamed leeks and smoked haddock alongside braised lamb shoulder with merguez, couscous and harissa. A couple who enjoyed 'tender and succulent' duck noted that the tables are sufficiently close together to observe other people's approval of their own food. Desserts should tempt with creamed rice pudding with caramelised citrus fruits or macadamia nut brittle. The wine list provides wider choice than might be expected, nor is it restricted to France. House Bordeaux is £9.25.

Dining-rooms where music, either live or recorded, is never played are signalled by No music *in the details at the end of an entry.*

CHEF: Gilbert Roussett PROPRIETOR: Magno Coliadis OPEN: Mon to Fri L 12 to 2.30, Mon to Sat D 5.30 to 11.30 MEALS: alc (main courses £8 to £14). Set L £13.50 (2 courses) to £16.50, Set pre-theatre D £9.95 (2 courses), Set D £13.50 (2 courses) to £16.50 SERVICE: 12½% CARDS: Access, Amex, Delta, Diners, Visa DETAILS: 55 seats. Private parties: 65 main room. Vegetarian meals. Children's helpings. Smart dress preferred. Wheelchair access. Music. Air-conditioned

Mandarin Kitchen

map 13

14–16 Queensway, W2 3RX COOKING 2
TEL: 0171-727 9012 and 9468 COST £15–£45

Seafood of the freshest kind is what distinguishes this large Chinese restaurant opposite Queensway tube station. Scottish lobsters, crabs, eels and other species are kept alive until required, and the kitchen makes use of everything from jellyfish, sea cucumbers and geoduck (Alaskan king clam) to carp and yellow croaker. This year's postbag contains fulsome recommendations for all quarters of the menu. Steamed scallops with black-bean sauce, fried king prawns with coconut sauce, sizzling pomfret with mandarin sauce, green pepper stuffed with king prawns, and eel with pork and straw mushrooms have all drawn an enthusiastic response. Added to this are dishes such as cucumber with preserved hot cabbage, deep-fried shredded smoked chicken, black pepper veal chop, 'Cantonese spicy goulash casserole pot', and duck every which way. As an accompaniment, try 'excellent' Singapore noodles or a parcel of unusual vegetables wrapped in lotus leaves with a bowl of steamed rice. Service can be 'slow' and the waiters may sometimes seem 'self-absorbed', but they do their job efficiently. Some reporters feel that the place is geared towards parties ordering lavish feasts (there are several tables large enough to seat more than a dozen people) and that couples fall to the bottom of the pecking order, but the food compensates. Jasmine tea tastes freshly brewed, and the wine list offers a useful range of three dozen quite appropriate bottles with realistic mark-ups. House wine is £7.50.

CHEF: Mr Man PROPRIETOR: Mr S.Cheung OPEN: all week noon to 11.30 CLOSED: 25 and 26 Dec MEALS: alc (main courses £5 to £25). Set L and D £8.90 (2 courses) SERVICE: not inc CARDS: Access, Amex, Diners, Switch, Visa DETAILS: 110 seats. Private parties: 20 main room. Vegetarian meals. Children welcome. Smart dress preferred. Music. Air-conditioned

Mantanah £

NEW ENTRY map 12

2 Orton Buildings, Portland Road, SE25 4UD COOKING 2
TEL: 0181-771 1148 COST £18–£31

Mantanah is one of a growing band of Thai restaurants cooking up a storm in the outer reaches of the capital. From the outside it doesn't look much at all, standing in a row of shops by a railway bridge on a busy street a few steps from Norwood Junction railway station. Meals are eaten in a fairly small downstairs room with unvarnished wooden floorboards, a few silk paintings of Thai figures and some curious-looking enamel fish on one wall. This is a family business, run with care and civility: proper hot towels are brought when you sit down.

The menu is long, wide-ranging and uncompromisingly authentic, with few concessions to Western tastes. Vegetarians have plenty to choose from, and there is also a section devoted to native dishes from north-east Thailand (where the owner's wife hails from): highland tribe (sic) is an 'extremely tender' pork curry cooked to dryness with roasted peanuts on the side and pickled garlic to garnish. Somtum is an 'utterly delicious' green papaya salad judiciously spiced with baby chillies. There are also some family inventions – for example, golden triangle (three little rice-paper cases with different fillings); chicken and pumpkin curry; sliced beef with green beans, bean sprouts, red wine and dried chillies; and steamed rice-cake with a stuffing of Chinese leeks. Benchmark dishes – Thai fish-cakes with sweet chilli sauce, a superbly balanced version of tom yum soup, pahd taie noodles with ground peanuts, and fried rice – are handled with exemplary skill and confidence. Desserts are not a strong point. Singha Thai beer is a safe bet, and there is saké and a minimal wine list, with house wine at £7.15.

CHEF: Tym Srisawatt-Yeoh PROPRIETORS: Mr and Mrs K.S. Yeoh OPEN: Tue to Sun D only 6.30 to 11 CLOSED: 25 and 26 Dec, 1 Jan MEALS: alc (main courses £5.50 to £6.50). Set D £12.95 to £16 SERVICE: not inc, card slips closed CARDS: Access, Amex, Visa DETAILS: 40 seats. Private parties: 40 main room. Vegetarian meals. Children's helpings. Smart dress preferred. No cigars in dining-room. Wheelchair access. Music. Air-conditioned

Mas Café

map 13

6–8 All Saints Road, W11 1HH — COOKING 1
TEL: 0171-243 0969 — COST £22–£35

'Like a cross between a brasserie in an art gallery and a provincial railway waiting-room that has been "improved" by a designer,' suggested a visitor to this casual West London rendezvous. Walls are washed in blues, yellows and pinks, whose brightness may be fading thanks to 'one of London's smokiest restaurant atmospheres'. Noise can also be a hazard when it has a full complement of 20- and 30-somethings. The barely legible menu swims with the tide of Italian-style dishes – chicken liver crostini, or braised squid with shrimp stuffing – and relies on grilling to impart flavour to lamb chops, poussin or steak.

Among Italianate successes have been pan-fried gnocchi alla romana, and ravioli filled with spinach, egg and garlic in a walnut sauce. Refinement is not the name of the game: roast pheasant is 'a big helping, virtually half a bird, plonked on the plate rather unceremoniously'; milled black pepper is used liberally; and vegetables have not always pleased. There has been praise, however, for a light pastry tart with a creamy fish filling, and a polenta-like slab of 'scorza' served with a pile of firm, succulent oyster mushrooms flavoured with tarragon. A brunch menu operates at weekends. Service is by a band of 'modern' young women with Mediterranean accents. Three dozen wines contribute to perceived value, staying commendably below £20. There are no half-bottles, but house wine is £2.25 a glass.

CHEF: Sam Kennef PROPRIETORS: David Stacey and Ian Alexander OPEN: Sat and Sun brunch 11 to 4.30, all week D 7 to 11.30 (10.30 Sun) MEALS: alc (main courses £4 to £9.50) SERVICE: not inc, card slips closed; 12.5% on parties of 6 or more CARDS: Access, Delta, Switch, Visa DETAILS: 70 seats. Private parties: 25 main room. Vegetarian meals. Children's helpings. Wheelchair access. Music

Melati map 15

21 Great Windmill Street, W1V 7PH COOKING 1
TEL: 0171-437 2745 and 734 6964 COST £19–£37

'The best of its type in town,' affirms a London reporter who knows his way around. Melati has been a consistent source of genuine Malay/Indonesian food since 1981 and continues to please, despite the fact that it is in a narrow Soho street surrounded by sex shops and strip clubs. It feels and looks like a café, with pine-furnished rooms on three floors and not much space between tables; it is also open throughout the day, although the kitchen has been known to run out of steam towards the end of a long session. It pays to have some prior knowledge of the cuisine if you want to get the best from the 140 or so dishes on the menu. Reporters have enjoyed vegetarian starters, such as satays, pergedel (potato cake), hot-and-sour soup, and spring rolls. The kitchen can also get to grips with such classics as laksa soup, beef rendang, and fried chicken with chilli, not to mention an abundance of seafood, ranging from kari kepala ikan (fish-head curry) to sotong asam manis (squid fritters in sweet-and-sour sauce). Also look for the section devoted to vegetables and salads, which embraces everything from cold gado-gado and rujak to tumis terong (aubergines in tamarind sauce with what the menu calls 'tiny fishes'). Big plates of noodles and composite dishes such as nasi ramas are handy for a high-speed lunch. Jasmine tea and Tiger or Bintang beer are appropriate drinks. House wine is £8.45.

CHEFS: Mr Hasyim and S. Alamsjah PROPRIETORS: S. Alamsjah and Margaret Ong OPEN: all week noon to 11.30 (12.30 Fri and Sat) MEALS: alc (main courses £5 to £7). Set L and D £16.50 (2 courses) to £21.25 (inc wine) SERVICE: not inc, card slips closed CARDS: Access, Amex, Diners, Visa DETAILS: 120 seats. Private parties: 40 main room, 40 private room. Vegetarian meals. Children welcome. Smart dress preferred. Wheelchair access (1 step). Music. Air-conditioned

▲ *Le Meridien Hotel, Oak Room*  map 15

21 Piccadilly, W1V 0BH COOKING 3
TEL: 0171-734 8000 FAX: 0171-437 3574 COST £31–£90

Everyone is pleased to see you at the Meridien, which is wonderfully reassuring if you have just fought your way through heaving crowds outside. Feel care slide away. You know you will be called upon to make weighty and difficult decisions about food and wine, but beyond that you will feel no hint of trauma for the next few hours. You are shown into a beautiful room with pale oak panelling – 'a cross between *fin de siècle* and Sir Terence Conran' – in calming shades of pink, grey-green, cream and beige, lit with gleaming cut-glass chandeliers and populated with an all-French team of waiters in immaculate black and white.

Nibbles arrive with menus, which are grand luxe, and again at the large tables with large chairs and lots of space. The menu gourmand weighs in at 'forty-six pounds' (which is how prices are written) and offers a taster of seven dishes from the *carte*, three of them fish, two of them desserts. Or there is a lighter and rather ordinary-sounding three-course meal at twenty-eight pounds which also includes a glass of very good ordinary wine per course. At one meal the *carte* offered a neat pile of white crab meat and plump pearl barley dressed in colza oil which tasted 'much like toasted hazelnut oil, and is obviously very big in Joigny where the advisory chef Michel Lorrain has his restaurant'. Lobster meat was perched on top of this, and round the plate were 'daubs of intensely reduced lobster bisque with the consistency of sticky glue and the taste of all the lobsters in the world reduced down to this one patch. A very big success.' Another saucing hit was the rouennaise that came with juicy nuggets of roast breast of duck with crispy chargrilled skin. Both dishes were highlights of an inspection meal in which other flavours were less convincing, and a 'truffle risotto' (served with fillet of lamb) was neither truffley nor a risotto.

Desserts have included chocolate ganache on a cushion of puffed rice with a praline sauce, and one of slices of thinly cut deep-fried crispy pineapple layered with pineapple sorbet, with 'decorative daubs of mashed bananas and lime mousse around the perimeter'. 'I would bear this in mind as a tranquil haven in the middle of a particularly busy part of London, but could probably find somewhere better to eat for the price,' concluded one. Wines are mostly high French at hefty prices, with little below £20 except half-bottles, though house French is £15.50.

CHEF: Dominique Zunda PROPRIETOR: Le Meridien Hotel OPEN: Mon to Fri L 12 to 2.30, Mon to Sat D 7 to 10.30 CLOSED: first week Jan, first 3 weeks Aug MEALS: alc (main courses £21 to £25). Set L £24.50, Set D £28 to £46 SERVICE: not inc CARDS: Access, Amex, Delta, Diners, Switch, Visa DETAILS: 45 seats. Children welcome. Jacket and tie. Wheelchair access (also WC). Music. Air-conditioned ACCOMMODATION: 266 rooms, all with bath/shower. TV. Phone. Air-conditioned. Room only £268 to £315. Rooms for disabled. Children welcome. Baby facilities. Afternoon teas. Swimming-pool

Le Mesurier

map 13

113 Old Street, EC1V 9JR — COOKING 1*

TEL: 0171-251 8117 FAX: 0171-608 3504 — COST £27–£40

If Le Mesurier were a stone-built cottage in some north Lancashire market town, it would feel at one with its surroundings. Transferred to the bustle of Old Street, serving lunches to business people behind discreet Venetian blinds, it comes to seem an improbable oasis. The fact that it is now entering its second decade shows that the City is grateful for it.

The small à la carte menu offers three choices at each stage for food that is light but well-conceived in terms of flavour. A puff-pastry tartlet of monkfish, or sardine and potato terrine, makes a diverting starter, while main courses generally offer one fish and two meat. The former resist the temptation to go for simplicity for its own sake: deep-fried crab and seaweed parcel, or cod with a sauce containing avocado, peanuts and ginger testify to that. Fashionable touches in meat dishes show that the cooking style is not set in stone. Pork escalope comes with tapénade and a tomato sauce; beef fillet is garnished with basil and deep-fried capers. Choose from the likes of chocolate cake, pear gratin or apple beignets if your tooth is sweet, assorted French cheeses if not. Finish with unlimited 'excellent coffee – some of the best around'. It all takes place in 'a haven of civilisation and discretion'. The short wine list does its job within a limited compass, and keeps prices reasonable. House French is £9.

CHEFS: Gillian Enthoven and Loic Le Pape PROPRIETOR: Gillian Enthoven OPEN: Mon to Fri L 12 to 3 (D party bookings only) CLOSED: 1 week Christmas, 3 weeks Aug MEALS: alc (main courses £8 to £12) SERVICE: 12.5% (optional), card slips closed CARDS: Access, Amex, Diners, Switch, Visa DETAILS: 26 seats. Private parties: 26 main room. Smart dress preferred. No pipes in dining-room. Wheelchair access. No music

Mijanou

map 14

143 Ebury Street, SW1W 9QN — COOKING 3
TEL: 0171-730 4099 FAX: 0171-823 6402 — COST £42–£58

Here is a little island of consistency in the eddying whirlpool of London restaurant fashion. The location, for all that it is essentially central, feels oddly off the beaten track. The interior is modestly proportioned and not especially luxurious, though the stained glass and cheery yellow murals go some way to lightening what might otherwise be unprepossessing spaces at both ground and basement levels. 'Artisanale' is how Sonia Blech describes her cooking style, indicating that, while its principal accent is French, it is not in the formal mode of classic cuisine. The occasionally recherché combinations have the feel of a domestic cook experimenting. Descriptions of dishes may be lengthy, but the words 'very light' crop up as a kind of disclaimer in four items on one menu.

What turns up on the plate may be more straightforward than its billing suggests. A mousse terrine of duck and foie gras at a winter lunch was 'very herby and light with a slightly granular texture'. John Dory was paired with whiting, and baked under a coat of courgette slices with a tomato sauce containing 'a fashionable hint of chilli'. Game is given all the accompaniments it can handle: saddle of venison is sauced with juniper, elderberry and gin and comes with a 'Tatin' of apples and shallots, while noisettes of wild boar are bolstered with a ragoût of Toulouse sausage, green lentils and spätzli. Puddings keep up the tempo with Caribbean pancakes of banana, pineapple and coconut flamed with Malibu, and a 'quite delicious' version of cassata made with pistachios, cashews, chocolate and marrons glacés. Coffee comes with 'irresistible' petits fours. People appreciate the friendliness of the approach, and a vegetarian described the non-meat cookery as 'outstanding'.

Neville Blech runs a retail venture, The Wine Treasury, as well as officiating at the drinking in Mijanou. The partnering of wine and food is taken seriously: menus are annotated so that dishes refer to suitable wines from the stylistically arranged list. If there were world enough and time, you could weigh these suggestions carefully, but you might miss the rest of the list. Suffice to say that there are pages of superb wines at eminently fair prices, the choices supremely assured in every section. Many are available by the glass, and bottle prices open at £10.50.

CHEF: Sonia Blech PROPRIETORS: Neville and Sonia Blech OPEN: Mon to Fri 12 to 2, 7 to 11 CLOSED: 2 weeks Christmas, 1 week Easter, 3 weeks Aug MEALS: alc (main courses £16). Set L £13.50 (2 courses), Set D £38.50 SERVICE: not inc CARDS: Access, Amex, Diners, Visa DETAILS: 30 seats. 6 tables outside. Private parties: 24 main room, 20 private room. Vegetarian meals. Children welcome. Smart dress preferred. No smoking in 1 dining-room. No music. Air-conditioned

Mr Kong £ map 15

21 Lisle Street, WC2H 7BA COOKING 2*
TEL: 0171-437 7341 and 9679 COST £18–£42

Soho's Chinatown restaurants are notoriously volatile: new stars flicker briefly in the firmament, reputations are quickly dashed, addresses and chefs come and go with relentless regularity. Mr Kong seems to be as solid as a rock, a bastion of consistency in an area where the casualty rate is high. It can get congested at peak times, with its small tables crammed close together, and the atmosphere can be smoky. The pink tablecloths have seen plenty of service, but one regular visitor observed that the walls have been given a coat of white paint above the dado, and there are multi-coloured embroideries to jazz things up.

The menu is long and predominantly Cantonese, although the extended list of chef's specials takes the cooking into the realms of satay eels, sauté chicken with mango and asparagus, and 'dragon wistlers' (pea shoots) with dried scallops. The food now rates as among the best of its kind in London – witness thick slices of shredded lamb spiked with pieces of strong ginger, bean curd stuffed with crabmeat, and fried beef balls attractively splayed open and served with whole fish balls and Chinese greens. It is also worth asking for hot and spicy spare-ribs in a paper bag (a renowned dish not listed on the menu). Vegetables, such as stir-fried aubergines with mushrooms, are timed to perfection, and Peking duck is an authentic version with beautifully glazed skin, good pieces of meat served on prawn crackers, and 'exceptionally thin' pancakes for wrapping. The waiters are generally friendly, attentive and relaxed. Jasmine tea is free, and the wine list is 'quite respectable by Chinatown standards'. House wine is £7.

CHEFS: K. Kong and Y.W. Lo PROPRIETORS: K. Kong, Y.W. Lo, M.T. Lee, K.C. Tang and C.Y. Chan OPEN: all week noon to 1.45am CLOSED: 4 days Christmas MEALS: alc (main courses £5.50 to £15). Set L £8.80 to £11 (2 courses), Set D £8.80 (2 courses) to £22. Minimum £7 D SERVICE: net prices CARDS: Access, Amex, Diners, Visa DETAILS: 115 seats. Private parties: 40 main room. Vegetarian meals. Children welcome. Music. Air-conditioned

Mitsukoshi map 15

Dorland House, 14–20 Regent Street, SW1Y 4PH COOKING 2*
TEL: 0171-930 0317 FAX: 0171-839 1167 COST £33–£98

The pre-occupations of this Japanese restaurant in the basement of a department store are business and formal dining, although it also attracts a few casual West End visitors with its lunch-time menus. One reporter thought the smart, formal dining-room had a rather detached, institutional feel, with its clever lighting, etched-glass screens, beautiful woodwork and arty Rennie Mackintosh-style chairs. Visual impact counts for a great deal here: for example, a fascinating array of porcelain dishes, stoneware and basketry of different colours and shapes is used to match the food and echo the seasons.

There is a *carte*, but most people are attracted by the set menus and formal kaiseki banquets. The aptly named Mitsukoshi Dinner (the menu specifying that it includes 'typical and traditional Japanese dishes') shows the sheer quality of the cooking and the unfailing attention to detail. Proceedings begin on a high note with an appetiser consisting of a slice of cooked beef, plus a tiny sliver of fish-cake gilded with pink roe and a miniature sprig of broccoli with a dab of plum purée on top. Impeccably fresh sashimi is made up of luxury cuts of tuna, yellowtail and sea bass adorned with a fresh nettle-like shizo leaf. Tempura and grilled salmon are near-faultless examples of the genre, while the classic trio of rice (garnished with minuscule fish and dried seaweed), miso soup and strikingly coloured pickles are all you would expect from a restaurant of this standard. Others who have sampled the sushi dinner describe it as a no-expense-spared extravaganza. The food is undeniably high class, although one reporter concluded with some trepidation that he would not want to pay his own money to eat here, but was glad he had been through the experience. Prices are sky-high and there is an obligatory 15 per cent service charge as well as a cover charge ('What cover? Our tables had no cloths!'). Green tea is an acceptable brew, but the wine list inhabits the Japanese expense-account world of three-figure clarets and burgundies, plus the obligatory line-up of whiskies. The cheapest bottle on the list is a 1987 Liebfraumilch at £15.

CHEF: Jiro Shimada PROPRIETOR: Mitsukoshi (UK) Ltd OPEN: Mon to Sat 12 to 2, 6 to 9.30 MEALS: alc (main courses £4.50 to £27). Set L £15 to £60, Set D £30 to £60. Cover £1.50 SERVICE: 15%, card slips closed CARDS: Access, Amex, Diners, Visa DETAILS: 80 seats. Private parties: 24 main room, 12 and 24 private rooms. Children welcome. Jacket and tie. Music. Air-conditioned

Miyama

map 15

38 Clarges Street, W1Y 7PJ — COOKING 3
TEL: 0171-499 2443 FAX: 0171-493 1573 — COST £24–£70

Miyama puts on a modern, international face. Three-dimensional Japanese artwork covers the walls, tropical plants are carefully positioned throughout the dining-room, and the Muzak might be quiet repetitions of Vivaldi's *Four Seasons*. Service is from pleasant waitresses who waft around in traditional costumes of various designs. Proprietors-cum-chefs Fumio Miyama and Mr Miura match style and courtesy with consummate artistry in the kitchen.

The menu is as classic as they come, taking in zen-zai appetisers, sashimi, sunomono (vinegared salads), grills, rice and noodles, plus specialities prepared at the table. Alternatively, order one of the set menus based on tempura, or on sushi, or on teriyaki. Edamame (salted soya beans cooked in their pods) are beautifully fresh; shime saba consists of a delicately marinated fillet of mackerel; nasu agedashi is a superb broth containing a thick circular slice of aubergine with tempura batter on and around it. The quality of sushi and sashimi is outstanding, miso soup has depth and finesse, pickles are technicoloured.

The cooking is generally first-class and the food is reckoned to be good value, although one reporter who seems to have eaten in the teppanyaki basement found little to applaud: 'very fishy' salmon and 'uninteresting' salad typified her meal. Saké comes in cups of differing patterns, or there is Japanese beer and a predictable European wine list. House wine is £10. A second branch, City Miyama, is at 17 Godliman Street, EC4. Tel: 0171-489 1937.

CHEFS/PROPRIETORS: Mr T. Miura and Mr F. Miyama OPEN: Mon to Fri L 12 to 2.30, all week D 6 to 10.30 MEALS: alc (main courses £10 to £16). Set L £12 to £18, Set D £34 to £42 SERVICE: 15% CARDS: Access, Amex, Delta, Diners, Switch, Visa DETAILS: 67 seats. Private parties: 30 main room, 5 and 10 private rooms. Vegetarian meals. Children welcome. Music. Air-conditioned

Monkeys

map 14

1 Cale Street, Chelsea Green, SW3 3QT — COOKING 2
TEL: 0171-352 4711 — COST £22–£59

Monkeys pays homage to our simian cousins in a converted town house on Chelsea Green, pictures of primates crowding its walls. Over the course of a decade and a half, it has found its niche among the smart set of SW3, without noticeably going overboard for the cosmopolitan voguishness that characterises newer openings. Returnees are greeted volubly, and an atmosphere of calm civility reigns.

Another sort of homage is paid by Thomas Benham's cooking, this time to France. Two fixed-price dinner menus supplement a *carte*, all offering the kinds of dishes that sustained classic restaurants in London before the first sun-dried tomato was discovered. Meals may kick off with a terrine, either of brill, salmon and scallops, or veal sweetbreads and wild mushrooms, or perhaps a warm salad of foie gras. Main courses plumb the sauce repertoire old and new, as in stuffed sea bass with red pepper sauce, or sauté mignon of venison with chestnuts and port. Game in season is given more overtly English treatment, and there is also grilled calf's liver and bacon for the diehards. Desserts, too, fly both flags: crêpe mille-feuille with Cointreau, or treacle tart with custard, cream or ice-cream. Chocolate soufflé with coffee ice-cream should send you swooning towards the petits fours. House wines from Bouchard are £11.

CHEF/PROPRIETOR: Thomas Benham OPEN: Mon to Fri 12.30 to 2.30, 7.30 to 11 CLOSED: 2 weeks Easter, last 3 weeks Aug MEALS: alc (main courses £14 to £19.50). Set L £15 to £35, Set D £22.50 to £35. Minimum £17.50 D SERVICE: not inc CARDS: Access, Delta, Switch, Visa DETAILS: 45 seats. Private parties: 30 main room, 12 private room. Children's helpings. Smart dress preferred. No pipes in dining-room. Wheelchair access (3 steps). No music. Air-conditioned

Mon Plaisir

NEW ENTRY map 15

21 Monmouth Street, WC2H 9DD
TEL: 0171-836 7243 and 240 3757 — COOKING 1
FAX: 0171-379 0121 — COST £22–£50

For more than 20 years, Alain Lhermitte's bistro has been a fixture of old Covent Garden. It is just as Gallic as can be. The house colours are the 'tricolour', the floors are tiled, the layout encourages table-to-table chat. French is the chosen tongue. Although the kitchen has no truck with modernity, loyal supporters have noticed a few changes of late: 'There was a time [not so long ago] when the cooking seemed to have slumped into the world of "pile on the plate with not much care but plenty of peasant-style gusto", but the cooking has gained definition, flavours are now more distinct and presentation is noticeably meticulous.' A set-lunch menu and plats du jour augment the *carte*, which is a familiar run through French onion soup, rillettes of duck, Dover sole grenobloise, and fillet of beef with morels. A well-timed fillet of salmon dotted with a few peppercorn-sized capers and set on a pile of crunchy mange-tout cut into diamond shapes alongside a twirl of buttery tagliatelle was reckoned to be a well-composed, cohesive effort. Reporters have also praised a neat salad of ballottine of chicken, calf's liver with a deeply flavoured tarragon sauce, and a skilfully wrought tart of summer fruits on a pool of crème anglaise. Pre-theatre meals ('tables to be vacated by 8pm') are also worth knowing about. The wine list is sound, old-fashioned and reasonably affordable. Another branch, Mon Petit Plaisir, is at 33 Holland Street, W8, 0171-937 3224.

CHEF: Daniel Gobet PROPRIETOR: Alain Lhermitte OPEN: Mon to Fri L 12 to 2.15, Mon to Sat D 6 to 11.15 CLOSED: 24, 25 and 31 Dec, 1 Jan MEALS: alc (main courses £8.50 to £15), Set L £13.95, Set pre-theatre D £13.95 SERVICE: 12.5% (optional) CARDS: Access, Amex, Delta, Diners, Switch, Visa DETAILS: 96 seats. Private parties: 28 main room, 25 in private rooms. Vegetarian meals. Chiildren's helpings. Wheelchair access (1 step). Music. Air-conditioned

Moshi Moshi Sushi £ NEW ENTRY map 13

Unit 24, Liverpool Street Station, EC2M 7QH COOKING 1
TEL/FAX: 0171-247 3227 COST £10–£18

Something strange is happening high above platform 1 at Liverpool Street Station. Queues are gathering to eat sushi in a colourful and surprisingly comfortable room lit by paper lanterns, with high stools lined up along a counter. Anyone who tires of the sight of flashing knives and fingerwork can always gaze below and watch the trains go by. Like many things Japanese, this extraordinary set-up was born out of ingenious simplicity: the food is served on a conveyor belt and different patterns on each plate signify how much individual items cost. Behind the counter half a dozen operatives work at a fantastic rate, while still managing to be charming.

The food is not only fun, it is also good quality. The system is as follows: waiters bring drinks and miso soup as ordered; they also hand you a dish of soya sauce when you sit down. Tea is self-service, drawn from an urn standing on the side counter. The rest of the kit – chopsticks, toothpicks, paper napkins, jars of pickled ginger, 'squeeze bottles' of wasabe (green horseradish) – is on the counter. You simply pick and choose as the plates move along. Passing before you might be tuna, salmon, sea urchin, cuttlefish, scallop, akegai (ark-shell) and tamago (omelette); there are large and small morsels wrapped in nori, and hand-rolled specialities such as grilled salmon skin with spring onion. Prices are commendably low and quantities are generous by sushi bar standards. Lunch boxes are available to take away. Half a dozen wines, starting at £6.90, are listed on a paper notice.

CHEFS: Shinji Nakamura and Toshimizu Nagaura PROPRIETOR: Caroline Bennet OPEN: Mon to Fri 11.30 to 9 CLOSED: 2 weeks Christmas MEALS: alc (main courses £2.40 to £3.60). Set L and D £4.50 to £9.50 SERVICE: not inc CARDS: Access, Delta, Visa DETAILS: 56 seats. Private parties: 24 main room. Vegetarian meals. Children welcome. No smoking in dining-room. Wheelchair access. Music. Air-conditioned

Museum Street Café map 15

47 Museum Street, WC1A 1LY COOKING 2*
TEL: 0171-405 3211 COST £23–£35

Mark Nathan and Gail Koerber's restaurant, now entering its seventh year, is a classic of its kind. It feels like a café, although it is 'not the place for just a cup of tea'. Discreet from the outside, and with modern pictures helping to make the most of what feels a like a small corridor, it offers a warm welcome that develops into efficient and friendly service. It delivers wholesome and simply prepared food, cooked with appropriate skill and enough imagination to give an upbeat feel. 'Simple excellence and tastefulness' is how one reporter described it.

The menu choice is limited, often to two or three items per course, and chargrilling is the preferred cooking method, applied to veal chop, corn-fed chicken, tuna and the like. But it might also take in a salad consisting of grilled leeks, roasted fennel, olives and Parmesan shavings, before roasted cod with rosemary and anchovy butter, and then almond cake with figs cooked in red wine. At a November meal one reporter enjoyed richly flavoured red pepper soup, with crème fraîche helping to give it a gloriously smooth texture, then pork and leek sausages on green beans with a tomato marmalade, and a 'first-rate rendition' of tarte Tatin. Vegetables are well prepared. Olives and bread are put on the table to start the meal off. Espresso coffee is good, although it is charged by the cup. Two dozen wines are cannily chosen and fairly priced, with five available by the glass. House Vin de Pays d'Oc – Marsanne and Merlot – are £7.90.

CHEFS/PROPRIETORS: Mark Nathan and Gail Koerber OPEN: Mon to Fri 12.30 to 2.30, 6.30 to 9.45 CLOSED: 1 week Christmas, 1 week Feb, 1 or 2 weeks summer MEALS: Set L £12 (2 courses) to £15, Set D £17 to £21 SERVICE: not inc CARDS: Access, Delta, Switch, Visa DETAILS: 37 seats. Private parties: 15 main room. Children welcome. No smoking in dining-room. Wheelchair access (2 steps; also WC). No music. Air-conditioned

Neal Street Restaurant

map 15

26 Neal Street, WC2H 9PS COOKING 2
TEL: 0171-836 8368 FAX: 0171-497 1361 COST £41–£73

Antonio Carluccio's restaurant and next-door delicatessen are best known for championing the mushroom cause. Although 'wild' mushrooms are now industry standard on smart menus, many people merely pay lip service to the idea, fulfilling their obligation by combining cultivated ones with the unmistakable taste of dried ceps or porcini soaked in water. Carluccio, on the other hand, has roamed and foraged for his own, making a commercial success out of his passion for fresh fungi and truffles. At its best, the enthusiasm shows in wild mushroom soup, halibut with honey fungus and Judas ears, or a simple sauté of whatever fresh mushrooms are to hand. Likewise, in season there can be few finer dishes than baked eggs with white truffle shaved over them.

Modern pictures cover the cream-painted brick walls of the long, narrow, early-Conran dining-room, while a plate of good black olives with ciabatta and focaccia breads sets the Italian mood. Pasta might come with smoked fish roe (bottarga), and fried scallops have appeared with seaweed and lime, while main courses can be as hearty as veal kidney with morels, or venison with porcini and polenta chips. Among straightforward desserts such as tiramisù, or a glass of vin santo with cantuccini biscuits to dip in, is a frozen zabaglione with balsamico. 'Service varies according to which member of staff you deal with' but comes in at 15 per cent anyway. That, and the generally high prices, are the main brake on full-blooded endorsement. Italian wines naturally dominate the list, and prices can be high, but by avoiding the Barolos and super-Tuscans it is possible to

drink very well for around £20 to £25. House Rosso Altesino from Tuscany and Donna Fugata from Sicily are around £13.

CHEF: Nick Melmoth-Coombs PROPRIETOR: Antonio Carluccio OPEN: Mon to Sat 12.30 to 2.30, 7.30 to 11 CLOSED: 1 week Christmas and New Year MEALS: alc (main courses £13 to £19.50) SERVICE: 15%, card slips closed CARDS: Access, Amex, Diners, Visa DETAILS: 65 seats. Private parties: 26 private room. Vegetarian meals. Children welcome. Smart dress preferred. Wheelchair access (1 step). No music. Air-conditioned

Nico Central

map 15

35 Great Portland Street, W1N 5DD — **COOKING 3**
TEL: 0171-436 8846 FAX: 0171-355 4877 — **COST £32–£41**

Like Simply Nico, the other satellite of Chez Nico at Ninety Park Lane (see entries, London), Nico Central runs on a diet of comforting, rather rich but soundly cooked dishes at prices that reporters consider fair. 'A dinner of crab ravioli, baked brill and tarte Tatin for £26 is well worth it.' The dining-room's light wood, modern prints and mirrors help to make it feel airy and spacious at lunch-time, while small spotlights change the mood for dinner.

Dishes don't break new ground. Here are simple classics of mushroom tart with poached egg and béarnaise sauce, marinated salmon with herb blinis and sour cream, or risotto of ceps. They can be as British as grilled ribeye of Scottish beef with horseradish sauce or as French as foie gras and chicken liver pâté with toasted brioche. Either way, the change of chef during 1995 seems to have made little difference to the overall style or treatment. There are still nine or ten choices per course, and the kitchen still has a slightly nonchalant way with luxuries. The foie gras with which a pigeon breast is stuffed, for instance, isn't even referred to on the menu, but it adds an extra dimension of reassurance and is neatly countered by a small pile of choucroute and a layer of creamy mashed potato.

Long-running Nico desserts include lemon tart and chocolate marquise, among intriguing alternatives such as a warm croissant and apricot terrine. Although one reporter found service 'perfect', others consider it the weak link in the operation: there is 'lots of activity, but to no great purpose', said one, and there have also been complaints of lost bookings and long waits. Wines are the same as at Simply Nico: a good international mix, with most interest in the £20 to £30 bracket, ten half-bottles, and four house wines by the glass from £3.

CHEF: André Garrett PROPRIETORS: Nico and Dinah Jane Ladenis OPEN: Mon to Fri 12 to 2, Mon to Sat D 7 to 11 CLOSED: 10 days Christmas, 4 days Easter, bank hol Mons MEALS: Set L £19 (2 courses) to £23.50, Set D £26 SERVICE: net prices, card slips closed CARDS: Access, Amex, Diners, Visa DETAILS: 55 seats. Private parties: 20 main room, 10 private room. Vegetarian meals. No children under 5. Smart dress preferred. No pipes in dining-room. No music. Air-conditioned

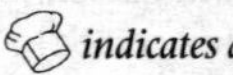

indicates a change of chef since last year's **Guide.**

'Enquiry about the cheeses brought some confusion, since the proprietor was in hospital. ''The man who knows isn't nere,'' said the waitress, ''but we have our own names for them. This is the squidgy one, this is the mouldy one....''' **(On eating in Wales)**

Nicole's

NEW ENTRY map 15

158 New Bond Street, W1Y 9PA COOKING 1
TEL: 0171-499 8408 FAX: 0171-499 7522 COST £33–£48

A trend of recent times is for designer clothes shops to sprout their own restaurants, and here is Nicole Farhi's contribution. It comes as something of a relief to find that the place is not remotely as self-conscious as may be feared. 'Had we still been in the period of power dressing, I may well have felt intimidated, but now that casual and unconstructed is the rule, even us overweight tent-wearers can relax' was one sparklingly candid summation. Cream walls, natural wood and white linen keep things feeling fresh, and the food – would you believe? – is Mediterranean.

Seared beef fillet with pecorino, grilled tuna with deep-fried green beans and anchovy mayonnaise, and veal with Serrano ham and fettuccine are the drill, and indeed eyebrows might have been raised if they weren't. Pigeon – 'a pinkish and tender limb' – has good flavour, and comes with a faintly extraneous salad of watercress and blood orange. Grilled brill, 'beautifully cooked and obviously very fresh', reposes on lightly cooked spinach, but has been accompanied by a leek and mushroom fritter 'the size of a tennis ball'. Caramelised apple pudding with custard suggests that not everyone is weight-watching: a 'lovely rich fudgy surface, light in texture, and in a vast helping'. Italy is not neglected even at dessert stage, though, so zuccotto with chocolate, and pannacotta with strawberry sauce are there as well. Espresso is 'excellent – hot and strong'. Service is mainly by 'cheerful and efficient lads'. Any of the 30 wines on the list may be drunk by the glass. House French is £8.50 a bottle.

CHEF: Annie Wayte PROPRIETOR: N.F. Restaurants Ltd OPEN: Mon to Sat L 12 to 3.30 (4 Sat), Mon to Fri D 6.30 to 10.45 MEALS: alc (main courses £13 to £14.50). Cover £1. Minimum £12 L SERVICE: 12.5% (optional), card slips closed CARDS: Access, Amex, Delta, Diners, Switch, Visa DETAILS: 91 seats. Private parties: 80 main room. Vegetarian meals. Children's helpings. Smart dress preferred. Music. Air-conditioned

Nosh Brothers

map 12

773 Fulham Road, SW6 5HA COOKING 1*
TEL: 0171-736 7311 FAX: 0171-731 8529 COST £22–£41

This is now Nosh Brothers without the Nosh brothers, Mick and Nick, who didn't take the name with them when they left. But Chris Endeacott continues in the kitchen, and his cooking runs along essentially the same lines: a modern rendition of British dishes held together with a bit of international glue in the form of blinis with Beluga caviare, iced gazpacho, and tagliatelle with roast tomato and basil sauce. The modern, abstract, funky décor has little to do with the food, which contrives to present roast beef with Yorkshire pudding as a first course, by way of build-up to roast rack of lamb with celeriac rösti, or pan-fried calves' kidneys. Dishes such as smoked haddock risotto with a poached egg and deep-fried courgette flower, or rolled and stuffed belly of pork have enough about them to divert attention from the rock Muzak, while banoffi pie or pear Tatin with clotted cream make up for any lack of richness so far. With five or six items per course, the menu offers about as much choice as the short, functional list of wines, a few of which are served by the glass. House wine is £8.50.

CHEFS: Chris Endeacott and Claire Newbury PROPRIETOR: Fork Ltd OPEN: Mon to Sat D only CLOSED: 25 Dec, 1 Jan MEALS: alc (main courses £7 to £12.50). Set D Mon to Thur £10 (2 courses) SERVICE: 12.5% (optional), card slips closed CARDS: Access, Delta, Switch, Visa DETAILS: 65 seats. Private parties: 65 main room. Vegetarian meals. Children's helpings. No cigars/pipes in dining-room. Music. Air-conditioned

Noughts 'n' Crosses £ ✱

map 12

77 The Grove, W5 5LL — COOKING 2
TEL: 0181-840 7568 FAX: 0181-840 1905 — COST £23–£33

In a quiet residential street behind the Ealing Broadway shopping centre, Noughts 'n' Crosses mainly serves the local community: the owners reckon that about 80 per cent of customers are regulars and live nearby. Of the three rooms, one looks on to a patio garden that is floodlit at night. Anthony Ma used to live in Hong Kong, albeit 20 years ago, and the long menu thrives on a mix of French, Italian and Far Eastern ideas. Spinach gnocchi with walnut sauce and grated Parmesan shares the billing with steamed spicy Thai pork and crab meatball in cabbage leaves with coconut and chilli sauce. There is so much to choose from that regulars could easily eat once or twice a month and never have the same dish; in any case the menu changes every few weeks.

Upbeat flavours are the norm, and if a balsamic vinegar dressing doesn't do the job, then a tangy tamarind and coriander sauce probably will. Vegetables are good, while cheese fondue, or a puff-pastry case filled with field mushrooms and a gorgonzola sauce, do more than pay lip service to non-meat eaters. A meal which ended with almond coconut and citrus pudding, and an apple and blackcurrant tart, was considered 'excellent'. Service is very accommodating. The reasonably priced wine list includes a Tinto Barocca from South Africa. House Ch. Belingard from Bergerac is £8.90.

CHEF: Anthony Ma PROPRIETORS: Jörgen Kunath and Anthony Ma OPEN: Sun L 12 to 2, Tue to Sat D 7 to 10 CLOSED: 26 Dec to 5 Jan, Aug MEALS: Set L £11.95 (2 courses) to £15.40, Set D £15.60 (2 courses) to £19.50 SERVICE: not inc CARDS: Access, Amex, Switch, Visa DETAILS: 55 seats. 4 tables outside. Private parties: 55 main room, 25 private room. Vegetarian meals. Children's helpings. Smart dress preferred. No smoking in 1 dining-room. Wheelchair access (1 step). Music

Odette's 🍾

map 13

130 Regent's Park Road, NW1 8XL — COOKING 3
TEL: 0171-586 5486 and 8766 — COST £20–£50

The street has a 'village-like atmosphere', no doubt helped by the proximity of the village green, aka Primrose Hill. There is a garden room at the back, a wine bar downstairs and a mirrored dining-room that spills outside in fine weather: pedestrians and motorists provide the street theatre. Wherever you sit, a three-course lunch for £10 is what reporters consider a bargain, even though there is no choice. One winter offering was hare parfait with brioche, then smoked haddock and artichoke fish-cake 'topped with a perfectly runny poached egg and coated with a thick creamy hollandaise sauce', and pavlova with clementines and passion-fruit pulp. 'Maybe not the most balanced menu, but none the less delicious and wonderful value.'

The *carte* has some exotic combinations, including a soup of mooli, butter-bean and sage, another of roast fish with cardamom and orange, or a dish that teams confit of chicken with scallops and beetroot purée. Fine pastry tartlets work well, filled with sweet onion or with shredded celeriac, and risotto is properly done: on one spring occasion a main-course version came with young broad beans, shaved Parmesan and basil. Lightness of touch characterises many of the dishes, including crisp red mullet in a crab bourride, and quince and lemon cake that was 'as light as a fairy'. Yet there is good depth of flavour in gutsier items of calves' kidneys wrapped in caul, served with crunchy parsnip chips, a red onion compote and onion gravy.

The wine list is a lesson to any restaurant that cannot produce much of interest under £20, although quality, not price, is the basis for inclusion here. Bottles are arranged by style and weight, and 20 half-bottles are as welcome as the two dozen wines by the glass, including four excellent vins de pays d'Oc from La Serre at £10.95. Bin-ends and wines of the month add interest too. CELLARMAN'S CHOICE: Viognier 1993, Dumazet, £16.95; Barbera d'Alba Conca Tre Pile 1992, Conterno, £19.20.

CHEF: Paul Holmes PROPRIETOR: Simone Green OPEN: Mon to Fri L 12.30 to 2.30, Mon to Sat D 7 to 11 CLOSED: 2 weeks Christmas, bank hols MEALS: alc (main courses £8 to £14). Set L £10 SERVICE: not inc CARDS: Access, Amex, Diners, Visa DETAILS: 60 seats. 4 tables outside. Private parties: 30 main room, 8 private room. Vegetarian meals. Children's helpings. No music. Air-conditioned

Olivo

map 13

21 Eccleston Street, SW1W 9LX — COOKING 1
TEL: 0171-730 2505 — COST £22–£36

If you don't like olive oil and 'carbon streaks across your food', you might feel out of place here, observed a reporter who called in at this aptly named Italian restaurant not far from Victoria Station. The dining-room is jolly but rather cramped, and it heaves at lunch-time when the excellent-value set menu is on offer. The cooking is modern trattoria – lots of chargrilled meat, vegetables and fish, plus polenta, broad beans, risottos, rocket and gallons of the green, extra-virgin nectar. One of the owners is from Sardinia and the menu includes some interesting regional specialities: malloreddus is a pasta dish with fresh sausage and tomato sauce; sebadas is a dessert consisting of flour fritters stuffed with ewes' milk cheese and lemon, then doused with honey. Also look out for bottarga (grated dried grey mullet roe), and a salad of wind-dried tuna with green beans. The cover charge pays for bread, olives and, of course, olive oil. All in all, the food is reckoned to be 'good straightforward stuff'. Service can be a little slow at times. A handful of Sardinian bottles crops up on the short Italian wine list. House wine is £9.

CHEF: Sandro Medda PROPRIETORS: Jean-Louis Journade and Mauro Sanna OPEN: Mon to Fri L 12 to 2.30, Mon to Sun D 7 to 11 CLOSED: 1 week Aug MEALS: alc (main courses £9 to £11). Set L £13.50 (2 courses) to £15.50. Cover £1.30 SERVICE: not inc CARDS: Access, Amex, Switch, Visa DETAILS: 43 seats. No children under 5. Smart dress preferred. No cigars/pipes in dining-room. No music. Air-conditioned

192 🍷

map 13

192 Kensington Park Road, W11 2ES — COOKING 2
TEL: 0171-229 0482 — COST £21–£45

'Notting Hill restaurants have the best atmospheres of any in town,' maintains an experienced eater, issuing something of a challenge. Perhaps that is because the area feels like a true neighbourhood, and many places function as local meeting-points as opposed to momentary stopovers. 192 swung through the 1980s on a high roll, doing vanguard food when, in town, previous culinary fashions were dying. Many important chefs earned their stripes here, and Albert Clarke is the latest in the illustrious line.

Daily-changing menus follow the markets assiduously, and are made up of dishes that reflect the blend of rustic France and Italy with splashes of oriental that is today's favourite mixture. Starters range from light crab wun-tuns with cucumber noodles and soy to substantial pigeon breast with celeriac rémoulade and beetroot chips. Or there are pastas, soups, including one of artichoke and fennel of 'a dreamy texture and taste', and vegetarian dishes. For main courses, fish is treated imaginatively, as when John Dory is steamed and served with spiced cabbage and a lime and soy butter sauce. Grilled ribeye with béarnaise will satisfy more traditional temperaments. Macadamia nut brittle ice-cream is a dessert to get your teeth into, and a tart of mixed berries, white chocolate and almonds has been described as 'excellent'. A reporter comments that, if anything, value for money seems to be better than ever. The action all takes place in a pleasantly buzzy ambience, with service that observes the proprieties.

The wine list is a model of contemporary taste, the selections from the New World, such as Mulderbosch barrel-fermented Sauvignon from South Africa, as inspired as old-timers, like the rare white Nuits-St-Georges of Domaine de l'Arlot. Over half the list is available by the glass, which adds hugely to the allure. Prices start at £8.90 for a pair from Languedoc. CELLARMAN'S CHOICE: Bourgogne Blanc 'Les Sétilles' 1993, Olivier Leflaive, £16; Lussac St- Emilion 1990, Ch. de Lussac, £14.75.

CHEFS: Albert Clarke and Angus Henderson PROPRIETORS: Anthony Mackintosh, John Armit and Tchaik Chassay OPEN: all week 12.30 to 3 (1 to 3.30 Sun), 7 to 11.30 (11 Sun) MEALS: alc (main courses £6.50 to £13). Set L Mon to Fri £9.50 (2 courses), Set L Sun £13.50 SERVICE: not inc CARDS: Access, Amex, Diners, Switch, Visa DETAILS: 85 seats. 4 tables outside. Vegetarian meals. Children welcome. Wheelchair access. Music

Orsino 🍷

map 12

119 Portland Road, W11 4LN — COOKING 1
TEL: 0171-221 3299 FAX: 0171-229 6411 — COST £19–£45

Lest anyone doubt the striving for authenticity at Orsino and its big sister Orso in Covent Garden (see entry, below), the menus are painstakingly bilingual. Here, the room beyond the virtually concealed entrance is spacious and airy, the walls adorned with a complex arrangement of miniature shutters. Antipasti and pizzas are sometimes thought better than main courses and, as so often with Italian food, the very simplest things seem to work best. A reporter who evocatively described his focaccia with sun-dried tomatoes, black olives, sage and rosemary as 'a moist, chewy, salty, pungent window on the Mediterranean on a chilly grey

December day' felt less enthusiastic about the calf's liver that needed all the zest it could get from the garnish of lemon shreds. Puddings offer sustenance in the form of walnut and coffee torte or chocolate and pear tart with white wine sabayon. Espresso will wake you up. Service has on occasion been found 'slightly semi-detached'. Except for champagne, the wine list is wholly Italian, exhibiting some of the most exciting names around, with about half under £20. Halves? Forget it. House wines from Umbria are £9 a litre.

CHEF: Anne Kettle PROPRIETOR: Orsino Restaurants Ltd OPEN: all week 12 to 10.45 CLOSED: 24 and 25 Dec MEALS: alc (main courses £4 to £13). Set L £11.50 to £13.50 SERVICE: not inc CARDS: none DETAILS: 100 seats. Private parties: 8 main room, 25 private room. Vegetarian meals. Children welcome. No-smoking area. No music. Air-conditioned

Orso 🍷

map 15

27 Wellington Street, WC2E 7DA — COOKING 1

TEL: 0171-240 5269 FAX: 0171-497 2148 — COST £21–£46

'It merits a detour from the City, even at lunch,' writes a loyal supporter of this, the parent restaurant of Orsino (see entry, above). Gentle pastel shades lighten the large basement dining-room, reached from one of the West End's less obtrusive entrances. Martin Wilson, Orso's chef for ten years now, was among the first in the capital to move Italy's cuisine out of the humdrum ristorante norm of old. Antipasti allow the sunniest of flavours to speak for themselves, as in a warm salad of broad beans, peas, artichoke, Parma ham and mint, or bresaola with watercress and olives. Pizzette put many of the larger franchises to shame with toppings of spinach and pancetta, or aubergine and capers, while main courses display a bold rusticity in veal kidneys with garlic, parsley and white wine sauce, or lamb stewed with sun-dried tomatoes and cannellini beans served with grilled fennel. Finish with chocolate, orange and ricotta mousse, or Pecorino cheese and pear. Pedigree Italian wines span a price range from Orvieto Classico at £11 to Solaia 1990 at £70, both made by the house of Antinori. House wines from Umbria are £10.50 a litre.

CHEF: Martin Wilson PROPRIETOR: Orso Restaurants Ltd OPEN: all week noon to midnight CLOSED: 24 and 25 Dec MEALS: alc (main courses £10 to £13). Set L Sat and Sun £11.50 (2 courses) to £13.50 SERVICE: not inc DETAILS: 100 seats. Private parties: 8 main room. Vegetarian meals. Children welcome. No music. Air-conditioned

Osteria Antica Bologna 🍷 £

map 12

23 Northcote Road, SW11 1NG — COOKING 1*

TEL: 0171-978 4771 and 924 5648 — COST £18–£35

Back-to-the-roots Italian country cooking is Aurelio Spagnuolo's stock in trade and he tantalises his customers with the gusty flavours of his native Bologna, as well as straying south for inspiration. The presence of heavy wooden tables and chairs outside his restaurant – even on a cool May evening – are reminders that this place is an old-style osteria which just happens to be in London. There isn't much elbow room and formalities are kept to a minimum. At first glance the food is as robust as the décor, but dig a little deeper and you will find a surprisingly subtle range of flavours and textures, derived from a larder packed with authentic ingredients. An armoury of sausages, pancetta, cheeses of all kinds (from smoked Provola and Scamorza to Caciotta), pulses, artichokes, rocket and chillies are used to telling effect.

To start the ball rolling there are a dozen assaggi – little starters that can whet the appetite or be brought together for a summery communal meal. Dishes such as fried olives stuffed with mortadella sausage or caponatina di mare (a juicy salad with chunks of aubergine, seafood, olives and bread sauce) are the perfect lead-in to more substantial offerings, including a mighty lamb steak cooked pink with an earthy dark green lentil sauce, grilled cuttlefish with peppers and capers, or the house speciality – goat with tomato and almond pesto. Pasta comes in all shapes and sizes with all manner of multi-coloured flavourings: penne with tuna, olives, capers and chillies did the business for one reporter. Puddings are dynamite: try pera ripiene – a meltingly soft, chocolate-coated pear 'stuffed with Amaretto, honey and liqueur' floating in a pool of zabaglione and chocolate sauce. The wine list aims for good producers the length and breadth of Italy, but doesn't simply go for big names; it combines quality with interest and reflects the true variety of Italian wines, all at very fair prices. House Pugliese is £7.50, and around ten wines are available by the glass. CELLARMAN'S CHOICE: Biancolella dell'Isola d'Ischia 1992, D'Ambra, £14.50; Carignano del Sulcis 1991, Cantina Santadi, £9.90.

CHEF: Aurelio Spagnuolo PROPRIETORS: Rochelle Porteous and Aurelio Spagnuolo OPEN: Mon to Sat noon to 11 (11.30 Fri and Sat), Sun 12.30 to 10.30 MEALS: alc (main courses £5.50 to £9.50). Set L £7.50. Cover 70p SERVICE: not inc, card slips closed CARDS: Access, Amex, Switch, Visa DETAILS: 75 seats. 5 tables outside. Private parties: 30 main room. Vegetarian meals. Children's helpings. Wheelchair access. Music. Air-conditioned

Osteria Basilico £

map 13

29 Kensington Park Road, W11 2EU — COOKING 1
TEL: 0171-727 9957 and 9372 FAX: 0171-229 7980 — COST £20–£33

'Not for twin-sets and pearls,' warned one reporter of this busy, informal café-style Italian. Its popularity means that 'you need patience and a sense of humour to book by phone. Staff appear to speak limited English: "You come now, you share table, you go by 9.15."' The place is so packed that conversation drowns out the music, but by the time the meter runs out the chances are that you and everybody else sharing the bare wooden tables will have had a good time.

The Osteria runs on pasta, grilled fish and vegetables, toasted bread, gallons of olive oil and mountains of tomatoes. It doesn't pretend to be anything other than simple and rustic in its appeal, and doesn't bother with fancy or expensive ingredients: a chargrilled steak or baked halibut is the furthest it goes. The food is 'better than average', concluded one who enjoyed a 'dessert of the day' that was a white chocolate mousse in a dark chocolate sauce, with a strawberry garnish. If nothing on the perfunctory under-£10 wine list appeals (no producers, no vintages), ask for the special list of ten rather better bottles.

CHEF: Alex Palano PROPRIETOR: A. Tiraboschi OPEN: all week 12.30 to 3 (4.30 Sat, 3.15 Sun), 6.30 to 11 (10.30 Sun) CLOSED: 25 and 26 Dec, 1 Jan SERVICE: 10% (optional) CARDS: none DETAILS: 100 seats. 5 tables outside. Private parties: 50 main room. Vegetarian meals. Children welcome. No cigars/pipes in dining-room. Music

Le Palais du Jardin NEW ENTRY map 15

136 Long Acre WC2E 9AD COOKING 1
TEL: 0171-379 5353 FAX: 0171-379 1846 COST £22–£42

This well-appointed busy brasserie in the heart of Covent Garden is certainly making its presence felt. Expansions due in September and November 1995 will make it three times the size it was when it first opened in 1992, giving a total of 450 seats. In an atmosphere of infectious bustle, the smooth-running service is a miracle of unobtrusiveness, the tables sufficiently close to each other for you to get to know your neighbours. Chefs perform behind glass at the back. 'It all looks very classy,' says a reporter.

The bilingual menus indicate that the food is resolutely French, although an exception is made for calf's liver and bacon, fish-cakes, and bangers and mash. A starter of baby scallops and spinach scattered with crisp lardons and dressed with garlic butter is tasty enough, and baked goats' cheese with a hazelnut crust and a roasted pear is an intelligent combination. Fruits de mer are something of a speciality: mussels, prawns, lobster and oysters are available in a variety of preparations or all together on a platter. Meat dishes can be more elaborate, and successfully so, as in venison in a herb mousse with a filo parcel of leeks and wild mushrooms and a redcurrant sauce. Vegetables, charged extra, come in fairly petite portions. A reporter who was pleasantly surprised to find the kitchen offering a chocolate soufflé in such hurly-burly was impressed by the result, although the raspberry sauce that was poured into it was less appreciated. Expansion can sometimes upset the equilibrium of places such as this, but in the meantime the Palais is hitting the target. The short wine list is a run-of-the-mill French selection, with house wines at £8.50.

CHEF: Winston Matthews PROPRIETOR: Le Palais du Jardin Ltd OPEN: restaurant all week 12 to 3.30, 5.30 to 12 (all day Sun); oyster bar 10am to midnight (11pm Sun) CLOSED: 25 and 26 Dec MEALS: alc (main courses £7 to £12.50) SERVICE: 12.5% (optional) CARDS: Access, Amex, Delta, Diners, Switch, Visa DETAILS: 150 seats. 10 tables outside. Private parties: 40 main room. Vegetarian meals. Children's helpings. No smoking in 1 dining-room. Wheelchair access (2 steps; also WC). Music. Air-conditioned

People's Palace NEW ENTRY map 13

Royal Festival Hall, SE1 8XX COOKING 1
TEL: 0171-928 9999 FAX: 0171-928 2355 COST £22–£46

It may sound like a vast Chinese restaurant cloned from Peking, and reminded one reporter of 'the huge restaurants I have eaten in in Moscow', but in fact it is more of a modern British brasserie, serving up smoked haddock fish-cake, jellied ham with piccalilli, roast beef sandwich with fried eggs and capers, or crispy roast pork belly. The Festival Hall location is not to everybody's taste: 'about as welcoming as a railway station on a wet Sunday evening' for one reporter. Nevertheless, it has been a source of regret that over 40 years such a national institution has been unable to field a restaurant to match its cultural significance until now.

The dining-room is large, high and white, with well-spaced, dark-grey tables, and some colour from the Gary Rhodes merchandising. Fortunately this versatile chef is able to be in several places at once: cooking at the Greenhouse (see entry,

London) and here, at the same time as appearing on your TV screen. Fresh ingredients simply cooked, and the idea of 'real food for real people', is appealing. The three-course set-meal was not the compromise one reporter was expecting, but turned out to be 'a real bargain'. However, standards are uneven: disappointments have included mashed potatoes, poorly timed fish, and some puddings. How far its populist aims can co-exist with those of an up-market restaurant remains to be seen. More inexpensive wines on the short list would help, although eight white and six red are available by the glass from £1.80.

CHEF: Gary Rhodes PROPRIETOR: Capital Hotel OPEN: all week 12 to 3, 5.30 to 11 CLOSED: 25 Dec MEALS: alc (main courses £5.50 to £15). Set L and D £10.50 (2 courses) to £13.50 SERVICE: not inc, net prices CARDS: Access, Amex, Delta, Diners, Switch, Visa DETAILS: 185 seats. Private parties: 270 main room. Vegetarian meals. Children's helpings. Wheelchair access (also WC). Music. Air-conditioned

Le P'tit Normand map 12

185 Merton Road, SW18 5EF COOKING 1
TEL: 0181-871 0233 COST £17–£33

Normandy's northern border extends to Southfields, where this wholeheartedly traditional and well-supported bistro in a parade of shops draws in a healthy postbag of plaudits year on year. Tablecloths are predictably red and white checked, the printed menu is supplemented by daily blackboard dishes, and calvados will be set on fire at the drop of a tarte Tatin. Seafood pancakes are a good bet to start, although mussels prepared in the alsacienne manner (with bacon, white wine and cream) have proved popular with reporters. Main courses may take in generous fish panaché, pheasant breast in port or lamb fillet with pleurottes. Vegetables have been found 'fresh but overcooked', while the cheeseboard, fruit tarts and well-made ice-creams round things off nicely. The 'delightful and exceptionally friendly' service is almost always singled out for praise. A short but functional French wine list does no more than it absolutely needs to. House wines are £7.95.

CHEF/PROPRIETOR: Philippe Herrard OPEN: Sun to Fri L 12 to 2.30, all week D 7 to 10 (10.30 Fri and Sat) MEALS: alc (main courses £7.50 to £9.50). Set L £9.95, Set L Sun £11.95 SERVICE: 12.5% (optional), card slips closed CARDS: Access, Amex, Delta, Diners, Visa DETAILS: 40 seats. Private parties: 20 main room, 20 private room. Vegetarian meals. Children's helpings. Smart dress preferred. No pipes in dining-room. Wheelchair access. Music

Pied-à-Terre map 15

34 Charlotte Street, W1P 1HJ COOKING 3*
TEL: 0171-636 1178 FAX: 0171-916 1171 COST £30–£59

It is surprising how a restaurant that opened its doors only in 1991 seems to have been there for ever. That's Charlotte Street for you. The long, thin dining-room is 'strikingly austere', with light grey walls and mixed canvases and prints. It has a sense of space, clean lines, and is well lit. 'Out of a spartanish setting came an array of inventive, well-executed, perfectly flavoured dishes, including a tonne of petits fours.' Richard Neat is a resourceful chef who does not let his solid grounding in classic techniques inhibit a good idea, yet who rarely strays into exotica. Hence he pairs a skate wing with poached egg, or foie gras with choucroute, and combines snails with morel mushrooms, asparagus and fondant potato.

Offal and shellfish are favourite ingredients, from a salad of pig's head with brains and gherkins, to roasted scallops with an oyster sauce, seaweed purée and cardamom. One reporter enjoyed a dish of roasted veal sweetbreads on a pea purée with a creamy onion sauce and a scattering of morels, another sang the praises of a frothy cappuccino-like asparagus bouillon ('as if somebody had been blowing the soup through a straw') with grilled langoustines. More than one cooking method may be used in a single dish, as in deep-fried duck confit served with white bean casserole, or roasted guinea-fowl with a Parmesan and saffron risotto. There is a heartiness and richness about the food that builds up during the course of a meal.

The more expensive menu can seem pricey, although good black olives start the ball rolling and, if you count the oyster appetiser and the excellent pre-dessert crème brûlée, the three courses turn into five. Puddings range from a chocolate soufflé with a cherry sorbet in a chocolate box to a simpler roasted plum tart, Tatin-style, tasting rather bitter from the burnt caramel, served with a separate bowl of crème fraîche as thick as clotted cream. The maître d' is sharp, confident, cheerful, informative, and the wine waiter is just as proficient: he knows what you have ordered and will proffer customised advice on the largely French collection of superior bottles. House vin de pays is £14.

CHEF: Richard Neat PROPRIETORS: Richard Neat and David Moore OPEN: Mon to Fri L 12.15 to 2.15, Mon to Sat D 7.15 to 10.45 CLOSED: Christmas and New Year, last 2 weeks Aug, bank hols MEALS: Set L £16.50 (2 courses) to £39.50, Set D £33 (2 courses) to £39.50 SERVICE: net prices, card slips closed CARDS: Access, Amex, Delta, Diners, Switch, Visa DETAILS: 40 seats. Private parties: 40 main room, 12 private room. Children's helpings. Smart dress preferred. Wheelchair access. No music. Air-conditioned

Pizzeria Castello £ — map 13

20 Walworth Road, SE1 6SP — COOKING 1
TEL: 0171-703 2556 — COST £14–£22

'The pizza here is vastly better than at the commercial chains,' writes a supporter. The simple formula works, and standards are maintained. The crust is half the secret: made from good dough, and done medium thick unless you ask for it thinner, which one reporter recommends. A seasoned reporter enjoyed an Americana pizza for its 'excellent base, and extremely generous portions of high-quality peppery salami, cheese and tomatoes'. The usual permutations and combinations of topping ingredients yield a choice of 15 items, with extras available for the DIY brigade. Starters and pasta dishes, plus daily blackboard specials, ring the changes. Wines on the 40-strong list include 'the dread Liebfraumilch', but make up for it with some good Italian reds for around £10 to £15. House Valpolicella, Soave and Bardolino from Bolla are £6.90 a bottle, £1.80 a glass.

Card slips closed *in the details at the end of an entry indicates that the total on the slips of credit cards is closed when handed over for signature.*

CHEF: F. Arrigoni PROPRIETORS: Renzo Meda and Antonio Proietti OPEN: Mon to Fri noon to 11, Sat 5 to 11 CLOSED: bank hols MEALS: alc (main courses £3.50 to £6) SERVICE: not inc (10% for 7 or more) CARDS: Access, Amex, Delta, Switch, Visa DETAILS: 150 seats. Private parties: 30 main room. Vegetarian meals. Children's helpings. Smart dress preferred. Wheelchair access (also WC). Music. Air-conditioned

Le Pont de la Tour 🍾 map 13

36D Shad Thames, Butlers Wharf, SE1 2YE COOKING 3
TEL: 0171-403 8403 FAX: 0171-403 0267 COST £24–£72

'It is best to have been before in order to find it,' advised one. 'No matter how many times I go to Butlers Wharf I always get lost,' confessed another, noting that the signs along Shad Thames are designed more for artistic effect than usefulness. Once found, the long, thin dining-room of the gastrodrome's senior restaurant (see also Blue Print Café, Butlers Wharf Chop House and Cantina del Ponte) is a fairly simple and elegant bit of Conranism, a pleasant contrast to the packed and noisy seafood bar and grill through which it is necessary to squeeze in order to get to and from the outside world. There are views of the river and Tower Bridge for those facing north.

Seafood is prominent, from plain oysters or crab to lobster mayonnaise or simple grilled Dover sole. Overall, a good balance is achieved between these lighter dishes and heartier ones, such as a rich fillet of beef with a ballottine of foie gras, or braised lamb shank. Meatless items in Italian vein have included 'squidgily moist' tomato, mozzarella and pesto tart that uses (and oozes) buttery puff pastry, while a plate of roasted red pepper with tomato flesh and garlic ('very Delia Smith') is partnered by a rather Middle Eastern loosely packed mound of bits of aubergine and a minted yoghurt dressing.

Apart from an occasional distraction, as when smoked bacon overpowers the fat, juicy scallops it encloses, the cooking is well judged. A sophisticated saddle of rabbit, for instance, is boned, stuffed with a tarragon-flavoured filling, sliced into sections and served with a strong mustardy sauce. Vegetables are priced and ordered separately, and you get a large portion: glistening green beans, perhaps, or mashed potato with crunchy spring onion. 'Simple but effective' is the gist of pudding reports, from a feuilleté of strawberries with good pastry, to lengths of sharp-tasting rhubarb with a circle of shortbread and some strands of crystallised lemon peel.

The only cloud on the horizon concerns the cost. 'I am not sure we had £130-worth of enjoyment,' concluded a typical couple, although the reduction in service charge from 15 to 12½ per cent following the *Guide*'s comments last year is a small crumb of comfort. 'The wine list covers everything,' noted one, 'except inexpensive bottles.' To be fair, about 20 good wines under £20 are picked out to make life easier, and quality is never in question throughout the list. Mickey Mouse prices owe much to the mature vintages on offer. Allow extra time to read through the list, or take advice. House Vin de pays d'Oc, Dom. Virginie is £10.75. CELLARMAN'S CHOICE: Matanzas Creek Chardonnay 1992, Sonoma, California, £35.95; Graves, Ch. Rahoul 1989, £28.50.

🍾 *denotes an outstanding wine cellar;* 🍷 *denotes a good wine list, worth travelling for.*

CHEF: David Burke PROPRIETORS: Sir Terence Conran, Joel Kissin and David Burke OPEN: restaurant Sun to Fri L 12 to 3, Mon to Sat D 6 to 11.30; bar and grill Mon to Sat 11.30 to 11.30, Sun noon to 11 CLOSED: 5 days Christmas, Good Fri MEALS: restaurant alc D (main courses £14.50 to £18.50). Set L £26.50, Set pre- and post-theatre D 6 to 6.45 and 10.30 to 11.30 £19.50; bar and grill alc (main courses £6 to £13). Sat brunch 11.30 to 3 £14.95 (2 courses) to £17.95, Sun brunch (main courses £10 to £14.50) SERVICE: 12.5%, card slips closed CARDS: Access, Amex, Diners, Visa DETAILS: restaurant 105 seats, bar and grill 65 seats. 33 tables outside. Private parties: 9 main room, 20 private room. Vegetarian meals. Children welcome. Wheelchair access (also WC). No music in restaurant

Poons £

map 15

4 Leicester Street, WC2H 7BL — COOKING 1
TEL: 0171-437 1528 FAX: 0171-458 0968 — COST £14–£49

'Within earshot of the Swiss Centre clock' are the directions provided by one couple who have watched Poons move from a café (complete with 'chipped china spoons' and 'plastic reinforced teapot spouts') to a bright and rather upmarket venue done out with gleaming white walls, light wood and metal-framed chairs, and tables covered with cloths. They had to admit, in a moment of nostalgia, that they quite missed 'the dinge'. The kitchen still delivers big portions of authentic Cantonese food at prices that inhabit the more affordable end of the Soho Chinatown market. Wind-dried duck, pork and sausages are the Poon family's claim to fame, but you can also get one-plate meals, casseroles, hotpots and a fair list of more unusual specials such as 'very tender' steamed duck slices with plums, quick-fried milk, mashed tofu with lotus seeds, and steamed Dover sole prettily strewn with tangerine peel, spring onions and ginger. Service is matter-of-fact, but quick and accurate. Drink tea and Tsingtao beer. House wine is £6.50.

CHEF: Yuan Jin He PROPRIETOR: W.N. Poon OPEN: all week 12 to 11.30 CLOSED: 24 to 27 Dec MEALS: alc (main courses £4 to £15.50), Set L and D £14 to £17 (min 2) SERVICE: not inc CARDS: Access, Switch, Visa DETAILS: 120 seats. Private parties: 60 main room, 20 private room. Vegetarian meals. Children welcome. No music. Air-conditioned

Quaglino's

map 15

16 Bury Street, SW1Y 6AL — COOKING 2
TEL: 0171-930 6767 FAX: 0171-839 2866 — COST £22–£58

If large restaurants come to signify London's optimism in the 1990s – some are already open, more are promised – then Quaglino's will undoubtedly be seen as one of the boldest and most imaginative. 'It is a wonder that Conran has been able to make it happen,' muses a reporter. But Sir Terence Conran has, in style and with considerable flair, from the antipasti bar and the staircase that turns every arrival into an event, to the glamorous pillared dining-room, and hard stainless-steel and glass surfaces that amplify the chatter. The place has more buzz than a swarm of bees. 'It has a theatrical air that makes me feel OK about spending money,' confesses one reporter, though others are less diverted by the circus. 'While the whole effect is a triumph of logistics, I don't think this means that special dispensation should be made for the food marking.' Indeed not.

The enormous turnover means that freshness is never in question, so oysters and plates of shellfish with mayonnaise score highly, while the 'cooking' may be approximate. It follows Anglo-French lines – roast cod with artichoke mash, shoulder of pork with crackling and apple sauce – but in a wholesome sort of way, respecting appetite and enthusiasm more than refinement. While grilled lemon sole and chips might come 'perilously close to something I could get from the chippy at the end of the road', Thai fish-cakes are suitably spiced and carefully cooked, and the flavour of spinach and Parmesan tart with rich crumbly pastry has real bite. 'The lack of a non-smoking area is boring,' writes one reporter, adding that 'they seem to have taken your point about service charge to heart. It is now 12.5 per cent.' The youthful and up-to-date wine list commendably keeps the balance under £20, and house vin de pays d'Oc from Dom. Virginie is £10.95.

CHEF: Martin Webb PROPRIETORS: Sir Terence Conran, Joel Kissin, Keith Hobbs and Tom Conran OPEN: all week 12 to 3, 5.30 to 12 (1am Fri and Sat, 11pm Sun) CLOSED: 2 days Christmas MEALS: alc (main courses £9.50 to £15.50). Set L and pre-theatre D £13.50 SERVICE: 12.5%, card slips closed CARDS: Access, Amex, Diners, Visa DETAILS: 338 seats. Private parties: 10 main room, 40 private room. Vegetarian meals. Children welcome. Wheelchair access (also WC). Music. Air-conditioned

Quality Chop House map 13

94 Farringdon Road, EC1R 3EA COOKING 2
TEL: 0171-837 5093 COST £23–£44

Combine Victorian Values with Back to Basics and this is what you get. Historically one of the founders of informal 1990s eating, though less overtly influential than some, Charles Fontaine produces an attractive mixture of English and French dishes, from corned-beef hash with fried egg, to roast snails in garlic butter. He does it from a small kitchen (you can watch him doing it) near the Mount Pleasant sorting office. The Victorian premises have been restored, but the bench seating is as character-building as it must have been a century ago, and the 'progressive working-class caterer' ethic is just as strong.

Anglo-French strands come together in Toulouse sausages with mash and onion gravy, or salmon fish-cake with sorrel sauce, and while avocado and prawn cocktail may seem stuck in a rut, warm asparagus with Pecorino is less so. Salads figure prominently – Caesar, for example, or smoked herring and warm potato – and where eggs are not fried they are probably poached: perhaps in another salad with smoked bacon and mushroom. The 16-ounce grilled T-bone steak is strictly for the workers, chips are good, and treacle sponge comes with custard. A short, modern wine list, with four or five wines by the glass, is backed up by a few English beers. House wine is £9.

CHEF/PROPRIETOR: Charles Fontaine OPEN: Sun to Fri L 12 to 3 (4 Sun), all week D 6.30 (7 Sun) to 11.30 CLOSED: 24 Dec to around 3 Jan MEALS: alc (main courses £6 to £13) SERVICE: not inc DETAILS: 48 seats. Private parties: 12 main room. Vegetarian meals. Children's helpings No cigars/pipes in dining-room. No music. Air-conditioned

'The pork reminded me of Tutankhamun: preserved for all that time in recognisably porky form, then as soon as it is exposed to the fork of a diner it crumbles immediately.'
(On eating in Norfolk)

Quincy's

map 13

675 Finchley Road, NW2 2JP — COOKING 1
TEL: 0171-794 8499 — COST £32–£39

'We don't pretend to be anything special but we try to be,' David Wardle says modestly of his well-supported neighbourhood restaurant in Child's Hill. People appreciate the welcoming ambience of its womb-like interior, with pine tables set close together, and the 'prompt and affable' service that will make even first-timers feel like regulars. David Philpott's set-price menus essay some bold experiments, encompassing oriental and Mediterranean influences in the modern way. Gnocchi with sun-dried tomatoes, black olives and goats' cheese delivered 'powerful flavours' one wet November evening, while roast lamb cooked *à point* with pea purée, roast garlic and a rosemary jus pleased one man no end. A fish dish always features in the daily-changing menu, and is imaginatively cooked: Thai-style sea bass had perfect texture for one but was perhaps a little over-soyed. Mushroom Stroganov with saffron risotto offers vegetarians plenty of flavour; meat-eaters may be tempted by calves' kidneys with *sauce diable* or venison with spiced quince and peppercorns. British puds, such as treacle tart with caramel ice-cream and 'light and fluffy' bread-and-butter pudding, are pronounced 'excellent'. A commendably international wine selection is grouped only by colour but offers sound value and some good producers. House Duboeuf is £9.

CHEF: David Philpott PROPRIETOR: David Wardle OPEN: Tue to Sat D only 7 to 11 CLOSED: 1 week Christmas MEALS: Set D £25 SERVICE: not inc CARDS: Access, Amex, Visa DETAILS: 30 seats. Private parties: 10 main room, 16 private room. Vegetarian meals. Children's helpings. Music. Air-conditioned

Ragam

map 15

57 Cleveland Street, W1P 5PQ — COOKING 1
TEL: 0171-636 9098 — COST £12–£39

'A little gem of a place' is the widely held view of this likable restaurant opposite Middlesex Hospital. The décor has been spruced up, with lilac and pink paintwork, striped Regency-style wallpaper and four mini-chandeliers dangling from the ceiling, but the atmosphere is as informal as ever. Waiters are casually domestic – 'more carpet slippers and cardigans than tunics and bow ties,' commented one reporter who comes here a lot. The menu is unchanged: what it offers is an assortment of South Indian vegetarian dishes backed up by a full contingent of curry-house favourites. Lamb dhansak is 'a world away from Parsee richness', but none the worse for that; chicken dupiaza is a good version, although 'chilly chicken' was the star dish of one meal. Vegetables such as green beans with shavings of lightly browned coconut, and brinjal bhaji are consistently good. Specialities such as masala dosa, uthappam (a chilli-laden, pizza-style pancake), and kaalan (a Keralan curry made with mango, yoghurt and coconut) have also been heartily endorsed. Drink lassi or lager.

The Guide *always appreciates hearing about changes of chef or owner.*

CHEFS: J. Dharmaseelan and G.K.C. Nair PROPRIETORS: J. Dharmaseelan, T. Haridas and S. Pillai OPEN: all week 12 to 3, 6 to 11.15 (11.50 Fri, 10.50 Sat) CLOSED: 25 and 26 Dec MEALS: alc (main courses £2.50 to £7) minimum £6.50 SERVICE: not inc, card slips closed CARDS: Access, Amex, Diners, Visa DETAILS: 36 seats. Private parties: 40 main room, 20 private room. Vegetarian meals. Smart dress preferred. Children welcome. Wheelchair access (also WC). Music. Air-conditioned

Rani £

map 12

7 Long Lane, N3 2PR — COOKING 2
TEL: 0181-349 4386 and 2636 FAX: 0181-349 4386 — COST £17–£29

The décor in the Pattni family's converted shop might be described as 'smart and cleverly utilitarian': it is certainly a world away from the clichés of most curry-houses. Red and white colour schemes, glass-topped tables and a band of waiters and waitresses from around the world set the tone of the place. Most agree that Rani delivers some of the best Gujarati cooking in London. No eggs, fish, meat or animal fats (apart from some dairy products) are allowed on the premises, but the kitchen scores with the subtlety of its flavours and textures: after sampling several starters, one reporter concluded that 'there is crunch, aroma, a mild touch of heat and at times a searing jolt' to the bhajias, samosas and cold snacks such as dhai vada and aloo papri chat.

Much of the impact comes from dazzling home-made pickles and chutneys: fresh coriander bound with crushed peanuts; coconut marinated in yoghurt; green chillies and carrot in a mustard dressing. Vegetables also get plenty of votes: stuffed aubergine and potato curry is the current favourite, although banana methi, and cauliflower with peas have been mentioned too. It's also worth exploring the daily specials: spinach with split mung beans on Tuesday, undhia (balls of chickpea flour and fenugreek with exotic vegetables) on Saturday. Breads are a fascinating assortment, while carrot halva and gulab jamun are popular desserts. Set meals are excellent value, and the special version for children is an admirable idea. Early and late diners may get a reduction in price, discount cards are an incentive to return, and the menu is available in braille. Lassi and falooda are soothing accompaniments, with Cobra beer and house wine at £8.60 on the modest list of drinkable wines. As we went to press, a new branch was due to open at 3 Hill Street, Richmond, Surrey TW9 1SX, telephone 0181-332 2322: reports, please.

CHEF: Sheila Pattni PROPRIETOR: Jyotindra Pattni OPEN: all week D only 6 to 10.30 CLOSED: 25 Dec MEALS: alc (main courses £6.50 to £10). Set D £8.40 to £13. Minimum £10 Sat SERVICE: not inc, card slips closed; 10% for parties of 7 or more CARDS: Access, Amex, Delta, Switch, Visa DETAILS: 90 seats. Private parties: 56 main room, 23 private room. Vegetarian meals. Children's helpings. Smart dress preferred. No smoking in 1 dining-room. Wheelchair access (1 step). Music

£ *indicates that it is possible to have a three-course meal, including coffee, a half-bottle of house wine and service, at any time the restaurant is open (i.e. at dinner as well as at lunch, unless a place is open only for dinner), for £20 or less per person.*

'Dan Quayle seems to have had a hand in at least one part of the menu, which listed ''potatoe cage'' among its offerings.' (On eating in Wiltshire)

Ransome's Dock 🍷 map 12

35–37 Parkgate Road, SW11 4NP COOKING 2*
TEL: 0171-223 1611 FAX: 0171-924 2614 COST £22–£42

This aquatically blue restaurant overlooks a stretch of canal hard by Albert Bridge. Window tables afford sunny views in summer, but can be draughty in winter. Martin Lam's modern, imaginative food stirs many to raptures. Good-value set lunches are available on weekdays. The evening à la carte array offers a wider range of dishes such as caramelised endive and Gruyère tart, celeriac rémoulade with Norfolk smoked eel, basil oil and couscous, or grilled Barbary duck breast with blood orange sauce and smoked garlic mash. Daily fresh fish might include John Dory with roasted vegetables. At the weekend extra brunch-type dishes are added to the menu, such as scrambled eggs and toasted muffin accompanied by bacon or smoked salmon.

A regular reporter praised an 'excellent and generous' sirloin steak that came with a simple red wine jus. Another recommended the fish specials as 'well worth going for' – particularly a cod, squid and sole ragoût. Star desserts are a prune and armagnac soufflé pronounced 'out of this world', or baked banana served with dark rum, orange, cardamom and cream, plus organic ice-creams from Rocombe Farm in Devon. One old hand presiding over a lunch party of three generations noted contentment all round. Service can be 'a bit rushed' on occasions, but mostly copes. The commendably catholic wine selection is arranged stylistically and offers plenty of affordable bottles. Te Mata Sauvignon Blanc from New Zealand, Dom. Cauhapé's dry Jurançon, Dolcetto from Mascarello and Cornas from Colombo indicate the sureness of touch. There is also an abundance of dessert wines. House selections start at £10. CELLARMAN'S CHOICE: Cape Mentelle Sauvignon Blanc 1994, Margaret River, W. Australia, £16.50; Crozes-Hermitage 1991, Alain Graillot, £18.50.

CHEF: Martin Lam PROPRIETORS: Martin and Vanessa Lam OPEN: Mon to Fri noon to 11, Sat noon to midnight, Sun noon to 3.30 CLOSED: Christmas MEALS: alc (main courses £9 to £14.50). Set L Mon to Fri £11.50 SERVICE: not inc CARDS: Access, Amex, Delta, Diners, Switch, Visa DETAILS: 65 seats. 8 tables outside. Private parties: 50 main room. Car park (D and weekends). Vegetarian meals. Children's helpings. Smart dress preferred. No pipes in dining-room. Music. Air-conditioned

Rasa **NEW ENTRY** map 12

55 Stoke Newington Church Street, N16 OAR COOKING 1*
TEL: 0171-249 0344 COST £23–£35

Rasa (the name means 'taste') is as much about culture as cooking. It stands inauspiciously on Stoke Newington Church Street, and from the outside you might never guess that it was a restaurant of distinction. The kitchen specialises in the vegetarian cooking of Kerala (according to some, the most civilised and enlightened state on the Sub-continent), and it celebrates the region's most famous annual festival, 'Onam', with music, dance and, of course, food. The red and green dining-room feels serene, Eastern classical music plays, and everyone is bowled over by the beguiling charm of Sivadas and Alison Padmanabhan.

The menu jumps between the familiar and the esoteric, taking in tea-shop snacks, festive specialities and dishes from village homes. Flavours are subtle and finely tuned. Home-made pickles are brilliant: try the ferociously sour lemon version, or the mixture of carrot, ginger and green chillies. Among the starters you might go for banana boli (slices of plantain in a crisp, bright yellow batter served with an 'extraordinary' peanut and ginger sauce; sukian (nuggets of mung beans mixed with coconut); or crisp thayir vadai dumplings spiked with green chillies and ginger. Dosas and avial sound a reassuring note, but also look for appam – a curious cross between a pancake and a waffle made from rice flour and served with soothing paal (a potato stew flavoured with coconut milk). Also recommended is moru kachiathu, which the menu describes an 'everyday curry from Travancore homes', consisting of sweet mangoes and green bananas cooked together with yoghurt and curry leaves. Tamarind rice and lemon rice are impeccable, and breads are skilfully done. Lassi is the ideal accompaniment, although there is also a cheap and cheerful wine list. House wine is £6.50.

CHEF: Kumar Moorkoth PROPRIETOR: Sivadas Padmanabhan OPEN: all week 12 to 2.30, 6 to 11 (midnight Fri and Sat) CLOSED: 25 and 26 Dec MEALS: alc (main courses £8 to £10) SERVICE: not inc CARDS: Access, Amex, Delta, Diners, Visa DETAILS: 42 seats. 12 tables outside. Private parties: 25 main room. Vegetarian meals. Children welcome. Smart dress preferred. No smoking in dining-room. Wheelchair access (1 step; also WC). Music. Air-conditioned

▲ *The Regent [renamed Landmark] London* map 13

222 Marylebone Road, NW1 6UD COOKING 3
TEL: 0171-631 8000 FAX: 0171-631 8080 COST £31–£64

Much has been written about the atrium at the Regent hotel (or the Landmark London, as it renamed itself as we went to press). Despite its gargantuan scale, with palm trees towering into eight storeys of daylight, it remains a comfortingly far cry from the traffic on Marylebone Road, and one of the more peaceful places in the capital in which to drink a dry Martini. The main dining-room is turning out cooking of great style and daring within the often stultifying confines of an international five-star hotel.

While it once had a pronounced northern Italian accent, the menu seems now to be edging into more cosmopolitan waters. Veal carpaccio with aged balsamic vinegar clearly still pays homage to Italy, but where to place a panaché of asparagus and artichoke with dandelion and quail's egg in a loganberry vinaigrette? Main courses run the gamut from straightforward grills of calf's liver through lamb cooked with courgette fritters on truffled risotto, to the confusing Szechuan-style glazed duck with bok choy on couscous. A starter of ravioli of sea bass with a lobster sauce demonstrates correct fish cookery and a good sauce. A simple reduction of red wine, cooking juices and cream provides the right note of intensity for an excellent piece of beef fillet surrounded by new potatoes, courgettes and caramelised onions. But it's an odd philosophy that stimulates culinary imagination with two courses and then delivers puddings on a trolley. Gâteaux and bowls of fruit are the order of the day. Chocolate cake has been praised, as has the coffee – 'strong and full of flavour'. While service is fully as gracious as the context requires, it can seem a little slow. Italy is the principal focus of the wine list, with shorter selections from France, Spain and the New World that are by no means token. The inevitable problem is price, with

only a few bottles under £20. Pieropan's Soave has more character than most, but perhaps not £23-worth. House wines start at £18.

CHEFS: Ralph Porciani and Roger Peters PROPRIETOR: The Lancaster Landmark Hotel Company Ltd OPEN: Sun to Fri L 12 (12.30 Sun) to 3,all week D 7 to 11 MEALS: alc (main courses £17 to £22). Set L Mon to Fri £21.50, Set L Sun £29 (inc wine), Set D £29 SERVICE: net prices, card slips closed CARDS: Access, Amex, Diners, Visa DETAILS: 110 seats. Private parties: 12 main room. Car park. Vegetarian meals. Children's helpings. Smart dress preferred. Wheelchair access (also WC). Music. Air-conditioned ACCOMMODATION: 309 rooms, all with bath/shower. TV. Phone. Air-conditioned. B&B £218 to £306. Rooms for disabled. Children welcome. Baby facilities. Pets by arrangemet. Afternoon teas. Swimming-pool

Riva

map 12

169 Church Road, SW13 9HR COOKING 2
TEL: 0181-748 0434 COST £23–£46

Riva, in a parade of shops set back from the road, has been a seminal influence on a number of chefs and critics alike. Andrea Riva and Francesco Zanchetta have brought northern Italian food, with its simple ideas and good ingredients, to a market that is weary of borrowed clichés. They have done it with an understanding that has belied the straightforward list of ingredients of which the menu is composed. Their focus is that part of Italy between the Alps and the Po which falls into Lombardy and Veneto. Given the Adriatic influence, fish usually features strongly, as in a mix of clams, shrimps and cuttlefish in a garlic-flavoured wine broth, or fish-cakes made from tuna, crab and salt-cod and served with a spicy sauce.

Flavours can be as strong as horseradish with thick chunks of smoked salmon tartare, or a honey and mustard sauce with sturgeon, both items appearing on the same plate. Main courses have produced rabbit with spätzli and a lemon-flavoured onion sauce, and pigeon legs on mashed potatoes with a sauce of onions and raisins. Desserts have included maize and almond crumble soaked in vin santo with mascarpone, and an OK version of zabaglione. A short list of predominantly northern Italian wines runs all the way from Sassicaia down to house Tocai and Merlot at £9.75.

CHEF: Francesco Zanchetta PROPRIETOR: Andrea Riva OPEN: Sun to Fri L 12.15 to 2.30, all week D 7 to 11 (11.30 Fri and Sat, 9.30 Sun) CLOSED: Christmas, Easter, last 2 weeks Aug, bank hols MEALS: alc (main courses £6 to £12.50) SERVICE: 10%, card slips closed CARDS: Access, Delta, Switch, Visa DETAILS: 50 seats. 2 tables outside. Private parties: 40 main room. Vegetarian meals. Children's helpings. Smart dress preferred. No cigars/pipes in dining-room. Wheelchair access (also WC). Music. Air-conditioned

River Café 🍷

map 12

Thames Wharf Studios, Rainville Road, W6 9HA COOKING 3
TEL: 0171-381 8824 FAX: 0171-381 6217 COST £29–£54

The minimalist warehouse conversion – refurbished since last year – looks out across the Thames. It is a cool, stylish room that comes into its own on clear days like a 'spring Sunday, with the sun streaming through the big windows'. Whatever else such a chromed and hard-edged room does, 'it doesn't cosset'. The modern Italian food, on the other hand, can be very satisfying. It pushes the idea

of simplicity to its limits, 'beyond fashion and vogue', in a way that looks so easy that some feel they could do it at home just as well. But 'brilliant simplicity' like this is deceptive. It takes skill to buy well, to cook accurately and to combine flavours in a way that seems 'just right'.

The food's transparency derives in part from chargrilling, the principal cooking method, applied to lamb, calf's liver, turbot, scallops and a whole basket of Mediterranean vegetables alike. A wood-burning oven has now been installed, and pan-roasting produces good results, as in a partridge with pink breasts, crisp skin and a thyme stuffing. Their own-label olive oil is the main moisturising agent, emulsions use vinegar from named super-Tuscan estates, and salsas and pesto feature. Rocket is the first-choice salad green, polenta is never far away – it even crops up with lemon as a pudding – and if you don't eat sour-dough bruschetta at least once during the meal, you are just not trying. 'Honest raw materials mucked about with as little as possible' is a fair assessment of the style. Puddings impress too, including pannacotta with grappa and raspberries, and a rich moist wedge of chocolate and chestnut cake served with a smooth zabaglione ice-cream tasting strongly of marsala.

A few take issue with the prices, one describing the food as 'annoyingly good: the bill is so high, we tried to find a reason not to return'. Service can be efficient and unobtrusive, but it can also be offhand and show 'no evidence of much knowledge of the food'. The reason for last orders as early as 9.30 is that the licence requires the premises to be vacated by 11pm. The notes have disappeared from the wine list and, although precious little comes from south of Tuscany, the selection is a zestful celebration of some of Italy's most fascinating flavours, not least among dessert wines. House wine is £9.50. CELLARMAN'S CHOICE: Tocai, Enofriulia 1994, Collio, £14; Salice Salentino Riserva 1990, Candido, £13.

CHEFS: Rose Gray, Ruth Rogers and Theo Randall PROPRIETORS: Richard and Ruth Rogers, and Rose Gray OPEN: all week L 12.30 (1 Sun) to 3, Mon to Sat D 7.30 to 9.30 CLOSED: 1 week Christmas, bank hols MEALS: alc (main courses £11 to £18) SERVICE: 12.5%, card slips closed CARDS: Access, Amex, Delta, Switch, Visa DETAILS: 95 seats. 15 tables outside. Private parties: 100 main room. Car park D. Children's helpings. Wheelchair access (also WC). No music

Royal China

map 13

13 Queensway, W2 4QJ COOKING 2
TEL: 0171-221 2535 COST £23–£58

The black and chrome décor with its gold-lacquered wall panelling may not be everyone's cup of jasmine, but there's little doubt that this classy restaurant is capable of serving up some 'very fine' Chinese food. The kitchen shows its Cantonese roots with a premier-league selection of around 50 dim-sum (served from noon to 5pm): perfectly cooked baby scallop dumplings, spanking-fresh prawn and coriander dumplings 'bursting with flavour' and refreshingly unslimy cheung-fun have all been endorsed. The menu is a catholic mix of Mandarin and Szechuan dishes bolstered by a few curiosities.

If you are looking for a challenge, order poached king clam with garlic and soya sauce, oyster and chive omelette, marinated shin of beef with jellyfish, or a hotpot of chicken with bean curd and salt-fish. Otherwise, settle for double-cooked pork, chicken in yellow-bean sauce, or sizzling squid with chilli and black-bean sauce. Impeccable ingredients and clear, distinctive flavours are what impress most. Service is suitably charming and courteous. A handful of well-chosen French and Italian wines are alternatives to saké. House wine is £8.50. A second branch is in Putney (3 Chelverton Road, SW15 1RN, Tel: 0181-788 0907).

CHEFS: Simon Man and Wai Hung Law PROPRIETOR: Playwell Ltd OPEN: all week noon to 11.15 (10.30 Sun) CLOSED: 23 to 25 Dec MEALS: alc (main courses £5 to £15). Set L and D (minimum 2) £20 to £26 SERVICE: 12.5% CARDS: Access, Amex, Delta, Diners, Switch, Visa DETAILS: 100 seats. Private parties: 85 main room, 15 private room. Vegetarian meals. Children welcome. Smart dress preferred. Music. Air-conditioned

RSJ 🍷

map 13

13A Coin Street, SE1 8YQ COOKING 2
TEL: 0171-928 4554 COST £23–£38

Coin Street is not the loveliest locale, and some complain that RSJ is difficult to find (aim for the intersection with Stamford Street), but it is worth persevering for the accomplished cooking and agreeable ambience that await. Pre-South Bank diners will find their schedules as well as their hunger catered for more than competently. It all happens on two levels – simple brasserie fare on the ground floor and more elaborate cooking upstairs – with the physical fitness of staff serving both areas rigorously tested but not found wanting.

The cooking, under the supervision of Ian Stabler, has evolved gently over the years, drawing the best from passing fashion without going headlong into ill-advised trendiness. In the restaurant, a good-value set-price menu of three courses plus coffee doesn't for once feel like the poor relation of the *carte*. A meal consisting of pigeon, quail's eggs, avocado and Roquefort salad, followed by roast lamb with French beans, black olives and saffron mash, and finishing with spiced apricot and pear crumble with crème fraîche, sounds likely to satisfy most appetites. Confit of duck on garlic mashed potatoes proved enormously popular among a birthday gathering. As much thought goes into puddings, such as Austrian plum cake with brown-bread ice-cream or vanilla cream with poached apples and hazelnut sablé, as into the rest of the menu. The same is true of the vegetarian dishes, which have a distinctly modern Italian twist. Service is amiable and helpful.

The wine list has long been a legend. Nigel Wilkinson's passion is for the Loire, often skimmed over in conventional lists (what chance has Chinon when crowded out by clarets?); here celebrated in its true glory with the best vintages and producers, the region has two pages to itself. Savennières-lovers have eight to choose from. The botrytised wines – such exemplary value compared with Sauternes – go on and on. Halves are generously provided too. House wines from Anjou are £9.75. CELLARMAN'S CHOICE: Saumur Champigny 1990, Dom. de Nerleux, £14.95; Coteaux de l'Aubance, Cuvée Prestige 1992, V. Lebreton, £15.95.

CHEF: Ian Stabler PROPRIETOR: Nigel Wilkinson OPEN: Mon to Fri L 12 to 2, Mon to Sat D 6 (5.45 Sat) to 11 CLOSED: bank hols MEALS: alc (main courses £9 to £12). Set L £15.95, Set D £15.95 SERVICE: 10%, card slips closed CARDS: Access, Amex, Switch, Visa DETAILS: 90 seats. 6 tables outside. Private parties: 10 main room, 16 and 30 private rooms. Vegetarian meals. Children welcome. No cigars/pipes in dining-room. Music. Air-conditioned

Rules map 15

35 Maiden Lane, WC2E 7LB COOKING 2
TEL: 0171-836 5314 FAX: 0171-497 1081 COST £28–£47

London's oldest restaurant approaches its bicentennial in confident stride. Famed when it opened for its 'porter, pies and oysters', it now offers in its amiably clubby confines a repertoire that ploughs much the same furrow. A jar of marinated herrings, fruity game preparations, thick-crusted pies and substantial puddings form the backbone, although there are occasional forays into the modern world, as in seared mackerel with tomato, pesto and herbed vinaigrette. One vegetarian discovered that three of the five options relied on Stilton for flavour. Rules is much more at ease catering for customers like the gentleman on his way to the Coliseum who stopped off for potted shrimps, a breast of 'surprisingly bony' partridge, a wodge of Stilton, half a bottle of claret and a pot of Earl Grey. One diner's description of the grouse as 'uncomfortably high' will be music to the ears of many game fans. She went on to say of the sticky toffee pudding that she 'couldn't imagine it being done better anywhere'. Moans and groans surface occasionally over the speed of service, despite the fact that the waiters are 'computerised', but the general atmosphere remains 'extremely jolly'. The wine list is compact but apposite, even if, with so much game around, you might expect a little more from Burgundy than an indifferent Passe-tout-grains. House wines are £8.50.

CHEFS: Neil Pass and Frank Wilkinson PROPRIETOR: John Mayhew OPEN: all week noon to midnight CLOSED: 23 to 26 Dec MEALS: alc (main courses £12 to £13). Set L Sat and Sun (2 courses) £12.95, Set pre-theatre D £12.95 (2 courses), Set afternoon meals 3 to 5 pm £7.95 (2 courses) SERVICE: not inc CARDS: Access, Amex, Delta, Switch, Visa DETAILS: 140 seats. Private parties: 10 main room, 18 to 60 private rooms. Vegetarian meals. Children welcome. No pipes in dining-room. Wheelchair access. No music. Air-conditioned

Sabras £ map 12

263 High Road, Willesden Green, NW10 2RX COOKING 2
TEL: 0181-459 0340 COST £17–£28

Hemant and Nalinee Desai started by supplying packets of Bombay mix to a few shops in London before opening their own sweet centre in 1972. A year later Sabras was born (the name means 'all taste' – it is also a word for 'salt'). More than two decades on, Hemant tells us that his 'enthusiasm is still sparkling'. Lunch has been abandoned, but the evening trade has picked up noticeably and it is wise to book.

The location is a dejected neighbourhood close to Willesden bus garage, yet the restaurant has pride, dignity and civility written all over it. The menu has been jazzed up, complete with a few personal quips, but it is serious stuff and few would argue against the view that the kitchen delivers some of the finest Gujarati vegetarian food in London. Some dishes are available only on certain days: home-made garlic and coriander chutney on Tuesday and Wednesday, banana-flavoured raita on Thursday and Friday, moong dhal with cherry tomatoes on Saturday and Sunday, for example. Farsan snacks are highly praised: patra (yam leaves rolled around a spicy flour-based mixture then sliced) and samosas are excellent. Hyderabadi masala dosai – its crisp outside impregnated with black pepper and roasted cumin – has also been praised. Added to this are all kinds of vegetables, ranging from spinach cooked with garlic and yoghurt to karela-bataka (sliced bitter gourd with potatoes and lemon), plus slow-cooked 'sun-dried' dhals and a good showing of breads and rice. Thalis are served until 8.30pm. Sweet lassi is the perfect non-alcoholic accompaniment, although Sabras also has its own beer and wine club. It is one of the few Indian places with a beer list offering such curiosities as Swedish Pripps and Russian Zhiguli. The wine list is equally global. House wine is £8.50.

CHEFS/PROPRIETORS: Hemant and Nalinee Desai OPEN: Tue to Sun D only 6.30 to 10.30 MEALS: alc (main courses £4 to £6). Set D £10 to £12.50 SERVICE: not inc CARDS: none DETAILS: 32 seats. Private parties: 32 main room. Vegetarian meals. Children welcome. Smart dress preferred. Wheelchair access. Music

Saga £✱

map 15

43–44 South Molton Street, W1V 1HB COOKING 1*
TEL: 0171-408 2236 FAX: 0171-629 7507 COST £17–£90

Saga plays to an almost exclusively Japanese audience in one of Mayfair's most glitzy shopping streets. You can expect to pay serious money here and expectations are high, even if the results do not always inspire superlatives. On the ground floor is a sushi bar, discreetly hidden from view behind a screen. Downstairs is the main restaurant, a labyrinth of eating areas with bare, varnished oak tables lit by ceiling-spots and box-shaped lamps. Elegance exudes from every corner and service is extremely courteous.

The long menu covers most of the classic repertoire and a choice of set meals offers the prospect of a satisfying run through the whole range of cooking styles and techniques, rounded off with miso soup, rice and pickles. Highpoints from recent samplings have included an assortment of little appetisers including 'tenderly cooked' eel in aspic, and a mini-mound of wild-rice paste dotted with sesame seeds. Clear soup is a delicate broth loaded with unidentifiable baby mushrooms, prawns and seaweed; tempura scores highly with succulent ingredients and the lightest of batter. Noodles are decent enough. As a finale, a plate of sliced fruits 'in lovely condition' provides pleasant relief and refreshment. To drink, there is green tea, a choice of sakés and shochu spirits, not to mention Japanese beers and a short, fairly priced wine list. House wine is £12.90.

CHEF: M. Kikuchi PROPRIETOR: K. Hashimoto OPEN: all week 12.30 to 2.30, 6.30 to 10 CLOSED: 25 Dec, 1 Jan MEALS: alc (main courses £6.50 to £22). Set L £6.50 to £12, Set D £37 to £55. Cover £1 D SERVICE: not inc L, 15% D CARDS: Access, Amex, Delta, Diners, Switch, Visa DETAILS: 100 seats. Private parties: 30 main room. Vegetarian meals. Children welcome. No smoking in 1 dining-room. No music. Air-conditioned

'We hadn't been for many years, but the owners emerged from the kitchen at the end of the meal and wanted to chat. They claimed to remember us, so either we are unforgettable or they don't have many customers.' (On eating in Hampshire)

All entries in the Guide *are rewritten every year, not least because restaurant standards fluctuate. Don't rely on an out-of-date* Guide.

▲ *St George's Hotel, The Heights* NEW ENTRY map 15

Langham Place, W1N 8QS COOKING 3
TEL: 0171-636 1939 FAX: 0171-753 0259 COST £31–£52

'Rather grim-looking' is how the hotel is viewed, but an express lift whisks you up to the fifteenth floor, where a bar awaits and a long, thin modernised dining-room ensures that most tables enjoy a good view of offices, tower blocks, indeed anything to the west of Broadcasting House. 'It is much nicer to be looking outwards from St George's than the other way round,' concluded one. This would appear to be another part of the Forte plan to conquer the world with cooking, following on the success at Grosvenor House (see Chez Nico at Ninety Park Lane) and the Hyde Park Hotel (see entry), among others. Adam Newell has not yet reached those sorts of heights, but his Roux training has undoubtedly helped to produce a good technical grounding, and his cooking also displays some genuinely inventive touches.

Tarte Tatin is a common device used in all three courses, including a starter of peppers and seared foie gras, and one of bananas to finish. Risottos might be made with black ink or pearl barley, pasta appears as lasagne of pheasant and Savoy cabbage, or tortellini of roasted artichoke, and the fashionable savoury cappuccino has used both lobster and chanterelles. Ingredients are good, and sometimes unusual. One reporter spotted deep-fried cockscombs, 'crispy yet slightly chewy', that came with a ballottine of chicken. Mediterranean input is strong, as in a thin tart of rouget and tapénade with rouille sauce, but there are earthier dishes too, of rump of lamb with smoked bacon and flageolet beans, for instance.

One of the benefits, and perhaps drawbacks, of a big kitchen is that it has time to do such things as make tortellini of wild mushrooms simply to partner a poached loin of rabbit. If the brigade were smaller the food might be simpler, which would probably be to its advantage. On the other hand, meals offer plenty of choice. Servers are dressed in beige smock tops, and communication does not appear to be a forte (so to speak). Water is £4 a bottle (a contender for the record) and six wines are served by the glass in the large 175ml size unless you stipulate a standard measure. A quick run through the major wine-producing regions turns up enough for both ordinary drinkers and corporate entertainers, though not many halves. House wine is from £11.95.

CHEF: Adam Newell PROPRIETOR: Forte Hotels (UK) Ltd OPEN: Mon to Fri L 12 to 2.30, Mon to Sat D 7 to 10.30 (11 Fri and Sat) MEALS: alc D (main courses £10 to £15.50). Set L £19.50. Min £19.50 L, £20 D SERVICE: not inc CARDS: Access, Amex, Diners, Visa DETAILS: 65 seats. Private parties: 100 main room, 12 private room. No children under 3. Smart dress preferred. No cigars/pipes in dining-room. Wheelchair access (also WC). Music. Air-conditioned ACCOMMODATION: 84 rooms, all with bath/shower. TV. Phone. Air-conditioned. B&B £142 to £154. Children welcome. Afternoon teas

---

The Guide *is totally independent, accepts no free hospitality, and survives on the number of copies sold each year.*

'I had chargrilled sirloin steak with a thyme-flavoured wine sauce. Obviously there had been a lot of vegetarians in recently as the steak was huge.' (On eating in Wiltshire)

St John

NEW ENTRY map 13

26 St John Street, EC1M 4AY — COOKING 2
TEL: 0171-251 0848 and 4998 FAX: 0171-251 4090 — COST £24–£42

St John is a one-off, an original that deals largely, but not exclusively, in offal. It has a mission. Those who eat only lamb chops, rump steak and pork fillet are missing out on some very tasty dishes indeed. Many restaurants get as far as oxtail and stop, but Fergus Henderson carries right on through the middle and out the other end. This 'nose-to-tail eating' is invigorating for those to whom variety matters, and sad that it has all but disappeared from our tables. Given that tongue, trotters and brisket are among the less expensive cuts, it is surprising that the recession has not winkled them out in greater numbers before now. The setting is an old Smithfield smokehouse painted white, with nooks, crannies, and flights of steps leading in all directions. 'The whole place has the feel of an Escher print.'

It may be trendy, and it may be the sort of place that only London could support, but any idea that a converted warehouse means a casual approach to the food is wide of the mark. Fergus Henderson (previously at the French House Dining Room; see entry, London) takes his ingredients seriously and turns them into appealing dishes. The celebrated roast bone-marrow with parsley salad satisfies curiosity as much as appetite, but grilled ox-tongue with beetroot, lambs' tongues stew, pot-roast brisket, and lamb's trotter with faggot are more substantial. And if you ask for pigeon you get the entire bird. Even plain boiled chicken is 'strongly flavoured, with lovely gelatinous lickable bits'. Meatless dishes are not neglected (asparagus and potato tart with poached egg, for example), and fish might appear in the form of cuttlefish with cracked wheat, or an eel, bacon and clam stew. Treacle custard pie and steamed plum pudding are for schoolkids of all ages. Service has been 'informed, confident and genuine', and the wines are, for some reason, entirely French (bar Tokai) and very young. Vin de table begins at £8.95.

CHEF: Fergus Henderson PROPRIETOR: Trevor Gulliver OPEN: restaurant all week L 12 to 3 (3.30 Sun), Mon to Sat D 6 to 11; bar Mon to Sat 11am to 11pm, Sun 12 to 3 MEALS: alc (main courses £6 to £13); bar meals available SERVICE: not inc CARDS: Access, Amex, Delta, Diners, Switch, Visa DETAILS: 100 seats. Private parties: 150 main room, 20 private room. Vegetarian meals. Children welcome. Wheelchair access (also WC)

Salloos

map 14

62–64 Kinnerton Street, SW1X 8ER — COOKING 2
TEL: 0171-235 4444 — COST £27–£51

It says a great deal about this sophisticated Pakistani restaurant that it has had the same chef for almost 30 years – a feat that few comparable establishments could match. Consistency is its strength, although quality comes at a high price in this village enclave of Knightsbridge. In many ways Salloos is a neighbourhood eating-place, although most of the locals are a moneyed crowd ('one of the diners had a diamond ring in which the diamond was wider than her finger,' observed one reporter). The upstairs dining-room feels cosy, with subdued lighting, paintings of Indian scenes on the walls and carvings set into white wooden panels.

The menu is dominated by meat and fish, most of which are subjected to the classic tandoori treatment. The results are highly impressive: lamb chops, for example, are 'beautifully tenderised for at least 24 hours in a marinade full of fresh spices' before being skewered and cooked to order. Curries are equally outstanding because spicing is so accurate. One seasoned reporter (if you will forgive the pun) reckoned that intensely flavoured chicken korai was one of the best dishes of its kind that he had eaten. Dhal is excellent, ditto chana (whole chickpeas cooked to perfect softness). Salloos also delivers brilliant breads: light, fluffy nan and tandoori paratha, for example. Rice is tip-top and served in realistic quantities (unlike some places, where you can almost count the individual grains). The hefty cover charge pays for poppadums and 'excellent home-made chutneys'. Some find the service pushy and hectoring, although it is rarely less than courteous. Like everything else, the wine list is pricey, although the section from Corney & Barrow offers fair value. House wine is £12.50.

CHEF: Abdul Aziz PROPRIETOR: Mohammed Salahuddin OPEN: Mon to Sat 12 to 2.30, 7 to 11.15 MEALS: alc (main courses £10.50 to £14.50). Set L £16, Set D £25. Cover £1.50 SERVICE: 15%, card slips closed CARDS: Access, Amex, Delta, Diners, Switch, Visa DETAILS: 65 seats. Private parties: 65 main room. Vegetarian meals. No children under 6 after 8pm. Smart dress preferred. No music. Air-conditioned

Les Saveurs 🍷 map 15

37A Curzon Street, W1Y 8EY **COOKING 4**
TEL: 0171-491 8919 FAX: 0171-491 3658 **COST £36–£80**

Given the Curzon Street location, and the fact that this does not obviously appear to be a restaurant, 'you feel as if you are stepping, not quite licitly, into a private Mayfair club'. Eating is done in the 'top-swank Japanese corporate' basement. This is a civilised restaurant offering a suitably exalted style of cooking, which is serious but also enjoyable, with that extra 'zing' that lifts it out of the ordinary. That Les Saveurs is reaching maturity can be gauged from the prices. The opening offer was perhaps too good to last, but three courses for £42 are still worth it if you grit your teeth, and the cheaper set lunch is considered 'first-class value'.

The style is ultra-modern, French-based and notable for its innovative spicing and combinations, such as eel fritters on a herb purée, foie gras with Thai spices, roast cod with chorizo, or praline terrine with crispy rice. Innovation does not mean seat-of-the-pants experimental. This is all carefully considered and researched, as in a first course of fanned slices of pink pigeon with 'a nice smoke pungency' generously dressed with a mild vinaigrette, on a plate scattered with 'soft, mushy, well-seasoned' fresh white haricot beans. In another first course, three mounds of chopped raw mackerel shared a bowl of clear, delicately flavoured buttery fish stock with three warm, slithery oysters, some slices of Jerusalem artichoke and diced tomato flesh.

Not all dishes are electrifying, but they generate enough voltage to power favourable reports – for example, two medallions of veal with an 'intense flavour' (and how common is that for veal?), lightly peppered and seared, with three quenelles of 'heavenly' truffle risotto that were cheesy and properly gluey, with a little veal stock reduction. Puddings are no less inventive, one of them a 'regally risen' hot lime soufflé in a napkin-shrouded dish, into which the waiter poured viscously runny acacia honey. 'The sharpness of the lime, the sweetness and exotic floral note of the honey, and the lightness, were exemplary. A triumph,' concluded an inspector, which was more than could be said for a sickly sweet chocolate madeleine with vanilla sauce at the same meal.

Generally, dishes don't waste time on unnecessary garnish: 'all the little doodles of sauce and greenery are edible.' Bread and nibbles might be improved. Service is as courteous as can be, and not in the least overbearing, although staff have to concentrate hard on busy evenings to keep everything on schedule. Many of the wines are the kind to dream about rather than actually buy. Their pedigree is unquestioned, from *grand cru* burgundies to first-growth clarets, all in wonderful profusion. A fine-tooth comb is needed to get change from £20 – south-west France is the place to look – and even house wine is £17.50.

CHEF: Joël Antunès PROPRIETOR: Fujikoshi UK Ltd OPEN: Mon to Fri 12 to 2.15, 7 to 10.30 CLOSED: 2 weeks Dec to Jan, 2 weeks Aug, bank hols MEALS: Set L £17 (2 courses) to £42, Set D £38 to £42 SERVICE: not inc CARDS: Access, Amex, Delta, Diners, Switch, Visa DETAILS: 55 seats. Private parties: 50 main room, 10 private room. No children under 10. Jacket and tie. No pipes in dining-room. No music. Air-conditioned

▲ *The Savoy, Grill Room* — map 15

Strand, WC2R 0EU — COOKING 3
TEL: 0171-836 4343 FAX: 0171-240 6040 — COST £41–£85

'What a place! What a meal! What service! What a hangover! And Bob says, what a bill!' So began one enthusiastic account of dinner. Poor Bob. The evening starts with someone parking your car, and proceeds to the American Bar where it is possible to make a meal of the mixed nuts, olives and constantly replenished crisps. 'We made our drinks last while the pianist played some of my requests. It was all so Scott Fitzgeraldy that we had to tear ourselves away to the restaurant', where the seating is so luxuriously comfortable and the service so solicitous 'that I have decided to recover from my next major illness here'.

The Grill is not all carving and flambéing, although anybody ordering roast meat will find the relevant trolley wheeled to the table. Daily specials of sausage and mash or Lancashire hotpot are served at lunch-time, and honey-roast ham or sirloin of beef at dinner. The menu deals largely in old-fashioned British hotel favourites (written in stilted French, of course), from dressed crab, Dover sole and lobster to lambs' kidneys, veal sweetbreads, and pan-fried pigeon or rosettes of lamb, but the cooking is sound and carefully done. Luxuries are well handled, including a terrine of foie gras, with 'cool, amber, slippery jelly around the pieces of meltingly soft dark liver', and a salad of langoustines on a colourful pile of leaves bathed in a piquant dressing which 'fulfilled the role of appetiser to perfection'. Meaty set pieces appeal too, from fillet of beef in a rich creamy sauce speckled with pieces of black truffle, 'the whole plate redolent of the subtle perfume', to 'lamb casserole with knobs on': large chunks cooked long and slowly, with lots of green lentils, all bound in a rich glossy sauce.

Puddings are designed to lift flagging spirits: 'fabulous' honey ice-cream ringed with fat, juicy raspberries, or summer pudding with 'masses of sweet syrupy juice that blended with the dollop of thick cream'. As to staff, 'there seems to be a spring in everyone's step, and friendly civility hits just the right note'. Questions are answered courteously and knowledgeably, and at the end of the evening 'our car was parked in the forecourt, keys in the ignition, when we emerged at approximately the time we expected'. Wines in the Grill and River Restaurant are similar: bulging with fine burgundy and classy claret at prices you would expect, with plenty of interest for those prepared to pay up to £30 a bottle. For the rest of us, house wine is £15.70.

CHEF: David Sharland PROPRIETOR: Savoy Group plc OPEN: Mon to Fri L 12.30 to 2.30, Mon to Sat D 6 to 11.15 MEALS: alc (main courses £16.50 to £21.50). Set pre-theatre D 6 to 7 £27 (2 courses) to £29.75 SERVICE: not inc CARDS: Access, Amex, Delta, Diners, Switch, Visa DETAILS: 85 seats. Private parties: 10 main room, 4 to 80 private rooms. Vegetarian meals. Jacket and tie. No pipes in dining-room. Wheelchair access by arrangement. Music. Air-conditioned ACCOMMODATION: 202 rooms, all with bath/shower. TV. Phone. Air-conditioned. B&B £180 to £295. Deposit: 1 night's stay. Rooms for disabled. Children welcome. Baby facilities. Afternoon teas. Swimming-pool (*The Which? Hotel Guide*)

▲ *The Savoy, River Restaurant* map 15

Strand, WC2R 0EU COOKING 2*
TEL: 0171-836 4343 FAX: 0171-240 6040 COST £37–£114

The River Restaurant is noted for its view of the Thames, and shares black-coated male waiters, and much of the food, with the Grill Room (see entry, above), although the result does not seem to wow reporters to quite the same extent. Prices are similar, too, whether for luxuries such as fricassée of lobster and sole, marinated salmon in caviare cream sauce, or more humble asparagus with hollandaise sauce. The menu also incorporates kidneys and sweetbreads alongside roast beef with Yorkshire pudding or breast of pigeon, adding crêpes suzette for a bit of old-fashioned pyrotechnical theatre, and as an alternative to crème brûlée and other stalwarts from the trolley. There is a list of desserts too, for the likes of chocolate and vanilla soufflé that wouldn't survive a trolley.

Other items add interest, from a ragoût of wild mushrooms with lentil cake to omelette Arnold Bennett. A menu entitled 'régime naturel' means whatever you want it to mean, but seems to be light and free from meat and cream, offering vegetable broth with soft-boiled quail's eggs, and linguine with peas and mint. Meats such as beef and venison are generally cooked pink, although an occasional item might inadvertently end up with rather more cooking than intended. There is ample choice, and if it all seems bewildering, consider the five-course seasonal menu that includes a choice glass of wine to accompany each course: terrine of goose liver and chicken breast with an Alsace Gewurztraminer, for example, or breast of duck with 'turnip marmalade' and a glass of Ch. Paveil de Luze 1989 from Margaux. Service is 'helpful, courteous and efficient', and wines are similar to those in the Grill.

CHEF: Anton Edelmann PROPRIETOR: Savoy Group plc OPEN: all week 12.30 to 2.30, 6 to 11.30 (10.30 Sun) MEALS: alc (main courses £22.50 to £30.50). Set L Mon to Sat £27.50, Set L Sun £24.50, Set pre-theatre D 6 to 7 £27 (2 courses) to £29.75, Set D Sun to Thur £32.90 to £55, Set D Fri and Sat £39.50 to £55 SERVICE: 15%, card slips closed CARDS: Access, Amex, Delta, Diners, Switch, Visa DETAILS: 200 seats. Private parties: 50 main room, 4 to 80 private rooms. Vegetarian meals. Children welcome. Jacket and tie. No pipes in dining-room. Wheelchair access by arrangement. Music. Air-conditioned ACCOMMODATION: See entry above for details.

▲ *The Savoy, 'Upstairs'* map 15

Strand, WC2R 0EU COOKING 2
TEL: 0171-836 4343 FAX: 0171-240 6040 COST £28–£51

Both the Grill Room and River Restaurant (see entries above) offer a chance to eat before or after the theatre (for which the Savoy is handily placed), but this informal all-day restaurant appeals, being even more flexible and cheaper into the bargain. A couple who dived in late one evening enjoyed tomato and mozzarella salad followed by fish-cake and (to a lesser extent) a version of kedgeree. Fish is the star of the show and generally works well, whether simple dressed crab or rock oysters, or else clam chowder, pan-fried red mullet, or cold wild salmon. One option is a kind of fishy 'thali' that includes smoked salmon with scrambled eggs, coleslaw king prawn, crabmeat, oyster and red mullet, and a tomato salsa. Sherry trifle, and rhubarb and orange meringue pie finish things off. Service may lack the polish of the more formal dining-rooms. Wines are not as informally priced as they might be, but thanks to a Cruvinet machine there are usually around nine or ten rather smart ones available by the glass (Puligny-Montrachet, for instance) from £6 to £9. House wine is £15.70 a bottle.

CHEF: David Sharland PROPRIETOR: Savoy Group plc OPEN: Mon to Fri noon to midnight, Sat 5 to midnight CLOSED: bank hols MEALS: alc (main courses £7 to £14). SERVICE: not inc CARDS: Access, Amex, Diners, Visa DETAILS: 36 seats. Private parties: 10 main room. Vegetarian meals. Children welcome. Smart dress preferred. No pipes in dining-room. No music. Air-conditioned ACCOMMODATION: See the Savoy, Grill Room for details

Shaw's 🍷 map 14

119 Old Brompton Road, SW7 3RN COOKING 2
TEL: 0171-373 4472 and 7774 FAX: 0171-370 5102 COST £27–£53

A sense of affluence and calm seems to come from the light pastel walls, large gilded mirrors and subtle lighting of this dining-room, although Shaw's is not blessed with the acres of space between tables that would take it into the luxury class. The place is designed for 'mature tastes and sensibilities', and the food brings reassurance – in the form of foie gras terrine with apple jelly, or chicken breast with spinach dumplings – to the comfortably off. What the operation lacks in edgy excitement it makes up for in quiet satisfaction.

Frances Atkins is particular about her supplies, specifying wild rather than farmed salmon and venison, and dived rather than dredged scallops. A streak of Englishness runs through, from roast pink fillet of lamb with a tian of tongue to queen of puddings, and behind apparent simplicity on the plate may lie some deft and lengthy preparation, as in stuffed rabbit cooked with ham knuckle, prunes, armagnac and leek, and served with pasta and a mustard sauce. 'Gutsy bouillons' and good sauces are a hallmark. Service is overseen by the amiable and gentlemanly Gerald Atkins, who epitomises the appeal of the restaurant. Bread, according to one reporter, does not appear to have improved, although wines are as good as ever, assembled with an eye for quality and fairly priced, not least in Italy. House wine is £13.50. CELLARMAN'S CHOICE: Sancerre, Dom de Nozay 1993, Benoist, £18.50; Coldstream Hills Reserve Pinot Noir 1992, Yarra Valley, Australia, £20.

CHEF: Frances Atkins PROPRIETORS: Gerald and Frances Atkins, Sir Neil and Lady Shaw, David Banks and Torunn Fieldhouse OPEN: Sun to Fri L 12 to 2 (3.30 Sun), Mon to Sat D 7 to 10, post-theatre supper 10.30 to 11.30 CLOSED: Christmas and New Year, Easter, first 2 weeks Aug MEALS: Set L £14 (2 courses) to £17.50, Set D £26.75 (2 courses) to £29.75; set post-theatre D £14 (2 courses) to £17.50 SERVICE: not inc L, net prices D, card slips closed CARDS: Access, Amex, Delta, Diners, Switch, Visa DETAILS: 44 seats. 3 tables outside. Private parties: 34 main room. Vegetarian meals. Children welcome. Smart dress preferred. Wheelchair access (1 step). No music. Air-conditioned

Simply Nico

map 13

48A Rochester Row, SW1P 1JU — COOKING 3
TEL: 0171-630 8061 FAX: 0171-355 4877 — COST £32–£48

'We arrived at 8.30pm and the party was in full swing, with a healthy din in several languages.' The dining-room is a long corridor painted a soothing shade of lemon yellow, with pink added to the mix for warmth, and bands of mirrors around the walls at waist height. Tables are close together. 'I enjoyed the meal, the ambience and the service,' wrote one, although others have found the noise a bit much. There is little difference in price between the set lunch and the set dinner, yet it is lunch that elicits applause for value. Perhaps that is because, as one reporter perceptively put it, 'the food is more safe lunch food than exciting dinner food'.

The repertoire comforts with just enough luxury, but doesn't flaunt it. Supplements for foie gras (a 'melt-in-the-mouth experience of decadent self-indulgence'), beef and sea bass are considered niggly, though the choice of rarely less than ten items per course is generous. Fish soup with Parmesan, rouille and toasts was 'as good as anything we've encountered in the South of France', claimed a traveller, while another found the contrast in texture and taste between warm, slithery smoked salmon and cold, crunchy celeriac to be 'interesting'. The balancing act of sweet and sharp is generally well handled, as between sweet braised endive and a lemon and oil dressing that accompanied a fillet of sea bass.

The food may need more fine-tuning than it sometimes gets, with 'heavy' accompaniments for fish, and a few simply 'dull' items; even mainstays such as the chips and lemon tart have had their ups and downs, the chips just right for some, not crispy enough for others. For one reporter, the caramelised lemon tart had 'that ten-egg-yolk flavour about it', and was 'one of the best ever: thick, sharp, palate-cleansing, with the minimum of pastry'. One experienced diner summed up the widespread feeling that 'the food tasted as if it was in safe hands'. Service meanwhile has varied from 'arrogant' – and pushy in the case of wine – to 'excellent'. One found it 'amusing, witty and with that cocky arrogance that works when it is allied with knowledge'. Some 50 reliable bottles from around the world are well chosen for interest and flavour, at pretty standard mark-ups. There are ten half-bottles, and four wines available by the glass from £3.

'I had lamb rogan josh, and began to suspect that the words ''rogan josh'' translate as ''mutton dressed as''.' (On eating in Edinburgh)

CHEF: Jim Johnson PROPRIETORS: Nico and Dinah Jane Ladenis OPEN: Mon to Fri L 12 to 2, Mon to Sat D 7 to 11 CLOSED: 10 days Christmas, 4 days Easter, bank hol Mons MEALS: Set L £21 (2 courses) to £24, Set D £26 SERVICE: net prices, card slips closed CARDS: Access, Amex, Diners, Visa DETAILS: 45 seats. Private parties: 20 main room. No children under 5. Smart dress preferred. No pipes in dining-room. No music. Air-conditioned

Singapore Garden Restaurant map 13

83–83A Fairfax Road, NW6 4DY COOKING 1*
TEL: 0171-328 5314 FAX: 0171-624 0656 COST £23–£52

'This place gets reviewed regularly in *The Straits Times,'* comments a reporter who clearly knows her way around. The cooking in this popular family-run restaurant is laced with authenticity, and the menu has its share of interesting Nonya regional dishes as well as so-called 'hawker' street food seldom found outside Singapore. The satays, ho jien (oyster omelette), chilli crab and kway teow (broad rice noodles with all kinds of meaty tit-bits) have all been given the seal of approval. But it also pays to delve into the more challenging seafood specials: sambal skate served on a banana leaf, Assam curried fish with okra, or squid blachan. To finish – or as a sustaining 'drink' throughout the meal – try chendol, a blend of coconut milk, ice and green-dyed soft noodles with palm sugar and aduki beans. This is a happy-go-lucky venue: families with children appear at lunch-time, and in the evening it's often an intriguing mix of young, affluent Chinese and Asians, old colonials taking a trip down memory lane and 'brash businessmen loudly proclaiming their globe-trotting credentials'. It gets 'chock-a-block', but service copes admirably. Singapore Tiger beer is the best accompaniment; otherwise, there is saké or house wine at £8.95. Singapore Garden II is at 154 Gloucester Place, London NW1 6DJ, Tel: 0171-723 8233.

CHEF: Mrs S. Lim PROPRIETOR: Singapore Garden Restaurant Ltd OPEN: all week 12 to 2.45, 6 to 10.45 (11.15 Fri and Sat) MEALS: alc (main courses £5.50 to £18). Set L and D £16. Minimum £10 D SERVICE: not inc CARDS: Access, Amex, Diners, Visa DETAILS: 100 seats. 4 tables outside. Private parties: 100 main room, 60 private room. Vegetarian meals. Children welcome. Smart dress preferred. No cigars in dining-room. Music. Air-conditioned

Snows on the Green map 12

166 Shepherd's Bush Road, W6 7PB COOKING 2
TEL: 0171-603 2142 FAX: 0171-602 7553 COST £21–£38

'Provincial European cooking' is the declared orientation here, for which read Italy, Spain and the South of France. The restaurant itself adds to the effect, especially when the sun is shining. Calmly and pleasantly run, it was also, for one, 'visually cooling in the heat of July, an outpost of Mediterranean civilisation in the midst of a slightly scruffy area'. Mediterranean cooking is not, of course, exclusive to Shepherd's Bush, but here of all places it is the studied avoidance of cliché that impresses, at least for first and second courses.

Dishes may sound quixotically blunt – foie gras, fried egg and vinegar – but what arrives on the plate usually convinces doubters. Flavours that sound brash turn out to be better balanced than expected. A summer starter of beetroot in olive oil had four strips of smoked eel draped across the roughly diced root, together with a blob of horseradish cream. The whole avoided unnecessary saltiness and was appreciated for its simplicity, 'not to mention the beautiful colours'. On another occasion, pigeon breast was topped with black pudding and accompanied by cabbage-wrapped bacon and onion, an assemblage that threatened to topple into over-richness but just held the line. Olive oil finds its way into most stages of a meal, from the dish for sopping bread in, in mashed potato, to a dessert that pairs a slice of Roquefort with a half-fig. Imagination peters out somewhat by dessert stage, and the menu chooses to follow the familiar repertoire of lemon tart, crème brûlée and tiramisù. Wines adopt the modern approach, comprising French, Italian and New World bottles at sensible enough prices. House French is £9.50.

CHEF/PROPRIETOR: Sebastian Snow OPEN: Mon to Fri and Sun L 12 to 3, Mon to Sat D 7 to 11 MEALS: alc (main courses £8 to £11.50). Set L £11.50 (2 courses) to £13.50 SERVICE: not inc CARDS: Access, Delta, Switch, Visa DETAILS: 75 seats. Private parties: 50 main room, 30 private room. Vegetarian meals. Children's helpings. No cigars/pipes in dining-room. Wheelchair access. Music. Air-conditioned

Soho Soho

map 15

11–13 Frith Street, W1V 8TS — COOKING 1

TEL: 0171-494 3491 FAX: 0171-437 3091 — COST £20–£53

A central Soho location and a leaning towards French Mediterranean food is a good marketable combination, and indeed for one reporter this was a welcome 'taste of Provence on a cold and dreary Monday night'. The ground-floor rôtisserie is a busy meeting-place and purveyor of less expensive dishes that make much of pasta, salads, omelette and chips, fish and vegetables, while the upstairs restaurant is quieter; for window tables the street below provides a good side-show. As we went to press, a general refurbishment was under way.

In truth, not all the food is strictly provençale, although credentials are well established in a dish such as grilled tuna steak served on red peppers stewed with salt-cod and garnished with a potato and olive timbale. Some of the food might look slightly old-fashioned in today's context, as in a wine and garlic velouté sauce for Dover sole for instance, but peppers and tomatoes abound, and at its best the food is 'full of vibrancy and life'. Simpler dishes, as so often, work best, and tender steak with crisp frites would fall into this category. Crème brûlée and lemon tart are among the puddings. Staff are polite and helpful, and a broadly Mediterranean selection of wines backs up the more traditional regions. Eight house wines begin at £3.25 a glass.

CHEF: Laurent Lebeau PROPRIETOR: Groupe Chez Gérard Ltd OPEN: restaurant Mon to Sat 12 to 3, 6 to 11.45; rôtisserie Mon to Sun noon to 12.45am (12 Sun) MEALS: restaurant alc (main courses £12 to £14.50); rôtisserie alc (main courses £6 to £9.50). Set pre-theatre D restaurant 6 to 7.30 Tue to Sat and 6 to 11.45 Mon £15.20 (2 courses) to £17.60. Cover £1.50 restaurant SERVICE: 12.5% (optional), card slips closed CARDS: Access, Amex, Delta, Diners, Switch, Visa DETAILS: restaurant 60 seats, rôtisserie 30 seats. 6 tables outside. Private parties: 60 private room. Car park for restaurant customers after 6.30. Vegetarian meals. Children's helpings. Wheelchair access. Music. Air-conditioned

Sonny's

map 12

94 Church Road, SW13 0DQ NEW CHEF

TEL: 0181-748 0393 FAX: 0181-748 2698 COST £24–£45

The restaurant is a well-used local, in a row of shops with its own delicatessen next door. Walk through the café-bar to the bright, airy, casual dining-room with its chrome-framed chairs with cream leather seats, linen cloths and paper napkins. The kitchen has been in a state of flux recently, since Redmond Hayward left. Peter Harrison arrived too late for us to receive any reports, or to inspect, hence no cooking mark this year, but the modern-style menu continues with first courses of fish soup with rouille and croûtons, risotto of Serrano ham and peas, and chicken and foie gras terrine. Main courses might include casserole of rabbit and baked polenta, seared blue-fin tuna with aubergine relish, or rump of lamb with flageolets. Vanilla bavarois or chocolate marquise bring up the rear, and the short wine list is as catholic as the food, starting at £8.75 a bottle, with a dozen available by the glass.

CHEF: Peter Harrison PROPRIETOR: Rebecca Mascarenhas OPEN: restaurant all week 12.30 to 2.30 (3 Sun), Mon to Sat D 7.30 to 11; café all week 10 to 6 CLOSED: bank hols MEALS: alc (main courses £8.50 to £14.50). Set L £13.50 (2 courses) SERVICE: not inc CARDS: Access, Amex, Visa DETAILS: 100 seats. Private parties: 10 main room, 20 private room. Vegetarian meals. Children welcome. Smart dress preferred. No cigars/pipes in dining-room. Music. Air-conditioned

The Square 🍷

map 15

32 King Street, SW1Y 6RJ COOKING 3

TEL/FAX: 0171-839 8787 COST £40–£63

The tranquillity of St James's made the evening atmosphere 'most agreeable' for one reporter, despite his being shoehorned into the window table of a full house. The minimal adornment consists of 'an artistic array of primary colours in simple shapes, tastefully arranged', and adds to the feeling that this is still a restaurant with its finger on the pulse. Apart from perhaps a rump of lamb with white-bean purée and a confit of artichokes, which is hardly old-fashioned anyway, the cooking makes its impact with a modern array of fish, vegetables and fowl, the generally light effect of which is appreciated.

The repertoire remains fairly constant, and the accomplishment is a tribute to what can be achieved when a chef sticks around instead of moving on to the next golden opportunity. Philip Howard has been here from the start in 1991, overseeing a menu that deals in crisp onion pizza with a sauté of ceps, escabèche of mackerel with mozzarella and tapénade, and a salad of new potatoes with salsify and truffles. Among fish dishes that have met with approval were two at a spring meal: half a grilled lobster 'slopping over with butter powerful with the savour of rosemary', and a fish soup that was 'a deep, thick, russet-coloured liquidised version with buckets of cream in it', and which came with a side-plate of grilled red mullet sitting on a pile of salad leaves that our surprised inspector 'couldn't help feeling was a bit of another dish really'.

At one meal roast squab pigeon arrived sectioned into parts, with breasts rubbed in coarse salt (softly textured 'without losing the required density'), the legs 'good for gnawing', and a 'dark satisfying gaminess' pervading all. The sense of clarity is carried through to desserts of caramelised banana tart, or a 'metaphorical mille-feuille' (997 leaves short of its quota) consisting of three wafer-thin slices of dark chocolate sandwiching a nicely granular pistachio cream, enlivened by a sharp-flavoured orange sauce. Since last year the evening *carte* has disappeared, leaving only a rather expensive fixed-price menu. Indeed, price, whether for just mineral water or for the whole meal, is one of the main grumbles. Excellence on the wine list doesn't come cheap either. Clarets and burgundies are extensive and tip-top, but even the usual bolt-holes of Italy or Australia afford little financial relief, which is provided by a handful of youthful regional French wines. Ten wines are available by the glass from £3.75.

CHEF: Philip Howard PROPRIETOR: Nigel Platts-Martin OPEN: Mon to Fri L 12 to 2.45, Mon to Sat D 6 to 11.45, Sun D 7 to 10 CLOSED: Christmas, bank hols L MEALS: alc L (main courses £13 to £18). Set D £32 (2 courses) to £38 SERVICE: not inc CARDS: Access, Amex, Delta, Diners, Switch, Visa DETAILS: 65 seats. Private parties: 10 main room, 20 private room. Children welcome. Smart dress preferred. Wheelchair access (also WC). No music. Air-conditioned

Sree Krishna £

map 12

192–194 Tooting High Street, SW17 0SF — COOKING 1
TEL: 0181-672 4250 and 6903 — COST £15–£34

'We chose Sree Krishna because of cost and the fact that we wouldn't have to change,' noted a couple who needed reviving after a hard day's work. Unbeatable value, informality and 'smiling' waiters are part of the attraction. The restaurant's trump card is authentic South Indian vegetarian cooking with a bias towards the Kerala coast. Rava dosais ('the big square flat ones') and cylindrical masala dosais are now bolstered by a version for carnivores that is stuffed with mince as well as the usual spicy mix of potatoes and onions. A few 'exotic starters' such as fish fry and cashew-nut pakora appear alongside vadai (fried gram-flour doughnuts), uthappam (a spicy pizza-style pancake with green chillies and tomatoes) and other meatless specialities. The vegetable dishes are highly rated, and the menu also features a full slate of curry-house stalwarts from bhunas to birianis. Drink lassi or lager, or house wine at £7.

CHEF: Mullath Vijayan PROPRIETORS: T. Haridas and family OPEN: all week 12 to 3, 6 to 11 (12 Fri and Sat) CLOSED: 25 and 26 Dec MEALS: alc (main courses £2 to £7). Minimum £5 SERVICE: 10%, card slips closed CARDS: Access, Amex, Diners, Visa DETAILS: 120 seats. Private parties: 60 main room, 60 private room. Vegetarian meals. Children welcome. Smart dress preferred. Wheelchair access (also WC). Music. Air-conditioned

Sri Siam

map 15

16 Old Compton Street, W1V 5PE — COOKING 2
TEL: 0171-434 3544 — COST £18–£46

In May 1995 Sri Siam moved from its original premises to a bigger and better site next door. Things were still in a state of flux as we went to press, but the place seems set to continue in much the same way. The layout is similar: two dining areas separated by a thick wall with large oblong 'windows' set in it. Semi-abstract designs of fish and leaves have been stencilled on to the stone-grey walls, a few artefacts and embroideries lighten the tone and there are flowers on the tables. It feels smart, and service remains polite even under pressure.

Set lunches continue to draw favourable comments, but it pays to give proper consideration to the full menu, which spans much of the Thai repertoire. Satays, spring rolls, stuffed chicken wings and fish-cakes are accurate, finely flavoured examples of the cuisine, and deep-fried 'golden bags' (crispy parcels stuffed with a fishy mix) have been excellent. Dishes such as plameuk krapow (stir-fried squid with chilli and 'holy basil') and a yellow curry of king prawns with coconut milk and spices are well executed, while the northern Thai speciality larb – a salad of pork, beef or chicken with ground roasted rice and a sour lime dressing – is well worth a try. Noodles and rice are up to the mark. Sri Siam and its sister Sri Siam City (see entry, below) tell us they are the only Thai restaurants in the UK with a full vegetarian menu 'approved by the Vegetarian Society'. The wine list is a useful selection tilted towards the New World; otherwise, go for Singha beer. House French is £8.80.

CHEF: W. Rodpradith PROPRIETOR: Thai Restaurants plc OPEN: Mon to Sat L 12 to 3, all week D 6 to 11.15 (10.30 Sun) MEALS: alc (main courses £6 to £9.50). Set L £10.50, Set D £15.50 SERVICE: 12½% (optional) CARDS: Access, Amex, Diners, Switch, Visa DETAILS: 120 seats. Private parties: 140 main room, 30 private room. Vegetarian meals. Children welcome. Music. Air-conditioned

Sri Siam City

map 13

85 London Wall, EC2M 7AD — COOKING 2
TEL: 0171-628 5772 FAX: 0171-628 3395 — COST £23–£36 29

The younger sibling of Sri Siam (see entry, above) attracts both sharp-suited City types and the culture-vultures who descend on the nearby Barbican. The setting sounds like archetypal 1990s EC2: you enter a modern office block and descend to the restaurant, passing 'a splendid wooden throne *en route*'. At the front of the peachy-pink dining-room is a bar done out in shades of green, where drinks can be taken and menus perused.

The repertoire of around 70 dishes is virtually identical to the Soho original, although prices (including those for set meals) are higher across the board. Flavours are vivid, and chilli is used to create liveliness rather than sheer heat. Starters such as satays, fish-cakes, and stuffed chicken wings are capably prepared, phad phed talay is a fresh-tasting assortment of stir-fried seafood with herbs, and yam woonsen is exactly what you might expect from a salad of vermicelli glass noodles with finely minced meat and vegetables tossed in. Among the soups, tom kah gai (chicken broth with coconut) has been a shade more convincing than prawn tom yum. Rice is reckoned to be 'adequate', not 'as fragrant as the best Thai'. Ripe fresh fruit makes a good finale, or try nam kang sai – crushed ice with sweetcorn, lychees and grass jelly topped with rose syrup, ice-cream and roasted peanuts. The wine list is more extensive than at Sri Siam, and it pays proper attention to vintages and producers from both the Old and New Worlds. House wine is £8.95.

All main entries are fully indexed at the back of the Guide.

CHEF: Pongchan Lerdjirakul PROPRIETOR: Thai Restaurants plc OPEN: Mon to Fri 11.30 to 8 CLOSED: 24 to 26 Dec, 1 Jan, bank hols MEALS: alc (main courses £7 to £10.50). Set L and D £14.90 to £24.90 SERVICE: 12.5% (optional), card slips closed CARDS: Access, Amex, Diners, Switch, Visa DETAILS: 140 seats. Private parties: 180 main room. Vegetarian meals. Children welcome. Wheelchair access (also WC). Music. Air-conditioned

Stephen Bull

map 15

5–7 Blandford Street, W1H 3AA COOKING 2*
TEL: 0171-486 9696 FAX: 0171-490 3128 COST £32–£48

Marylebone High Street still functions as an old-fashioned browsing and shopping street, and Stephen Bull's – just round the corner in Blandford Street – is 'still absolutely in vogue' with its awning and frontage in crisp black and grey. Bull's restaurants have always demonstrated an eye for detail and design, and refurbishment has produced an exuberant mixture of lemon yellow and peppermint green that contrives to feel 'very cool, very elegant', helped by a polished wooden floor, discreet lighting and an artful use of mirrors. 'Compared with previous meals here, the arrival of new chef Mercy Fenton has meant no more than business as usual,' concluded one visitor. The cooking remains modern, light, 'very Stephen Bull', and in keeping with the elegant interior.

Fish, vegetables and fowl outnumber standard farmyard protein, as is fast becoming the norm: unless you count oxtail faggots, only ribeye of beef is old-school. Otherwise, the menu is a happy mix of leaf salad with roast peppers, terrine of John Dory with Mediterranean vegetables, and escabèche of mackerel. Standard Bull favourites – twice-cooked goats' cheese soufflé, fish with lentils, and pairings of plaice with morel mushrooms and duck with shiitakes – are enlivened with accompaniments from lemon couscous to green mango chutney. An inspector was impressed with the cooking of fish, from fillets of sea bass to a risotto of 'sweet, fresh' scallops and mussels with broad beans for 'background crunch', the whole thing pulled together with thyme-flavoured fish stock, though he was less taken with some unbalanced or shy flavourings: this is cooking that requires confidence and conviction.

A dessert on the theme of chocolate, however, produced four different variations – ice-cream, light and dark mousses, and crunchy brownie – 'each with its own character and nuance', and espresso coffee to finish is very good indeed. Wines are as zestful as the food, and decently priced. One reporter who was entertaining a winemaker from Bordeaux found he could do so in proper style, thanks to nearly 100 bottles that tap some of the world's most informed winemaking. Gems abound, half-bottles are fair, and the list opens at £10.50. CELLARMAN'S CHOICE: Pacherenc du Vic-Bilh, Ch. Bouscassé 1992, Brumont £17; Syrah, Les Collines de Laure 1992, Jean-Luc Colombo, £16.50.

CHEF: Mercy Fenton PROPRIETOR: Stephen Bull OPEN: Mon to Fri L 12.15 to 2.15, Mon to Sat D 6.30 to 10.45 CLOSED: 1 week Christmas, bank hols MEALS: alc (main courses £11.50 to £14.50) SERVICE: not inc, card slips closed CARDS: Access, Amex, Visa DETAILS: 55 seats. Children's helpings. No cigars/pipes in dining-room. Wheelchair access (1 step). No music. Air-conditioned

indicates a change of chef since last year's Guide.

Stephen Bull's Bistro 🍷 map 13

71 St John Street, EC1M 4AN COOKING **2***
TEL: 0171-490 1750 FAX: 0171-490 3128 COST £26–£42

Not that long ago the location would have seemed strange: close to Smithfield Market of course, which is useful for a restaurant, but not exactly at the centre of things. Now, especially given that St John (see entry) and a few others have set up shop nearby, the area looks increasingly handy for both West End and City, as well as for Barbican refugees. At the bistro the bold colours remain, but since last year the bar, good for an early-evening beer, has gone: a victim of the pressure on tables for food. Instead, there is a new seafood bar by the entrance, where customers can graze from a short shellfish menu.

Although for a time he moved to Stephen Bull's main operation at Blandford Street (see entry, previous page), Stephen Carter is back as the chef here, producing food that can be both light and satisfying, with a strong bias towards Europe, yet without the mindless flourishes that bedevil many kitchens. Fish plays a central role, from the Seafood Bar's crab mayonnaise, or lobster salad with truffle potatoes, to grilled skate with pasta and tomato butter. Carter's leaning towards Iberia is evident in Spanish mackerel with courgettes, red peppers and garlic cream, and a plate of Spanish delicacies (including cheese, chorizo and quince paste), though risotto, lasagne, and grilled ribeye of beef spread the net wider, as do puddings from sticky toffee to rice brûlée with oranges and pecans. Four dozen youthful wines reflect a good range of current winemaking styles and practices, from barrel-fermented Spanish Chardonnay to unfiltered Alsace, squeezing good value out of South Africa, California, Italy and Australia. House wine is £9. CELLARMAN'S CHOICE: Viñas del Vero Chardonnay 1992, Spain, £12; Vacqueyras 1990, Dom. Le Couroulu, £17.50.

CHEF: Stephen Carter PROPRIETOR: Stephen Bull OPEN: Mon to Fri L 12 to 2.15, Mon to Sat D 6.30 to 11 CLOSED: 1 week Christmas, bank hols MEALS: alc (main courses £8.50 to £10.50) SERVICE: not inc, card slips closed CARDS: Access, Amex, Visa DETAILS: 125 seats. Private parties: 60 main room. Children's helpings. No cigars/pipes in dining-room. Wheelchair access (1 step). Music. Air-conditioned

Stepping Stone NEW ENTRY map 12

123 Queenstown Road, SW8 3RH COOKING **2**
TEL: 0171-622 0555 FAX: 0171-622 4230 COST £21–£39

The name may suggest a converted pub in the leafy shires, but the reality is an impeccably modish metropolitan eatery on the arterial road through Battersea: a hard-edged pair of rooms, done in vibrant midnight blue and dark caramel, that were formerly the premises of L'Arlequin. Staff wear jeans and the house T-shirt, proceedings are clamorous, but things flow smoothly and the olives are great.

The food is essentially Mediterranean, refracted through a Californian prism, minimising the use of both dairy fat and cliché. Start with a tart of ricotta, yellow tomato and marrow with baby artichoke, or spider crab with mayonnaise, then go on to boiled ox-tongue in hay dressed with hard-boiled egg and capers. When the combinations work, they can be pretty impressive, as in a first course of griddled cuttlefish with spinach and red peppers, the fish 'tender and satisfying', all the ingredients retaining their own characters. Sausages of the day may be chicken embedded with pink Paris mushrooms, enlivened with a giant grilled red chilli. More griddling comes into play for a main-course of 'superbly tasty' scallops with a Chinese dressing, while vegetables include lightly steamed sugar-snaps and green beans tossed in butter and parsley and 'bursting with flavour'. 'First-class' ice-creams made in-house are the mainstay of the dessert list. A 'rich and smooth' ginger version accompanies figs poached in red wine and spices, while pecan pie comes with a scoop of pecan and maple syrup ice. The well-chosen wine list offers an array of contemporary labels at a good range of prices, and shows that life isn't all Chardonnay and Cabernet. A scattering of halves and wines by the glass will cater for all appetites. Prices open at £8.50, and there are five beers from Belgium – and one from Fulham.

CHEFS: Theodore Kyriakov, Laura Greenfield and Bill Groenen PROPRIETORS: Gary and Emer Levy OPEN: Sun to Fri L 12 to 2.30 (3 Sun), Mon to Sat D 7 to 11 MEALS: alc (main courses £7 to £14.50). Set L Mon to Fri £10 (2 courses), Set L Sun £11.50 (2 courses) to £15 SERVICE: not inc; 10% for parties of 6 or more CARDS: Access, Amex, Diners, Visa DETAILS: 56 seats. Private parties: 56 main room. Vegetarian meals. Children's helpings. No smoking in 1 dining-room. Wheelchair access. Music. Air-conditioned

Suntory map 15

72–73 St James's Street, SW1A 1PH COOKING 3*
TEL: 0171-409 0201 FAX: 0171-499 0208 COST £30–£129

Suntory lives and breathes expense-account affluence: its purpose in life is to entertain, feed and cosset the big guns of the Japanese business world. The cost can be frighteningly high, but you are unlikely to come here on the off-chance with money in your own pocket. Every detail is meticulously thought out, every polite gesture has to be paid for – although prices do include service. There is, however, a way to eat here affordably: come for lunch and order one of the daily menus. On Wednesday, £15 will pay for udon noodles in miso soup and prawn tempura in rice ball; on Saturday you will be offered Japanese-style steak and assorted sashimi.

The evening repertoire in the ground-floor dining-room plunges straight into Japanese haute cuisine with all of its ethereal lightness, delicate flavours and eye-opening visual artistry. It says a great deal about the clientele that gyuu-sashimi (sliced raw beef) and grilled foie gras with teriyaki sauce share the billing with maguro yama-kake (raw tuna with grated yam), unagi-kabayaki (broiled eel with sweet soy sauce) and asari sakamushi (steamed clams with saké). One-pot dishes such as shabu-shabu and yose-nabe (cooked in a special ceramic pan) are prepared at the table with assistance from a waitress. Below the main dining-room is a teppanyaki bar where chefs work up a sweat over iron hotplates, grilling chateaubriand with prawns, 'lamb chops monkey's favourite' (with sauté bananas), lobster and other luxury seafood. Order saké or wine with your meal and the bill will rocket skywards. House wine is £14.

CHEF: K. Kato PROPRIETOR: Suntory Ltd OPEN: Mon to Sat 12 to 2, 6 to 10 CLOSED: Christmas and Easter MEALS: alc (main courses £18 to £42). Set L £15 (2 courses) to £35, Set D £49.80 to £68 SERVICE: net prices, card slips closed CARDS: Access, Amex, Delta, Diners, Switch, Visa DETAILS: 120 seats. Private parties: 100 main room, 60 and 70 private rooms. Vegetarian meals. Children's helpings. Smart dress preferred. Wheelchair access. No music. Air-conditioned

Le Suquet

map 14

104 Draycott Avenue, SW3 3AE — COOKING 1*
TEL: 0171-581 1785 FAX: 0171-225 0838 — COST £21–£50

Set up by Pierre Martin in 1976 as a gastronomic outpost of France in a fashionable quarter of London, Le Suquet continues to woo the crowds. The menu hasn't moved on a great deal in 20 years: fresh fish is the name of the game and the repertoire is based on regular deliveries of oysters, clams, mussels, langoustines and other delicacies. This is backed up by classic treatment of skate, turbot, salmon, cod and anything else that the markets can provide. Simplicity generally wins the day: 'The best sole meunière I have eaten!' raved one reporter. The carnivorous contingent is offered the likes of confit of duck, steaks and beef bourguignon. After a shaky patch, the staff seem to have pulled their socks up and service is reckoned to be courteous and friendly. The wine list is short, French and unfussy. House wine is £9.50.

CHEFS: Phillipe Moron and Jean-Yves Darcel PROPRIETOR: Pierre Martin OPEN: Mon to Fri L 12 to 2.30, D 7 to 11.30, Sat and Sun all day 12.30 to 11.30 MEALS: alc (main courses £10 to £15). Set L £12. Cover £1 SERVICE: 15% (optional), card slips closed CARDS: Access, Amex, Delta, Diners, Switch, Visa DETAILS: 70 seats. 6 tables outside. Private parties: 16 main room, 16 private room. Children welcome. Smart dress preferred. Music. Air-conditioned

Surinder's

map 13

109 Westbourne Park Road, W2 5QL — COOKING 1
TEL: 0171-229 8968 — COST £21–£26

Dedicated followers of fashion may think that old-school French cooking has had its day, but there are still devotees who will travel some distance (from Belfast in one case) to join locals in this likeable neighbourhood bistro. They come for 'ample' helpings of estouffade de boeuf, calf's liver normande, Barbary duck with cherries, saddle of lamb with tarragon, and sole dieppoise. Surinder makes regular trips to London's wholesale markets for supplies and his handwritten fixed-price menu with a choice of six starters and main courses is remarkable value. The mainly French wine list is also good value, with a few higher-priced bottles included for those special-occasion meals. House wine is £8.95.

CHEF/PROPRIETOR: Surinder Chandwan OPEN: Tue to Sat D only 7 to 11 CLOSED: Aug MEALS: Set D £14.95 SERVICE: 10%, card slips closed CARDS: Access, Amex, Visa DETAILS: 45 seats. Private parties: 45 main room. Children's helpings. Smart dress preferred. Wheelchair access (2 steps). No music

Tabac

NEW ENTRY map 13

46 Golborne Road, W10 5PR — COOKING 2
TEL/FAX: 0181-960 2433 — COST £19–£39

'This little patch of W10 is the epitome of cool today,' comments a former Notting Hill Billy. Golborne Road, she adds, is 'all very '90s' and Tabac fits in perfectly. The frontage is lavender-blue, the interior looks adequately stark and yet adequately vibrant with much bare wood and a minimal amount of decoration.

Food here is in keeping; the tone is fiercely modern and the menu hops around the world picking up a legume here, a salsa there. Which isn't surprising when you realise that Pip Wylie learned her craft in the kitchens of the First Floor and the River Café (see entries, London).

Italy is emblazoned everywhere, although some have also detected a Mexican wave in the background. The bread basket is 'a treasure trove' full of the kind of stuff that you could happily munch all night. Courgette soup with a zingy dose of fresh ginger is spot-on in texture and a splendid shade of green. Colour is also what distinguishes ceviche of scallops (apart from the stunning freshness of the molluscs themselves), while vegetarian enchilladas lurk amid a jungle of 'dangerous-looking spiky leaves (dandelion?)' and 'heat-blasted' cherry tomatoes. Carnivorous main courses keep up the momentum: brilliantly timed grilled fillet of beef with a sweet potato gratin; salmon baked in sea salt with broad beans, peas and aïoli; roast lamb shank with garlic mash and gremolata, for example. After the devastating news that chocolate mousse cake was off the menu, one couple sought solace in summer pudding, although they might have opted for passion fruit brûlée or ice-cream with tamarillos. Service throughout is well-intentioned and fairly clued-up. The wine list journeys to some obscure destinations, but the choice is varied and prices are not prohibitive; cocktails and imported beers form the back-up. House wine is £8.95.

CHEF: Pip Wylie PROPRIETORS: Bennie Neville and Pip Wylie OPEN: Tue to Sun L 11 to 3.45, all week D 7.30 to 11 CLOSED: 24 and 25 Dec MEALS: alc (main courses £4.50 to £12) SERVICE: not inc CARDS: Access, Amex, Diners, Visa DETAILS: 80 seats. Private parties: 40 main room. Vegetarian meals. Children's helpings. Smart dress preferred. Music. Air-conditioned

Tamarind

NEW ENTRY map 15

20 Queen Street, W1X 7PS — COOKING **2**
TEL: 0171-629 3561 FAX: 0171-499 5034 — COST £26–£47

Those with long memories may recall that this Mayfair site once housed Tiberio, a venue much frequented by Frank Sinatra and his pack during the 1960s. How things change. Tamarind is a worldly-wise, jet-setting Indian restaurant, about as far removed from a balti café as you can get. Emily Todhunter (darling of restaurant designers) has turned this basement into a chic dining-room that oozes sumptuous charm, modish tranquillity and deliberate artiness. The colour schemes are sandy-golden, with shades of brown on the bare-boarded floor, mighty gilded columns, curving wrought-iron chairs and panel displays of saris. A tamarind 'seed-pod' motif runs through everything. As if to emphasise the internationalism of the whole set-up, the staff seem to be keen on mixing groovy cocktails.

By contrast, chef Atul Kochhar was brought in direct from Delhi, and his cooking is currently making people sit up and take notice. He has constructed a grade-one North Indian menu that makes much of the output from two giant tandoori ovens (you can watch the action through glass screens). Free-range chickens, lamb, quails, chunks of paneer and vegetables are all subjected to impeccable treatment. What lifts Tamarind above most of the current competition is the accuracy of the spicing, not to mention the quality of the raw materials. There may be suggestions of cumulative richness, but portions are restrained and there's seldom any feeling of being 'over-stuffed'. Examples from one meal included shakarkand ki chaat (roasted sweet potatoes zinged up with ginger), and an assertively spiced dish of pan-fried chicken livers. From the list of curries, try murgh shajehani (chicken breasts in a golden saffron sauce) or a spot-on version of that much-abused Kashmiri classic, rogan josh. Vegetables and pulses maintain the balance between clarity and earthy richness: bhindis are caringly handled, aubergines are wonderfully smoky, while dahl bukhari (black lentils) is all about pungent intensity. Breads play a starring role (roti laced with chilli, paratha with fenugreek, for example), and basmati rice is up to scratch. Prices are steep, even by Mayfair standards, but Tamarind also offers a brilliant-value set-lunch menu that is far from wallet-stretching. Salted lassi and Cobra beer are alternatives to the showy wine list. House wines start at £9.50.

CHEF: Atul Kochhar PROPRIETOR: Indian Cuisine Ltd OPEN: Mon to Fri L 12 to 3, all week D 6 to 11.30 CLOSED: 25 to 30 Dec MEALS: alc (main courses £5.50 to £18). Set L £13.50 (2 courses) SERVICE: 12.5% CARDS: Access, Amex, Diners, Switch, Visa DETAILS: 90 seats. Private parties: 90 main room. Vegetarian meals. Children's helpings. Smart dress preferred. Music. Air-conditioned

La Tante Claire 🍷

map 14

68 Royal Hospital Road, SW3 4HP
TEL: 0171-352 6045 and 351 0227 COOKING 5
FAX: 0171-352 3257 COST £32–£101

The scale of Tante Claire appeals. It is a single room, light and fresh, with mirrors, pastelly pictures in solid glass frames, and coloured chair covers to suit the mood. This is no adjunct to a hotel, but a single-minded venture, the vision of one man who has cooked here for nearly 20 years – and after all this time he remains at the stove, in charge of everything – producing top-class French cooking with a bias to his native Gascony. Foie gras and truffles take their place alongside such 'humble' items as the famous pig's trotter, a dish that has inspired many imitative tributes from chefs up and down the country. Even the foie gras, simple enough to sauté perhaps, might arrive on a potato 'galette' that deserves a prize for being made from the thinnest strands of potato imaginable, 'yet they still had taste and texture: remarkable!'

'No superlative can describe how good it is,' enthused one reporter, who felt that at £26 for lunch he was robbed. Not the reporter – Pierre Koffmann. One such lunch opened with an escabèche of red mullet: two fillets 'reeking of the sea and fennel', on a bed of thin pasta strips. Around it were carrot slices and bits of tomato, with blobs of coriander leaf purée and an occasional coriander seed. 'The whole thing was a gloriously heady dish in which all the flavours were intense.' A fillet of salmon followed, just cooked, on a bed of choucroute, with a couple of pieces of smoked bacon that partnered the fish amazingly well. Finally a tarte truffée au chocolat that was 'rich yet light, dark, and not too sweet'. Mineral water is part of the set lunch package, and service is included, as it is on all the menus.

The repertoire extends beyond south-west France, to Provence for a layered terrine of pepper and aubergine with artichoke, held together with a tasty jelly, and further afield for a roast fillet of lamb cooked shepherd's-pie style, and one wrapped in couscous and a cabbage leaf: steamed pink, and sliced open to reveal 'delightful flavours of saffron in the couscous, excellent lamb, and just a dribble of jus to add moisture'. Few restaurants escape criticism entirely. One reporter was disappointed by over-salting and 'unexceptional' vegetables, while another who has had 'splendid meals here in the past' felt let down by 'tasteless duck and lamb'. And in true French fashion, smoking is permitted. But in general Tante Claire offers an unbeatable standard of French cooking, right down to the simplest pudding. 'In the City, an option without any added features is called a plain vanilla. Obviously not many people have tasted Tante Claire's vanilla ice-cream of indescribable richness.' Friendly courtesy is a hallmark of the service. Classy French wines are naturally the order of the day, but lesser regions, including the south-west, offer more chance for modest spenders. Half-bottles are generous, and the wine waiter knows his stuff. House Ch. de Lastours from Corbières at £17.80, and Domaine de Villeroy-Castellas Sauvignon Blanc at £12, are good.

CHEF/PROPRIETOR: Pierre Koffmann OPEN: Mon to Fri 12.30 to 2, 7 to 11 MEALS: alc (main courses £24.50 to £35). Set L £26. Minimum £45 D SERVICE: net prices CARDS: Access, Amex, Delta, Diners, Visa DETAILS: 43 seats. Private parties: 48 main room. Children's helpings. Jacket and tie. No pipes in dining-room. Wheelchair access (1 step; also WC). No music. Air-conditioned

Tate Gallery Restaurant NEW ENTRY map 13

Millbank, SW1P 4RG COOKING 1
TEL: 0171-887 8877 FAX: 0171-887 8902 COST £26–£45

'Rites of Passage' was the name of an important exhibition at the Tate in summer '95, and it might well have been applied to the restaurant over the years. Once so English that it pursued a fondness for Elizabethan recipes for a time, it has now opened the door to the wider world, to let in, for example, roasted vegetables in a lime dressing with couscous. Rex Whistler's serene half-length mural has witnessed the gradual evolution, as has Michael Driver, who has been responsible for the cooking since 1978.

The style is still undoubtedly English. Asparagus and quail's eggs are unified by a competent herb dressing incorporating balsamic vinegar, poached salmon trout is served cold as a main course, while well-roasted leg of lamb, aromatic with garlic and rosemary, comes with honest-to-goodness gravy. Fish receives more adventurous treatment: chilled salmon soup, or a warm skate salad with soy vinaigrette and rösti potatoes, for example. A thin apple tart with cinnamon ice-cream had nicely risen puff, but would have been better served warm. Otherwise, there is chocolate truffle torte or a selection of Neal's Yard cheeses. Whatever else has changed, 'the cosseting service thankfully remains'. The wine list was once a monument. While no longer so extensive, it retains a core of French classics, many of them fully mature, at prices that will induce a contented glow. House French is £11.50. A good collection of malt whiskies is also kept.

CHEF: Michael Driver PROPRIETOR: Trustees of the Tate Gallery OPEN: Mon to Sat L only 12 to 3 CLOSED: 24 to 26 Dec, 1 Jan, Good Friday, May Day bank hol MEALS: alc (main courses £7 to £16). Set L £13.50 (2 courses) to £16.50. Minimum £6.95 SERVICE: not inc, card slips closed CARDS: Access, Delta, Switch, Visa DETAILS: 102 seats. Private parties: 30 main room. Vegetarian meals. Children's helpings. No-smoking areas. Wheelchair access (also WC). No music. Air-conditioned

Tatsuso

map 13

32 Broadgate Circle, EC2M 2QS — COOKING 3
TEL: 0171-638 5863 FAX: 0171-638 5864 — COST £33–£108

Tatsuso is a Japanese restaurant that functions, quite literally, on two levels. Go through the door and you are immediately in a spacious room devoted to the dramatic pleasures of teppanyaki – the process of grilling and barbecuing meat and fish in full view of customers. Below stairs is the main restaurant, where diners can explore the complex artistry of wasoku (traditional Japanese cuisine). The setting is dominated by a great variety of woods of differing shades, contrasting with the off-white walls and occasional flourishes of black and gold panelling. Service is formal, but pleasant with it. The *carte* is a long, complex affair, and there are also daily specials, which are generally recited on demand, plus a variety of set-price meals. What impresses is not only the delicacy and refinement of the cooking, and the freshness of the ingredients, but also the presentation, which is immaculate without resorting to ostentatious carving or superfluous garnishes. Sashimi is state-of-the-art stuff: up to eight different species of fish, perfectly chilled and gilded simply with three whole shizo leaves. Appetisers, such as squid with sea urchin paste, are dazzling, and the menu also feature sunomono salads, grilled and braised dishes, tempura, and deep-fried specialities such as bora nebuka-age (grey mullet with leeks) plus one-pot meals. Rice, pickles and other essentials are exemplary and sweets are reckoned to be some of the best of their kind in London. All of this comes at a price, but you can get an affordable taste of the whole experience by going for one of the cheaper set menus. House wine is £13.50.

CHEFS: Mr Maehara and Mr Yamana PROPRIETOR: Terriibroadgate Ltd OPEN: Mon to Fri 11.30 to 2.30, 6.30 to 9.45 CLOSED: bank hols MEALS: alc (main courses £8.50 to £31). Set L £23 to £75, Set D £21 to £75. Minimum £15 L, £25 D SERVICE: 13% CARDS: Access, Amex, Diners, Switch, Visa DETAILS: 130 seats. Private parties: 60 main room, 6 and 8 private rooms. Vegetarian meals. Children's helpings. Smart dress preferred. Music. Air-conditioned

Thai Garden £

map 12

249 Globe Road, E2 0JD — COOKING 2
TEL: 0181-981 5748 — COST £17–£32

The surprising smartness and gentrification of this East End street reminded one visitor of the King's Road beamed across to Bethnal Green: the black frontage of the Thai Garden sits well among its neighbours. Beyond the door is a neat, functional dining-room with a wooden floor, bentwood chairs around well-spaced tables, and walls decorated with colour photographs of fruit and vegetables.

The menu eschews meat and poultry in favour of a 60-strong line-up of fish and vegetarian dishes. Ingredients are fresh and ideas are intriguing, although there seems to be a preponderance of prawns and pomfret among the seafood and a surfeit of mushrooms for vegetarians. Even so, this is high-quality, authentic Thai cooking. Soups – always a benchmark – show a near-perfect balance of spicing, flavours and textures: tom khar (cauliflower with coconut and galanga) has been outstanding, while po taek includes a brilliantly fresh assortment of crab claws, squid and other fishy items. Som tum salad hides a remarkably subtle tinge of raw papaya, satays are up to the mark, while gaeng som is a light, sour curry packed with prawns, French beans and other crisp titbits. The kitchen also succeeds when it sets out to imitate meat classics, as in pahd woon sen (a meatless version of fried vermicelli noodles with a 'gently chilli-hot' assortment of eggs, mushrooms and vegetables). Rice is perfectly fragrant, and grainy-textured Thai custard makes a refreshing finale. The fixed-price lunch menu (also served until 7.30 in the evening) is an affordable trip through the full works. Singha Thai beer and jasmine tea are the preferred accompaniments, but a handful of workaday wines is also on offer, with house wine at £6.50.

CHEF: Naphaphorn Duff PROPRIETORS: Suthinee and Jack Hufton OPEN: Mon to Fri L 12 to 2.45, Mon to Sat D 6 to 10.45 CLOSED: bank hols MEALS: alc (main courses £4.50 to £7). Set L £7.50, Set D (before 7.30pm) £7.50 (2 courses) to £21 SERVICE: 10%, card slips closed CARDS: Access, Delta, Visa DETAILS: 32 seats. Private parties: 20 main room, 14 private room. Vegetarian meals. Children's helpings. No smoking in 1 dining-room. Wheelchair access (1 step). Music

Thailand

map 12

15 Lewisham Way, SE14 6PP — COOKING 2
TEL: 0181-691 4040 — COST £20–£44

Kamkhong Cambungoet (now Mrs Herman) was brought up in the northern Thai village of Ban Kwao, but these days she can be found in the kitchen of this extraordinary little restaurant in one of the 'seediest parts of London'. If you are looking for cool serenity, waitresses in full costume and an atmosphere of ethnic exoticism, this is not the place for you. Some reporters are put off by the weird décor (a map of South-east Asia set in the ceiling, a platinum disc on one wall), the all-pervasive smokiness of the place and young children disrupting any semblance of calm.

People make the trek because the food is something special. The menu, which runs to some 90 dishes, is spelled out in clear, plain English with no tricky Thai names to get your tongue round. The result, according to those who know, is fearsomely good food, full of incendiary heat when it needs to be, but subtly soothing at other times. Soups, such as hot-and-sour prawn with lemon grass, bergamot and galanga, are reckoned to be first-rate, and one reporter waxed ecstatic about a dish piled high with 'wonderful' mussels in a thick curry sauce imbued with powerful ginger, mint and spring onion. Prawn fried rice has been beautifully fragrant. On the down side, there have been niggles about fish curry ('every single mouthful contained several bones'), and stir-fried broccoli drenched in a cloying glutinous sauce. The section devoted to Laotian specialities is well worth exploring: try hot-and-sour green papaya with chilli and fish sauce, or chargrilled steak with lime juice and pounded toasted rice and herbs, for example. Desserts include some bizarre curiosities: black sticky sweet rice with coconut, black beans and sweet potato sounds strangest of all. To drink there is Singapore Tiger beer as well as a short list of affordable wines, with house Sicilian at £8.50.

The Guide *always appreciates hearing about changes of chef or owner.*

CHEF/PROPRIETOR: Mrs G. Herman OPEN: Tue to Sat D only 6 to 10.30 CLOSED: 25 Dec, 1 Jan MEALS: alc (main courses £6 to £11). Set D £25 SERVICE: not inc, card slips closed CARDS: Access, Amex, Visa DETAILS: 25 seats. Private parties: 25 main room. Vegetarian meals. Children welcome. Music. Air-conditioned

Tokyo Diner ✱ £

map 15

2 Newport Place, WC2H 7JJ — COOKING 1

TEL: 0171-287 8777 FAX: 0171-434 1415 — COST £7–£17

The Japanese have a phrase for cafés like this: they call them 'o-shokuji-dokoro', or 'fixed-meal places'. Englishman Richard Hills reckoned that he could introduce Londoners to this idea, so he converted a launderette on a Chinatown street corner, fitted it out with wooden benches, stools and cheery paper lanterns and tried to make the whole experience as much fun as possible. He knew exactly what he had to do: keep prices down, strip off the veneer of cultural formality and go for authenticity while avoiding any 'rude shocks for the Western palate'. The result is high-quality fast food (ideal for the location, close to theatreland), no bookings, and payment by cash only.

Dominating the menu is a choice of bento meals assembled in elegant lacquered boxes with square compartments containing rice (cooked in filtered water), noodles with prawns, sashimi and potato salad, plus the centrepiece component – salmon teriyaki, braised beef with ginger, or a mixed fry of fish and chicken in a light, crispy batter, for example. This is also one of the few outlets where you can sample the novelty of Japanese curry, a curiously mild dish that is accompanied by fukujinzuke (bright red pickled radish). If you want fish and finger food, there is also a sushi bar at one end of the diner. Tea comes free, or go for Kirin beer or saké; house wine is £6.50.

CHEF: Sueharu Hamaue PROPRIETOR: Richard Hills OPEN: all week noon to midnight MEALS: Set L and D £3.45 to £11.90 SERVICE: none CARDS: none DETAILS: 75 seats. Vegetarian meals. Children welcome. No smoking in 1 dining-room. Wheelchair access. Music. Air-conditioned

La Truffe Noire

map 13

29 Tooley Street, SE1 2QF — COOKING 2

TEL: 0171-378 0621 FAX: 0171-403 0689 — COST £26–£74

Tooley Street is not one of London's more beguiling thoroughfares, although the area is being continually re-developed and improved with buildings such as the Hays Galleria – and there is always the London Dungeon. Across the road, La Truffe Noire is on two floors in a Grade II listed building. The natural constituency of this classy French restaurant has always been the City, and it has had to adapt to the effects of what the owners call 'management downsizing' (redundancies among the dealers) on its pace of business. As a result, it has opened the High Note jazz bar in the basement which provides 'bittersweet jazz and blues to take [dealers'] minds off the markets' on Thursday and Friday evenings. At other times one-course meals, with a glass of wine thrown in, are available for under £10.

For those not quite so constrained, the *carte* in the main restaurant still offers an extensive choice of imaginative French cooking seasoned with lively oriental influences. Reporters all agree that Philippe Roth knows how to deliver flavours: plaudits are received particularly for 'delightfully light' grilled foie gras with ginger and orange, game terrine with shallot marmalade, and Thai king prawns with spicy noodles. Meats are sensitively cooked, as in duck breast with apple and calvados, or sauté quails stuffed with pancetta and sage, accompanied by grilled aubergine and walnuts. Standards are kept high with desserts such as pear sable with acacia honey and passion-fruit soufflé, and the French cheeses are properly looked after. Service is helpful and amiable. The wine list is mainly typical French offerings and prices have been kept down by including fewer older bottles, with New World representatives at appealing prices. A good selection of bottled beers from around the world is also available. House French is £8.

CHEF: Philippe Roth PROPRIETORS: Mr and Mrs M. Alam-Ahmed OPEN: Mon to Fri 12 to 2.30, 7 to 10.30 CLOSED: 23 Dec to 2 Jan MEALS: alc (main courses £10 to £25). Set L and D £13 (2 courses) to £17 SERVICE: 12½%, card slips closed CARDS: Access, Amex, Delta, Diners, Switch, Visa DETAILS: 45 seats. 10 tables outside. Private parties: 50 main room, 15 to 45 private rooms. Vegetarian meals. Children welcome. Smart dress preferred. No cigars/pipes in dining-room. Wheelchair access (1 step) restaurant only. Music. Air-conditioned

Turner's

BARGAIN 1996 LUNCH

map 14

87–89 Walton Street, SW3 2HP — COOKING 4

TEL: 0171-584 6711 FAX: 0171-584 4441 — COST £26–£55

A relaxed atmosphere, attractive menu and the ability to deliver high-quality food consistently combine to make Turner's a favourite of many reporters. It is not, at first glance, the most likely candidate. Culinary fireworks are few, and this is not cutting-edge cuisine. But it is satisfying and well turned out, in an atmosphere that is 'peaceful, tranquil, civilised and comfortable'. The blue and yellow colour scheme is all-pervasive, but not oppressive. 'It gives a warm and welcoming feel.' The prints on the wall are of paintings by a different Turner.

The menu offers a goodly number of options, including two, three, or (at dinner) four courses for a fixed price, as well as a more extensive menu at £32 for two courses. If that sounds a lot of money, remember that service is included, and that lunch remains one of London's great bargains: three courses of exceptionally good food 'for little more than you might pay at a motorway service station'. This is a 'must' for anybody reeling from London prices in general. Although first courses can sound predictable (smoked salmon, salade niçoise, chicken liver pâté with foie gras), ingredients are immpeccable and carefully judged.

The foundation is 'high-quality animal protein which avoids exotica', such as roast rack of English lamb, or prime rib of grilled beef with a bone marrow and garlic sauce. Reporters have enjoyed a slab of beef 'of flawless quality', cooked rare and served on a bed of thinly sliced potato, sitting on a reduction of the cooking juices with red wine, and a brill steak with a simple tomato and herb crust on a bed of spinach in a butter-based dill-flavoured sauce. Bread is good, but cheese is only a modest plated selection. Complaints are few and far between, with slow service taking most of the flak. Brian Turner may or may not put in an appearance, but in general staff are courteous, efficient and good at 'not getting in the way'.

A choice of ten puddings (on the expensive menu) is generous by any standards, and the assiette, which changes daily, is 'a complex affair involving five desserts and three pools of sauce'. Pastries, parfaits, mousses and chocolate desserts are all of a standard, with special mention for a fluffy ginger sponge with gooey caramel sauce. Wines are very French and very good, but not cheap, although it is worth remembering that wine prices also include service. House wine is £13.50, or £4 a glass.

CHEFS: Brian Turner and Jonathan Bibbings PROPRIETOR: Brian Turner OPEN: Sun to Fri L 12.30 to 2.30, all week D 7.30 to 11.15 (Sun 10) CLOSED: 1 week Christmas, bank hols MEALS: Set L £9.95 (2 courses) to £13.50, Set L Sun £19.50, Set D £23.50 (2 courses) to £26.50 SERVICE: net prices, card slips closed CARDS: Access, Amex, Delta, Diners, Switch, Visa DETAILS: 52 seats. Private parties: 50 main room. Children's helpings. Smart dress preferred. Wheelchair access (2 steps). Music. Air-conditioned

Two Brothers £ map 12

297–303 Regents Park Road, N3 1DP COOKING 1*
TEL: 0181-346 0469 COST £17–£35

Brothers Leon and Tony Manzi are the front men at this brightly lit, smart fish and chip shop in a parade on Regents Park Road. We are 'not yer avridge chippy!' writes Tony. The tables are bare and the interior is more café than restaurant, but the service remains very welcoming and efficient. The major plus-points here are the daily supplies of fish from Billingsgate, Peterhead and Newlyn, backed up by oysters and mussels air-freighted from Ireland; chips are Maris Piper potatoes cooked in groundnut oil, vinegar is the real thing (not 'non-brewed condiment'), and the brothers make their own tartare sauce. The result is fish and chips out of the top drawer, whether it be 'really excellent' haddock, skate, plaice on the bone or lemon sole. If you want your fish cooked in matzo meal, you have only to ask and pay an extra 50p. Starters and sweets have not always met with such enthusiasm, but the wine list more than makes amends: it is a 'surprisingly good', well-annotated selection with some creditable stuff from the New World, as well as the Loire and elsewhere. House wine is £8.85.

CHEFS/PROPRIETORS: Leon and Tony Manzi OPEN: Tue to Sat 12 to 2.30, 5.30 to 10.15 CLOSED: bank hols (exc Good Friday), last 2 weeks Aug MEALS: alc (main courses £6 to £14) SERVICE: not inc, card slips closed CARDS: Access, Amex, Switch, Visa DETAILS: 90 seats. Children's helpings. No babies or pushchairs after 6.30pm. No smoking in 1 dining-room

Union Café NEW ENTRY map 15

96 Marylebone Lane, W1M 5FP COOKING 2
TEL: 0171-486 4860 COST £25–£44

The large, bright, open room is a hop, skip and a jump from Oxford Street. With the kitchen in full view, and with light wood, plain white walls, lots of window and bare, well-spaced tables, it has a fresh, clean feel. 'I like the look of the place,' wrote one who exempted the green paint from this acclamation. It conveys the strong feeling that there are no tricks up anybody's sleeve, and serves plain, straightforward, what-you-see-is-what-you-get sort of food: sea bass with vegetables and aïoli, smoked haddock with spinach and hollandaise, or pizza. Although not a café to drop into for a quick bite (the pace is unhurried), there are simple plates of cold meats or cheese with good olives and bread (focaccia and sour-dough are made in-house) to satisfy one-dish appetites.

Simplicity and freshness are the key, which is not to say skill is not involved. Quite the reverse. Knowing what to buy, and when to stop fiddling with it, produces first-class soups (including mushroom with soured cream, paprika and dill), grilled corn-fed chicken breast with spring onions and carrots, and a dessert of crisp pears on thin, crumbly shortcrust pastry, set in a moist, almond frangipane. The Itali-fornian food may be café-like, but the care and attention are more restaurant-like. This is casual, everyday food produced with a sense of purpose. Espresso is good, although a double is still tiny and refills add to the bill. A dozen wines from £9 (half of them by the glass) are backed up by Wyken cider, Black Sheep ale, and thick fruit-based 'smoothies'.

CHEFS/PROPRIETORS: Caroline Brett and Sam Russell OPEN: Mon to Fri 12.30 to 10pm, plus breakfast 10am to noon CLOSED: 2 weeks Christmas, last 3 weeks Aug MEALS: alc (main courses £8.50 to £12). Minimum £10 12.30 to 2, 7.30 to 10 SERVICE: not inc for bills less than £80, 12½% for bills over £80, card slips closed CARDS: Access, Delta, Switch, Visa DETAILS: 60 seats. Private parties: 60 main room. Vegetarian meals. Children welcome. Wheelchair access. No music

Upper Street Fish Shop £

map 13

324 Upper Street, N1 2XQ
TEL: 0171-359 1401

COOKING 1
COST £12–£25

Islington locals regularly descend on Alan and Olga Conway's auspicious chippie after watching the 'flicks' at the Screen on the Green across the road. Others make the trek from much farther away: 'They were amazed we had come all the way from Beaconsfield,' reported one couple who thought the place was 'wonderful – just like Yorkshire'. It is unpretentious, it often gets cramped and the queues are never-ending, but no one seems to mind and the owners provide free plates of chips while you are waiting for a table. Fish soup, smoked salmon pâté and ice-cream are made on the premises to well-tried family recipes: the rest is fish every which way (deep-fried, grilled, poached, baked), backed up by chips, mushy peas and pots of tea, and rounded off with old-fashioned English puds. The café is unlicensed, but the Conways have been operating a successful bring-your-own policy (no corkage) for more than 15 years.

CHEF: Stuart Gamble PROPRIETORS: Alan and Olga Conway OPEN: Tue to Sat L 12 to 2 (3 Sat), Mon to Sat D 5.30 to 10 CLOSED: bank hols MEALS: alc (main courses £6 to £9.50). Minimum £6. Unlicensed but bring your own (no corkage) SERVICE: not inc CARDS: none DETAILS: 50 seats. Children's helpings. Wheelchair access. No music. Air-conditioned

£ *indicates that it is possible to have a three-course meal, including coffee, a half-bottle of house wine and service, at any time the restaurant is open (i.e. at dinner as well as at lunch, unless a place is open only for dinner), for £20 or less per person.*

Vegetarian Cottage ✱ £

map 13

91 Haverstock Hill, NW3 4RL
COOKING 1
TEL: 0171-586 1257
COST £13–£23

The décor of this useful local restaurant – between Campden and Hampstead – is a smart, modish mixture of bright lights, tall black chairs and oriental artwork on otherwise bare walls, but what makes the place interesting is its food. The Cottage is one of the few establishments almost wholly devoted to the vegetarian aspect of Chinese cuisine, although the menu also offers a clutch of seafood dishes. Starters tend to be in the deep-fried mould of wun-tun, spring rolls and sliced yam rolls, while main courses are generally based on bean curd, vegetables and fungi. Black moss is paired with braised Chinese mushrooms or used as a 'Buddha's cushion' for mixed vegetables; all kinds of vegetables and nuts are served in a crispy potato basket or wrapped in lotus leaves; wheat gluten is stir-fried with chilli and black-bean sauce. On the fish side, reporters have enjoyed crab and sweetcorn soup, and steamed scallops served in the shell with a spicy sauce laced with ginger. Rice and noodles are adequately handled. Australian house wine is £6.80.

CHEF: C.K. Wong PROPRIETORS: Y.K. Tsui and S.W. Chu OPEN: Sun L 12 to 3, all week D 6 to 11.15 MEALS: alc (main courses £4.50 to £15). Set L Sun £8, Set D £11.80 to £13.50. Minimum £8 SERVICE: not inc CARDS: Access, Visa DETAILS: 60 seats. Private parties: 30 main room, 20 private room. Vegetarian meals. Children welcome. Smart dress preferred. No smoking in 1 dining-room. Music. Air-conditioned

Villandry Dining Room ✱

map 15

89 Marylebone High Street, W1M 3DE
TEL: 0171-224 3799 and 487 3816
COOKING 1
FAX: 0171-486 1370
COST £24–£47

Business is brisk, service is frantic and you sit at little tables elbow to elbow with everyone else, but no one seems to mind. It is all fast, furious fun. The 'Dining Room' is part and parcel of a first-rate deli, and the sight and aroma of pungent cheeses, hams and sausages are enough to whet most people's appetites. You can come here for breakfast and the place opens for dinner one evening each month, but lunch is what the Carrarinis' set-up is all about. The menu is short, changes daily, and many dishes run out quickly, so arrive early for the best choice – as well as the best seats. Plates of charcuterie, crudités and Irish smoked salmon are fixtures, soup might be potato and herb with parsley pesto, and there are main-course sized salads (warm new potatoes with roasted tomato, Morteau sausage and a thick grain mustard vinaigrette, for example). Another choice might be fillet of brill with balsamic vinegar sauce, Parmesan-breaded lamb chops with potato and courgette gratin, or a mixed grill. Cheese is a sound way of rounding things off; otherwise opt for tarte Tatin, a fruit compote or crème fraîche ice-cream. The monthly-changing wine list is dictated by supplies from Legrand of Paris; also look for the range of imported bottled beers. House wine is £10.90.

CHEF: Rosalind Carrarini PROPRIETORS: Jean-Charles and Rosalind Carrarini OPEN: Mon to Sat L only 12.30 to 2.30 MEALS: alc (main courses £7 to £10) SERVICE: not inc, card slips closed CARDS: Access, Amex, Switch, Visa DETAILS: 50 seats. Private parties: 40 main room. Vegetarian meals. Children's helpings. No smoking in dining-room. Wheelchair access. No music. Air-conditioned

Wagamama £

map 15

4 Streatham Street, WC1A 1JB — COOKING 1
TEL: 0171-580 9365 FAX: 0171-323 9224 — COST £13–£27

Japanese socio-cultural correctness dictates that this is 'a non-destination food station', as the notes to the menu explain, although most of us would call it a fast-food noodle bar. There are no bookings, queues generally spill out on to the street, and you are not encouraged to take your time: 'Good value and lingering over meals are, unfortunately, not compatible,' claims the management. The ideology of Wagamama is a bizarre mix of high-tech and squeaky-clean environmentalism: orders are handled by means of electronic pads, smoking is banned, chopsticks are made from disposable bamboo ('a fast-growing, readily renewable resource'). To satisfy the demands of 'positive eating and positive living' the menu is high on the 'raw energy' derived from noodles, salads and rice. There are no starters, although side dishes can be treated as such, and no desserts. Flavours are varied, although Japanese authenticity has been coloured by influences from China and South-east Asia. Ramen noodle soups are topped with heaps of chicken, seafood, or steak and mixed with greens and seaweed and spiked with chilli oil. Soba noodles are pan-fried with shiitake mushrooms, bean sprouts, fish-cake, tofu and all manner of titbits. The main accompaniments are little dishes of such things as gyoza (grilled chicken dumplings) and edamame (salted soya beans in their pods). Service is multi-ethnic, 'brisk but not brusque'. The drinks list tells its own tale: free green tea, 'body-cleansing' juices, calpico (Japanese yoghurt) and 'revitalising' herbal Amé for the health-conscious; saké, plum wine with soda and ice, and some organic wines for the drinkers. House wine is £6.90. As we went to press we learned that a second branch is due to open at 12–26 Lexington Street, W1R 3HS, in December 1995: reports, please.

CHEF: Ayumi Meada PROPRIETOR: Wagamama Ltd OPEN: all week 12 (12.30 Sat and Sun) to 11 (10 Sun) CLOSED: 25 Dec to 2 Jan MEALS: alc (main courses £4 to £6). Set L £5.80 to £6.80 (2 courses), Set D £5.80 to £6.80 (2 courses) SERVICE: not inc CARDS: Delta, Switch DETAILS: 104 seats. Private parties: 104 main room. Vegetarian meals. Children welcome. No smoking in dining-room. No music. Air-conditioned

Waltons

map 14

121 Walton Street, SW3 2HP — COOKING 2
TEL: 0171-584 0204 FAX: 0171-581 2848 — COST £22–£66

Waltons exists in a cocooned world all of its own. Printed curtains are tightly drawn against the hubbub, no hint of daylight is permitted, and arriving here is rather like entering a hermetically sealed capsule. Despite the positive gaudiness of the décor, the mood might be described as dignified and discreet – a predominantly male domain that is ideally suited to corporate entertaining. Mock Louis XV chairs are grouped around luxuriously laid tables where bowls sit upon plates, plates upon larger plates, and larger plates on stainless steel salvers. What you get is 'grand service for a non-grand price and old-fashioned good manners', in the words of one who highly recommended the fixed-price lunch (the best deal in the place).

John Coxon has been elevated to the position of head chef, but little else changes. The cooking has conservative English nuances, but the proliferation of truffles, caviare and foie gras suggests that it still courts the old world of haute cuisine. However, the presence of sun-drenched Mediterranean ideas – roasted artichoke and grilled pepper salad with balsamic dressing, pan-fried scallops with black tagliatelle and saffron sauce, and calf's liver with pancetta – makes the whole set-up even more difficult to pigeonhole. Meals tend to finish in safe territory, with raspberry mille-feuille, hot plum and almond tart or Grand Marnier crème brûlée. Cheese is true-blue Stilton. The wine list is voluminous and presented with reverence, each page separated with a sheet of tissue paper as if part of a rare printing. France steals the limelight (although the New World, Italy and Spain have their say in passing), and mark-ups are not unreasonable. House wine is £9.50.

CHEFS: Paul Hodgson and John Coxon PROPRIETOR: Roger Wren OPEN: all week 12.30 to 2.30 (2 Suns and bank hols), 7.30 to 11.30 (7.00 to 10.00 Sun and bank hols) CLOSED: L 25 Dec, 26 Dec MEALS: alc (main courses £10.50 to £20). Set L Mon to Sat £14.75, Set L Sun £18.75, Set D Mon to Sat after 10pm £21 (2 courses) SERVICE: not inc CARDS: Access, Amex, Delta, Diners, Switch, Visa DETAILS: 90 seats. Private parties: 45 main room, 6 to 20 private rooms. Vegetarian meals. Children's helpings. No music. Air-conditioned

Wilsons

NEW ENTRY map 12

236 Blythe Road, W14 0HJ — COOKING 1
TEL: 0171-603 7267 — COST £22–£34

If you hear bagpipes in Shepherds Bush, the chances are that the drone is emanating from Wilsons, a charming little restaurant not far from Brook Green. Tablecloths are clannish tartans of many colours ('frugally cut, so anyone wearing a kilt would have to sit discreetly', noted a reporter from Wales), while stags' horns and a shelf of rare malt whiskies help to reinforce the Highland image. The place is, not surprisingly, run by two Scots: eponymous Bob Wilson takes care of the drinks, his partner cooks. The menu is short and modern British with a few oriental leanings. The Celtic tendency doesn't extend much further than haggis with mash and swede, salmon fish-cakes and Finnan haddock pudding ('a compressed kedgeree'), but there is plenty of enthusiasm here, if not dazzling panache. A giant grilled mushroom is filled with spinach and mozzarella, and plump duck sausages sit on sauerkraut with a 'rustic-looking' juniper sauce. Chocolate mousse is a rich 'Aero-like' dessert, and lemon posset refreshes the parts that need refreshing. Cafetière coffee and a well-considered dram round things off in true Scottish fashion. The short wine list has some big names – Cloudy Bay, Guigal, for example – although prices struck one reporter as somewhat 'erratic'. House wine is £8.25.

CHEF: Robert Hilton PROPRIETORS: Robert Wilson and Robert Hilton OPEN: Sun L (winter only) 12.30 to 2.30, Mon to Sat D 7 to 11 MEALS: alc (main courses £6.50 to £9.50) SERVICE: 12.5% (optional), card slips closed CARDS: Access, Amex, Delta, Visa DETAILS: 44 seats. Private parties: 44 main room. Vegetarian meals. Children's helpings. Music. Air-conditioned

Wiltons

map 15

55 Jermyn Street, SW1Y 6LX COOKING 3
TEL: 0171-629 9955 FAX: 0171-495 6233 COST £30–£85

In case you were in any doubt about the tone set at Wiltons, the menu cover shows a rather supercilious lobster in a shiny topper brandishing a cane in one claw and a glass of champers in the other. Camouflaged discreetly among the gentlemen's tailors and art dealers of St James's, the restaurant boasts a series of booths where, to quote the management, 'captains of industry may conduct their business in private'. Wiltons is about British heritage catering, that heady mix of scrupulous formality, Continental luxuries (two ounces of Beluga caviare for £75) and sherry trifle. Ross Hayden has been at the stoves for ten years but, despite the fact that the main *carte* seems carved in tablets of stone, the many daily specials offered alongside it suggest that he is allowed licence for thoughtful creativity.

Our inspectors, testing the range, were hugely impressed with a large wineglass lined with crisp iceberg lettuce crammed full of expertly dressed crabmeat mixed with pale pink marie-rose and with a nip of Tabasco to sharpen it. Marinated salmon is a giant's portion, the thickly meaty slices fringed with dill, the waitress ladling a dollop of dill sauce at the table. Fish accounts for much of the main-course business: baked cod is robustly matched with twirls of bacon and artichoke bottom in a 'very garlicky' herb butter, and sea bass is daringly grilled and served with spinach and ginger. The latter comes to the table on the bone (Wiltons does not nanny its fish-eaters as most modern restaurants do), but the timing is spot-on, and even an over-exuberant puddle of soy sauce doesn't unbalance the dish. Crème brûlée has a 'pleasant, firm texture and quite lemony flavour', while sherry trifle is liberally boozed and has good custard, plenty of red fruit and the requisite 'lashings' of whipped cream. There are lashings of service too, which will all seem very stiff at first, but relax: it is perfectly friendly and considerate and will do its utmost to please, right down to the somewhat over-zealous chilling of white wines and perhaps even the application of smelling salts after the bill has been delivered. House wine starts at £13.50.

CHEF: Ross Hayden PROPRIETOR: Wiltons (St James's) Ltd OPEN: Sun to Fri 12 to 2.30, 6 to 10.30 MEALS: alc (main courses £10 to £28.50). Set L Sun £19.75. Cover £1 SERVICE: not inc CARDS: Access, Amex, Diners, Visa DETAILS: 100 seats. Private parties: 40 main room, 18 private room. No children under 8. Jacket and tie. Wheelchair access (1 step). No music. Air-conditioned

'The cheese waiter seemed very fond of a cheese that was four years old. I was not sure whether to sing Happy Birthday to it or eat it.' (On eating in Monte Carlo)

'More than half the other guests were from North America, so we felt like locals.' (A Welsh reporter in Scotland)

Zen Central

map 15

20 Queen Street, W1X 7PJ — NEW CHEF

TEL: 0171-629 8089 and 8103 FAX: 0171-493 6181 COST £33–£69

The smart modern surroundings, approachable Chinese food and Westernised service are typical of the small Zen chain, which is currently undergoing a few changes. Black chairs, grey carpets, white walls and acres of glass and mirror may look a bit 1980s nowadays, but the comfort factor is high, as perhaps it should be given the Mayfair prices. The arrival of a new chef occurred too late for us to receive reports or to inspect, but in the past the food has been happy to borrow from Thailand and Malaysia, with a few luxury ingredients thrown in, and to eschew MSG. Wines are unusually good, with countries outside France offering change from £20. House wine is £12, or £3.50 a glass.

CHEF: Wai Hung Ho PROPRIETOR: Tealeaf Ltd OPEN: all week 12 to 2.30, 6.15 to 11.15 (10.45 Sun) CLOSED: 4 days Christmas MEALS: alc (main courses £10 to £40). Cover £1 SERVICE: not inc CARDS: Access, Amex, Delta, Diners, Visa DETAILS: 95 seats. Private parties: 100 main room. Vegetarian meals. Children welcome. Smart dress preferred. Wheelchair access. Music. Air-conditioned

Zoe

map 15

3–5 Barrett Street, St Christopher's Place, W1M 5HH COOKING 2

TEL: 0171-224 1122 FAX: 0171-935 5444 COST £21–£40

Zoe continues to be compared favourably with other restaurants in which Antony Worrall-Thompson is involved. Its lively ambience extends from the ground-floor café, which serves food from 11.30am to 11.30pm, to the 'bright and crisp' basement dining-room, where the plain wooden floor results in quite a lot of noise. The menus offer masses of colourful choice, with ideas pillaged from all over the culinary world and descriptions that know how to stir curiosity. Starters of rustic vegetable soup with bean and chickpea falafels, and chargrilled crumpets with home-cured foie gras, and a main course of marinated spatchcocked chicken with stir-fried mooli, mange-tout, broccoli and bean sprouts all appeared on one spring menu in the restaurant. Although one reporter was disappointed with a main dish of 'stringy' calf's liver, others have cited particularly memorable sweet potato and yam soup, wild mushroom and celery risotto with white truffle oil, 'excellent' blue cheese and asparagus tart with spinach, and 'sinfully scrumptious', sticky fig pudding with clotted cream and coffee ice. House wines from Duboeuf are £8.45.

CHEFS: Antony Worrall-Thompson and Conrad Melling PROPRIETOR: Zen Group OPEN: Mon to Fri L 11.30 to 2.30, Mon to Sat D 6.30 to 11.30 CLOSED: bank hols MEALS: alc (main courses £7.50 to £12) SERVICE: not inc CARDS: Access, Amex, Delta, Diners, Switch, Visa DETAILS: 150 seats. 15 tables outside. Private parties: 30 main room. Vegetarian meals. Children welcome. Music. Air-conditioned

'As I arrived early, and the rest of the place was empty, I exchanged thoughts with the owner on life, the state of the catering trade, and whether no-shows should be burnt at the stake or simply garotted.' (On eating in Bristol)

London round-ups

Eating out in London is largely a question of picking the location that offers the right kind of food for the occasion. To assist *Guide* readers, the round-up section provides details of a range of restaurants, bistros, and cafés that are well worth a visit but do not merit a full entry. Each is included for a specific reason: you will find lunchtime bolt holes for shoppers, good hotel dining-rooms, cafés in department stores, chippies, Cantonese soup kitchens, up-and-coming brasseries, even a new star or two in the making. Entries are based on readers' recommendations, often backed up by inspectors' reports. In some cases we have put an establishment in the round-ups rather than in the main-entry section because there are changes in the air or because there has been a dearth of votes in its favour. Reports on these places are especially welcome, as they enable us to extend our overall coverage of good food in the capital.

Price guide For a three-course meal, including half a bottle of house wine, coffee and service per person:

£ = £15 or under
££ = £15-£30
£££ = £30-£40
££££ = over £40

Albero & Grana SW3
89 Sloane Avenue map 14
0171-225 1048
Flashy Chelsea tapas bar and restaurant with stunning technicolour décor, a 'buzzy Euro-chic atmosphere' and brilliant service. The kitchen deals in exciting ideas, although results have been mixed. Lasagne of black pudding is the signature dish; otherwise the menu spans everything from vibrant salads and mussels with black rice, to Segovian-style suckling pig. **£££–££££**

Aroma W1
1B Dean Street map 15
0171-287 1633
Perfectly sited where tourist Oxford Street meets Soho media-land, this upbeat, technicolour cafe is 'an enjoyable place to take time out'. It serves some of the best coffee in town (tall glasses of café latte are brilliant), the music may be full-volume Colombian, and the food is a wholesome mix of trendy sandwich combos, seasonal salads and patisserie. Branches at: 36A St Martins Lane, WC2, 0171-836 5110; 273 Regent Street, W1, 0171-495 4911; West One Centre, 381 Oxford Street, W1, 0171-495 6945; 168 Piccadilly, W1, 0171-495 6995; Unit 2/35 Bishopsgate Arcade, EC2, 0171-374 2774; Aroma in Books Etc., 120 Charing Cross Road, WC2, 0171-240 4030; Royal Festival Hall, Belvedere Road, SE1, 0171-928 0622. Aroma has also reached Essex, with an outlet in the Lakeside Shopping Centre, West Thurrock. **£**

Arts Theatre Café WC2
6–7 Great Newport Street map 15
0171-497 8014/240 7760
Just off Leicester Square tube in a basement below the children's theatre, this café is a little gem. The kitchen puts its faith in top-drawer ingredients (breads and olives are outstanding) and the cooking is robust, peasant-style Italian. Pasta is a good bet, roasted vegetable soup comes with bagna cauda, steak is grilled Tuscan-style and John Dory is served the Sicilian way with couscous salad. The Italian wine list hits the button. **££**

Balzac Bistro W12
4 Wood Lane map 12
0181-743 6787
A long-serving BBC bolt hole just down the road from the Television Centre and

reckoned to be a more tempting option than the staff canteen. The décor is lived-in, service is amiable and the value-for-money is fair. Wild mushrooms with polenta is a signature dish, but the menu also includes fresh fish cooked the old way (sole Colbert, and sea bass sauce Maltaise, for example). ££

Bedlington Café W4
24 Fauconberg Road map 12
0181-994 1965
'Crowded, cheap and fun' café serving lively Thai food to the Chiswick set. The evening menu blasts its way through satays, soups, curries and noodles, and also features a helping of specialities from Laos. Unlicensed, but you can bring your own wine (50p corkage). £

Belgo Centraal WC2
50 Earlham Street map 15
0171-813 2233
Frenetic Covent Garden offshoot of Belgo Noord in Chalk Farm (see main entry). Reach the restaurant and beer hall via a hydraulic lift, then wait for the ladies to direct you to a seat. Order massive helpings of mussels with chips, drink beer and don't be fazed by waiters dressed in monks outfits. Set lunches are brilliant value: 'Psycho Kilo' is a kilo of molluscs in a lidded pot plus a bottle of Hoegaarden, all for £5. £–££

Bentley's W1
11–15 Swallow Street map 15
0171-734 4756
Opened in 1916, this famous emporium still trades on the grandeur of a bygone era. Crystal chandeliers and polished woodwork suggest a gentlemen's club, and the menu still has oysters, Dover soles and lobster for the old guard. Elsewhere, California and Italy have their say, with monkfish terrine wrapped in prosciutto, grilled dorade with mushroom risotto, and steamed fillet of cod with Puy lentils and tapénade. Excellent British cheeses. ££–£££

Beotys WC2
79 St Martin's Lane map 15
0171-836 8768/8548
One of the longest-running hits in the West End, and a favourite with early-evening theatregoers. Since 1945 the Frangos family has specialised in generous Continental cooking with Greek overtones: most people opt for the fixed-price menus and authentic dishes such as spinach and garlic pancakes, swordfish kebabs, souvlakia, moussaka and baklava. Service is attentive and speedy when it needs to be. £££

Blenheim NW8
21 Loudoun Road map 13
0171-625 1222
A recent addition to the growing list of reincarnated London pubs devoted to affordable brasserie-style food. The setting is a grand-looking 'snow white' building in St John's Wood with a porticoed entrance and tables outside. Salmon fish-cakes with pesto mayo and crisp, coarse-cut chips share the billing with salads, pasta, burgers and a few homespun puds. 'Interesting' wine list. ££

Books for Cooks W11
4 Blenheim Crescent map 13
0171-221 1992
Immensely useful day-time café at the back of London's best-known foodie bookshop. After browsing or buying, customers can peruse the tiny menu: perhaps lemon, yoghurt and garlic soup; mixed mezze; tagine of chicken served with spiced salmon couscous; ginger and mascarpone cheesecake. Rock-bottom prices. £

Café Rouge W8
2 Lancer Square map 13
0171-938 4200
The Kensington branch of this chain epitomises the style and intentions of the whole group. All offer affordable French food at fair prices, with casual 'Parisienne' atmosphere to match. Early birds, shoppers, business lunchers and

theatregoers have a choice of salads, steak sandwiches, dishes such as coq au vin and great coffee. There are over 30 branches in the London area; find one near you.

Caffé Graffiti NW3
71 Hampstead High Street map 13
0171-431 7579 and 433 1372
Eat on the pavement terrace and watch Hampstead at play or sit in the long, pleasant dining-room surrounded by modern lithographs and paintings. The menu is a lively mix of dishes gleaned from the world larder: reporters have enjoyed sweetcorn chowder with Gorgonzola crostini, spinach gnocchi, calf's liver with bubble and squeak, and tarte Tatin. Service is youthful and efficient. ££

Caraffini SW1
61–63 Lower Sloane Street map 14
0171-259 0235
Boisterous Italian opened by Paulo Caraffini, formerly head waiter at nearby Como Lario (see main entry). Expect pasta with plenty of modern twists (pumpkin tortelloni, tagliolini with crab and courgettes), various risottos, and mains ranging from scampi with artichokes to chargrilled baby chicken. Booking essential. ££

Casale Franco N1
134–137 Upper Street map 13
0171-226 8994
Usefully situated just off Upper Street, but in a state of flux as we went to press. The owners tell us they are refurbishing the dining-room, rejigging the menu and building a new wood-burning oven. It seems likely that pizzas and pasta will remain the major draw, with trattoria stalwarts available for those who want something else. Reports on the new set-up, please. £££

Chez Gérard W1
8 Charlotte Street map 15
0171-636 4975
The Fitzrovia branch of this mini-group of restaurants is a long, thin dining-room with close-packed tables, lots of noise and French waiters who practise English only if they have to. Go for the steaks (onglet and châteaubriand are the stars) and enjoy 'the world's best frites'. Incidentals such as baguettes, olives and cappuccino are great. Drink whatever suits the food. Branches also at: 31 Dover Street, W1, 0171-499 8171; 119 Chancery Lane, WC2, 0171-405 0290. ££

China China W1
3 Gerrard Street map 15
0171-439 7511
Lively Cantonese canteen that specialises in fair-value one-plate meals. Have a bowl of noodle soup topped with barbecued pork or roast duck, order chilli oil on the side and fill up with some Chinese greens if you're famished. Plates of roast meat on rice are good too. £

Condotti W1
4 Mill Street map 15
0171-499 1308
Go for the pizzas. This flashy, up-market West End venue serves decent versions on thin, accurately cooked bases. Good garlic bread, strong espresso, plus a few gutsy Italian wines or Peroni beer to wash it all down. Service is as sharp as a knife. ££

Diwana Bhel-Poori NW1
121 Drummond Street map 13
0171-387 5556
Drummond Street has a fair sprinkling of Indian vegetarian cafés and restaurants, and this is reckoned to be the best of the bunch. Tables are bare, ethnic artefacts adorn the walls, and the cooking is genuine. Make a meal from starters and snacks, or opt for one of the thalis. Don't miss the brilliant lassi and kulfi. £

L'Escargot Doré W8
2–4 Thackeray Street map 13
0171-937 8508
This particular snail is hidden away in a backwater behind Kensington High Street, but is worth seeking out for decent classic French food. The eponymous

molluscs are doused in garlic and butter, sea bass is cooked wirh lemon grass sauce, and sabayon of fresh fruits is a good sweet. Coffee is excellent and service never falters. Snacks are available in the ground-floor brasserie. More reports, please. ££

Florians N8
4 Topsfield Parade map 12
0181-348 8348
Up-to-the-minute Italian food is served in the dining-room at the back of this useful Crouch End address. Expect dishes such as black tagliolini with seafood and rocket, chargrilled lamb's liver with sage oil and marinated courgettes, baked rabbit with grilled polenta, and terrine of pine kernels and moscato. Light meals are available all day in the bar. Reasonably priced Italian wines and lots of grappas. ££

Formula Veneta SW10
14 Hollywood Road map 14
0171-352 7612
Ultra-smart establishment offering back-to-the-roots Italian cooking in a setting dominated by motor-racing photographs. Excellent broad-bean soup, sophisticated pasta dishes such as fettucine with sausage and wild mushrooms, plus risottos and seafood; also look for specials including pig's trotter with lentils. Tempting Italian wine list. Eat in the courtyard on fine summer evenings. ££

Green Cottage NW3
9 New College Parade, map 13
Finchley Road
0171-722 5305 and 7892
'Like a Soho Chinese restaurant whisked out of context into Swiss Cottage.' The cooking is 'genuine' and the menu spans everything from stewed duck with mixed vegetables, and steamed belly pork with taro, to barbecued meats and noodles. Also look for the ambitious vegetarian section: stir-fried bean curd with chilli, fish-flavoured aubergine, and Buddha's Cushion. Friendly service. £

La Grignote NW3
77 Heath Street map 13
0171-433 3455
Pure bistro – right down to its red paintwork and blue gingham curtains – this Hampstead eating-house is endearingly run by a French couple. Recommendations have spanned everything from warm salad of smoked duck breast, and tomato tarte Tatin, to roast pheasant on a 'rouille' of sweet potato, and grilled lamb cutlets with minted cabbage. Crème brûlée runs out quickly. ££

Haandi NW1
161 Drummond Street map 13
0171-383 4557
A good-value carnivorous alternative to the clutch of Indian vegetarian places in Drummond Street. The best deal is the buffet lunch, which features an impressive display of pickles, curries, vegetables, rice and nan bread. The ground-floor dining-room fills up fast. £

Ikkyu W1
67 Tottenham Court Road map 15
0171-436 6169 and 636 9280
Set in a basement a few doors from Goodge Street tube, this Japanese is at its best at lunch-time, when there are affordable set meals based on grilled fish, peasant-style hotpots and noodles. Prices of other items such as sashimi and yakitori are also commendably low. ££

Kartouche SW10
329–331 Fulham Road map 14
0171-823 3515
A place for 'brash fun' in Chelsea's Golden Mile. There are no bookings: watch the Porsches pull up outside and do a bit of star-watching. The menu is as modern as they come: saffron risotto with smoked chicken and garden peas, Jamaican jerk chicken with wild rice and Cajun spiced salmon with fried banana and avocado salsa are typical. There is plenty of inspirational stuff on the wine list. ££

King's Road Café SW3
Habitat, 208 King's Road map 14
0171-351 1211
High-quality in-store café meticulously bedecked with Habitat furniture, designer crockery and huge indoor trees in terracotta pots. The lunch menu is short, modern and Mediterranean, taking in gutsy soups, lively salads, loads of oily ciabatta, and dishes such as involtini of roast peppers. Home-made cakes and cappuccino please the shoppers at any time of day. £

Kym's SW1
70–71 Wilton Road map 13
0171-828 8931
Handy venue for a Chinese meal close to Victoria Station and the local theatres (special deals are available for visitors to the shows). The menu is a long run through the staples of Peking and Szechuan cuisine, with dishes such as poached prawns in soy and chilli sauce, drunken fish, sizzling beef and double-cooked pork singled out for praise. Light, airy surroundings, helpful service. ££

Lemonia NW1
89 Regents Park Road map 13
0171-586 7454
Long-running venue off Primrose Hill serving up meze and a clutch of tried-and-tested Greek-Cypriot favourites. Also look for more enterprising daily specials, such as fresh artichokes with broad beans and grilled swordfish with okra. Three-course weekday lunches are a bargain for those who like peace and quiet; families descend on the place at weekends. ££

Manzi's WC2
1–2 Leicester Street map 15
0171-734 0224
Go through the door and put your watch back 60 years. The Manzi family set the tone for Continental fish cookery a very long time ago, and their time-warp of a restaurant now seems curiously out of kilter with Soho in the '90s. However, if you are in Leicester Square and fancy the experience, go for the grilled fish and chips and skip the rest. ££–£££

Le Metro SW3
28 Basil Street map 14
0171-589 6286
Worth knowing about if you need a change of scene after a morning's shopping at Harrods or Harvey Nick's. The smart, modern basement is reached via steps almost next to the Capital Hotel (see main entry section), whose chef also supervises this kitchen. The short menu aims for day-time satisfaction in the shape of pigeon terrine with sultana chutney, chicken risotto, roast chump of lamb and plum and almond tart. Wines are 'potentially very good'. ££

Mezzanine SE1
National Theatre map 13
0171-928 3531
Equally useful if you are peckish before a show at the National or simply want 'a quick jaunt out of the stuffiness of the city'. Service is prompt, portions are sensibly restrained and the food is lively without going overboard. Salmon fish-cakes, marinated duck breast with green vegetables, ribeye steak and cold rice pudding brûlée have pleased the punters. ££

Le Midi SW6
488 Fulham Road map 13
0171-386 0657
Cosy little restaurant off Fulham Broadway, with French and Mediterranean décor, 'light music' and food to match. The *carte* lists dishes such as salade niçoise, chargrilled fish with sun-dried tomato salsa, and fillet of lamb in puff pastry with garlic sauce. ££

Namaste E1
30 Alie Street map 13
0171-488 9242
The word is that this mould-breaking East End Indian is currently delivering some of the most distinctive food of its kind in the capital. Chef's specials set the tone: deep-fried oysters, wild rabbit tikka, stuffed

grouse, monkfish cooked with dried raw mango and cokum berries. The regular menu has a heavy Goan and South Indian presence as well as keeping faith with the north. Plans are afoot to move to larger premises; more reports, please. **££**

New Loon Fung **W1**
42-44 Gerrard Street map 15
0171-437 6232/ 439 0458
Next door to the Loong Fung Supermarket and a useful choice for daytime dim-sum if you are cruising Chinatown at the weekend. All kinds of things, from curried whelks to scallop dumplings, are brought to the table direct from the kitchen and the results are well up to scratch. Cantonese dishes also available from the full menu. **£**

New Mayflower **W1**
68–70 Shaftesbury Avenue map 15
0171-734 9207
The original Mayflower acquired a new name, new owners and a new chef shortly before we went to press. Little else seems set to change. The cooking has its feet firmly in the Cantonese camp, with a heavy bias towards seafood and esoteric ingredients. One-plate rice and noodle dishes are available after 11pm. Note the unusual opening hours: 5pm to 4am. Reports on the new regime, please. **££–£££**

Newport **WC2**
8 Great Newport Street map 15
0171-240 1551
The setting is a large basement that has been turned into a good-looking, modern dining-room. Breads and pasta are home-made, and dishes such as seared tuna with pickled vegetables, mixed seafood with black noodles, and baked chocolate tart with orange compote have been praised. A change of chef was about to take place as we went to press. More reports, please. **££**

New World **W1**
1 Gerard Place map 15
0171-434 2508
Currently the leader of the pack in Soho Chinatown when it comes to dim-sum dispensed from heated trolleys (as opposed to dishes that are served straight from the kitchen). This vast Cantonese arena seats several hundred on three floors; there is bags of space, the atmosphere is vibrant and staff cope well. 'Exact and distinct' flavours set the kitchen apart from its rivals. **££**

Odin's **W1**
27 Devonshire Street map 15
0171-935 7296
A collection of pictures belonging to the late Peter Langan brightens up proceedings in this courteously run, club-like establishment. The kitchen was peddling British food long before the current fad began, and you will find such things as kedgeree with quail's eggs, oxtail with lentils, and rice pudding, though prices are high. **££££**

Panda Si Chuen **W1**
56 Old Compton Street map 15
0171-437 2069
A useful Soho address for anyone wanting a taste of Szechuan food, Authentic items include cold, herb-marinated beef, pelmeni (wun-tun) in hot-and-sour soup, croaker fish with chilli, tea-smoked duck and red-cooked aubergine. The mirrored room is quite smart and service is pleasant. **££–£££**

Il Passetto **WC2**
230 Shaftesbury Avenue map 15
0171-836 9391
At the Covent Garden end of Shaftesbury Avenue, Passetto generally pleases theatergoers with its seasoned version of Pavarotti trattoria cooking. Trolleys of antipasti and desserts are wheeled up and down the aisle in the narrow dining-room, service comes with smiles and gestures. **££**

Patisserie Valerie W1
R.I.B.A., 66 Portland Place map 15
0171-580 5533
The most recent addition to a small but legendary band of independent pâtisseries, first opened in Soho in 1926. After a stroll round the free exhibitions in the Royal Institute of British Architects, settle down to 'zippy orange juice, great cappuccino, first-class croissants', or one of the seductively calorific cakes and pastries. Lunches are light, fast and great value. Branches also at 44 Old Compton Street, W1, 0171-437 3466; 215 Brompton Road, SW3, 0171-823 9971; Patisserie Valerie at Maison Sagne, 105 Marylebone High Street, W1, 0171-935 6240; 8 Russell Street, Covent Garden, WC2, 0171-240-0064. **£**

Pierre Victoire 0171-823 2070
9 William Street map 14
SW1
The Knightsbridge address of this chain is a premier site; all follow Pierre Levicky's formula of affordable food in functional surroundings. The set lunch is unbeatable value, although, judging by reports, some outlets clearly impress more than others. There are many branches in and around London including: 6 Panton Street, Haymarket, SW1, 0171-930 6463; 136 Upper Richmond Road, Putney, SW15, 0181-789 7043; 11 Charlotte Street, W1, 0171-436 0248 **££**

Poons WC2
27 Lisle Street map 15
0171-437 4549
The original branch of the Poon family's little empire is a higgledy-piggledy café on Lisle Street serving big helpings of wind-dried duck, sausages and bacon, plus a forthright contingent of Cantonese soups, hotpots and one-plate meals. Very cheap. **£**

Prince Bonaparte W2
80 Chepstow Road map 13
0171-229 5912
Born again in Westbourne Park, this revamped Victorian pub now doubles as a neighbourhood drinking place and '90s dining-room. Order at the bar and pay in advance. The blackboard menu flits between tradition (steak and kidney pudding, smoked haddock fish-cakes) and globetrotting (sweet potato, roast garlic and oregano soup; kimchee and tiger prawn ramen; chargrilled salmon with polenta). Staff are 'incredibly nice'. **£**

Rebato's SW8
169 South Lambeth Road map 12
0171-735 6388 and 582 8089
The mother of all London tapas bars and an enduring old-stager offering 'wonderful-value' restaurant food with a recognisable Spanish accent. Fish specials are the best bet, otherwise the menu spans everything from zarzuela and paella to grilled lamb cutlets with garlic mayonnaise, steaks and a trolley load of creamy desserts. Drink the house Torres. **££**

Ritz Hotel W1
Piccadilly map 15
0171-493 8181
The unashamed luxury of the Ritz and its sumptuous Louis XVI restaurant provides a fitting backdrop for David Nicholl's increasingly assured cooking. Fixed-priced lunches bring forth dishes such as truffle and herb risotto with scallops; pig's trotters with lentils, sweetbreads and leeks; and provençale vegetable tart, plus daily roasts from the trolley. The evening *carte* inhabits another realm where price seems irrelevant. Service is impeccable, the pace is measured. **£££–££££**

Rotisserie W12
56 Uxbridge Road map 12
0181-743 3028
Well-hung Aberdeen Angus steaks cooked on a genuine French rotisserie justifiably steal the show in this popular place close to Shepherds Bush tube. Otherwise opt for rack of lamb, Barbary duck breast with fruit chutney, corn-fed chicken with rosemary or fillet of salmon.

Drink South African Castle lager or one of the New World wines. **££**

San Remo **SW13**
195 Castelnau map 12
0181-741 5909
Modest from the outside, this highly popular Italian has a relaxed atmosphere and a standard menu of trattoria classics. Expect anything from pasta with 'lots and lots' of clams to 'flamed cake'. The specials board attracts plenty of interest. **££**

Selfridge Hotel, Fletcher's **W1**
Orchard Street map 15
0171-408 2080
An 'island of tranquillity' and a favoured lunch spot on the first-floor of the Selfridge hotel. Chef Mark Page aims high and his menu reads well, although dish descriptions may be somewhat erratic. Fish is well handled (fillet of halibut with butter-bean cassoulet, for example) and pastry-work is good. A decent, reasonably priced wine list helps things along. **££–£££**

Soulard **N1**
113 Mortimer Road map 13
0171-254 1314
No pretensions, but good, honest bistro food in pleasing surroundings. The owners are French and the 'well-thought-out' menu sticks to basics: moules, lamb with flageolet beans, 'surprisingly delightful' crème brûlée. Service is friendly and well informed. **££**

Spread Eagle **SE10**
2 Stockwell Street map 12
0181-853 2333
Historic tavern opposite the Greenwich Theatre now functioning as a 'dining-room' specialising in authentic French cooking. Regularly changing menus feature dishes such as feuilleté of veal sweetbreads with shredded leeks, monkfish with roasted garlic and olives, and pan-fried salmon with croûtons, lime and capers. Pre-theatre suppers are excellent value. Live jazz in the cellar every Thursday evening. **£££**

Surya **NW6**
59-61 Fortune Green Road map 13
0171-435 7486
A reliable choice for North Indian vegetarian cooking in Hampstead. The Tiwaris offer a short menu of bhel-pooris, dosas and vegetables, backed up by more enterprising daily specials: stuffed green peppers and lotus steam curry, for example. Service is 'unfailingly charming'. Open evenings and for excellent-value buffet lunches on Sunday. **£**

Thistells **SE22**
65 Lordship Lane map 12
0181-299 1921
Handy if you live in the far reaches of Dulwich and are keen on quirky décor. The setting is a former David Greig shop with lots of tiling, marble and drapes at the windows. Sami Youssef offers snacks, business lunches and full meals from a well-tried repertoire with Middle Eastern echoes. 'Wonderful' bread and generally good raw materials. **£–££**

Toff's **N10**
38 Muswell Hill Broadway map 12
0181-883 8656
The owner of this highly rated Muswell Hill chippie is Mr Ttoffalli – hence the truncated name. Its virtues are simple: fresh fish (anything from haddock to halibut), light batter, good-quality chips; all the details are spot-on, from good gherkins to choice cups of tea. Pick a table at the back of the shop or take your place in the queue for the take-away counter. **£**

Vasco & Piero's Pavilion **W1**
15 Poland Street map 15
0171-437 8774
A long-running West End Italian with a distinctive personal style and a happy atmosphere. Modern fixed-priced menus offer plenty for those who don't want meat, and the cooking generally succeeds.

reporters have enjoyed sauté mushrooms with courgettes and pancetta, herb-crusted cod with a tomato and basil sauce, and slices of rare fillet of beef on a pile of bitter leaves. Home-made pasta and 'sensational' gnocchi are also endorsed. ££

Wakaba NW3
122A Finchley Road map 13
0171-586 7960
Discreetly situated opposite Finchley Road tube station, this Japanese restaurant provides good-quality food and friendly service amid slightly austere surroundings. You can sit at the bar where chefs carve and assemble sushi; otherwise there is plenty of space at the tables. ££

Wodka W8
12 St Albans Grove map 14
0171-937 6513
Fun-loving Kensington bolt hole that lives up to its name with a mind-blowing collection of flavoured vodkas, supported by a menu with Polish overtones and a nod to current fashion. Expect anything from 'featherlight' blinis, pierogi dumplings and roast suckling pig to fish-cakes with basil and pine-nut mayonnaise, or chargrilled squid. ££

Zafferano SW1
15 Lowndes Street map 14
0171-235 5800
A newish Knightsbridge Italian that is on the way up. Olive oil is used with a free hand and pasta is a star turn: pappardelle with tiny broad beans, and linguine with crab and chilli have drawn praise. Other high points from recent meals have included sliced ox-tongue with gherkins and a potent herb sauce, roast rabbit with polenta, and veal kidneys with artichoke and lentils. Lemon and mascarpone tart is a winning sweet. More reports, please. ££

England

ALDEBURGH Suffolk map 6

Lighthouse **NEW ENTRY**

77 High Street, Aldeburgh IP15 5AU COOKING 2
TEL/FAX: (01728) 453377 COST £15–£28

Sara and Peter Hill are delighted to be back in Aldeburgh. After leaving the nearby Regatta (see entry), they moved to Hedgehog Hall in Kelsale, but are now resident in this converted high street shop. Theirs is a hive of industry. In high season they are open seven days a week for coffee, light lunches, teas and dinners; they also sell cakes and do outside catering. As winter approaches they will probably batten down the hatches on Sunday nights and Mondays.

It is a place that buzzes with life, although the décor is restful. The strength of the set-up is its reliance on specialist local suppliers for everything from smoked fish to ice-cream. Seafood is a strong suit: oysters are always available, Cromer crab (a 'well-groomed' specimen) comes with herby green mayonnaise, grilled tuna and squid are served with red peppers and Parmesan, and roast salmon arrives on Puy lentils with coconut and lemon grass. Lamb also receives good reports: either roasted or pan-fried and accompanied by a mushroom and pine-nut risotto. An undoubted highlight was a thick piece of fillet steak, 'roasted blue', sliced in two and flanked by horseradish-spiked mash with 'superb' caramelised shallots and a rich brown sauce. Desserts include Sara's renowned bread-and-butter pudding, and a perfectly made toffee and walnut tart. Peter runs the front of house, ably assisted by a couple of waitresses. The wine list relies heavily on deliveries from Adnams, packs a lot of interest into a short space, and is very fairly priced. Nine house wines are all under £10 a bottle.

CHEF: Sara Fox PROPRIETORS: Sara Fox and Peter Hill OPEN: all week 12 to 2.15, 7 to 10.15 CLOSED: winter Sun D and Mon L and D MEALS: alc (main courses £4 to £8). Set D £13.50 (2 courses) to £15.75 SERVICE: not inc, card slips closed CARDS: Access, Delta, Visa DETAILS: 70 seats. 2 tables outside. Private parties: 40 main room, 40 private room. Vegetarian meals. Children's helpings. Smart dress preferred. No smoking in 1 dining-room. Wheelchair access (1 step). No music

'By the end of the evening, after one of the lads from the bar had dropped a tray of glasses on the floor, the waitresses were all giggling uncontrollably as if relieved that they had somehow got through yet another stressful evening without themselves causing a major disaster.' (On eating in Wales)

Regatta ⁂

171–173 High Street, Aldeburgh IP15 5AN — COOKING 1

TEL/FAX: (01728) 452011 — COST £23–£36

The bright, nautically themed Regatta is done out in pastel colours and offers a choice of either bar or restaurant to eat in, with seafood constituting one of the main strands. A Mediterranean theme runs through the menu in the form of gazpacho, or fish soup served with rouille and croutons, while warm chorizo sausage with roast peppers and olive salad, locally smoked salmon, and a 'cassoulet' of giant prawns with buttered noodles show the breadth of its compass. Otherwise, cod might be simply fried with chips, or 'toasted' with creamed leeks, while fishy variety is provided by flounders with herbs and oil, or roast skate with seaweed sauce. Good pasta, and 'real chicken nuggets' on a children's menu delighted one reporter, while spotted dick with custard might take its place alongside crème brûlée, ice-creams and sorbets. Cooking is subject to ups and downs, but service is friendly. Robert Mabey appears to be cooking here as well as at Mabey's Brasserie (see entry, Sudbury). House wine is £7.50.

CHEF: Robert Mabey PROPRIETORS: Robert and Johanna Mabey OPEN: June to Sept all week and Oct to May Wed to Sun 12 to 2.30, 6 to 10 MEALS: alc (main courses £8 to £12) SERVICE: not inc, card slips closed CARDS: Access, Amex, Switch, Visa DETAILS: 80 seats. Private parties: 30 main room. Vegetarian meals. Children's helpings. Smart dress preferred. No smoking in 1 dining-room. Wheelchair access (3 steps; also WC). No music

---

ALDERHOLT Dorset — map 2

Moonacre

Fordingbridge Road, Alderholt SP6 3BB

TEL: (01425) 653142 — COOKING 2

off B3078, between Cranborne and Fordingbridge — COST £17–£33

For some, the Moonacre is a neighbourhood bolt hole dealing in midweek suppers and Sunday lunches; for others – many of whom make the trek from distant conurbations – it is the venue for a special evening out. Barbara Garnsworthy aims to please all comers. As a country cook working in a whitewashed cottage within reach of the New Forest and the downlands of Cranborne Chase, she is tuned in to the seasons and knows her way round the local food scene. Her notes and comments read as follows: 'Mallard, teal, partridge and pheasant were plentiful this year. Hares are still scarce here, so local shoots don't kill them. Bumper harvests of wild mushrooms, ceps, horn of plenty and chicken of the wood have been dried and preserved in oil, as well as used fresh. Keynston Mill asparagus and Trelane blueberries are both excellent.'

In her kitchen you might find pickled cherries (served with pigeon breast and pork terrine), curried peach chutney (the perfect spicy foil to celery and Stilton pâté), and jars of medlar jelly that might be used to accompany roast partridge. Those who have eaten well here have singled out 'light as a feather' Brie in filo pastry with pesto, a three-cheese soufflé that was 'timed to perfection', scallops cooked with bacon, mushrooms, basil and white wine, and roast loin of venison on a bed of braised lentils with wild mushrooms. Dishes of help-yourself vegetables are left in the centre of the table. To round things off, you might opt for brown bread ice-cream or white chocolate and coconut cheesecake. The welcome is warm and service is attentive without becoming obtrusive. The list of three dozen wines is a thoughtful, varied selection with interesting names and realistic prices. House wine is £7.50.

CHEF: Barbara Garnsworthy PROPRIETORS: Barbara Garnsworthy and Edward Bourke OPEN: Sun L 12 to 2, Tue to Sat D 7 to 10 CLOSED: 2/3 weeks spring MEALS: alc (main courses £7 to £12). Set L Sun £12, Set D Tue to Thur £9 (2 courses) to £11 SERVICE: not inc, card slips closed CARDS: Access, Visa DETAILS: 40 seats. Private parties: 40 main room. Car park. Vegetarian meals. Children's helpings. Wheelchair access (1 step). No music

ALNWICK Northumberland map 10

John Blackmore's

1 Dorothy Foster Court, Narrowgate,
Alnwick NE66 1NL COOKING 2*
TEL: (01665) 604465 COST £20–£43

The building, not far from the castle, dates from 1631 and looks cosier from inside, with stripped-pine doors, pine tables and chairs, terracotta tiles and pretty curtains. The feel is warm if 'unsophisticated', and the food is varied and slightly old-fashioned in its generous use of cream.

Menus incorporate quite a bit of fish, from smoked cod with noodles in a creamy curry sauce to a partnership of poached haddock and Craster smoked salmon in a creamed tarragon sauce. Hot fish and vegetable mousses are not uncommon, including one of carrot served with sauté scallops and creamed coriander sauce. Alcohol shows up in a port sauce for mignons of venison with chicken livers, while fillet of beef might be served with a whisky and mushroom sauce. The pace is relaxed and there are no double bookings, but service can be perceived as slow. The 20 wines are mostly under £20, and the list includes 10 half-bottles. House wine is £8.50.

CHEF: John Blackmore PROPRIETORS: John and Penny Blackmore OPEN: Tue to Sat D only 7 to 9 CLOSED: Jan MEALS: alc (main courses £12 to £16). Set D Tue and Wed £18.50 (inc wine) SERVICE: not inc CARDS: Access, Amex, Diners, Visa DETAILS: 28 seats. Private parties: 28 main room. Vegetarian meals. Children's helpings. No children under 5. Smart dress preferred. No smoking in dining-room. Wheelchair access (1 step). Music

ALVECHURCH Hereford & Worcester map 5

The Mill NEW ENTRY

Radford Road, Alvechurch B48 7LD COOKING 2
TEL: 0121-447 7005 FAX: 0121-447 8001 COST £19–£39

Carl Timms has been a part of the Midlands restaurant scene for many years and he is now to be found in the kitchen of this converted mill in a quiet village not far from the M42. Original beams divide the dining-room into sections, floral curtains hang at the windows and tables are crisply laid with lemon cloths. The owners are extremely courteous, and service is thoroughly professional. Regulars who knows Timms's cooking feel that his new menu is 'a touch ordinary' and that this set-up may be pandering too much to 'steak-eating

Saturday-night-type people'. Even so, there's little doubt that he can still deliver the goods: 'excellent' confit of duck with orange and endive makes a good starter, while his sure touch with fish shows in a perfectly timed escalope of salmon with a 'rich, buttery, nicely sorreled sauce'. Forays to Birmingham market might bring lobsters and Dover sole, monkfish (served with saffron and lime) and sea bass (with a vermouth sauce and baby vegetables). Herb-crusted rack of lamb is cooked 'vaguely pink' and accompanied by fresh spinach, moist rösti and a 'very professional' rosemary sauce.

Desserts end things on a high note: a 'very lovely' caramelised rice pudding is served cold with orange sauce; date and walnut pudding has just the right texture and the accompanying butterscotch sauce is spot-on. The extensive wine list covers all the world's main growing regions, descriptions are knowledgeable, prices fair. The cheapest house wine is £7.50.

CHEF: Carl Timms PROPRIETORS: Stefan, Geoffrey and Vivienne McKernon OPEN: Sun L 12.30 to 2, Tue to Sat D 7 to 9 (9.30 Sat) MEALS: alc (main courses £9.50 to £13.50). Set L Sun £13.50, Set D Tue to Thur £11.50 (2 courses) to £13, Set D Fri and Sat £13.50 (2 courses) to £15. Minimum £9.50 SERVICE: not inc CARDS: Access, Amex, Visa DETAILS: 38 seats. Private parties: 38 main room. Car park. Vegetarian meals. Children welcome. Smart dress preferred. No pipes in dining-room. Music

AMBERLEY West Sussex map 3

▲ *Amberley Castle, Queen's Room*

Amberley BN18 9ND
TEL: (01798) 831992 FAX: (01798) 831998
on B2139, between Storrington and Bury Hill

COOKING **2***
COST **£28–£69**

'It would be foolish to deny the contribution that the surroundings make to the sum of pleasure provided at Amberley,' ran a report. Not far from Arundel, it is indeed one of the better preserved of England's medieval castles, imposingly turreted and floodlit at night. Inside, some dubious touches 'take off some of the polish': cuddly toys are not everybody's cup of tea. The restaurant, known as the Queen's Room, is on the first floor, 'a long, lofty, barrel-vaulted room', slightly younger than the castle itself but quite venerable enough.

New chef Simon Thyer arrived in June with an Australian-stamped passport and a CV full of country-house pedigree. His predecessor had taken the cooking here into more ambitious realms and it seems to be the intention to keep it there. Certainly the *carte* will leave nobody in any doubt as to the seriousness. Among the dishes to expect might be paupiette of smoked salmon and crab dressed with salmon eggs and dill, warm salad of rabbit and foie gras with cider dressing and apple crisps, and a main-course tartlet of chicken and hazelnuts garnished with 'lozenges' of leek in a Gewurztraminer sauce.

There are good-value fixed-price menus as well, which don't stint on the elaboration, as was evident in a fine mussel and clam rice dish – not quite the risotto it claimed to be – with saffron and a fritter of lemon balm. Calf's liver with bacon and caramelised apple, and a sauce based on Dubonnet, showed careful cooking of the main ingredient, though greater vibrancy came in a lemon tart balanced by a sauce of sweet orange. Aniseed fans might go for a liquorice bavarois with orange and Galliano sauce. Service is amiable. There are

some quality wines on the list, but the choices below £20 are a little on the pedestrian side.

CHEF: Simon Thyer PROPRIETORS: Martin and Joy Cummings OPEN: all week 12.30 to 2, 7.30 to 9.30 MEALS: alc (main courses £16 to £22.50). Set L £16.50 (2 courses) to £19.50, Set D £27.50 SERVICE: not inc, card slips closed CARDS: Access, Amex, Delta, Diners, Visa DETAILS: 50 seats. 6 tables outside. Private parties: 48 main room, 12 private rooms. Car park. Children welcome. Jacket and tie. No smoking in dining-room. No music ACCOMMODATION: 15 rooms, all with bath/shower. TV. Phone. B&B £95 to £275. No children under 7. Afternoon teas. Garden

---

AMBLESIDE Cumbria **map 8**

▲ *Rothay Manor*

Rothay Bridge, Ambleside LA22 0EH
TEL: (01539) 433605 FAX: (01539) 433607 **COOKING 2**
off A593 to Coniston, ¼m W of Ambleside **COST £18–£44**

The loyal following that the Nixons have built up at Rothay Manor since they opened in the 1960s is affirmed by a couple who have themselves been coming here for a quarter of a century: 'Service is efficient and friendly, the atmosphere civilised and relaxed, and the food is always imaginative and well cooked.' The Manor is in the heart of Lakeland – a short distance from the northern edge of Windermere – and so is the culinary style. Menus, priced according to how many courses you want (up to five plus coffee) offer a choice from three for first course and main with either a soup or sorbet in between. Puddings are followed by cheese. Simplicity and complexity sit side by side; you may opt to start with Cumbrian air-dried ham with melon, or paupiettes of smoked salmon filled with trout tartare on a pepper coulis. Inventiveness in main courses extends to a sauce of lemon and lime with monkfish on stir-fried vegetables, and chicken breast stuffed with Cumberland ham, Gruyère and onions. Vegetables are individually sauced or herbed, and suit some dishes better than others. Courgette and lime soup was for one diner 'fine and subtly flavoured' but slightly overpowered by a buttery taste when croûtons were sprinkled on it, while a breast of duck with spinach, cooked pink as requested, came up trumps. Finish with the likes of chocolate and orange gâteau or lemon syllabub. Much cheer is to be had from the wine list, which explores most of its represented countries thoroughly at prices that encourage flexibility. Many good growers have been chosen in Burgundy, the Rhône and the Loire, there are some fine German Rieslings, and the small California selection is an intelligent one. Four house wines (including, alas, Blue Nun) are £10 each. CELLARMAN'S CHOICE: Chardonnay 1992, Dom. Leasingham, Clare Valley, S. Australia, £10.90; Cépage Viognier 1993, Verget, £15.80.

'My companion was describing [from the menu] ''crostini of ricotta marinated with marjoram and mint'', followed by ''insalata di acciughe fritti with chillies on sourdough bruschetta''. ''Humph,'' she said, ''first cheese on toast, and now sardines on toast.''' **(On eating in London)**

CHEFS: Jane Binns and Colette Nixon PROPRIETORS: Nigel and Stephen Nixon OPEN: Mon to Sat L 12.30 to 2, Sun L 12.45 to 1.30, all week D 7.45 to 9 CLOSED: 3 Jan to 9 Feb MEALS: alc L (main courses £7). Set L £11, Set D £22 (2 courses) to £28 SERVICE: not inc, card slips closed CARDS: Access, Amex, Diners, Switch, Visa DETAILS: 70 seats. Private parties: 12 main room, 32 private room. Car park. Vegetarian meals. Children's helpings. Smart dress preferred. No smoking in dining-room. Wheelchair access (also WC). No music. Air-conditioned ACCOMMODATION: 18 rooms, all with bath/shower. TV. Phone. B&B £78 to £128. Deposit: £60. Rooms for disabled. Children welcome. Baby facilities. Afternoon teas. Garden (*The Which? Hotel Guide*)

AMERSHAM Buckinghamshire map 3

King's Arms

30 High Street, Old Amersham HP7 0DU COOKING 1*
TEL: (01494) 726333 FAX: (01494) 433480 COST £19–£45

Holding pride of place on the old High Street, this Tudor inn looks every inch the classic market town hostelry. The black and white frontage, the flower-festooned courtyard and the beamed bar – complete with alcoves and an inglenook – reinforce its image of old English gentility. By contrast the dining-room offers the prospect of modern Anglo-French cooking in revamped surroundings that are 'high on atmosphere'. Gary Munday's menus are peppered with in-vogue ideas: smoked tuna appears on a salad dressed with rosemary and horseradish, grilled duck breast is served with a zingy combination of lime and ginger, while a trio of lamb (kidney, liver and cutlet) receives a sauce of tomato, basil and red wine. Weekday set lunches are a highly affordable deal. Occasional disappointments can cloud the picture, but the cooking generally wins approval. Regular gastronomic events and seafood extravaganzas are popular attractions. A strong European presence provides most interest on the respectable wine list. Chilean house wine is £8.50.

CHEF: Gary Munday PROPRIETOR: John Jennison OPEN: Tue to Sun L 12 to 2, Tue to Sat D 7 to 9.30 CLOSED: 25 to 31 Dec MEALS: alc (main courses £13 to £15.50). Set L £8.50 (2 courses) to £11.50, Set L Sun £14.50. Set D Tue to Fri £17, Set D Sat £25. Minimum £8.50 L, £13 D SERVICE: not inc CARDS: Access, Amex, Delta, Diners, Switch, Visa DETAILS: 30 seats. Private parties: 48 main room, 12 to 48 private rooms. Car park. Vegetarian meals. Children welcome. Smart dress preferred. No cigars/pipes in dining-room. No music

APPLETHWAITE Cumbria map 10

▲ *Underscar Manor* $*

Applethwaite, nr Keswick CA12 4PH
TEL: (01768) 775000 FAX: (01768) 774904 COOKING 3
off A66, 1½m N of Keswick COST £27–£52

There is a sense of the lavish at Underscar, both inside and out. Sweeping views down to Derwentwater make this one of the more dramatic settings in a county not short on competition in that department, while the attention to interior detail in the Italianate house itself is of an impressively high order. The conservatory dining-room allows you to feast your eyes on the ambient magnificence, while scampering squirrels, 'cavorting badgers' and 'a flock of nosy guinea-fowl' provide a diverting floorshow in the foreground.

The cooking is very much in contemporary Lakeland vein, but shows a painstaking desire to balance flavours appositely in dishes that may contain a number of elements. This comes across in a first course of home-smoked salmon served in a thick slice with a spicy tomato concassé, asparagus tips and mange-tout to one side, deep-fried cabbage strips on top, the gentle smoking of the fish adding depth to the overall impact. A cheese and herb soufflé sounds simple enough, its 'soft and moist but not runny' middle demonstrating great timing, but add some chopped smoked haddock and 'a swathe of red-pepper purée' to a buttery sauce and it moves up through several gears. At dinner a soup – spicy lentil in October – is served while you await main courses, which major in meat: guinea-fowl with chicken livers on pasta with an orange sauce, perhaps, or Norfolk squab roasted with a slice of foie gras and served with creamed cabbage and bacon and a madeira sauce. Vegetables are refreshingly simple, but 'all tasting wonderful'.

One group in December had an assortment of 'seasonal' desserts: Christmas pudding agreeably laced with rum, a brandy-snap basket filled with strawberries, crème caramel and sticky toffee pudding, 'all fresh, delicate and tasty'. Cheeses are notably well kept. Service is 'formal and correct, but very cordial', and the flourishing of silver domes continues relentlessly.

Classical France is the chief preserve of the wine list. If your lottery numbers come up, note that the Fine Wines are mostly very fine. As for the rest, a smattering of New World bottles affords relief alongside some youthful clarets and workaday wines from elsewhere in Europe. House French is £11.50.

CHEF: Robert Thornton PROPRIETORS: Pauline and Derek Harrison, and Gordon Evans OPEN: all week 12 to 1, 7 to 8.30 (9 Sat) MEALS: alc (main courses £16.50 to £18) Set L £18.50, Set D £25. Minimum £18.50 L, £21 D SERVICE: not inc, card slips closed CARDS: Access, Amex, Switch, Visa DETAILS: 50 seats. 4 tables outside. Private parties: 40 main room, 20 private room. Car park. Vegetarian meals. No children under 12. Smart dress preferred. No smoking in dining-room. No music ACCOMMODATION: 11 rooms, all with bath/shower. TV. Phone. D,B&B £85 to £250. Deposit: 25%. Garden (*The Which? Hotel Guide*)

ARNCLIFFE North Yorkshire map 8

▲ *Amerdale House*

NEW ENTRY

Arncliffe, Littondale, nr Skipton BD23 5QE
TEL/FAX: (01756) 770250 COOKING 2
off B6160, 7m NW of Grassington COST £31–£37

Amerdale, formerly the manor house of Arncliffe estate, is late Victorian (with older origins) and set on the edge of a peaceful village. It is a small-scale and personal operation, and guests soon find themselves in conversation with each other. The dining-room overlooks the front garden and fields beyond, and the daily-changing dinner menu is four courses, with a balanced choice of three items to begin, one of which is generally fruity, then a second course of soup or fish.

The food can be as homely as Whitby crab salad with lime mayonnaise, a butter-fried sandwich of smoked ham and Gruyère cheese (a sort of croque monsieur) or steamed jam sponge with custard. But Nigel Crapper also turns out deep-fried sweetbreads in a crispy breadcrumb coating with a piquant sauce, and grilled polenta with tomato sauce and Parmesan shavings. Fish tends to be meaty and grilled – from halibut to salmon to Dover sole – although it has also included fresh-tasting plaice with curried orange butter, which may be overdoing things a bit. The kitchen is on firmer ground with roast leg of Dales lamb studded with rosemary and garlic, which comes with a tasteful gravy jus. Vegetables vary with the main course, and are 'carefully cooked, retaining some crispness'.

There are usually two puddings: at one meal a rich and 'properly made' apple and raspberry crème brûlée, and a relatively light version of treacle tart with a thin, flaky pastry base and real custard. The other option is home-made oatmeal biscuits with local cheese: Coverdale, Blue Wensleydale, Silverdale or Ribblesdale goats'. The Crappers are 'a charming couple, genuinely warm and professional but approachable', and there are some good names and reasonable prices on the wine list. Wakefield Cabernet Sauvignon, by the way, is from Australia, not Yorkshire. Regional French starts the ball rolling at £8.35.

CHEF: Nigel Crapper PROPRIETORS: Paula and Nigel Crapper OPEN: all week D only 7 to 8.30 CLOSED: Nov to Mar MEALS: Set D £24 SERVICE: not inc, card slips closed CARDS: Access, Visa DETAILS: 22 seats. Private parties: 22 main room. Car park. Children's helpings. Smart dress preferred. No smoking in dining-room. No music ACCOMMODATION: 11 rooms, all with bath/shower. TV. B&B £40.50 to £67. Baby facilities. Garden (*The Which? Hotel Guide*)

ASENBY North Yorkshire map 9

Crab & Lobster

Asenby YO7 3QL
TEL: (01845) 577286 FAX: (01845) 577109 COOKING 2
off A168, between A19 and A1 COST £20–£50

The crustaceans have made their home in a thatched seventeenth-century country pub east of Ripon in surroundings characterised by the owners as 'bohemian antique mish-mash'. Whatever the definition, the place has genuine character. You can eat either brasserie food ordered at the bar from a bewilderingly wide choice (baked scallops, parsnip and pear soup, lobster thermidor, and roast woodpigeon are among the offerings) or avail yourself of the full restaurant menu.

Michael Pickard cooks dishes of considerable panache, some of which may sound quite unlikely in the context of a Yorkshire pub. Escalope of foie gras with toasted brioche and caramelised oranges has more than a touch of swank, while main courses take in the likes of halibut 'chunk' with a tomato compote and crisp onions, or medallions of venison with Agen prunes, cranberries and pasta. One reporter characterised it all as 'huge portions of very ambitious food on immense plates', a verdict that might sound the death-knell were the cooking not brought off with such convincing élan. Desserts, too, pile on the style, a five-course gourmet menu offering chilled passion-fruit and vanilla soufflé with macerated red fruits and strawberry purée. House wines from France are £8.50.

CHEF: Michael Pickard PROPRIETORS: David and Jackie Barnard OPEN: all week L 12 to 2.30, Mon to Sat D 6.30 to 10 CLOSED: 25 Dec MEALS: alc (main courses £10.50 to £19.50). Set L £13.75 SERVICE: not inc, card slips closed CARDS: Access, Amex, Delta, Switch, Visa DETAILS: 100 seats. 20 tables outside. Private parties: 65 main room, 20 and 50 private rooms. Car park. Vegetarian meals. Children's helpings. Smart dress preferred. Music

ASHBOURNE Derbyshire map 8

▲ *Callow Hall*

Mappleton Road, Ashbourne DE6 2AA
TEL: (01335) 343403 FAX: (01335) 343624
¾m NW of Ashbourne, turn left off A515 at crossroads with Bowling Green pub on left; Mappleton Road first on right

COOKING 1*
COST £21–£48

The Spencer family has been baking and catering for the citizens of Ashbourne since the late eighteenth century, Callow Hall being only the most recent example of their indefatigable enterprise. Industrious home production is the kitchen's foundation: salmon is smoked, bacon is cured and Ashbourne gingerbread is baked for tea within the hall's confines. The scale may initially seem grand, but the dining-room is a comfortable place and the tone of service refreshingly friendly. Set-price dinners offer four courses plus coffee, the second course a choice of fish or sorbet. The style of cooking marshals some interesting combinations without going overboard. Starters might be a pigeon breast with avocado and spring onions, a simple soup, or a classic sauté of scallops with spinach and bacon. Fish is mostly traditionally prepared, although monkfish tail with tapénade appeared one night. Stuffings bulk out the meat dishes: apricot or even mango may be used for guinea-fowl, a more familiar herbed filling for loin of lamb with celeriac. The speciality pudding is Callow flan, an almond, apple and mincemeat tart with apricot glaze. Otherwise, chocolate mousse, fruit salad or warm fruit tarts are the order of the day. Those who stay overnight enjoy the extensive breakfast menu and the 'glorious views' of woodland and the Peak District.

The wine list does France proud, though the coherent ordering by price or vintage called for last year is still not in sight. Other regions are less good but prices are easier, and there are plenty of halves. House French is £9.75 (white) and £9.50 (red).

CHEFS: David and Anthony Spencer PROPRIETORS: David and Dorothy Spencer, and Anthony Spencer OPEN: Tue and Sun L (other days by arrangement) 12.30 to 1.30, Mon to Sat D (Sun residents only) 7.30 to 9.15 MEALS: alc (main courses £13 to £17). Set L £14.75, Set D £29.50 SERVICE: not inc CARDS: Access, Amex, Diners, Visa DETAILS: 60 seats. Private parties: 35 main room, 20 and 35 private rooms. Car park. Vegetarian meals. Children's helpings. Smart dress preferred. No smoking in dining-room. No music ACCOMMODATION: 16 rooms, all with bath/shower. TV. Phone. B&B £65 to £130. Rooms for disabled. Children welcome. Baby facilities. Pets by arrangement. Garden. Fishing (*The Which? Hotel Guide*)

'Certainly this young waitress was getting hands-on-experience – the cheese was served with her fingers.' **(On eating in Wales)**

ASTON CLINTON Buckinghamshire map 3

▲ *Bell Inn* 🍷 £✱

Aston Clinton HP22 5HP
TEL: (01296) 630252 FAX: (01296) 631250 COOKING 1
on A41, between Tring and Aylesbury COST £35–£56

Once the haunt of political dignitaries and their minions, this bastion of Home Counties conservatism clings to its tweed-suited image with dogged resilience. The dining-room, which one visitor thought was like a work of art with its autumnal scenes painted on the walls, is still etched with staid solidity: the synchronous lifting of cloches continues unabated. Reports suggest that Giles Stonehouse, after a slightly shaky start last year, has now found his feet in the kitchen. The cooking does not try to startle and it seldom takes risks: it is reliable rather than racy. Meals revolve around a choice of set menus and a short *carte*: the legendary Bell Inn smokies and specially reared Aylesbury ducks are still there, and fish is popular. Baked salmon with 'potato scales' on a beurre blanc with a light tomato sauce, and grilled fillet of brill with chive butter sauce have both been praised. Reporters have also commended strongly flavoured wild-mushroom soup, and breast of chicken stuffed with walnut and Stilton mousse. Any tendency towards richness in first and main courses is tempered by light desserts such as kumquat parfait with pear coulis, or lemon tart with candied lemon and orange zest.

Classic French wines form the backbone of the list, but there is good support from the New World and other sections such as sparkling and dessert wines; half-bottles are generous. Prices, though, can be high. A couple of pages of house wines simplify choice, beginning at £12.95 for vin de pays Chardonnay and Merlot. CELLARMAN'S CHOICE: Vidal Sauvignon Blanc 1993, Hawkes Bay, New Zealand, £18.75; Médoc, Ch. La Tour St-Bonnet 1992, £19.75.

CHEF: Giles Stonehouse PROPRIETOR: M.D.G. Harris OPEN: all week 12.30 to 1.45, 7.30 to 9.45 MEALS: alc (main courses £13 to £16). Set L £13.50 (2 courses) to £17, Set D £25 SERVICE: not inc, card slips closed CARDS: Access, Amex, Delta, Switch, Visa DETAILS: 150 seats. 9 tables outside. Private parties: 68 main room, 24 to 200 private rooms. Car park. Vegetarian meals. Children's helpings. Smart dress preferred. No smoking in dining-room. Wheelchair access (also WC). Music ACCOMMODATION: 21 rooms, all with bath/shower. TV. Phone. B&B £50 to £80. Rooms for disabled. Children welcome. Baby facilities. Pets welcome. Afternoon teas. Garden (*The Which? Hotel Guide*)

AYLESBURY Buckinghamshire map 3

▲ *Hartwell House* 🍷 £✱

Oxford Road, Aylesbury HP17 8NL
TEL: (01296) 747444 FAX: (01296) 747450 COOKING 2*
on A418, 2m from Aylesbury towards Oxford COST £30–£74

The building is arguably one of the finest examples of a restored country house in England. It stands in 90 acres of sweeping grounds, complete with croquet lawn and a herd of cows that obligingly fulfils the rural expectation. The Historic House Hotels group of which Hartwell House is part (along with Middlethorpe Hall, see entry, York, and Bodysgallen Hall, see entry, Llandudno, Wales) has done as good a job as it is possible to do, and probably spent as much money as it is possible to do. 'Dinner guests may feel they are helping to foot the bill,' suggested one, which of course they are. A supplement of £7 for a fillet of sea bass – even though this is a long way from the sea – seems a bit much, though it would probably not have bothered Louis XVIII, who lived here for five years in the early nineteenth century.

Dinner in the pale yellow dining-room – 'very grand, very formal' – is a choice of eight to ten alternatives per course, and the kitchen is at home with contemporary ideas, such as carpaccio of monkfish and tuna with a potato and balsamic salad. Indeed, fish is a strong suit. Two reporters approved red mullet on salad leaves, and halibut 'at the peak of freshness' with a Gruyère and brioche crust. The style is as innovative as a warm chicken sausage with wild mushrooms and lentils on creamed potatoes, and the cooking is precisely timed.

The menu changes seasonally, and summer pudding, or pistachio parfait on a confit of kumquats might be among the attractions. There are canapés to start and petits fours to finish. Lunch offers less choice and could be a bargain, though anybody who just wants a look at the place might consider afternoon tea at a mere £9.50. Wines are generally high-quality, with prices to match, and though the lower reaches are not neglected you have to hunt for affordable bottles. House French is from £11.90. CELLARMAN'S CHOICE: Fairview Estate Pinot Gris 1993, South Africa, £17; Fairview Estate Shiraz 1992, South Africa, £17.

CHEF: Alan Maw PROPRIETOR: Historic House Hotels Ltd OPEN: all week 12.30 to 1.50, 7.30 to 9.40 MEALS: Set L £18.70 (2 courses) to £24.50, Set D £39.50 SERVICE: net prices, card slips closed CARDS: Access, Amex, Delta, Diners, Switch, Visa DETAILS: 80 seats. Private parties: 60 main room, 18, 30 and 60 private rooms. Car park. Vegetarian meals. No children under 8. Jacket and tie. No smoking in dining-room. Wheelchair access (also WC). Music ACCOMMODATION: 45 rooms, all with bath/shower. TV. Phone. B&B £107 to £253. Rooms for disabled. No children under 8. Pets welcome in bedrooms only. Afternoon teas. Garden. Swimming-pool. Fishing (*The Which? Hotel Guide*)

BARNARD CASTLE Co Durham map 10

Blagraves House

30–32 The Bank, Barnard Castle DL12 8PN COOKING 2*
TEL: (01833) 637668 COST £21–£36

Blagraves is the kind of house that tourist brochure designers dream about. Its photogenic mix of mullioned windows, oak panelling, crested ceilings and vaulted cellars is pure Olde English; log fires burn in winter, flowers fill the hearth during the summer. As a bonus, the place lists Oliver Cromwell among its great guests of the past. However, owners Kenneth and Elizabeth Marley are not content simply to trade on history. Their cooking moves with the times, menus change monthly and their style is a fulsome version of modern British, underpinned by home baking, preserving and sound domestic enterprise, although they are not averse to conjuring up classics such as beef Wellington when required. A couple who dined from the *carte* found much to praise, in particular warm fish terrine with Chablis sauce, potted rabbit with gammon, and braised oxtail boned and stuffed with shallots and bacon. Others have endorsed the excellent-value weekday set-price menu, which offers wholesome stuff such as gnocchi with smoked bacon and local Cotherstone cheese, roast chicken with a spicy coriander-flavoured risotto, and sea bream with watercress. Puddings might include raspberry brûlée and coconut ice-cream. Service is attentive without veering into over-familiarity. The wine list does the trick with a modest selection of keenly priced bottles from most major countries. House wine is £7.95.

CHEFS/PROPRIETORS: Kenneth and Elizabeth Marley OPEN: Tue to Sat D only 7 to 9.30 MEALS: alc (main courses £8 to £14). Set D Tue to Fri £13.50 SERVICE: not inc, card slips closed CARDS: Access, Delta, Switch, Visa DETAILS: 26 seats. Private parties: 26 main room, 40 private room. Vegetarian meals. Children welcome. Smart dress preferred. No smoking in 1 dining-room. Music

BARNET Hertfordshire **map 3**

Mims

63 East Barnet Road, Barnet EN4 8RN COOKING 2*
TEL: 0181-449 2974 FAX: 0181-447 1825 COST £22–£38

There isn't much to arrest the attention on East Barnet Road, and Mims could be just another mediocre neighbourhood bistro. Reports, however, continue to attest that this impression would be way off the mark. Here is no 'frenetic ambition to win celebrity status' (for all Ali Al-Sersy's Roux Brothers tutelage) – just a restaurant that has been 'commendably patient in doing what it set out to accomplish'. Readers' reports are emphatic about the excellent value, especially at lunch-time, the 'unimposing and leisurely' approach and the sheer quality of the food. This is the best restaurant for miles around.

Much of what the scrawled fixed-price menus attempt is quite daring in conception. This is not a kitchen to shy away from pyrotechnic flourishes, but most of what is attempted comes off. Witness a starter of 'supremely savoury' sauté chicken livers and mushrooms laid on a 'pasta sheet' to collect the cooking juices which delivered wondrous intensity of flavour. Garlic is steamed to provide the creamy base for a soup with plenty of fresh parsley. The chargrill makes its presence felt, perhaps a shade clumsily in a main course of seared salmon with similarly singed courgettes in a salad, but the treatment of roast duck was more apposite: robustly done to an almost Cantonese degree, it was accompanied by 'astonishing' outer leaves of cabbage, fresh and crunchy, and a subtle sauce that involved foie gras.

Puddings show a simpler touch but still impress for technique in a 'pie' of red-hot fried banana slices, a properly tart lemon tart, and strikingly presented white chocolate mousse. Good coffee and breads contribute to the air of contentment. The wine list is principally French, with an unexceptional smattering from elsewhere, with choices that are solid but not stimulating. Prices, however, are kept in check. House French is £9.50.

CHEF: Ali Al-Sersy PROPRIETORS: Ali Al-Sersy and M. Zahrah OPEN: Sun noon to 10.30, Tue to Fri L 12 to 3, Tue to Sat D 6.30 to 11; during Dec all week 12 to 3, 6.30 to 11 MEALS: Set L £9.50 (2 courses) to £13.50 Set D £15 (2 courses) to £19 SERVICE: not inc CARDS: Access, Delta, Switch, Visa DETAILS: 45 seats. Private parties: 50 main room. No children under 6 L. Smart dress preferred. No cigars/pipes in dining-room. Wheelchair access (1 step). No music

BARNSLEY South Yorkshire map 9

Armstrongs 🍷

6 Shambles Street, Barnsley S70 2SQ COOKING 1
TEL: (01226) 240113 COST £19–£39

Armstrongs is a lively place near the town hall and might be described as Barnsley's best shot at café society. Unobtrusive jazz and potted plants set the tone in the dining-room. Nick Pound served his apprenticeship with Stephen Bull (see entries, London) during the 1980s and his cooking is English revivalist, plundering the globe for uncluttered ideas and inspiration. Menus change each month: in April you might find pasta with asparagus and garden peas, Moroccan marinated chicken with vegetable couscous, and fillets of baby halibut with preserved lemon, capers and red onion. To follow there might be plum and cinnanon tart with Amaretto ice-cream or iced butterscotch meringue cake with orange julienne sauce. Weekday lunches provide some lighter touches and the early-evening menu (7 to 8pm, Tuesday to Friday) is an affordable bet. A relatively short but reliable and interesting list of realistically priced wines begins in the South of France at £8.95. CELLARMAN'S CHOICE: Vins de Pays de l'Ardèche, Prestige Chardonnay 1993, Vignerons Ardèchois £11.75; Tempranillo 1991, Bodegas Ochoa, Navarra, £12.95.

CHEF/PROPRIETOR: Nick Pound OPEN: Tue to Fri L 12 to 2, Tue to Sat D 7 to 10 MEALS: alc (main courses £8 to £13). Set D Tue to Fri 7 to 8 £12.95 SERVICE: not inc CARDS: Access, Amex, Delta, Switch, Visa DETAILS: 60 seats. Private parties: 40 main room, 20 and 30 private rooms. Vegetarian meals. Children welcome. Wheelchair access (1 step). Music

BARNSTAPLE Devon map 1

Lynwood House £

Bishops Tawton Road, Barnstaple EX32 9DZ
TEL: (01271) 43695 FAX: (01271) 79340 COOKING 1*
1m S of town centre, before A377 roundabout COST £20–£55

It looks like the sort of building that might have become a nursing home but didn't: solid, Victorian, on a corner plot on the outskirts of Barnstaple. Pot plants and candles in the dining-room add to the 'comfortable middle-class suburban feel'. The Robertses have been here for 27 years, refreshed in their efforts now and again as more family members come on stream. They currently offer a short *carte* that is supplemented with lighter options that include salads, and a set-price business lunch.

The style is plain cooking that doesn't try to impress with gestures beyond the kitchen's capabilities. Fish is a strong suit, with sole, scallops, hot-smoked salmon and a full-flavoured chunky fish soup of white fish, salmon and shellfish all added just in time to cook through. One inspector looking for faults in this dish confessed himself defeated. Crispy roast duck, fillet steak and pot-roast partridge are among the meat options, and vegetables are given proper care and attention. The richness of double cream, not entirely unexpected in Devon, makes its presence felt in puddings such as chocolate truffle mousse and crème caramel. The well-stocked cellar offers a good range of quality and prices, and house wine is £8.75.

CHEFS: Ruth Roberts and Matthew Roberts PROPRIETORS: John, Ruth, Matthew and Christian Roberts OPEN: Mon to Sat 12 to 2, 7 to 10 (9.30 winter) MEALS: alc (main courses £12.95 to £21). Set L £11.95 to £13.95 SERVICE: not inc CARDS: Access, Amex, Delta, Diners, Switch, Visa DETAILS: 60 seats. Private parties: 60 main room, 20 private room. Car park. Vegetarian meals. Children welcome. Smart dress preferred. No smoking in dining-room. Wheelchair access (also WC). Music ACCOMMODATION: 5 rooms, all with bath/shower. TV. Phone. B&B £40.50 to £60.50. Children welcome. Pets welcome

BARTON-UPON-HUMBER Humberside map 9

Elio's £

11 Market Place, Barton-upon-Humber DN18 5DA COOKING 1
TEL: (01652) 635147 COST £15–£43

Twelve years of sound practice have made Elio Grossi's little trattoria on Barton's market-place a firm favourite in an area not liberally endowed with good eating. Regulars who eat here every month say that, despite its being rather cramped on a busy Saturday night, 'the quality never falters'. The menus mix some straightforward Italian cooking – grilled sardines, chicken cooked in wine and cream, Venetian-style calf's liver with onions, and a range of pizzas – with some thought-provoking daily specials. Fish is the freshest, and is as competently handled in the simple grilling of a Dover sole as in the agrodolce saucing of baby halibut with citrus juices, herbs and butter. A spring diner who started with fettuccine cooked with mushrooms, smoked bacon and cream thought it 'the best pasta I have had for a long time'. Desserts tend to let the side down somewhat when the predictable Italian gelati misti and zabaglione are trundled out, but March saw Elio flaming apple crêpes in calvados at the table, so perhaps things are looking up. Good coffee comes, of course, with amaretti. Wines are a standard Italian selection, and the list presumes you will not need to know who made them or in what years. House Tocai and Merlot from the Veneto are £8.95.

CHEFS: Elio Grossi, N. Lyons and L. Kuyath PROPRIETOR: Elio Grossi OPEN: Mon to Fri L 12 to 2, Mon to Sat D 6 to 10.30 (11 Sat) CLOSED: 2 weeks Aug MEALS: alc (main courses £7 to £18). Set L £7.95, Set D (2 people, inc wine) Mon to Fri £24.50 SERVICE: not inc Mon to Fri; 10% Sat; card slips closed CARDS: Access, Amex, Delta, Diners, Visa DETAILS: 40 seats. Private parties: 18 main room, 12 and 18 private rooms. Vegetarian meals. Children's helpings. Smart dress preferred. No smoking in 1 dining-room. Wheelchair access (1 step). Music

BARWICK Somerset map 2

▲ *Little Barwick House*

SOMERSET 1996 FLAVOUR

Barwick BA22 9TD
TEL: (01935) 23902 FAX: (01935) 20908 COOKING 3
off A37, take second left opposite Red House pub COST £31–£40

Little Barwick is house and home for Christopher and Veronica Colley; it seems almost incidental that they run it as a personable, if 'slightly eccentric', hotel.

Their captivating Georgian dower house is set in more than three acres of grounds on the edge of the village, and it continues to woo visitors with its informality. Dinners are priced according to the number of courses taken. What impresses is the uncluttered approach, the emphasis on flavour rather than fashion, and the commitment to local produce. Fish is from West Bay, beef and lamb are reared in the Vale of Taunton, game is from nearby sources, and many vegetables are grown by a green-fingered schoolteacher in Sherborne. The result is a repertoire of soups, pies and steaks fleshed out with dishes such as honey-glazed confit of duck on a bed of fresh pasta and rack of lamb with mint and cucumber sauce. Weekly specials add interest: warm salad of quail's eggs with smoked bacon, medallions of venison with blackcurrant and port sauce, or baked fillets of sole with tarragon cream sauce. Puddings take care with textures and tastes, and span the range from lime sorbet to steamed treacle pudding, to a little pot of chocolate. Barwick House is also a happy hunting ground for vegetarians, who might be offered a warm salad of avocado and toasted pine-nuts with slivers of Parmesan, grilled vegetable tartlet with herb butter sauce, or stuffed peppers with cherry tomatoes, shallots and feta cheese. The substantial wine list roams far and wide, but prices are kept in check and half-bottles are not neglected. House wines are £9.60.

CHEF: Veronica Colley PROPRIETORS: Christopher and Veronica Colley OPEN: Mon to Sat D only 7 to 9 MEALS: Set D £17.50 (2 courses) to £22.90 SERVICE: not inc, card slips closed CARDS: Access, Amex, Visa DETAILS: 40 seats. Private parties: 40 main room, 18 private room. Car park. Vegetarian meals. Children's helpings. No smoking in dining-room. No music. Air-conditioned ACCOMMODATION: 6 rooms, all with bath/shower. TV. Phone. B&B £48 to £78. Deposit: £20. Children welcome. Pets welcome. Garden (*The Which? Hotel Guide*)

BASLOW Derbyshire map 9

▲ *Fischer's Baslow Hall*

DERBYSHIRE 1996 CLASSIC

Calver Road, Baslow DE45 1RR COOKING 4
TEL: (01246) 583259 FAX: (01246) 583818 COST £29–£54

Opinion is divided as to the aesthetic qualities of this Edwardian hall, close to Chatsworth House in the sheep-strewn Peak District National Park, but the Fischers have avoided standard country-house décor in favour of an approach that imitates the styles of bygone eras. Some love it, some don't. What counts is the amount of care that goes into everything from main constituents down to incidentals. Cooking is based on both a sound understanding of the importance of good ingredients and a mastery of classic techniques. The apparently effortless results belie the work that has gone into them.

The skills come together impressively in a first course of lamb's sweetbreads and kidneys, with an impeccably flavoured soubise, and in another of pan-fried scallops, each sitting on a thin slice of potato, with a terrific vinaigrette that combines freshness with spiciness and earthiness: a 'brilliant and sophisticated' touch of exotica. Freshness is striking, timing is spot-on, roasts are properly rested, and textures and consistencies are carefully handled. Duck breast (first sauté then roasted) combines crisp skin, a layer of fat that was 'definitely worth eating', and juicy, supple, flavourful meat; draped elegantly over a baked cake of grated potato, and surrounded by a carefully haphazard scattering of vegetables, the dish appeals both in its detail and as a whole. The tailoring of vegetables specifically to each main course deserves the praise it gets.

Puddings are technically immaculate and beautifully presented. A teardrop of white chocolate (with none of the blandness white chocolate is prone to) is served with warm raspberries and a chocolate sorbet, 'which is about as good as a chocolate sorbet can be'. A mille-feuille of oranges and pears is a double-decker sandwich of crisp pastry and wedges of fruit, served on a translucent citrus sauce with a thick, rich, yolky scented custard. Service errs on the formal side and is too stiff for some, but Susan Fischer's hostessing receives praise. As to value, note that the set-dinner price includes mineral water, coffee and copious extras. Café Max, in another room, offers lower prices, and a more laid-back menu along the lines of goats' cheese tartlet with tomato and thyme, cod and salmon fish-cakes, and gratin of rhubarb with stuffed prunes. The wine list aims for quality rather than bargains, but bottles under £20 (including dry Jurançon, Australasian whites, Beaujolais and a couple of Rhônes) are worth drinking. House wine is £10.50. CELLARMAN'S CHOICE: Meursault 1992, Michelot, £30; Crozes-Hermitage 'Les Meysonniers 1991, Chapoutier, £20.

CHEF: Max Fischer PROPRIETORS: Max and Susan Fischer OPEN: Sun to Fri L 12 to 2, Mon to Sat D 7 to 9.30; Sun D residents only CLOSED: 25 and 26 Dec MEALS: Set L £16.50 (2 courses) to £19.50, Set D £36 SERVICE: not inc, card slips closed CARDS: Access, Amex, Diners, Visa DETAILS: 76 seats. 4 tables outside. Private parties: 40 main room, 12 to 40 private rooms. Car park. No children under 10 after 7 pm. Smart dress preferred. No smoking in dining-room. Wheelchair access (3 steps; also WC). No music ACCOMMODATION: 6 rooms, all with bath/shower. TV. Phone. B&B £70 to £120. Deposit: £50. Children welcome. Baby facilities. Afternoon teas. Garden (*The Which? Hotel Guide*)

BATH Avon map 2

▲ *Bath Spa Hotel, Vellore Restaurant*

Sydney Road, Bath BA2 6JF COOKING 2
TEL: (01225) 444424 FAX: (01225) 444006 COST £28–£78

Mimosa-coloured walls, heavy curtains, chandeliers and stripey fabric on the chairs make the large Vellore dining-room – formerly the ballroom – feel comfortable and coolly elegant. At dinner a tinkly pianist plays nothing too aurally demanding, which seems to suit the food, relying as it does on simple partnerings of good ingredients. Parma ham, bresaola and carved melon may be all right, but as a third of a £35 menu it seems a bit steep. The other two-thirds might be baked turbot followed by tiramisù. When the cooking does get going, though, it really shifts, with first courses of monkfish tempura with stir-fried vegetables in a mirin and rice wine sauce, or baked pâté of foie gras with chicken livers and wild mushrooms plus papaya chutney and herb bread.

A dinner *carte* has been introduced since last year, with plenty of choice, supplemented by four menus called Collectives, for two people or more, though pretence reaches new heights (or is it depths?) when five fishy courses for £27.50 per person are billed as 'ichitology' (sic). Accompaniments are strong on appeal: a bitter-tasting endive cream to cut through the sweet saltiness of a sauce for sweetbreads; smoked garlic jus with lamb; or sweet potato purée and braised shallots with veal. Though the food may lack a distinctive personality, desserts are well executed, including a passion-fruit soufflé with coconut ice-cream. Cheeses are fine. Wines are expensive: even local Elm Crosshouse wine is £17.50. The Alfresco restaurant is open all week for lighter and less expensive dishes.

CHEF: Jonathan Fraser PROPRIETOR: Forte plc OPEN: Sun L 12.30 to 2, all week D 7 to 10 MEALS: alc (main courses £13 to £23.50). Set L Sun £16.50, Set D £35 SERVICE: not inc, card slips closed CARDS: Access, Amex, Delta, Diners, Switch, Visa DETAILS: 100 seats. Private parties: 140 main room, 8 to 140 private rooms. Car park. Vegetarian meals. Children's helpings. Jacket and tie. No smoking in dining-room. Wheelchair access (also WC). Music. Air-conditioned ACCOMMODATION: 98 rooms, all with bath/shower. TV. Phone. B&B £109 to £179. Rooms for disabled. Lift. Children welcome. Baby facilities by arrangement. Pets by arrangement. Afternoon teas. Garden. Swimming-pool

Clos du Roy

1 Seven Dials, Saw Close, Bath BA1 1EN COOKING 2*
TEL: (01225) 444450 FAX: (01225) 460218 COST £20–£38

The restaurant is in the new Seven Dials development next to the theatre, a large semi-circular room on the first floor with french windows all around the curved wall, opening on to a small but pretty wrought-iron balcony. 'It looks as if it was designed to be a piano bar,' given the decorative musical motifs and the ivory-coloured baby grand which is played during the evening. Competition in Bath is intense. For one reporter Clos du Roy is the benchmark, while another has found it disappointing. But Philippe Roy goes out of his way to be accommodating: the set-price and à la carte menus at both lunch and dinner, and pre- and post-theatre meals, are generous to a fault.

'This must be one of the last redoubts of nouvelle cuisine,' according to one reporter, 'at least as far as the portions go.' Certainly presentation is taken seriously, and the foundation is French, but there are plenty of items that a British chef might well include in his or her repertoire, from carrot and orange soup, through steamed fillet of salmon with a tarragon butter, to profiteroles filled with butterscotch ice-cream covered in chocolate sauce. Saucing is along conservative lines – thyme-flavoured with venison fillet, burgundy-infused for a pan-fried sirloin of Scotch beef – and the same selection of vegetables is likely to appear with everything. Puddings from chef patissier Alain Dubini hold their own: a milk chocolate and cinnamon mousse is served with vanilla and apple sauce, and a passion-fruit charlotte is glazed with a bitter chocolate gelée. Service is efficient and pleasant, and wines are mostly French, helpfully arranged by style, with a fair selection of half-bottles. House wine is £8.95.

CHEF/PROPRIETOR: Philippe Roy OPEN: all week 12 to 2.30, 6 to 10.30 CLOSED: 25 Dec MEALS: alc (main courses £13). Set L £8.95 (2 courses) to £11.95, Set D £18.50, Pre- and post-theatre menu SERVICE: not inc, card slips closed CARDS: Access, Amex, Delta, Diners, Visa DETAILS: 80 seats. 5 tables outside. Private parties: 100 main room. Vegetarian meals. Children's helpings. Smart dress preferred. Wheelchair access (also WC). Music

Waiter to customer: 'Oh, I don't know what [port] we've got. They're just a load of old bottles to me. Come and have a look.'' ' (On eating in London)

Hole in the Wall

16 George Street, Bath BA1 2EH — COOKING 3
TEL/FAX: (01225) 425242 — COST £19–£35

Anybody who thinks of a hole in the wall as a cash dispenser is probably too young to remember this restaurant in its heyday under George Perry-Smith. It is testament to his enduring influence that older reporters still take his tenure here as the benchmark, hoping to recapture early excitement. Those who recall the far-off prices can be disappointed, which is rather unfair on the present team. An air of quiet competence pervades the two rooms. Smokers have bare wooden tables and chairs, non-smokers have a smart modern room with colourful abstract paintings, and displays of oils, bottles, jars and other comestible paraphernalia.

The Hole offers a varied output with plenty of choice on the *carte*, keeps abreast of the times and combines traditional British and Mediterranean ideas with reasonable panache, from warm salad of monkfish with Carmarthen ham and mushrooms to daube of beef with mild horseradish dumplings, from chicken breast kebab on couscous for lunch to a rich and unctuous lamb shank for dinner. At one meal a main course of lambs' tongue with liver and kidneys – 'all browny-grey, in a brown sauce' – followed a thin pastry spread with pesto and tomato (both fresh and sun-dried), on top of which rested two slices of grilled goats' cheese; anchovy and chopped black olives in an oily dribble around the edge added to the simple delight of 'flavour without blur'.

Interest is sustained in puddings of mulled figs and kumquats with white chocolate ice-cream, wimberry tartlet, or a gently warm rice pudding that is 'tasty without relying on nutmeg', served with a compote of stoned plums: 'a simple dish done well'. Young, competent, unobtrusive staff oversee the pleasantly informal operation and serve wines from the concise, up-to-the-minute, youthful list. There are no passengers on it, so careful is the selection – virtually every wine is a gem – and prices are reasonable. Over 20 wines are available by the glass from £2 to £5.50, and house French is around £10. CELLARMAN'S CHOICE: St-Hallett Cabernet/Merlot 1992, Barossa Valley, S. Australia, £17.50; Graves, Ch. Beauregard 1993, £16.

CHEFS: Christopher Chown and Adrian Walton PROPRIETORS: Christopher Chown and Gunna á Trødni OPEN: Mon to Sat 12 to 2, 6 to 11 MEALS: alc (main courses £12; any 3 courses £19.50). Set L £9.50 (2 courses) to £11.50 SERVICE: not inc CARDS: Access, Amex, Switch, Visa DETAILS: 70 seats. Private parties: 16 main room. Vegetarian meals. Children welcome. No smoking in 1 dining-room. No music. Air-conditioned

▲ *Queensberry Hotel, Olive Tree*

Russel Street, Bath BA1 2QF — COOKING 2
TEL: (01225) 447928 FAX: (01225) 446065 — COST £20–£46

Those used to dimmed lights, deep-pile carpets and hushed formality in hotel restaurants may find the Olive Tree a pleasant surprise. The room is unexpectedly light and airy for a basement, not large but made to feel spacious by the careful positioning of tables and by the ceramic-tiled floor.

The kitchen team, led by Stephen Ross, ploughs a robust Mediterranean furrow that takes in Provence (for fish soup and rouille), Italy (for polenta with mushrooms and courgettes) and Morocco (for chicken couscous with onions and peppers). An inspection dinner began in fine style with a dish of chargrilled, caramelised scallops on a bed of wilted spinach and toasted pine-nuts. Asparagus and salmon risotto impressed for the earthiness of the two principal ingredients. A main course of monkfish was helped by a copious sauce of white wine, onions, cream and dill. Another good sauce, a meat reduction with rosemary and garlic, partnered rump of 'chewy' lamb with haricot beans. EU health regulations are probably to blame for the 'positively icy' temperature at which the otherwise fine cheeses were served, the charcoal-coated goats' and the Camembert in particular standing out. A sweeter tooth might go for iced ginger meringue with a poached pear and advocaat cream, or hot chocolate pudding with chocolate sauce. Service is commended both for friendliness and knowledgeability. The smallish wine list is adequate rather than imaginative, Australia providing respite from the duller French selections. House vin de pays d'Oc is £10.50.

CHEFS: Stephen Ross, Janice Wilmot and Mathew Prowse PROPRIETORS: Stephen and Penny Ross OPEN: Mon to Sat L 7 to 10 (9 Sun), all week D 7 to 10 (9 Sun) CLOSED: 1 week Christmas MEALS: alc (main courses £9.50 to £13.60). Set L £9.50 (2 courses) to £11.50, Set D Mon to Fri £17, Set D Sun £14.50 (2 courses) to £16.50. SERVICE: not inc CARDS: Access, Amex, Delta, Switch, Visa DETAILS: 50 seats. Private parties: 30 main room, 16 private room. Vegetarian meals. Children's helpings. No smoking in dining-room. Wheelchair access (3 steps; also WC). Music ACCOMMODATION: 22 rooms, all with bath/shower. TV. Phone. B&B £84 to £164. Rooms for disabled. Children welcome. Baby facilities. Afternoon teas. Garden (*The Which? Hotel Guide*)

▲ *Royal Crescent Hotel, Dower House*

15–16 Royal Crescent, Bath BA1 2LS — COOKING 2
TEL: (01225) 739955 FAX: (01225) 339401 — COST £27–£62

The Dower House is at the back of the hotel, across the garden. It is decorated in cream, terracotta and grey-green, with banquettes around the room, and more than its share of transatlantic visitors. Riches abound, judging by the foie gras: made into tortellini with sweetbreads and served with a truffle dressing, or used to partner squab pigeon served with wood mushrooms and glazed turnips. Steven Blake puts a lot of effort into the preparation, making a pithiviers of chicken livers to accompany marinated and sauté chicken, and making crab rösti on which to rest a wing of skate. The expensive ingredients and workmanship together contribute to the high cost, particularly on the *carte*, though the set-price lunch brings things down to earth.

Onion-related flavours are popular with the kitchen, as in a shallot dressing for a salad of rabbit, a spring onion and chilli dressing for marinated red mullet, or onion confit with beef fillet, although the sharpness of vinegar often counters any sweetness. Service, one reporter thought, lacked the common touch. 'This,' she felt, examining the bill, 'was not real life.' Wines are arranged by style and subdivided by country, making what is called the 'smooth, medium-bodied red wine' section the longest on account of the pedigree burgundies and clarets. The New World helps to keep prices down. House Vin de pays du Gers is £11.95.

CHEF: Steven Blake PROPRIETOR: Queens Moat Houses plc OPEN: all week 12.30 to 2, 7 to 9.30 (10 Sat) MEALS: alc (main courses £11 to £20.50). Set L £18.50, Set D £30 SERVICE: not inc, card slips closed CARDS: Access, Amex, Delta, Diners, Switch, Visa DETAILS: 66 seats. Private parties: 80 main room, 24, 40 and 45 private rooms. Car park. Vegetarian meals. Children's helpings. Smart dress preferred. Wheelchair access (1 step). Music ACCOMMODATION: 46 rooms, all with bath/shower. TV. Phone. B&B £111 to £312. Rooms for disabled. Children welcome. Afternoon teas. Garden (*The Which? Hotel Guide*)

Woods

9–13 Alfred Street, Bath BA1 2QX — NEW CHEF
TEL: (01225) 314812 FAX: (01225) 443146 — COST £16–£33

Right in the historic heart of old Bath, next to the Assembly Rooms, the Prices' spacious restaurant brings a sense of occasion to the business of eating, whether it be wine tutorial dinners or the efforts of Kooky the Clown on the first Sunday of every month. The kitchen has had some diverting turns of its own, and following a plate of crudités the choice may extend to Japanese tuna burgers, pheasant with blackcurrants, and 'Woods' puds' such as steamed pecan and toffee pudding, or chocolate terrine with lime and orange sauce. Or it may not. Tony Edwards and Lee Davidson took over the kitchen just as we went to press, leaving us no time for feedback – so reports are welcome. The small, predominantly French wine list offers a good spread at level-headed prices, and a slate of varied house wines from £9 may all be taken by the glass.

CHEFS: Tony Edwards and Lee Davidson PROPRIETORS: David and Claude Price OPEN: all week L 12 to 3, Mon to Sat D 6 to 11 CLOSED: 24 to 26 Dec MEALS: alc (main courses £4 to £11.50). Set L £11, Set D Mon to Fri £12 to £19.95 SERVICE: not inc CARDS: Access, Visa DETAILS: 120 seats. 8 tables outside. Private parties: 70 main room, 40 private room. Vegetarian meals. Children's helpings. No cigars/pipes in dining-room. Wheelchair access (2 steps; also WC). Music

BEAMINSTER Dorset — map 2

▲ *Bridge House*

3 Prout Bridge, Beaminster DT8 3AY — COOKING 2
TEL: (01308) 862200 FAX: (01380) 863700 — COST £21–£43

The house is a thirteenth-century clergyman's dwelling – 'a solid, welcoming, grey-stone building' – on Prout Bridge at one end of this Hardyesque country town. The immaculately manicured lawn, pleasant sitting rooms and trim pink dining-room all convey an impression of calm civility.

Jacky Rae came to cook in 1994, and has added some personal touches to the food while maintaining continuity with the style of her predecessor. This is essentially English country cooking, absorbing some of today's preoccupations without unduly complicating matters. The fashionable salad of breakfast foods to start – black pudding, bacon, fried croûtons and a poached egg – was judged 'very good' at an inspection meal, while another first course of tagliatelle with marinated salmon in a dill cream sauce scored highly for accuracy of cooking. Main-course meats may have stuffings: spinach and garlic cream cheese in pork tenderloin, and walnuts and grapes in a brace of quail which were 'first-class, perfectly cooked with a rich wine sauce'. Hollowed-out bulbs of fennel doubled as receptacles for some of the other vegetables. Classic desserts are competently rendered, from two-colour chocolate ganache torte on a thin pastry base, to agreeably tangy lemon mousse. Extras include walnut bread and canapés, although diners might need to be dextrous to cope with the amuse-gueules of tomatoes filled with prawns in marie-rose sauce that arrived plateless. Good truffles come with the cafetière coffee. The personable service adds to 'an enjoyable experience'. Wines are listed in the modern way, with nationalities co-existing in ascending order of price. There are some good growers, an enterprising choice of special recommendations and, even at the top end, fair prices. Five house wines are £8.45.

CHEFS: Jacky Rae and Peter Pinkster PROPRIETOR: Peter Pinkster OPEN: all week 12.30 to 2, 7 to 9 MEALS: Set L £10.95 (2 courses) to £12.95, Set D £14.95 (2 courses) to £16.95 SERVICE: not inc, card slips closed CARDS: Access, Amex, Diners, Visa DETAILS: 40 seats. 4 tables outside. Private parties: 48 main room, 16 private room. Car park. Vegetarian meals. Children's helpings. Smart dress preferred. No smoking in dining-room. No music ACCOMMODATION: 13 rooms, all with bath/shower. TV. Phone. B&B £49 to £92. Deposit: £25. Rooms for disabled. Children welcome. Baby facilities. Afternoon teas. Garden (*The Which? Hotel Guide*)

BECKINGHAM Lincolnshire map 6

Black Swan

Hillside, Beckingham LN5 0RF
TEL: (01636) 626474 COOKING 2
off A17 to Sleaford, 6m E of Newark-on-Trent COST £18–£43

More than ten years have passed since Anton and Alison Indans first welcomed customers to their whitewashed 400-year-old building by the banks of the River Witham. Today, the place feels reassuringly lived-in and all is comfortable: beams and an open fire define the décor, while displays of fresh and dried flowers add the necessary touches of colour. The Indanses recently acquired a full licence, and are now open for lunch as well as dinner. Their *carte* invites a flexible approach to eating: some starters are available in full-sized portions, you can opt for a single dish or a full meal, and the repertoire is bolstered by open sandwiches and salads during the summer months (when the riverside garden comes into its own).

There's a touch of invention about the cooking, backed up by the kind of confidence that comes from handling classic ideas well. 'Excellent' twice-baked cheese soufflé, warm quail galantine with apricots and sage, and grilled red mullet salad garnished with fried green chillies and squid start the proceedings. Main courses could range from Dover sole with lemon and watercress sauce to roast loin of lamb with a mint-tinged bean cassoulet with home-made lamb sausage. Pork fillet in filo pastry has been first-rate, tender and flavoursome, while summer pudding and home-made hazelnut ice-cream completed one party's 'leisurely, enjoyable meal, served with white gloves'. Coffee and home-made chocolates provide the final flourish. Sunday lunch is a popular family event, when children under 11 eat for free, providing there is 'one child per adult'. The wine list is short and enticing, although details of producers are thin on the ground. House wine is £8.20.

CHEFS: Anton Indans and Claire Rogers PROPRIETORS: Anton and Alison Indans OPEN: Tue to Sun L 12 to 1.30, Tue to Sat D 7 to 10 CLOSED: 1 week Feb, 2 weeks Aug MEALS: alc (main courses £8 to £15). Set L Sun £12.50 SERVICE: not inc CARDS: Access, Visa DETAILS: 40 seats. 4 tables outside. Private parties: 28 main room, 12 and 28 private rooms. Car park. Vegetarian meals. Children's helpings. Smart dress preferred. No smoking in dining-room. Wheelchair access (also WC). Music

BECKINGTON Somerset map 2

▲ *Woolpack* **NEW ENTRY**

Warminster Road, Beckington BA3 6SP
TEL: (01373) 831244 FAX: (01373) 831223 COOKING 3
off A36, in centre of village COST £24–£43

Condemned felons on their way to the gallows were once allowed a last tipple at the Woolpack before their appointment with the hangman. This sixteenth-century coaching-inn now presides over cheerier scenes in the centre of an unblemished Cotswold village, happily bypassed by the Bath to Warminster road. It is a carefully renovated building, long and low, divided into three areas for eating, the most recent a rear extension overlooking an Italianate courtyard replete with 'small cypresses and classical floodlit statuary'.

Previously at the Well House in Cornwall (see entry, St Keyne), David Woolfall has brought a lustre to the cooking that this well-kept country pub deserves. Whether Beckington or Battersea, England expects to see the likes of goats' cheese, sun-dried tomato, and pesto crostini on menus these days, but there is a richly inventive mind at work beyond the strong Mediterranean showing and a great deal of confidence. A serving of excellent gravad lax, for instance, is brought into even sharper focus by accompaniments of herring in a mustardy marinade, strips of pickled squid and a compote of fennel. These are not bashful flavours, but all work well together. Pork tenderloin is a successful main course, four hefty slices given fortifying support by chopped chorizo and 'a nice dollop of Puy lentils'. To finish, lemon tart with a fine dense raspberry coulis, and a brandy-snap cornet of rhubarb parfait on a cinnamon sauce are brought off with equal aplomb. Occasionally, the drive for maximum impact can overpower a dish, but the outlook is generally promising. Service is 'smart' in every sense.

You will need all your wits about you for the wine list, as the logic of its layout is not immediately intelligible. Its quality, however, makes the effort worth while. A good little Loire selection together with delights such as L.A. Cetto's Petite Sirah from Mexico make for an inspired choice at sane prices. Ten house wines are commendably offered at a uniform cost – £8.50 – and eight of them may be taken at £2 glass.

CHEF: David Woolfall PROPRIETOR: West Country Village Inns Ltd OPEN: all week 12 to 2, 7 to 10 (9 Sun) MEALS: alc (main courses £6 to £14) SERVICE: not inc, card slips closed CARDS: Access, Delta, Switch, Visa DETAILS: 80 seats. 8 tables outside. Private parties: 50 main room, 20 private room. Car park. Vegetarian meals. Children's helpings. No smoking in 1 dining-room. Wheelchair access (4 steps; also WC). No music ACCOMMODATION: 12 rooms, all with bath/shower. TV. Phone. B&B £49.50 to £84.50. Deposit: £20. Children welcome. Pets by arrangement. Afternoon teas. Garden

BERWICK-UPON-TWEED Northumberland map 11

▲ *Funnywayt'mekalivin*

41 Bridge Street, Berwick-upon-Tweed TD15 1ES COOKING 2*
TEL: (01289) 308827 COST £15–£32

'What a blessing to find this brilliant oasis of civilisation in a virtual desert!' exclaimed a happy reporter, who wondered what Northumberland had done to deserve it. The old building has been decorated and is now 'terribly smart in an understated way', with a mix of modern furniture and a collection of oddments that seem to have been acquired bit by bit. 'Elizabeth Middlemiss is a really good cook,' summed up one, on the basis of simple ideas successfully executed. There is no fuss or show, just a pride in what she does and a concentration on essentials. It is a very personal style, well suited to the small scale, although one reporter remarked on the resemblance of some dishes to those of Hilary Brown at La Potinière (see entry, Gullane, Scotland). There may be no choice on the dinner menu (it depends on circumstances) but soup usually gets things off to a good start: 'light and not too strongly cheesy' Stilton and celery, or 'well-balanced' carrot and apple.

Next might be gravad lax of Tweed salmon, or toasted goats' cheese with an apple and ginger chutney, or for one reporter a delicate prawn and avocado mousse that 'actually tasted of fresh prawns'. Main courses come with appropriate vegetables – potatoes cooked in Sauternes, and cabbage with garlic, for example, with a casserole of Berwick lamb cooked with apricots and spices – and puddings have included 'properly done crème brûlée' and a 'rich, creamy and very lemony' lemon tart. Generous use of dairy products can make meals seem rich for some. The moist, flavoursome home-made bread comes into its own at the 'near-faultless' breakfast, along with Craster kippers and even better coffee than at dinner. Service is friendly, knowledgeable and efficient, and the five courses at dinner just keep coming. Lunch is a more informal affair along the lines of crab pâté or smoked salmon roulade. Twenty-odd sensible wines under £20 include house Australian at £8.50.

CHEF/PROPRIETOR: Elizabeth Middlemiss OPEN: Tue to Sat L 11.30 to 2.30, Wed to Sat D 7.30 to 8 CLOSED: 25 and 26 Dec, 1 Jan MEALS: alc L (main courses £5 to £6). Set D £22.50 SERVICE: none, card slips closed CARDS: Access, Switch, Visa DETAILS: 32 seats. Private parties: 18 main room. Vegetarian meals. Children's helpings. No smoking while others are eating. No music ACCOMMODATION: 3 rooms. TV. B&B £25 to £40. Deposit: £10. Children welcome. Pets by arrangement

BEXHILL East Sussex map 3

Lychgates

5A Church Street, Old Town, Bexhill TN40 2HE COOKING 2
TEL: (01424) 212193 COST £25–£35

Nineteen ninety-six will see the Tysons clock up ten years in their 'pretty cottage' a mile from the sea in the old town, next to the church. Theirs is a 'well-run, family business in a lovely and comfortable old house', and the kitchen offers its own adaptation of French cooking. 'Simple presentation with a twist' is how one reporter described it, adding that 'a lot of thought and time goes into the food'. Opening times are limited, but the two-course Saturday lunch might run to scrambled egg with ratatouille followed by fillet of plaice with tomato, thyme and cream.

Menus change every month or so, and three-course dinners are extended to five by starting with two savoury items and a sorbet before the main business. A spring meal began with French onion soup followed by salad of skate, sorbet, then fillet steak pan-fried with honey (a favourite addition), mustard and cream. The presence of cream and alcohol – a tot of whisky in a casserole of rabbit, for instance – can add to the richness, although one reporter enjoyed a summer meal of asparagus with melted butter, poached salmon with new potatoes, and crème brûlée with a thick topping (other opinions about the crème brûlée have differed). Service is all very homely. A couple of dozen wines mostly under £20 suit the circumstances. House French is £8.75.

CHEF: John Tyson PROPRIETORS: John and Sue Tyson OPEN: Sat L 12.30 to 2, Wed to Sat D 7 to 10.30; lunches other days by arrangement CLOSED: 2 weeks during school hols, bank hol Mons MEALS: Set L £10 (2 courses), Set D £18.50 to £21.95 SERVICE: not inc, card slips closed CARDS: Access, Visa DETAILS: 24 seats. Private parties: 18 main room. Children's helpings. No cigars/pipes in dining-room. Wheelchair access. Music

BIBURY Gloucestershire map 2

▲ *The Swan*

Bibury GL7 5NW COOKING 2*
TEL: (01285) 740695 FAX: (01285) 740473 COST £23–£50

William Morris called Bibury 'the most beautiful village in England'. It is a conservation area, with a wildfowl reserve owned and managed by the National Trust, and Arlington Row, a medieval agricultural building later converted into cottages. For the Cotswolds, the village is mercifully unspoilt. The seventeenth-century creeper-clad Swan is opposite the bridge over the River Coln, with a courtyard for al fresco eating. 'Looking at the building from outside, one would never imagine it to be so luxurious inside.' The bar and brasserie are modern and informal, open all day, while the dining-room is high-ceilinged and quite grand, with draped curtains and glittering chandeliers.

The cooking adopts a contemporary and largely French stance, turning out such things as a warm salad of pigeon breast with a ravioli of wild mushrooms, and pan-fried red mullet with potato purée and a red pepper and tomato dressing. Even the puddings – chocolate marquise, tarte Tatin, and crème brûlée – are generally French-inspired. Dinner always begins with 'a taste of Bibury trout', quickly grilled, with an intensely reduced grain mustard sauce, while a soup or sorbet is slotted between first and main courses. Some dishes can be rather convoluted, as when thick chunks of duck breast, crusted with orange and breadcrumbs, are accompanied by slices of first-rate black pudding, peppered and roasted pear, and a parcel of mousseline wrapped in smoked salmon, all in a port wine sauce. Simpler items tend to work better, such as a glazed pithiviers pastry case filled with goat's cheese and herbs, or a risotto of squid and its ink, covered with lemon and garlic. Salt is used liberally.

This is an ambitious hotel with an ambitious chef, but an inspector found 'the style more impressive than the substance'. The price of dinner invites comparison with some of the country's top restaurants, raising expectations that are not always fulfilled. Service could be improved, but incidentals are good, from freshly baked white and brown rolls to the petits fours with coffee. Wines range far and wide, and there are some wonderful bottles and half-bottles, but prices are on the high side. The cheapest half-bottle of sweet wine, for example, is £16.25. House Australian white and California red are £13.10.

CHEF: Guy Bossom PROPRIETORS: Mr and Mrs J.A. Furtek OPEN: Sun L 12.30 to 2.30, all week D 7.30 to 9.30 MEALS: Set L Sun £15.95, Set D £35 SERVICE: net prices, card slips closed CARDS: Access, Amex, Delta, Switch, Visa DETAILS: 80 seats. Private parties: 80 main room, 12 private room. Car park. Children's helpings. Smart dress preferred. No smoking in dining-room. Wheelchair access (also WC). No music ACCOMMODATION: 18 rooms, all with bath/shower. TV. Phone. B&B £86 to £210. Deposit: £50. Rooms for disabled. Children welcome. Baby facilities. Afternoon teas. Garden. Fishing (*The Which? Hotel Guide*)

BILBROUGH North Yorkshire map 9

▲ *Bilbrough Manor* **NEW ENTRY**

Main Street, Bilbrough YO2 3PH
TEL: (01937) 834002 FAX: (01937) 834724 COOKING 2*
off A64, between York and Tadcaster COST £18–£56

Blue signs lead to the pebble-dash manor, with its grandish entrance hall, log fires, rag-rolled green walls, exposed stone and big settees. Antiques abound, including a couple of grandfather clocks, one of them in the oak-panelled pink-curtained dining-room. Luxuries are not in short supply on the menu either, which uses a mousseline of foie gras to stuff a chicken, Sevruga caviare to decorate a grilled fillet of sea bass, and lobster either in ravioli, as part of a salad, or cooked thermidor. 'Just a bit passé' is how one reporter described this expense-account style of eating. The recession seems to have sent most other country-house hotels round to the back of the butcher's to ask for ox-cheek or a pig's trotter, but Bilbrough doesn't stint, which tends to make it 'a bit pricey'.

Nevertheless, the ingredients themselves are good. At one meal, slices of veal kidney were sandwiched between rounds of filo pastry, with trompette mushrooms in a well-reduced sauce, and a pile of 'angel hair' celeriac and leek on top. It was autumn, and chanterelles appeared in the next course beside a breast of pheasant, with more angel hair on top, while the soufflé was blackcurrant. An inspector wondered about the wisdom of the 'fussy and rather overwrought' style of cooking that brings a plate of six vegetables to table, and partners a fillet of venison with a compote of pear, cranberries and orange peel as well as pan-fried foie gras. However, lighter and less elaborate dishes are available at lunch-time. Service might be sharper, given the kitchen's ambition. The wines include a fair spread from around the world, although quality is mixed under £20. Five house wines are £11.95, or £2.50 a glass.

'When the chef [and owner] solicited our comments I expressed some reservations, to which her only response was ''Win some, lose some''.' (On eating in Norfolk)

CHEF: Andrew Jones PROPRIETORS: Mr and Mrs Colin Bell OPEN: all week 12 to 2, 7 to 9.30 MEALS: alc (main courses £14.50 to £18.50). Set L £14.50 (2 course) to £16.50, (both inc wine), Set D £20 (2 courses) to £30 SERVICE: not inc CARDS: Access, Amex, Diners, Visa DETAILS: 80 seats. 4 tables outside. Private parties: 50 main room, 10 to 50 private rooms. Car park. Vegetarian meals. Children's helpings. Jacket and tie. No smoking in dining-room. Wheelchair access (also WC). Music ACCOMMODATION: 15 rooms, all with bath/shower. TV. Phone. B&B £77 to £150. No children under 10. Baby facilities. Afternoon teas. Garden

---

BILLESLEY Warwickshire map 5

▲*Billesley Manor* 🍷

Billesley B49 6NF
TEL: (01789) 279955 FAX: (01789) 764145 COOKING **2***
off A46, 3m W of Stratford-upon-Avon COST **£26–£57**

Billesley Manor, converted into a hotel in 1980, has a long history. It was mentioned in the Domesday Book; later on, Shakespeare was a frequent visitor, and some historians claim that he wrote *As You Like It* here.

Mark Naylor's cooking does not go in for excess elaboration, nor does it plunge headlong into Mediterranean voguishness (even though a menu in spring included a wild mushroom, sweet pepper and tomato risotto). The country-house style comes across in John Dory in puff pastry on a Chablis sauce, while smoked duck confit with foie gras and shallots dressed with an apple and balsamic chutney delivers real depth of flavour. Lemon sole may not be the most opulent of fish, but stick some salmon mousse in it and add smoked salmon to the sauce and it becomes a different proposition. A main-course dish of steamed chicken with a basil mousse and mushroom risotto has also come in for praise. Desserts have a classic French tilt to them: prune and armagnac soufflé, warm pear tart with hazelnut ice-cream, and crêpes suzette. The English and French cheeses served with walnut bread are highly commended, as is the efficient and discreet service. Zind-Humbrecht Alsace, Durup Chablis and a range of pedigree clarets and burgundies contribute to a noteworthy French list. Other sections are less illustrious but more competitively priced. An extensive spread of half-bottles is available, and house wines from south-west France are £10.75. CELLARMAN'S CHOICE: Montagny *premier cru* 'Les Monts Cuchots',1991, Dom. Steinmaier, £22.75; Chinon, Clos de Danzay 1989, £29.25.

CHEF: Mark Naylor PROPRIETOR: Queens Moat Houses plc OPEN: all week 12.30 to 2, 7.30 to 9.30 (10 Fri and Sat) MEALS: alc (main courses £15 to £19). Set L £18, Set D £27.50 SERVICE: not inc, card slips closed CARDS: Access, Amex, Diners, Visa DETAILS: 75 seats. 6 tables outside. Private parties: 40 main room, 14 to 100 private rooms. Car park. Vegetarian meals. Children's helpings. Jacket and tie D. No cigars/pipes in dining-room. Wheelchair access. No music ACCOMMODATION: 41 rooms, all with bath/shower. TV. Phone. B&B £99 to £180. Children welcome. Baby facilities. Afternoon teas. Garden. Swimming-pool (*The Which? Hotel Guide*)

'I asked the head waiter if I could have a copy of the menu.... He rushed off, and then got Chef to sign it. Chef came out and waved. Waiters beamed in many different languages.' (On eating in London)

BIRCH VALE Derbyshire map 8

▲ *Waltzing Weasel*

New Mills Road, Birch Vale SK12 5BT
TEL: (01663) 743402 FAX: (01663) 743402 COOKING 1*
on A6015, ½m W of Hayfield COST £19–£37

Michael Atkinson used the Waltzing Weasel as his local when he was a student living just down the road. On hearing that the place was due to be sold, he and his wife bought it 'on a whim and a prayer'. Success has not gone to their heads, and they have ensured that this is still a thriving village pub as well as an easy-going restaurant-with-rooms. The machine-free bar, with its rough-stone walls and warming fire, is where the drinkers congregate for pints of well-kept real ale and light meals: lunch is a lavish carvery of hot and cold collations, while suppers are fleshed out with starters and puddings from the restaurant menu. Visitors looking for something special tend to book a table in the dining-room, where they can gaze through mullioned windows and admire the spectacular vista of Kinder Scout. The menu is set-price for two or three courses, and George Benham keeps things simple. His links with reliable suppliers show up in starters such as 'superb' fresh-water crayfish tails with garlic mayonnaise, and smoked leg of lamb with redcurrant jelly. Main courses continue the theme with poussin stuffed with ham and leeks, beef Wellington, or poached salmon with shrimp sauce. Then it's back to the nursery and to school for treacle tart with custard, and bread-and-butter pudding dabbed with chunky marmalade. Service is enthusiastic, and the wine list is a well-chosen, reasonably priced slate with enough variety to suit most palates and pockets. House wine is £8.75.

CHEF: George Benham PROPRIETORS: Michael and Linda Atkinson OPEN: all week 12 to 2, 7 to 9 MEALS: alc L (main courses £6.50 to £12.50). Set D £19.50 (2 courses) to £23.50 SERVICE: not inc, card slips closed CARDS: Access, Amex, Delta, Switch, Visa DETAILS: 26 seats. 2 tables outside. Private parties: 36 main room, 12 private room. Car park. Vegetarian meals. No children under 5. Smart dress preferred. Wheelchair access (1 step). No music. Air-conditioned ACCOMMODATION: 8 rooms, all with bath/shower. TV. Phone. Air-conditioned. B&B £45 to £95. Deposit: £20. No children under 12. Pets welcome. Garden (*The Which? Hotel Guide*)

BIRDLIP Gloucestershire map 2

▲ *Kingshead House* 🍷

Birdlip GL4 8JH
TEL: (01452) 862299
½m off A417 between Gloucester and Cirencester, COOKING 2
on B4070 towards Stroud COST £30–£39

The bare wooden floors of this seventeenth-century coaching-inn are shiny with age, and behind it stretches a long garden where the Knocks grow their own herbs, including the now rare comfrey. Lunch is a flexible arrangement, with food served either in the bar or dining-room, from one course upwards. It can be as straightforward as a plate of smoked salmon with home-made bread, grilled merguez sausage with tabbouleh and yoghurt, or a main course of wild rabbit casserole with mashed potato and red and green cabbage, followed by mocha truffle with coffee sauce.

Dinner brings three or four courses at a set price, but the style remains much the same. Judy Knock's cooking runs along well-oiled Anglo-French lines, from brandade of smoked haddock in puff pastry with celery sauce to Cointreau ice-cream with chocolate chips, by way of hot salt duck with lentils, and home-made mushroom ravioli. Fish is often steamed, perhaps with a fondant of leeks. Rack of lamb with a herb crust and pea purée is a regular, as is breast of pigeon with spicy stuffed cabbage and tapénade, while a warm covered tart filled with cheese and served with an onion sauce is a typical meatless option for main course. Good value is a priority on the wine list. Quality and interest are high, but much of it manages to sail easily under £20 a bottle. Half-bottles are fair, and house wine begins at £9.80 (£1.80 a glass). CELLARMAN'S CHOICE: Sancerre, Dom. des Godons 1993, Raimbeau-Pineau, £16.80; Médoc, Ch. Potensac 1986, £19.50.

CHEF: Judy Knock PROPRIETORS: Judy and Warren Knock OPEN: Tue to Fri and Sun L 12.30 to 1.45, Tue to Sat D 7.30 to 9.45 CLOSED: 26 and 27 Dec, 1 Jan MEALS: alc L (main courses £7.50 to £12). Set L Sun £16.50, Set D £22.50 (2 courses) to £24.50 SERVICE: not inc CARDS: Access, Amex, Diners, Visa DETAILS: 34 seats. 3 tables outside. Private parties: 34 main room. Car park. Vegetarian meals. Children's helpings. Smart dress preferred. No smoking while others eat. Wheelchair access. Music ACCOMMODATION: 1 room, with bath/shower. TV. B&B £33 to £56. Deposit: 10%. Children welcome. Small pets by arrangement. Garden

BIRKENHEAD Merseyside map 8

Beadles

15 Rosemount, Oxton, Birkenhead L43 5SG COOKING 1
TEL: 0151-653 9010 COST £22–£32

Since 1977 Roy and Bea Gott have 'rendered a public service' to Merseyside by sustaining their civilised neighbourhood restaurant. 'They maintain their strength,' observes a loyal supporter, who adds that it is 'the kind of place to which one could happily return very regularly without becoming sated or bored'. The setting is a Victorian building – complete with its original frontage dating from 1846 – in the conservation area of Oxton village. Inside there is not much in the way of décor, although Roy's collection of prints is worth more than a passing glance. The heating may be courtesy of Calor gas, the chairs could do with renewing, and the tables are simply laid with paper napkins and ordinary crockery – but the food is what matters.

Supplies, especially fish, are procured with diligence, and Bea Gott's menu jumps happily between reassuring classicism and global eclecticism. Gnocchi with home-made pesto, calf's liver with braised onions and marmalade sauce, and beef fillet with a horseradish-scented redcurrant sauce share the billing with warm Thai duck salad, hot-and-sour Sri Lankan prawns, and confit of duck with spiced butter-beans. Puddings feature home-made ice-creams and sorbets as well as strawberries in elderflower syrup, and coffee and praline syllabub. Some seven different varieties might grace the cheeseboard, and the coffee is reckoned to be first-class. Roy Gott's wine list is an enthusiast's choice, with only champagne breaking the £15 barrier. House wine is £7.

CHEF: Bea Gott PROPRIETORS: Roy and Bea Gott OPEN: Tue to Sat D only 7.30 to 9 CLOSED: 2 weeks Aug to Sep MEALS: alc (main courses £7.50 to £10.50) SERVICE: not inc; 10% for parties of 6 or more CARDS: Access, Delta, Switch, Visa DETAILS: 32 seats. Private parties: 34 main room. No children under 7. No smoking before coffee. Wheelchair access (1 step). Music

BIRMINGHAM West Midlands **map 5**

Chung Ying £

16–18 Wrottesley Street, B5 4RT COOKING 1
TEL: 0121-622 5669 FAX: 0121-666 7051 COST £20–£66

Birmingham's Chinese quarter is developing fast: it now sports a herbal centre and a genuine Cantonese takeaway, as well as some new restaurants and grocers. Chung Ying is one of the old-stagers – although it has been given a lick of bright green and red paint on the outside, in keeping with the 'house style' of its neighbours. The interior also struck one reporter as brighter than before, with big colourful lampshades and linen canopies ballooning over parts of the ground-floor dining-room. Service, thought the same reporter, remains 'fast and slick', with 'efficiency counting for more than good humour'.

The mighty dragon of a menu runs to more than 300 items, with plenty of strength in the contingent of dim-sum and one-plate rice and noodle dishes. Shanghai dumplings with brown-rice vinegar dip, hand-moulded minced-beef balls, Chinese sausage cheung-fun, and deep-fried shredded squid, plus a parcel of glutinous rice in lotus leaves would make an affordable lunch. Otherwise, go for massive helpings of stewed duck with plum sauce, spiced pork chops with 'special sauce' on rice ('glorious, succulent, sticky meat'), plus 'seductively slimy' braised dried mushrooms with seasonal greens. The sheer span of the menu means inevitably that some dishes work better than others: sometimes flavours are too timid, at other times too assertive, but when the kitchen is on target, the food is excellent in a 'rough-and-ready' way. House wine is £9.50.

CHEF/PROPRIETOR: Siu Chung Wong OPEN: all week 12 to,to 11.30 (11 Sun) CLOSED: 25 Dec MEALS: alc (main courses £6.50 to £17). Set D £13 to £45 (min 2 to 6) SERVICE: not inc CARDS: Access, Amex, Delta, Diners, Switch, Visa DETAILS: 250 seats. Private parties: 120 main room, 120 private room. Vegetarian meals. Children welcome. Smart dress preferred. Wheelchair access (2 steps). Music. Air-conditioned

Chung Ying Garden £

17 Thorp Street, Birmingham B5 4AT COOKING 2
TEL: 0121-666 6622 FAX: 0121-622 5860 COST £20–£39

The front-runner in Birmingham's revitalised Chinese quarter continues to serve an impressive range of tip-top Cantonese food in surroundings that are stylish and elegant without being stuffy. The place is lively, properly organised, well paced and manned by a team of sharp waiters who can 'respond at a glance to eye contact and discreet sign language'. One reporter, who called in for a dim-sum lunch one Saturday, found the place bustling with 'lots of Chinese families – three generations, eight to a table – plus couples taking a break from shopping, and a few students'. The choice now runs to some 60 items, but highlights on that occasion included steamed king prawns and vegetable dumplings with 'a full-blooded' filling; deep-fried wun-tun topped with a drizzle of sweet-and-sour sauce and strands of sweet preserved vegetables; steamed spare-ribs with plum sauce ('tender and authentically chewy at the same time'); and little sausages of fragrantly spiced minced beef wrapped in wrinkly egg pasta. 'Very fresh, no short cuts, distinct flavours across the board,' was the verdict. The remainder of the menu is a mighty assemblage of casseroles, hotpots, one-plate rice and noodle dishes, and more esoteric specialities, such as sliced fillet of beef with ground walnuts, quick-fried dry squid and shredded jellyfish with celery, and steamed pork pie with preserved egg. House wine is £9.50 a litre.

CHEF/PROPRIETOR: Siu Chung Wong OPEN: all week 12 to 11.30 (10.30 Sun) CLOSED: 25 Dec MEALS: alc (main courses £6 to £11). Set D £12 to £18 SERVICE: not inc CARDS: Access, Amex, Diners, Switch, Visa DETAILS: 350 seats. Private parties: 200 main room, 30 to 70 private rooms. Vegetarian meals. Children welcome. Wheelchair access (also WC). Music. Air-conditioned

Maharaja £

23–25 Hurst Street, Birmingham B5 4AS — COOKING 1*
TEL: 0121-622 2641 — COST £16–£35

For more than 25 years this discreet city-centre restaurant has been delivering some of the most satisfying Punjabi and Mughlai food in Birmingham. Chef Bhupinder Waraich has been in command of the kitchen since 1982 and his presence has no doubt helped to sustain the consistency of the cooking. The menu is finely tuned and untouched by trendiness. Accurately spiced and freshly flavoured curries and tandoori dishes are the mainstays, although vegetables and dhals often steal the show: in particular, look for sag paneer (spinach with curd cheese) and kamal kakri and mater (lotus roots with peas). It's also worth asking about daily specials not listed on the menu: chicken badami, lamb bara kebab and tandoori fish all feature from time to time. The setting consists of two unshowy dining areas (one in the basement) with pink cloths, blue fabric chairs and a fascinating collection of oriental paintings and prints on the walls. Service is in tune with the mood of the place: unfailingly gracious without putting on airs and graces. Drink lassi, Cobra lager or the house wine (£6.95 a bottle).

CHEF: Bhupinder Waraich PROPRIETOR: Mr N.S. Batt OPEN: Mon to Sat 12 to 2.15, 6 to 11.15 MEALS: alc (main courses £5.50 to £7.50). Set L and D £10.90. Minimum £7 SERVICE: 10%, card slips closed CARDS: Access, Amex, Diners, Switch, Visa DETAILS: 62 seats. Private parties: 30 main room. Vegetarian meals. Children welcome. Smart dress preferred. Wheelchair access (1 step; also WC). Music. Air-conditioned

'It is hard to generalise about the clientele. They cover a wide range, from the middle-aged advertising executive who thought (wrongly) that he recognised my companion to the noisy Australian opposite who thought (also wrongly) that he was amusing.'
(On eating in London)

BIRTLE Greater Manchester map 8

▲ *Normandie*

Elbut Lane, Birtle BL9 6UT
TEL: 0161-764 3869 and 1170 FAX: 0161-764 4866 COOKING 3*
off B6222, 3m NE of Bury COST £21–£51

Nobody has a good word for the building from the outside. After the short but promising trip up a rugged little lane, reporters expect more of a show. It is slightly better from the inside, looking out through the picture window over the Manchester conurbation, although the furnishings and trappings of marble-topped tables, Spanish arches, horsey pictures and polystyrene-tiled ceiling fail to excite enthusiasm. What a blessing the kitchen has a more astute eye for taste, design and balance, offering a *carte* of six choices for each of the three courses, and a markedly simpler weekly set menu.

Pascal Pommier's cooking generally follows the seasons, making good use of game in autumn and casseroles in winter, and turning to lighter-cooked fish and vegetable dishes in spring and summer. On one spring menu hot goats' cheese in filo pastry came with a red-pepper relish, while a layered vegetable 'mosaic' combined green beans, button mushrooms, tomato, spring onions, leeks, red pepper, salsify and strips of carrot in a jellified stock, surrounded by a light olive oil dressing. Fish can be impressive too, from a pre-meal offering of escabèche of mackerel to a first course of sweet, nutty roasted scallops served on sliced potatoes and surrounded by a creamy, grain-mustard sauce for pleasantly acidic contrast. 'I cannot imagine a better fish-cake,' claimed one reporter of his main course, which came with a lemon sauce. Not all dishes reach the same high standard, however. 'A mixture of excellence and ordinariness' is a common experience with the food this year. Tuna is not always pink, as promised, but cooked through, which makes it hard-going, and pork has been described as 'flavourless', suggesting that buying is not as sharp as it might be. Cheese can be disappointing too – cold, and of no particular quality – yet tasty game terrine and good fillet steak restore confidence, and sticky toffee pudding and bread are consistently good.

The owners are on the ball, but otherwise service, while polite and correct, can be slow and sombre. The wine list is an unstuffy selection that deals in quality yet keeps its feet on the ground with regard to prices. There is much good and varied drinking under £20, but enough headroom among more expensive bottles for those with the inclination to splash out, plus a fair spread of half-bottles. House Merlot and Sauvignon Blanc are £11.95. CELLARMAN'S CHOICE: The Brothers Vineyards Chardonnay 1992, Marlborough, New Zealand, £19.95; Côte de Beaune, Maranges 1998, Paul Chevrot, £24.50.

CHEF: Pascal Pommier PROPRIETORS: Gillian and Max Moussa OPEN: Tue to Fri L 12 to 2, Mon to Sat D 7 to 9.30 CLOSED: 2 weeks from 26 Dec, 1 week Easter, bank hols (open 25 Dec) MEALS: alc (main courses £11 to £20). Set L £12.50 (2 courses) to £15, Set D £18.95 SERVICE: none, card slips closed CARDS: Access, Amex, Delta, Diners, Switch, Visa DETAILS: 60 seats. Private parties: 50 main room. Car park. Vegetarian meals. Children welcome. Smart dress preferred. No cigars/pipes in dining-room. Wheelchair access (1 step; also WC). Music ACCOMMODATION: 23 rooms, all with bath/shower. TV. Phone. B&B £49 to £79. Children welcome. Garden

BISHOP'S TACHBROOK Warwickshire **map 5**

▲ *Mallory Court*

Harbury Lane, Bishop's Tachbrook CV33 9QB
TEL: (01926) 330214 FAX: (01926) 451714 COOKING 3
off B4087, 2m S of Leamington Spa COST £34–£81

'High-class food in high-class surroundings' is how one reporter saw it. The manor-house may not be architecturally distinguished, but the garden is well kept, Rollers gleam in the drive, the bright lounge is scattered with carefully arranged cushions and magazines, and the dining-room is oak-panelled. Those hoping to spend a lot of money are allowed every opportunity. Dinner is £30 for three courses, £60 for six (one of which is coffee) and there is a *carte* along the same lines. Stephen Shore took over the kitchens early in 1995, cooks in modern Anglo-French mode, and brings a high level of technical expertise to the operation.

At one meal two large pinkish lamb chops were spread with mint mousseline and sweetbreads that were held in place with caul fat, an ambitious dish that impressed for its culinary double somersaults, although taste-wise a few cloves of powerfully smoked garlic swept all except the lamb before them. Food should be taste-led, not technique-driven, and so the cooking works best when it gives ingredients the limelight, as in a grilled fillet of Cornish sea bass – 'delightful, fresh, meaty, tender, moist, all a sea bass should be' – with shelled broad beans in a creamy saffron sauce. This was true too in a first course that built up from a base of lightly seared artichoke heart through slices of wonderfully gamey quail to pieces of glistening duck liver fresh from the pan: all much lighter than it sounds, and brilliantly effective because of its directness. At other times the art of garnish is raised to a high level, and since garnish is only garnish, its wisdom is questioned.

A lot of work goes into puddings, from plates of different chocolate desserts, or ice-creams and sorbets, to a hot lemon soufflé, 'well risen, then punctured by the waitress who poured in a sharp raspberry sauce. We watched in admiration as it re-inflated for a few moments.' The combined acidity of the lemon and raspberries was well countered by a piece of shortbread biscuit, a simple and effective idea. Young staff help to keep the whole thing relaxed. Wines are cleverly chosen, with a good spread of vintages where it matters, and excellent producers throughout. They are not quite matched by the service they deserve, and prices are high, but eight good wines by the glass start at £3.95. CELLARMAN'S CHOICE: Wairau River Sauvignon Blanc 1993, Marlborough, New Zealand, £22.50; Rioja Contino Reserva 1988, Laguardia, £28.75.

CHEF: Stephen Shore PROPRIETORS: Allan Holland and Jeremy Mort OPEN: all week 12.30 to 2, 7 to 9.45 MEALS: alc (main courses £22 to £24.50). Set L £19.50 (2 courses) to £23.50, Set D £30 to £60 SERVICE: none, card slips closed CARDS: Access, Amex, Delta, Diners, Switch, Visa DETAILS: 50 seats. 6 tables outside. Private parties: 25 main room. Car park. Vegetarian meals. No children under 9. Smart dress preferred. No cigars/pipes in dining-room. Wheelchair access (2 steps). No music ACCOMMODATION: 10 rooms, all with bath/shower. TV. Phone. B&B £115 to £215. No children under 9. Afternoon teas. Garden. Swimming-pool

BLACKPOOL Lancashire map 8

September Brasserie

15–17 Queen Street, Blackpool FY1 1PU COOKING 2
TEL: (01253) 23282 COST £20–£41

The small dining-room of this hairdressing-'n'-restaurant combo near the North Pier is on the first floor, above the salon. Pat (The Hair) Wood and Michael (The Food) Golowicz joined forces in 1989, and have developed a bright and enthusiastic style of cooking. They call it 'creative' and 'eclectic', which is PR-speak for the wholesale borrowing and adapting of anything that takes their fancy. And very welcome it is too in Blackpool. The dinner menu offers three or four items per course, and among the good ingredients fish stands out particularly. Scallops feature in a salad; lobster and crab join lentils in a soup; and halibut makes an appearance covered in a Szechuan pepper crust and served with caramelised shallots. It is the flashes of flavour in accompaniments that give the food a bounce: lemon grass here, tomato chutney there, not to mention creamed parsnips and plums with saddle of wild boar. And who else serves collapsed dark chocolate soufflé with yoghurt water-ice? Not all experimental flavour combinations work equally well, but everything is usually done with enough brio to carry the day. Wines run from the traditional (Jobard's Meursault) to the wacky (Duxoup's Napa Gamay) on a short but wide-ranging list of generally good quality. House wines begin at £10.80.

CHEF: Michael Golowicz PROPRIETORS: Michael Golowicz and Pat Wood OPEN: Tue to Sat 12 to 2, 7 to 9.30 CLOSED: 2 weeks summer, 2 weeks winter MEALS: alc (main courses £5.50 to £14). Set D £15.95 SERVICE: not inc, card slips closed CARDS: Access, Amex, Delta, Diners, Switch, Visa DETAILS: 40 seats. Private parties: 40 main room. Vegetarian meals. Children's helpings. Smart dress preferred. Music

BLACKWATER Cornwall map 1

Pennypots

Blackwater TR4 8EY
TEL: (01209) 820347 COOKING 3
off A30, ¾m W of village centre COST £29–£46

The atmosphere in this 'pretty and cottagey' whitewashed roadside house is homely and inviting, the pace leisurely and relaxed. Jane Viner oversees the front-of-house with assistance from 'polite and helpful' staff. A Cornish location ensures a ready supply of good fish and shellfish throughout the year, which is well suited to the light treatment it receives at Kevin Viner's hands. 'I do not believe in excess stuffing or wrapping,' he writes, preferring to show off the primary flavours of scallops with a simple herb butter sauce, or of red mullet and ocean perch with a caper and lemon butter sauce. The menu offers plenty of variety from sauté foie gras on a potato-cake through twice-baked cheese soufflé to venison fillet with a game mousse. The style is accomplished without being fussy, skilful but not showy, 'inventive, yet seldom over the top'.

Saucing makes use of stocks, wine, oil and home-grown herbs, adding rosemary to a madeira sauce for pan-fried fillet of beef, and basil to a saffron sauce for steamed fillets of turbot and sea bass. Vegetables are not integral to the dish, except perhaps when cod fillet (with a crab and herb crust) is placed on a bed of ratatouille. Instead, a 'never-ending' selection might take in carrots flavoured with orange and coriander, or a purée of parsnips and shallots with cream, plus potatoes in some form: sliced and baked with cream and nutmeg, for instance. A separate vegetarian menu might take in an open ravioli of tofu, mushrooms and asparagus with a hot oil and balsamic dressing, or mushrooms in filo pastry with a hazelnut sauce.

Bread is baked in-house, a good selection of nibbles gets things off to a tasty start, and old-fashioned rich puddings might include bread-and-butter with clotted cream, a plate of chocolate puds in which orange, black cherries and kirsch also feature, 'wonderful' sticky toffee pudding and crème brûlée. Wines make use of the New World for the value it offers, and go to France for some classic tastes, helpfully indicating the degree of sweetness for whites and body for reds, and generally balancing prices well. House Vin de Pays d'Oc from Domaine Virginie is £7.95.

CHEF: Kevin Viner PROPRIETORS: Jane and Kevin Viner OPEN: Tue to Sat D only 7 to 9.30 CLOSED: 4 weeks winter MEALS: alc (main courses £12 to £14.50) SERVICE: not inc, card slips closed CARDS: Access, Visa DETAILS: 30 seats. Private parties: 22 main room, 10 private room. Car park. Vegetarian meals. Children's helpings. No smoking in dining-room before 10pm. Wheelchair access (1 step). Music

BLANDFORD FORUM Dorset map 2

▲ *La Belle Alliance* 

White Cliff Mill Street, Blandford Forum DT11 7PB
TEL: (01258) 452842 FAX: (01258) 453727
turn right at end of market square into Salisbury Road then bear left at first junction into Shaftesbury Road; La Belle Alliance is 300yds from turning on right-hand side

COOKING 1*
COST £21–£41

The generously proportioned Edwardian town house, set back from the road on the outskirts of town, is a functional building, the wear and tear now being addressed by 'serious refurbishment' from the new owner. Edward Moss – whom some readers may remember from his time at Le Provençal in Salisbury (in the *Guide* from 1974 to 1983) – took over shortly after the last edition of the *Guide* went to press. Dinner in the spacious and rather formal dining-room is a choice of two, three or four courses, beginning perhaps with an ambitious spicy tomato and scallop bisque with a prawn and scallop soufflé, or chicken liver pâté with a home-made chutney or relish. Despite a monthly-changing menu that describes dishes in detail, the result on the plate is not as elaborate as might be expected, and flourishes are generally avoided.

'Edward Moss certainly can cook, and he takes a lot of care over ingredients and presentation,' concluded an inspector. Although inconsistencies suggest that he may take his eye off the ball from time to time, flavours can be well judged: an ordinary-sounding salad of red and green peppers on a few partly dried tomatoes with slivers of red onion was made to sing with the addition of some bright fresh basil, marjoram, rosemary and spearmint leaves. Service is generally more competent than experienced. 'My party of three were the only diners, but the staff of two could not remember who was having what.' The 70 moderately priced wines, mostly French, include 11 house wines from £9.50, available by the glass from £1.90.

CHEF: Edward Moss PROPRIETORS: Edward Moss and Robin Wrigley OPEN: Sun L 12 to 2, Tue to Sat D 7 to 9.30; weekday L by arrangement MEALS: Set L Sun £13.95, Set D £15.50 (2 courses) to £23.50 SERVICE: not inc, card slips closed CARDS: Access, Amex, Delta, Diners, Switch, Visa DETAILS: 35 seats. Car park. Vegetarian meals. Children's helpings. Smart dress preferred. No smoking in dining-room. Wheelchair access. Music ACCOMMODATION: 6 rooms, all with bath/shower. TV. Phone. B&B £48 to £66. Rooms for disabled. Children welcome. Pets welcome

BOLLINGTON Cheshire map 8

Mauro's

88 Palmerston Street, Bollington SK10 5PW COOKING 1
TEL: (01625) 573898 COST £21–£43

'A former Co-op building in a "Hovis"-type village. Hanging baskets and décor to blend in with locality' is how Vincenzo Mauro describes the setting of his popular Italian restaurant. Extension into the next-door premises means that the place now has a fully fledged bar, where lunchtime snacks are served from Monday to Friday. However, most of the action takes place in an up-market dining-room that reminded one visitor of a verandah restaurant in Portofino that had been shifted indoors. Mediterranean green, orange and yellow are the house colours, the mood is one of serious intent and the cooking aims higher than light-hearted provincial trattorias.

The results have drawn a mixed response from readers in recent months: some suggest that both cooking and service have suffered as a result of expansion and that the set-up sometimes overreaches itself. But there is plenty on the plus side. The 'capacious' hors d'oeuvre trolley gets good notices, and the best options among main courses are home-made pasta and fish specials (baked sea bass, red snapper and 'faultless' monkfish with tomato and garlic sauce have been singled out). Creamy gâteaux, parfaits and meringues are displayed on the sweets trolley. The wine list is a single-minded trawl through the Italian regions with some champagnes representing France. Mauro's also claims to have 'the largest selection of grappas in the north-west'. House wine is £8.50.

CHEF/PROPRIETOR: Vincenzo Mauro OPEN: Mon to Fri L and first Sun L in month 12 to 2, Mon to Sat D 7 to 10 MEALS: alc (main courses £8.50 to £16); bar snacks Mon to Fri L SERVICE: not inc; 10% on parties of 6 or more CARDS: Access, Amex, Delta, Visa DETAILS: 48 seats. Private parties: 60 main room. Vegetarian meals. Children's helpings. Smart dress preferred. Wheelchair access (also WC). Music

'I was particularly taken with the ladies' loo, which had a wonderful stained mirror, a marble topped dresser with a serious plant, and a sink in an old wooden surround with lots of big fluffy white towels. There was also a small fireplace with iron grate, dried flowers and a very desirable wooden advertising poster for cigarettes. Given a power shower, I could live in a bathroom like that.' (On eating in Wiltshire).

BOLTON ABBEY North Yorkshire map 9

Devonshire Arms, Burlington Restaurant

Bolton Abbey BD23 6AJ
TEL: (01756) 710441 FAX: (01756) 710564 NEW CHEF
at junction of A59 and B6160, 5m NW of Ilkley COST £29–£59

The Bolton Abbey estate, where this seventeenth-century coaching-inn-turned-luxury-hotel stands, has for generations belonged to the Dukes of Devonshire. Much of the décor has been freighted over from Chatsworth, so expect high civility, good oil paintings and lashings of antiques. Gavin Beedham left as we went to press. His position is taken by Andrew Nicholson, who, as sous-chef for two years, will be as familiar as anyone with the repertoire of dishes. Among these have been sea bass with roast peppers and aubergine, beef fillet topped with a mousse of black pudding on parsnip rösti, and chocolate muffins with banana cream. Details have been impressive, from breads to 'outstandingly good' Sumatra coffee. Service is normally 'swift, competent and friendly', and the wine list offers plenty to go at, with the price range not that bad once you escape the big French regions. House wines start at £10.95. Reports please.

CHEF: Andrew Nicholson PROPRIETORS: Duke and Duchess of Devonshire OPEN: all week 12 to 2, 7 to 10 (9.30 Sun) MEALS: Set L £17.95, Set D £28.95 SERVICE: 10%, card slips closed CARDS: Access, Amex, Diners, Switch, Visa DETAILS: 70 seats. Private parties: 20 main room, 10 to 24 private rooms. Car park. Vegetarian meals. No children under 12. Jacket and tie. No smoking in dining-room. Wheelchair access (also WC). No music ACCOMMODATION: 40 rooms, all with bath/shower. TV. Phone. B&B £95 to £150. Rooms for disabled. Children welcome. Pets welcome. Afternoon teas. Garden. Swimming-pool. Fishing (*The Which? Hotel Guide*)

BOSTON SPA West Yorkshire map 9

Café Provence £

NEW ENTRY

174 High Street, Boston Spa LS23 6BW
TEL: (01937) 845625 COOKING 1*
on Collingham to Tadcaster road, 4m W of Tadcaster COST £18–£36

Take one cream-painted Georgian building in a reserved North Country spa town, put it in the hands of David Barnard, who also owns the Crab & Lobster, Asenby (see entry), and you have the recipe for a fireworks display. Look for the French flag flying outside and 'Café Provence' scrawled in blue and purple script over the frontage. The entrance is downstairs, past the balti takeaway, the hairdresser and the greengrocer; once inside, you are confronted by an ancient bike, a worn settee and rows of books. Continue up through to the main restaurant, where the music is jazz and blues and the colours are primary. Knick-knacks are dotted all around to delight and surprise: 'On our table was a round raffia box; we opened it and out popped a paper snake!'

The menu is written on a 'movable blackboard' and fish runs riot: bowls of moules marinière, tureens of pale-orange provençale fish soup, and a savoury tarte Tatin piled with smoked salmon, olives and chives all get a look-in. You are also likely to see plates of charcuterie, ravioli of chicken and chives, and mushroom rissoles with courgettes. Sandwiches come with some lively fillings, while desserts include a splendid example of lemon tart, as well as mixed fruit terrine and rhubarb parfait. Look out for the special lunchtime events: champagne and gossip for the ladies on Tuesday, sport on TV every Saturday. Service is 'jeans and waistcoat casual'. France dominates the reasonably priced wine list; 50cl 'pots' of house Georges Duboeuf are £5.50.

CHEF: Kevin Searl PROPRIETOR: David Barnard OPEN: Tue to Sat 12 to 2.30, 6 to 10 CLOSED: first week Jan MEALS: alc (main courses £7 to £13.50). Set D before 7pm £10.95 SERVICE: not inc, card slips closed CARDS: Access, Amex, Delta, Switch, Visa DETAILS: 60 seats. 2 tables outside. Private parties: 24 main room. Vegetarian meals. Children's helpings. Smart dress preferred. No smoking in 1 dining-room. Music

BOTTESFORD Leicestershire map 5

La Petite Maison

1 Market Street, Bottesford NG13 0BW
TEL: (01949) 842375 COOKING 1
just off A52 Nottingham to Grantham road COST £18–£40

As its name suggests, this 'little house' is a modest Continental bistro, with a garden for al fresco meals and a stone-floored dining-room full of pine, corn dollies and prints. Everyone applauds the 'outstanding' home-baked breads served straight from the oven, and Sunday lunch rates as a good-value family occasion. Otherwise, the menu is a sound selection of French paysanne dishes often based on locally procured ingredients, including game from Belvoir Castle, Stilton and soft fruit. A typical day's offerings might include home-made seafood ravioli, roast duckling with sage and onion sauce, pan-fried calf's liver, and wild mushroom risotto. Reporters have also singled out robust beef broth, smoked haddock gratin, and pink fillet of lamb stuffed with a light chicken mousseline. Vegetables are prepared with care, as are desserts, such as iced caramel parfait, and white chocolate and strawberry terrine. Coffee comes with 'hand-crafted' petits fours. Service has been described as 'brusque' by one, though 'attentive but not intrusive' by yet another. The wine list is an affordable slate with some creditable stuff from France and the New World. House wine is £8.95.

CHEF: Adrian Hutchinson PROPRIETORS: Andrew and Beverley Goodson OPEN: Tue to Sun L 12 to 2, Mon to Sat D 7 to 10 CLOSED: first 2 weeks Jan MEALS: alc (main courses L £6 to £11, D £11 to £14). Set L £10.95, Set D £14.95 SERVICE: not inc CARDS: Access, Amex, Delta, Switch, Visa DETAILS: 58 seats. 2 tables outside. Private parties: 38 main room, 18 private room. Car park. Vegetarian meals. Children's helpings. No smoking in dining-room. Wheelchair access (also WC). Music

See inside the front cover for an explanation of the symbols used at the tops of entries.

The 1997 Guide *will be published before Christmas 1996. Reports on meals are most welcome at any time of the year, but are particularly valuable in the spring (no later than June). Send them to* The Good Food Guide, *FREEPOST, 2 Marylebone Road, London NW1 1YN. Or e-mail your report to guidereports@which. co. uk.*

BOUGHTON LEES Kent map 3

▲ *Eastwell Manor*

Eastwell Park, Boughton Lees TN25 4HR
TEL: (01233) 635751 and 219955
FAX: (01233) 635530 COOKING 2
on A251, 3m N of Ashford COST £29–£64

The estate in which Eastwell resides accounts for a fair-sized chunk of Kent, and provides the Manor's kitchens with hare and game birds in season. Although there has been a manor of one sort or another here since the time of William the Conqueror, the present Jacobean-style house dates from 1926. Its ornate plaster ceilings and carved oak panelling now form the backdrop for Ian Mansfield's vivid culinary flair. The menu price is fixed for three courses plus coffee, with one of the options a dearer 'seasonal menu', although there is nothing unseasonal about the ordinary one. A six-course tasting menu for whole tables offers the likes of quail, artichoke and foie gras salad, John Dory with mussels in a saffron and parsley broth, spiced shin of veal braised with fennel and carrots, then cheeses and two desserts.

Simpler dishes such as marinated shiitake mushrooms with tomatoes and coriander, smoked salmon with new potatoes and caviare, and chocolate and almond tart appear on the three-course menus, and all receive plaudits. Good petits fours have been appreciated by more than one visitor. The 'most attentive and helpful' service extended on one occasion to one of the waiters braving a winter downpour in order to rescue a couple's car from the car park. Wines are well spread and well chosen, though prices are high. Around 100 bottles are supplemented by magnums and a generous supply of halves. House wine is around £15.

CHEF: Ian Mansfield PROPRIETOR: Queens Moat Houses OPEN: all week 12.30 to 2, 7.30 to 9.30 (10 Fri and Sat) MEALS: Set L £19.50 to £42, Set D £28.50 to £42 SERVICE: not inc, card slips closed CARDS: Access, Amex, Diners, Visa DETAILS: 80 seats. Private parties: 95 main room, 20, 40, 65 private rooms. Car park. Vegetarian meals. Children's helpings. Smart dress preferred. No smoking in dining-room. Wheelchair access (2 steps; also WC). Music ACCOMMODATION: 23 rooms, all with bath/shower. TV. Phone. B&B £107.50 to £255. Rooms for disabled. Lift. Children welcome. Pets welcome. Afternoon teas. Garden (*The Which? Hotel Guide*)

BOURNEMOUTH Dorset map 2

Sophisticats

43 Charminster Road, Bournemouth BH8 8UE COOKING 2
TEL: (01202) 291019 COST £27–£39

'These are honest and friendly people trying to please, and serving a slightly old-fashioned cuisine in rather kitsch surroundings,' summed up one reporter. Some find the cat theme, from logo down to cat-shaped fondants with coffee, 'naff' and 'tasteless', while others don't seem to mind. As for the food, the simpler dishes such as 'stunningly fresh' crab in a salad have been appreciated most, though elaboration seems to be a speciality of the house, and is counter-productive. What chance does a fresh piece of sole have after being poached in Noilly Prat with sun-dried tomatoes, then 'finished' with cream and lychees?

Indeed, cream, cheese and alcohol in sauces contribute to the 'old-fashioned' impression of many of the dishes, although it is also possible to eat Dover sole simply grilled with butter, or a venison pie with a good suet pastry top. 'Dishes of the month' add interest. One portion of vegetables may well be enough for two people, while puddings that have met with approval include Black Forest crêpes, praline mousse with caramel sauce, and a layered gâteau of brandy-soaked sponge and chocolate mousse. Service is friendly and informal, 'if slightly eccentric at times', and one reporter found smokiness a problem. The straightforward wine list stays mostly under £20, with house French at £8.25.

CHEF: Bernard Calligan PROPRIETORS: John Knight and Bernard Calligan OPEN: Tue to Sat D only 7 to 9.30 CLOSED: 2 weeks Jan, 2 weeks Aug MEALS: alc (main courses £10.50 to £12) SERVICE: not inc CARDS: none DETAILS: 34 seats. Private parties: 16 main room. Children welcome. Wheelchair access (also WC). Music

BOWNESS-ON-WINDERMERE Cumbria map 8

Porthole Eating House

3 Ash Street, Bowness-on-Windermere LA23 3EB COOKING 2
TEL: (01539) 442793 FAX: (01539) 488675 COST £17–£50

'The food at the Porthole is very good, as your *Guide* says,' wrote one. 'Not anything new, but very well done.' A fixture in the area since the early 1970s, the restaurant inhabits a seventeenth-century cottage kitted out with bare tables, and offers a warm welcome. The menu may strike a chord of recognition in anybody familiar with high-street Italian restaurants up and down the country, for there is everything from Parma ham with melon to spaghetti bolognese and chicken saltimbocca. It is not even all Italian, hence lamb moussaka, beef Stroganov, and Burgundian chicken in a wine, cream and mushroom sauce. In a concession to local gastronomy, Windermere char is potted (with toast) to begin, or grilled and served with a wine and butter sauce for a main course.

Cutting-edge it may not be, but the Porthole still pleases reporters for its solid achievement. Fillet steak Rhône-style was 'perfectly done, as blue as I like it', with a trio of pink, green and black peppercorns in a beef stock sauce, while 'snails Italian-style' came with 'just the perfect amount of garlic' for one reporter. The wine list has enthusiasm stamped all over it: there are a dozen Alsace Gewurztraminers (four of them Vendange Tardive), a splendid collection of German wines (including some 1976 Mosels and Rheingaus) and good Spanish and Italians. One reporter ordered a wine from the Quintarelli collection, 'which brought a smile of delight to the owner's face'. Old and rare spirits look interesting, though Judy Berton's liqueur made from Lyth Valley damsons may be more of a bargain. House Italian is £9.50. CELLARMAN'S CHOICE: Côte de Beaune, Les Pierres Blanches, 1990, Dom. Ponelle, £16; Chambolle Musigny, Hauts Doix 1990, Drouhin, £24.

''Is it local?'' the next table enquired, on discovering there was ostrich on the menu.'
(On eating in Lancashire)

CHEF: Michael Metcalfe PROPRIETORS: Gianni and Judy Berton OPEN: Sun, Mon, Wed to Fri L 12 to 3, Wed to Mon D 6.30 to 11 CLOSED: Jan and Feb MEALS: alc (main courses £5.50 to £15) SERVICE: not inc, card slips closed CARDS: Access, Amex, Delta, Diners, Visa DETAILS: 40 seats. 8 tables outside. Private parties: 40 main room, 30 private room. Vegetarian meals. Children's helpings. Music

BRADFIELD COMBUST Suffolk **map 3**

▲ *Bradfield House*

Bradfield Combust IP30 0LR
TEL: (01284) 386301 **COOKING 1**
on A134, 4m S of Bury St Edmunds **COST £27–£39**

The brick and timber-framed house is seventeenth-century, and the décor has remained unchanged since the new owners took over early in 1995. Douglas Green has worked with Frances Atkins (both at Farleyer House in Aberfeldy – see entry – and at the Old Plow in Speen) and is now going solo. An idea of the style can be gleaned from one couple lunching in summer who enjoyed marinated salmon, cream of mushroom soup with real depth of flavour, roast poussin, and tender rare beef, finishing with rhubarb fool. A few old-fashioned ideas surface, such as avocado with coronation chicken and mango chutney, and some savoury dishes indulge in striking contrasts: grilled halibut explores the sweet-sharp continuum, being glazed with honey and given a warm lemon and lime vinaigrette.

Sauces tend to use alcohol quite a bit, from red wine for a dish of lamb and potatoes wrapped in filo pastry, to Riesling for a fillet of trout, or madeira as a marinade for pork tenderloin: all of them, incidentally, from one menu. Steamed syrup pudding or pears poached in port are satisfying ways to round things off. Good bread is baked in-house, service is on the smart and formal side. A 40-bottle and slightly unbalanced wine list includes some good white burgundy and Italian red, as well as a dozen half-bottles. Prices are fair, beginning with four house wines under £10.

CHEF: Douglas Green PROPRIETORS: Douglas Green, Gordon Green and Moya Green OPEN: Tue to Sun L 12.15 to 2.15, Tue to Sat D 7.15 to 9.15 MEALS: alc (main courses £7.50 to £12.50). Set L and D £15.50 (2 courses) to £19.50 SERVICE: not inc CARDS: Access, Diners, Switch, Visa DETAILS: 30 seats. 3 tables outside. Private parties: 20 main room, 15 private room. Car park. No children under 5. Jacket and tie D. No smoking in dining-room. Wheelchair access. Music ACCOMMODATION: 4 rooms, all with bath/shower. TV. Phone. B&B £45 to £80. Deposit: £25. Children welcome. Baby facilities. Pets welcome. Garden

BRADFORD West Yorkshire **map 8**

▲ *Restaurant Nineteen*

North Park Road, Heaton, Bradford BD9 4NT **COOKING 3**
TEL: (01274) 492559 FAX: (01274) 483827 **COST £35–£43**

'The sitting-room in this small restaurant overlooking Lister Park has been renovated since our previous visit,' wrote one, 'with lavish drapes, newly upholstered chairs and attractive lighting.' Refurbishment of the dining-room, though, has been put on ice until funds allow. Bradford is not such a thriving place as its near neighbour, Leeds. The two dining-rooms are domestic in scale, with salmon-pink walls and well-spaced tables. 'Glassware and crockery are impeccable', and service by a young team is professional, knowledgeable and friendly.

Dinner is three courses with four or five items a time, along the lines of 'tender and juicy' slices of roast quail arranged on a bed of rocket, accompanied by corn fritters and a sweet plum sauce, then salmon and turbot with lemon grass and coriander, followed by poached pear with vanilla ice-cream. Some starters can seem like miniature versions of a main course without the vegetables, like the thigh and leg of chicken with wild mushrooms in a cream sauce that one reporter ate, while others are a meeting-point for perhaps one too many ideas, as in a braised knuckle of ham with rabbit fillet and rissoles with mushrooms and pulses. An inspector felt that components of some dishes didn't seem to have much affinity for one other, and that not all the flavours had the impact they should, although raw materials were first-class. 'We felt the kitchen was capable of better things.'

Puddings have included 'smooth, sweet' Amaretto ice-cream with a compote of dried apricots, and a tall glass filled with Tia Maria ice-cream trifle topped with leaves of dark chocolate. One reporter ordered poached peaches just to see what the accompanying basil ice-cream tasted like. Wines are sensibly chosen and priced, taking advantage of good modern wine-making, and the list provides ample choice from around the world within the compass of a hundred or so bottles, four of them available by the glass from £2.75. CELLARMAN'S CHOICE: Bianco 1993, Avignonesi, £12; Rioja, Contino Reserva 1988, £18.50.

CHEF: Stephen Smith PROPRIETORS: Stephen Smith and Robert Barbour OPEN: Tue to Sat D only 7 to 9.30 (10 Fri and Sat) CLOSED: 1 week Christmas, 1 week June, 2 weeks Aug to Sept MEALS: Set D £25 SERVICE: not inc CARDS: Access, Amex, Delta, Switch, Visa DETAILS: 36 seats. Private parties: 36 main room. Car park. No children under 10. No cigars/pipes in dining-room. Music ACCOMMODATION: 4 rooms, all with bath/shower. TV. Phone. B&B £65 to £75. No children under 10. Garden (*The Which? Hotel Guide*)

BRADFORD-ON-AVON Wiltshire map 2

▲ *Woolley Grange*

Woolley Green, Bradford-on-Avon BA15 1TX
TEL: (01225) 864705 FAX: (01225) 864059 NEW CHEF
on B3105, 1m NE of Bradford-on-Avon COST £24–£48

Woolley Grange's colourful brochure explains that this is a Jacobean stone manor house in 14 acres of gardens and paddocks. It also makes the point that children are particularly welcome: there is a nursery in the old coach house with a full-time nanny, a games room and a separate eating area with its own daily-changing menu of shepherd's pie, chicken nuggets and pizza. Parents can come away with their children, then lose them while they address their own needs. All very civilised. 'Like so many country-house hotels,' writes a senior reporter, 'Woolley Grange really needs to be experienced for a weekend break' to get the full benefit.

The house has 'old, desirable rugs tossed with abandon all over the place' and its share of antiques. The bright modern paintings in the pastel-coloured dining-room make an impact 'like Lewis Carroll on Ecstasy'. Stephen Morey took over the kitchen for a while, then left for Homewood Park (see entry, Hinton Charterhouse), and Peter Stott was promoted from sous to head chef as we went to press. It is likely the cooking will continue in the same vein, producing mainstream dishes, along the lines of steamed mussels, grilled sirloin steak and twice-baked goats' cheese soufflé. Cheeses are good, and wine prices can be high, although graded mark-ups make the better wines better value. The list is an enterprising selection that combines classics with lesser known but interesting wines from odd corners of the vinous world. House Duboeuf is £10.50. CELLARMAN'S CHOICE: Bergerac, Sauvignon Blanc, Ch. la Jaubertie, £16; Jamesons Run 1991, Coonawarra, S. Australia, £22.50.

CHEF: Peter Stott PROPRIETORS: Nigel and Heather Chapman OPEN: all week 12.15 to 2, 7.15 to 10 MEALS: alc (main courses £9 to £14). Set L Sun £17. Set D £28 SERVICE: not inc, card slips closed CARDS: Access, Amex, Delta, Diners, Switch, Visa DETAILS: 70 seats. 6 tables outside. Private parties: 20 main room, 12 and 20 private rooms. Car park. Children welcome. Smart dress preferred. No smoking in dining-room. Wheelchair access (1 step; also WC). No music ACCOMMODATION: 20 rooms, all with bath/shower. TV. Phone. B&B £90 to £170. Rooms for disabled. Children welcome. Baby facilities. Dogs welcome exc in dining-room. Afternoon teas. Garden. Swimming pool (*The Which? Hotel Guide*)

BRAITHWAITE Cumbria map 10

▲ *Ivy House*

Braithwaite CA12 5SY
TEL: (01768) 778338 FAX: (01768) 778113 COOKING 1
just off B5292 Keswick to Braithwaite road COST £25–£30

The 'strange' dark-green ambience of Ivy House reminded one visitor of a 'Disneyland haunted house'; others with less vivid imaginations simply enjoy the prospect of dining at their leisure in the elegant surroundings of the Shills' ever-evolving hotel. Dinner is served in a distinctive beamed dining-room and the cooking seems firmly rooted in the traditions of the Lakeland country-house, even though it occasionally veers off into the exotic realms of pork satay, or salmon and monkfish cooked with sherry, coriander, paprika and cream. The four-course menu has a few long-running dishes – steak au poivre, rack of lamb with rosemary and mint gravy, Gressingham duck with black cherries and madeira – and these continue to get their share of praise.

Starters such as avocado with smoked mackerel and balsamic vinaigrette or seafood mousse could be followed by 'fantastic' pea soup or a sorbet. To finish, there might be white chocolate mousse or sticky toffee pudding, although one visitor needed nothing more than a plate of fresh fruit with cream to complete a meal full of simple pleasures. Good wine merchants such as Adnams and Bidendum contribute to a list that stays mostly under £20. House wines are less than £10. CELLARMAN'S CHOICE: Mitchell Riesling 'Watervale Vineyard' 1992, South Australia, £12.25; Gran Reserva Cabernet Sauvignon 1991, Portal del Alto, Chile, £11.50.

CHEFS: Wendy Shill and Peter Holten PROPRIETORS: Nick and Wendy Shill OPEN: all week D only 7.30 (one sitting) CLOSED: Jan MEALS: Set D £18.95 SERVICE: not inc CARDS: Access, Amex, Delta, Diners, Switch, Visa DETAILS: 32 seats. Private parties: 20 main room. Car park. Children welcome. Smart dress preferred. No smoking in dining-room. Music ACCOMMODATION: 12 rooms, all with bath/shower. TV. Phone. B&B £30 to £60, D,B&B £47 to £94. Deposit: £20. Children welcome. Baby facilities. Pets by arrangement. Afternoon teas. Garden (*The Which? Hotel Guide*)

BRAMPTON Cumbria map 10

▲ *Farlam Hall*

Brampton CA8 2NG
TEL: (01697) 746234 FAX: (01697) 746683 COOKING **2**
on A689, 2½m SE of Brampton (not at Farlam village) COST **£38–£45**

Once the home of wealthy Victorian industrialists, Farlam Hall was purchased by the Quinion family in 1975 as 'an empty house with no furniture'. Twenty years on it tells a different story. The Quinions have been joined by the Stevensons, and together they have shaped and decorated the interior without sacrificing its nineteenth-century origin: 'lovingly collected paintings' line the walls, stuffed animals and toby jugs are dotted around and heavy drapes hang at the windows. As the evening draws to a close, ludo, chess and cards are set out on coffee-tables in the lounge. It is all very 'country-house party', and Joan Quinion ('resplendent in a long taffeta dress') orchestrates proceedings impeccably. From the formal dining-room, guests can gaze out on to the landscaped Victorian garden, complete with its ornamental lake and manicured lawns.

Dinner is a set-price, four-course affair that kicks off with an excellent selection of breads. A typical meal might begin with 'gently smooth' chicken liver parfait with spicy home-made plum chutney and toasted fruit-loaf, or strips of salmon marinated in walnut oil, white wine and lemon juice. A sorbet precedes the main course, which may be poached halibut with a deep orange saffron sauce or medallions of local beef with a red wine sauce. Cheeses are English, and puddings range from a raspberry brûlée of 'industrial strength' to 'excellent' sherry and sultana ice-cream. The list of around 40 wines offers a reasonable, if not dazzlingly interesting, choice over a fair price range. House wine is £12.75.

CHEF: Barry Quinion PROPRIETORS: the Quinion and Stevenson families OPEN: all week, D only 8 for 8.30 (one sitting); L on Mother's Day, Easter Sun, 25 Dec and 1 Jan CLOSED: 26 to 30 Dec MEALS: Set D £28 SERVICE: not inc, card slips closed CARDS: Access, Amex, Switch, Visa DETAILS: 40 seats. Private parties: 28 main room. Car park. No children under 5. Smart dress preferred. No cigars/pipes in dining-room. Wheelchair access (2 steps). No music ACCOMMODATION: 12 rooms, all with bath/shower. TV. Phone. D,B&B £95 to £210. No children under 5. Afternoon teas. Garden (*The Which? Hotel Guide*)

'Our main courses took ages to arrive. Finally the head waiter popped round to our table to explain that "there was a queue in the kitchen".'
(On waiting to eat in Worcestershire)

BRAY Berkshire map 3

▲ *Waterside Inn* 🍷

Ferry Road, Bray SL6 2AT
TEL: (01628) 20691 FAX: (01628) 784710 COOKING **4***
off A308 Maidenhead to Windsor road COST £38–£107

The setting has been described as 'magical' even on a cold, blustery February day, which is good going, and even if the décor does not have reporters in raptures (fortunately the Thames, waiters and other diners provide distraction), it plays attractively with reflections and refractions in spotlights, mirrors and candlelight. The appeal is classic and conservative French cooking of an exceptionally high order. In place of bold and direct flavours, we get refined and subtle ones. If the Waterside appears oblivious to what is happening in the culinary world beyond its doors, then it doesn't seem to mind.

Menus are totally *en français*, of course, and consist of a generous *carte*, plus a *menu exceptionnel* that abstracts some items, trims them for size and arranges them into a four-course spread (plus mid-meal sorbet) for two people. Meals begin with a nibble of something over an aperitif, then an amuse-gueule at table – all light and restrained curtain-raisers for the show that is about to begin. One reporter who went expecting 'mouthgasms' remained unmoved, wondering if the place were simply living on its reputation. But it isn't. Although some dishes, such as pasta filled with a rough mousse of crab and lobster, may sound very ordinary, freshness and flavour lift them into the superlative category. A marbled terrine of chicken, artichoke and foie gras, served with a scoop of cauliflower cream, produces 'gorgeous combinations of flavours and textures'.

The brevity of the cooking times for meat 'is exactly what is needed to bring out the brilliance of the raw materials'. At one meal a duck arrived for two people, 'shown to us whole, then carved into thin, supple, decidedly pink slices at table'. The bird had been poached in jasmine tea, producing a gently smoky flavour, then roasted with honey to crisp the skin. It came with a 'sticky, subtly cinnamon-flavoured sauce', plus potatoes, mange-tout, and a duck-shaped vol-au-vent of flaky pastry filled with creamed cauliflower. Sauces tend to be small stock-based pools that add to 'the amazing intensity of flavours', and while the food may be less innovative, less daring, than some expect, the combinations are subtle and come close to perfection. Hot raspberry soufflé for an inspector was 'perfect in flavour, perfect in texture'. The waiter cut it open and poured in more 'sheer raspberriness' in the form of a sauce.

Service has drawn mixed reports. A request for plain tap-water was refused on the grounds that the restaurant serves only bottled water, and while one felt that 'staff are faintly bored with the whole deal', another was impressed that 'they see to it that every customer has a wonderful evening'. Other niggles have generally concerned smoking (the tables have ashtrays), poor bread, and the policy of stating that service is included but then leaving a blank space for 'gratuity' on the credit card slip. One reporter felt that £6 for a cup of coffee was a bit cheeky, but it does come with brilliant petits fours that are an art form in themselves. Wines are as French as the rest of the operation, and prices tend to astonish ordinary mortals, although house wine is £18 and you can buy a glass of Ch. Talbot 1987 for £5. CELLARMAN'S CHOICE: Chablis, Selection des Frères Roux 1989, £28; Pessac-Léognan, Ch. La Parde Haut Bailly 1989, £23.50.

CHEFS: Michel Roux and Mark Dodson PROPRIETOR: Michel Roux OPEN: Wed to Sun L 12 to 2 (2.30 Sat and Sun), Tue to Sun D 7 to 10 CLOSED: 5 weeks from 26 Dec; Sun D Nov to Mar MEALS: alc (main courses £26 to £34). Set L £29.50 to £66, Set D £66. Minimum £30 SERVICE: net prices CARDS: Access, Diners, Switch, Visa DETAILS: 75 seats. Private parties: 80 main room, 8 private room. Car park. Vegetarian meals. No children under 12. Smart dress preferred. No cigars in dining-room. Wheelchair access (1 step). Music ACCOMMODATION: 7 rooms, all with bath/shower. TV. Phone. B&B £130 to £205. Deposit: £60. No children under 12

BRIGHOUSE West Yorkshire map 8

Brook's

6 Bradford Road, Brighouse HD6 1RW COOKING 1*
TEL: (01484) 715284 FAX: (01484) 712641 COST £19–£35

Classic '30s jazz, window blinds and bare floorboards set the mood in Darrell Brook's cool but lively restaurant. The pace can be fast, so ask to wait between courses if you want a leisurely meal. Before seven o'clock in the week there is an 'early bird' menu at a special price; otherwise, dinner revolves around a short weekly menu (fixed-price for two or three courses) and the kitchen plunders the globe for inspiration. On a typical evening you might find Thai beef salad with crispy noodles, deep-fried haggis with parsnip sauce, and pan-fried king prawns and Italian bacon circled around chopped black olives and pesto ('I really enjoyed this,' remarked an inspector). Specials, such as Spanish chicken terrine with gazpacho coulis, chateaubriand, and chargrilled venison cutlet with blackcurrant jus and onion marmalade flesh out the repertoire. Also look for the unusual version of gravlax made from smoked haddock. Darrell Brook tells us that his bread-and-butter pudding has 'a big following', although chocolate mocha ganache with sauce anglaise has also received praise. To finish, you can retreat to the upstairs lounge for coffee, or stay seated and create an arty doodle on the paper tablecloth using the wax crayons provided (the best exhibits are given pride of place on the walls). The short wine list fits the bill admirably and prices are fair. House wine is £7.50.

CHEF: Richard Ullah PROPRIETOR: Darrell Brook OPEN: Mon to Sat D only 6 to 11 CLOSED: 1 week summer MEALS: Set D £14.95 (2 courses) to £18.95, 'early bird' menu £11.95 (Mon to Fri 6 to 7pm) SERVICE: not inc CARDS: Access, Visa DETAILS: 55 seats. Private parties: 65 main room, 20 private room. Vegetarian meals. Smart dress preferred. No smoking in dining-room.Wheelchair access (1 step). Music

BRIGHTON East Sussex map 3

Black Chapati

E. SUSSEX 1996 MAVERICK

12 Preston Circus, New England Road,
Brighton BN1 4GW COOKING 2
TEL: (01273) 699011 COST £20–£34

'Brilliantly idiosyncratic as ever,' confirms one who has supported this unlikely restaurant since its early days. Don't be put off by the location. The Black Chapati is 'plonked down in an arcade of shops in an area of light industrial development and burger bars', and the décor is a bizarre mix of black menus on black tables

and prints of sheet music on white walls. Tables are so tightly crammed in that 'someone wanting to go to the toilet can result in half the diners having to stand up and shuffle about'. Despite the problems, service is pleasant and unfussy, although Stephen Funnell's 'direct' attitude to his customers may ruffle a few feathers.

The food refuses to be pigeonholed: one reporter described it as 'a flagrant Europeanisation of Indian cooking'. In truth, it is an extraordinary kaleidoscope of Asian strands seen through Western eyes. Here is a kitchen that can conjure up 'light' crab soup with coriander and pork wun-tuns, smoked duck breast with lentil salad and mustard sauce, and a brilliant dish of haddock with ginger, tamarind and Thai rice. The menu also promises grilled guinea-fowl with herb couscous, bhel pooris, braised chicken South Indian style, and a vegetarian thali composed of half a dozen precisely cooked, subtly spiced dishes. When it comes to desserts, Europe wins the day with first-rate crème brûlée, apple crumble and stewed plums with fromage frais and polenta. The wine list is short and lively, but most people opt for imported bottled beers or cider: *cidre breton* is 'the chef's favourite drink', but the weekly 'guest' could be Perry's traditional brew from Somerset. House wine is £8.50.

CHEFS/PROPRIETORS: Stephen Funnell and Lauren Alker OPEN: Tue to Sat D 7 to 10.30 CLOSED: 1 week Christmas, 1 week Jun MEALS: alc (main courses £8.50 to £11). Set L Sun buffet £8.95 SERVICE: 10%, card slips closed CARDS: Access, Amex, Delta, Switch, Visa DETAILS: 30 seats. 2 tables outside. Private parties: 10 main room. Vegetarian meals. Children welcome. Wheelchair access. Music

One Paston Place

1 Paston Place, Brighton BN2 1HA — COOKING 2
TEL: (01273) 606933 FAX: (01273) 675686 — COST £22–£42

As we went to press, Langan's Bistro had a face-lift, not to mention a hip replacement and an organ transplant. The name and décor may have changed, but Mark Emmerson remains at the stoves, producing confident renditions of gutsy dishes from Provence and Gasgony, combining technical consistency with impeccable raw materials. A Midlands couple on a gastro-tour of Brighton enjoyed 'extremely tasty' marinated salmon with rillettes of the same fish and then 'excellent' guinea-fowl on red cabbage and raisins – 'despite the strength of these flavours, the essential taste of the fowl was still discernible'. Other good dishes have been substantial mushroom and sorrel soup, well-dressed salad of bacon and duck confit, and braised legs of rabbit on a tapénade. The French accent wears off a little at dessert stage, where you might find sticky toffee pudding and apple crumble, although a version of crème brûlée with a topping of ground roasted hazelnuts made a better-than-usual variant on that much-modified dish. Espresso is good and strong. The wine list is standard bistro French with the sole exception of the California fizz Cuvée Napa. House wines from Duboeuf are £8.80.

CHEF: Mark Emmerson PROPRIETOR: Coq d'Or Restaurant Co Ltd OPEN: Sun and Tue to Fri L 12.30 to 2.15, Tue to Sat D 7.30 to 10.15 MEALS: alc (main courses £14 to £15). Set L £12.50 (2 courses) and £14.50. Cover 75p SERVICE: 10%, card slips closed CARDS: Access, Amex, Delta, Diners, Visa DETAILS: 45 seats. Vegetarian meals. Children welcome. No pipes. Wheelchair access. Music. Air-conditioned

Terre à Terre

NEW ENTRY

7 Pool Valley, Brighton BN1 1NY — COOKING 1*
TEL: (01273) 729051 — COST £22–£33

'Gosh,' exclaimed an unrepentant carnivore who chanced upon this 'café of sorts' a short hop from the Palace Pier. In a setting of folding chairs, varnished wood tables 'like school desks', watercolours and fuschias in vases, you will be offered confidently flavoured vegetarian food with hardly a hint of sanctimony or self-denial. The menu lists seven or so choices at each stage, and highlights dishes that are vegan. Portions are hearty, prices are very fair. As a 'heart-warming starter', try a large timbale of caponata with broad shavings of Parmesan and a scattering of whole toasted almonds, which is eaten with slices of garlicky focaccia plus a heap of salad leaves. The 'generous platter' of tapas is another popular way to start a meal.

Even bigger are multi-layered main dishes: something called sweet potato and pink peppercorn bullas appears as two hefty patties jazzed up with chilli, piled with a sour-cream raita-like dressing, topped in turn with 'seemingly home-made' mango chutney. Around all this is a lake of tomato salsa dotted with black beans, but that is not all: add some more salad and a little collection of chargrilled vegetables to complete 'another groaning plateful'. Desserts also show plenty of invention: marinated apricots with cassis sauce, blackened banana, or 'two-tone' cappuccino and chocolate mousse served on a heap of squashed prunes marinated in cognac. The short wine list promises 'traditional stuff at decent prices'. House wine is £7.50.

OPEN: Tue to Sun L 12 to 5.45, all week D (exc Mon winter) 6 to 10.30 MEALS: alc (main courses around £7) CARDS: none SERVICE: not inc DETAILS: 46 seats. Private parties: 24 main room. Vegetarian meals. Children's helpings. No smoking in 1 dining-room. Wheelchair access. Music

Whytes

33 Western Street, Brighton BN1 2PG — COOKING 1*
TEL: (01273) 776618 — COST £27–£32

Ian and Jane Whyte say they are aiming to provide 'honest cooking with friendly service in a cosy atmosphere'. The consensus appears to be that they are succeeding on all three counts in their converted whitewashed cottage a few yards from Brighton's western seafront. Menus are centred on perennial favourites such as half a roasted crispy duckling, and best end of lamb with basil-scented Mediterranean vegetables. Vegetarian dishes mobilise plenty of flavour, as in a leek, wild mushroom and Gruyère strudel sauced with grain mustard, and local fish is used enthusiastically, perhaps in a simple pairing of poached brill and sole with a classic sauce of wine, cream and chives. A refugee from central London, praising 'the best meal out I've had for a long time', happily recalled a dinner that ended with a 'wonderful almond slice with nutty ice-cream and butterscotch sauce', and only wished she lived nearer. The serviceable French wine list offers good-value drinking. House wines are from £7.95.

CHEF: Ian Whyte PROPRIETORS: Ian and Jane Whyte OPEN: Mon to Sat D only 7 to 10 MEALS: Set D £15.50 (2 courses) to £18.95. Minimum £15.50 SERVICE: not inc CARDS: Access, Amex, Visa DETAILS: 36 seats. Private parties: 30 main room, 14 private room. Vegetarian meals. Children welcome. Music

BRIMFIELD Hereford & Worcester map 5

▲ *Poppies* 🍷 £✱

The Roebuck, Brimfield SY8 4NE
TEL: (01584) 711230 FAX: (01584) 711654 COOKING 3*
on A49, 4m S of Ludlow COST £31–£60

Poppies is part of the Roebuck, a village pub with accommodation. The bar may not look inspiring, but part of the attraction is that nobody stands on ceremony. 'The drinks order was called across the bar, one at a time, and we were served the same way.' Perhaps this relaxed approach helps to explain some of the differing views of service, which has been judged 'attentive, charming and efficient' as well as 'chaotic, inadequate and appalling', although there is no doubting the personal effort that Carole Evans puts into running the whole show. The bar menu alone is worth a visit, with Helford oysters, a pot of crab, black pudding, or smoked haddock and tarragon tart, mostly between £5 and £9.

The dining-room is a contrast, with comfortable chairs and plenty of space. 'Carole Evans is an excellent and creative cook', and also a thoroughly modern one. She uses organic produce wherever possible, and doesn't stand still: 'during the past 12 months my cooking has become much lighter, with less-heavy sauces,'she writes. The set lunch is normally a choice between two dishes per course, while the evening *carte* offers a more generous six or eight. 'It is not cheap, but it is good value.' Olives and 'delicate savouries' are followed by a pre-meal offering, such as green pea and lettuce soup, and then anything from crab ravioli to tomato and pesto tart, from oxtail en gelée to a ragoût of plump green asparagus with wild mushrooms and pasta. Even grilled Lakeland char makes an appearance, as does Herefordshire beef, tender pink Welsh lamb, and pan-fried sea bass. Ingredients are first-class.

A good spread of British cheeses (some unpasteurised) is backed up by bread-and-butter pudding, hot chocolate soufflé, and ice-cream presented in sheets of caramel 'like a stained-glass lantern'. The intelligently chosen wines are sold at fair prices, whether from the New World or the more extensive French collection. They include a generous supply of half-bottles, although it is worth staying the night to take advantage of the full ones, as well as the malt whiskies and breakfast. House wine starts at £12.50. CELLARMAN'S CHOICE: Vins de Pays de la Haute-Vallée de l'Aude, Chardonnay 'Les Aigles' 1992, £13; Parker Terra Rossa Cabernet Sauvignon 1991, Coonawarra, S. Australia, £20.50.

CHEF/PROPRIETOR: Carole Evans OPEN: Tue to Sat 12 to 2, 7 to 9.30 MEALS: alc D (main courses £18.50 to £22.50). Set L £20. Bar meals available SERVICE: not inc, card slips closed CARDS: Access, Delta, Switch, Visa DETAILS: 40 seats. 4 tables outside. Private parties: 40 main room, 16 private room. Car park. Vegetarian meals. Children's helpings. Smart dress preferred. No smoking in 1 dining-room. Wheelchair access. No music ACCOMMODATION: 3 rooms, all with bath/shower. TV. Phone. B&B £45 to £60. Deposit: £30. Children welcome. Pets by arrangement (*The Which? Hotel Guide*)

BRISTOL Avon map 2

Bell's Diner £

1 York Road, Montpelier, Bristol BS6 5QB
TEL: 0117-924 0357 FAX: 0117-924 4280
take Picton Street off Cheltenham Road (A38) – runs into York Road
COOKING 2
COST £17–£34

When Shirley Ann Bell opened this 'slightly off-beat' diner in 1976 her intent was, as one of her partners says, 'to emulate the basic honesty of approach of the traditional French family-run restaurant'. Two decades later the place still fulfils its aims, although it is thoroughly in tune with the trends of the 1990s. The ambience has been described as 'rustic', with paper cloths on the tables and 'meagre furniture', but most reporters agree that the cooking generally hits the button.

The menu is set-price for three courses, with supplements charged for various dishes at each stage. The menus change from week to week as new ingredients find their way into the kitchen. Much of the produce – including the bread – is from local sources, although fish is delivered twice weekly from Cornwall. Descriptions of dishes often read like a litany of components and ingredients, but there are plenty of surprises in store. Seared scallops might be accompanied by an unexpected mint and Jerusalem artichoke purée, or paired with lentil and anchovy dressing. Stilton soufflé gets a lift from 'excellent' onion and pear marmalade, while a main course of crisply chargrilled salmon is served with a fiery tomato and chilli salsa, although the addition of avocado butter struck one reporter as an unnecessary embellishment. A sauce of lime, ginger and honey with braised guinea-fowl has been described as 'very good and balanced'. Desserts may include prune and armagnac tart with mascarpone, and there is generally a plate of unpasteurised British farmhouse cheeses to round things off. Good coffee comes with home-made fudge. The wine list is a lively and affordable assemblage of bottles from enterprising growers; also look for Smiles Exhibition, sold by the jug, and EKU wheat beer. Eight house wines start at £8.

CHEFS: Peter Taylor, Chris Wicks and Shirley Ann Bell PROPRIETORS: Shirley Ann Bell, Peter Taylor and Mark Hall OPEN: Sun L 12.30 to 3, all week D 6.30 to 10 (10.30 Sat by arrangement, 8.30 Sun) CLOSED: 1 week from Aug bank hol MEALS: Set L Sun £10.50, Set D £12.75 SERVICE: not inc; 10% for parties of 8 or more CARDS: Access, Switch, Visa DETAILS: 60 seats. Private parties: 28 main room, 18 private room. Vegetarian meals. Children's helpings. No smoking in dining-room. Music

Harveys

12 Denmark Street, Bristol BS1 5DQ
TEL: 0117-927 5034 FAX: 0117-927 5003
COOKING 3
COST £22–£56

For the best part of two centuries Harveys the wine merchant has used these medieval cellars for storing and bottling wine for its customers, and the museum that now forms part of the underground operation is well worth a visit. The restaurant has been here for over 30 years, stabilising since 1992 under the direction of Ramon Farthing. 'Harveys is back where it belongs,' claims a regular reporter who had not visited for some time, adding that 'it is very expensive, but worth it, like any great classic.' Deep carpets, eighteenth-century paintings and prints, and various vinous memorabilia combine to give it 'a wonderful blend of opulence and mystery'.

The food has a sound classic foundation yet is very much up to date, dealing in some elaborate but eye-catching ideas. As unlikely as it sounds, a chicken and black olive sausage, flavoured with coriander, is served with creamed potato and a sauce of chicken livers and pineapple. Crisp breast of duck comes with a peach Tatin, while a soup of white haricot beans is accompanied by a smoked garlic cream with baked ham and mustard pastries. Despite the apparent complication, dishes work splendidly, with 'exemplary' pheasant casserole, and rack of lamb cooked 'exactly as ordered'. If it does all seem too much, there is an escape clause: ingredients will be cooked more simply on request.

British and Irish cheeses make an impressive finale, from Irish Gubbeens or Cashel Blue to unpasteurised Cheddar or Shere, while puddings range from a hot passion-fruit soufflé served with white chocolate sauce to a chilled rice pudding topped with caramelised pears and served with a cinnamon sabayon. Staff are distinguished not only by friendliness but also by a high level of knowledge about wine and food. Their help may be necessary to find a good match of wine with the food, given the kaleidoscope of flavours; there are so many wines that something is bound to work. The list is tilted heavily towards France, with a magnificent display of claret culminating in vintages of Ch. Latour dating back to 1934. Elsewhere there is good drinking at more affordable prices. If in doubt, begin with a sherry and finish with port. House wine is £12. CELLARMAN'S CHOICE: Sancerre 1992, Prieur, £19; Sonoma County Clos du Bois Merlot 1992, California, £18.

CHEFS: Ramon Farthing and Paul Dunstane PROPRIETOR: John Harvey and Sons OPEN: Mon to Fri L 12 to 1.45, Mon to Sat D 7 to 10.45 CLOSED: bank hols MEALS: alc (main courses £17 to £20). Set L £16, Set D £29 SERVICE: net prices, card slips closed CARDS: Access, Amex, Delta, Diners, Switch, Visa DETAILS: 120 seats. Private parties: 70 main room, 50 private room. Car park. Vegetarian meals. No children under 8. Smart dress preferred. Music. Air-conditioned

Howards

1A–2A Avon Crescent, Hotwells, Bristol BS1 6XQ — COOKING 1
TEL: 0117-926 2921 — COST £20–£39

This pair of Georgian terraced houses built on a curve has been transformed into an attractive restaurant on two floors, the upper one more formal, the ground floor more like a bistro, with lots of flowers and plants. A seasonally changing *carte* is supplemented by a set-price, no-choice, three-course menu, and by fish of the day listed on the blackboard: perhaps grilled salmon with leeks and a basil dressing, or poached monkfish with asparagus and chive butter. Sometimes the urge to experiment gets the better of David Short, who offers a baked filo parcel of smoked chicken and mango with Cumberland sauce, or rosettes of lamb with a crab flan and Madras sabayon. But ingredients and presentation are good, and the simpler dishes seem to work best: a warm salad of 'lovely grilled scallops, full of flavour', for example, that came with a rather busy salad, or a 'tender and flavoursome' duck breast served with a rich pâté wrapped in bacon. Puddings range from strawberry and rhubarb gratin to a rich, creamy raspberry crème brûlée. Service has see-sawed from 'lacklustre' to 'energetic and rushed'. The 50-strong wine list keeps prices sensibly in check. House wine is £7.25.

CHEF: David Short PROPRIETORS: Christopher and Gillian Howard OPEN: Mon to Fri L 12 to 2.30, Mon to Sat D 7 to 11 CLOSED: Christmas, bank hols MEALS: alc (main courses £9.50 to £14.50). Set L £13, Set D Mon to Fri £15 SERVICE: not inc; 10% for parties of 8 or more CARDS: Access, Amex, Diners, Visa DETAILS: 65 seats. Private parties: 25 main room, 40 private rooms. Vegetarian meals. Children welcome. Smart dress preferred. No-smoking area. Wheelchair access (1 step). Music

Hunt's

26 Broad Street, Bristol BS1 2HG COOKING 3
TEL/FAX: 0117-926 5580 COST £21–£44

The heart of Bristol's old commercial district is surprisingly compact in scale. Parking in the narrow streets can be a nightmare, even after business hours, so find some other way of getting here, if you can. Hunt's is opposite the Colston Hall, in premises where tea and coffee were once traded.

In a city well served by conspicuous culinary talent, Andrew Hunt has done well to establish and maintain his high reputation, particularly through the recession. The style is essentially French, with one or two Italian borrowings, the emphasis gently placed on fish. Smoked salmon trout is rolled around prawns for a light starter, while smoked haddock soufflé has ground coriander and a dill cream. Globe artichoke forms the centre of a labour-intensive first course, filled with a duxelles of wild mushrooms and pine-nuts, coated in brioche crumbs and baked. Some traditional preparations are evident in main courses of guinea-fowl with apples and calvados, Trelough duck breast with spiced plums, or calf's liver and bacon with a purée of parsnip. Salmon with scallops in a sauce that included coriander was rated highly at a summer dinner; at a winter lunch it was baked and came with 'a gorgeously creamy but light lemon sauce'.

Desserts cooked to order may take in Normandy apple and almond tart with butterscotch sauce or a hot soufflé, such as cranberry and Cointreau. Rice pudding is given a tweak by being made into an iced confection that turns up with a poached pear and a sabayon of Poire Williams. The appetisingly fat olives that come at the outset are mentioned in dispatches, and vegetables are well prepared and copious. The mainly French wine list has some good growers at generally reasonable prices. Choice isn't especially wide, though, and more halves would help. House wines start at £9.50.

CHEFS: Andrew Hunt PROPRIETORS: Andrew and Anne Hunt OPEN: Tue to Fri L 12 to 2, Tue to Sat D 7 to 10 (10.30 Sat) CLOSED: 1 week Easter, 1 week end Aug, 10 days Christmas MEALS: alc (main courses £13 to £16). Set L £10.95 (2 courses) to £12.95 SERVICE: not inc, card slips closed CARDS: Access, Amex, Delta, Switch, Visa DETAILS: 35 seats. Private parties: 26 main room. Children's helpings. Smart dress preferred. Wheelchair access (1 step). Music

'On a quiet lunch-time the waiters appeared to do very little, but in a most professional way.' (On eating in London)

Lettonie 🍷

9 Druid Hill, Stoke Bishop, Bristol BS9 1EW COOKING **4**
TEL: **0117-968 6456** FAX: **0117-968 6943** COST **£28–£56**

'Yes, it is in an anonymous parade of shops, with an awful plastic awning, and nowhere to park, but it was a meal I thoroughly enjoyed.' Reporters are unanimous in their praise for this Bristol oasis, and their view is that it offers value for money. 'My husband and I took my parents out for dinner and we achieved a first: everyone was thrilled with everything.' Another was 'calmed and revived by the cool interior on a hot day, and enjoyed one of the finest meals ever'. Lettonie is testament to the fact that good food doesn't need swanky surroundings. A 'simple but comfortable room' such as this suffices, and friendly service contributes to the feeling of well-being. Siân Blunos is a natural hostess.

The cheaper set menus offer limited choice, while the more expensive one imposes a small supplement for Sevruga caviare sprinkled over scrambled duck's egg, flambé in Latvian vodka, and served with hot blinis 'of perfect lightness' and a large measure of vodka (with a choice of plain, black pepper, or lemon grass). This is a signature first course of 'bold showmanship, and the extra £3.50 was well spent'. It is also one of the few signs of Martin Blunos's East European background, although a preference for game, offal and pasta also marks out his distinctive approach.

Pasta is often paired with fish, and might come in the form of a light tortellini of tasty langoustine, or of pike with a crayfish cream sauce, while game might include loin of venison with a lentil crust. The flavour and stickiness of offal finds much support, from stuffed pig's trotter, or braised lambs' tongues in pastry with onion marmalade, to 'a beautifully done package of oxtail off the bone on a rich stock with braised turned vegetables'. The cooking works in combinations too, as in a dish of lamb cutlets 'immaculately tender and properly pink', accompanied by a coarse and very gamey terrine made from lambs' tongues and kidneys, 'a powerful counterpoint to the delicacy of the cutlets, and beautifully judged'.

Puddings are rich and satisfying, and among successes have been a 'spot-on' chocolate marquise served with a poached pear, and a caramel nut ice in a tuile with raspberry coulis, although by this stage of the meal rapture is sometimes reserved more for looks than taste. The cheese selection is exceptional. Wines are predominantly French and generally mainstream, with some less-well-known producers helping to keep prices under control. A fair selection of half-bottles, a few bin-ends, and a wine waiter who knows his business add to the appeal, as does a short list of house wines at £2.90 a glass. CELLARMAN'S CHOICE: Cloudy Bay Sauvignon Blanc 1994, Marlborough, New Zealand, £19.80; Graves, Ch. Le Bonnat 1989, £22.80.

CHEF: Martin Blunos PROPRIETORS: Martin and Siân Blunos OPEN: Tue to Sat 12.30 to 2, 7 to 9 CLOSED: 2 weeks Christmas, 2 weeks Aug MEALS: Set L £17.95 to £34.50, Set D £23.50 (Tue to Thur) to £34.50 SERVICE: not inc CARDS: Access, Amex, Switch, Visa DETAILS: 24 seats. Private parties: 24 main room. Children's helpings. Wheelchair access (1 step). Music

See the inside of the front cover for an explanation of the 1 to 5 rating system for cooking standards.

Markwicks

43 Corn Street, Bristol BS1 1HT — COOKING 3*
TEL/FAX: 0117-926 2658 — COST £25–£50

This is Stephen and Judy Markwick's very personal show. Her presence out front is invaluable; his domain is the kitchen, where he perhaps remembers the days when he was a pupil of West Country gastro-guru George Perry-Smith. Their restaurant is in the vaults of an old bank building in the commercial quarter of the city; it reminded one visitor of a 'nineteenth-century club crossed with a 1950s Paris bistro'. In reality that means a cool, peach-coloured room that looks like an advertisement for twentieth-century art: vivid modernist pictures hang on the walls, Art Deco stained-glass bunches of grapes mask the ceiling lights, the lamp standards are chrome.

Stephen Markwick cooks with the seasons. His inspiration comes from France and the Mediterranean, and he gets an obvious kick from both fish and offal. His treatment of seafood yields first-class dishes: succulent scallops with a creamily moist risotto of sun-dried tomatoes and Parmesan; roasted John Dory on a bed of braised squid with a rich stew of red wine and oranges beneath; or an 'absolutely superb' ménage of hake, sole (with a baked pesto crust), monkfish (firm but delicate), salmon (rich and flaky) and squid (just slightly singed), further complemented by a delicate crab sauce with just the faintest hint of fennel. 'You can't cook better than this,' reflected one happy diner. The kitchen can also deliver lightly seared sweetbreads with madeira sauce and tagliatelle, or lambs' offal tart ('the best starter I've ever tasted'). Markwicks' carré d'agneau is 'a classic', and there is also glowing acclaim for guinea-fowl with apples and calvados, and breast of duck with roasted shallots, Puy lentils and Sauternes sauce.

The memorable line-up of desserts might include lemon tart, home-made sorbets and ice-creams, Grand Marnier pancakes, and a 'startlingly good' rhubarb and elderflower meringue that sounds like the very essence of England in June. Bread is baked in-house and very good it is, too. Prices are exceedingly fair, with lunch, in particular, outstanding value. A sensible rapport between quality and price informs the wine list, which offers variety and choice yet keeps to a manageable size. Over a dozen house wines are bang-on, starting at £10. CELLARMAN'S CHOICE: Thelema Mountain Vineyards Sauvignon Blanc 1994, South Africa, £14.50; Ribera del Duero Crianza 1989, Felix Callejo, £16.50.

CHEFS: Stephen Markwick and Sara Ody PROPRIETORS: Stephen and Judy Markwick OPEN: Mon to Fri L 12 to 2, Mon to Sat D 7 to 10.30 CLOSED: 10 days Christmas, 1 week Easter, 2 weeks Aug, bank hols MEALS: alc (main courses £14.50 to £16.50). Set L £13.50 (2 courses) to £16, Set D £21.50 SERVICE: not inc, card slips closed CARDS: Access, Amex, Visa DETAILS: 40 seats. Private parties: 20 main room, 6 and 20 private rooms. Vegetarian meals. Children's helpings. No music

Melbournes

74 Park Street, Bristol BS1 5JX — COOKING 1*
TEL: 0117-922 6996 — COST £15–£26

'This is the kind of place you could take your mother to on her birthday, your boy- or girlfriend for a meal out, or a business colleague to clinch a deal. This was a lunch-time, but they were all there that day!' observed one highly satisfied customer. In the evening Melbournes fairly buzzes with noise, heat and action, and tables are hard to come by: one long-suffering diner was confronted by a 'human wall' of people queueing around the servery. It is easy to see the attractions: the décor and atmosphere are convivial (bright prints, big plate-glass windows, a dining area on two levels, low lights), the food is dependable and great value, and though licensed, the restaurant has a no-corkage policy on bring-your-own wine. Lunch is from both a *carte* and a set-price menu, while dinner is set price for two or three courses. The cooking is Anglo-French with Mediterranean leanings and ideas lifted from exotic cookery books. Fish is well thought of, whether it be poached salmon with hollandaise or tuna with Cajun spices, but the kitchen also turns out 'fair' guacamole, warm pigeon salad, stuffed roast pheasant and 'honest' steak with green peppercorn sauce. 'Decent' puddings include tarte Tatin or orange and chocolate mousse. Cheeses are English. Service is generally brisk and cheerful, although the pace may slacken at peak times. The good-value wine list is tilted towards the New World, and additional selections are chalked on blackboards. House wine is £6.50.

CHEFS: C.J. Cowpe and R.A. Smith PROPRIETORS: A.P. Wilshaw, N.J. Hennessy and C.J. Cowpe OPEN: Tue to Fri and Sun L 12 to 2 (3 Sun), Mon to Sat D 7 to 10.30 MEALS: alc L (main courses £6.50 to £9.50). Set L £8 (2 courses) to £9.50, Set L Sun £10 (2 courses) to £11.50, Set D £13.25 (2 courses) to £15 SERVICE: 10%, card slips closed CARDS: Access, Amex, Delta, Diners, Switch, Visa DETAILS: 100 seats. Private parties: 50 main room. Vegetarian meals. Children's helpings. No cigars/pipes in dining-room. Wheelchair access (1 step). Music

Muset

16 Clifton Road, Clifton, Bristol BS8 1AF COOKING 1*
TEL/FAX: 0117-973 2920 COST £23–£38

A fan sums up the enduring appeal of this sprawling, jam-packed place: 'The great thing is that you can (by taking your own wine, already paid for) always keep the bill below £40, have a decent skinful of grub, and count on regular, not unthoughtful international-tourist cuisine without a trace of condescension on your part or theirs.' In all, the Muset is 'a remarkable venture'.

Chef Paul Baker quotes extensively, 'even magnificently', from the Caribbean, Mediterranean, Pacific and Baltic: no doubt behind the scenes he possesses a good library. High turnover suggests some mass production, and some dishes have been known to fall flat, but there is also plenty to celebrate: 'first-rate' sardines, 'a good dollop' of scrambled egg with smoked salmon, and coq au vin done properly 'with a once-live cockerel, not a dummy' have all been recalled with enthusuiasm. Monkfish is handled well, as are pheasant and pigeon (perhaps roasted with bacon, potato-cake and port sauce). Puddings might be strawberry cream slice or chocolate marquise. If you forget to raid your own cellar or visit the off-licence (corkage is free), there is also a dependable wine list drawn from good worldwide sources. House wine is £7.25.

CHEF: Paul Baker PROPRIETOR: Muset Partnership OPEN: all week D only 6.30 to 10.30 MEALS: Set D £12.95 (2 courses) to £14.95 SERVICE: 10% (optional), card slips closed CARDS: Access, Amex, Delta, Diners, Switch, Visa DETAILS: 140 seats. Private parties: 40 main room, 25 and 40 private rooms. Vegetarian meals. Children's helpings. Smart dress preferred. Music. Air-conditioned

Rocinantes

85 Whiteladies Road, Bristol BS8 2NT — COOKING 1
TEL: 0117-973 4482 — COST £18–£35

Rocinantes wears its ecological heart on its sleeve: 'All our meat and most of our vegetables are organically produced, our eggs are free-range and we do not use farmed fish or fish from over-trawled waters. All our food is prepared without the use of microwaves or aluminium cookware.' So reads the 'Green Note' at the top of the menu. But this is no outpost of new-age puritanism. Just the opposite. Breakfast is served until 11am. Some people come just for drinks – 'everything is served,' a reporter tells us, 'in ubiquitous cheap tumblers which suit the mood of the place' – but most of the young and lively crowd are looking for good food as well.

Tapas in the broadest sense of the word is the mainstay. There are 'small' dishes, 'medium-sized' dishes and all kinds of options mostly dictated by a fondness for full-blooded Mediterranean flavours. A party of five who ordered a selection as long as your arm singled out raw beef with horseradish cream, 'the sausages!', smoked cod brandade and crab tart, but they might just as well have mentioned chickpea salad, steamed mussels with salsa verde, or pincho moruno (skewered lamb marinated in olive oil, cumin, saffron and lemon juice). If a conventionally structured meal is what you are after, the short *carte* of daily specials runs through such dishes as grilled pigeon breast with rocket salad, poached salmon with tomato butter, and Belgian chocolate mousse. Jugs of sangria and 'frozen' margarita make a racy accompaniment, or choose something from the short wine list. House Spanish is £7.95.

CHEFS: Barny Haughton and Heather Staten PROPRIETORS: Barny Haughton and Matthew Pruen OPEN: Mon to Sat breakfast 9 to 11, L 12 to 3, D 6 to 11, Sun brunch 10 to 3, D 6 to 10.30 MEALS: alc (main courses £7.50 to £12) SERVICE: not inc; 10% for parties of 6 or more CARDS: Access, Amex, Delta, Switch, Visa DETAILS: 90 seats. 6 tables outside. Private parties: 45 main room, 30 private room. Vegetarian meals. Children welcome. Wheelchair access (3 steps; also WC). Music

---

BROADHEMBURY Devon — map 2

Drewe Arms

Broadhembury EX14 0NF
TEL: (01404) 841267 — COOKING 2*
off A373, between Cullompton and Honiton — COST £26–£38

'No rules and regulations' is how the Burges describe their comfortable pub, which focuses on offering a cornucopia of fresh fish and shellfish. The interior is idiosyncratically decorated, as all good pubs should be, the walls adorned with the work of local artists (a set of charcoal nudes diverting the eye on one occasion). Even when the pub is bustlingly full, the atmosphere remains one of 'relaxed charm'.

The food is classical and unpretentious; the popularity of the place reflects the fact, perhaps, that people tend to be happier with simpler treatments when it comes to impeccably fresh fish. Langoustines can be dunked in garlic mayonnaise, crab comes smartly dressed, and marinated herring is chased down with a glass of aquavit. Main courses are sympathetically sauced: chive butter for Dover sole, anchovy butter for more robust halibut, and à la mode ginger and lemon grass for steamed sea bass. The seriously determined may plump for a seafood selection with an option of half a crab or half a lobster, while those not in the mood for fish (which would seem a strange affliction here) may have the likes of loin of venison with a wild mushroom sauce. Ice-creams are made on a nearby farm. 'The food was stunning, very simply cooked but executed to perfection,' commented one reporter. A pleasingly broad selection of wines is arranged by grape variety, with more reds than you might expect in a place dealing predominantly with seafood. Prices are fair and halves are plentiful. House wines start at £7.90.

CHEFS/PROPRIETORS: Kerstin and Nigel Burge OPEN: all week L 12 to 2, Mon to Sat D 7 to 10 MEALS: Set L and D £17.95 SERVICE: not inc CARDS: none DETAILS: 40 seats. 8 tables outside. Car park. Children welcome. Jacket and tie. No smoking in dining-room. Wheelchair access (1 step; also WC). No music

BROADWAY Hereford & Worcester map 5

▲ *Collin House* £*

Collin Lane, Broadway WR12 7PB
TEL: (01386) 858354 COOKING 1*
on A44, 1m NW of Broadway COST £20–£37

The sixteenth-century house is 'small-scale, domestic, intimate, and very Cotswold', with a charming semi-wilderness for a garden, flagstoned floors, mullioned windows, and walls covered in pictures. 'The style of the menu and food has been very consistent over the years,' wrote an inspector who has visited at frequent intervals, although the proprietorial grip may be loosening slightly these days. Judith Mills retired from the kitchen in 1993, and although the cooking is still technically competent, it lacks the strikingly fresh appeal it once had. Incidentals from bread to nibbles to petits fours are in need of an upgrade too. What might have been acceptable five years ago now seems less so, although one regular considers that it serves 'a good honest English meal', citing a Stilton pâté with herbs and garlic, roast leg of lamb 'with a separate jug of real stock-made gravy', and a traditional apricot sponge pudding with ice-cream, all for £15 at lunch.

There are also bar lunches, 'Cotswold suppers' available early evening, and a three-course dinner with a generous choice, where price is determined by the main dish. 'Nicely made' home-cured gravad lax with smoked salmon mousse, and spinach pasta mixed with rough chunks of mushrooms in a creamy sauce have been endorsed, although richness can build up since cream runs through the menu: with a dash of cinnamon in a sauce for scallops, monkfish and crayfish, and in an excellent damson ice-cream. Comfort, and an amiable, solicitous atmosphere, has always been one of Collin House's strongest suits. A list of around 60 wines combines mature vintages of claret with some good producers from the New World. French house wine is £9.85.

CHEFS: Mark Brooks and Anthony Ike PROPRIETOR: John Mills OPEN: all week 12 to 1.45, 7 to 9 CLOSED: 24 to 29 Dec MEALS: Set L £15, Set D £16 to £24; bar meals available SERVICE: none, card slips closed CARDS: Access, Visa DETAILS: 24 seats. 5 tables outside. Private parties: 34 main room. Car park. Vegetarian meals. No children under 6 D. Smart dress preferred. No smoking in dining-room. Wheelchair access (1 step; also WC). No music ACCOMMODATION: 7 rooms, all with bath/shower. B&B £45 to £87. Deposit: £40. Children under 7 by arrangement. Garden. Swimming-pool (*The Which? Hotel Guide*)

▲ *Dormy House*

Willersey Hill, Broadway WR12 7LF — COOKING 2
TEL: (01386) 852711 FAX: (01386) 858636 — COST £25–£61

Dormy House sits on a hill a little off the A44, a mile or so from the tourist bustle of Broadway. The interiors are pleasingly pastoral; tapestries of English fruits adorn the dining-room chairs and are reproduced on the menus, and the approach, according to a pair of weekenders, is 'sensitive and professionally orchestrated'.

Alan Cutler arrived in spring 1994 and first reports suggested that he needed to find his feet. Good things have since been heard, of innovation and originality, and the consensus is that the cooking is on a marked upward swing. The fairly pricey *carte* offers a broad spread of choice and is supported by a set-price menu of starter, sorbet, main and pudding, and a gourmet menu of five courses with coffee. Dishes may sound quite complex but have perceptible culinary logic to them. Monkfish terrine comes with a mild curry mousse and a mango coulis spiked with coriander. Smoked duck carpaccio has a contrasting support of caramelised Victoria plums. 'The hallmark of successful experimentation' was illustrated for one couple by a main-course dish that paired seared escalopes of tuna with grilled scallops in a sauce made from smoked gazpacho ingredients – tomatoes, peppers, onions and garlic. Colourful artistry comes to the fore in puddings. A caramel trio brings together a miniature crème caramel, a hot soufflé and ice-cream in a nest of spun sugar, and hot apple and rhubarb filo tart is served on a toffee and whisky sauce. Coffee comes with well-made petits fours. The wine list will delight a classicist for its scrupulous attention to the major French regions. Choices from elsewhere seem a touch old-fashioned, although there are a handful of quality German Rieslings, and Argentina, Chile and Lebanon are represented too. Halves are copious. Ten French house wines open at £8.95, and five of them are available by the glass.

CHEFS: Alan Cutler and Simon Boyle PROPRIETOR: Jorgen Philip-Sorensen OPEN: all week 12.30 to 2, 7 to 9.30 (9 Sun) CLOSED: 25 and 26 Dec MEALS: alc (main courses £18 to £19.50). Set L £15 (2 courses) to £17, Set D £26.50 to £33 SERVICE: not inc CARDS: Access, Amex, Delta, Diners, Switch, Visa DETAILS: 80 seats. Private parties: 40 main room, 8 and 14 private rooms. Car park. Vegetarian meals. Children's helpings. Smart dress preferred. No smoking in 1 dining-room. Music ACCOMMODATION: 49 rooms, all with bath/shower. TV. Phone. B&B £60 to £145. Children welcome. Baby facilities. Pets welcome (not in public rooms). Afternoon teas. Garden (*The Which? Hotel Guide*)

The Guide *always appreciates hearing about changes of chef or owner.*

▲ *Lygon Arms* ✱

High Street, Broadway WR12 7DU — COOKING 2*
TEL: (01386) 852255 FAX: (01386) 858611 — COST £32–£68

Broadway might be a Merchant-Ivory film set. A bustling thoroughfare scythes through the centre of an aspic-dipped village of Cotswold stone. On one side, woollens and postcards may be bought, on the other – in pride of place – the Lygon Arms loftily surveys the scene. 'The most famous inn in England,' claims the Savoy Group, although the age-dark wonky panelling, mounted stags' heads and creaking floorboards are the historic veneer for swimming-pool, steam-room and beauty salon. Formality emanates from every pore.

Roger Narbett succeeded Clive Howe in the kitchens just as we were going to press last year, but the grandiose style of the food continues uninterrupted. The main business is à la carte, though there is also a fixed-price three-course lunch and dinner menu and the same for vegetarians. The cooking is certainly ambitious, although occasionally some items may not quite live up to the glamour of their billing. A terrine of chicken, apple and black pudding with Pommery mustard dressing has been surprisingly bland given its ingredients, for example, though a tart of caramelised red onions and curd cheese, on the other hand, scored highly for its combination of sweet onion and sharp cheese and for the very good pastry. Medallions of Cornish monkfish might come with marinated vegetables provençale and a tangy tomato and basil salsa, and fillet of beef has been considered 'excellent'. Vegetables arrive on side-plates with their own little forks, the menu curiously warning that 'guests may find our vegetables lightly cooked'. Classical technique is mobilised all the way through to dessert stage, where a soufflé glacé of Grand Marnier with chocolate sauce is attractively presented on a sponge base soaked in the liqueur. The wine list is as appropriately classical as you would expect in the surroundings, but it also makes room for the New World. Bottles are energetically marked up for the most part, but there is just enough choice under £20 to accommodate tighter budgets. House French is £12.

CHEF: Roger Narbett PROPRIETOR: Savoy Group plc OPEN: all week 12.30 to 2, 7.30 to 9.15 (9.30 Sat) MEALS: alc (main courses £16 to £20.50). Set L £20.50, Set D £32 SERVICE: not inc, card slips closed CARDS: Access, Amex, Diners, Visa DETAILS: 120 seats. Private parties: 95 main room, 12 to 95 private rooms. Car park. Vegetarian meals. Children's helpings; no children under 3 D. Jacket and tie. No smoking in dining-room. Wheelchair access (also WC). No music ACCOMMODATION: 65 rooms, all with bath/shower. TV. Phone. B&B £106 to £229. Deposit: 1 night's stay. Rooms for disabled. Children welcome. Pets welcome. Afternoon teas. Garden. Swimming-pool (*The Which? Hotel Guide*)

BROCKENHURST Hampshire — map 2

Le Poussin ✱

The Courtyard, Brookley Road,
Brockenhurst SO42 7RB — COOKING 3*
TEL: (01590) 623063 FAX: (01590) 622912 — COST £24–£43

The Poussin is a popular bird. Our postbag is once again bursting at the seams with enthusiastic testimonials, from the London couple who ate 'the best meal we have eaten in 1994' here, to the young lady aged five who gave wholehearted approval to the coq au vin and a dessert of two chocolates before sinking into the petits fours. The Aitkens have worked hard to perfect what they do, and the overwhelming consensus is that they have attained an exalted level of achievement.

To reach the restaurant, look for the Bestsellers bookshop on Brookley Road and drive under the adjacent archway into the tiny courtyard beyond. This may look a little scruffy, but inside is a smart dining-room of Lilliputian dimensions, the small tables lavishly dressed but topped with paper. Alexander Aitken's cookery is very much a product of its New Forest location, with mild Mediterranean overtones to show that time has not passed him by. Wild mushrooms are sauté with rosemary cream and served with home-made tagliatelle, salmon from the Itchen is covered with tapénade and bedded on sweet peppers, and wild pork ('wild boar crossed with local pig,' the menu explains) is braised with Muscat wine and prunes. Soufflés draw the most breathless plaudits, whether for the glazed twice-baked cheese version as a starter – 'superb and so light' – or for the hot dessert variants, like 'sublime' passion-fruit, or banana into which caramel sauce is decanted. The trio of meats remains a stalwart main course for those of stout appetite: beef fillet, best end of lamb and venison haunch with a rosemary-flavoured red wine sauce might take some digesting, you may think, but a reporter found it 'tender, rich and succulent'. White chocolate terrine moved one woman to rhapsodies. The occasional tale of unfocused flavours and service tending to the cooler side of formal does surface, but by and large contentment reigns.

The wine list specialises in great French classics, with a short selection from elsewhere at the end. Clarets and burgundies include some venerable bottles from fine vintages, which helps to push up the overall price average, but there is a good range of halves as well as wines by the glass. Bottle prices start at £10.50.

CHEF: Alexander Aitken PROPRIETORS: Alexander and Caroline Aitken OPEN: Wed to Sun L 12 to 1.30, Wed to Sat D 7 to 9.30 MEALS: Set L Wed to Sat £10 (2 courses) to £15, Set L Sun £12.50 (2 courses) to £17.50, Set D £20 (2 courses) to £25 SERVICE: not inc CARDS: Access, Visa DETAILS: 25 seats. 3 tables outside. Private parties: 30 main room. Car park. Children welcome. Smart dress preferred. No smoking in dining-room. No music

BROMSGROVE Hereford & Worcester map 5

▲ *Grafton Manor*

Grafton Lane, Bromsgrove B61 7HA
TEL: (01527) 579007 FAX: (01527) 575221 COOKING **2**
1½m SW of Bromsgrove, off B4091 COST **£31–£52**

Grafton has had its ups and downs in recent years, but now seems back on track. The Manor was founded before the Norman Conquest, though the present red-brick house dates from the early eighteenth century. It is an L-shaped building, with an arched sandstone portal on one arm and a fifteenth-century private chapel on the other. Interiors are ornate, the lounge done strikingly in maroon and blue, the dining-room in olive and gold. So far, so classical.

There is little classicism in Simon Morris's cooking, however. He describes it as 'modern English with a strong Indian influence': hence menus that include chicken terrine with cardamom and spinach with a sweetcorn and coriander sauce, and salmon baked with spiced tomatoes served with aubergine and apple infused with asafoetida. At an inspection meal a first-course terrine of hare larded with bacon, dried figs and angelica with medlar jelly was a brave and largely successful marriage of flavours. Simpler and even better was a dish of fresh tagliatelle sauté until al dente with strips of salami and pesto – a triumph of textural contrasts, it all 'came together beautifully'. Simple and good vegetables are served separately. Desserts can include Bramley apple cake, and a tart of apples, raisins and nuts with a thin custard. Service is pleasantly unpretentious. Wine prices are high, though quality is generally ordinary. House wines start at £10.75.

CHEF: Simon Morris PROPRIETORS: the Morris family OPEN: Sun to Fri L 12.30 to 1.45, all week D 7.30 to 9 (7.30 only Sun, one sitting) MEALS: Set L £20.50, Set D £24.95 to £31.50 SERVICE: not inc, card slips closed CARDS: Access, Amex, Diners, Switch, Visa DETAILS: 45 seats. Private parties: 45 main room, 20 and 120 private rooms. Car park. Vegetarian meals. Children welcome. Smart dress preferred. No smoking in dining-room. Wheelchair access (2 steps). No music ACCOMMODATION: 9 rooms, all with bath/shower. TV. Phone. B&B £85 to £125. Rooms for disabled. Children welcome. Baby facilities. Garden. Fishing (*The Which? Hotel Guide*)

BROXTED Essex map 3

▲ *Whitehall*

Church End, Broxted CM6 2BZ
TEL: (01279) 850603 FAX: (01279) 850385 COOKING 2*
off B1051, 3m SW of Thaxted COST £31–£61

The trim white-fronted manor-house dates from Elizabethan times, and its current owners, the Keanes, are careful custodians of its innate charm. The house itself has a walled garden overlooked by the church, and the gnarled beamed interiors have been conscientiously preserved. Gary Rhodes once cooked here, and there has been fairly rapid turnover since.

Last year saw the arrival of Stuart Townsend, who looks set fair to take the cooking into another class altogether. The evening format is a set-price menu with a sorbet after the starter. Cooking achieves a high degree of proficiency, and the choice is wide given the country-house parameters. Langoustines sauté with trompettes-de-mort bring two good components together with a lobster cream sauce that avoids excess richness, while a generously constituted game sausage comes on potato rösti with a deeply flavoured sauce of purée beetroot. Main-course meats receive robust treatment, including noisettes of lamb casseroled and bedded on soft pearl barley with red cabbage and an expressive stock. A wide choice of extra vegetables is offered at no further cost.

Dessert plates tend to come decked with flowers under a snowfall of icing sugar, although the central features don't need such prettying up. A portion of banana and toffee crumble on a thin pastry base is appropriately caramelised, and a pyramid of chocolate wafers entombs milk chocolate mousse with a tangy rasberry coulis. Great care is taken over appetisers and petits fours, adding to an air of practised professionalism. Despite all the mod cons, the hotel 'still manages to have the feel of a family home', which is of course exactly what it is. Six house wines are priced from £12.

CHEF: Stuart Townsend PROPRIETORS: the Keane family OPEN: Sun to Fri L 12.30 to 2, all week D 7.30 to 9.30 MEALS: Set L £10 (2 courses) to £19.50, Set D £27.50 (2 courses) to £37.50 SERVICE: not inc, card slips closed CARDS: Access, Amex, Diners, Visa DETAILS: 56 seats. Private parties: 120 main room, 16 and 40 private rooms. Car park. Vegetarian meals. Children's helpings. Smart dress preferred. No cigars/pipes in dining-room. Wheelchair access (also WC). No music ACCOMMODATION: 25 rooms, all with bath/shower. TV. Phone. B&B £75 to £155. Rooms for disabled. Children welcome. Baby facilities. Afternoon teas. Garden. Swimming-pool (*The Which? Hotel Guide*)

BRUTON Somerset map 2

Truffles

95 The High Street, Bruton BA10 0AR COOKING **2**
TEL: (01749) 812255 COST £23–£41

If nourishing the local community is one of the functions of an all-round provincial restaurant, then Truffles succeeds admirably. It certainly draws a loyal following and, doubtless, is a godsend for parents visiting their children boarding at the town's public schools. Denise and Martin Bottrill are a well-travelled couple who soak up culinary ideas as well as the sun during their trips abroad. A glance at one of their fixed-price monthly menus will probably tell you where they have been recently – it could be Provence, Thailand or Africa. One couple who ate here in April found much to enjoy: watercress and potato soup tasting of itself, a terrine of rabbit and hare spiked with pistachios and served with a rocket salad that gave the whole thing just enough bite, and perfectly cooked fillet of beef with a port and Stilton sauce ('a model of its kind') – although the addition of grapes and walnuts seemed to contribute little to the dish. Boned leg of chicken stuffed with a 'superb' foie gras mousse on an earthy wild mushroom sauce has also received acclaim.

Desserts tend to follow the same path, with an undercurrent of richness and elaboration: Truffles' gâteau is an 'absolutely sinful and delicious' concoction topped with 'divine' home-made brown meringues, while fig ice-cream is served in a chocolate cup with a lemon cream sauce. Endless coffee comes with an assortment of home-made petits fours in a brandy-snap basket. Denise Bottrill runs the front-of-house single-handedly and manages to remain charming under pressure. France and the New World share top billing on the wine list, which is a dependable selection dotted with a few high-class surprises. House red is £10.50.

CHEF: Martin Bottrill PROPRIETORS: Denise and Martin Bottrill OPEN: Sun L 12 to 2, Tue to Sat D 7 to 9.30; Tue to Sat L by arrangement MEALS: Set L Sun £13.95, Set D £20.95 SERVICE: not inc, card slips closed CARDS: Access, Visa DETAILS: 20 seats. Private parties: 24 main room. Vegetarian meals. No children under 6. Smart dress preferred. Wheelchair access (1 step). No music

'The waiters were so anxious not to upset the kitchen's timing that they served my wife's first course while she was in the lavatory, intoning a description of the dish as they placed it in front of an empty chair.' (On eating in London)

BUCKLAND Gloucestershire map 2

▲ *Buckland Manor*

Buckland WR12 7LY
TEL: (01386) 852626 FAX: (01386) 853557 COOKING 2
off B4632, 2m SW of Broadway COST £31–£80

This beautiful manor house of warm Cotswold stone is reached by a drive lined with daffodils in spring. It is next to the church, which dates, like the original house, from the thirteenth century, and since all the rooms seem to be about the same size this makes for a large hall and a rather small dining-room. Despite the formality of ties for gents, polished French service, domes for dinner and a tendency to pile on the extras (nibbles, amuse-gueules, Melba toast, sorbet and a cake stand of petits fours), the food appeals for its grasp of French basics, from potted duck rillettes to tarte Tatin.

Saucing can be as simple as langoustine butter with turbot, or a light rosemary jus for fillet of lamb. But the kitchen goes to a lot of trouble with some of the accessories, from a sweetcorn and Parma ham mousse that is piled into a poached breast of chicken, to the rest of the lamb dish, which includes a breadcrumb and herb coating, a herb pancake and puff pastry. Interesting ideas include a warm mousseline of chicken and Somerset Brie served with a Sauternes sauce, and a trio of citrus desserts that combines lemon tart, grapefruit mousse and orange sorbet.

The wine list is a book, with every item annotated, and although mark-ups are standard there is nevertheless plenty of reasonably priced drinking, and the range and quality are impressive. New World classics are worth considering, though France is particularly well stocked and difficult to resist. Italy now features in strength, and there are over 100 half-bottles. House wines and French country wines offer good drinking up to around £15, with around 20 by the glass. CELLARMAN'S CHOICE: Fixin Blanc, Clos Moreau 1989, Dom. Geoffroy, £24; St-Julien, Ch. Gruaud-Larose 1983, £39.

CHEF: Martyn Pearn PROPRIETOR: Roy and Daphne Vaughan OPEN: all week 12 to 1.45, 7.30 to 9 MEALS: alc (main courses £18.50 to £24), Set L £22.50 to £26.90, Set D £55 SERVICE: not inc CARDS: Access, Amex, Visa DETAILS: 40 seats. Private parties: 10 main room. Car park. No children under 12. Jacket and tie. No smoking in dining-room. No music ACCOMMODATION: 14 rooms, all with bath/shower. TV. Phone. B&B £150 to £325. No children under 12. Afternoon teas. Garden. Swimming-pool (*The Which? Hotel Guide*)

BUCKLAND Oxfordshire map 2

▲ *Lamb Inn* £

NEW ENTRY

Lamb Lane, Buckland SN7 8QN
TEL: (01367) 870484
just off A420, midway between Kingston Bagpuize and Faringdon COOKING 1
COST £18–£40

It would be difficult to find a quieter location than the hamlet of Buckland, where the eighteenth-century Lamb Inn is hidden away 'down a road full of potholes'. Inside, the inn is fresh and understated, with beams festooned with hops. Paul Barnard's aim is to offer imaginative Anglo-Continental cooking several cuts above traditional pub fare. Menus are geared to the seasons, and cast the net wide for duck rillettes, salmon in filo pastry, veal escalope in marsala sauce, and roast grouse with all the trimmings. An occasional adventurous dish such as warm curried fruits with wild rice is given house room. Old-fashioned afters include summer pudding, junket, baked banana with rum and top-flight sticky toffee. Service is solicitous. A thoroughly commendable wine list has been put together, with a good choice of attractive wines at unpretentious prices. Five house wines are available at £1.60 the glass, or £8.95 the bottle.

CHEF/PROPRIETOR: Paul Barnard OPEN: all week 12 to 2 (2.30 Sun), 6.30 to 9.30 (7 to 9 Sun) MEALS: alc (main courses £4.50 to £13). Set L Sun £15.95 SERVICE: not inc, card slips closed CARDS: Access, Delta, Switch, Visa DETAILS: 80 seats. 10 tables outside. Private parties: 65 main room, 15 private room. Car park. Children's helpings. Music ACCOMMODATION: 4 rooms, all with bath/shower. TV. Phone. B&B £35. Deposit: £10. Children welcome. Afternoon teas. Garden

BURNHAM MARKET Norfolk map 6

Fishes'

Market Place, Burnham Market PE31 8HE COOKING 1*
TEL: (01328) 738588 COST £18–£35

The holiday season in this part of north Norfolk seems to run throughout the year, judging by the queues and crowds that jostle for tables in Gillian Cape's casual restaurant. Booking is advisable if you want to be sure of a seat – even at lunch-time. The setting is a double-fronted Georgian house on the village green and the décor is all 'jade-green' and 'dark turquoise' walls, varnished wooden tables, with a settee and open fire thrown in for good measure. All comers are happily accommodated: there is no standing on ceremony, dress is casual, and you might find yourself in company with tourists, locals and off-duty clergy from nearby Walsingham. The menu is built around local seafood, home-smoked fish, salads and a few meaty items such as home-baked ham. Although the repertoire doesn't change a great deal, reporters continue to endorse the potted shrimps, home-cured gravlax with mustard sauce and a shot of aquavit, 'famed' salmon fish-cakes with crab sauce, and whole lemon sole with herb butter. Rounding things off are Norfolk treacle tart with soured cream, sorbets and home-made ice-creams. Affordable whites dominate the wine list, which includes some local stuff from Elmham House; James White's Suffolk cider and apple juice are also on show. House wine is £8.50.

CHEFS: Gillian Cape and Paula Ayres PROPRIETOR: Gillian Cape OPEN: Tue to Sun L 12 to 2, Tue to Sat D 6.45 to 9.30 (9 weekdays in winter) CLOSED: 25 Dec, last 3 weeks Jan MEALS: alc (main courses £6 to £13). Set L £8.95 (2 courses) to £12.25 SERVICE: not inc, card slips closed CARDS: Access, Amex, Delta, Diners, Switch, Visa DETAILS: 44 seats. Private parties: 12 main room. Children's helpings. No children under 5 after 7.30. No cigars/pipes in dining-room. No smoking while others eat. Wheelchair access (1 step). Music

An asterisk (*) after the 1 to 5 cooking mark at the top of an entry signifies that the Guide *and its readers think that the restaurant is a particularly fine example within its rating.*

BURTON UPON TRENT Staffordshire map 5

▲ *Dovecliff Hall*

Dovecliff Road, Stretton, Burton upon Trent DE13 0DJ
TEL: (01283) 531818 FAX: (01283) 516546 COOKING 1
¾m off A38, between Stretton and Rolleston COST £21–£50

The 'unusually lovely' gardens of this Georgian house are at the same time extensive and formal, yet romantic enough to contain fountains, statues of cherubs, pergolas and roses by the score. The trouble the Hines have taken to restore it all is plain to see, and the 'garden feeling' extends to the dining-room, where menus offer set-price options and a *carte* whose price is determined by the main course. The list of dishes is rather long, and the territory as familiar as baked filo parcels of Brie with a Waldorf salad, eggs Benedict, or grilled sirloin steak with chips.

The highlight of an inspection meal was a pair of herby fish-cakes made from salmon and crab, coated in breadcrumbs and given a parsley sauce. In general, saucing is rather heavy on cream and butter by today's standards, and might be considered one of the least successful aspects of the cooking. Puddings are mostly in the British mould of bread-and-butter – though made with double cream and raisins soaked in Cointreau – or, in June, new season's rhubarb fool with home-made shortbread biscuits. On the wine list, good claret is backed up by Jadot Burgundies and Spanish wines from Torres, but Italy and Australia are worth a look. A dozen wines around £12 are available by the glass from £2.50. House wine is £12.50 and £13.50.

CHEFS: Hilary Hine, Bryan Kime and Ian Johnson PROPRIETORS: Mr and Mrs N.O. Hine OPEN: Tue to Fri and Sun L 12 to 2, Mon to Sat D 7 to 9.30 CLOSED: 1 week Christmas, 1 week spring, 2 weeks summer MEALS: Set L £9.50 (2 courses) to £11.50. Set L Sun £13.95. Set D £18.50 to £29.50 SERVICE: not inc CARDS: Access, Amex, Diners, Visa DETAILS: 85 seats. 3 tables outside. Private parties: 85 main room, 16 and 60 private rooms. Car park. Vegetarian meals. Children's helpings. Smart dress preferred. Wheelchair access (also WC). Music ACCOMMODATION: 7 rooms, all with bath/shower. TV. Phone. B&B £75 to £105. Children welcome. Garden. Fishing

BURY ST EDMUNDS Suffolk map 6

Mortimer's ✱ £

30–31 Churchgate Street, Bury St Edmunds IP33 1RG COOKING 1
TEL: (01284) 760623 FAX: (01284) 761611 COST £18–£40

This is the older of the two Mortimer's (its sibling is in Ipswich; see entry) by some three years. The enduring popularity of both shows that a good number of people appreciate sound seafood cookery. The extensive menus get you going with staples such as crab pâté with toast, rollmops in sherry, Loch Fyne oysters and scrambled eggs with smoked salmon. Main courses are prepared in a variety of ways. Brill may be grilled and served with a prawn and dill butter, sea bream sauced with tomatoes, peppers and basil, or monkfish steamed and served with a sauce of red wine, mushrooms and onions. Vegetables are simple, and the fish itself is resonantly fresh. One reporter rued the niggling little charge for bread, which comes ready-buttered. Puddings include blackcurrant bavarois, and chocolate pot laced with Navy rum. Service is 'friendly and efficient'. The wine list is principally of whites and offers much wider choice than you might expect. Prices are kept in check, and there is a good spread of half-bottles. House French is £7.45.

CHEFS: Kenneth Ambler and Hannah Jolly PROPRIETORS: Kenneth Ambler and Michael Gooding OPEN: Mon to Fri L 12 to 2, Mon to Sat D 7 to 9 (6.30 to 8.15 Mon) CLOSED: 24 Dec to 5 Jan, 2 weeks Aug MEALS: alc (main courses £7.50 to £16) SERVICE: not inc CARDS: Access, Amex, Delta, Diners, Switch, Visa DETAILS: 72 seats. Private parties: 12 main room, 12 private room. Children's helpings. Smart dress preferred. No smoking in 1 dining-room. Wheelchair access (1 step; also WC). No music

CALSTOCK Cornwall map 1

▲ *Danescombe Valley Hotel*

Lower Kelly, Calstock PL18 9RY
TEL/FAX: (01822) 832414 COOKING 2*
1m W of Calstock on riverside road COST £33–£39

The restaurant is open for a little over half the year, and then for only five sessions a week, and then can take only a dozen people. This is a small-scale operation, domestic in both size and nature. The Smiths are the sort of amateurs who obviously keep their love of the food business in perspective, and thus refreshed. Local supplies feed through into a simple no-choice menu that expresses the gentler mode of country cooking: not country-house cooking, which is far too flash by comparison, and not entirely British, because Anna Smith's Italian background often comes to the fore, as in, for example, first courses of asparagus baked with Parma ham, or baked goats' cheese with roasted tomatoes.

One spring meal opened with Italian herb omelette, followed by spiced duck breast with honey and soy sauce, then cheese – unpasteurised cheeses from the West Country are a fixture – and finished with a ricotta and pear strudel. Main courses on other evenings have been Tamar salmon roasted with a horseradish crust, or baked in a paper bag with bacon and aromatic rosemary, and served with vegetables from the Tamar valley. Apple puffs with honey ice-cream, and mascarpone and chocolate tart have been among the puddings. The enthusiastic wine list naturally has a soft spot for Italy, and is arranged partly by grape variety, which includes Arneis, Greco and Savagnin whites, and Dolcetto and Negroamaro among the reds. There are mainstream bottles too, but the temptation to explore is encouraged by very attractive prices – most under £20. The Smiths add: 'Any of the medium-priced wines from our list are opened for use by the glass.'

CHEF: Anna Smith PROPRIETORS: Martin and Anna Smith OPEN: Fri to Tue D only 7.30 (one sitting) CLOSED: Nov to Mar (exc Christmas) MEALS: Set D £27.50 SERVICE: none, card slips closed CARDS: Access, Amex, Diners, Switch, Visa DETAILS: 12 seats. Private parties: 12 main room. Car park. No children under 12. No smoking in dining-room. No music ACCOMMODATION: 5 rooms, all with bath/shower. B&B £70 to £120. Deposit: £50. No children under 12. Garden (*The Which? Hotel Guide*)

CAMBRIDGE Cambridgeshire map 6

Midsummer House

Midsummer Common, Cambridge CB4 1HA COOKING 1
TEL: (01223) 69299 COST £36–£60

There have been major changes in kitchen and ownership since last year. Hans Schweitzer and the team went off to the Sandy Lane Hotel, Barbados, a new chef came and went, and Jonathan Bishop has now been installed since March 1995, since when reports have been mixed. The walled Victorian house overlooks the common, and contains a number of small dining-rooms plus a conservatory that can suffer from extremes of temperature. The food is as ambitious as a game pithiviers with lentils and wild mushrooms in a deep red port basting jus, and dishes can be highly wrought. 'Over-fussy' is how one reporter described the style, with main courses of lamb or pavé of beef overwhelmed by vegetables, or a first course of smoked duck breast given salad leaves, blobs of avocado mousse, skinned tomato, deep-fried apple slices (crispy but cold), a scattering of chervil and chives, and a light sweet calvados dressing.

The elaborate style is perhaps more appropriate for desserts, which have included a successful raspberry and grenadine soufflé served with a nougat mousse, and a passion-fruit parfait covered in a spun-sugar cage, partnered by a dark chocolate mousse in a brandy-snap basket and an apricot crème anglaise. Bread is home-made, service is 'sir' and 'madam' but can wilt under pressure, and prices of both food and drink are high. House wine is £15.

CHEF: Jonathan Bishop PROPRIETOR: Crown Society OPEN: Tue to Fri and Sun L 12 to 2, Tue to Sat D 7 to 10 CLOSED: 26 Dec and 1 Jan MEALS: Set L £17 (2 courses) to £30, Set D £24 (2 courses) to £38 SERVICE: not inc CARDS: Access, Amex, Visa DETAILS: 70 seats. Private parties: 14 main room, 8 and 14 private rooms. Vegetarian meals. Children's helpings. Jacket and tie. Music

Twenty Two

22 Chesterton Road, Cambridge CB4 3AX COOKING 2
TEL: (01223) 351880 COST £28–£40

A short trot from Cambridge city centre is this 'homely but elegant' Victorian dining-room owned by two lecturers from the local catering college and staffed by some of their students. Amid unfussy décor and neatly dressed tables with candles, the 'extremely friendly' attitude makes this a justifiably well-supported neighbourhood restaurant.

Ian Reinhardt earned an extra stripe when he moved up to head chef in May 1995, and has retained his predecessor's formula. That is a set-price dinner menu of four courses, including a properly dressed mixed-leaf salad after the first course, with an optional fish course available for another £4.50. An inspector was fired with enthusiasm by a 'superb' squid salad, tiny tender rings 'beautifully presented' on salad leaves with a confidently flavoured ginger dressing. Breads may very well be built into first courses, for example in soused mackerel with soda bread and a sweet mustard sauce, or olive bread with Gorgonzola and walnuts. While presentation is generally immaculate throughout, dishes can sometimes want for seasoning: a fillet of poached pork served with a sweetish apple mousse has been reported as having had 'only a passing acquaintance with the salt', as did the spätzli. Lightly cooked lambs' liver of fair quality comes garnished imaginatively with a pile of chopped liver sitting on a disc of red onion polenta. Desserts are a forte. Banana terrine with coconut ice-cream might tempt the curious. Elderflower parfait has been described as 'faultless – highly scented and perfectly textured', recumbent on a slice of Granny Smith and given a two-tone coulis of apricot and raspberry. Equal pains are taken over the petits fours.

The wine list is a model of sharpness and brevity. Its stopovers in regions outside France may be limited to one each of red and white, but selections have a keen eye on the quality–price ratio. The house quartet at £8.50 and £10.50 takes in France, Hungary and Australia. CELLARMAN'S CHOICE: Vins de Pays d'Oc, Les Jamelles 1993, Viognier, £13.95; Ch. Musar 1987, Gaston Hochar, Lebanon, £15.95.

CHEF: Ian Reinhardt PROPRIETORS: David Carter and Louise Crompton OPEN: Tue to Sat D only 7 to 10.45; L by arrangement CLOSED: 1 week Christmas MEALS: Set D £19.95 SERVICE: not inc CARDS: Access, Amex, Switch, Visa DETAILS: 30 seats. Private parties: 34 main room, 12 private room. Vegetarian meals. No children under 11. Smart dress preferred. No cigars/pipes in dining-room. Music

CAMPSEA ASH Suffolk map 6

▲ *Old Rectory*

Campsea Ash IP13 0PU
TEL/FAX: (01728) 746524 COOKING 2
on B1078, 1m E of A12 COST £26–£35

There is something irresistibly enticing about this highly distinctive converted rectory: peace and tranquillity are two of its strongest assets, and the noisiest disturbance is likely to be the whirr of an occasional train on the East Suffolk coastal line or a car on the B1078. Forget any notions of de-luxe hotel service; this is Stewart Bassett's home, a place that he shares with friends and strangers.

Stewart's efforts in the kitchen are highly regarded. He offers a fixed-price three-course dinner menu with plenty of choice across the board; there is now a fully fledged separate menu for vegetarians too. One typically fine evening kicked off with poached sea trout with samphire and a white wine and butter sauce, then rack of lamb from a butcher in Halesworth whom Stewart has been using for some 20 years, before a lightly textured variation on strawberry crumble. It sounds simple, but the results are excellent. On another night you might choose terrine of salmon and halibut, breast of guinea-fowl with wild mushrooms, then sticky toffee pudding. Pair the menu with the wine list and you have the ingredients for serious pleasure. The fairly priced and wide-ranging list includes good Alsace from Faller, some old claret, seven vintages of Ch. Musar, a few sweet Loires and a varied selection of half-bottles. House wine is £9.50.

'The pistachio nuts would have needed the dexterity, determination and incisors of a squirrel to break into.' (On eating in London)

CHEF/PROPRIETOR: Stewart Bassett OPEN: Mon to Sat D only 7.30 to 8.30 CLOSED: Christmas MEALS: Set D £17.50 SERVICE: not inc CARDS: Access, Amex, Diners, Visa DETAILS: 40 seats. Private parties: 36 main room, 12 and 18 private rooms. Car park. Children's helpings. Smart dress preferred. No smoking in dining-room. Music ACCOMMODATION: 9 rooms, all with bath/shower. B&B £32 to £50. Deposit: £15. Children welcome. Pets welcome. Garden (*The Which? Hotel Guide*)

CANTERBURY Kent map 3

▲ *Sully's*

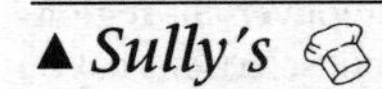

County Hotel, High Street, Canterbury CT1 2RX COOKING 1*
TEL: (01227) 766266 FAX: (01227) 451512 COST £23–£40

Everyone seems to have something to say about the décor at Sully's, but pinpointing its style is no easy matter. Nineteen-seventies opulent is probably as near as you get to defining the windowless dining-room, with its bare brick walls, plain mirrors, a slab of plastic panelling, and a battery of ceiling lights masquerading as a chandelier. But all these pale into insignificance when you are confronted by the sheer pinkness of the décor. The point about Sully's is that it is a 'charming provincial restaurant' serving the needs of a mixed clientele ranging from tourists to local senior citizens.

New chef François Garcin arrived towards the end of 1994 armed with an impressive CV and plenty of ideas. The considered view is that he has started well, but needs to iron out a few inconsistencies and find a more assertive touch. The table d'hôte remains, but the *carte* has been abandoned in favour of a second fixed-price menu (two or three courses) built around seasonal specialities (although venison casserole with chocolate pasta in spring struck one reporter as 'mind-boggling'). However, there is plenty to applaud: 'brilliant' steamed crab dumplings, tartare of scallops and oysters (a 'gentle introduction' for those who have never eaten oysters before), and pink magret of duck with 'little rolls of crisp, crisp skin', pan-fried asparagus and a madeira jus, for example. Puddings generally work well: plum and whisky pancake soufflé with apricot coulis, and a trio of chocolate desserts have been enjoyed. The wine list is dominated by France, although Italy, Germany and Australia provide the most affordable drinking. House wine is £10.50.

CHEF: François Garcin PROPRIETOR: Laughing Water Hotels Ltd OPEN: all week 12.30 to 2.30, 7 to 10 MEALS: Set L £13.50 (2 courses) to £25, Set D £17 (2 courses) to £25 SERVICE: not inc CARDS: Access, Amex, Delta, Diners, Switch, Visa DETAILS: 50 seats. Private parties: 18 main room, 30 to 130 private rooms. Car park. Vegetarian meals. Children's helpings. Smart dress preferred. No pipes in dining-room. Wheelchair access (also WC). No music. Air-conditioned ACCOMMODATION: 73 rooms, all with bath/shower. TV. Phone. B&B £70.50 to £112. Deposit: 1 night's stay. Rooms for disabled. Children welcome. Baby facilities. Afternoon teas

---

indicates a change of chef since last year's Guide.

Dining-rooms where music, either live or recorded, is never played are signalled by No music *in the details at the end of an entry.*

CARLTON North Yorkshire map 9

▲ *Foresters Arms* £

Carlton, nr Leyburn DL8 4BB
TEL/FAX: (01969) 640272 COOKING 1
off A684, 4½m SW of Leyburn COST £19–£46

A long, narrow, winding drive leads to this seventeenth-century pub, whose stone floor, oak beams and draught beers were all that one visitor hoped for. The menu is long and ambitious, taking in baked crab and asparagus gâteau, a parfait of chicken livers with 'clean, natural flavours', ham and egg, lots of fish, and anything from smoked ham hock with mushy peas to pot-roast poussin for main course. The kitchen can turn out excellent stock-based sauces – with 'sweet, pink, tender loin of lamb' at one meal – although a main course of 'excessively garnished' roast sea bream with prawns was in the view of an inspector 'such a mixture of flavours as to be just too much'. Puddings use a lot of chocolate, and a fair bit of hot sponge and vanilla sauce between them. Drink cask-conditioned Yorkshire ales, or peruse the mainly French wine list and try to spot a bargain. House wine is £8.95.

CHEF/PROPRIETOR: B.K. Higginbotham OPEN: Tue to Sun L 12 to 2, Tue to Sat D 7 to 9.30 MEALS: alc (main courses £7.50 to £15) SERVICE: not inc, card slips closed CARDS: Access, Delta, Visa DETAILS: 60 seats. 6 tables outside. Private parties: 30 main room, 30 private room. Car park. Vegetarian meals. Children's helpings. Smart dress preferred. No smoking in 1 dining-room. Wheelchair access. Music ACCOMMODATION: 3 rooms, all with bath/shower. TV. Phone. B&B £30 to £55. Deposit: £20. Children welcome. Pets welcome. Afternoon teas

CARTERWAY HEADS Northumberland map 10

▲ *Manor House Inn* £

Carterway Heads, Shotley Bridge DH8 9LX
TEL: (01207) 255268 COOKING 1
on A68, 3m W of Consett COST £13–£26

'A useful roadhouse near Consett,' decided one reporter of this whitewashed, stone-built low-beamed pub. A friendly welcome and a fast drink get things off to a good start; easy chairs and sofas share the room with dining tables, and a blackboard supplements the written menu. Half a dozen choices such as grilled Craster kippers or cheese soufflé can be taken as either a first or main course. While a few dishes explore the territory of smoked chicken and Brie croissant, and baked aubergines with pesto, the general thrust is along the more traditional lines of Cumberland sausage and mash with mustard sauce, or cold roast beef with a peach and apple chutney. To anyone who wonders what spiced lamb koftas with minted couscous and raita are doing here, the answer is not much, and the advice is to stay with the plainest food: grilled halibut, baked salmon, or grilled lamb chops. The same goes for puddings – bread-and-butter, sticky toffee – although raspberries sandwiched between crisp, ginger-spiced tuile biscuits with a lot of cream were considered successful. The wine list is short, but most bottles are also available by the glass.

CHEFS: Jane Pelly, Elizabeth Fielding, Neil Hyton and Peter Tipplady PROPRIETORS: Anthony and Jane Pelly, and Elizabeth Fielding OPEN: all week 12 to 2.30, 7 to 9.30 (9 Sun) CLOSED: 25 Dec MEALS: alc (main courses £3.50 to £9). Set L and D Mon to Sat £16.50 SERVICE: not inc, card slips closed CARDS: Access, Delta, Visa DETAILS: 100 seats. 5 tables outside. Private parties: 50 main room. Car park. Vegetarian meals. Children's helpings. No smoking in 1 dining-room. No music ACCOMMODATION: 4 rooms, all with TV. B&B £22 to £38.50. Children welcome. Baby facilities. Garden

CARTMEL Cumbria **map 8**

▲ *Uplands*

Haggs Lane, Cartmel LA11 6HD
TEL/FAX: (01539) 536248
2½m SW of A590, 1m up road opposite Pig and Whistle

COOKING 3*
COST £20–£39

Lovely views and peace and quiet are the backdrop to Tom Peter's classy and accomplished cooking and Diana Peter's sympathetic handling of customers. They are old Tovey hands, and style their operation 'in the Miller Howe manner' (see entry, Windermere), but Uplands has its own style and no need to trade on another's reputation. The mustard-coloured pebble-dash house is late Victorian, with an individual approach to décor. The lounge is a forest of squat table-lamps, and a gentle pinkness suffuses the room. Most wall space is covered with prints from New York's Metropolitan Museum of Art.

'We haven't really changed our style of cooking, and we certainly don't re-invent ourselves every couple of years,' write the Peters. Like all restaurateurs who know their customers well, they are happy to stick with a style that works and one that people expect. Something customers expect is a whole loaf for each table, 'with a gentle, sweet sticky maltiness about it', and a bread knife to cut it with. 'We keep a supply of plastic bags,' writes Diana Peter, 'for all the people who ask to take the remains home with them.' Accompanying the bread may be poached scallops, or a big tureen of excellent Jerusalem artichoke soup. Do they keep a supply of buckets for people to take the remains of this home too?

Game is from nearby Holker Hall, vegetables are grown locally, and fish comes from Fleetwood, ending up as baked sea bass on a fennel and Pernod sauce or a hot sole soufflé. Tastes are distinct, controlled, simple but effective, from pork fillet hotted up with mustard and flavoured with sage, to four fillets of bouncy sole wrapped around gently smoked salmon and spears of thin asparagus. Four accompanying vegetables are the norm. Popular puddings include chocolate mousse, passion-fruit ice-cream, and hot spiced apricot pie with a sweet butterscotch sauce. 'For consistency, Uplands is in a class of its own,' writes a regular, and only one reporter during the year has disagreed with the general picture. The balanced list of 40-odd wines stays comfortably low in price.

'We do not sell Malibu. I cannot remember the last time we were asked for it, and in ten years only one regular customer drinks it. She brings her own and consumes a whole bottle during the course of an evening.' (On eating in the North of England)

CHEF: Tom Peter PROPRIETORS: John Tovey, and Tom and Diana Peter OPEN: Tue to Sun 12.30 for 1, 7.30 for 8 CLOSED: 1 Jan to 23 Feb MEALS: Set L £14, Set D £25.50 SERVICE: not inc, card slips closed CARDS: Access, Amex, Visa DETAILS: 28 seats. Private parties: 28 main room. Car park. No children under 8. Smart dress preferred. No smoking in dining-room. Wheelchair access (2 steps; also WC). No music ACCOMMODATION: 5 rooms, all with bath/shower. TV. B&B £44 to £88. No children under 8. Pets welcome in bedrooms only. Garden (*The Which? Hotel Guide*)

CASTLE CARY Somerset map 2

▲ *Bond's*

Ansford Hill, Castle Cary BA7 7JP
TEL/FAX: (01963) 350464 COOKING 1*
on A371, 400yds past station towards Wincanton COST £20–£38

Kevin and Yvonne Bond's country hotel was known to eighteenth-century coach travellers as the Half Moon Inn. The period feel has been nicely preserved behind its creeper-clad exterior, and the small dining-room keeps things on a level-headed domestic scale.

The monthly-changing fixed-price dinner menu is supplemented by a daily offering that capitalises on the best of what's available. Yvonne Bond's cooking has paid due heed to trends elsewhere, absorbing some Mediterranean and Middle Eastern influences, for example, while never losing sight of sound culinary logic. The benchmark first-course breakfast salad of black pudding, bacon and poached egg is here, but fried in a wok and dressed with a warm vinaigrette of orange and mint, while rabbit and pistachio sauces flavoured with basil come with mashed parsnip and potato and a sherry butter sauce. Desserts cover fashionable territory: orange and Marsala trifle with mascarpone, or caramelised rice-pudding with mango and apricot purée, while the toffee pudding is not merely sticky but 'icky sticky'. 'The food is excellent and always a delight,' says a loyal supporter. A youngish team keeps things ticking over well. A modest wine list of international standards is sensibly priced, and all five house wines, from £8.50 the bottle, are served by the glass.

CHEF: Yvonne Bond PROPRIETORS: Kevin and Yvonne Bond OPEN: all week 12 to 2, 7 to 9.30 CLOSED: 1 week Christmas MEALS: Set D £12.50 to £19.75; light L available SERVICE: not inc, card slips closed CARDS: Access, Visa DETAILS: 20 seats. 2 tables outside. Private parties: 18 main room. Car park. Vegetarian meals. Children's helpings. Smart dress preferred. No music ACCOMMODATION: 7 rooms, all with bath/shower. TV. Phone. B&B £38 to £116. Deposit: £40. Babies welcome. No children under 8. Afternoon teas. Garden (*The Which? Hotel Guide*)

'There was a strange crunchy deep-fried wun-tun thing perched on top. I had noticed several other diners bite this, look at it in bewilderment and then put in on their side plates. I tasted it and did the same. When I asked the head waiter why it was there, he said that people were always asking that and he would have a word with the chef Monday morning.' (On eating in London)

CASTLE COMBE Wiltshire map 2

▲ *Manor House Hotel*

Castle Combe SN14 7HR
TEL: (01249) 782206 FAX: (01249) 782159 COOKING 3
on B4039, 3m NW of junction with A420 COST £27–£75

A pretty village is the setting for the Manor House, a fifteenth-century Cotswold-stone delight. The estate encompasses parkland and a golf course, and a river runs through it. Above the vast stone fireplace in the oaken entrance hall, the house proudly displays its armorial credentials. Not unexpectedly, the tone at dinner is formal. Staff are 'very well trained', and mineral water is treated like champagne. Menu descriptions are florid – 'diver-caught scallops draped in a satay sauce' – but the cooking at an inspection dinner showed that Mark Taylor is well up to the challenge of his rarefied surroundings. His food is essentially English, he says, which means that it borrows cheerfully from many other culinary cultures. Witness the technique in a first-course soufflé of bacon, shallots and morels into which was poured a 'gorgeous, deep-brown morel sauce': both texture and flavour were formidable.

A main course of roast Trelough duck with vanilla and cinnamon sauce and sour cherries offered sliced breast and a 'beautifully sticky and rich' confit of the leg, with a sauce of wondrous flavour contrasts. Vegetables are built in to the main dish – on this occasion a potato galette, smooth pea purée and spinach. 'Technically faultless' they may have been, but perhaps lacked excitement. A dessert of gratiné rice pudding with plums and a pastry case filled with plum ice-cream, was a nice idea for all that it looked a bit of a puddle. Appetisers and petits fours are proffered in reckless abundance, quality varying from one mouthful to the next. The refresher-course sorbet of lime and mint did its job well, but the cafetière coffee could have done with stiffening up. The kitchen could probably afford to go a little easier on the frills and furbelows. There are some fairly high prices to justify, but imagination and skill are sufficient to warrant these. Sheets of classics form the backbone of the wine list, and mark-ups are high. There is a broad house selection that limits itself to £20, and a fair spread of halves, but the bulk is pretty intimidating. Prices start at £14.50.

CHEF: Mark Taylor PROPRIETOR: Manor House Hotel Ltd OPEN: all week 12 to 2, 7 to 10 MEALS: alc D (main courses £19 to £23). Set L £16.95, Set D £32 SERVICE: not inc, card slips closed CARDS: Access, Amex, Diners, Switch, Visa DETAILS: 70 seats. 12 tables outside. Private parties: 90 main room, 10 to 20 private rooms. Car park. Vegetarian meals. Children's helpings. Smart dress preferred. No smoking in dining-room. Wheelchair access (3 steps; also WC). Music ACCOMMODATION: 40 rooms, all with bath/shower. TV. Phone. B&B £111 to £372. Rooms for disabled. Children welcome. Baby facilities. Pets welcome. Afternoon teas. Garden. Swimming-pool. Fishing (*The Which? Hotel Guide*)

indicates that smoking is either banned altogether or that a dining-room is maintained for non-smokers. The symbol does not apply to restaurants that simply have no-smoking areas.

CHAGFORD Devon map 1

▲ *Gidleigh Park*

WEST COUNTRY 1996 LUNCH

Chagford TQ13 8HH
TEL: (01647) 432367 and 432225
FAX: (01647) 432574
from Chagford Square turn right at Lloyds Bank into Mill Street, take right fork after 150 yards, follow lane for 1½m

COOKING 4*
COST £33–£76

'Always a wonderful place to visit,' began one reporter, sinking into the deep cushions in the drawing-room. The atmosphere is supremely relaxed and not in the slightest bit stuffy, with service that is 'unobtrusive, but there when you need it'. Freshness and 'perfect balance' – not least between the first-class ingredients and the methods of cooking – characterise the food. 'A truly stunning meal,' summed up an inspector, impressed by the uniformly high standard throughout. As if that were not enough, the price of lunch has come down. 'I can assure you this is not from desperation,' writes Paul Henderson who, when he joined the *Financial Times* Lunch for a Tenner scheme, suddenly realised that not everybody wanted to pay £40, even though service is included. The current lunchtime prices must be strong contenders for the best-value lunch in the West Country.

Dinner begins (in summer at any rate) on the terrace with an array of superior amuse-gueules, and continues at table with a small cup of 'flawless, creamy textured, strongly flavoured lobster bisque'. Michael Caines's food has a classical foundation as well as an openness to other ideas and a degree of controlled invention about it. One or two reporters remark on its richness. Foie gras and lentil soup 'with a texture like satin' is 'the ultimate comfort food' for one. Oriental flavourings play a part too, usually the headier ones: ginger and lemon grass, for instance, in a delicate sauce for sweet, firm, succulent crab ravioli, or (with the addition of orange and fennel) for roasted brill, the fish thick and timed to perfection.

Fish, indeed, comes in for consistently high praise, from a salad of plump scallops, briefly seared to be crisp outside and 'like mother-of-pearl' inside, and dressed with truffled vinaigrette, to wild salmon roasted hard on one side, with an array of vegetables in the peak of condition. Even the gutsier cooking – a breast of pigeon on a potato galette in an intense reduction of the cooking juices, with chanterelles and oyster mushrooms – is 'beautifully judged and faultless'. Balance and contrast feature in desserts too, from crème brûlée with a very fine crisp topping, looking more tanned than substantial, to a feathery-textured hot pistachio soufflé served with the same flavour of ice-cream. Cheeses are good, and successful breads owe something to French flours and a good oven.

'I can't remember the last time I saw a wine list so reasonably priced, since the mark-ups reduce in relative terms as the wines become more expensive.' Burgundy runs from simple Mâcon-Villages to *grands crus*, while Alsace and Italy both get serious treatment. Claret and burgundy vintages go back a long way, as do some of the American wines, among which it is also good to see Bonny Doon, Jade Mountain and Qupé varietals. Bin-ends need to be ordered by 5pm 'in order that we can find them', while the Cruvinet machine ensures a good supply of wines by the glass from around £4.

CHEF: Michael Caines PROPRIETORS: Paul and Kay Henderson OPEN: all week 12.30 to 2, 7 to 9 MEALS: Set L Mon to Thur £15 (2 courses) to £50, Fri and Sat £20 (2 courses) to £50, Sun £25 (2 courses) to £50, Set D £50 to £55 SERVICE: net prices, card slips closed CARDS: Access, Amex, Diners, Switch, Visa DETAILS: 40 seats. Private parties: 20 main room. Car park. Children welcome. Smart dress preferred. No smoking in dining-room. No music ACCOMMODATION: 14 rooms and cottage, all with bath/shower. TV. Phone. D,B&B £200 to £365. Children welcome. Baby facilities. Pets welcome. Afternoon teas. Garden. Fishing

CHEDINGTON Dorset map 2

▲ *Chedington Court* 🍷

Chedington DT8 3HY
TEL: (01935) 891265 FAX: (01935) 891442 COOKING 1
off A356, 4½m SE of Crewkerne COST £31–£38

Chedington is an imposing mock-Elizabethan mansion built in the 1840s on the Dorset–Somerset border, with delightful views of rolling countryside. Granite fireplaces and heavy bookshelves give a solid feel, but the décor is unshowy. 'Handsome and comfortable,' thought one. The daily-changing menu is set in the simple and traditional ways of a quiche (with bacon, cheese and mushrooms), mussels in white wine and cream, and baked fillet of salmon with lemon hollandaise. 'We have now discontinued the fish course as many people found five courses too much,' write the Chapmans. Even so, the remaining four courses can be a lot for some.

Crusts and stuffings are common devices: bacon and hazelnut crust for black bream, or a moist roast breast of guinea-fowl stuffed with sausagemeat, chestnuts, prunes and thyme. Performance is uneven, from vivid orange pimento mousse 'in a steak and kidney pie shape' with vibrant taste and real kick, to good fresh brill let down by 'a gloupy mixture of cream, butter and cheese'. Desserts come on a trolley. Apricot and chocolate cake, described as a crunchy mix of oats, nuts, dark chocolate and soft apricots, 'would have been more at home at a church fête'. Presentation has left something to be desired, or to be improved – from 'tatty menus' and local radio wafting out of the kitchen, to jelly-mould mousses – but service is friendly and efficient.

The strong suits on the wine list are Bordeaux, Burgundy and Germany, backed up by a good spread from Australia and the USA. A run of Beaujolais under £20, and a German red wine, show that the list repays exploration. It is also very generous with half-bottles. House vin de pays is from £7.50. CELLARMAN'S CHOICE: Beaujolais Blanc 1993, Ch. des Tours, £15.50; Brouilly 1993, Ch. des Tours, £15.50.

CHEFS: Lindsay Wakeman and Hilary Chapman PROPRIETORS: Philip and Hilary Chapman OPEN: all week D only 7 to 9 CLOSED: Jan MEALS: Set D £27.50 SERVICE: none, card slips closed CARDS: Access, Amex, Visa DETAILS: 28 seats. 2 tables outside. Private parties: 8 main room, 14 private room. Car park. Vegetarian meals. No children under 10 D. Smart dress preferred. No cigars/pipes in dining-room. Wheelchair access (2 steps; also WC). Music ACCOMMODATION: 10 rooms, all with bath/shower. TV. Phone. D B&B £82 to £184. Deposit: £30. Children welcome. Afternoon teas. Garden (*The Which? Hotel Guide*)

CHEESDEN **Greater Manchester** map 8

French Connection NEW ENTRY

Edenfield Road, Cheesden, nr Rochdale OL12 7TY
TEL: (01706) 50167
from M66 junction 1, take the Rochdale road for 2½ miles

COOKING 2*
COST £23–£47

The moorland provides a starkly evocative backdrop for any restaurant, and that seems to be particularly true in the case of French Connection, a thoughtfully converted pub on the Rochdale to Edenfield road. Outside, thought one reporter, 'the scene is reminiscent of *Wuthering Heights*', which makes the welcome within all the warmer.

Andrew Nutter's connection is that he cooked in France for a while, taking charge here when his father bought the place in 1993. Twin flags on the menu, and bilingual prose, announce the dual culinary orientation. You either eat à la carte or take the chef's six-course tasting menu. The techniques in evidence are mainly French, but ingredients bring you back home; crispy Bury black pudding wun-tuns with mixed vegetables in an oriental dressing is 1990s Britain if ever a dish was. A salad of lobster and asparagus is neatly presented, its little pools of marie-rose sauce a long way from the banal norm, and the same patient attention is evinced in the generously proportioned main courses. Guinea-fowl is grilled and sauced with a stock scattered with pink peppercorns, while fillet steak is two chunks of beef on garlicky dauphinois, the meat 'absolutely first-class, and perfectly timed as ordered'.

For dessert caramelised lemon tart has a top that is properly crisped, 'the custard sharp and intense, the pastry light', or how about chocolate and pistachio soufflé pudding with a milkshake sauce? Cheeses may be on the humdrum side, but incidentals are impressive – appetising canapés, decent bread and full-blooded coffee with home-made petits fours. 'I got the impression,' commented a reporter, 'that this was a place that was developing and had by no means reached its full potential' – always an exciting time in the life of a restaurant. Not surprisingly, the main business of the wine list is in France with a smattering of New World bottles as well. Clarets and burgundies look fairly youthful, a good spread of halves is available, and prices are reasonable. House wines start with French Connection red and white, which, provocatively enough, are Australian, at £9.80.

CHEF: Andrew Nutter PROPRIETORS: the Nutter family OPEN: Tue to Sat 12 to 2, 7 (6.30 Sat) to 9.30 (10 Sat), Sun noon to 9 CLOSED: first 2 weeks Aug, bank hol Mons MEALS: alc (main courses £7.50 to £17). Tasting menu D £27.50 SERVICE: not inc CARDS: Access, Delta, Switch, Visa DETAILS: 54 seats. Private parties: 54 main room. Car park. Vegetarian meals. Children's helpings. Smart dress preferred. No smoking in dining-room. Wheelchair access (also WC). Music

'French waiters are proud of their profession in itself, while English waiters often see it as a stepping stone to potentially greater things, which probably never happen.'
(On eating in London)

CHELSWORTH Suffolk map 6

▲ *Peacock Inn* NEW ENTRY

The Street, Chelsworth IP7 7HU
on B1115 between Stowmarket and Sudbury COOKING 1
TEL: (01449) 740758 COST £18–£31

'I have never known a place change so much,' said a Suffolk man after a visit to this revamped Tudor inn overlooking the grounds of Chelsworth Hall. Since taking over in 1994, Nigel and Carol Ramsbottom have stamped their mark on the place with a vengeance. The décor is still an 'olde-worlde' blend of beams, inglenooks and exposed brickwork, but the food is what really attracts. The menu is chalked on a blackboard and you can eat anywhere: in summer, the wonderfully luxuriant garden, with its all-embracing white canvas parasol, is highly recommended.

Nigel Ramsbottom spent some time in the kitchens of the Walnut Tree Inn, Llandewi Skirrid (see entry, Wales) and it shows. There's no doubting the Mediterranean bias (chargrilled squid marinated in chillies, pan-fried salmon with a pesto crust, Italian sausages with butter-beans, for example), but the British flag flies high with lovage and celery soup, smoked haddock topped with Welsh rarebit (courtesy of Gary Rhodes) and lambs' liver with onions and mash. Those with a trencherman's appetite might like to tackle the massive braised knuckle of pork subtly infused with garlic, rosemary and white wine. Vegetables and salads struck one reporter as rather uninspiring, although things perked up again with glazed lemon tart and chocolate loaf with coffee sauce. Real ales are on handpump, and the short wine list provides plenty of creditable drinking by the bottle or glass. Eleven house wines start at £8.99, though some on the list are even cheaper than that.

CHEF: Nigel Ramsbottom PROPRIETOR: Old English Pub Co Ltd OPEN: all week L 12 to 2, Tue to Sat D 7 to 9 MEALS: alc (main courses £6 to £10.50) SERVICE: not inc CARDS: Access, Switch, Visa DETAILS: 45 seats. 12 tables outside. Private parties: 25 main room. Children welcome. Smart dress preferred. Music ACCOMMODATION: 4 rooms. TV. B&B £25 to £45. Children welcome. Garden

CHELTENHAM Gloucestershire map 5

Le Champignon Sauvage 🍷

24–26 Suffolk Road, Cheltenham GL50 2AQ COOKING 3*
TEL: (01242) 573449 COST £26–£52

To describe the Champignon as a French restaurant seems increasingly to miss the point as time passes. So much successful cross-fertilisation has taken place in the cooking style that to give it the unvarnished tag 'français', despite the laboriously bilingual descriptions on the menu, seems almost mischievous. The food exhibits a broader-based complexity and daring, but regulars have come to understand the intention and are rewarded with menus that don't know the meaning of the word 'cliché'.

The setting is a terraced knock-through on one of Cheltenham's busier thoroughfares, the understated greys of the dining-room offset with brightly painted plates and modern paintings. Menus are set-price according to the number of courses taken. David Everitt-Matthias is a canny purchaser of materials as well as a dab hand at presentation, more often than not with the main element supported on some assertively flavoured base. Chestnut polenta is the resting-place for a duck sausage, while stuffed Cotswold rabbit surmounts a choucroute made of turnip and is partnered with black pudding, and undyed smoked haddock is paired with cockle couscous in squid ink. 'The cooking was faultless,' said the reporters who ate these things, 'with clear strong flavours and a good contrast of textures.' Creativity continues into dessert stage, in iced gingerbread soufflé with orange and liquorice sorbet, or assiette bretonne: a mixture of buttery Breton prune cake, pressed apple terrine, prune and armagnac ice-cream and a cider syrup. Helen Everitt-Matthias runs the front-of-house single-handedly, which means that the pace of service can be seen as 'relaxed' or 'boringly slow', depending on whether time presses.

The wine list goes in search of the best and is not confined exclusively to France. Albert Mann's Alsace grand cru Gewurztraminer or Coudoulet de Beaucastel Rhône red will grace any occasion, but there is also Corbans New Zealand Chardonnay and Clos du Val Pinot Noir from California. Although quality does push up prices, there is enough under £20 to provide decent choice. House French starts at £8.50. CELLARMAN'S CHOICE: Châteauneuf-du-Pape 1990, Dom. de Terre Ferme, £23.95; Côtes du Frontonnais, Ch. la Colombière 1989, Villaudric, £11.50.

CHEF: David Everitt-Matthias PROPRIETORS: David and Helen Everitt-Matthias OPEN: Mon to Fri L 12.30 to 1.30, Mon to Sat D 7.30 to 9.30 CLOSED: 24 Dec to 4 Jan, bank hols MEALS: Set L £12.50 (2 courses) to £17.50, Set D £18.50 to £33 SERVICE: not inc CARDS: Access, Amex, Diners, Visa DETAILS: 30 seats. Private parties: 30 main room. Children welcome. Smart dress preferred. No cigars/pipes in dining-room. Wheelchair access (1 step; also WC). No music. Air-conditioned

Mayflower

32–34 Clarence Street, Cheltenham GL50 3NX
TEL: (01242) 522426 and 511580 COOKING 1*
FAX: (01242) 251667 COST £14–£44

'Happiness is when you hang the wallpaper correctly,' proclaim the Chinese words on the pink-papered walls of this popular restaurant. Frilly Austrian blinds billow at the windows, tables are lit by candles under little lampshades. The effect is 'Regency oriental'. This is a 'good outpost' for reliably cooked food, although prices are far from Chinatown café and you won't find anything in the way of duck's webs or fish lips. Instead, the menu sweeps its way through the Cantonese, Pekinese and Szechuan repertoire, taking in dishes such as steamed scallops (accompanied by a bowl of soy sauce fired up with ginger and chopped green chillies), sizzling crispy lamb, and deep-fried spiced fish slices. Lobster and duck appear in various guises, and there has also been praise for Buddha's hot-pot – a meatless extravaganza of vegetables, bean thread noodles and fungi that almost converted one reporter to vegetarianism. Ingredients are fresh, presentation is neat, and service is polite, willing and speedy. The wine list is a thoughtfully selected slate of around 80 bins that are well above the Chinese average. Australian house wine is £8.95.

CHEFS: Mrs M.M.Kong and Mr C.F.Kong PROPRIETORS: the Kong family OPEN: Mon to Sat L12 to 1.45, all week D 5.45 to 10.45 (11.15 Fri and Sat) CLOSED: 24 to 27 Dec MEALS: alc (main courses £6.50 to £9.50). Set L £6.50, Set D £16 (2 courses) to £27.50 SERVICE: not inc CARDS: Access, Amex, Delta, Diners, Switch, Visa DETAILS: 120 seats. Private parties: 80 main room, 40 private room. Vegetarian meals. Children welcome. Smart dress preferred. Wheelchair access (2 steps). Music. Air-conditioned

Staithes Restaurant

12 Suffolk Road, Cheltenham GL50 2AQ
TEL: (01242) 260666 COOKING 1*
on A40, S of town centre at junction with Bath Road COST £23–£41

The attention to cleanliness at Staithes is such that 'a polite notice outside suggests that customers should wipe their feet before going in', while the lavatories have earned paeans from readers – 'bright, shining and impeccable' – and won a national award. Close by Cheltenham Boys' College, the Lucases' small neighbourhood restaurant attracts emphatic support from readers who enjoy luxuriating in 'the atmosphere of a pleasant dining-club'. The cooking is robust and homely with the emphasis on simplicity, the range represented by creamy pea and ham soup, halibut from Cornwall with a horseradish and herb crust, and sliced duck magret with cassis and blackcurrants. 'When dishes appear, they live up to their description,' commented one reporter, while another found the flavours in main courses 'lovely – delicate but distinct'. Paul Lucas makes a mean bread-and-butter pudding, and other desserts that delight include peach and mango parfait with mango coulis, white chocolate and hazelnut terrine with caramel sauce, and banana crème brûlée. Service is 'top-class'. A brief wine list on one side of the menu is serviceable rather than exciting but at least, with the exception of champagnes, everything is under £20. House French is £9.95.

CHEF: Paul Lucas PROPRIETORS: Heather and Paul Lucas OPEN: Mon to Sat D only 7.30 (7 Sat) to 10; L by reservation only CLOSED: 1 week Christmas, 2 weeks summer, bank hol Mons MEALS: alc (main courses £7 to £14) SERVICE: not inc, card slips closed CARDS: Access, Amex, Diners, Visa DETAILS: 24 seats. Private parties: 24 main room, 10 private room. Vegetarian meals. Children over 8 by arrangement. Smart dress preferred. No smoking in dining-room. Wheelchair access (1 step). Music

CHESTER Cheshire map 7

▲ *Chester Grosvenor Hotel, Arkle*

Eastgate Street, Chester CH1 1LT COOKING 4
TEL: (01244) 324024 FAX: (01244) 313246 COST £30–£73

Grosvenor Estates Holdings is a Duke of Westminster company, and horsey overtones persist at the hotel's restaurant because Anne, Duchess of Westminster, owned the racehorse Arkle. Luxuries don't come cheap, but the restaurant sets out to provide the best. Drinks and nibbles – including warm canapés – are taken in the library to piano accompaniment. The dining-room is held up by massive white pillars, greenery dangles from the conservatory-type roof, and oil-paintings, including one of Arkle, decorate the walls. Tables are far apart: annoying if you want to overhear somebody else's conversation, perfect if you want privacy for your own. Choice is lavishly provided: 'There arrived first of all a trolley laden with no less than 19 different kinds of bread, all home baked. Remarkable.'

The menu oozes French, although one might wonder why, if they use local rabbit in a dish, they don't use the local language to describe it. And the practice of writing prices as 'eighteen pounds and twenty-five pence' is a mite ridiculous. But after eating food of this quality such quibbles all but vanish. The six-course menu gourmand (sic) at thirty-seven pounds (they've even got us doing it now) is recited by the manager, a bit of a bore for him since it changes only quarterly, but it is a *tour de force*. At one meal it began with ham hock and chicken in a beetroot sauce, before a small piece of halibut with scallops in a bouillabaisse sauce, then a lime sorbet. Main course was slices of lamb on a bed of mashed potato with asparagus and garlic cloves, followed by a selection of cheeses from the board, ending with a strawberry soufflé.

Of course there is no stinting on luxuries, but they are intelligently used. The beauty of this food is more than skin deep. Duck liver comes with a brawn and crackling salad, beef fillet with shredded tongues and glazed goats' cheese, and venison saddle with wild mushroom dumplings. Sauces are cleverly contrived, and globe artichoke (with a whipped mousseline of crab, roasted lobster and gazpacho vinegar) is 'simply brilliant.' Nor does the pace slow with desserts, which might include a trio of hot and cold caramel puddings, or a savarin of prunes with armagnac ice-cream and orange preserve. Lunch is less elaborate.

Service is unobtrusive, obliging and honest: if somebody doesn't know the answer to your question he will go and find out. Chefs often receive all the acclaim, but the restaurant manager can be just as important to overall enjoyment. Step forward, Jenner Harding, and take a bow. 'There is nothing wrong with the wines apart from the prices,' noted one reporter, although there are enough bottles under £20 to provide some choice. The selection from France is tip-top, and half-bottles are plentiful. CELLARMAN'S CHOICE: Viognier, Dom. St Hilaire 1993, £19; Beaune *premier cru* 'Epenottes' 1989, Vallet Frères, £44.

CHEF: Paul Reed PROPRIETOR: Grosvenor Estate Holdings OPEN: Tue to Sun L 12 to 2.30, Mon to Sat D 7 to 9.30 CLOSED: 25 and 26 Dec, first week Jan MEALS: alc D (main courses £18 to £21.50). Set L £18 (2 courses) to £22.50, Set D £37 SERVICE: not inc CARDS: Access, Amex, Diners, Visa DETAILS: 45 seats. Vegetarian meals. Children's helpings. Jacket and tie. Music. Air-conditioned ACCOMMODATION: 86 rooms, all with bath/shower. TV. Phone. Air-conditioned. B&B £145 to £243. Rooms for disabled. Children welcome. Baby facilities. Afternoon teas

---

CHICHESTER West Sussex map 3

Droveway

30A Southgate, Chichester PO19 1DR COOKING 1
TEL: (01243) 528832 COST £25–£50

The large Georgian-style dining-room, although not exactly cosy, is attractively furnished. Jonas and Elly Tester keep things on the hop, whipping up enthusiasm by organising lots of events and producing a quarterly newsletter, taking post-theatre bookings, and offering an Anglo-French *carte* in the evening on top of the fixed-price options. Dishes can sound ambitious, as in raw scallops on a bed of creamed celeriac with truffle vinaigrette, but omelette Arnold Bennett brings things back to earth.

Other ideas range from a quail and artichoke salad through blanquette of sole with asparagus (the fish is usually good) to what some consider the highlight: puddings such as made-to-order bread-and-butter with Grand Marnier, or a bitter chocolate fondant filled with Bailey's cream liqueur, with a white chocolate sauce. A short range of exotic teas and coffees follows. One edition of the Droveway's newsletter points out that the new Euro-measures for glasses of wine which came into effect on 1 January 1995, and which specify a capacity of either 125 or 175 millilitres, are particularly convenient because the average wine bottle contains approximately 4.2857 of the larger-sized glasses. They offer a French red and Australian white by the glass, a 12-strong moderately priced house selection, and 20 other hand-picked bottles.

CHEF: Jonas Tester PROPRIETORS: Elly and Jonas Tester OPEN: Tue to Sat 12.30 to 2, 7 to 10 CLOSED: first 2 weeks Jan MEALS: alc D (main courses £10 to £17.50). Set L £12 (2 courses) to £15, Set D £19.50 SERVICE: not inc, card slips closed CARDS: Access, Amex, Delta, Switch, Visa DETAILS: 40 seats. Private parties: 32 main room. Vegetarian meals. Children's helpings. No smoking in 1 dining-room. Music

CHILGROVE West Sussex map 3

▲ *White Horse Inn*

Chilgrove PO18 9HX

TEL: (01243) 535219 FAX: (01243) 535301 COOKING 1

on B2141, between Chichester and Petersfield COST £26–£47

The long white inn, covered in wistaria and climbing roses, faces a clear stretch of the South Downs, uninhabited as far as the eye can see. Pink plush décor and wine memorabilia account for much of the inside, overseen by Barry Phillips, who is 'what you would call a character'. The food goes in for ravioli of pigeon and spinach with chive jus, baked filo parcels of leeks with a Stilton sauce, and usually includes an offal dish, such as lambs' kidneys, or calf's liver with red onion marmalade and madeira sauce. At inspection, vegetables, pudding and incidentals such as bread, coffee and petits fours let the side down, although a first-course dish of fillet of red mullet with an orange and walnut salad, and a main-course breast of Barbary duck were thoroughly enjoyed.

A few luxuries along the lines of caviare, foie gras and lobster come into play, and there is a vegetarian main course and a daily fish dish. Puddings are recited. Accommodation is now available in nearby Forge Cottage – useful for those who wish to take advantage of one of the country's outstanding wine lists. Claret is the strong suit: 16 vintages of Ch. Pétrus, and two dozen of Ch. Mouton-Rothschild are typical of the scale, although one reporter felt that the monthly-changing wines offered by the glass are 'interesting and kept in good condition, which is of much more use than being offered all the different clarets in existence'. Half-bottles abound, as do first-rate Germans, and there are over 20 half-bottles of South African dessert wine. Prices are realistic, usually shaved just enough to encourage a doubting drinker to have a go, and everything on the list is laid out simply and well. All you need is an afternoon to look through it. CELLARMAN'S CHOICE: Muscadet, Cuvée de Millénaire 1993, Marquis de Goulaine, £12.95; Van Loveren, Blanc de Noir Rosé 1994, Robertson, South Africa £11.50.

CHEF: Neil Rusbridger PROPRIETORS: Barry Phillips and Neil Rusbridger OPEN: Tue to Sun L 12 to 2, Tue to Sat D 7 to 9.30 (10.30 in summer) CLOSED: last week Oct, 3 weeks Feb MEALS: alc (main courses £10.50 to £17.50). Set L £17.50, Set D £23; bar meals available SERVICE: 10%, card slips closed CARDS: Access, Delta, Diners, Switch, Visa DETAILS: 70 seats. 3 tables outside. Private parties: 34 main room, 10 and 34 private rooms. Car park. Vegetarian meals. No children under 14. Smart dress preferred. No cigars/pipes in dining-room. Wheelchair access. No music. Air-conditioned ACCOMMODATION: 5 rooms, 3 with bath/shower. TV. Phone. B&B £35 to £70. Rooms for disabled. Garden

CHINNOR Oxfordshire **map 2**

CHILTERN 1996 ECCENTRIC

Sir Charles Napier

Sprigg's Alley, nr Chinnor OX9 4BX
TEL: (01494) 483011
off B4009, take Bledlow Ridge turn from Chinnor, 2m up hill

COOKING 2*
COST £30–£44

Follow the road as it snakes its way uphill towards Bledlow Ridge and you might easily drive straight past the Sir Charles Napier. From the outside it could be just another Chilterns country residence, but the red-brick façade conceals all manner of delights. First, glance round the car park and the garden (a typically unpredictable blend of wildness and wayward cultivation) and you cannot miss the sculptures: massive polished pigs, hippos, voluptuous nudes and spindly constructions of rusty metal reinforce the feeling that you have stumbled on to an open-air art exhibition. Inside, it is pure eccentricity: a shambolic clutter of battered armchairs and sofas, junk-shop curios, paintings, effigies. The dining-room is full to the brim with tables and chairs of every description, and the cutlery consists of EPNS spoons and bone-handled knives.

But culinary cobwebs and backward glances have no place in Batiste Tolu's kitchen. His food is neat, sharply defined and modern, although he is no dedicated follower of fashion. Fish is his strong point, fresh flavours, timing and clarity his trade marks: witness crab-cakes with lime and coriander, roast scallops with sorrel and bacon, and baked fillet of sea bass with a silky-smooth lemon butter sauce. Puddings have included a rich banana tarte Tatin and light Bakewell tart, but the best way to finish is with cheese: the selection is British and Irish, and the quality is as good as you will find anywhere (Blue Shropshire, Cashel Blue, Swaledale and Devon Garland have all been brilliant). Service is youthful, well-informed and perfectly in tune with the casual mood of the place.

The wine list is bursting with enthusiasm at every turn: in its broad scope, its insistence on flavour and character (look to the Rhône and New World for variety), its championing of lesser-known wines alongside more familiar ones, and its mission – to encourage, through modest mark-ups, good drinking at all levels. Don't forget the Wadworth real ale or the enterprising digestifs. CELLARMAN'S CHOICE: Polish Hill Riesling 1994, Clare Valley, S. Australia, £14.95; Saumur Champigny 'Vieilles Vignes' 1989, Filliatreau, £18.95.

CHEF: Batiste Tolu PROPRIETOR: Julie Griffiths OPEN: Tue to Sun L 12 to 2.30 (12.30 to 3.30 Sun), Tue to Sat D 7 to 10 MEALS: alc (main courses £9.50 to £13.50). Set L Tue to Fri £12.50 (2 courses), Set D £14 (2 courses). Licensed, but you may also bring your own: corkage £5 SERVICE: 12.5% (optional), card slips closed CARDS: Access, Amex, Switch, Visa DETAILS: 75 seats. 10 tables outside. Private parties: 45 main room, 30 and 45 private rooms. Car park. Vegetarian meals. No children under 8 D. No cigars/pipes in dining-room. Wheelchair access. Music

CHOBHAM Surrey map 3

Quails

1 Bagshot Road, Chobham GU24 8BP COOKING 1
TEL: (01276) 858491 COST £21–£43

A converted shop in a small parade, Quails sets out its stall for the Surrey crowd. On weekdays, regional French fixed-price menus operate alongside the *carte* at dinner. Reporters seem unable to agree about the décor: is it 'pleasant and restful', or 'a bit seedy'? Pastel colours, curtains draped over poles, agreeable pictures and dainty Florentine candlesticks set the scene. Mrs Wale runs the front-of-house efficiently. Christopher Wale tries hard to deliver a mix of Gallic classics and eclectic modern dishes, and he has a sure touch. Appropriately, quail is handled with style: the bird is wrapped in smoked bacon, stuffed with mushrooms and leeks, then cooked 'prettily pink'. Saddle of roe-deer with cassis and green peppercorns also hits the button, as does roast poulet noir with an orange-coloured ragoût of peppers. Of the fish dishes, poached salmon with sorrel sauce has been better received than halibut 'unhappily teamed' with rocket salad and an assertive sun-dried tomato salsa. Similarly, skilfully executed mocha parfait in a white chocolate 'ramekin' easily overshadows 'stodgy, unpalatable' spotted dick. At lunch-time there is a lighter menu of brasserie-style dishes. The wine list aims to complement the food; it focuses on France and provides plenty of satisfying drinking at reasonable prices. House wine is £9.50.

CHEF: Christopher Wale PROPRIETORS: the Wale family OPEN: Tue to Fri and Sun L 12.30 to 2, Tue to Sat D 7 to 10 MEALS: alc (main courses £7.50 to £13). Set L Sun £12.95, Set D Tue to Fri £13.95 (2 courses) to £15.95 (inc wine) SERVICE: not inc; 10% for parties of 8 or more CARDS: Access, Amex, Diners, Switch, Visa DETAILS: 40 seats. Private parties: 40 main room. Car park. Children welcome. Smart dress preferred. Wheelchair access. Music. Air-conditioned

CHRISTCHURCH Dorset map 2

Splinters

12 Church Street, Christchurch BH23 1BW COOKING 1
TEL/FAX: (01202) 483454 COST £23–£39

Splinters takes great advantage of its setting: it is in a Grade II listed building standing in the shadow of Christchurch's 900-year-old priory. Inside, the main restaurant consists of three rooms done out with pine woodwork and Laura Ashley wallpaper: choose between the high-sided Private Booth, the intimate Cellar Room festooned with wine bottles or The Parlour. The bar area – complete with Lloyd Loom furniture – doubles as Number II Brasserie (10.30am to 2.30pm), and meals often finish in the old-style comfort of the first-floor drawing room. Reports confirm that new chef Eamonn Redden has settled in well and is producing some very creditable food from a menu that is a mix of eclectic modern dishes and classic revivals, plus one or two quirky inventions (shrimp and oyster junket with leek sauce, or roast scallops with strawberries and green peppercorn sauce). Warm salad of black pudding, bacon, tomatoes and quails' eggs was 'a jolly little breakfast' for one reporter, although it was slightly overwhelmed by its balsamic dressing. The list of recent recommendations also includes hot soufflé of smoked haddock with parsley sauce, roast Gressingham duck, and brochette of caramelised autumn fruits on a bed of 'excellent' creamed rice pudding. Splinters has links with the Chocolate Society, so you can always expect a dessert such as Valrhona chocolate noodles with cappuccino sauce. The 'cheese dome' holds a fine selection of British farmhouse choices served with orange and walnut bread. The owners are helpful and service is generally spot-on. Wines are reasonably priced and include five by the glass. House French starts at £9.50.

CHEF: Eamonn Redden PROPRIETORS: Timothy Lloyd and Robert Wilson OPEN: all week 10.30 to 2.30, 7 to 10.30 CLOSED: 2 weeks Jan MEALS: Set L £11.50 (2 courses) to £14.50, Set L Sun £13.50, Set D £19.50 to £22.50 SERVICE: not inc CARDS: Access, Amex, Diners, Switch, Visa DETAILS: 40 seats. Private parties: 12 main room, 22 private room. Vegetarian meals. Children welcome. Smart dress preferred. Wheelchair access. Music

CLAYGATE Surrey map 3

Le Petit Pierrot

4 The Parade, Claygate KT10 0NU COOKING 1*
TEL: (01372) 465105 FAX: (01372) 467642 COST £24–£34

'[I was] restored to life after a hard day!' commented a reporter who reckoned that the curative powers of this family-run French restaurant were just what the doctor might have ordered. Everyone who comes here seems to mention the happy, relaxed atmosphere of the place and the quality of the service. Most are also keen to sing the praises of Jean-Pierre Brichot's endeavours in the kitchen. His cooking is dyed-in-the-wool French and his fixed-price menus (lunch changes fortnightly, dinner every six weeks) are peppered with classics such as escalope of sea trout with chive butter sauce, rack of lamb with a herb crust, and calf's liver with raspberry vinegar sauce. Sliced breast of Gressingham duck (sometimes gilded with honey and sesame seeds) has been praised, along with crème brûlée tinged with saffron. The wine list continues the Gallic theme with a short slate of fair-priced bottles from the major growing regions. House wine is £9.25.

CHEF: Jean-Pierre Brichot PROPRIETORS: Jean-Pierre and Annie Brichot OPEN: Mon to Fri L 12.15 to 2.30, Mon to Sat D 7.15 to 10.30 CLOSED: bank hols MEALS: Set L £9.95 (2 courses) to £16.85, Set D £18.95 SERVICE: not inc CARDS: Access, Amex, Diners, Visa DETAILS: 32 seats. Private parties: 34 main room. No children under 9. Smart dress preferred. No pipes in dining-room, cigars permitted after meals. Music. Air-conditioned

CLITHEROE Lancashire map 8

Auctioneer

New Market Street, Clitheroe BB7 2JW COOKING 2
TEL: (01200) 27153 COST £21–£54

The view from the Auctioneer has changed beyond recognition. The restaurant itself hasn't moved, but the market square has been extensively reconstructed in local stone. Themed menus still feature regularly, whether it be Italian lakes and mountains, or Normandy and Brittany. Whatever the style, people feel that Henk Van Heumen brings off most of what he attempts. 'Very consistent cooking, and the welcome and service' were the justification for one couple's return visits. A lunchtime *carte* supplements the various fixed-price menus that may offer dishes such as watercress and shrimp soup, or a main-course pairing of venison and woodpigeon sauced with port and mushrooms. There is no sense of novelty for its own sake, which is undoubtedly one of the reasons for the consistency. 'Surprisingly tasty' fresh-water prawns on an Italian menu came with 'refreshingly sweet-sour' marinated peppers and courgettes. A pre-Christmas dinner delivered Goosnargh turkey escalope with an 'exceptional' sauce of brown-cap mushrooms and tarragon. Traditional puddings may include Dutch apple pie or sachertorte with blueberries, but a chocolate truffle ice-cream served with a coulis of peach and sweet Jurançon showed a readiness to invent. Good coffee with chocolates rounds things off in style. A competent wine list features a bargain selection headed 'Just A Tenner'. Otherwise, most regions are given a quick look-in, and there is a comprehensive selection of halves. House burgundy is £10.25.

CHEF: Henk Van Heumen PROPRIETORS: Henk and Frances Van Heumen OPEN: Wed to Sun 12 to 1.30, 7 to 9 (9.30 Sat) MEALS: alc L (main courses £7 to £12). Set D £16.75 (2 courses) to £21.75 SERVICE: not inc CARDS: Access, Amex, Delta, Switch, Visa DETAILS: 48 seats. Private parties: 24 main room, 24 private room. Vegetarian meals. Children's helpings. Smart dress preferred. No smoking in 1 dining-room. Music

COCKERMOUTH Cumbria map 10

Quince & Medlar £

13 Castlegate, Cockermouth CA13 9EU COOKING 1
TEL: (01900) 823579 COST £19–£31

'We want our customers to enjoy the food for what it is,' write the Le Vois, 'not to be reminded that it doesn't contain meat.' This is a laudable aim. The restaurant is up a short hill leading off the main street, but inside all is calm and civilised, with a Victorian feel to the net-curtained dining-room. Tables have light green cloths, flowers and candles.

A choice from the half-a-dozen dishes per course might produce French onion tart, a layered aubergine gâteau and a warm orange sponge with Cointreau sauce. A problem that one reporter identified was that the kitchen lacks the confidence to serve something with only a few ingredients. A mixed vegetable and chickpea fricassee, for example, was attractively spiced with cumin, coriander, turmeric and ginger, spooned into a cornet-shaped poppadum, accompanied by a slightly dry pile of wild rice layered with slices of sweet potato, plus a salad of shredded carrot, pasta swirls and half a dozen other things. Service is friendly but has struck more than one reporter as slower than necessary. This does not seem to sway the opinion that this is 'a pleasant place'. Wines offer a more than adequate choice, including a handful of organics, and house French at £6.80.

CHEFS/PROPRIETORS: Colin and Louisa Le Voi OPEN: Tue to Sun D only 7 to 9.30 CLOSED: 2 weeks Jan, and Sun and Mon New Year to Easter MEALS: alc (main courses £7 to £8) SERVICE: not inc, card slips closed CARDS: Access, Visa DETAILS: 26 seats. Private parties: 14 main room. Vegetarian meals. No children under 5. Smart dress preferred. No smoking in dining-room. Music

COGGESHALL Essex map 3

Baumann's Brasserie

4–6 Stoneham Street, Coggeshall CO6 1TT COOKING 1
TEL: (01376) 561453 FAX: (01376) 563762 COST £16–£41

'Attractive décor, a buzzing atmosphere and attentive service' mark out the brasserie territory, and the legacy of Peter Langan persists in the varied collection of paintings. If you can't quite place the style of dishes, you are not alone: neither can Mark Baumann. 'With an Austrian mother and of Swiss descent, I have Germanic dishes and some British ideas' – and lots more besides. The mixed ancestry produces roast breast of goose on a compote of apples, and wild venison with spätzli, as well as Huntingdon fidget tart, and a dish of wilted lettuces with salt-beef in English mustard vinaigrette with a toasted onion bagel. The food is not without its lighter side – a pea soup, for example, is named London Particular – and the three-course set lunch is good value, as is the minimal wine list. Mark Baumann and Douglas Wright share the cooking here and at the North Hill Exchange Brasserie at 19 North Hill, Colchester.

CHEFS: Mark Baumann, Douglas Wright and Jason Shaw PROPRIETOR: Baumann's Brasserie Ltd OPEN: Tue to Fri and Sun L 12.30 to 2, Tue to Sat D 7.30 to 9.30 (10.30 Fri and Sat) CLOSED: first 2 weeks Jan MEALS: alc (main courses £11 to £15). Set L £9.95 SERVICE: not inc, card slips closed CARDS: Access, Switch, Visa DETAILS: 80 seats. Private parties: 80 main room. Children's helpings. Smart dress preferred. Wheelchair access (also WC). Music

COLCHESTER Essex map 3

Warehouse Brasserie $*

12 Chapel Street North, Colchester CO2 7AT COOKING 2
TEL: (01206) 765656 COST £16–£33

The Warehouse has got the brasserie ambience just right. There may not be much of the boulevard Montparnasse about Chapel Street, but the dimensions of this building and the buzzing, chattery atmosphere within show that Colchester has caught the bug. The vibrant colour scheme and different dining levels also play their part, as does the extensive menu of diverse culinary influences. Classic brasserie dishes, such as duck rillettes with French bread, sauté scallops with tomato and basil, and chicken breast with mustard cream sauce, constitute the core of the operation. Forays into the unexpected might include roast sea bass stuffed with spring vegetables seasoned with lime and ginger, or a vegetarian dish of spiced chickpea and almond samosas with warm coriander chutney and wild rice. A lamb mixed grill that used the chump, neck and liver in a sweetish stock and wine reduction was judged 'wonderful' by a man who could have stood the meat a little rarer. Even a simple-sounding puff pastry tart of mushrooms and garlic with a side salad turns out to be 'very rich and substantial'.

For dessert, brown-bread ice-cream made to a Victorian recipe with lashings of brandy delivers lots of flavour, or there may be distinctly more modern pecan and praline parfait with chocolate sauce. Cafetière coffee is strong and plentiful. The 'friendly and efficient' service and low prices have helped ensure a firm bedrock of repeat custom. When your bin-ends include a Chinese Chardonnay, nobody can fault you for enterprise. Wines are grouped stylistically, giving most regions (not forgetting Essex) a look-in, and prices are fair, with nearly everything offering change from £20. Largely French and Australian house wines start at £7.75.

CHEFS: Anthony Brooks, Mark Burley and Cheryl Hilham PROPRIETORS: Anthony Brooks and Mel Burley OPEN: all week L 12 to 2, Mon to Sat D 7 to 9.30 CLOSED: 25 and 26 Dec, L Good Fri, Easter Mon MEALS: alc (main courses £7 to £12). Set L £7.95 (2 courses) to £9.95 SERVICE: not inc, card slips closed CARDS: Access, Amex, Delta, Switch, Visa DETAILS: 90 seats. Private parties: 100 main room. Vegetarian meals. Children's helpings. No smoking in 1 dining-room. Wheelchair access (1 step). No music. Air-conditioned

---

COLERNE Wiltshire map 2

▲ *Lucknam Park*

Colerne SN14 8AZ
TEL: (01225) 742777 FAX: (01225) 743536 COOKING 3*
off A420 at Ford, 6m W of Chippenham COST £35–£73

This is a hotel in the grand manner: a creeper-clad Palladian mansion in extensive grounds – if you call 500 acres extensive – approached by a mile-long avenue of trees. Staying here is 'like spending the weekend in *Country Living* magazine, only more sumptuous and very relaxing'. The gardens are hedged with fine yew, and the large public rooms are tastefully decorated and comfortably furnished, with crystal chandeliers and stags' heads to hold the upward gaze. There is an inexhaustible supply of staff, who are always there when you need them, but not otherwise, which suits reporters very well.

Michael Womersley left at the beginning of June 1995 after six years at Lucknam to set up on his own at the Three Lions at Stuckton (see entry), and Alexander Venables moved up from sous-chef to take full control of the kitchen. Some items on the menu remain virtually unchanged, including a dish of glazed scallops and tender langoustines with a little cylinder of spinach mousse. Though it may be short on thrills, a puff pastry case filled with wild mushrooms and asparagus, with a champagne sauce, shows the kitchen's sound grasp of essentials. The style is modern, there is some fine cooking, and the handling of classic sauces is extremely good, including an excellent demi-glace with a rare fillet of pan-fried beef which made it 'the dish of the evening' for an inspector.

Slices of ripe pear sandwiched between almond tuile biscuits, served with cinnamon ice-cream, and a rich, moist, hot chocolate cake with crème anglaise both ran it a close second. The cheeseboard is impressive, with a good range from Britain and France, including a couple made from goats' milk on a farm just outside Bath, and a choice of coffee blends and teas brings things to a satisfactory conclusion. The wine list is an encyclopedic and enthusiastic romp through some very good vineyards. Leave all thoughts of bargains at the door, but be prepared for excellence and a good spread of vintages. If in doubt, ask for advice. One couple enjoyed a 'stunning' vin de pays Syrah at £18, taken instead of a more expensive St-Joseph on the wine waiter's recommendation. House claret and Chardonnay are £15 a bottle, house burgundy and Viognier £4 a glass. CELLARMAN'S CHOICE: Reuilly 1993, Aujard-Mabillot, £20; Chénas 1991, Dom. des Ducs, £21.

CHEF: Alexander Venables PROPRIETOR: Lucknam Park Hotels Ltd OPEN: all week 12.30 to 2, 7.30 to 9.30 MEALS: Set L £24.50, Set D £42.50 SERVICE: not inc CARDS: Access, Amex, Delta, Diners, Switch, Visa DETAILS: 85 seats. Private parties: 80 main room, 10 to 28 private rooms. Car park. Vegetarian meals. No children under 12. Jacket and tie. No smoking in dining-room. Wheelchair access (also WC). No music ACCOMMODATION: 42 rooms, all with bath/shower. TV. Phone. B&B £110 to £450. Children welcome. Baby facilities. Afternoon teas. Garden. Swimming- pool (*The Which? Hotel Guide*)

COLN ST ALDWYNS Gloucestershire map 2

GLOS 1996 PUB

▲ *New Inn*

NEW ENTRY

Coln St Aldwyns GL7 5AN COOKING **2**
TEL: (01285) 750651 COST £21–£34

The New Inn is not new at all: it dates from the days of Good Queen Bess, who decreed that 'there should be a coaching-inn within a day's travel of every major centre of population', as the inn's brochure states. Almost twenty monarchs later, this grey-stone building is still in the business of dispensing hospitality, although its visitors are now likely to be on the National Trust trail and the Cotswold sightseeing run. Owners Brian and Sandra-Anne Evans have given the interior a feel of stylish gentility. The beamed bar (where you can sample high-quality traditional English food and real ales) is pure country-pub. By contrast, the restaurant is a subtly lit room painted yellow, with wildlife prints on the walls, candles on the tables and fresh flowers everywhere. Chef Tony Robson-Burrell is a man on his way up if early reports are anything to go by. His fixed-price dinner menu is an enticing read, with ideas that are trendy but with results that are convincing and cohesive. Witness a starter of fillets of red mullet on a bed of minutely diced 'ratatouille-type vegetables' topped by a mound of crisp, shredded, deep-fried vegetables, the whole thing surrounded by a tomato vinaigrette; or else a mighty tournedos cooked blue as requested, gilded with a slice of foie gras, all resting on a rough pea purée wreathed with coarsely chopped morels. Otherwise, there might be a salad of grilled crottin cheese with endive, air-dried tomatoes and crostini, or a breast of chicken with pesto mash and beetroot sauce. Desserts are serious home-made offerings such as morello cherry muffin with cherry ice-cream, or apricot crème brûlée. The Anglo-French cheeseboard is also worth a considered look. The short, affordable wine list was being 'enhanced and expanded' as we went to press. House wines start at £8.75.

CHEF: Tony Robson-Burrell PROPRIETORS: Brian and Sandra-Anne Evans OPEN: Sun L 12 to 2.15, all week D 7.30 to 9.30 MEALS: Set L Sun £13.50, Set D £21; bar meals available SERVICE: not inc, card slips closed; 10% for parties of 6 or more CARDS: Access, Amex, Switch, Visa DETAILS: 40 seats. 15 tables outside. Private parties: 20 main room, 20 private room. Car park. Vegetarian meals. Children's helpings. Smart dress preferred. No cigars/ pipes in dining-room. Wheelchair access (also WC). No music ACCOMMODATION: 11 rooms, all with bath/shower. TV. Phone. B&B £45 to £90. Deposit: £40. Children welcome. Baby facilities. Afternoon teas. Garden

COLSTON BASSETT Nottinghamshire map 5

Martins Arms

NEW ENTRY

School Lane, Colston Bassett NG12 3FN
TEL: (01949) 81361 COOKING 1
off A46 Leicester to Newark road, 4m S of Bingham COST £24–£47

Colston Bassett's early reputation hinged on the fact that it was beset by the plague. Nowadays the village is synonymous with arguably the finest Stilton in the land. The Martins Arms was once a farmhouse owned by the squire in this estate village. Much of the action takes place in the bar, where muddy-booted walkers, farm managers and business types sup quietly on pints of real ale and sample dishes from a bar menu that mixes local pubbiness (ploughman's are served with Stilton and Melton Mowbray pork pie, for example) with more ambitious brasserie-type stuff. Formal meals are taken in the convivial, Victorian-style dining-room festooned with brass, velvet and polished wood. The short menu (in a folder complete with a potted history of the village) majors in modern-sounding dishes such as black pudding with leek and bacon ragoût, monkfish with asparagus and vermouth, and some wacky desserts including black coffee jelly with fromage frais, as well as beer pudding with banana toffee sauce. The list of 30 wines from Lay & Wheeler is a reliable choice with plenty of variety and sound drinking. House wine is £8.95.

CHEFS: Salvatore Inguanta, Ashley Hackett and Kevin Pole PROPRIETORS: Lynne Strafford Bryan and Salvatore Inguanta OPEN: all week L 12 to 1.45, Mon to Sat D 7 to 9.45 MEALS: alc D (main courses £13 to £17). Set L £15.95 SERVICE: not inc CARDS: none DETAILS: 30 seats. 9 tables outside. Private parties: 30 main room, 16 private room. Car park. Vegetarian meals. No children under 14. Smart dress preferred. No music

COOKHAM Berkshire map 3

Alfonso's

19–21 Station Hill Parade, Cookham SL6 9BR COOKING 1
TEL: (01628) 525775 COST £20–£36

This family-run restaurant is 'a bit of a surprise, hidden away in a parade of shops, but well worth a visit'. Reporters appreciate the congenial atmosphere, the warm service – always sensitive to the occasion – and the reasonably priced food. The menu doesn't change much, apart from the addition of a couple of 'specials' as occasion warrants, and beams a little Mediterranean sunshine on to some British staples. Lobster terrine is a perennial favourite, and other fish dishes include a soup flavoured with basil, orange and saffron, and steamed sea bass fillets with olive oil and tomatoes. 'The best pigeon I've ever tasted,' said one reporter of a roasted bird flavoured with thyme, while another praised the breast of chicken filled with a chicken mousse and served with a champagne beurre blanc. Puddings might include fruit tartlet, or savarin with kiwi-fruit on saffron cream. Around 40 wines, 10 of them Spanish, stay happily below £20. House French is £8.95.

CHEFS: Richard Manzano and Simon Hall PROPRIETORS: Mr and Mrs Alfonso Baena OPEN: Mon to Fri L 12.30 to 2, Mon to Sat D 7 to 10 (10.30 Fri and Sat) CLOSED: 2 weeks Aug, bank hols MEALS: Set L £12.50 to £16.50, Set D £16.50 SERVICE: not inc CARDS: Access, Amex, Diners, Visa DETAILS: 34 seats. Private parties: 34 main room. Car park. Vegetarian meals. No children under 8. Smart dress preferred. No pipes in dining-room. Wheelchair access. Music

COPPULL MOOR Lancashire map 8

Coppull Moor

311 Preston Road, Coppull Moor PR7 5DU COOKING 2
TEL: (01257) 792222 COST £24–£39

The setting – a former pub with two dining-rooms – is charming and improving, thanks to more paintings and ornaments. It is also going from strength to strength, according to one visitor, who reckons that four courses and coffee for £22.50 is exceptional value. There appears to be a feeling of greater confidence about the enterprise now that it has found its feet, which is expressed most convincingly in plans as we go to press to extend the kitchen to over twice its original size. The main thrust of the food, meanwhile, remains much as it was: to offer a wide variety of distinctive flavours, helped along by marinades and stuffings, and sauces of mustard, lime, curry or mint.

A May meal gives the idea. It began with lemon-scented clams and home-made pasta flavoured with dill, served with deep-fried salty salmon – 'an inspired combination' for the reporter – and was followed by celery and cauliflower soup with herb-scented rolls straight from the oven. Medallions of prime-quality beef were served with 'a magnificent array of imaginative vegetables' including 'superb' potatoes roasted in duck fat, beetroot in sherry, sweet lemon-scented carrots, and exemplary beans. And why settle for one dessert when you can have several? Ask for the assiette and you might end up with a plateful of peach crumble, 'superlative' lemon tart with 'wonderful pastry and a sharp lemon filling', good ice-cream and sticky toffee pudding. Sunday brunch is a leisurely affair. 'After they have eaten, many retire to the lounge with their tea or coffee and either have a little nap or finish off the papers,' writes Barry Rea. Wines, mostly under £20, are an odd mixture of very ordinary and very good, but 'customers may choose any wine to be served by the glass'.

CHEFS: Barry Rea and Mark Pilling PROPRIETOR: Barry Rea OPEN: Sun L 11.30 for 12 (one sitting), Tue to Sun D 8 for 8.30 (one sitting) MEALS: Set L £17.50, Set D Tue to Thur £22.50, Fri to Sat £26.50 SERVICE: none, card slips closed CARDS: Amex, Diners DETAILS: 26 seats. Private parties: 12 private room. Car park. Vegetarian meals. No children under 14 D. Smart dress preferred. No smoking in dining-room. Wheelchair access. Music

CORSCOMBE Dorset map 2

Fox Inn £ NEW ENTRY

Corscombe DT2 0NS
TEL/FAX: (01935) 891330 COOKING 1
off A356, 6m SE of Crewkerne COST £18–£32

'The Fox will always be a pub, not a restaurant,' insists landlord Martyn Lee, who has been custodian of this seventeenth-century village inn since 1988. This is a free house with all the right ingredients: a thatched roof, stone floors, a slate bar counter with casks of real ale lined up behind it, open fireplaces and roses round the door. It is also a 'rabbit warren' of a place with lots of little rooms, lavatories that are 'impossible to find without a guide' and cheery, smiling staff. The arrival of chef Will Longman from the Three Horseshoes, Powerstock (see entry, England round-ups), has given the cooking a boost. Soups, salads, and steaks are fixtures, but the best dishes are listed on the blackboard of specials. Fish from West Bay is the star of the show: fried squid with garlic and herb butter, 'superb' fresh turbot on a bed of fennel, and cod with crabmeat sauce. Other people may be tempted by mushroom pancakes, wild boar sausages with mash, or spicy Cajun duck casserole. Desserts include Italian-style ice-creams, although one reporter was completely won over by a gooey treacle tart. Apart from draught beers and East Chinnock Farmhouse cider, the Fox has a useful little wine list with some well-chosen bottles at down-to-earth prices. House wine is £8.

CHEF: Will Longman PROPRIETOR: Martyn Lee OPEN: all week 12 to 2.30, 7 to 9 (9.30 Fri and Sat) CLOSED: 25 Dec MEALS: alc (main courses £5 to £12) SERVICE: not inc CARDS: none DETAILS: 48 seats. 5 tables outside. Private parties: 20 main room, 20 private room. Car park. Vegetarian meals. Children welcome. No music

CORSE LAWN Gloucestershire map 5

▲ *Corse Lawn House Hotel*

Corse Lawn GL19 4LZ
TEL: (01452) 780771 FAX: (01452) 780840 COOKING 3
on B4211, 5m SW of Tewkesbury COST £26–£57

'An admirable part of Gloucestershire's eating scene,' maintained one, while another who had not eaten here for some time thought it 'better than ever'. Twelve acres of gardens and fields in peaceful, pretty countryside, emphasise the rural attraction. The pond in front of the Queen Anne house (a listed building) used to be a coach wash, now home to families of waterfowl that entertain you over a drink. Inside, pale colours, soft lighting and walls full of pictures maintain the feel of an old house in the country, as opposed to a country house.

More than one reporter has noted the dining-room's formal feel, despite this being a family-run place, though the upholstered chairs are 'very comfortable for protracted sitting'. Both lunch and dinner offer fixed-price meals and a *carte*, so there is plenty to go at, from hot crab sausage or crisp lobster pancake through to haunch of venison with cinnamon sauce and flageolets. Attempts to nail the style to a precise point on the Anglo-French continuum are doomed to failure, thanks to deft use of lemon grass and coriander here, chutneys and relishes there, along with home-smoked salmon or lamb with a lentil crust and colcannon potato. There is also a 'rough-hewn' quality about the food, from an amuse-bouche of 'two hefty quiches the size of jam tarts' to dark pink pigeon breast with a 'livery smooth taste'.

At around five options per course, vegetarian meals offer fair choice. French onion tart with hollandaise, wild mushroom pancake, and aubergine fritters have featured, and one carnivorous reporter was particularly impressed with the selection of vegetables at dinner. Puddings range from grilled brochette of tropical fruit with brandy butter, to 'exquisite' passion-fruit sorbet, and there are unpasteurised English and French cheeses. Occasional niggles have surfaced, for both food (beef that was promised 'rare and bloody' turning up well done) and service (slow). Those who take dinner, bed and breakfast reckon they get the best deal. Flexibility is increased by the more informal bistro, which serves less expensive food (all dishes priced at under £10), and offers the chance to eat either a snack or a full meal. The wine list is sensitive to the need for modest drinking, drawing on the New World and what the list describes as 'the little wines of France' for assistance. Nevertheless there is plenty of headroom in the classic regions for more expansive drinking, including some lovely old vintages. Half-bottles are generous, and house vin de pays is £9.95. CELLARMAN'S CHOICE: Haut-Médoc, Ch. Villegeorge 1980, £18.50; Rully, Ch. de Rully 1991, Antonin Rodet, £24.70.

CHEF: Baba Hine PROPRIETORS: the Hine family OPEN: all week; 12 to 2, 7 to 10 MEALS: alc (main courses £13 to £19). Set L £12.50 (2 courses) to £15.95, Set D £23.50; bistro meals available SERVICE: not inc, card slips closed CARDS: Access, Amex, Diners, Visa DETAILS: 50 seats. 10 tables outside. Private parties: 75 main room, 15 and 35 private rooms. Car park. Vegetarian meals. Children's helpings. Wheelchair access (also WC). No music ACCOMMODATION: 19 rooms, all with bath/shower. TV. Phone. B&B £65 to £110. Rooms for disabled. Children welcome. Baby facilities. Pets welcome. Afternoon teas. Garden. Swimming-pool (*The Which? Hotel Guide*)

CRANLEIGH Surrey map 3

La Barbe Encore

Freeland House, High Street, Cranleigh GU6 8AE COOKING 1
TEL: (01483) 273889 COST £28–£38

In this 'virtually unreconstructed tea-shoppe' (the words of one reporter), Jean-Pierre Bonnet flies the tricolour with great tenacity. The menus are in two languages, the walls are covered with Tin-Tin posters and, just in case the penny hasn't dropped, accordion ballads resound through the small, divided dining-room. This is a French restaurant.

The cooking is centred on classic preparations, interspersed with some cautious departures, such as pork medallions with *'currie chutney d'oignons'*. A pile of shredded pork confit strewn with good smoked bacon and surrounded by lentils is a great Gascony-style opener, but surprisingly muted flavours have been in evidence in a terrine of red mullet and aubergine. Although a main course of daube provençale was found a little dry by one reporter, roasted guinea-fowl with fennel and onion stuffing and served with a mound of 'accurately cooked' cabbage met with approval. Puddings may include pear Tatin, which, as so often, isn't really Tatin but a straight pear tart with acceptably thick slices of fruit, and an 'extremely mighty' mousse of fromage frais served with strawberries in red wine. Good strong coffee ends things on a high note. Service is very willing. A fairly priced wine list is predominantly French, of course, but it does dip a toe into the southern hemisphere. House wines are £9.25.

CHEF: Jean-Pierre Bonnet PROPRIETORS: Ann and Jean-Pierre Bonnet OPEN: Tue to Fri and Sun L 12 to 2, Tue to Sat D 7 to 10 MEALS: Set L £15.95 (2 courses), Set D £18.95 (2 courses) SERVICE: not inc, card slips closed CARDS: Access, Amex, Switch, Visa DETAILS: 60 seats. Private parties: 70 main room. Vegetarian meals. Children's helpings. Smart dress preferred. Music

CROSTHWAITE Cumbria map 8

▲ *Punch Bowl Inn* £

LAKELAND 1996 PUB

NEW ENTRY

Crosthwaite LA8 8HR
TEL: (01539) 568237
FAX: (01539) 568875

COOKING 1
COST £15–£26

Crosthwaite is strung out along a minor road at the upper end of the Lyth Valley, famous for its damsons, and the pub – for that is what it is – stands next to the church. Steven and Marjorie Doherty have upped sticks from the Brown Horse at Winster (in the *Guide* last year) to move 3.2 miles down the road and set up on their own. Rough white plaster walls, horse brasses and red velour bar stools remain resolutely in pub mode, but the food is way above grub standard. 'One of the best meals I have eaten for the price,' maintained one reporter. Steven Doherty might easily have fetched up at a swanky address charging the earth, but has chosen to follow the saintlier example of his hero Franco Taruschio at the Walnut Tree Inn (see entry, Llandewi Skirrid, Wales) and offer simply good food in informal surroundings.

Knives and forks are wrapped in paper napkins, and sandwiches are listed on a board behind the bar; there is no standing on ceremony. Mr Doherty's training at Le Gavroche has left vestigial traces along the lines of soufflé suissesse (which at £3.50 marginally undercuts the original), but jumbo prawns in a crispy batter with tartare sauce, and baked layers of aubergine and polenta topped with mozzarella, are his own idea. Fish is well bought and properly cooked – seared salmon with a topping of olives, herbs, tomatoes and garlic for instance – and puddings might include poached pear in vanilla syrup with raspberry cream, or chocolate truffle cake with coffee sauce. Drink Theakston, or a guest beer such as Charles Wells Bombardier, or try a bottle from the short list of sensibly chosen wines, mostly under £10.

CHEFS: Steven Doherty and Andrew Macpherson PROPRIETORS: Steven and Marjorie Doherty OPEN: all week 12 to 2, 6 to 9 CLOSED: 25 Dec MEALS: alc (main courses £5.50 to £7). Set L and D Sun £7.50 (2 courses) to £9.50 SERVICE: not inc, card slips closed CARDS: Access, Delta, Switch, Visa DETAILS: 80 seats. 4 tables outside. Private parties: 10 main room. Car park. Vegetarian meals. Children's helpings. Smart dress preferred. No smoking in 1 dining-room. Music ACCOMMODATION: 3 rooms, all with bath/shower. TV. B&B £25 to £40. Deposit: £10. Children welcome. Afternoon teas

CROYDE Devon map 1

▲ *Whiteleaf at Croyde*

Croyde EX33 1PN
TEL: (01271) 890266

COOKING 2
COST £20–£31

The Wallingtons have put the brake on. 'We are well into our 60s, and although we are not in any way incapacitated we would like not to work as hard in the future as we have in the past.' Bed and breakfast (a feast in itself) continues as before, but the week's other eating possibilities have been trimmed to four nights in season, and see what the winter brings: it is worth ringing to check, as plans were not finalised as we went to press. The 1930s boarding-house appearance can be deceptive. 'As one gets to know the place better, one finds there is more to it than meets the eye,' volunteered one reporter who had spotted some of the antiques. The lounge is spacious and comfortable, and the dining-room opens on to the garden.

The menu remains ambitiously long, with a dozen or so choices at each of the three courses, nicely balancing traditional and modern ideas. Dishes reflect the roving eye of an 'amateur' rather than an obsession with fashion, which is very welcome both in itself and for a change. Steak and kidney pie has a suet crust, smoked haddock rarebit comes with tomato salad, and local huss is stuffed with crabmeat in puff pastry. Pasta is a regular, perhaps with asparagus and smoked salmon, or with pesto, and the location is reflected in rack of Devon lamb, and in strawberries and clotted cream to finish. The cellar has been run down to half a dozen house wines (from £8) in view of retirement plans, but there may still be some bin-ends left.

CHEF: David Wallington PROPRIETORS: David and Florence Wallington OPEN: Thurs to Sun D only 7 to 9.30 CLOSED: Thur and Sun in winter; 2 weeks May, 2 weeks Sept or Oct, 23 Dec to Feb MEALS: alc (main courses £8.50 to £12) SERVICE: none, card slips closed CARDS: Access, Visa; £2.50 surcharge on credit card transactions DETAILS: 14 seats. 2 tables outside. Private parties: 20 main room. Car park. Vegetarian meals. Children's helpings. Smart dress preferred. No smoking in dining-room. No music ACCOMMODATION: 3 rooms, all with bath/shower. TV. Phone. B&B £35 to £62. Deposit: £25. Children welcome. Baby facilities. Pets welcome in bedrooms only. Garden (*The Which? Hotel Guide*)

CRUDWELL Wiltshire map 2

▲ *Crudwell Court*

Crudwell, nr Malmesbury SN16 9EP
TEL: (01666) 577194 FAX: (01666) 577853
on A429, 3m N of Malmesbury

COOKING 1*
COST £18–£43

The dining-room at the back of this seventeenth-century rectory has well-spaced tables, wicker chairs, stripped-wood shutters and a very English view of the formal garden and Cotswold-stone village church. The cooking remains on an even keel and fits in well with the relaxed country feel. Lunch is a small-choice two-course affair (three on Sundays) of perhaps soup, followed by grilled monkfish with wild mushrooms, while the set-dinner menu is more ambitious. The price for this varies according to choice of main course, and there is a hefty £6 supplement for Scotch smoked salmon.

Soft herring roes poached in wine with cream and tarragon, or fillet of sea trout with scallops and fennel, show a confidence with fish, while meats generally come with soothing sauces: watercress with baked guinea-fowl, or shallot and port for roast lamb. The vegetarian main-course option might be something like a crêpe basket filled with a vegetable and nut risotto. Puddings have included strawberry cheesecake, and pear poached in red wine with cinnamon macaroons; good filter coffee comes with petits fours. Wines are carefully chosen (by a Master of Wine) with a decent spread across Old and New Worlds, and prices are generally fair. House French or Australian is just under £10. CELLARMAN'S CHOICE: Haut-Médoc, Ch. Sénéjac 1990, £17; Crozes-Hermitage, Mule Blanche 1993, Jaboulet, £14.25.

CHEF: Chris Amor PROPRIETOR: Nick Bristow OPEN: all week 12 to 2, 7.30 to 9.45 MEALS: Set L Sun £11.50, Set L Mon to Sat £7.50 (2 courses), Set D all week £19.50 to £25.95 SERVICE: not inc, card slips closed CARDS: Access, Amex, Diners, Visa DETAILS: 80 seats. Private parties: 50 main room. Car park. Vegetarian meals. Children's helpings. Smart dress preferred. No smoking in dining-room. Wheelchair access (also WC). Music ACCOMMODATION: 15 rooms, all with bath/shower. TV. Phone. B&B £50 to £143. Children welcome. Baby facilities. Pets welcome in bedrooms only. Afternoon teas. Garden. Swimming-pool (*The Which? Hotel Guide*)

CUMNOR Oxfordshire map 2

Bear & Ragged Staff **NEW ENTRY**

Appleton Road, Cumnor OX2 9QH COOKING 1*
TEL: (01865) 862329 FAX: (01865) 865366 COST £23–£47

The Buchans have moved from the Fish at Sutton Courtenay (in last year's *Guide*) to this fourteenth-century stone-built farmhouse close to Oxford, bringing with them much of their repertoire, and their familiar choice between more or less formal eating-places: a flagstoned bar for light meals, or a split-level dining-room to the rear, with bare tables to eat off, and prints and some original watercolours to look at. The latter offers a fine old mix of Anglo-French food, including sauté foie gras with sweet-and-sour onions, a warm salad of black pudding with sauté potatoes and poached egg, and veal sweetbreads with rösti and mustard.

More straightforward fillet of lamb, roast breast of duck, and Aberdeen Angus beef take their place alongside fish from Cornwall: grilled sea bass or red mullet with horseradish fish-cakes, or a tail of sole with strips of smoked bacon in puff pastry with a caramelised sauce. A meal shortly after the new owners took over indicated a wobbly performance, with errors in timing recorded by a 'miffed' reporter who felt that prices were a bit high in the circumstances. 'Given their achievements at the Fish, the food must surely improve,' she concluded charitably, though a smooth chestnut parfait with slivers of prune on top went some way towards making amends. The pocket-sized wine list has a few serviceable bottles under £20, including house wine at £9.50.

'The lamb would have benefited from having had more of a social life, run around with some friends, developed a few bad habits and a bit more muscle.'
(On eating in London)

CHEFS: Bruce Buchan, Glenn Varley and Chris Dando PROPRIETORS: Bruce and Kay Buchan OPEN: all week 12 to 2.15, 7 to 10 MEALS: alc (main courses £12 to £15). Set L Sun £11.95 (2 courses) to £13.95 SERVICE: not inc, card slips closed CARDS: Access, Amex, Delta, Diners, Switch, Visa DETAILS: 65 seats. 6 tables outside. Private parties: 40 main room. Car park. Vegetarian meals. Children's helpings. Smart dress preferred. No cigars/pipes in dining-room. Music

DARLINGTON Co Durham map 10

Cottage Thai

94–96 Parkgate, Darlington DL1 1RX COOKING 1
TEL: (01325) 361717 COST £12–£35

Despite the somewhat unprepossessing frontage and location opposite the Civic Theatre ('good for evening trade,' says a reporter) and next to the magistrates' court ('good for lunchtime trade unless otherwise detained,' she adds), this is an engaging restaurant authentically decked out in Thai style. Wall-hangings, carved wooden screens, statues of deities and china elephants are dotted around the dining-room; rattan chairs are arranged around polished square tables, and food is eaten with gilded Thai cutlery. One area is partitioned off with low tables and cushions for formal banquets. Music plays in the background and smiling waitresses glide around.

The 70-dish menu stays with the reliable backbone of Thai cuisine ('nothing too daring for Darlington'), but everything is freshly prepared, flavours are clear and there is plenty of visual contrast. It 'felt like good home cooking', commented a lunch-time visitor, who enjoyed crispy spring rolls with sweet chilli sauce, kanoom cheep (dim-sum) with a garlicky soy sauce, and green chicken curry with a 'lively aromatic flavour' derived from lemon grass and Thai basil. Salads, stir-fries and noodle dishes are the principal back-ups. Set lunches are a cheap and cheerful introduction to the full menu. Drink Singha Thai beer or jasmine tea. House wine is £7.75.

CHEF/PROPRIETOR: Malinee Burachati OPEN: Mon to Sat 12 to 1.30, 6.30 to 10 CLOSED: 2 weeks mid-Aug MEALS: alc D (main courses £6.50 to £9). Set L £5.45 (2 courses) to £5.95, set D £14.95 to £23.95 SERVICE: not inc CARDS: Access, Amex, Switch, Visa DETAILS: 50 seats. Private parties: 60 main room. Vegetarian meals. Children's helpings. Smart dress preferred. Wheelchair access (also WC). Music

Victor's

84 Victoria Road, Darlington DL1 5JW COOKING 2*
TEL: (01325) 480818 COST £26–£32

Times are hard. The Robinsons have now scrapped lunches, except for bookings of six or more, because trade was so slack it was uneconomical to open. They have been here since 1984, doing all the right things, using locally produced and seasonal food, cooking it fresh and moving gently with the times. Reporters have found the excellent food good value; and in an effort to refute the 'somewhat scruffy' description in last year's *Guide*, the Robinsons have even redecorated the interior and laid new carpets. What more, one wonders, can a restaurant do?

Evening meals continue as before, with a monthly-changing menu of four courses, the second a no-choice soup or sorbet. The Anglo-French style tempts with smoked haddock fish-cakes or tomato and black-olive tartlet to begin, followed by grilled salmon with sweet-and-sour leeks, steak and Guinness pie, or roast stuffed pigs' kidneys on a potato pancake. Buying is adept and the cooking skilled. Simple-sounding dishes taste more interesting than they might appear, while flavours shine through in the more complex ones. Cheeses may include Swaledale, Ribblesdale, Cotherstone or 'Yorkshire feta'. Puddings are recited – chocolate refrigerator cake, for example – and the tiny wine list is as much a bargain as everything else. Amazingly, virtually all the wines on the list, apart from champagne, are available by the glass from £1.25 to £2.25.

CHEFS/PROPRIETORS: Peter and Jayne Robinson OPEN: Mon (bookings only) to Sat D only 7.30 to 10.30 CLOSED: 1 week Christmas MEALS: Set D £20 SERVICE: not inc, card slips closed CARDS: Access, Amex, Diners, Visa DETAILS: 30 seats. Private parties: 30 main room. Children welcome. Wheelchair access (2 steps). Music

DARTMOUTH Devon map 1

Billy Budd's

7 Foss Street, Dartmouth TQ6 9DW COOKING 1
TEL: (01803) 834842 COST £13–£34

This small bistro is in a pedestrianised street, with a few more-or-less nautical pictures to remind you that it is no more than a hundred yards from the water. At lunch Billy Budd's operates more like a café, an effect which the wooden tables and chairs do nothing to dispel. The short blackboard menu might include a homely leek and potato soup, an omelette, a salad, or perhaps a crisp-skinned roast chicken leg with garlic butter and 'circular chips'. The simple rustic appeal derives from food that is plainly served and which, in the evening, might take in roast duck with plum sauce, John Dory with pesto topping, or goujons of sole ('an old Billy Budd standard, but none the worse for that'). Wines are in similar vein, with simple drinking rarely breaking the £12 barrier. Australian house wine is £8.50.

CHEF/PROPRIETOR: Keith Belt OPEN: Tue to Sat (and bank hols) 12 to 2, 7.30 to 9.30 CLOSED: 1 week Nov, 4 weeks Jan to Feb MEALS: alc (main courses £3.50 to £13). Minimum £10.95 D SERVICE: not inc, card slips closed CARDS: Access, Switch, Visa DETAILS: 35 seats. Private parties: 15 main room. Vegetarian meals. No children under 11. Smart dress preferred. No cigars/pipes. Music

Carved Angel

2 South Embankment, Dartmouth TQ6 9BH COOKING 4
TEL: (01803) 832465 FAX: (01803) 835141 COST £37–£63

'We have always found it a treat to go there, and still do.' The Tudor frontage and harbour view continue to please, as does the seamless flow between 'immaculate and purposeful' open-plan kitchen and now smoke-free dining-room. The importance of this integral arrangement has not escaped reporters, aware of the direct line between quality of ingredients and end result. The restaurant's opinion is similar: it wants customers to 'see right into the heart, which promotes a proper attitude to food'. This is not a place for reverence and awe, but rather a place at which to appreciate that there are no secrets, no sleight of hand, just the simple transformation of first-class ingredients into dishes that generally delight. Staff work in both departments, so are well informed about the food.

The foundation is a long-standing reliance on carefully bought local foods, particularly fish, among them an array of sea bass, turbot, brill, shellfish, red mullet, octopus, shark and cuttlefish. One reporter was there 'when a large sack of scallops was delivered by the man who had just caught them', and an inspector enjoyed a dish of them 'just seared, almost translucent', on a bed of lentils and Indian spices, as well as salmon trout, with 'samphire providing just the right astringent contrast to the creamy champagne sauce'. Beef, lamb, venison, partridge, pigeon, teal and woodcock are also on the doorstep, as well as vegetables, herbs and soft fruit.

The straightforwardness of the food can leave some reporters wondering where the fireworks are. 'At these prices I expect something remarkable,' wrote one who dined on 'three little pieces of monkfish the size of postage stamps,' while some who come away unhappy about 'bland food' and 'haphazard service' are a little shocked that they have done so. 'To find fault with the Carved Angel is rather like questioning the Archbishop of Canterbury's commitment to the Church of England.' Quibbles about bread, chewy duck and pigeon, and slow service can take the edge off it all, but supporters are equally adamant about their enjoyment. What is remarkable for them is that food can be so simple and so good at the same time. In the end it may come down to price – £40 for two courses at dinner – although there is good value to be had, particularly at lunch-time, with two light courses for £15, and free meals for the under-fives. The inclusion of everything in the price – water, nibbles of smoked haddock beignets or baby bream kebabs, coffee, petits fours and service, and excepting only wine – is a great plus. It seems that we must either take the place on its own terms, or leave it.

The exemplary wine list is an enthusiast's collection of interesting bottles from a wide variety of sources at generally affordable prices; it keeps up to date, never stints on quality, and doesn't lose its head to ostentation. Aperitifs and digestifs by the glass are legion, and half a dozen house wines are £3 a glass. CELLARMAN'S CHOICE: Meursault 1982, Ampeau, £41.25; Cape Mentelle Shiraz 1991, Margaret River, W. Australia, £15.

CHEFS: Joyce Molyneux and Nick Coiley PROPRIETORS: Joyce Molyneux, Meriel Matthews, Nick Coiley and David Shepard OPEN: Tue to Sun L 12.30 to 2, Tue to Sat D 7.30 to 9.30 CLOSED: 6 weeks from 2 Jan MEALS: alc L (main courses £16 to £24.50). Set L Tue to Sat £15 (2 courses) to £29, Set L Sun £30, Set D £40 (2 courses) to £45 SERVICE: net prices, card slips closed CARDS: Delta, Switch DETAILS: 50 seats. Private parties: 40 main room, 12 and 20 private rooms. No smoking in dining-room. Children's helpings. Smart dress preferred. Wheelchair access. No music

---

'I am always impressed by peeled broad beans. I know it is something we should all do, as natural as cleaning our teeth, but how many of us can put our hands on our hearts and remember the last time we peeled a broad bean?' (On eating in London)

DEDHAM Essex map 6

▲ *Fountain House*

Dedham Hall, Brook Street, Dedham CO7 6AD COOKING 1
TEL: (01206) 323027 COST £23–£30

Overlooking the pond and gardens of Dedham Hall, this historic fifteenth-century cottage is a sheer delight, providing pleasures of all kinds for budding artists (painting courses are held frequently) and for tourists visiting Constable country. The Fountain House is valued for its cosy intimacy, relaxed mood and honest cooking. Wendy Sarton works to a weekly-changing fixed-price dinner menu that has yielded plenty of good things, including herrings in soured cream ('with just the right balance between sweetness and astringency'), vegetarian pancakes provençale, beef Wellington, and breaded pork fillet with tomato sauce. Desserts are a mixed bag: strawberry vacherin, and mandarin cheesecake have been more impressive than a 'panaché' of ice-creams which was no more than three balls of different kinds in a dish.

The wine list's cogent and sensible layout begins with Australian varietals and proceeds through California, Rhône rangers and some Italian jewels to France, where Alsace gets equal billing with Bordeaux. In short, this is a commendably unintimidating list, made especially friendly by some astonishingly good prices, and full of excitement too. Half-bottles are generous to a fault, and eight house wines don't break the £10 barriers.

CHEF: Wendy Sarton PROPRIETORS: James and Wendy Sarton OPEN: Sun L 12.30 to 2, Tue to Sat D 7 to 9.30 MEALS: Set L £16.50, Set D £18.50 SERVICE: not inc, card slips closed CARDS: Access, Delta, Switch, Visa DETAILS: 34 seats. Private parties: 50 main room. Car park. Vegetarian meals. Children's helpings. Smart dress preferred. No smoking in dining-room. Wheelchair access (1 step). Music ACCOMMODATION: 6 rooms, all with bath/shower. TV. B&B £34 to £57. Children welcome. Garden

▲ *Le Talbooth*

Gun Hill, Dedham CO7 6HP
TEL: (01206) 323150 FAX: (01206) 322309 COOKING 3
on B1029, off A12, 6m NE of Colchester COST £22–£57

It won't be long before Gerald Milsom clocks up a half-century at Le Talbooth. The riverside setting is admired by all; indeed, it would be difficult for the house to get any closer to the River Stour without actually being in it. Inside, the table-settings in the timbered dining-room are crisp and proper, the dining chairs upholstered and high-backed.

The kitchen has seen a fair degree of turnover lately, but it is a measure of the dedication with which the Talbooth is run that standards have not lurched. None the less, the arrival of Terry Barber in spring 1995 does seem to have lifted things noticeably. The fixed-price menus and daily roasts bolster a *carte* that is divided, invidiously you may feel, into 'traditional' and 'creative' sections. There is much to impress by eating creatively. Sympathetic cooking of shellfish is on show in a first course of lightly browned scallops with garlicky tiger prawn tails in the scallop shells, on a generous bacon salad. Timbale of crab and marinated salmon is a labour-intensive dish – a non-gelatinous crab mousse with thickly sliced fish, served with two sauces and a caviare garnish. Meat dishes are deeply classical: herb-crusted rack of lamb is carved in the dining-room, and comes with crisp vegetables provençale and a rosemary jus, while an accurately cooked piece of mature tournedos arrives in an intense madeira reduction, with tenderly sticky morsels of oxtail, soft artichoke and creamy mash. A dab hand at pastry is evident in a shortbread almond tart flavoured with Glayva, accompanied by brown-bread ice-cream, while banana ice-cream comes with sticky toffee pudding with butterscotch sauce. Coffee arrives with chocolate truffles. The overall impact of this style of country-house cooking is fairly weighty, but when brought off with such panache and using such good ingredients, it can exercise a powerful pull. Service, punctilious almost to a fault, enhances the whole experience.

The seriousness of the wine list bears witness to the proximity of Colchester specialists Lay & Wheeler. The wines don't come cheap, but those from the best Bordeaux châteaux and burgundy growers never do. Even in the New World, the pedigree of producers such as Simi in California, Henschke in Australia and Martinborough in New Zealand ensures that a premium must be paid. However, there are three pages of half-bottles (the third taking in just dessert wines) and a fairly priced house selection of great interest. Prices open at £9.95. CELLARMAN'S CHOICE: Henschke Riesling 1990, Eden Valley, Australia, £17.95; Montagne St Emilion, Ch. Montaiguillon 1990. £18.95

CHEF: Terry Barber PROPRIETOR: Gerald Milsom OPEN: all week 12 to 2 (5 Sun in winter), 7 to 9 (9.30 Sat) CLOSED: Sun D in winter MEALS: alc (main courses £12.50 to £19). Set L Mon to Fri £12.50 (2 courses) to £15, Set L Sun £19.95, Set D Mon to Sat £16.95 (2 courses) to £19.95 SERVICE: 10%, card slips closed CARDS: Access, Amex, Switch, Visa DETAILS: 80 seats. Private parties: 80 main room, 34 private room. Car park. Vegetarian meals. Children's helpings. Smart dress preferred. No cigars/pipes in dining-room. Music ACCOMMODATION: 10 rooms, all with bath/shower. TV. Phone. B&B £85 to £140. Rooms for disabled. Children welcome. Garden (*The Which? Hotel Guide*)

DENMEAD Hampshire map 2

Barnards

Hambledon Road, Denmead PO7 6NU
TEL: (01705) 257788 COOKING 2
on B2150, 2m NW of Waterlooville COST £21–£38

'Barnards provides very good food for an astonishingly good price,' reckoned one. The setting is a 'minimalist' interior with few frills – just bare brick walls softened by swags of yellow fabric over the windows – but tables are not crowded. Since last year the Barnards have added three lunchtime openings, offering the same food at the same price as dinner, as well as a brasserie lunch menu along the lines of a hot beef baguette and salad, baked potato with prawns, or minced beef pancakes with cheese sauce. One reporter enjoyed a fixed-price dinner of mussels in wine and cream sauce, sliced fillet steak, and a rich chocolate mousse. Throw in canapés, include petits fours in the price of coffee, and the 'excellent value' becomes apparent.

The *carte* changes every six weeks, and the style is simple food 'with a French influence', as David Barnard says. A reliance on dairy products reveals itself in a butter sauce (for scallops), a cheese sauce (for lobster) and a cream sauce (for duck), and in the ever-popular baked Swiss cheese soufflé. Salmon is locally smoked, lobster comes from Portsmouth, and vegetables are grown by friends of the family. A vegetarian option is always available. Lemon meringue tart, and profiteroles with a coffee-cream filling are among desserts. Thirty-odd straightforward round-the-world wines include house Duboeuf at £8.25.

CHEF: David Barnard PROPRIETORS: David and Sandie Barnard OPEN: Wed to Fri L 12 to 1.45, Tue to Sat D 7 to 9.45 CLOSED: 1 week Christmas, 2 weeks Aug MEALS: alc (main courses £10 to £16). Set L and D £14.50 SERVICE: none, card slips closed CARDS: Access, Amex, Delta, Diners, Switch, Visa DETAILS: 38 seats. Private parties: 34 main room, 34 private room. Vegetarian meals. Children's helpings. Smart dress preferred. No smoking in 1 dining-room. Music

DINTON Buckinghamshire map 3

La Chouette

Westlington Green, Dinton HP17 8UW
TEL/FAX: (01296) 747422 COOKING 1
off A418, 4m SW of Aylesbury COST £19–£59

The quiet village of Dinton is an unlikely setting for a Belgian restaurant. The former pub is decorated with pictures of birds, reflecting the owner's hobby, and goes in for a more studied kind of cooking than the mussels-and-chips formula. The one-man band sometimes surprises – M. Desmette appears to do both cooking and serving at times – and not everybody takes to his front-of-house style, nor to the service charge he awards himself, but the food is alive to the seasons. On a spring menu, morel mushrooms appeared on toast and in a sauce for duck breast, while asparagus came as a mousseline, as a partner for turbot, and cooked 'Flemish-style'. Although the menu may not give much away – 'a Belgian recipe' is a common description – M. Desmette fills in the gaps and makes sure his dishes are not burdened by excessive ingredients or unnecessary treatments. Puddings receive less attention than the rest. The £10 three-course no-choice lunch is promised 'in less than an hour', while the £20 meal includes two glasses of wine. More wines under £20 would suit the food better, although the Belgian beers are difficult to resist. House vin de pays is £10.

CHEF/PROPRIETOR: Frédéric Desmette OPEN: Sun to Fri L 12 to 2, (Sun only if booked 2 days in advance), Mon to Sat D 7 to 9 MEALS: alc (main courses £9.50 to £16.50). Set L £10 to £36, Set D £20 to £36 SERVICE: 12.5%, card slips closed CARDS: Access, Amex, Visa DETAILS: 40 seats. 4 tables outside. Private parties: 40 main room. Car park. Children's helpings. Smart dress preferred. No cigars/pipes in dining-room. Wheelchair access (2 steps; also WC). Music

DISS Norfolk map 6

▲ *Salisbury House* £✶

84 Victoria Road, Diss IP22 3JG COOKING 2
TEL/FAX: (01379) 644738 COST £19–£45

Sir John Betjeman described Diss as 'the perfect English market town', and this well-preserved Victorian house on the outskirts in trim, spacious grounds has the feel of a private home. Meals in the restaurant follow a fixed-price format according to how many courses you take, with a modest choice at each stage, except for the second, which is always a set fish dish. Barry Davies's style is British country-house with the very faintest of French intonations. Avocado mousse with tomato vinaigrette might crop up anywhere across the Channel, but poached chicken breast with scallops and mushrooms in a curry cream sauce is less likely to. The accuracy of the cooking is illustrated by a dish of boned skate with an expressive ginger butter sauce, and baked red mullet with a delicately spiced gazpacho purée. Sauce-making skill is demonstrated in the piquant reduction that comes with sliced fillet of lamb arranged around a timbale of leeks and mushrooms. Vegetables are plentiful and imaginatively treated.

Peaches poached in champagne with strawberry cream make a sumptuous summer dessert. A more elaborate construction around a citrus theme juxtaposes a slice of lemon tart with folded mini-crêpes spooned with an orange butter sauce and a lime parfait of sufficient bite to mitigate the sweetness of the other items. The 'attentive but relaxed' service copes well, and Barry Davies finds time to speak to everybody. The wine list makes a good attempt at covering as much territory as it can at a reasonable range of prices, all seemingly calculated to the nearest 5p. But exercise patience and hunt through, because there are some rewarding choices. House French is £8.55 (white) and £8.80 (red).

The bright, informal bistro serves such dishes as onion and coriander soup, salade niçoise with fresh tuna, and pan-fried fillet of lamb with a madeira jus, and has a wide selection of wines at under £12 a bottle.

CHEF: Barry Davies PROPRIETORS: Barry and Sue Davies OPEN: restaurant Tue to Sat D only 7.30 to 9.15; L by appointment; bistro Tue to Fri L 12.15 to 1.45, Tue to Sat D 7.15 to 9.15 CLOSED: 1 week Christmas, 2 weeks Aug MEALS: restaurant Set L and D £18.50 to £30; bistro alc (main courses £6 to £7) SERVICE: not inc CARDS: Access, Visa DETAILS: restaurant 20 seats, bistro 14. 2 tables outside. Private parties: 22 main room, 14 and 22 private rooms. Car park. Children's helpings. Smart dress preferred. No smoking in dining-rooms. Music ACCOMMODATION: 3 rooms, all with bath/shower. TV. B&B £39 to £70. Deposit: £10. Children welcome. Baby facilities. Garden (*The Which? Hotel Guide*)

Weaver's Wine Bar

Market Hill, Diss IP22 3JZ — COOKING 1
TEL: (01379) 642411 — COST £17–£32

William and Wilma Bavin continue to serve the denizens of Diss from their converted 500-year-old chapel at the top of Market Hill. The cream- and brown-painted house may look lopsided with age, but history is one of its assets. The interior is divided up by exposed timbers and brickwork, and big windows provide views of the action on the street. Tables are massive slabs of bare polished wood: 'Lucky me, to get the one with the pink Art Deco lamp,' observed a visitor. At lunch-time two good-value set menus operate, and the place packs with shoppers and business people tucking into pork satay, roast cod, and lamb steak with garlic and tarragon butter. Dinner is a more elaborate affair. Ingredients are excellent and the cooking is sure, although at an inspection meal there was probably one component too many on the plate. Superb medallions of beef, for example – sliced open to reveal the bloodiness within – come on a mound of chickpea and marscarpone 'pâté' with roasted peppers and chilli-spiked lentils.

Vegetarians have a choice of five or so main courses. The range of desserts might gain from something light among the crumbles, flans and pavlova, but cranberry and orange upside-down sponge with a muscatel syrup and custard has been pronounced a winner. The place is run with happy good humour, plenty of friendly chat and no standing on ceremony. The wine list, from Adnams and other sources, casts its net wide for value and quality. House wine is £8.45.

CHEF: William Bavin PROPRIETORS: William and Wilma Bavin OPEN: Mon to Fri L 12 to 1.30, Mon to Sat D 7 to 9 MEALS: alc D (main courses £9 to £12). Set L £7.95 (2 courses) to £9.95, Set D Mon to Fri £10 SERVICE: not inc, card slips closed CARDS: Access, Delta, Diners, Switch, Visa DETAILS: 80 seats. Private parties: 40 main room, 50 private room. Vegetarian meals. Children's helpings. Smart dress preferred. No smoking before 2 L, 9.30 D. Music

DORCHESTER Dorset map 2

Mock Turtle

34 High West Street, Dorchester DT1 1UP COOKING 1
TEL: (01305) 264011 COST £27–£38

The Hodder family's relaxed high-street restaurant continues to get the thumbs-up from locals and holidaymakers looking for good value and simply cooked fresh food. The two-course set lunches must be one of the best deals in the area: around £10 pays for 'tender' kidney and mushrooms en croûte, then a ragoût of sole, salmon, scallops and prawns with a plentiful helping of al dente vegetables. Fish from West Bay, Poole and Weymouth is the mainstay of the dinner menu: whole brill, Dover sole and lemon sole are simply shown the grill, while other species might be dressed up (monkfish is roasted with garlic butter, délices of salmon gets a dill and saffron sauce). Meat-eaters and vegetarians are accommodated with the likes of lamb cutlets in filo pastry, and tomato and leek tart. Puddings, such as warm pecan pie or spiced orange brûlée, are reckoned to be 'excellent'. Service is charming and friendly. Eldridge Pope – Dorchester's brewery-cum-wine merchant – is responsible for the well-spread, good-value wine list; beer-drinkers can also sample bottles of Royal Oak and Hardy Country Bitter. House wine is £8.50.

CHEF: Raymond Hodder PROPRIETORS: Raymond, Alan and Vivien Hodder OPEN: Tue to Fri L 12 to 2, Mon to Sat and Sun bank hols D 7 to 9.30 CLOSED: bank hol Mons D MEALS: Set L £10 (2 courses), Set D £16.50 (2 courses) to £19.50 SERVICE: not inc CARDS: Access, Delta, Switch, Visa DETAILS: 55 seats. Private parties: 20 main room. Vegetarian meals. Children's helpings. No cigars/pipes in dining-room. Wheelchair access (1 step; also WC). Music

'The next table had an intriguing mix of people, including one who looked like the Dalai Lama. He launched into a plate of foie gras in a most un-Buddhist fashion and was a joy to watch. If he was the Dalai Lama, I'm converting to Buddhism next week. He was also the only man in the restaurant who was not required to wear a tie, which my husband thought most unfair.' (On eating in London)

DORCHESTER Oxfordshire map 2

▲ *George Hotel* 🍷 NEW ENTRY

High Street, Dorchester OX10 7HH
TEL: (01865) 340404 FAX: (01865) 341620 **COOKING 1***
on A423, 4m NW of Wallingford **COST £30–£50**

The well-preserved eighteenth-century carriage standing outside announces the George, although the whitewashed building itself is a good 300 years older than that. Images of England's patron saint adorn the hotel, and the dining-room is a long glassed extension looking on to a water-garden. David Allison has cooked in and around Oxford for some years, and brings to the George a style of relaxed British modernism with French embellishments. Unlikely sounding assemblages turn out rather well, as witnessed by a man who began a meal with half an apple marinated in Muscadet, filled with a mousse of Stilton, walnuts and banana, and topped with a tarragon-flavoured sabayon. A more classic fish terrine uses salmon and sole of palpable quality with a lemon and herb butter. A certain excess in saucing has been noted on one or two occasions. Blackcurrant with venison needs careful handling if it is not to overwhelm, but the rosemary and honey jus with lamb has been 'enjoyably intense'. Multi-layering of flavours is let rip in dessert courses, demonstrated by a brandy-snap basket filled with mascarpone, bananas and Bailey's, and topped with vanilla ice-cream and chocolate sauce. Cheesecake of the day may be a better bet: the apricot version comes with fanned fresh fruit on an admirably light mousse. There is evidence enough in our reports to suggest that the George is on a sharp upward course. Not the least attraction is a wonderfully enthusiastic wine list. Predominantly French, it covers the regions in exhaustive detail, with a fine collection of clarets and much else besides at demonstrably fair prices. House wine is £7.75.

CHEF: David Allison PROPRIETOR: Neville and Griffin Ltd OPEN: all week D only 7 to 9.30 (9 Sun) MEALS: alc (main courses £11.50 to £18); bar L and D available SERVICE: not inc CARDS: Access, Amex, Delta, Diners, Switch, Visa DETAILS: 28 seats. 7 tables outside. Private parties: 40 main room. Car park. Vegetarian meals. No children under 9. Smart dress preferred. Music ACCOMMODATION: 18 rooms, all with bath/shower. TV. Phone. B&B £55 to £85. Rooms for disabled. Children welcome. Baby facilities. Pets welcome. Afternoon teas. Garden (*The Which? Hotel Guide*)

DORKING Surrey map 3

Partners West Street £✗

2–4 West Street, Dorking RH4 1BL **COOKING 2**
TEL: (01306) 882826 **COST £23–£45**

The sixteenth-century building is on two levels, in a narrow road just off the high street that is full of antique shops. The downstairs bar and dining-room are used mostly for parties, while upstairs the main dining-room is all creaking floors and beams, with a restless patterned carpet. The menus, however, have stopped fidgeting, and have settled into a simple format. Of the two, the fixed-price one offers limited choice, while the *carte* lists loads of dishes, but – in the evening – at a price.

Among the options are half a dozen (mostly fish) that may be taken either as a first or main course, including Cornish crab-cakes with braised vegetables, and lobster sausages. Meat dishes mentioned in despatches include pan-fried calf's liver with lots of spinach leaves, tender pork and braised lamb, although more flavour in sauces would help things along no end. Puddings can be nutty, including pecan pie, and layers of praline with poached plum. An otherwise standard wine list includes the local Denbies, a short but classy claret section, a dozen half-bottles; and house French is £10.95, or £2.50 a glass. Partners Brasserie (see entry, North Cheam) is under the same management, and owner Tim McEntire divides his time between them.

CHEF: Paul Boyland PROPRIETOR: Partners Restaurants plc OPEN: Sun to Fri L 12 to 2, Mon to Sat D 7 to 9.30 MEALS: alc (main courses £6 to £16). Set L £11.95, Set D £15 SERVICE: not inc CARDS: Access, Amex, Delta, Diners, Switch, Visa DETAILS: 45 seats. Private parties: 35 main room, 20 to 35 private rooms. Vegetarian meals. Children welcome. Smart dress preferred. No smoking in dining-room. Wheelchair access (1 step). Music. Air-conditioned

DORRINGTON Shropshire map 5

▲ *Country Friends*

Dorrington SY5 7JD
TEL: (01743) 718707 COOKING 3
on A49, 5m S of Shrewsbury COST £33–£45

Brick-built and bang on the A49, Country Friends could do with a bit of cheering up inside, perhaps a few flowers to relieve the numerous browns and make up for low-wattage lamps. But real wood burns in the fireplace, and all the effort obviously goes into the food. Twice-baked soufflés are as well received as they are presented: a Parmesan one with fillet of sole, or one with a crunchy top tasting faintly of celeriac and strongly of Gruyère.

A regular customer feels that the cooking 'lacks metropolitan panache' and 'seems to have settled into a predictable mould'. A kindlier interpretation might be that the style is pleasantly provincial, does not seek to rock any boats, and makes good use of Trelough duck from Hereford, local rabbit, pheasant, and 'superb' venison that comes with port sauce and Puy lentils. While not afraid to try new ideas, the kitchen does seem reluctant to give up well-tried favourites, as if it needs a shove to keep it moving. Nevertheless, the buying and cooking skills are sound enough. The set menus offer half a dozen items per course. 'Fish is always imaginatively presented,' according to one reporter, while another enjoyed three tightly rolled fillets of Dover sole – fresh, moist and firm – in a sandy-coloured mussel sauce made from fish stock and cream.

If there is a common thread to reports, it is the view that more distinctive flavouring might not go amiss, although puddings are exempt from this reproach, especially pineapple and hazelnut ice-cream on a blackcurrant coulis, and a dense lemon tart. Bread is good, vegetables meet with mixed success, and the food can get a bit pricey for some people's comfort at £21.50 for two courses, especially at lunch. The wine list is a selection from around the world, with variable mark-ups, a fair spread of styles and four house wines that include Louis Latour's Chardonnay de l'Ardèche at £10.50.

CHEF: Charles Whittaker PROPRIETORS: Charles and Pauline Whittaker OPEN: Tue to Sat 12 to 2 (plus L last Sun of each month), 7 to 9 (9.30 Sat) CLOSED: 2 weeks July MEALS: Set L and D £21.50 (2 courses) to £28.65 SERVICE: not inc CARDS: Access, Amex, Switch, Visa DETAILS: 40 seats. Private parties: 40 main room. Car park. Vegetarian meals. Children welcome. No smoking in dining-room. Wheelchair access. No music ACCOMMODATION: 3 rooms, 1 with bath/shower. D B&B £60 to £98. Children welcome. Garden

DREWSTEIGNTON Devon map 1

▲ *Hunts Tor House*

Drewsteignton EX6 6QW
TEL: (01647) 281228

COOKING 2*
COST £25–£33

The house is tucked away in the corner of a small square, easily missed even in such a small village as Drewsteignton. 'William Morris with touches of art nouveau' is what it's like inside, with Victorian-style net curtains ensuring a bit of privacy. 'Planning restrictions allow us to take only eight people,' write the Harrisons, who make a virtue of the problem by giving a level of personal service that few can match. They offer no printed menus, and no choice in the three-course meal (except to add cheese and make it four), but dislikes are discussed when booking, which is necessary. One couple who stipulated 'no onions' found this didn't present a problem.

There are no frills, but 'all the ingredients are honest and well prepared'. Fish and vegetable dishes have included fish soup with aïoli, skate with black butter, or red pepper mousse with sun-dried tomato vinaigrette. The Harrisons also use some organic produce, but don't shy away from boldness, whether in spicing, or in the simple heartiness of, say, guinea-fowl roasted with garlic and smoked bacon. Dishes may sound healthy until you get to the puddings, although even here they are not excessively rich, running to rice-pudding with fruit compote, for example, or iced lemon soufflé with orange brandy sauce. 'We came away feeling that we had eaten a most enjoyable meal with a simple, well-balanced menu that left us feeling satisfied but not bloated,' concluded one couple. The atmosphere may be 'more correct than jolly', although fellow diners can soon change that. There are no half-bottles (except for a champagne) on the short wine list, and nothing by the glass, but much of the list stays comfortably under £20.

CHEF: Sue Harrison PROPRIETORS: Sue and Chris Harrison OPEN: all week D only 7.30 (one sitting) CLOSED: end Oct to early Mar MEALS: Set D £17 to £19 SERVICE: not inc CARDS: none DETAILS: 8 seats. Private parties: 8 main room. No children under 10. Smart dress preferred. No smoking in dining-room. Music ACCOMMODATION: 4 rooms, all with bath/shower. TV in 3 rooms. B&B £27 to £65. Deposit: £10. Children welcome. Pets welcome in bedrooms only.

'The next table sent back the cheese selection because it had come straight from the fridge and was too cold. The customer suggested five seconds in the microwave. The waiter nodded, took it away, and returned with it a couple of minutes later.' (On eating in Lancashire)

DRYBROOK Gloucestershire map 5

Cider Press ✱

The Cross, Drybrook GL17 9EB COOKING 2
TEL: (01594) 544472 COST £23–£42

The nearby Forest of Dean is an Area of Outstanding Natural Beauty, which attracts its share of visitors. Those who make it to the Cider Press find a gently paced country restaurant with a strong line in fish 'which the chef brought out to show us in all its glory before choosing'. Mussels, 'heaps of them', are steamed with the customary bouillon of olive oil, garlic, lemon and parsley, while roast monkfish gets a no-nonsense Mediterranean dousing of garlic, tomatoes, olives and wine. 'The style of cooking has never consciously followed any particular school,' writes Bernadette Fitzpatrick, a position that few would challenge, given a repertoire that takes in sea bass cooked with ginger, spring onion and soy sauce in a foil parcel, as well as turbot with elderflower butter sauce.

Meats are free-range, with pheasant and venison putting in an appearance alongside fillet of beef. Vegetables are steamed, cheeses are mostly British, often local, and you get the whole board to help yourselves from. Double chocolate mousse is a perennial favourite among puddings, and steamed sponge with plums 'was accompanied by ice-cream, of all things, but it tasted fine'. The place is friendly and relaxed. The short wine list includes a few organic wines, and Bernadette Fitzpatrick tells us that she has made a conscious effort to expand the choice of wines under a tenner, – a policy which we would like to think might bring a blush to the cheeks of all those restaurants that cannot even find anything under £20. House wine is £7.95, or £1.60 a glass.

CHEF: Christopher Challener PROPRIETOR: Bernadette Fitzpatrick OPEN: Wed to Sat D only 7 to 10.30; Sun and Mon D and Wed to Sun L by arrangement only MEALS: alc (main courses £10 to £16) SERVICE: not inc CARDS: Access, Delta, Visa DETAILS: 24 seats. 2 tables outside. Private parties: 30 main room. Children welcome. Smart dress preferred. No smoking in dining-room. Wheelchair access (also WC). Music

EAST BOLDON Tyne & Wear map 10

Forsters

2 St Bedes, Station Road, East Boldon NE36 0LE
TEL: 0191-519 0929 COOKING 2
on main Newcastle to Sunderland road COST £21–£40

'My style of cooking is simply food that I would like to eat myself,' writes Barry Forster. 'A lot of my repertoire is tried and trusted dishes that work well – the main thing is consistency.' Such words of wisdom would do well to constitute a sort of oath for chef-restaurateurs, particularly when – as here – they run their kitchens unaided. Sited on a suburban shopping parade, Forsters may feel a trifle cramped when full, but nobody seems to mind. A *carte* that takes in half a dozen choices per course is accompanied by a set-price menu for all except Saturday nights. Benedict variations are played around the theme of a poached egg on a toasted muffin, sometimes with smoked salmon, avocado and hollandaise ('wonderful – highlight of the evening'), at others with grilled mushrooms and béarnaise. Moules marinière are given a Thai twist with curry spices, chilli and coconut milk. Traditional meat dishes include rack of lamb with a herb and mustard crust, venison with braised red cabbage and chestnuts, and Lunesdale duck with Grand Marnier sauce and crisply fried onions.

Desserts are crowd-pleasers: crème brûlée, sticky toffee pudding with dates and walnuts, or prune and brandy ice-cream, for example. Plates of Stilton and Cheddar are served with a glass of port. A man who was disappointed to hear Muzak and to find himself sitting behind a chain-smoker was still happy to praise the 'excellent food'. The wine list is not in order of country, age or price, but only colour, and it contains enough judiciously chosen bottles from all over to be worthy of a more coherent approach. Prices are sane, and there is a good scattering of half-bottles. House Duboeuf is £7.65.

CHEF: Barry Forster PROPRIETORS: Barry and Sue Forster OPEN: Tue to Sat D only 7 to 10 CLOSED: 1 week Christmas, 1 week May, 1 week Sept, bank hols MEALS: alc (main courses £12 to £14). Set D Tue to Fri £15 SERVICE: not inc CARDS: Access, Amex, Diners, Visa DETAILS: 28 seats. Private parties: 30 main room. Car park. Children's helpings. Smart dress preferred. No cigars/pipes in dining-room. Music

EASTBOURNE East Sussex map 3

▲ *Grand Hotel, Mirabelle*

Jevington Gardens, Eastbourne BN21 4EQ COOKING 3*
TEL: (01323) 410771 FAX: (01323) 412233 COST £25–£54

'You dine well, and in considerable comfort,' summed up one visitor to this swish seaside hotel. Make your way through miles of wide, softly carpeted corridor to the quiet, cool Mirabelle dining-room and admire its extravagant use of space. 'They like you to sit in the bar area first so that they can bring a tiny canapé – terribly fiddly to make and quite delicious – while you read the menu.' Then comes another morsel – a light vol-au-vent of smoked haddock in a creamy mustardy sauce, perhaps – before you begin to eat what you ordered. Keith Mitchell remains executive chef, joined since last year by Mark Jones as head chef, though the food shows every sign of consistency in both style and standard.

The cooking is classic, and sufficiently interesting without having recourse to anything fussy, taking in a clear oxtail consommé with parsley dumplings, sauté medallions of veal with caraway-scented cabbage and smoked bacon, and a hot apple and pear Tatin with brown bread ice-cream. The kitchen does not overreach itself, but sticks to what it does well, including, at one meal, a warm salad of intensely flavoured asparagus that was 'crisp without being chewy, as if roasted', with wild mushrooms and a creamed balsamic vinaigrette. Typically firm and confident control showed itself in a breast of just-pink densely textured guinea-fowl with a mousseline of leeks in a crisp, light pastry lattice with a well-judged madeira jus, and vegetables that included tiny purple mange-tout.

Clear and true flavours continue into desserts of sharply defined lemon tart, softly textured armagnac and praline mousse, and an orange sorbet in a tuile basket. Fixed-price dinners are 'stunning value, a real bargain', including, as they do, three well-planned courses and lots of incidentals. Real care is taken over these – 'I'd come here for the bread alone' – and the petits fours are rather better than the coffee itself. 'This is a generous place and it leaves one with a sense of well-being,' concluded an inspector. The wine list is under review as the *Guide* goes to press and is to be re-introduced in late 1995.

CHEFS: Keith Mitchell and Mark Jones PROPRIETOR: De Vere Hotels OPEN: Tue to Sat 12.30 to 2.30, 7 to 10 CLOSED: first 2 weeks Jan MEALS: alc (main courses £19.50 to £22). Set L £15.50 (2 courses) to £18.50, Set D £22.50 to £28.50. Minimum £15.50 L, £22.50 D SERVICE: none, card slips closed CARDS: Access, Amex, Diners, Visa DETAILS: 60 seats. Private parties: 50 main room. Car park. Vegetarian meals. Children's helpings. Smart dress preferred. No cigars/pipes in dining-room. Wheelchair access (also WC). Music. Air-conditioned ACCOMMODATION: 164 rooms, all with bath/shower. TV. Phone. B&B £91.50 to £170. Deposit: £50. Rooms for disabled. Children welcome. Pets welcome. Afternoon teas. Garden. Swimming-pool

EAST BUCKLAND Devon map 1

▲ *Lower Pitt*

East Buckland EX32 0TD
TEL/FAX: (01598) 760243 COOKING 1*
2m N of A361, 4m NW of South Molton COST £23–£33

Picture the scene: a sixteenth-century farmhouse festooned with honeysuckle in season, with old ploughs out front, a patio for al fresco drinks, and a sloping kitchen garden at the back where herbs and vegetables are grown organically. This is house and home to Jerome and Suzanne Lyons, the 'quiet, respectful' hosts who run Lower Pitt, on the fringes of Exmoor, as a beguiling restaurant-with-rooms. Inside there are two comfortable lounges (complete with log fires, even in May) and a narrow, whitewashed dining-room with a conservatory extension jutting out into the virtually wild garden. Jerome Lyons manages to lay his hands on plenty of West Country produce – local venison, for instance – plus organically reared Trelough duckling from Herefordshire, and he conjures up a variety of country-style dishes spiced with a few ethnic fire-bombs. Cornish hot-smoked salmon with grain mustard mayonnaise, herby chicken terrine, and game bourguignonne might share the billing with Kashmiri-style lamb, and stir-fried Thai prawns with cashew-nuts and lemon grass. Vegetables vary from day to day, cheeses are English, and the choice of desserts could include white chocolate terrine and tiramisù as well as sticky toffee and date pudding. Overnight guests have raved about the breakfasts. The wine list kicks off with around a dozen house selections (from £8.90), and the remainder is an affordable, wide-ranging slate backed up by a page of half-bottles.

CHEF: Suzanne Lyons PROPRIETORS: Jerome and Suzanne Lyons OPEN: Tue to Sat D only 7 to 9 (9.30 Sat) CLOSED: 25 Dec, 1 Jan MEALS: alc (main courses £9 to £10.50). Minimum £9 SERVICE: not inc, card slips closed CARDS: Access, Amex, Delta, Switch, Visa DETAILS: 32 seats. 3 tables outside. Private parties: 16 main room, 16 private room. Car park. Vegetarian meals. No children under 12. Smart dress preferred. No smoking in dining-room. No music ACCOMMODATION: 3 rooms, all with bath/shower. D,B&B £50 to £110. Deposit: 10%. No children under 12. Garden (*The Which? Hotel Guide*)

All entries in the Guide *are rewritten every year, not least because restaurant standards fluctuate. Don't rely on an out-of-date* Guide.

EAST GRINSTEAD West Sussex map 3

▲ *Gravetye Manor*

Vowels Lane, East Grinstead RH19 4LJ
TEL: (01342) 810567 FAX: (01342) 810080 COOKING 3
off B2028, 2m SW of East Grinstead COST £36–£86

Don't be put off if you seem to be getting nowhere. Gravetye is some way off the beaten track. The approach is spectacular, sweeping up to high views of the Weald, and down through heavily wooded lanes that twist and turn in the 1,000 acres of forest which encircle the Elizabethan manor house. It is an amalgam of mullioned windows, creepers and gables of different ages, brought together in grey-yellow stone, and surrounded by William Robinson's English Natural Garden, which one reporter considered 'integral to the experience' and well worth devoting an hour to admire. Inside, all is wood panelling, subdued light and a pervading smell of woodsmoke. Authentic melts seamlessly into repro, so that everything – from abundant flower arrangements and ample seats to drapes, thick rugs and stone floors – is of a piece. 'National Trust with knobs on' was one view.

Mark Raffan took over the kitchen from Stephen Morey (now at Homewood Park Hotel – see entry, Hinton Charterhouse) in June 1995, having previously worked at Gravetye before taking time out to cook for King Hussein of Jordan and the vegetarian Queen Noor. The kitchen's accomplishment is impressive, showing well at inspection in a fillet of cod cooked perfectly moist and flakey, with mussels, clams and fried potato ribbon: 'soundly put together, with flavours firmly correct.' Luxuries abound, of course, as befits the setting, and some dishes remain as before, including one of quail with black pudding, poached quail's eggs and fondant potato. Raffan's desire to impress, however, can result in gestures that divert attention from the main business. An individual lemon tart, for example, with crisp sweet pastry, an excellent filling, and a crisp brûlée top – brilliant by itself – was given an intensely flavoured raspberry sorbet and a net of spun sugar, both rather pointless in the context. There is no doubting the skill, though, and individual flavours are generally very good. Service eases the way in accomplished fashion. Staff are young, incredibly enthusiastic, and drawn from all over Europe. They combine warmth with light good humour, and are knowledgeable, efficient and responsive. One reporter felt that unforced enjoyment of this unique place transcended the high cost: VAT at 17.5% is added to the entire account. Wines are not cheap either, but quality is indisputably high and the choice vast, with vintages galore and plenty of half-bottles and magnums strewn about. Germany is treated as seriously as anywhere else outside France, and the preoccupation throughout is bankable certainty rather than novelty. House Chardonnay and Pinot Noir are £15.50. CELLARMAN'S CHOICE: Riesling d'Alsace 1991, Trimbach, £17; St-Estèphe, Ch. de Pez 1975, £46.

---

indicates a change of chef since last year's Guide.

denotes an outstanding wine cellar; *denotes a good wine list, worth travelling for.*

CHEF: Mark Raffan PROPRIETORS: the Herbert family OPEN: all week 12.30 to 2.30, 7.30 to 9.30 (10 Sat, 9 Sun) CLOSED: 25 Dec D exc for residents MEALS: alc (main courses £16 to £28 – plus VAT). Set L £22, Set L Sun £28, Set D £28 – all plus VAT SERVICE: inc plus VAT, card slips closed CARDS: Access, Switch, Visa DETAILS: 50 seats. Private parties: 8 main room, 20 private room. Car park. Vegetarian meals. Children's helpings. No children under 7. Smart dress preferred. No smoking in dining-room. Wheelchair access (male WC). No music ACCOMMODATION: 18 rooms, all with bath/shower. TV. Phone. B&B £109 to £223 – plus VAT. Deposit: 1 night's tariff. No children under 7 exc babies. Baby facilities. Garden. Fishing (*The Which? Hotel Guide*)

EAST WITTON North Yorkshire map 8

▲ *Blue Lion* £

NEW ENTRY

East Witton DL8 4SN
TEL: (01969) 624273 FAX: (01969) 624189
on A6108 Masham to Leyburn road, 2m SE of Middleham

COOKING 1
COST £17–£45

'When I was a lad and stopped off at a country pub in the Yorkshire Dales it was a choice between chicken and scampi in the basket,' mused a North Country reporter of long standing. Places such as the Blue Lion have changed all that. The setting may be a nineteenth-century coaching-inn – complete with flagstoned floors, settles and an open fireplace – but the kitchen lives in the modern world. Owners Paul and Helen Klein are the driving force, ably supported by staff who are pleasant, knowledgeable and genuinely interested in serving their customers.

The restaurant menu (dinners and Sunday lunch only) is written on blackboards and reads well: here you will find warm mussel and Stilton tart with saffron sauce, skate wings with creamed celeriac and a caper and almond butter sauce, and glazed lime tart with gin sabayon. Sometimes the cooking is up to the minute (warm salad of tender scallops with sun-dried tomatoes), sometimes classically robust (grilled lamb steak with a herb-spiked tomato sauce). Desserts might include 'delicious' raspberry crème brûlée, and hazelnut and chocolate tart with white chocolate ice-cream. Similarly adventurous stuff can also be eaten in the bar. The wine list is extensive, accurately described and offers sound selections from around the globe. Sixteen house wines (including 11 by the glass) start at £8.25.

CHEF: Chris Clarke PROPRIETORS: Paul and Helen Klein OPEN: restaurant Sun L 12 to 2.15, all week D 7 to 9.30, bar food all week 12 to 2.15, 7 to 9.30 MEALS: alc (main courses £7.50 to £15). Set L Sun £10.95 SERVICE: not inc CARDS: Access, Delta, Switch, Visa DETAILS: 80 seats. 8 tables outside. Private parties: 40 main room, 16 private room. Car park. Vegetarian meals. Children's helpings. Wheelchair access (also WC). No music ACCOMMODATION: 9 rooms, all with bath/shower. TV. Phone. B&B £39.50 to £70. Children welcome. Baby facilities. Pets welcome. Afternoon teas. Garden

---

'The wine waiter was totally charming and was one of those men who really have to be flirted with. Anything else would have been rude. I duly obliged.'
(On eating in London)

EDENBRIDGE Kent map 3

Honours Mill

87 High Street, Edenbridge TN8 5AU COOKING 3
TEL: (01732) 866757 COST £21–£45

Above the bar, the dining-room is simple, light and comfortable, a successful blend of ancient and modern. 'Lovely setting, charming building, willing and eager service' was how one reporter saw it. Meals are set-price only. The cheaper alternative at lunch-time and dinner offers more restricted choice and simpler fare, so a meal might consist of a salad of chicken livers with bacon and croûtons, oxtail casserole and the dessert of the day. At dinner half a bottle of house wine is included in the price of the cheaper meal. The view is that this option is the one to pick for value: 'admirable, well presented and cooked'. In any case the simpler dishes generally work better.

They really go to town on the more expensive dinner menu, throwing their heart and soul (as well as lobster, caviare and wild mushrooms) into it. A mixture of lobster and sole in a salmon mousse comes with a butter sauce, while a rich meaty stew is crammed with salt pork, oxtail, lambs' tongue and confit of duck. Rice pudding is served with roast apples and a caramel sauce. There is a feeling that the kitchen may be sailing close to the wind with this menu, given the price. 'A little too much for Edenbridge' is one view. Nevertheless, there is enthusiasm for snails in pastry, smoked trout and eel on a crêpe Parmentier, excellent veal kidneys and bisquit glacé. The largely French wine list has some good bottles and some high mark-ups, but all prices include service. House wine is £10.15, or £2.20 per glass.

CHEF: Martin Radmall PROPRIETORS: Neville, Duncan and Giles Goodhew OPEN: Tue to Fri and Sun L 12.15 to 2, Tue to Sat D 7.15 to 10 CLOSED: 2 weeks after Christmas MEALS: Set L Tue to Fri £15.50 to £32.75, Set L Sun £23.50, Set D Tue to Fri £26 (inc wine), Set D Tue to Sat £32.75 SERVICE: net prices CARDS: Access, Amex, Visa DETAILS: 38 seats. Private parties: 38 main room. Children's helpings. Smart dress preferred. No music

ELY Cambridgeshire map 6

Old Fire Engine House

25 St Mary's Street, Ely CB7 4ER COOKING 1
TEL: (01353) 662582 COST £24–£38

Few external clues tell you that this unassuming brick-built eighteenth-century townhouse a hop and a step from the cathedral is a restaurant. Terri Kindred's cooking is informed by research into old English recipes, particularly of the last century. Small modifications are made to the menu from one session to the next, and the choice of dishes is wide. There are always a couple of soups that use strong vegetable flavours like celeriac or Jerusalem artichoke. Grilled plaice comes with garlic and mushrooms, salmon with a fennel hollandaise. Black olives are used in a casserole of pigeon and bacon, while vegetarians may be tempted by the likes of mushroom and cashew-nut loaf with ratatouille. The proximity of a 'screeching toddler' could not interrupt one man's enjoyment of his beef braised in Guinness and port, while another party found themselves offered second helpings of both loin of pork and vegetables, and – unable to choose between apple pie and treacle tart – were unhesitatingly told, 'Have both'. Puddings are where the Englishness is most apparent, the syllabubs and burnt creams backed up by agreeably boozy sherry trifle. Readers praise the friendliness of service.

The wine list completely belies the modesty of the surroundings. Enthusiasts will find much to mull over, especially in the main French regions, where the choices are disarmingly fine and buttressed by bargain bin-ends. Exhaustive tasting notes will guide the beginner. House white from Bulgaria and red from Chile are £7.

CHEF: Terri Kindred PROPRIETORS: Ann Ford and Michael Jarman OPEN: all week L 12.30 to 2, Mon to Sun D 7.30 to 9 CLOSED: 2 weeks from 24 Dec, bank hols MEALS: alc (main courses £11 to £14) SERVICE: not inc CARDS: Access, Switch, Visa DETAILS: 36 seats. 8 tables outside. Private parties: 36 main room, 22 private room. Car park. Vegetarian meals. Children's helpings. No smoking in 1 dining-room. No music

EMSWORTH Hampshire map 2

Spencers

36 North Street, Emsworth PO10 7DG COOKING 2*
TEL: (01243) 372744 COST £21–£46

Gas lamps flicker in the upstairs dining-room at the Spencers' cosy Victorian place in Emsworth's main thoroughfare, and faded books on overhead shelves add to the feeling of quaint antiquity. A long, narrow room with partitioned booths on either side, it reminded one reporter of a railway carriage. Although he still cooks himself, Denis Spencer drafted in the talents of Gary Collins in late 1994 to head up the kitchen. The restlessly inventive tone of the food is maintained, with Mediterranean and Javanese influences adding interest to the Anglo-French core of the menus.

Wrapping items in various kinds of pastry is a favoured technique, and an inspector noted that while many dishes rely on cream sauces for their impact, great proficiency was evident throughout the meal. A filo money-bag of mussels with salmon mousse on a beurre blanc strewn with shredded carrot is brought off with convincing aplomb, everything cooked just so, even the filo 'appetisingly browned'. Cream sauces for main-course meats are augmented by madeira for lightly cooked strips of beef fillet, and mint and mustard for well-trimmed lamb cutlets. Two ways with potatoes (mashed and topped with sun-dried tomatoes, or sauté with much rosemary) have been the focus of the vegetable dishes.

Puddings can be 'nice but naughty': blackcurrant and orange mousse on a jelly base comes with two corresponding syrups, while both bitter and milk chocolate sauce accompany profiteroles filled with vanilla cream. Chocolate pralines are served with cafetière coffee. The 'well-dressed and well-trained waiting staff' contribute to what one regular says is always 'a jolly good evening'. The compact wine list is basically French, supplemented by a handful of Australians, a pair from South Africa and a lone German. Choices are sound rather than thrilling, but prices are commendably restrained, with even the more expensive items representing fair value. House Australian is £9.50.

CHEFS: Denis Spencer and Gary Collins PROPRIETORS: Denis and Lesley Spencer OPEN: Tue to Fri L 12 to 2, Tue to Sat D 7.30 to 10.30 CLOSED: 25 and 26 Dec MEALS: alc L (main courses £7.50 to £10.50). Set D £17.50 (2 courses) to £23.50 SERVICE: not inc, card slips closed CARDS: Access, Amex, Delta, Switch, Visa DETAILS: 44 seats. Private parties: 24 main room, 10 private room. Vegetarian meals. Children welcome. Smart dress preferred. No cigars/pipes until 10 at D. Music. Air-conditioned

EPWORTH Humberside map 9

Epworth Tap £

9–11 Market Place, Epworth DN9 1EU
TEL: (01427) 873333 COOKING 2
3m S of M180, junction 2 COST £19–£35

'My local watering-hole,' admits a Humberside reporter who adds that 'every village should have such a place.' The unpretentiousness of the Tap is infectious and praise seems to be shared equally between John Wynne's 'incredible' wine list and Helen Wynne's cooking. Most fish now comes up from Brixham, and cheeses (of perfect temperature and ripeness) are supplied by Iain Mellis of Edinburgh, a British farmhouse specialist. The Wynnes have also turned part of their lawn into a herb garden, which helps to give a fresh twist to the repertoire. High points from recent meals have included 'creamy' leek and potato soup, and daube of venison and pork with prunes and garlic (both served with exemplary vegetables). Otherwise, you might expect chicken breast with orange and lemon, pan-fried fillet of turbot, and rack of lamb with mint and honey, followed by crème brûlée or sticky toffee pudding.

Wines continue to delight and surprise for their generosity in range and value. Some older vintages – of claret, for example – are a snip, and it even makes financial sense to drink burgundy here. How often does that happen? 'Are people beginning to tire of New World Chardonnay and Sauvignon Blanc?' asks John Wynne. If so, there is no shortage of alternatives, although little from South Africa as yet. Advice, if you need it, is informed and genuine. House French starts at £7.95. CELLARMAN'S CHOICE Sancerre, La Grande Côte 1993, Cotat, £20; Côte Rôtie, Les Jumelles 1983, Jaboulet £22.

CHEF/PROPRIETOR: Helen Wynne OPEN: Wed to Sat D only 7.30 to 9.15 (9.30 Sat) CLOSED: 2 weeks after Christmas MEALS: alc (main courses £7.50 to £12.50). Set D £17.50 SERVICE: not inc, card slips closed CARDS: Access, Amex, Delta, Switch, Visa DETAILS: 65 seats. Private parties: 24 main room, 24 private room. Children's helpings. No children under 7. Smart dress preferred. No smoking in 1 dining-room. Music

ERPINGHAM Norfolk map 6

▲ *Ark*

The Street, Erpingham NR11 7QB
TEL: (01263) 761535 COOKING 2
on A140 Cromer road, 4m N of Aylsham COST £18–£37

'We went to Norfolk for the weekend thinking of crab and duck, but so did everyone else,' observed a family from Berkshire who eventually found a table at the Ark. 'As we were the last to arrive we had to have what was left. Given that I did not set out to have chicken livers, monkfish, cheese, and a pear, prune and armagnac tart, it all went down very well,' the writer concluded. Sheila and Mike Kidd's restaurant-with-rooms started life as a two-up, two-down flint cottage; it was a pub for over a hundred years, and the interior is still a maze of nooks and crannies on different levels. Supper at the Ark is based around a fixed-price menu (have two, three or four courses), and the style might be summed up as comfortingly British with French and Italian undercurrents and the occasional Far Eastern fling (Cantonese-style braised shin of beef, for example). Fish is from the east coast, vegetables are home grown and bread is baked in-house; the Kidds also find time to cure their own gravlax. Delving into their repertoire, you might be taken by pork, chicken liver and chard pâté with spiced damsons, duck with aubergines and fresh ginger, or a vegetarian stew of fennel, artichokes and mushrooms under a cream cheese crust. In addition to tarts of various kinds, the pudding list might also feature apple and redcurrant crumble, chocolate pithiviers, and almond meringue cake with strawberries. Not many restaurants manage to muster ten house wines at around £8, but the entire engaging round-the-world list here is well chosen and fairly priced. CELLARMAN'S CHOICE: Bourgogne Blanc 1993, Dom. Henri Clerc, £15; Crozes-Hermitage 1991, Cave de Tain L'Hermitage, £17.50.

CHEFS: Becky and Sheila Kidd PROPRIETORS: Sheila and Mike Kidd OPEN: Sun L 12.30 to 2, Tue to Sat D 7 to 9 (9.30 Sat) MEALS: Set L Sun £12.50, Set D £20.50. Minimum £17.50 D SERVICE: not inc CARDS: none DETAILS: 36 seats. Private parties: 36 main room, 8 and 16 private rooms. Car park. Vegetarian meals. No children under 7 D. Smart dress preferred. No smoking in dining-room. No music ACCOMMODATION: 3 rooms, 2 with bath/shower. TV. D,B&B £90 to £110 (double rooms). Deposit: £25. Rooms for disabled. Children welcome. Baby facilities. Pets welcome. Garden

EVERSHOT Dorset map 2

▲ *Summer Lodge*

Evershot DT2 0JR *NEW CHEF*

TEL: (01935) 83424 FAX: (01935) 83005 COST £17–£57

Last year's entry for Summer Lodge welcomed the arrival of Edward Denny in the kitchen and looked forward to a period of stability after previous upheavals. Alas, it was not to be. Denny's departure was followed by a brief interregnum with a chef from Cliveden, who was in turn succeeded by Donna Horlock. As we go to press Tim Ford has arrived from Homewood Park Hotel (see entry, Hinton Charterhouse), bringing him full circle, since he used to be a sous-chef here. Such frenetic activity is fortunately belied by the outward aspect of the Lodge, a smart dower house set in Hardyesque tranquillity, indeed boasting a sitting-room designed by the great man during a break from novel-writing.

The pattern is normally a set-price dinner of four or five courses, changing daily. Tim Ford is conscientiously seasonal and a skilled presenter. His style is squarely in the country-house idiom, often based on classic partnerships, and among his dishes might be oxtail consommé with horseradish dumplings, pigeon salad with black pudding and beetroot, and some that build impressive-looking towers of ingredients. Solicitous service – mostly by 'charming girls' – extends to the sugaring of cups for the cafetière coffee.

The wine list is a hugely exhaustive collection that casts its net democratically wide, in terms of both geography and pricing. Fine German Rieslings get the generous outing they deserve, Italian producers (including Maculan, Deltetto and Avignonesi) are of the best, California and Australia are well represented, and the French choices – particularly in Bordeaux – are superb. There are plenty of halves too. Prices open at £9.85 for a South African Gewurztraminer.

CHEF: Tim Ford PROPRIETORS: Nigel and Margaret Corbett OPEN: all week 12.30 to 1.45, 7.30 to 9 MEALS: Set L £9.75, Set D £32.50 SERVICE: not inc, card slips closed CARDS: Access, Amex, Diners, Switch, Visa DETAILS: 50 seats. 10 tables outside. Private parties: 50 main room, 6 and 20 private rooms. Car park. Vegetarian meals. Children's helpings. Smart dress preferred. No smoking while others are eating. Wheelchair access (also WC). No music ACCOMMODATION: 17 rooms, all with bath/shower. TV. Phone. B&B £100 to £225. Deposit: £50. Rooms for disabled. Children welcome. Pets welcome. Afternoon teas. Garden. Swimming-pool (*The Which? Hotel Guide*)

EVESHAM Hereford & Worcester map 5

▲ *Evesham Hotel, Cedar Restaurant* 🍷

Coopers Lane, off Waterside, Evesham WR11 6DA COOKING 1
TEL: (01386) 765566 FAX: (01386) 765443 COST £16–£39

One Thomas Watson made this half-timbered mansion out of an old farmhouse in the mid-sixteenth century, having bought it for roughly the price of today's dinner for two with wine. The Jenkinsons have raised idiosyncrasy to an art form over the last few years, both in the hotel décor – a What the Butler Saw machine will have been installed next to the swimming-pool by the time you read this – and in the menu-writing that will test fixed grins to the utmost. Cock-a-leekie with prunes, baked salmon on curried apple sauce with oyster mushrooms, or quails in cherry brandy with pink grapefruit beckon to the unwary, but there are more down-to-earth dishes too. Pancakes filled with spinach and ricotta worked well at a summer meal, as did the lunchtime sole that came as a 'useful boneless twirl' paired with samphire in a dill cream sauce. Cod baked in Parma ham and sauced with red wine and butter is the best sort of modern cooking. Among the customised desserts, such as Sue's Sweety Pie and Chocolate Oblivion, are some arresting ideas: an ice-cream of crème de cacao and calvados served with caramelised apple slices, or black coffee jelly on nutmeg sauce.

The drinks department is where all the stops are pulled out. This is the place to drink artichoke liqueur, Tunisian fig spirit and Wray's over-proof rum. The Jenkinsons have not stocked French or German wines since 1977. Although they list wines of every other provenance from Peru to the Republic of Ireland, the Australian, Californian and New Zealand sections are all outstanding. House wines from Concha y Toro in Chile are £9.60. CELLARMAN'S CHOICE: Castel Pujol Museo Carrau 1989, Uruguay, £14.50; Cricket Hill Chardonnay 1993, South Africa, £11.60.

CHEF: Ian Mann PROPRIETORS: the Jenkinson family OPEN: all week 12.30 to 2, 7 to 9.30 CLOSED: 25 and 26 Dec MEALS: alc (main courses £7 to £16.50) SERVICE: net prices, card slips closed CARDS: Access, Amex, Delta, Diners, Switch, Visa DETAILS: 55 seats. Private parties: 12 private room. Car park. Vegetarian meals. Children's helpings. No cigars/pipes in dining-room. No music ACCOMMODATION: 40 rooms, all with bath/shower. TV. Phone. B&B £54 to £84. Children welcome. Baby facilities. Pets welcome in bedrooms only. Afternoon teas. Garden. Swimming-pool (*The Which? Hotel Guide*)

EXETER Devon map 1

Lamb's

15 Lower North Street, Exeter EX4 3ET COOKING 1
TEL: (01392) 54269 FAX: (01392) 431145 COST £26–£44

The Aldridges say that their kitchen can be seen from part of the Victorian Iron Bridge nearby, sometimes drawing a little crowd. If the spectators thought of venturing in, they would find the experience rather more rewarding. Lamb's occupies two storeys of an eighteenth-century town house, the lower room done in muted greens with piscine cartoonery adding the right note of levity.

Carolyn Seath stepped up to head chef in the summer of 1994 and has brought a lighter touch to the inventive bistro-style cooking. A springtime meal opened with crab in filo with Thai seasonings a little strong on the chilli, but none the less enjoyable. 'Firm and fresh' monkfish made a good main course sauced with a red-pepper cream and pesto, while 'well-seasoned and succulent' wild boar from Exmoor came parcelled up in cabbage leaves and served with crisp onion rings and a concentrated jus. Vegetables may include courgettes smeared with strongly herbed tomato concassé and 'delicious' creamed white cabbage. Desserts show confident technique in 'faultless' caramelised lemon tart with crème anglaise, and a well-rendered mango parfait with a passion-fruit coulis. Home-made petits fours include fruit-flavoured truffles and crystallised orange peel. The reliably friendly service is full of enthusiasm, and the willingness to experiment with good ingredients makes Lamb's extremely welcome in Exeter. Wines offer a brisk international selection for under £20, and there's a slightly more expensive set of 'Classic Wines' at reasonable mark-ups with a good spread of halves. California house wines from Fetzer are £9.

CHEF: Carolyn Seath PROPRIETORS: Ian and Alison Aldridge OPEN: Tue to Fri L 12 to 2, Tue to Sat D 6 to 10 CLOSED: 2 weeks from 24 Dec MEALS: alc (main courses £9.50 to £15.50). Set L £10, Set D Tue to Thur £17 SERVICE: not inc CARDS: Access, Amex, Delta, Switch, Visa DETAILS: 42 seats. 2 tables outside. Private parties: 26 main room, 26 private room. Vegetarian meals. Children welcome. Smart dress preferred. No smoking in 1 dining-room. Wheelchair access. Music

▲ *St Olaves Court Hotel*

Mary Arches Street, Exeter EX4 3AZ COOKING 2*
TEL: (01392) 217736 FAX: (01392) 413054 COST £23–£50

'We sat in the garden under a mulberry tree,' one chap reminisced. 'What could be better on a hot summer's day?' The setting was the walled garden of St Olaves Court, within pealing distance of the cathedral. Some interior redecoration has taken place, with colours picked out to enhance the building's Georgian charm. A triumvirate of chefs runs the stoves, and the co-operative approach clearly pays dividends. In the last couple of years extraneous frills in the cooking have been sheared away, a wider trend that is nearly always to be welcomed.

The *carte* offers half a dozen choices per course, and there's a separate set menu – offered at both lunch-time and in the evening – of lighter dishes that may include pesto-crusted cod with chive cream, or roast chicken breast on ribbon vegetables and a tomato and basil sauce. The full menu offers the likes of venison mousse baked in breadcrumbs with a celeriac purée and morel essence, sauté scallops with fish tortellini and ginger butter, or roast lamb with its liver and sweetbreads on a madeira and tarragon jus. A lasagne of chicken livers made a good opener to a summer lunch, and the finishing touch of summer pudding with clotted cream has also been praised. Rosemary ice-cream with peach coulis is a novel idea for dessert. Despite the odd hiccup, St Olaves remains firmly established on a high plateau, the 'excellent, friendly' service playing its own role efficiently too. The soundly chosen, mainly French wine list offers concise selections at manageable mark-ups. Devon's Sharpham Vineyard is accorded a look-in, and there may well be some attractive bin-ends. House French starts at £10.50.

CHEFS: Jason Horn, John Winstanley and Jos Davey PROPRIETORS: Raymond and Ute Wyatt, and Peter Collier OPEN: Mon to Fri L 12 to 2, all week D 6.30 to 9.30 CLOSED: 1 to 7 Jan MEALS: alc (main courses £12.50 to £17.50). Set L and D £10.50 (2 courses) to £13.50 SERVICE: not inc, card slips closed CARDS: Access, Amex, Delta, Diners, Switch, Visa DETAILS: 63 seats. 5 tables outside. Private parties: 45 main room, 8 to 18 private rooms. Car park. Vegetarian meals. Children's helpings. Smart dress preferred. No cigars/pipes in dining-room. Wheelchair access (3 steps). No music ACCOMMODATION: 15 rooms, all with bath/shower. TV. Phone. B&B £65 to £90. Rooms for disabled. Children welcome. Baby facilities. Pets welcome in bedrooms only. Afternoon teas. Garden (*The Which? Hotel Guide*)

EYTON Hereford & Worcester map 5

▲ *Marsh Country Hotel*

Eyton HR6 0AG
TEL: (01568) 613952
off B4361, 2m NW of Leominster

COOKING 1
COST £30–£36

Martin and Jacqueline Gilleland have done a most thoughtful and sympathetic job in restoring this lovely medieval house. They have preserved most of the beams, stone floors and original trappings without turning it into a twee period piece; the garden is a delight at any time of the year, with its stream, lily pond and herbs. The atmosphere is quiet, and one reporter noted 'a tendency to converse in whispered tones', although Martin is a pleasant and chatty host. Jacqueline's cooking is defined by artful presentation, only occasionally at the expense of flavour. There is much to enjoy: wild mushrooms in filo pastry and cream had 'a good tang', while smoked trout mousse wrapped in smoked salmon, rare fillet of beef with a 'not-too-overwhelming' Stilton sauce, and Normandy pear tart have all received praise. Ancillaries include 'commendable' home-baked bread, decent cheeses and first-rate coffee with home-made chocolates. Eight wines (including local Bodenham Reichensteiner) are served

by the glass and the list is a well-spread selection with halves aplenty. House wines start at £10.

CHEF: Jacqueline Gilleland PROPRIETORS: Martin and Jacqueline Gilleland OPEN: Sun L 12.30 to 2, all week D 7.30 to 9 CLOSED: first 3 weeks Jan MEALS: Set L Sun £19.95, Set D £19.95 SERVICE: not inc, card slips closed CARDS: Access, Amex, Diners, Switch, Visa DETAILS: 24 seats. Private parties: 24 main room. Car park. Vegetarian meals. No children under 12. Smart dress preferred. No smoking in dining-room. No music ACCOMMODATION: 4 rooms, all with bath/shower. TV. Phone. B&B £80 to £110. Deposit: £25 per person. No children under 12 (except babies). Baby facilities. Garden (*The Which? Hotel Guide*)

FAVERSHAM Kent map 3

Read's

Painter's Forstal, Faversham ME13 0EE
TEL: (01795) 535344 FAX: (01795) 591200 COOKING 3*
on Eastling road, 2m S of Faversham COST £25–£53

On the outside the building may be a 'featureless 1960s block with blank brickwork punched through with even blanker picture windows', but the quality and skill of the cooking certainly command respect. David Pitchford has acquired an enviable reputation over the years; what people tend to admire about his cooking is its deceptive simplicity. Anyone who can elicit gasps for a dish of lightly cooked sea scallops with a salad of waxy potatoes clearly has a way with food. 'Such intense flavours' was the verdict on this dish: 'stylish, superbly executed, and so simple'. True, the potatoes were helped along with a splash of white truffle oil, but it is the 'simple' that rings most powerfully in that commendation. Most dishes on the set-price menus have that same aura of classic ideas either untampered with or reworked only minimally. Another first course of red mullet fillets on a saffron risotto offered 'spanking-fresh' fish and a gentle note of saffron. Steak au poivre is given a twist with cracked peppercorns, chopped bacon and a slice of black pudding. Otherwise, oriental flavourings may be used to productive effect, as in king prawns in thin batter with a chilli dip, or roast salmon on stir-fried vegetables and plum sauce. 'Outstanding' crème brûlée and pistachio parfait, are supplemented by a selection of miniature desserts and a chocoholic's platter on 'plates the size of tea-trays'. An inspector thought the bread 'excellent', the coffee only 'OK'. Add 'polite and attentive' service, and it begins to be clear why Read's is a winner.

The wine list too is a triumph, its confident touch evident in virtually every region it ventures into. Outside France the shrift may be fairly short, but the selections are representative and good. A prefatory listing of over 40 bottles under £20 is a laudable way of easing the unwary into the large selection. Halves are numerous too. House wines from France and Australia are £12. CELLARMAN'S CHOICE: Chablis *premier cru* Vaillons 1992, Fèvre, £21; Hamilton Russell Pinot Noir 1992, Hermanus, South Africa, £16.

CHEF: David Pitchford PROPRIETORS: David and Rona Pitchford OPEN: Tue to Sat 12 to 2, 7 to 10 MEALS: Set L £15.50, Set D £25 to £32 SERVICE: not inc, card slips closed CARDS: Access, Amex, Diners, Switch, Visa DETAILS: 40 seats. 3 tables outside. Private parties: 60 main room, 20 private room. Car park. Vegetarian meals. Children's helpings. Smart dress preferred. Wheelchair access (1 step). Music

FELSTED Essex map 3

Rumbles Cottage

Braintree Road, Felsted CM6 3DJ
TEL: (01371) 820996 COOKING 1
on B1417, between A130 and A120 COST £18–£36

Joy Hadley is a great experimenter: anyone who wants to test her latest inventions is free to do so, although it's wise to ask for what she calls the 'guinea-pig menu' when booking a table. Visitors who intend to run the gastro-gauntlet in her 400-year-old cottage might have to give a verdict on salad of king prawns with couscous, tomatoes and mange-tout, or breast of duck with walnut stuffing (using both fresh and pickled nuts) and apricot gravy. Convention can be turned on its head: desserts suddenly become savoury starters (tomato and pepper summer pudding, or smoked prawn egg custard, for example), while puddings may include halva and rose-water ice-cream, honey and thyme sorbet, or iced blueberry soufflé. Joy absorbs, borrows and adapts ideas from almost anywhere: imam bayaldi, tandoori chicken salad, poached salmon with kiwi-fruit sauce, and medallions of pork with mango sauce are examples from just one menu. Sunday lunch has been a great success, even on a hot afternoon 'not exactly conducive to gastronomic high points'. The wine list is a perfectly adequate collection of around 50 bins culled from reliable producers. House wines start at £7.95.

CHEF/PROPRIETOR: E. Joy Hadley OPEN: Sun L 12 to 2, Tue to Sat D 7 to 9 MEALS: alc D (main courses £11 to £12.50). Set L Sun £12.50, Set D Fri £10, Tue to Thur £12.50 SERVICE: not inc, card slips closed CARDS: Access, Visa DETAILS: 50 seats. Private parties: 22 main room, 8 to 22 private rooms. Vegetarian meals. Children welcome. Wheelchair access (1 step). No music

FOLKESTONE Kent map 3

Paul's

2A Bouverie Road West, Folkestone CT20 2RX COOKING 1
TEL: (01303) 259697 FAX: (01303) 226647 COST £23–£29

Paul and Penny Hagger have been here for 21 years and have watched the business grow until the long dining-room now seats 120. After all this time they seem to know what customers want. Freshness is remarked upon, and prices are reasonable: first courses and puddings mostly £2.95, main courses £9.95, with a £4.95 lunch offer of any starter plus vegetables and coffee. When that includes smoked trout fillets in horseradish butter, or hot duck liver and onion quiche served with a light sherry cream, the deal sounds attractive.

Dairy products have featured strongly for a long time. Dishes such as dressed crab baked with cream and Brie, or bream with a wine and cream sauce, can seem rather old-fashioned these days, but lighter and spicier sauces now make their mark as well, as in a chicken and lemon bratwurst in a tomato, chilli and garlic sauce. Vegetarian options are always available and have included sweet potato, eddoes, tomato, chilli and leeks baked together under a wholemeal crumble. Sweets are from the trolley. The wine list goes out of its way to find drinkable bottles below £20, although not all producers or vintages are credited.

It is well worth exploring the supplementary list of clarets (many from the 1983 vintage) at giveaway prices. House French is £7.95.

CHEFS: Penny and Paul Hagger, Eddie Pendlebury, Teresa Smith and Sue Clark PROPRIETORS: Paul and Penny Hagger OPEN: all week 12 to 2.30, 7 to 9.30 (10 Sat) CLOSED: Christmas MEALS: alc (main courses £10). SERVICE: not inc CARDS: Access, Visa DETAILS: 120 seats. Private parties: 80 main room, 40 private room. Car park at D. Vegetarian meals. Children's helpings. Wheelchair access (2 steps). No music

FORTON Lancashire map 8

El Nido £

Whinney Brow Lane, Forton PR3 0AE
TEL: (01524) 791254 COOKING 1
on A6, 1m S of M6 junction 33 COST £17–£41

The exterior suggests that this might have been a pub or a farmhouse at one time, but pictures of bullfights and country scenes remind you that El Nido is 'very heavily into the Spanish influence'. 'A good, competent restaurant with the added attraction of a bit of Continental glamour' just about sums it up. Tracey and René Mollinga have instituted a few changes of late: lunch has been abandoned (apart from Sundays), a good-value 'early-bird' menu is now available between 6 and 7pm (apart from Saturdays), and a batch of light, brasserie-style dishes, such as taco hotpot, Chinese beef, and pasta with mussels and pesto, has been added to the *carte*. Spain still has its say with tortilla, king prawns in garlic sauce, gazpacho, paella, and conejo Santa Cruz (rabbit cooked on the bone with wine, vegetables, chorizo, garlic and herbs). The list of home-made desserts is recited at the table. Twenty or so Spanish wines are the best and most quaffable options on the list. House Rioja is £8.25.

CHEFS: Lloyd Kenny and Tony Pool PROPRIETORS: René and Tracey Mollinga OPEN: Sun L 12 to 2, Tue to Sun D 6 to 10 MEALS: alc D (main courses £6 to £15). Set L Sun £8.95, Set D Tue to Fri and Sun 6 to 7 £9.95, Tue to Sat £15.50 SERVICE: not inc CARDS: Access, Delta, Switch, Visa DETAILS: 55 seats. 3 tables outside. Private parties: 45 main room. Car park. Vegetarian meals. Children's helpings. Smart dress preferred. Wheelchair access. Music. Air-conditioned

FOWEY Cornwall map 1

Food for Thought

Town Quay, Fowey PL23 1AT COOKING 2
TEL: (01726) 832221 FAX: (01726) 832060 COST £23–£48

It says a great deal about Martin and Caroline Billingsley's commitment and enthusiasm that they have managed to stay in business for more than 17 years despite capricious seasonal custom, without letting standards slip. The converted coastguard's cottage on the quay, with frilled curtains and pink carpets, goes in for fresh fish in a big way. Reporters speak highly of home-cured gravlax and firm-fleshed sea bass with orange butter sauce, but the undoubted stars are the local scallops. Whether they are pan-fried with garlic butter and herbs or paired with monkfish and mussels in saffron hollandaise, the results are 'brilliant'. Meat-lovers have also been well satisfied with an 'outstanding' warm salad of local pigeon with pine-kernels, and 'perfectly seasoned' roast rack of lamb with garden herbs. Green vegetables are served 'hot and crunchy', while sticky toffee pudding and 'dense' chocolate marquise with brandied prunes highlight the professionalism of the cooking. The wine list favours France, although it does make excursions to other parts of the globe. Prices are very fair, with house wines starting at £7.50.

CHEF: Martin Billingsley PROPRIETORS: Martin and Caroline Billingsley OPEN: Mon to Sat D only 7 to 9 CLOSED: Jan and Feb MEALS: alc (main courses £10 to £20). Set D £14.95 SERVICE: not inc CARDS: Access, Switch, Visa DETAILS: 38 seats. Private parties: 30 main room. Children's helpings. Smart dress preferred. Wheelchair access. No music

FRAMPTON ON SEVERN Gloucestershire map 2

Saverys

The Green, Frampton on Severn GL2 7EA
TEL: (01452) 740077 COOKING 2*
2½m NW of M5 junction 13 COST £32–£38

The story so far: one of the three peacocks that strut the green outside Saverys has had a toe amputated after a mishap with a fishing-line. Patricia Carpenter, taking pity on him, feeds him peanuts from the front door of the restaurant, where he has now become a regular customer, turning up without a booking and ordering lunch in a voluble screech. Meanwhile, the swans have had babies, eight of them, all doing well. And Saverys has been refurbished. *The Archers* has nothing on Frampton.

This 'idyllically English' village has the longest green in the country, not a bad prospect for a restaurant of the calibre of Saverys. Now in its tenth year, the restaurant enjoys an adamantly loyal bed-rock of regular customers who come back for some of the area's more imaginative cooking. Dinner may begin with a pistachio-flecked terrine of minced pork and pieces of chicken, the slice wrapped not in the usual bacon but in Parma ham, and garnished with blobs of boldly spiced mango and lime relish. Main-course rack of lamb, retaining 'just enough fat to give flavour', is roasted in a piece and carved into cutlets, accompanied by mounds of broad beans and a smooth buttery sauce spiked with horseradish (not the most convincing support for lamb but good enough in itself). A cornucopia of vegetables may include 'luscious and classical' dauphinois with much garlic.

Summer pudding – which 'smelled delicious and tasted just as good' – is a portion cut from a large one so as to minimise the amount of bread in the serving, crammed with whole berries and a 'gorgeously intense' raspberry coulis enlivened with cassis. With a scoop of excellent hand-made vanilla ice-cream, it constituted for one reporter a pudding made in heaven. Wines are a small but resourceful selection, the whites casting their geographical net wider than the reds. Reasonable prices begin with house wines at £8.50.

CHEFS: John Savery and Nicky Plumb PROPRIETORS: Patricia Carpenter and John Savery OPEN: Tue to Sat D only 7.15 to 9.15; L by arrangement CLOSED: 2 weeks Feb MEALS: Set D £22.95 SERVICE: not inc, card slips closed CARDS: Access, Delta, Switch, Visa DETAILS: 28 seats. Private parties: 30 main room. No children under 14. Smart dress preferred. No pipes in dining-room. Wheelchair access (1 step). Music

FRESSINGFIELD Suffolk map 6

Fox and Goose

Fressingfield IP21 5PB
TEL: (01379) 586247 FAX: (01379) 588107 COOKING 3
on B1116, 3½m S of Harleston COST £23–£49

A group who returned to the Fox and Goose after 30 years found the 'cosy, warm, welcoming' ambience seemingly uneroded by time, but a glance at the bar menu alone confirms the passing of the years. Sun-dried tomato tapénade on toast? There wasn't much of that about in the 1960s. Serious culinary intention is signalled on the menu by acknowledgements to the great (Simon Hopkinson) and the late, great (Jane Grigson), among others.

Ruth Watson and her team may safely be considered one of the pioneers of eclectic cooking, so whether you fancy Peking crispy duck with hoisin and the trimmings, rabbit stewed with beans and chorizo, or just potted Morecambe Bay shrimps and a slice or two of toast, the kitchen will not flinch. Some dishes, such as a starter of battered cod goujons with a chilli and garlic dip, are reminiscent of superior fast food, but the lightness and accuracy of flavour impress. Griddled squid with a mound of coriander hummus containing some whole chickpeas for texture has 'good robust flavours, the squid tasting of charcoal and a hint of chilli heat'. Sunday lunchers may pre-order roast beef sirloin with Yorkshire, horseradish and veg, and will find a pint of hand-pumped Adnams bitter or a glass of house red thrown in. Sticky toffee pudding and poire Belle Hélène are joined on the pudding list by 'iced lemon crystals' with lemon liqueur, and baked banana with orange syrup and cardamom ice-cream. Service is 'efficient and pleasant'.

The wine list is an exhaustive catalogue of super-fine vintages that will leave the devotee at a loss to know where to start. The easily baffled are thoughtfully given a sheet of affordable highlights, and Ruth and David Watson state on the main list that they will replace anything from that selection if it doesn't suit when tasted. The house selection starts at around £9.50. A fine run of vintage ports may tempt those with time to relax after eating.

CHEFS: Ruth Watson, Brendan Ansbro, James Perry and Max Dougal PROPRIETOR: Ruth Watson OPEN: Wed to Sun 12 to 2.15, 7 to 9.30 CLOSED: 2 weeks Christmas, 2 weeks mid-July MEALS: alc (main courses £9 to £13.50). Set L Wed to Sat £9.95 (2 courses) and £13.50 SERVICE: not inc DETAILS: 50 seats. 4 tables outside. Private parties: 24 main room, 24 private room. Car park. Vegetarian meals. Children's helpings. No cigars/pipes in dining-room. No music

FROME Somerset map 2

Croft's

21 Fromefield, Frome BA11 2HE
TEL: (01373) 472149 COOKING 1*
on B3090, ½m NE of Frome COST £18–£28

Frome boasts more listed buildings than any other town in Somerset, and Margaret Graham's modest restaurant is in one of them. The mood inside is that of an informal, relaxed bistro, with lots of beams, cottagey trappings, and well-spaced, country-style tables and chairs. 'Cooks are inevitably eclectic, magpie figures,' writes the lady of the house, and her short, fixed-price menus read like the gleanings of an enthusiastic collector: among the starters, filo parcels of lamb with aubergine purée line up alongside wild mushroom ravioli with thyme and bacon sauce. Main courses may include what the menu calls a 'green curry' of chicken breast with coconut and lime, or pan-fried lambs' liver and kidneys with madeira sauce. Desserts are the likes of brown sugar meringue and banana pancake with apricot sauce. The value for money is remarkable, and prices on the short wine list are hard to beat. House wine is £7.95.

CHEF/PROPRIETOR: Margaret Graham OPEN: Sun L 12 to 2, Wed to Sat D 7 to 9.45 (10 Sat) MEALS: Set L £10.50, Set D £14.95 SERVICE: not inc, card slips closed CARDS: Access, Visa DETAILS: 28 seats. Private parties: 20 main room, 12 private room. Vegetarian meals. Children's helpings. Smart dress preferred. No smoking in dining-room. No music

GATESHEAD Tyne & Wear map 10

▲ *Eslington Villa Hotel*

8 Station Road, Low Fell, Gateshead NE9 6DR
TEL: 0191-487 6017 and 420 0666
FAX: 0191-420 0667 COOKING 1*
on A6127, 2m S of Newcastle city centre COST £20–£47

A Victorian hotel in landscaped grounds with a conservatory dining-room facing a sweeping wooded lawn where rabbits gambol and even the odd fox sidles by: yes, this is Gateshead. Eslington Villa is justifiably proud of its pastoral aspect, and has put up swagged flowery curtains to press the point. Ian Lowrey cooks the kind of food the surroundings demand, a gentle rendition of modern British themes with nothing startling lying in wait, although sole fillets topped with coconut might raise an eyebrow. Cheese beignets with fresh tomato coulis are a favourite first course, or there may be tender pigeon slices in a salad dressed with raspberry vinaigrette. Fried sardines with garlic butter, and braised ham knuckle with butter-beans suggest that there is no inhibition about offering robust country dishes. More conventional grilled chicken breast with a cream sauce containing oyster mushrooms scores highly for flavour and texture, and lambs' liver is tender and intelligently offset with a restrained sauce of Meaux mustard. White chocolate truffle cake and sticky toffee pudding crop up regularly on dessert lists, but there is good pastry-work too in an apple tart with almond crème anglaise. Service pitches the mood just right. House wines from France and Australia are £8.95.

CHEF: Ian Lowrey PROPRIETORS: Nick and Melanie Tulip OPEN: Sun to Fri L 12 to 2, Mon to Sat D 6.30 to 10 MEALS: alc (main courses £16.50 to £17.50). Set L £9.95 (2 courses) to £13.95, Set D Mon to Fri £14.95 (2 courses) to £18.95 SERVICE: not inc CARDS: Access, Amex, Visa DETAILS: 60 seats. 3 tables outside. Private parties: 45 main room, 18 private room. Car park. Vegetarian meals. Children's helpings. Smart dress preferred. No smoking in dining-room. Wheelchair access. Music ACCOMMODATION: 12 rooms, all with bath/shower. TV. Phone. B&B £30 to £74.50. Rooms for disabled. Children welcome. Afternoon teas. Garden (*The Which? Hotel Guide*)

GEDNEY DYKE Lincolnshire map 6

Chequers

Main Street, Gedney Dyke PE12 0AJ
TEL/FAX: (01406) 362666
just off B1359, from Gedney roundabout on A17, 3m E of Holbeach
COOKING 1
COST £17–£33

Judith and Rob Marshall's Fenland free house continues to draw customers from far and wide. This is a pub where food is taken seriously. Fresh fish holds pride of place on the restaurant menu, and the kitchen rings the changes each day with specials such as sea bass with lime and ginger. There are roasts (local lamb with leek purée on madeira sauce, for instance) plus grills and South African bobotie, followed by treacle tart, or hazelnut and pear meringue. If you call in during the summer you might also be able to sample Lincolnshire chine with grain mustard dressing. Judith Marshall is keen on festive menus and special events: for example, 'healthy eating' (Caesar salad, then Cajun chicken with fresh fruit salsa) or 'hearty appetite' (Lincolnshire pork sausages with apples and potato mash, followed by bread-and-butter pudding with whisky sauce). The Chequers has a good line-up of real ales, plus a 50-strong list of quality wines supplied by Adnams. House wine is £7.25.

CHEFS: Judith Marshall and Sarah Tindale PROPRIETORS: Robert and Judith Marshall OPEN: all week 12 to 1.45, 7 to 9 (9.30 Fri and Sat, 8.30 Sun Apr to Oct) CLOSED: 25 and 26 Dec, D 1 Jan MEALS: alc (main courses £6 to £13) SERVICE: not inc, card slips closed CARDS: Access, Amex, Delta, Diners, Switch, Visa DETAILS: 54 seats. 4 tables outside. Private parties: 30 main room, 22 private room. Car park. Vegetarian meals. Children's helpings. No smoking in 1 dining-room. Music

GILLINGHAM Dorset map 2

▲ *Stock Hill*

Stock Hill, Gillingham SP8 5NR
TEL: (01747) 823626 FAX: (01747) 825628
off B3081, 1½m W of Gillingham
COOKING 2*
COST £27–£44

The Hausers have clocked up ten years in this late-Victorian mansion, adding value as they go. The latest development on their 11 acres is to re-stock an old lake with trout and carp, providing a less energetic sporting alternative to the croquet lawn and tennis court. The smart and comfortable house bears a strongly personal decorative stamp, with an inter-continental array of collectables from bronze Egyptian cats to, most striking of all, a couple of prancing Indian wooden horses.

The cooking bears an individual imprint too, due in part to Peter Hauser's Austrian background. Although most noticeable among desserts, it is also betrayed in smaller ways by the paprika-flavoured crème fraîche that accompanies home-cured herring fillet, or the frankfurter stuffing that goes into roast breast of guinea-fowl. A summer delicacy not to be missed, apparently, is sweetwater crayfish, served simply with a cucumber and dill salad. Choice on the four-course menu is generous, with a soup – cream of lovage, perhaps –

arriving after the first, and game and offal are not neglected. Given the Viennese penchant for cakes and desserts, it should come as no surprise to find them elbowing out the more usual country-house repertoire of sticky British ones – hence kugelhopf, Malakofftorte, and erdbeer stanitzel. The wine list offers good hunting almost everywhere, not least in the French provinces. A handful from Austria and the New World stay commendably under £20, while house Côtes de Roussillon and Muscadet are £13.50.

CHEFS: Peter Hauser and Lorna Connor PROPRIETORS: Peter and Nita Hauser OPEN: Tue to Fri and Sun L 12.30 to 1.45 (1.30 Sun), all week D 7.30 to 8.45 (8.30 Sun) MEALS: Set L £20, Set D £30 SERVICE: none, card slips closed CARDS: Access, Amex, Diners, Visa DETAILS: 24 seats. 2 tables outside. Private parties: 24 main room, 12 private room. Car park. Vegetarian meals. No children under 7. Smart dress preferred. No smoking in dining-room. Wheelchair access. No music ACCOMMODATION: 9 rooms, all with bath/shower. TV. Phone. D,B&B £105 to £240. Deposit: £60. No children under 7. Afternoon teas. Garden. Fishing (*The Which? Hotel Guide*)

GOLCAR West Yorkshire map 8

Weavers Shed

Knowl Road, Golcar HD7 4AN
TEL/FAX: (01484) 654284 COOKING 2
on B6111, 2m W of Huddersfield from A62 COST £17–£41

Golcar isn't the easiest place in the world to locate (keep your eyes peeled for the signs on the B6111), but once there you cannot miss the Weavers Shed. As its name suggests, this was originally a woollen mill, and owner Stephen Jackson has worked diligently to preserve as much of its original character as possible. Flagstones and wooden beams are everywhere. Heading up service is Shirley Bramald, who has been working here for as long as anyone can remember; the place would be very different without her. At lunch-time, there is an excellent-value set menu that deals in hearty stuff such as Yorkshire pudding with gravy, warm salad of black pudding, liver and bacon, and chicken in thyme sauce. Dinner is a more ambitious *carte,* with ideas lifted from some fashionable big-city addresses (framed menus from eminent establishments are dotted around the bar).

Tiger prawns in a frothy mushroom 'soup' sprinkled with cayenne is a well-handled first course; likewise pan-fried scallops heaped on to roughly chopped tomatoes and onions spiced with a curry-flavoured stock. Meaty main courses are well timed and pink: topside of venison with herb and butter sauce, and boned loin of lamb stuffed with apricots and pistachios have met with approval. The owners support local suppliers (their butcher is a hundred yards down the road) and reckon they will be 85 per cent self-sufficient in fruit, herbs and vegetables by the end of 1995. Desserts, such as cinnamon and apple crumble or sticky toffee pudding, rely on substance for effect. Perfectly ripe cheeses are served the traditional way with a wedge of fruity Old Peculier cake. The wine list is a carefully assembled selection of around 70 bins with representatives from most major countries. House wine is £8.95.

CHEFS: Ian McGunnigle, Stephen Jackson and Robert Jones PROPRIETOR: Stephen Jackson OPEN: Tue to Fri L 12 to 2, Tue to Sat D 7 to 10 CLOSED: first 2 weeks Jan, 2 weeks July to Aug, bank hols MEALS: alc D (main courses £10 to £14.50). Set L £10.95 SERVICE: not inc CARDS: Access, Amex, Switch, Visa DETAILS: 65 seats. Private parties: 40 main room, 30 private room. Car park. Vegetarian meals. Children's helpings. Smart dress preferred. Wheelchair access (2 steps; also WC). Music

---

GORING Oxfordshire map 2

Leatherne Bottel

Goring RG8 0HS
TEL: (01491) 872667 COOKING **2***
on B4009 out of Goring, 5m S of Wallingford COST **£32–£50**

Beware imitations! Some pubs in the area bear names with more than a passing resemblance to this, although it should soon become apparent whether or not you have hit the right one. It must have one of the most idyllic locations on the Thames and manages to be both rustic and elegant at the same time. Everybody feels relaxed, thanks partly to staff who are 'universally friendly and helpful'. Keith Read and Annie Bonnet put their garden to good use. 'Nasturtiums go into pasta and jelly, chive and clover flowers into butter, ginger and coriander into bread rolls, while sea bass gets roasted with lemon leaves.' Such liberal use of herbs produces strikingly aromatic dishes, while saucing, often no more than a trickle of olive oil, plain or flavoured, brings a freshness and lightness to the food. The accent is on clean flavours.

A single *carte* lists everything, with freedom to choose anything from a single course upwards, and lunch and dinner prices are consequently no different. This can either make lunch appear expensive or dinner cheap, depending on your point of view. Rarely does the cooking overstep the mark into excess or caricature, but makes the best of Far Eastern flavourings in a main course fish soup with miso, ginger, nori seaweed and ground green horseradish, or rare roast breast of local duck with black beans, ginger, spring onions and coriander. Surprisingly for this style of cooking, vegetarian items are few and far between. The short and youthful wine list is strangely bereft of half-bottles, although there is an offer to 'open any wine up to £20 in value for a half-bottle'. House French is £10.50.

CHEFS: Keith Read and Clive O'Conner PROPRIETORS: Keith Read and Annie Bonnet OPEN: all week L 12.15 to 2 (2.30 Sat and Sun), D 7.15 to 9 (9.30 Sat, 8.30 Sun) CLOSED: 25 Dec SERVICE: not inc, card slips closed CARDS: Access, Amex, Visa DETAILS: 60 seats. 25 tables outside. Private parties: 20 main room, 12 private room. Car park. Smart dress preferred. Wheelchair access. No music. Air-conditioned

---

'There are four happy looking Siamese cats around the large house, and I imagine that there is a very long queue of cats applying for a job here.' **(On eating in Devon)**

GRASMERE Cumbria map 8

▲ *Michael's Nook*

Grasmere LA22 9RP COOKING 3*
TEL: (01539) 435496 FAX: (01539) 435645 COST £38–£73

The grand old house is set back from the main road (turn off the A591 by the Swan pub at the northern end of Grasmere) and full of ancient wooden and antique furniture. The Giffords stick to the general Lakeland dinner formula – all guests arrive at around 7.30 and eat five courses – but the food is more inventive and interesting than most. Drinks and a first wave of nibbles are served (as indeed is everything) with a great degree of charm, and a log fire burns in the grate. A second hors d'oeuvre arrives at the bare wooden tables in the 'overwhelmingly red' and candlelit dining-room, on one evening an egg-cup full of pigeon consommé with a 'weeny dollop of sensationally good pigeon tartare' on a tiny triangle of melba toast.

Of the five courses the second is soup, the last cheese. There is ample choice, although the menu picks out a recommended selection which, while perfectly good, may lack the dash of other options. (The alternative 'gourmet menu' is six courses for an extra £10.) Ideas, techniques and ingredients are pleasingly varied, from braised boneless oxtail topped with foie gras, to a pan-fried smoked haddock cake with a herb sauce, to pink slices of rump of lamb on a bed of lentils, served with sweetbreads, gamey-tasting kidney, and a slice of tongue wrapped in a square of pasta. The cooking is accomplished and modern, but with a sound classic foundation. Kevin Mangeolles also makes good use of vegetables, in a turnip tarte Tatin with foie gras and shallot sauce, for example, or a Jerusalem artichoke mousse on a saffron and chive sauce. Occasional oddities surface, such as a summer pudding in April, but generally the food both convinces and delights. Soufflés come in for praise, particularly one with prunes and armagnac with an ice-cream of the same ingredients. The wine list has good depth in Bordeaux, some decent burgundies, some 1976 Germans, a lively New World section, and a very good choice of half-bottles. House French is around £12. CELLARMAN'S CHOICE: Fumé Blanc 'Valley Oaks' 1994, Fetzer Vineyards, California, £11.25; Cape Mentelle Zinfandel 1992, Margaret River, W. Australia, £16.15.

CHEF: Kevin Mangeolles PROPRIETORS: Mr and Mrs R.S.E. Gifford OPEN: all week 12.30 to 1, 7.30 to 8.15 MEALS: Set L £28.50, Set D £39.50 to £49.50 SERVICE: not inc CARDS: Access, Amex, Diners, Visa DETAILS: 50 seats. Private parties: 40 main room, 40 private room. Car park. Vegetarian meals. No children under 7. Jacket and tie. No smoking in dining-room. Wheelchair access (1 step). No music ACCOMMODATION: 14 rooms, all with bath/shower. TV. Phone. D,B&B £125 to £280. Deposit: £50. Children by arrangement. Afternoon teas (booking essential). Garden. Fishing

---

'Most of the rest of the clientele were American, at the larger tables in the centre of the room, while the smaller tables around the edge were English. It felt a bit like Custer's Last Stand.' (On eating in Avon)

▲ *White Moss House*

Rydal Water, Grasmere LA22 9SE

TEL: (01539) 435295 FAX: (01539) 435516 COOKING 3*

on A591, at N end of Rydal Water COST £36–£43

In common Lakeland fashion everybody meets at the appointed time in the pale green lounge of this eighteenth-century stone and slate building (once owned by Wordsworth – he wrote poetry in the porch) and says hello over drinks amid the bright floral chair covers. Since everybody eats the same until pudding, it makes sense to serve the whole room together, but the scale of the simple dining-room, with its wooden tables and floors, is too small and intimate for the system to feel regimented. The menu bears no price but offers good value: typically a soup, fish course, meat and four vegetables, then any of the three puddings and cheese (or the other way round for these two if you prefer), and coffee. The format hasn't altered since the Dixons opened their doors in 1980.

A well-rehearsed core repertoire throws up many of the same dishes in reports, including one soup of fennel, apple and almond, and another of carrot, coriander, lentil and orange that was 'subtly flavoured and delightfully textured'. Fishy delights have included two slices of salmon, one smoked, one poached, with a gently flavoured mustard and chive sauce. Rack of Westmorland Herdwick spring lamb has a more robust flavour than is usual for spring lamb, its mint-flavoured redcurrant sauce firmly anchored in the sensible British tradition; gentle acidulation appears to be a trademark. Quality and consistency mark out the food, portions are just right and the saucing is 'intense without being heavy or creamy'. Praise is heaped on the English cheeses, which are full of flavour and served at the right temperature, and on guardsman's pudding, a light wholemeal gingery sponge with a raspberry sauce and custard. Service is 'friendly but never intrusive'.

The stunning collection of wines is helpfully arranged by region within France, followed by comparable varietals from elsewhere: hence, New World Cabernets and Merlots follow clarets, for example. The compass of vintages within France is astounding, and if some of these wines were available at auction they would certainly fetch more than the prices asked here. At least ten wines are served by the glass. CELLARMAN'S CHOICE: Niederhausen Hermannsöhle Riesling 1976, Deinhard, £19.50; Pauillac, Ch. Pichon Lalande 1982, £52.

CHEFS: Peter Dixon and Colin Percival PROPRIETORS: Sue and Peter Dixon OPEN: Mon to Sat D only 8 (one sitting) CLOSED: mid-Dec to mid-Mar MEALS: Set D £27.50 SERVICE: not inc, card slips closed CARDS: Access, Visa DETAILS: 18 seats. Car park. Children's helpings. No toddlers. No smoking in dining-room. Wheelchair access. No music. ACCOMMODATION: 6 rooms, all with bath/shower. TV. Phone. D,B&B £60 to £174. Children welcome. Garden. Fishing (*The Which? Hotel Guide*)

The text of entries is based on unsolicited reports sent in by readers, backed up by inspections conducted anonymously. The factual details under the text are from questionnaires the Guide *sends to all restaurants that feature in the book.*

GREAT DUNMOW Essex map 3

▲ *The Starr*

Market Place, Great Dunmow CM6 1AX
TEL: (01371) 874321 FAX: (01371) 876337 COOKING 1
off A120, 9m E of Bishop's Stortford COST £25–£51

Orders are taken in the bar of this old coaching-inn – dishes aplenty are written up on a couple of blackboards – and consumed in the heavily beamed dining-room. Anglo-French-Italian food is the kitchen's currency, and among endorsements have been scallops with noodles and beurre blanc, crisp-skinned confit of duck with garlic mashed potato, and 'stunningly good' pear Tatin with pistachio ice-cream. Combinations can be intriguing, as in crab tart surrounded with segments of pink grapefruit topped with shavings of coconut, which in the context did not endear itself to the reporter, although another enjoyed his oxtail stew with prunes. Reporters have considered the intermediate sorbet at dinner 'unnecessary'. At inspection, lack of flavour in several items suggested that the kitchen might be dozing, though wines continue to please for their scope and quality, from French classics through antipodean value to an English white from nearby Mersea Island, and there is a fair spread of half-bottles. House French is around £3 a glass. CELLARMAN'S CHOICE: Coteaux du Languedoc, Picpoul de Pinet 1993, Hugues de Beauvignac, £12.95; Montagne St-Emilion, Ch. Montaiguillon 1990, £15.95.

CHEF: Mark Fisher PROPRIETORS: Brian and Vanessa Jones OPEN: Sun to Fri L 12 to 1.45, Mon to Sat D 7 to 9.30 CLOSED: first week Jan MEALS: alc L Mon to Fri (main courses £6.50 to £16). Set L Sun £16.50 (2 courses) to £21.50, Set L Mon to Fri £10 (2 courses), Set D £21.50 (2 courses) to £32.50 SERVICE: not inc CARDS: Access, Amex, Delta, Switch, Visa DETAILS: 45 seats. Private parties: 12 main room, 12 and 36 private rooms. Car park. Vegetarian meals. Children's helpings. Smart dress preferred. No smoking in dining-room. Wheelchair access. Music ACCOMMODATION: 8 rooms, all with bath/shower. TV. Phone. B&B £55 to £100. Rooms for disabled. Children welcome. Pets welcome (*The Which? Hotel Guide*)

GREAT GONERBY Lincolnshire map 6

Harry's Place

LINCS 1996 BAKER

17 High Street, Great Gonerby NG31 8JS
TEL: (01476) 61780 COOKING 3*
on B1174, 2m NW of Grantham COST £43–£68

This has to be one of the smallest restaurants in the country, a Georgian house on the outskirts of Grantham with room for only three tables, a maximum of ten people. It is well placed, a mile or so from the A1, and with a fast train service to London, so customers come from near and far. The menu is tiny as well – a choice of two items per course – and the wine list not much longer, but the dedication is heroic. Reporters are drawn into the Hallam routine, established over seven years: bookings only, three courses (with an optional fourth of cheese), and a meal that lasts all evening. Harry's is not the greasy-spoon the name might suggest, but a smartish dark pink room that is a study in pine of all ages, all overseen by Caroline Hallam, who is soon on first-name terms.

Two or three strands emerge from the careful style of cooking. First, baking is a forte, apparent from the basket of rough-hewn wholemeal bread, and the small puff pastry tartlets piled with mild goats' cheese, sweet tomato, black olive and a sprinkling of fresh herbs which arrive with drinks. A first-course pastry case containing a perfectly poached egg and bits of sweetcorn, covered in hollandaise sauce, is a triumph of the pastry-maker's art. Second, vivid fresh locally grown herbs are used in profusion, adding brightness to the vegetables that accompany main courses.

Ingredients are well sourced – Dee salmon, Filey lobster, corn-fed free-range chicken, Charolais beef whose pedigree Harry Hallam knows intimately – and cooking is precise. Flavours are simple and distinctive (roast breast of chicken gets a lift from lemon thyme, ginger and coriander, for example), although sometimes the balance can go askew, as in a first course of sauté chicken livers set in a sherry and black pepper jelly and served chilled, the pepper mightily strong and the Cumberland sauce very sweet. Hot soufflés of greengage or rhubarb figure among the puddings, along with lemon tart, and an outstandingly good caramel mousse brûlée in a ramekin: runny caramel in the bottom, feather-light vanilla mousse, and a dusting of icing sugar partially crisped on top. The dozen wines are rather expensive, with the cheapest half-bottle £15, and Montagny and Fleurie are served by the glass at £3.50.

CHEF: Harry Hallam PROPRIETORS: Harry and Caroline Hallam OPEN: Tue to Sat 12.30 to 2, 7 to 9.30; Sun and Mon L and D by arrangement CLOSED: 25 and 26 Dec, bank hols MEALS: alc (main courses £16 to £22.50) SERVICE: not inc CARDS: Access, Visa DETAILS: 10 seats. Private parties: 10 main room. Car park. No children under 5. No smoking in dining-room. Wheelchair access (1 step). No music

---

GREAT MILTON Oxfordshire map 2

▲ *Le Manoir aux Quat' Saisons*

Church Road, Great Milton OX44 7PD
TEL: (01844) 278881 FAX: (01844) 278847 COOKING 5
off A329, 1m from M40 junction 7 COST £41–£107

The Manoir is expensive, any fule kno that. But there is little point, judging from reports, in worrying what else you might have done with the £25 charged for a first course of wild salmon and caviare. The best way to enjoy it, having made the decision to go, is to forget the cost and simply take everything as it comes. 'Some details might have borne correction,' an inspector concluded, 'but one cannot help but be carried along by the sheer sweep of the restaurant's ambition and achievement. Overall, a superb meal and fine value for money too.'

Japanese involvement has met with acclaim – Japan's most celebrated chef spent a week here – and there seems to be increasing use of seaweed and sticky rice, and even greater striving for visual effect, although that has long been a Blanc forte. In this context the 'trois bouchées' of scallop tartare with shiso leaves, poached oyster in cucumber butter, and deep-fried seaweed purse of crab remains a favourite – although one reporter found herself 'marvelling more at the skill and ingenuity of the chef rather than swooning with pleasure over the flavours'. A 'brilliant variation on the theme of duck confit' with golden-brown duck jelly and a slice of black truffle, however, did the trick.

For another, a soufflé of crab in a fillet of sole was 'an utterly glorious dish', while poached breast of Landes chicken in truffle juice was 'a cracker, with the chicken cooked to perfection, stunning jus, utterly brilliant vegetables. A classic.' The garden's integral role in all this should not be overlooked. Vegetables are grown to precise requirements and could not be fresher: 'beetroot that fills the mouth with flavour', 'delicious asparagus', 'gorgeous deep-fried aubergine'. Given their impact – 'I was amazed that so much succulence and taste could ooze out of such a mundane vegetable as the turnip' – one feels it might be about time for M. Blanc to branch out into farming sheep, pigs, ducks and all the other animals on which he relies.

To follow, the 'caramel experience', despite sounding like a rather sticky ride at EuroDisney, is 'a marvellous compilation of different delicacies, including a darkly caramelised tarte Tatin, miniature crème caramel, a slice of wonderful caramelised apple, spun sugar, caramel ice-cream and a delectable nougatine parfait – wow!' No matter how intricate desserts appear, they invariably impress. Anything with chocolate and pistachio is worth having. Most reporters find the Manoir quite human, with friendly and helpful service – 'we felt deliciously pampered but not fussed over' – although some have found it lacking warmth.

Occasional niggles surface – of something not available, improvable bread, predictable petits fours, the price of drinks, and so on – which sometimes diminish the value of the encounter for their reporters, but many more write to say that meals are impossible to fault. 'Children of any age are not accepted; they are welcomed,' says the menu, and to prove it the restaurant has a £12 menu for children. Divide by three and some of the wine prices begin to seem quite reasonable. Allowing, say, £30, it is possible to find a good bottle, particularly from south-west France and the usual regional bolt holes, but wonderful burgundy and sensational claret are tempting for lottery-winners. Half-bottles are extensive. CELLARMAN'S CHOICE: Jurançon Sec 'Cuvée Marie' 1992, Alain Brumont, £30; Madiran Ch. Montus, 1989, Alain Brumont, £36.

CHEFS: Raymond Blanc and Clive Fretwell PROPRIETOR: Raymond Blanc OPEN: all week 12.15 to 2.30, 7.15 to 10.15 MEALS: alc (main courses £30 to £33). Set L £29.50 to £65, Set D £65 SERVICE: net prices CARDS: Access, Amex, Delta, Diners, Switch, Visa DETAILS: 100 seats. Private parties: 46 main room, 46 private room. Car park. Vegetarian meals. Children's helpings. Smart dress preferred. No smoking in 1 dining-room. Wheelchair access. Music. Air-conditioned ACCOMMODATION: 19 rooms, all with bath/shower. TV. Phone. D,B&B £175 to £375. Deposit: £150 per room. Rooms for disabled. Children welcome. Baby facilities. Pets welcome. Afternoon teas. Garden. Swimming-pool (*The Which? Hotel Guide*)

GREAT MISSENDEN Buckinghamshire map 3

La Petite Auberge

107 High Street, Great Missenden HP16 0BB COOKING 1*
TEL: (01494) 865370 COST £32–£46

Once over the threshold of these modest high-street premises you are immediately drawn into the intimate ambience of a genuine French restaurant. This is a quiet, cosy, relaxed place that moves along at an easy pace. Mrs Martel maintains her presence out front and knows when to chat and when to keep her distance. Mr Martel cooks, and his food draws consistently favourable reports. What he offers is a sound interpretation of French provincial cooking, although he occasionally gilds the lily with unnecessary slivers of truffles and pearls of caviare.

Asparagus in puff pastry is a popular starter (alternate spears of green and white served on an 'exact' butter sauce); otherwise there might be fish soup, a salad of smoked duck breast, or a 'superb' vegetable terrine with herb vinaigrette. Fish and meat are handled with equal confidence. One reporter praised meltingly fresh pan-fried scallops with a silky, golden saffron sauce, and fillets of John Dory on a bed of crunchy sauté leeks. Others have mentioned medallions of veal with beetroot and rösti, and sweetbreads in calvados sauce. Hot apple with cinnamon ice-cream is a favourite finale, and caramelised lemon tart is skilfully crafted. There is no house wine, but the short French list is completely reliable, with prices starting at £9.50.

CHEF: Hubert Martel PROPRIETORS: Mr and Mrs Hubert Martel OPEN: Mon to Sat D only 7.30 to 10.30 CLOSED: Christmas, bank hols MEALS: alc (main courses £14 to £16) SERVICE: not inc CARDS: Access, Visa DETAILS: 30 seats. Private parties: 30 main room. Children welcome. Smart dress preferred. Wheelchair access (also WC). Music

GRIMSTON Norfolk map 6

▲ *Congham Hall*

Grimston PE32 1AH
TEL: (01485) 600250 FAX: (01485) 601191 COOKING 2
off A148 or B1153, 7m E of King's Lynn COST £18–£50

A summer visitor to this brick-built, cream-painted Georgian manor-house was whisked straight through and out the other end, on to a patio with tables and 'large square sunbrellas', facing mature landscaped trees and a garden big enough to land a helicopter on. In fine weather meals can be eaten outside, at other times in the re-launched Orangery, as the dining-room styles itself, with mock bamboo garden chairs, and tables laid with elegant glasses. The kitchen turns out a lot of dishes: a couple of dozen savoury items at lunch-time, for example, from what the menu calls a 'working lunch' of soup, sandwiches and coffee for £7.50, to deep-fried plaice with chips and mushy peas, and a trio of chocolate mousses to follow.

Jonathan Nicholson's food is in contemporary country-house vein, taking in carpaccio of beef with a white truffle and chive dressing, poached oysters with pasta, and a ravioli of mixed shellfish in which thin pasta enclosed 'whizzed-up' crustaceans, in a sauce that 'tasted intensely of pulverised shells'. Another highlight was when a helicopter landed on the lawn (told you it was big enough), although this didn't detract from either a 'brilliant' offal sausage that came with a cassoulet of pork confit, nor from a first-class raspberry sorbet that partnered an improvable chocolate soufflé. The generosity and adaptability of menus are welcome, although an inspector felt that the trade-off seemed to be that proportionately less attention is paid to the construction and execution of individual dishes. Service is young and earnest. The wine list offers a few good bottles, though where it relies on négociants it lacks inspiration, and half-bottles might be improved. House wine is £11.50.

CHEF: Jonathan Nicholson PROPRIETORS: Christine and Trevor Forecast OPEN: Sun to Fri L 12.30 to 2, all week D 7.30 to 9.30 MEALS: alc L (main courses £4 to £15.50). Set D £24 to £32 SERVICE: not inc, card slips closed CARDS: Access, Amex, Diners, Visa DETAILS: 50 seats. 10 tables outside. Private parties: 50 main room, 20 private room. Car park. Vegetarian meals. No children under 12. Jacket and tie D. No smoking in dining-room. Wheelchair access (2 steps; also WC). No music ACCOMMODATION: 14 rooms, all with bath/shower. TV. Phone. B&B £65 to £185. Deposit: £20. No children under 12. Afternoon teas. Garden. Swimming-pool (*The Which? Hotel Guide*)

HALFORD Warwickshire map 5

Sykes House

Queen Street, Halford CV36 5BT COOKING 2
TEL: (01789) 740976 COST £36–£44

The idea of dining out in somebody else's home, where the small scale necessarily throws neighbouring tables into polite conversation with each other, may strike a note of tweeness. If so, consider booking the room with a single large oak table that takes between six and twelve, and filling it with friends. 'A good haunt for special occasions and foreign visitors,' remarked one who made a mental note to return. The sixteenth-century Cotswold-stone house is peaceful and attractive, and the Cunliffes organise a no-choice dinner of five courses for bookings only: 24 hours' notice is needed, which gives them time to deal with dislikes and allergies.

Spiced parsnip soup, or a summer vegetable broth is a likely way to begin, and may be followed by fish: fresh tuna Japanese-style on one occasion. Among other appealing ideas are a soup of potato, crayfish and watercress, a dish of frittered scallops on onion and parsley mash with lemon sauce, and a 'cheese' course of bitter salad leaves in a creamy Somerset Brie custard. Indeed, the cheese course is often more like a savoury: at one dinner a sliver of Stilton cheesecake served with oven-dried tomatoes and a dressed salad. Fillet of beef, breast of duckling with cornmeal dumplings, and grilled noisettes of Cotswold roe-deer have formed the centrepiece, while tarts of rhubarb, or gooseberry and crème fraîche have rounded things off. Meals begin with 'welcoming appetisers', as the menu describes them, and finish with 'little fancies', and the price also includes bottled water and coffee. Wines range from modest to swanky and are fairly marked up, with a changing selection of wines by the glass, given verbally, for around £2.50 to £3.50.

CHEF: David Cunliffe PROPRIETORS: David and Peggy Cunliffe OPEN: Wed to Sat D only 7.30 to 8.15 MEALS: Set D £32.50 SERVICE: none, card slips closed CARDS: Visa DETAILS: 24 seats. Private parties: 12 main room, 12 private room. Car park. Children welcome. Smart dress preferred. No smoking in dining-room. No music

All main entries are fully indexed at the back of the Guide.

'A waiter ushers you along a poorly illuminated passageway saying "mind the step" a few times as he gestures sweepingly to the obstacles. You are expected to remember them yourself on the way out.' (On eating in Norfolk)

HALIFAX West Yorkshire map 9

W. YORKS 1996 GOOD DEAL

NEW ENTRY

Design House

Dean Clough, Halifax HX3 5AX
TEL: (01422) 383242 COOKING 2
FAX: (01422) 322732 COST £19–£34

'Good food should be available at any level. It shouldn't be out of anybody's reach, whether it's just a sandwich, a jar of jam or a full meal.' These common-sense words from John Leach help to explain the Design House's drive. Dean Clough is a former carpet mill – solid, 'but not in the slightest bit satanic or depressing' – that has been sympathetically restored by entrepreneur and musician Sir Ernest Hall. An insurance company and an art gallery have found a home there, as has David Watson, who used to cook at Pool Court before it moved to Leeds (see entry).

It doesn't look like a mill from inside, now that it has been kitted out with chrome, glass, clean lines, curtains and artful curves, but there is jam for sale in the adjoining deli, along with honey, marmalade, bread, olive oil, wine and lots more. Salads and sandwiches are served at lunch-time, unless a plate of potted brisket, Scarborough woof with garlic butter, and a cup of coffee with change from a tenner is more up your street. The value impresses. So too does the free and easy style of smoked cod risotto, and boiled ham hock.

Reporters have enjoyed soups of Jerusalem artichoke and scallop, and pheasant and lentil, as well as resonant meaty dishes such as fillet of venison with spinach, turnip and fondant potatoes. Syrup sponge with custard is a recommended pudding. While there may be a few rough edges, the success rate is high. 'David Watson's cooking is even more confident than it was at Pool Court,' concluded one report. Service is friendly and the atmosphere relaxed. Beers (including Chimay and German wheat beer) are served in the right glasses, and wines are intelligently chosen, fairly priced, and arranged partly by style. Half a dozen are available by the glass from £2.

CHEF: David Watson PROPRIETOR: John Leach OPEN: Mon to Fri L 12 to 2, Mon to Sat D 6.30 to 10.30 CLOSED: 25 and 26 Dec MEALS: alc (main courses £6 to £10). Set L £9.50 (2 courses) to £12.75 SERVICE: not inc CARDS: Access, Amex, Switch, Visa DETAILS: 72 seats. Private parties: 72 main room. Vegetarian meals. Children welcome. Smart dress preferred. No pipes in dining-room. Wheelchair access (also WC). Music. Air-conditioned

HAMBLETON Leicestershire map 6

LEICS 1996 LUXURY

▲ *Hambleton Hall*

Hambleton LE15 8TH
TEL: (01572) 756991 FAX: (01572) 724721 COOKING 4
off A606, 3m SE of Oakham COST £37–£88

This represents some kind of perfection in the country-house genre. The mature gardens provide a luxuriant frame for the view down to Rutland Water, while the rooms are beautifully decorated without going over the top into country-house flummery. The restaurant combines an easy-going atmosphere with tight standards. The menu alters with the seasons, although details change with market availability. Luxury ingredients show up in a terrine of foie gras with leeks and a black truffle jelly, or another of lobster and monkfish with a salad of artichokes and lobster vinaigrette, but the view of reporters is that the seriously high prices on the *carte* are difficult to justify, and that the three-course no-choice daily set menu generally offers the best value.

One evening this began with five sweet king scallops arranged on braised chicory with scatterings of chanterelle and truffle, followed by a sauté of chicken with morel mushrooms in a creamy broth with young vegetables, a simple dish that scored for freshness and clarity of flavours. A light and wobbly hot caramel soufflé followed, served with caramel ice-cream in a small pastry tart. Aaron Patterson is a very accomplished chef, no doubt of that. His creations look good, flavour is a priority and techniques are impressive. Cold consommé of tomato with langoustines, for example, is 'spectacular in appearance and brilliant in flavour'.

There is a tendency to over-complicate, though, with arguably too many elements within one dish. How about a fillet of cod with hummus and Parma ham in a turkey juice scented with lemon grass and ginger? And quantities are generous. One reporter dined on pink Bresse pigeon, breasts filleted, legs bone-in, accompanied by sauerkraut and a sauce made from stock and Gewurztraminer; a large raviolo of light pasta was stuffed with wild mushrooms and topped with black truffle, and there was a cylinder of sliced potato as well. As the reporter observed, this is in danger of threatening rather than seducing, though he still managed to follow it with a light, porous savarin with succulent hot cherries and a sharp lemon verbena ice-cream.

'The Harts are to be congratulated on an outstanding training job,' ventured one impressed reporter about the staff. Most appear to be French, and can talk intelligently about the food. They are pleasant and helpful, from reception through waiting staff to the excellent sommelier who oversees a long list of extremely high quality, and not just in the classic regions. Price-banded 'wines of the moment' are a useful way of identifying interest and good value. CELLARMAN'S CHOICE: Azay le Rideau 1992, Dom. Pibaleau, £17.50; Bonny Doon 'Clos de Gilroy' Grenache 1993, Santa Cruz, California.

CHEF: Aaron Patterson PROPRIETORS: Tim and Stefa Hart OPEN: all week 12 to 2, 7 to 9.30 MEALS: alc (main courses £19 to £27). Set L and D £29.50 SERVICE: net prices, card slips closed CARDS: Access, Amex, Switch, Visa DETAILS: 60 seats. 4 tables outside. Private parties: 60 main room, 15 to 60 private rooms. Car park. Vegetarian meals. Children's helpings. Smart dress preferred. No cigars/pipes in dining-room. Wheelchair access (also WC). No music ACCOMMODATION: 15 rooms, all with bath/shower. TV. Phone. B&B £105 to £125. Rooms for disabled. Children welcome. Baby facilities. Pets by arrangement. Garden. Swimming-pool (*The Which? Hotel Guide*)

HAMPTON WICK Greater London map 3

Dijonnais

35 High Street, Hampton Wick KT1 4DA COOKING 1*
TEL: 0181-977 4895 COST £20–£45

There's no doubting the relaxed informality of Dijonnais. Some have likened it to 'a regular French country restaurant'. Much of its success is due to the combination of Jan Jolivet's charming presence out front and husband Lionel's cooking. The décor is all pastel colours, panelling and typically Gallic background music, and the kitchen delivers dependable French provincial cooking. Portions are generous, prices are commendably low. Reporters have been agreeably impressed by starters of fish soup, a choux bun filled with mushroom sauce, and a tartlet of quail's eggs with spinach, while main courses have included fanned slices of Barbary duck with cassis sauce, breast of pheasant with apricots and chestnuts, and poached sole with a 'delicate' lobster sauce. Meals often end on a high note: excellent apple tart with 'well-above-average' pastry, for example. The cover charge pays for peanuts, pleasant crudités with rich dips and fresh bread and butter. Wine-drinkers can take their pick from a modest selection of French bottles from reliable producers. House wine is £9.25.

CHEFS: Lionel Jolivet and Jerome Aurejac PROPRIETORS: Lionel and Jan Jolivet OPEN: Mon to Fri L 12 to 2.30, Mon to Sat D 6 (7 Fri and Sat) to 10 CLOSED: Easter, bank hols MEALS: alc (main courses £6 to £14.50). Set L £10 (2 courses), Set D £17.50. Cover £1 SERVICE: not inc CARDS: Access, Amex, Diners, Visa DETAILS: 29 seats. 1 table outside. Private parties: 25 main room. Vegetarian meals. Children's helpings. Wheelchair access (1 step). Music

Le Petit Max

97A High Street, Hampton Wick KT2 5NB — COOKING 3
TEL: 0181-977 0236 — COST £33–£42

'This is what *The Good Food Guide* is all about,' write a tender-hearted couple. 'Tracking down good food in scruffy surroundings. Great stuff.' If 'scruffy' sounds a trifle harsh, let it be noted that the little Max (elder sibling of Chez Max in London, see entry) is by day a caff called Bonzo's. In the evenings it is transformed – though not too dramatically – into a French bistro, with gingham tablecloths and service that doesn't stand on ceremony. When packed, it is very cramped ('a can opener would be required to extricate people once seated'). By the time this edition of the *Guide* reaches you, there will be more outside tables and the luxury of air-conditioning.

Simon Gale's cooking is essentially French, though fleshed out with the likes of imam bayaldi and gravad lax, and is capable of a high degree of polish. 'Delicious' tomato, basil and garlic soup was followed one summer evening by memorable chargrilled Angus steak in a thick red wine and redcurrant sauce, with pommes purée and french beans: 'We have not had one so good since 1975 in the Bois de Boulogne.' Another night saw sea bass pot-roasted in a 'remarkable' jus of mussels and saffron. Salmon done in the oven was served with a hollandaise and Jersey royals in June, exactly as many would do it at home. Good buying is evident at the margins: 'A carrot had one of the guests staring in amazement at how full of flavour it was.' Pear tarte Tatin with 'excellent thin' pastry is a favourite dessert, and there is classic crème brûlée, or straightforward strawberries and clotted cream in season. Good coffee, 'beautiful' olives and extremely crusty bread add to the satisfaction. There is no licence, so pick up your own bottle on the way and pay £2.50 to have it opened.

CHEF: Simon Gale PROPRIETORS: Max, Marc and Joanna Renzland OPEN: Tue to Sun L 3.30 to 4.30, Tue to Sun D 7 to 10.30 MEALS: Set L Sun £23.50, Set D £23.50. Unlicensed, but bring your own: corkage £2.50 SERVICE: 10% (optional) CARDS: none DETAILS: 32 seats. 4 tables outside. Private parties: 32 main room. No music

HARROGATE North Yorkshire map 8

La Bergerie

11–13 Mount Parade, Harrogate HG1 1BX COOKING 1
TEL: (01423) 500089 COST £23–£30

Jacques Giron serves French food with an emphasis on the south-west. The restaurant is two or three terraced properties joined together, with arches, candles, good linen and polished glasses. Although the atmosphere is a mite formal, staff are knowledgeable, friendly and helpful, and the food – of the kind that 'might be found in any village across the Channel' – has a convincing degree of authenticity. Brochette of green-lipped mussels and large, firm prawns comes with a particularly well-flavoured tomato sauce, 'a meal in itself' for one reporter, as is the long-standing house speciality, a huge portion of tasty cassoulet. Few things appear to be done by halves. Another speciality called 'tioro' (a Basque stew of monkfish, hake and shellfish) contains a week's supply of garlic. Not everybody makes it to the puddings, but a nicely browned gratin of orange in a sabayon sauce, or crème caramel with armagnac, is waiting for those who do. The modest French list includes a few good country wines. House red and white, of unspecified origin, are £8.50.

CHEF: Jacques Giron PROPRIETOR: Jacques Giron OPEN: Mon to Sat 12 to 2, 7 to 11 MEALS: Set D £14.50 to £16.50; lunch by arrangement only SERVICE: not inc CARDS: Access, Visa DETAILS: 40 seats. Private parties: 20 main room, 12 private room. Vegetarian meals. Children's helpings. No smoking in 1 dining-room. Wheelchair access (2 steps; also WC). Music

Drum and Monkey £

5 Montpellier Gardens, Harrogate HG1 2TF COOKING 2
TEL: (01423) 502650 COST £15–£37

For many visitors to Harrogate, the Drum and Monkey is a pleasant relief from the town's myriad conference hotels. The mood of this converted Victorian pub is generally jolly, although sometimes the pace can be rather slow; but there's no doubting the consistency of the cooking. Fish, mainly from the East Coast inshore boats, is given simple, classic treatment: sea trout is poached and served with asparagus hollandaise, scallops are wrapped in bacon, and fillets of sole are garnished with prawns and mushrooms or given the 'florentine' treatment. Lobster comes four ways; grilled Dover sole appears in four sizes. Seafood platters, pies and salads form the back-up. You might start with oysters or salmon and watercress mousse and round things off with tiramisù, treacle tart or frozen blueberry yoghurt. A simpler menu operates at lunch-time, when visitors can take pot luck for a table in the downstairs bar. The short, affordable list of around 40 wines is tilted towards youthful whites. House wine is £6.85.

CHEFS: Keith Penny and Tina Nuttall PROPRIETOR: William Fuller OPEN: Mon to Sat 12 to 2.30, 6.45 to 10.15 CLOSED: 24 Dec to 2 Jan MEALS: alc (main courses £4.50 to £13.50) SERVICE: not inc CARDS: Access, Switch, Visa DETAILS: 50 seats. Private parties: 8 main room. Children welcome. Wheelchair access. No music

Grundy's

21 Cheltenham Crescent, Harrogate HG1 1DH COOKING 1
TEL: (01423) 502610 COST £20–£37

The restaurant – green outside, pink inside – is in a Victorian terrace on Harrogate's 'Restaurant Row', and serves a fixed-price menu, with about four choices at each stage, as well as a longer *carte*. The reasonable prices don't happen by accident. Competition in the town is fierce, with restaurants caught between rising costs and squeezed margins. A few have closed. The Grundys hope their tight organisation, careful management and responsive kitchen will pay dividends.

Val Grundy is a self-taught cook who finds that occasional excursions into exotic flavours do not always please a conservative clientele, hence the conventional deep-fried Brie with cranberry and orange relish, or fillet of salmon with a watercress and cream sauce. The food may not be cutting-edge, but it does have a playful way with ingredients. Grilled Welsh goats' cheese on toasted brioche with pumpkin and ginger is novel, as is the hazelnut and carrot cream that comes with roast breast of marinated chicken. Vegetarians get a fair deal, and puddings are as homely as caramelised oranges in Grand Marnier, or summer pudding. White wines are listed in order of dryness, reds according to fullness of flavour, and both make good use of South Africa, the South of France, Australia and other regions to produce a simple but drinkable collection mostly under £15 a bottle. House wine is £8.50.

CHEF: Val Grundy PROPRIETORS: Chris and Val Grundy OPEN: Mon to Sat D only 6.30 to 10 CLOSED: 2 weeks Jan to Feb, 2 weeks July to Aug MEALS: alc (main courses £9 to £14). Set D £10.95 (2 courses) to £12.95 SERVICE: 10% (optional), card slips closed CARDS: Access, Amex, Delta, Switch, Visa DETAILS: 40 seats. Private parties: 36 main room. Vegetarian meals. Children welcome. No pipes. Music

Millers, The Bistro

1 Montpellier Mews, Harrogate HG1 2TG COOKING 2
TEL: (01423) 530708 FAX: (01423) 561021 COST £26–£49

Cramped French bistros have always been dear to the hearts of the British, and here is another. 'It looks quite twee from the outside with its shop-front windows,' commented reporters who, once inside, remarked that 'the tables for two are extremely tiny'. Basic décor and lack of elbow-room are all forgotten when the food arrives, starting with an appetiser of tapénade for spreading on 'fluffy' bread. Mediterranean fish soup is the approved version, down to the 'deep but not overpowering aniseed flavour' often missed elsewhere. 'Lovely moist' risotto black with octopus ink is topped with slices of roasted salmon – an 'outstanding' starter. Fish may be given a crust to sharpen its impact, whether it be parsley for baked cod, or tomato and cheese with turbot. A ball of noodles accompanying the latter 'merited credit for not being at all sticky'. Saddle of lamb is traditionally roasted and served with vegetables provençale and a tarragon jus. Purée potatoes with calf's liver one night tasted more of cream than of potato, but the liver itself was declared 'tender and mouth-watering, with a lovely deep reduced sauce'. Among the puddings, tarts and home-made ice-creams are normally good, or there may be challengingly rich chocolate marquise with strawberry purée. There are four French house wines, two at £8.95 and two at £10.95. Simon Gueller is planning to open a second restaurant, Rascasse in Leeds (TEL: 0113-244 6611), in autumn 1995.

CHEF: Simon Gueller PROPRIETORS: Simon and Rena Gueller OPEN: Tue to Sat 12 to 2, 7 to 10 CLOSED: Christmas, first 2 weeks Aug MEALS: alc (main courses £9.50 to £11.50). Cover £1 SERVICE: not inc CARDS: Access, Amex, Switch, Visa DETAILS: 40 seats. Private parties: 38 main room. Children's helpings. Wheelchair access (1 step; also WC). Music

HARROW Greater London map 3

Percy's

66–68 Station Road, North Harrow HA2 7SJ COOKING 1*
TEL: 0181-427 2021 FAX: 0181-427 8134 COST £25–£42

North Harrow is an altogether cheerier place for the presence of Percy's. It is a bare-boarded, reassuringly informal, neighbourhood restaurant linked umbilically to a 40-acre farm in Devon. Weekend runs bring back herbs, vegetables and saladings, about which Tony Bricknell-Webb is volubly clued up. Self-taught Tina runs the kitchen, whisking a mixture of culinary influences into some enticing dishes. Fresh crab salad on buckwheat blini, roast monkfish with smoked garlic butter, red pepper and spring onions, and loin of wild boar with mushrooms and madeira suggest a restlessly creative intelligence. 'Fresh, firm and tasty' monkfish steamed with tomato and fennel was a much admired dish, and hot chocolate pudding with truffle sauce and whipped cream was described as 'first-class' by one reporter. Occasionally, however, the impulse to complicate a dish threatens to capsize it, as in a pesto of marjoram, rosemary, garlic and olive oil which overpowered a lemon sole. But generally the bravery of Percy's output is acknowledged and commended. The wine list has developed well, and offers a confident international selection of top-drawer producers at reasonable prices. Menetou-Salon from Jean-Max Roger, Concha y Toro Chilean Cabernet and Ceretto Barolo are among the forthright flavours that should complement the food well. House wines start at £9.80.

CHEF: Tina Bricknell-Webb PROPRIETORS: Tony and Tina Bricknell-Webb OPEN: Tue to Sat 12 to 3, 6.30 to 10.30 CLOSED: 27 Dec to 2 Jan MEALS: alc (main courses £12 to £16). Set L £10 (2 courses) SERVICE: 10% (optional), card slips closed CARDS: Access, Amex, Delta, Diners, Switch, Visa DETAILS: 80 seats. Private parties: 50 main room. Car park. Vegetarian meals. No children under 10. Smart dress preferred. No smoking in dining-room. Wheelchair access. No music

Report forms are at the back of the book; write a letter if you prefer; or if you are on the Internet, e-mail us at guidereports@which. co. uk.

'Birthday boy got the assiette of assorted bits of ox cheek, pig's snout, tail and ear, lambs' kidney, liver etc. We were not, eventually, sure which bit belonged to which animal, but pleasurable grunts and snorts from the recipient worried us that there was more pig than anything else.' (On eating in Greater London)

HARVINGTON Hereford & Worcester map 5

▲ *Mill at Harvington*

Anchor Lane, Harvington WR11 5NR
TEL/FAX: (01386) 870688
S of B439 Evesham to Bidford-on-Avon road; avoid village
COOKING 2
COST £18–£43

The Mill, set in eight acres of grounds with willows shading its river frontage, was built in the mid-eighteenth century, and beer and bread have been made here, as its cast-iron bakery doors attest. The food philosophy takes consistency as its premise, ignoring the ideas that fashion throws up elsewhere. So there is no bashfulness about serving a cheese soufflé or a simple warm bacon and potato salad as starters, nor in offering rabbit pie or roast pork with apple sauce for Sunday lunch. Classics of more recent provenance attract praise, as in an 'utterly delicious' haddock mousse wrapped in smoked salmon with an hollandaise sauce. Choice of main course determines the price of dinner, and may include baked fillets of trout with strips of Morvan ham in a creamy shallot sauce, or half a Gressingham duck cooked crisp and sauced with orange and ginger. Criticisms sometimes surface over sauces that overwhelm their main ingredients, as in a curry concoction that came with veal. Butterscotch pudding can be good, coffee is comfortingly strong, and the service a model of helpful efficiency. 'From the warm welcome to the smiling goodbye,' reported one couple, 'we were looked after like old friends.'

For those who have time, the wine list is fleshed out with a digest of information on grape varieties. The section headings – 'dry wines getting heavier' – may sound like weather reports, but they announce some fine selections from around the world. Prices are kept within bounds, and there is a profusion of halves. House wines are £8.95. CELLARMAN'S CHOICE: Woodbridge Sauvignon Blanc 1992, Mondavi, California £12.50; Valdepeñas Gran Reserva 1984 'Señorio de los Llanos' 1984, Tempranillo, £11.25.

CHEFS: Jane Greenhalgh, Bill Downing and John Hunter PROPRIETORS: Simon and Jane Greenhalgh OPEN: all week 11.45 to 1.45, 7 to 9 CLOSED: 24 to 28 Dec MEALS: alc L (main courses £4 to £7). Set L £12.25 (2 courses) to £13.95, Set L Sun £11.75 (2 courses) to £13.95, Set D £21 to £28 SERVICE: not inc, card slips closed CARDS: Access, Amex, Delta, Diners, Switch, Visa DETAILS: 40 seats. 8 tables outside. Private parties: 40 main room, 14 private room. Car park. Vegetarian meals. Children's helpings. No smoking in dining-room. No music ACCOMMODATION: 15 rooms, all with bath/shower. TV. Phone. B&B £44 to £85. Rooms for disabled. No children under 10. Garden. Swimming-pool. Fishing (*The Which? Hotel Guide*)

HARWICH Essex map 6

▲ *Pier at Harwich*

The Quay, Harwich CO12 3HH
TEL: (01255) 241212 FAX: (01255) 551922
COOKING 1
COST £23–£49

The prospect of eating high-class fish and chips in a Grade II listed building overlooking the twin estuaries of the Stour and Orwell continues to lure crowds to this admirable quayside venue. The restaurant greatly cheered up one couple after a gastronomically disappointing holiday in Brittany, and did the trick for others on a wintry Saturday lunch-time. Cod and haddock stay fresh and moist in their coat of exemplary batter, and when the kitchen flexes its muscles the results are neat and meticulously balanced: marinated scallops are succulent and tasty, grilled fillet of sea bass is served on a bed of warm Chinese radish and red onion salad, and steamed roulade of Dover sole comes with a creamy vermouth sauce. Meat-eaters have their way with pan-fried medallions of beef, or chargrilled smoked chicken breast with tarragon sauce. Potato soup and vegetable samosas have kicked things off satisfyingly and, as a finale, you might find ice-creams, bread-and-butter pudding or Grand Marnier crème caramel. Good-value drinking throughtout the list at all levels owes a lot to suppliers Lay & Wheeler. Wines are up to date, but don't neglect the classics. CELLARMAN'S CHOICE: Stirling Hills Chardonnay 1994, Australia, £13,50; Côtes du Rhône-Villages 1991, Durieu, £15.50.

CHEF: Chris Oakley PROPRIETOR: Milsom Hotels (Dedham) Ltd OPEN: all week 12 to 2, 6 to 9.30 CLOSED: D 25 and 26 Dec MEALS: alc (main courses £6.50 to £15.50). Set L Sun to Fri (2 courses) £9.50 to £12.50, Set D £16.50 SERVICE: 10%, card slips closed CARDS: Access, Amex, Delta, Diners, Switch, Visa DETAILS: 80 seats. Private parties: 100 main room. Car park. Vegetarian meals. Children's helpings. No cigars/pipes in dining-room. Wheelchair access (2 steps). Music ACCOMMODATION: 6 rooms, all with bath/shower. TV. Phone. B&B £45 to £72.50. Children welcome (*The Which? Hotel Guide*)

HASLEMERE Surrey map 3

Fleur de Sel

SURREY 1996 NEWCOMER

NEW ENTRY

23–27 Lower Street, Haslemere GU27 2NY COOKING 3
TEL: (01428) 651462 FAX: (01428) 661568 COST £19–£43

Readers may be familiar with the knocked-together cottages on the raised pavement. For many years it was Morels, now renamed in honour of the high-quality French salt from Noirmoutier, whence Michel Perraud hails. More recently he was at Les Alouettes in Claygate, and Claygate's loss is very much Haslemere's gain, as reporters queue up to welcome the new venture. The room looks just as it did, very comfortable, with subdued jade green and peach fabrics and blue and yellow mottled walls. The welcome is gracious, the service good, although somewhat formal, by the junior French team.

Cooking is in the 'modern classical' mould of lobster-filled ravioli, or tian of lamb with an aubergine mousse, tomato and courgette. 'We had an excellent lunch at a reasonable price,' wrote one couple of the fixed-price daily-changing offering, in their case a 'deliciously light mousseline of turbot' with a tomato butter sauce, sliced breast of pheasant on braised Savoy cabbage, and a gratin of pineapple 'with a little chocolate in the sauce'. The midweek set-price menu looks a good deal, while the seasonally changing set-price *carte* offers plenty of choice. Some favourites have already become near-permanent fixtures, such as roast Gressingham duck, generously portioned, tender within, crisp without, in a sweet sticky sauce based on a good strong jus spiced with ginger.

Fish is well treated too, including at inspection, five ovals of sea bass topped with a pink shellfish mousse, light and fluffy, lightly spiced, in a good beurre blanc dotted with brilliant green petals of mange-tout. Although vegetables are good, they are the same for all main courses, while desserts meet with mixed success; among the better ones have been a crêpe soufflé with 'exquisitely contrasting orange and chocolate sauces', a crème brûlée – 'a perfect creamy base topped with perfect crunch' – and a brandy-snap flower holding an ice-cream made of black cherries and meringue: 'brilliant'. The entirely French wine list inclines more to reds, with some very smart clarets. House wine is £9.90, or £2.50 a glass.

CHEF: Michel Perraud PROPRIETORS: Michel and Bernadette Perraud OPEN: Tue to Fri and Sun L 12 to 2, Tue to Sat D 7 to 10 MEALS: Set L £9.50 (2 courses) to £12.50, Set D £21 (2 courses) to £26, plus Tue to Thur Set D £12.50 (2 courses) and £16.50 SERVICE: not inc CARDS: Access, Amex, Visa DETAILS: 50 seats. Private parties: 50 main room. Vegetarian meals. Children's helpings. Smart dress preferred. No cigars/pipes in dining-room. Wheelchair access. Music. Air-conditioned

HASTINGS East Sussex **map 3**

Röser's

64 Eversfield Place, St Leonards, Hastings TN37 6DB COOKING 3*
TEL: (01424) 712218 COST £24–£57

The 'very ordinary-looking' house is on the sea-front, opposite Hastings pier, where Hastings and St Leonards coalesce. Casual diners probably wouldn't give it a second look, which is just as well because the Rösers insist on bookings only. They are a husband-and-wife team who do just about everything themselves, serving up 'outstanding food for this area' among the wood panelling, 1960s-style cubicles and a collection of stuffed animals. The place may look like a tea-room, but the cooking is in a completely different class.

For a start the ingredients are tip-top. 'We have been picking our own ceps, chanterelles and pied de mouton mushrooms this year,' say the Rösers, who serve some fresh and preserve the rest. They also do their own smoking and curing, and make sausages of pork, venison and wild boar. Romney Marsh lamb crops up, as do locally landed fish, including John Dory, 'large, juicy, meaty scallops', and sea bass that might be served with coriander seeds, basil and tomato. One reporter enjoyed a 'wonderful' first course of pike soufflé, a generous warm mousse studded with little pieces of fish – no great kaleidoscope of flavours, perhaps, but a subtle contrast of intensities and textures.

There is, nevertheless, a robust side to the cooking, with 'really good helpings and really rich flavours', including first-class steaks, or roast pigeon breast, sliced wafer-thin, in a pool of deep, meaty sauce made with Cabernet Sauvignon vinegar. The interplay of flavours runs to puddings such as a white chocolate parfait complemented by a nicely bitter blood-orange caramel sauce. The quality of wines across the board is undisputed, from ineffably good claret and burgundy at the top down to short but effective selections in other mainstream regions and countries. Prices are not as high as in comparable establishments, and good, sensible drinking is possible for less than £20. House French is £9.95. CELLARMAN'S CHOICE: Montagny premier cru 1992, Leflaive, £21.50; Faugères, Ch. de la Liquière ' Vieilles Vignes' 1992, Vidal, £13.95.

CHEF: Gerald Röser PROPRIETORS: Gerald and Jenny Röser OPEN: Tue to Fri L 12 to 2, Tue to Sat D 7 to 10 MEALS: alc (main courses £13 to £16). Set L £16.95, Set D Tue to Fri £19.95 SERVICE: net prices, card slips closed CARDS: Access, Amex, Diners, Switch, Visa DETAILS: 30 seats. Private parties: 16 main room, 30 private room. Vegetarian meals. Children welcome. No cigars/pipes in dining-room. Wheelchair access (2 steps). No music

HAWORTH West Yorkshire map 8

▲ *Weaver's*

15 West Lane, Haworth BD22 8DU COOKING 1
TEL: (01535) 643822 COST £19–£40

The three knocked-together cottages manage to indulge in smartness and comfort and yet retain a period feel. The cooking styles itself 'honest northern', and cites in evidence smoked Ribblesdale cheese wrapped in air-dried ham, baked, and served with a warm potato salad, and pot-roast shoulder of Yorkshire lamb with spring vegetables and a reduction of elderberry wine. It makes a virtue of things like potato skins (deep-fried with a chive mayonnaise dip) but is not cheapskate when it comes to Pennine meat and potato pie with good beef and shortcrust pastry. Fish might come in a pie too, or baked or roasted. Butter and cream sauces are relieved by a few sharper ones: ginger and rhubarb for the well-cooked and boned duck, or gin and lime for locally reared, pan-fried calf's liver. 'Old school pud wi' custard' varies from day to day, and there is Victorian trifle, or chocolate and marshmallow brownies. The bargain fixed-price menu – similar food, just cheaper – operates early evening: order before 7.15pm, leave by 9pm. A good spread of wines at reasonable prices includes house French at £8.35.

CHEFS/PROPRIETORS: Colin and Jane Rushworth OPEN: Sun L (winter only) 12 to 1.30, Tue to Sat D only 6.45 to 9 CLOSED: 2 weeks Christmas, 2 weeks end July, Sun L Easter to Oct MEALS: alc (main courses £7 to £15). Set L Sun £9.95 (2 courses) to £11.95, Set D Tue to Fri before 7.15pm £9.95 (2 courses) to £11.95 SERVICE: not inc, card slips closed CARDS: Access, Amex, Delta, Diners, Switch, Visa DETAILS: 60 seats. Private parties: 16 main room, 16 private room. Vegetarian meals. Children's helpings. Smart dress preferred. No smoking in the dining-room. Music. Air-conditioned ACCOMMODATION: 3 rooms, all with bath/shower. TV. Phone. B&B £49.50 to £69.50. Deposit: £20. Children welcome (*The Which? Hotel Guide*)

HAYDON BRIDGE Northumberland map 10

General Havelock Inn

Radcliffe Road, Haydon Bridge NE47 6ER
TEL: (01434) 684376 COOKING 1
on A69, 6m W of Hexham COST £17–£33

An 'excellent pub', enthused one reporter about this green-painted hostelry with splendid lawns and a frontage by the River Tyne; it is a place that exudes warmth, comfort and civility. One reporter found the dining-room with its river view 'really cosy despite its high ceiling'. Ian Clyde is an obliging host and Angela runs the kitchen. Dinner is fixed-price for four courses and the cooking is generous, unfussy and ideally suited to the needs of visitors seeking a taste of old-style pub/restaurant food. Many fixture dishes are regularly mentioned: seafood pancake, thick wedges of crab tart, crispy duck with redcurrant jelly, and breast of chicken with tarragon. Vegetables are generally up to scratch, while puddings – such as poached pear with chocolate sauce or blackcurrant tart – are of a similar standard. A simpler, handwritten *carte* operates at lunch-time, when main courses range from roast loin of pork to baked fillet of plaice. The wine list is well spread, prices are fair and half-bottles show up well. House wines start at £7.

CHEF: Angela Clyde PROPRIETORS: Ian and Angela Clyde OPEN: Wed to Sun L 12 to 1, Wed to Sat D 7.30 to 8.45 CLOSED: first 2 weeks Jan, first 2 weeks Sept MEALS: alc (main courses £6 to £6.50). Set L Sun £12, Set D £19.50 SERVICE: not inc CARDS: none DETAILS: 28 seats. 1 table outside. Private parties: 28 main room. Children's helpings. Smart dress preferred. Wheelchair access (1 step; also WC). No music

HAYFIELD Derbyshire map 9

▲ *Bridge End*

7 Church Street, Hayfield SK12 5JE COOKING 2
TEL/FAX: (01663) 747321 COST £21–£44

Bring your hiking-boots and you can tramp up and down Kinder Scout to work up an appetite for dinner here. The village of Hayfield, a straggle of stone cottages on either side of the River Sett, is on the edge of the Peak District National Park, and Bridge End is in the middle of the village opposite the church. Inside, understated pine, dried flowers and knick-knacks present a suitably restrained backdrop for the cooking, which tends to the dramatic. Smoked haddock is simmered in cream with prawns and dill, wrapped up in smoked salmon, given a Cheddar topping and then grilled – a lot of work for a first course. Another starter presents wild rabbit in the form of a sausage of the saddle and leg meat with a pâté of the liver, accompanied by haricot beans and a tomato sauce, all adding up to a kind of cassoulet.

There is plenty going on in main courses too, such as roast corn-fed chicken with smoked bacon, baby onions and olives, the juices finished with white wine, served with polenta. The roast beef at Sunday lunch, cooked pink, has been pronounced 'excellent – tender and of lovely flavour, with good gravy and nice crisp Yorkshire'. Cheeses may include creamy Beenleigh Blue from Devon. Summer pudding is well rendered, and a dab hand is at work on dessert soufflés. Good coffee comes in large cafetières. Many would agree with the couple who praised the cooking as 'subtle and original'. The thoughtfully composed wine list has some fine French selections and a shorter but no less pedigree New World showing that includes wines from Elderton in the Barossa Valley and de Redcliffe from New Zealand. Mark-ups are computed so that they decrease proportionately as the base price goes up – a most sympathetic approach. House wines are £9.80.

CHEFS: Jonathan Holmes and Joanne Winch PROPRIETORS: Geoffrey and Barbara Tier OPEN: Sun L 12.30 to 2.30, Tue to Sat D 7.30 to 10 CLOSED: first week Jan MEALS: alc (main courses £9.50 to £15). Set L Sun £13 SERVICE: not inc CARDS: Access, Amex, Delta, Diners, Visa DETAILS: 50 seats. Private parties: 35 main room, 18 private room. Car park. Vegetarian meals. Children's helpings. Smart dress preferred. No smoking during meals. Music ACCOMMODATION: 4 rooms, all with bath/shower. TV. Phone. B&B £35 to £50. Children welcome. Baby facilities (*The Which? Hotel Guide*)

HELFORD Cornwall map 1

▲ *Riverside*

Helford TR12 6JU
TEL: (01326) 231443 FAX: (01326) 231103 COOKING 2
off B3293, 6m E of Helston COST £36–£43

This terraced restaurant overlooking Helford Estuary is certainly off most people's definition of the beaten track. It has been in the capable hands of Susie Darrell for eight years. Her reputation for good seafood cookery with a French orientation is solidly established, and regulars are warmly welcomed. The fixed price pays for a four-course menu with coffee; British and French cheeses are served before dessert, and there are no supplements. Elaboration is deliberately avoided. 'Plump and juicy' mussels come in a 'smooth and pungent' more or less marinière broth, while seafood pancakes generously filled with lobster, crab and scallops are given a creamy lobster sauce of powerful richness. Meat-eaters are not ignored: duck breast with a red wine and thyme sauce, and lamb fillet with its kidneys, sweetbreads and oyster mushrooms are accurately cooked and sauced. Mango parfait with passion-fruit syrup has assertive flavour. Otherwise you may be offered strawberry sablé with honey and mascarpone and a coulis of wild berries. Coffee needs strengthening a bit, but the petits fours that come with it had one family group squabbling over them. The place is usually, but not always, run with great bonhomie.

Choice in half-bottles alone – eight pages – would make the wine list worth travelling for. As a whole, it is well-nigh flawless, a treasure-house of the classical and the modern which offers many fully mature clarets, burgundies and Rhônes from the pick of the growers, and an authoritative selection from South Africa, all conscientiously annotated. In the context, prices are extremely fair. House wines include Louis Latour Mâcon-Lugny at £11.50 and a 1990 Côtes de Castillon claret for £12.50. CELLARMAN'S CHOICE: Hamilton Russell Chardonnay 1993, Hermanus, South Africa, £14; Cornas 1986, Clape, £27.60.

CHEF/PROPRIETOR: Susie Darrell OPEN: all week D only 7.30 to 9 CLOSED: Nov to end Mar MEALS: Set D £30 SERVICE: net prices, card slips closed DETAILS: 35 seats. 4 tables outside. Private parties: 12 main room. Car park. No children under 10. Smart dress preferred. Wheelchair access (2 steps; also WC). No music ACCOMMODATION: 6 rooms, all with bath/shower. TV. B&B £75 to £120. Rooms for disabled. Children welcome. Garden (*The Which? Hotel Guide*)

'Desserts were served by a Manuel lookalike who scurried in, asked who ordered which, plonked it down and then scurried out again.' **(On eating in Avon)**

HERSTMONCEUX East Sussex map 3

Sundial

Gardner Street, Herstmonceux BN27 4LA COOKING 2
TEL: (01323) 832217 COST £25–£70

A French auberge with an Italian chef in a Tudor house on the Weald has to be a recipe for success, and the fact that the Bertolis will before long be taking the Sundial into its fourth decade of operation is powerful testimony to that. The dining-room has been fashioned from a number of the old rooms amalgamated into one cosy, low-ceilinged space. The front-of-house is run with cool professionalism by Laure Bertoli, upstaged from time to time by her husband appearing in chef's whites. Outsized menus furnish plenty of choice, some dishes translated, others not. Starters are wholly traditional: prawns with garlic butter, smoked salmon roulade, game pâté en croûte. Experiments are tried in main courses that might see turbot fillets stuffed with a mousseline of scallops, or crisp duckling breast sauced with strawberries. Mixing and matching meats and offals is a regular technique: pigeon breasts come with lambs' kidneys in a mustard sauce, while the *assiette du boucher* has pheasant, lamb, beef and kidneys in port.

Desserts plough a timeless furrow of syllabub, profiteroles and the like. The wine list reflects the dual nationalities of the owners, a smattering of Italians among expensive French classical stuff. Some of the latter is astonishingly fine, and priced accordingly. At least the 1967 Ch. d'Yquem is kept decently under £600. Go to the less illustrious regions for relief. House Soave and Valpolicella come by the jug at £10.75.

CHEF: Giuseppe Bertoli PROPRIETORS: Giuseppe and Laure Bertoli OPEN: Tue to Sun L 12 to 2 (2.30 Sun), Tue to Sat D 7 to 9.30 (10 Sat) CLOSED: Christmas to 20 Jan, 3 weeks Aug to Sept MEALS: alc (main courses £15.50 to £25). Set L Tue to Sat £15.50 to £19.50, Set L Sun £27.50, Set D £24.50 SERVICE: 10%, card slips closed CARDS: Access, Amex, Delta, Diners, Visa DETAILS: 60 seats. 8 tables outside. Private parties: 60 main room, 20 private room. Car park. Children's helpings. Smart dress preferred. No smoking in dining-room. Wheelchair access (1 step; also WC). Music

HETTON North Yorkshire map 8

Angel Inn

Hetton BD23 6LT
TEL: (01756) 730263 FAX: (01756) 730363 COOKING 2*
off B6265, 5m N of Skipton COST £23–£36

Denis Watkins has put Hetton on the map, and attracts so much custom that the village is in danger of being swamped. He has also turned the Angel into an unlikely, but generally successful, meeting point for Lethersdale spring lamb and Mediterranean vegetables, or North Atlantic fish and eastern spices. The inn is a line of old stone buildings that have remained happily 'undisturbed by national brewery designers'. The casual bar and brasserie, with polished oak tables, farmhouse chairs and leaded and brass kitchen range, deal enthusiastically in rustic fish soup with aïoli, warm goats' cheese crostini, and pan-fried calf's liver with bubble and squeak. This inexpensive and spirited cooking has won many friends.

The restaurant dining-room is a contrast: more formal, but simple and comfortable, with 'good linen, cheap cutlery and big plates'. Although there is some overlap, it aims for more sophisticated food. In addition to filo pastry 'moneybags' filled with seafood, tomato tart with pesto, and what can be wonderful fresh fish of the day, there is a small but significant vein of hearty country cooking, in oxtail, steak and kidney pudding, and cassoulet. The menu tends to be rather static, though, and an October visitor was disappointed not to find any game on the menu. But much of the food pleases, not least the terrines: one 'an inspired mix of fibrous meaty ham and smooth, sweet foie gras pâté' served with a good onion marmalade and salad.

Techniques are mainly sound, dishes look good and portions are generous, but flavour is sometimes the casualty. By taking on breast of pigeon on a cep risotto, or filling ravioli with chopped scallops to accompany a fillet of turbot, the kitchen can seem rather out of its depth, as if striving hard to impress when it has no need to. Some, but not all, service is keen, knowledgeable and pleasant. Wines are a delight for their quality, interest, spread (although Burgundy and Bordeaux constitute the backbone), and for their pricing, which produces some refreshing bargains. The list has a good supply of half-bottles, a short 'hand-picked' selection of recommended wines under £15, and about 20 wines by the glass. CELLARMAN'S CHOICE: Mâcon Uchizy 1992, Dom. Talmard, £15.50; St Estèphe, Ch. de Marbuzet 1986, £19.65.

CHEF: John Topham PROPRIETORS: Denis and Juliet Watkins, and John Topham OPEN: restaurant Sun L 12 to 2, Mon to Sat D 6 to 9.30, bar and brasserie all week 12 to 2, 6 to 9.30 CLOSED: Second week Jan MEALS: alc bar and brasserie (main courses £6 to £11.50) restaurant set L Sun £17, Set D £22.95. Minimum £22.95 restaurant D SERVICE: not inc, card slips closed CARDS: Access, Delta, Switch, Visa DETAILS: 55 seats restaurant, 65 seats bar. 8 tables outside. Private parties: 40 main room. Car park. Vegetarian meals. Children welcome. Smart dress preferred in restaurant. No smoking in 1 dining-room. Wheelchair access. No music

HEXHAM Northumberland map 10

Black House

Dipton Mill Road, Hexham NE46 1RZ
TEL: (01434) 604744
on Whitley Chapel road, S of Hexham

COOKING 2*
COST £23–£45

The Black House is announced only by a discreet sign in black and white depicting a mallard. It is an old farmhouse, and entry to the restaurant is through a stable door. The split-level eating area is decorated in simple country style and run rather briskly by Chris Pittock, while wife Hazel cooks. Menus change monthly to capitalise on seasonal availability. Maryland crab-cakes may be a long way from home, but a terrine of pork, prune and pigeon with spiced pears and brioche is modern Britain all the way. An inspector was impressed by the novel technique used for the 'magnificent local asparagus'. It was blanched, then flash-roasted, and dressed in olive oil and balsamic vinegar. Main courses may include 'rich and juicy' king prawns with garlic, lemon and herb butter, or roast rack of Northumberland lamb – 'terrific-tasting, two-inch-thick meat' – with a sauce of redcurrants, ginger and orange accompanied by glazed onions. To finish there may be milk and dark chocolate mousse, or 'a timeless classic of strawberry tart'. Service is 'unintrusive and unpretentious'. French house wines are £9.75 a bottle.

CHEF: Hazel Pittock PROPRIETORS: Chris and Hazel Pittock OPEN: Sun L preceding bank hol 12.30 to 1.30, Fri and Sat D 7.30 to 9.30; D other days by arrangement CLOSED: 25 to 30 Dec MEALS: alc (main courses £8.50 to £16.50). Set L Sun £15.50 SERVICE: not inc, card slips closed CARDS: Access, Delta, Visa DETAILS: 26 seats. Private parties: 26 main room. Car park. Vegetarian meals. No children under 14. Smart dress preferred. No smoking in dining-room. Music

HINTLESHAM Suffolk map 6

▲ *Hintlesham Hall*

Hintlesham IP8 3NS
TEL: (01473) 652268 FAX: (01473) 652463 COOKING 3
on A1071 4½m W of Ipswich COST £28–£69

'I eat here about six times a year, always take the set lunch and have never had a poor dish,' comments a reporter. Such consistency – an elusive quality – builds confidence. Hintlesham, a Georgian-fronted Elizabethan house, is a model of good hotelkeeping, very grand but remarkably hospitable, and the kitchen has to run hard to keep up with the rest of the operation. Table-settings, décor and the magnificence of the dining-rooms inevitably produce a formal atmosphere, which staff do their best to soften while still preserving a high degree of discipline.

The variety of techniques applied to the cooking – steaming, poaching, grilling, braising, quick-frying, stewing – helps to bring diversity to the seasonally changing menu. Dishes can be elaborate, seeming to express the kitchen's exuberance as much as anything, although one reporter wondered whether, in return for a lot of money, the chef was merely making sure that customers received a lot of cooking. Alan Ford really goes to town on dishes, and in particular likes to wrap things up: braised vegetables are layered in filo pastry to accompany pigeon; breast of chicken, with a mushroom and herb farce, is encased in Parma ham; and an iced ginger and star-anise parfait is wrapped in a crisp tuile biscuit.

A 'comforting and successful' escalope of sweetly rich foie gras on a potato cake, surrounded by shredded oxtail in a wine-laden gravy, led one reporter to consider whether more than one meal here might be a daunting prospect. If it is, then the kitchen is willing to cook items more simply and plainly on request. Fish is particularly impressive, and details are looked after, including good granary, walnut and olive breads, first-class canapés, fine fruity olive oil, vegetables on a side plate, French and British cheeses, and coffee with home-made petits fours. Prices appear high but include service. The wine list is all-embracing, well chosen, with lots of Adnams favourites and much of interest below £20. Mark-ups may be justified on wines that have been cellared for some years, but are more difficult to accept on others. Half-bottles are plentiful, and house recommendations, from £12.50 a bottle, are helpful. CELLARMAN'S

CHOICE: Rioja Blanca 1993, Marqués de Mudela, £14.05; Gran Coronas Reserva 1988, Torres, £18.75.

CHEF: Alan Ford PROPRIETOR: Hintlesham Hall Ltd OPEN: Sun to Fri L 12 to 1.45, all week D 7 to 9.30 MEALS: alc (main courses £15.50 to £23). Set L £18.50, Set D Mon to Thur £24 SERVICE: net prices, card slips closed CARDS: Access, Amex, Diners, Switch, Visa DETAILS: 120 seats. Private parties: 81 main room, 14 and 42 private rooms. Car park. Vegetarian meals. Children's helpings. No children under 10 D. Jacket and tie. No smoking in dining-room. Wheelchair access (1 step; also WC). Music ACCOMMODATION: 33 rooms, all with bath/shower. TV. Phone. B&B £85 to £300. Children welcome. Pets welcome in bedrooms only. Garden. Swimming- pool. Fishing (*The Which? Hotel Guide*)

HINTON CHARTERHOUSE Avon

map 2

▲ *Homewood Park*

Hinton Charterhouse BA3 6BB

TEL: (01225) 723731 FAX: (01225) 723820

NEW CHEF

off A36, 5m SE of Bath

COST £29–£63

Such is the solicitude with which Homewood Park is run that, one foul January Sunday, the staff moved heaven and earth to keep the log fires going. The couple who wrote to us appreciated the efforts even more because they were the only two having lunch. In more clement weather, Homewood and its environs are a joy. The house is of ivied grey stone, the attractive Limpley Stoke valley undulates into the distance and Bath is close at hand. Homewood, for one couple, 'exuded friendliness' from the entrance hall onwards.

As we went to press Tim Ford left for Summer Lodge (see entry, Evershot) and Stephen Morey arrived after a short spell at Woolley Grange (see entry, Bradford-on-Avon) following his departure from Gravetye Manor (see entry, East Grinstead). His cooking has a classic foundation, taking in game terrine, and chicken boudin, as well as gutsier braised ham hock with lentils, and desserts such as Grand Marnier soufflé omelettes. Although some good bottles show up on the wine list, the selection overall is uneven, encompassing some tenderly youthful burgundies, maturer clarets and a 1979 Côtes du Roussillon Villages. There is a wine from Uruguay but nothing from Spain. House recommendations, including three English wines, are £12.50.

CHEF: Stephen Morey PROPRIETORS: Frank and Sara Gueuning OPEN: all week 12 to 1.30, 7 to 9.30 (10 Sat) MEALS: alc (main courses £18 to £20.50). Set L £17.50, Set D £28.50 SERVICE: not inc CARDS: Access, Amex, Delta, Diners, Switch, Visa DETAILS: 50 seats. Private parties: 40 main room, 25 private rooms. Car park. Vegetarian meals. Children's helpings. Smart dress preferred. No smoking in dining-room. Wheelchair access (also WC). No music ACCOMMODATION: 15 rooms, all with bath/shower. TV. Phone. B&B £85 to £150. Rooms for disabled. Children welcome. Baby facilities. Afternoon teas. Garden (*The Which? Hotel Guide*)

Prices quoted in the Guide *are based on information supplied by restaurateurs. The prices quoted at the top of each entry represent a range, from the lowest meal price to the highest; the latter is inflated by 20 per cent to take account of likely price rises during the year of the* Guide.

HOLDENBY Northamptonshire map 5

▲ *Lynton House*

Holdenby NN6 8DJ
TEL/FAX: (01604) 770777
between A50 and A428, E of Holdenby towards Church Brampton

COOKING 2
COST £19–£39

The Victorian rectory has taken well to its modest extensions – the one for drinks overlooks fields and grazing horses – which make it feel lighter and more spacious. The kitchen's energy is concentrated into the obligatory four courses at dinner, the second a sorbet or a tasty soup along the lines of pasta e fagioli or cappelletti in brodo. The food is neither completely modern nor particularly traditional, but slots Italian dishes of cannelloni or seafood risotto between rather more English braised saddle of venison or pheasant casserole. Beef usually carries a supplement.

The style has developed quite naturally from partners with different backgrounds, and it works to good effect in rural Northants. Some corners appear to be cut when it comes to ingredients, but pasta is made in-house and likely to be the pick of first courses – tortellini filled with ricotta and spinach at one spring meal – while fish is a good main-course bet: lemon sole with lobster sauce, perhaps, or bulging balloons of small squid stuffed with prawns and pesto. Puddings continue the Anglo-Italian theme with zuppa inglese, apple cream pie and Sicilian cheesecake. Wines range from humble Dolcetto to flamboyant super-Tuscans, with house wine at £10.75.

CHEF: Carol Bertozzi PROPRIETORS: Carlo and Carol Bertozzi OPEN: Tue to Fri L 12.30 to 1.45, Mon to Sat D 7.30 to 9.45 CLOSED: Christmas, 1 week spring, 1 week late summer, bank hols MEALS: Set L £12.50 (2 courses) to £17.75, Set D £21.25 SERVICE: none, card slips closed CARDS: Access, Amex, Visa DETAILS: 45 seats. 4 tables outside. Private parties: 80 main room, 20 private room. Car park. No children under 6. Smart dress preferred. No smoking in 1 dining-room. No cigars/pipes in other dining-room. Wheelchair access (also WC). No music ACCOMMODATION: 5 rooms, all with bath/shower. TV. Phone. B&B £49 to £55. No children under 6. Garden (*The Which? Hotel Guide*)

HOLT Norfolk map 6

Yetman's

37 Norwich Road, Holt NR25 6SA
TEL: (01263) 713320

COOKING 2
COST £30–£48

This old Norfolk cottage with low ceilings and beams is decorated to a high standard. The yellow paint, yellow curtains and yellow menus range from primrose to lemon and induce a permanent feeling of springtime freshness. Peter Yetman's matey philosophy is similarly cheerful, and 'laid-back and unpretentious' is his own assessment of the restaurant. Others may feel that some of the finer points are missing, but it is probably best to accept the idiosyncratic Yetman's lock, stock and barrel, or not at all. Once you are on the same wavelength, everything begins to make sense.

Fish and vegetables figure as prominently as meat on the shortish menu (two-, three- or four-course meals are the set deal), and without this kitchen some of the ingredients might never have bumped into each other, as when toasted North Barnet goats' cheese meets a Sicilian tomato salad. The quality of foodstuffs helps to turn apparently ordinary dishes into something special. Local mussels are poached in white wine and scattered with shredded leeks that do a fair (visual) impersonation of seaweed; local goose has a prune and celery stuffing; and a 'beautiful roll of soft, skinless, baked red pepper wrapped up with unbitter aubergine and olive oil' came with a scoop of creamy goats' cheese and bruschetta and 'tasted divine'. That same meal ended with 'a joyous heap of crunchy, fruity, chewy meringue studded with syrupy, crystallised ginger, pieces of dried fig and soft slices of pear – all very indulgent'.

Wines are chosen with care and served casually. The New World is prominent, with an excellent New Zealand section, but then quality is high throughout. Wines by the glass are tip-top, regularly updated, and usually cost between £3 and £4. Bottles are brought already opened, left on the table, and no tasting is offered. CELLARMAN'S CHOICE: Mulderbosch Vineyards Sauvignon Blanc 1994, Stellenbosch, South Africa, £12.95; Parker Cabernet Sauvignon 1989, Coonawarra, S. Australia, £21.50.

CHEF: Alison Yetman PROPRIETORS: Alison and Peter Yetman OPEN: Sat and Sun L 12.30 to 2 (by prior arrangement), Wed to Sun D (also Mon D summer) 7.30 to 9 MEALS: Set L £16.45 (2 courses) to £24.75, Set D £21.50 (2 courses) to £29.50. Minimum £16.45 L, £21.50 D SERVICE: not inc DETAILS: 32 seats. Private parties: 20 main room, 12 and 20 private rooms. Vegetarian meals. Children welcome. No smoking in dining-room. Wheelchair access (1 step). No music

HONLEY West Yorkshire map 8

Mustards & Punch

6 Westgate, Honley HD7 2AA COOKING **2**
TEL: (01484) 662066 COST £23–£38

Scott Hessel is no shrinking violet. Out of the Roux Brothers' stable via the Crab & Lobster, Asenby (see entry), he is intent on dazzling the conurbations of West Yorkshire with creative, contemporary cooking in surroundings that are uncompromisingly 1990s neighbourhood bistro. Change and improvement are his watchwords. He has put cloths on the tables and replaced the blackboards with a weekly printed menu – he even painted the multi-coloured logo on the cover.

His cooking is fiercely modern and comfortably classic by turns: Thai seared fillet salad and Belgian chocolate pithiviers have been in the repertoire since the beginning, but he is forever adapting ideas, reshaping, mixing and matching. Consider smoked haddock: it might appear as a mousse with smoked salmon tartare, as a croustade with poached egg and hollandaise, or fashioned into tempura with lemon-pickled salmon and vegetables. Hessel fills ravioli with goats' cheese (a popular starter, this), wild mushrooms, or roasted peppers and Taleggio. 'Gorgeous' salmon may be skewered with scallops, chargrilled and served on a coriander and tomato fondue, or encased in filo pastry with hake, while the old guard are wooed with steak and kidney pudding, calf's liver with shallot gravy and parsnip mash, and roast rump of lamb. Fresh fruit distracts from the richness of desserts such as mascarpone cheesecake or coconut crème brûlée. Occasionally things go awry – 'tough' sweetbreads, 'tasteless' saddle of rabbit and 'hard and cold' jam roly-poly clouded one occasion, for example – but these are isolated outbursts. Service is generally pleasant and speedy. Scott Hessel has also revamped his wine list, adding more details of growers and providing plenty of variety across the range. Drinkers with one eye on their bank balance can choose from an abundance of almost two dozen house selections, starting at £8.95.

CHEF/PROPRIETOR: Scott Hessel OPEN: Tue to Fri L 12 to 2, Mon to Sat D 7 to 10 (11 Sat) MEALS: alc (main courses £9 to £14). Set L £5 SERVICE: not inc, card slips closed CARDS: Access, Amex, Switch, Visa DETAILS: 60 seats. Private parties: 30 main room. Car park. Vegetarian meals. Children welcome. Smart dress preferred. No cigars/pipes in dining-room. Wheelchair access (1 step). Music. Air-conditioned

HORNCASTLE Lincolnshire map 9

Magpies

71–75 East Street, Horncastle LN9 6AA COOKING 1
TEL: (01507) 527004 COST £15–£32

'We don't ever want to become a faceless gastronomic temple,' says the Lee family, and indeed there seems little enough prospect of their tenacious local following permitting such an outrage. Fresh flowers, candles and vivacious décor make the most of the L-shaped dining-room, and a pleasant atmosphere of chatter fills the place. The culinary members of the Lee household are Matthew and Simon. Their fixed-price menus capitalise on local supplies, particularly for old breeds of meat. The roast loin of pork in cider gravy is Gloucester Old Spot, while locally reared Lincoln Reds provide sirloin steak – grilled and finished with shallots and mustard in a red wine sauce – and oxtail braised in madeira. Discreet dashes of fashion feature in salt-cod with potatoes and aïoli, tian of duck confit with red cabbage and apple, and roast sea bass with chicory and a vanilla sauce. Vibrancy continues through to dessert stage for white chocolate and prune terrine with armagnac ice-cream, and nougat glacé with passion-fruit coulis. Bread, vegetables and coffee are all up to the mark. Wines are listed in price bands, supplemented by a generous showing of pedigree bottles that mostly constitute good value. Seven house wines of varying provenance are all at the same price of £8 the bottle and £2 the glass.

CHEFS: Matthew and Simon Lee PROPRIETORS: the Lee family OPEN: Tue to Fri and Sun L 12.30 to 2, Tue to Sat D 7.15 to 9.45 CLOSED: first 2 weeks Jan MEALS: Set L £10, Set D £17 to £20 SERVICE: not inc CARDS: Access, Visa DETAILS: 40 seats. Private parties: 40 main room. No children under 4. Smart dress preferred. No smoking in dining-room. Music

HORTON Northamptonshire map 5

French Partridge

Horton NN7 2AP
TEL: (01604) 870033 FAX: (01604) 870032 COOKING 3
on B526, 5m SE of Northampton COST £28–£33

'Very good cooking, very good value' was one summing-up of this family-run restaurant a few miles from Northampton, now entering its fourth decade in the

Guide. The building is an old coaching-inn, mostly pre-1600, though the feel is more recent: Victorian has been suggested. In reality its heart is French provincial, given the two generations involved, the fixed-price four-course formula, the accomplished but not showy food executed with care and skill, the value, and even some of the dishes, from smooth, dark pink chicken liver parfait to lamb and duck cassoulet.

The menu works to an established routine, the second course usually fishy or mushroomy: on one occasion a piece of moist cod with a herb crust on a smear of light, sharp, unbuttery lemon sauce, or a pastry tartlet with mushroom duxelles, quail's eggs and hollandaise. 'A simple, standard classic' was the verdict on the tartlet, as it was on a crème brûlée done 'absolutely according to the book'. Four options each for first and main course may not sound a lot, but are usually enough. The Partridges pick up ideas from all over, including a Malayan-style baked chicken in a coconut cream and citrus marinade. Even Peruvian potatoes appeared at one meal: small new ones cooked with turmeric and a dash of something chilli-hot.

Sweets are generous to a fault, taking in chocolate marquise with coffee-bean sauce, and apricot rice brûlée, although savouries of mushrooms or soft herring roes on toast make a pleasant diversion. Meals are not rushed, and one reporter found Mary Partridge 'at her best in every way, advising on most acceptable wines at a very reasonable price', from a list that combines quality and value with enthusiasms from Burgundy to Germany by way of the Rhône and south-west France. The house selection of eight wines around £10 to £12 cleverly plays on eight grape varieties from Gamay to Jacquère. CELLARMAN'S CHOICE: Wirra Wirra Church Block 1992, McLaren Vale, S. Australia; Mercurey *premier cru* 1991, Juillot, £19.

CHEFS: D. C. and D. J. Partridge PROPRIETORS: D. C. and M. Partridge OPEN: Tue to Sat D only 7.30 to 9 CLOSED: 2 weeks Christmas, 2 weeks Easter, first 3 weeks Aug MEALS: Set D £23 SERVICE: net prices CARDS: none DETAILS: 50 seats. Private parties by arrangement. Car park. Vegetarian meals. Children welcome. No smoking in dining-room. Wheelchair access. No music

---

HUDDERSFIELD West Yorkshire map 9

Bradley's £

84 Fitzwilliam Street, Huddersfield HD1 5BB COOKING 1*
TEL: (01484) 516773 COST £14–£42

'The best thing that has happened around these parts for a long time' is a West Yorkshire reporter's verdict on this restaurant within walking distance of Huddersfield town centre. The dining-room occupies the ground floor of an old stone warehouse and the interior now consists of a split-level dining area with a stained glass and wooden bar tucked in one corner. Andrew Bradley and Jonathan Nichols have found staff with bags of enthusiasm. Jonathan heads the kitchen and his short printed menu is in the modern vein of warm salad of prawns, mushrooms and mange-tout, calf's liver with bubble and squeak, and vegetable tempura. Thickly sliced gravlax comes with a dill and grain mustard dressing, quiches are spot-on examples of the genre, and steaks are served with all manner of sauces. There are also well-reported specials such as roast monkfish with vermouth and dill sauce. Salads, vegetables and coffee have also been endorsed. A popular and great-value option – do check times in advance – is the daily-changing 'early bird' menu (the price includes half a bottle of house wine); you could make a pleasing supper of smoked mackerel mousse, lamb casserole and jam roly-poly. The 50-strong wine list has plenty of affordable bottles, especially from the New World. House wines start at £7.95.

CHEFS: Jonathan Nichols and Simon Garbutt PROPRIETORS: Jonathan Nichols and Andrew Bradley OPEN: Mon to Fri L 12 to 2, Mon to Sat D 6 to 10 (10.30 Fri and Sat) CLOSED: bank hols MEALS: alc (main courses £7.50 to £15). Set L £7.95 (2 courses) to £9.95, Set D £11.95 (Mon 6 to 9, Tue to Fri 6 to 7.30, Sat 6 to 7) SERVICE: not inc CARDS: Access, Switch, Visa DETAILS: 70 seats. Private parties: 70 main room. Car park. Vegetarian meals. Children's helpings. Smart dress preferred. Wheelchair access (also WC). Music. Air-conditioned

▲ *Lodge Hotel*

48 Birkby Lodge Road, Birkby,
Huddersfield HD2 2BG — COOKING 1*
TEL: (01484) 431001 FAX: (01484) 421590 — COST £19–£38

Perched on the edge of what is doomed to be known forever as *'Summer Wine* country', this popular small hotel offers Huddersfield an excursion into a wider culinary world than traditionally it may have been used to. In the setting of an immaculately tended dining-room, the fixed-price menus provide much food for thought. Parma ham, smoked venison and pastrami make a diverting first-course combination, as does pheasant with a crayfish and calvados sauce to follow. At dinner a soup course intervenes, with a choice of either French onion or the 'chef's renowned soup du jour'. Plaice with shrimps and lime juice at a spring Sunday lunch delivered good fish, although the citrus did rather predominate. Tagine of lamb with raisins, almonds and sweet tomatoes opens another window on Mediterranean cooking, while puddings work from a similarly vivid palette, including what the menu describes as 'New Orleans bread-and-butter pudding with bourbon cream'. Or there is a 'wonderful' cheeseboard. Vegetarians are more conscientiously catered for than at many other North Country places. The wine list does an exhaustive tour, taking in Kent, Surrey and Tasmania as well as the French regions. Prices are scrupulously fair, including Ch. Haut-Brion 1970 at £129, with house wines from Bergerac at £9.75.

CHEFS: Richard Hanson, Garry Birley and Kevin Birley PROPRIETORS: Garry Birley and Kevin Birley OPEN: all week L 12 to 2, Mon to Sat D 7.30 to 9.45 CLOSED: 26, 27 and 28 Dec MEALS: Set L £11.95, Set D £21.95 SERVICE: not inc, card slips closed CARDS: Access, Amex, Visa DETAILS: 62 seats. 4 tables outside. Private parties: 62 main room, 10 to30 private rooms. Car park. Vegetarian meals. Children's helpings. No children under 5 D. Smart dress preferred. No smoking in dining-room. Wheelchair access (also WC). Music ACCOMMODATION: 11 rooms, all with bath/shower. TV. Phone. B&B £45 to £70. Rooms for disabled. Children welcome. Baby facilities. Pets welcome in bedrooms only. Afternoon teas. Garden (*The Which? Hotel Guide*)

'My deep-fried pig's tail was rather like a pork grissini.'
(On eating in Greater London)

HUNSTRETE Avon map 2

▲ *Hunstrete House*

Hunstrete, Chelwood BS18 4NS
TEL: (01761) 490490 FAX: (01761) 490732 COOKING 2
off A368, 4m S of Keynsham COST £28–£70

This is a very English house, Georgian, and well furnished with antiques, porcelain and paintings. A popular spot for drinks, if the weather holds, is the courtyard, texturally rich with stone, terracotta and wood, plus a brace of silver pear trees. The inside feels stately – eighteenth-century portraits and thick green padded silk curtains with gold tassels hang in the dining-room – and dinner comes at appropriately stately prices. Robert Clayton's food is comfortably modern and generous, although roast tenderloin of pork stuffed with prunes shows that its roots are quite traditional. A few gestures play to the gallery, such as the puff pastry lid on a soup of spinach, smoked ham and truffle, or the cappuccino of wild mushrooms served with wild salmon and (domesticated) pickled cucumber. But ravioli of crab, or carpaccio of chargrilled beef is in the mainstream and none the worse for that.

Indeed, the balancing act between the low-risk food that many country houses indulge in and the desire to experiment is finely judged, producing mushroom boudin with creamed leeks and cep sauce, or grilled sea bass with trompettes-de-mort and a vanilla sauce. The garden supplies the kitchen with herbs, fruit and vegetables. Puddings include a passion-fruit soufflé with raspberry sauce, and demonstrate a contrasting mixture of tastes and temperatures in a pear and apple crumble with warm butterscotch sauce and apricot sorbet. Wines are good on the predominantly French list, but mark-ups are not friendly so prices soon break the £20 barrier. Half a dozen that stay below that are singled out as the house selection.

CHEF: Robert Clayton PROPRIETOR: Arcadian International plc OPEN: all week 12.30 to 2.30, 7.30 to 9.30 MEALS: alc D (main courses £12.50 to £22). Set L Mon to Sat £15, Set L Sun £19.50, Set D £29.50 SERVICE: not inc, card slips closed CARDS: Access, Amex, Delta, Diners, Switch, Visa DETAILS: 50 seats. 3 tables outside. Private parties: 50 main room, 12 and 30 private rooms. Car park. No children under 7. Smart dress preferred. No smoking in dining-room. Wheelchair access (also WC). No Music ACCOMMODATION: 23 rooms, all with bath/shower. TV. Phone. B&B £115 to £145. Rooms for disabled. Afternoon teas. Garden. Swimming-pool (*The Which? Hotel Guide*)

HURSTBOURNE TARRANT Hampshire map 2

▲ *Esseborne Manor* 

Hurstbourne Tarrant SP11 0ER
TEL: (01264) 736444 FAX: (01264) 736473 COOKING 1
on A343 1½m N of Hurstbourne Tarrant COST £28–£53

The late-Victorian country manor-house is set in two-and-a-half acres of gardens overlooking the Wessex Downs. A fixed-price lunch along the lines of leek and potato soup, mixed grill, and apple pie is served to local business folk, while a more adventurous *carte* comes into play in the evening (the set-price dinner has gone, coinciding with Nick Watson's arrival in the kitchen), offering about half a dozen choices at each stage, including savoury alternatives to pudding. Non-meat dishes appear to be on the increase, from a layered vegetable terrine or fish casserole to pasta dishes of linguine and pesto, or a ravioli of oriental-style mixed vegetables.

Saucing varies from a rich claret gravy with individual beef Wellington, to a warm chive vinaigrette with pan-fried sea bass. At inspection, meat dishes failed to shine, with the exception of chicken breast wrapped in bacon and stuffed with spinach, but puddings were very much on form, including a 'light but rich' chocolate bavarois in a chestnut-flavoured custard, and a trio of ice-creams in an almond basket with a warm butterscotch sauce. Wines hail from only three countries – France, Australia and New Zealand – but are from impeccable sources. Prices reflect the quality, but mark-ups are not greedy. House Australian is £12. CELLARMAN'S CHOICE: Cape Mentelle Chardonnay 1994, Margaret River, W. Australia, £23.80; Scotchmans Hill Pinot Noir 1993, Victoria, Australia, £23.90.

CHEF: Nick Watson PROPRIETORS: Michael and Frieda Yeo, and Simon Richardson OPEN: Sun to Fri L 12 to 2, all week D 7 to 9.30 MEALS: alc D (main courses £11.50 to £19). Set L £14 (2 courses) to £17.50 SERVICE: not inc, card slips closed CARDS: Access, Amex, Delta, Diners, Switch, Visa DETAILS: 40 seats. Private parties: 40 main room. Car park. Vegetarian meals. No children under 12. Smart dress preferred. Wheelchair access (also WC). Music ACCOMMODATION: 12 rooms, all with bath/shower. TV. Phone. B&B £69 to £112. Rooms for disabled. No children under 12. Garden (*The Which? Hotel Guide*)

HUXHAM Devon map 1

▲ *Barton Cross* 

Huxham, Stoke Canon EX5 4EJ
TEL: (01392) 841245 FAX: (01392) 841942 COOKING 1
at Stoke Canon, 5m N of Exeter on A396 COST £25–£38

The hotel, only five miles from Exeter city centre, is 'probably what an American tourist sees in his mind's eye when thinking of English country cottages'. Three seventeenth-century ones have been joined together, enclosing a courtyard garden 'where we sat for aperitifs and revelled in the tranquillity', and the older part of the building now forms the galleried dining-room. 'Paul Bending has returned to his home city after cooking for the rich and famous on private yachts in the Caribbean and Mediterranean,' write the new owners, so working in a kitchen that doesn't sway about must come as a huge relief to him. The fixed-price dinner menu offers a choice of six or seven items per course, along the lines of open ravioli of crayfish and asparagus, braised oxtail or venison steak, and tarte Tatin. Despite the proximity to the sea, fish does not play a leading role.

The kitchen, felt an inspector, may be trying too hard to make an impact, following fashion and striving for effect – intricate amuse-gueules, and butter carved into shapes, for instance – rather than concentrating its energy on more basic matters. '*"Faites simple"* should be carved over the mantelpiece' was the recommendation, which might also apply to a mid-meal pineapple and coconut sorbet ('just like a pina colada') that was considered rather sweet for a palate-cleanser. Nevertheless, honey and ginger ice-cream with butterscotch sauce, or chocolate pithiviers could round things off well. A warm welcome from the Hamiltons goes a long way, and the sensible list of reasonably priced wines begins with a handy selection of nine bottles around £10. More by the glass would help.

CHEF: Paul George Bending PROPRIETORS: Brian and Gina Hamilton OPEN: Mon to Sat 12 to 1.30, 7 to 9.30 MEALS: Set L £16.50, Set D £18.50 (2 courses) to £22.50 SERVICE: not inc, card slips closed CARDS: Access, Amex, Delta, Switch, Visa DETAILS: 35 seats. 4 tables outside. Private parties: 35 main room, 10 private room. Car park. Vegetarian meals. Children's helpings. Smart dress preferred. No smoking in dining-room. Wheelchair access. Music ACCOMMODATION: 7 rooms, all with bath/shower. TV. Phone. B&B £63.50 to £130. Rooms for disabled. Children welcome. Baby facilities. Pets welcome. Afternoon teas. Garden

ILKLEY West Yorkshire map 8

Box Tree *

35–37 Church Street, Ilkley LS29 9DR COOKING 3*
TEL: (01943) 608484 FAX: (01943) 607186 COST £35–£61

Here is one of British catering's more venerable institutions. An eighteenth-century farmhouse of Yorkshire stone and slate, it was purchased from the receivers in 1992 by the Avis family, who acquired the services of shooting-star chef Thierry Leprêtre-Granet the following year. The labyrinth of misshapen rooms is still crammed with the clutter of the previous owners, avid collectors of curios. Whether you see in them a thousand little gems of quixotic taste or a rising tide of tat will depend on your own sensibilities.

Madame Avis writes philosophically: 'One must look forward if one is not to be trapped in history.' Mindful of that exhortation, Leprêtre-Granet has given the menus a new spin while maintaining the feel of lavish elaboration that has always accounted for a large measure of the Box Tree's repute. While the orientation is identifiably French, there are traces of a more exploratory intelligence at work too. Red mullet and potato terrine with balsamic dressing appears among the starters alongside warm chicken liver mousse with a port sauce, while artichoke raviolo on pesto pleased one luncher mightily: 'a good idea, perfectly executed'. Main courses may offer woodpigeon breasts with swede purée in a sauce of red wine and walnut oil, or succulent duck leg confit scattered with sea salt and served on a cep fumet of great power.

The British and French cheeses are well looked after, as are dessert-lovers, who may enjoy a selection of vibrant sorbets garnished with fresh fruit and a mint syrup, or a roasted apple with blackcurrant and red wine coulis and cinnamon ice-cream. Service can be 'friendly and attentive', although two reporters found the front-of-house approach wanting: 'Madame Avis doesn't exactly encourage things to go with a swing.' The heavily Franco-centric wine list exhibits many fine bottles, making prices high, and half-bottles are thin on the ground. House selections represent decent value, however, starting at £9.75 for La Serre Sauvignon and Chardonnay.

CHEF: Thierry Leprêtre-Granet PROPRIETOR: The Box Tree Restaurant Ilkley Ltd OPEN: Tue to Sun L 12 to 2.30, Tue to Sat D 7 to 10.30 MEALS: alc L (main courses £15 to £18). Set L £22.50, Set D £29.50 SERVICE: not inc, card slips closed CARDS: Access, Amex, Visa DETAILS: 60 seats. Private parties: 32 main room, 16 private room. Children's helpings. Smart dress preferred. No smoking in dining-room. Wheelchair access. No music

IPSWICH Suffolk map 6

Kwok's Rendezvous £

23 St Nicholas Street, Ipswich IP1 1TW COOKING 1
TEL/FAX: (01473) 256833 COST £18–£32

When Thomas Kwok opened his restaurant in 1980, aromatic crispy duck was virtually unheard of in Suffolk. Nowadays it is common currency. If recent reports are anything to go by, there has been a surge of interest in the food at this unlikely Chinese rendezvous in a seventeenth-century Ipswich town house. The dining-room has been redecorated, but the menu is still based on a well-tried selection of Peking and Szechuan dishes with fish as a major attraction. Sole from the East Coast appears in five guises (the chu-chow version is pan-fried with ginger and garlic in a fish sauce spiked with lemon grass), prawns are a favourite option, and East Anglian eels are back again (although they are not advertised on the menu): Mr Kwok serves them with coriander, sesame oil and bamboo shoots or with hot Szechuan bean sauce. Other dishes include grilled chicken Peking-style, double-cooked pork, beef in oyster sauce and spicy Hunan noodles. Service is on the ball, and the presence of the eponymous chef/proprietor in and out of the kitchen is appreciated. Plans are afoot to re-introduce a special cut-price lunch menu aimed at business people. The wine list is dominated by fair-value bottles from the major French regions. House wine is £7.95.

CHEF/PROPRIETOR: Thomas Kwok OPEN: Mon to Fri L 12 to 1.45, Mon to Sat D 6.30 to 10.45 CLOSED: 2 weeks spring, bank hols MEALS: alc (main courses £4.50 to £6). Set L £14.95, Set D £14.95 to £16.95 SERVICE: not inc CARDS: Access, Amex, Visa DETAILS: 50 seats. Private parties: 70 main room. Vegetarian meals. Children welcome. Smart dress preferred. Wheelchair access (2 steps; also WC). Music

Mortimer's on the Quay £

Wherry Quay, Ipswich IP4 1AS COOKING 1
TEL: (01473) 230225 FAX: (01284) 761611 COST £18–£40

The younger of the two branches of Mortimer's is on the Ipswich dockside, but the theme is the same as the one in Bury St Edmunds (see entry): seasonal seafood classically prepared. Piscatorial pictures on the walls announce the single-minded intention; meat-eaters and vegetarians need not apply.

Choice on the *carte* is very wide, and generally supplemented with a couple of daily specials chalked on a blackboard. The standard of cooking remains sound and reliable. At one meal a 'prettily presented' platter of smoked items – Bradhan Rost (hot-smoked salmon), trout, eel and cod's roe – was followed by generous servings of main-course fish: salmon in a copious sauce of spinach, leek, sorrel and cream, and monkfish in a soupy sauce of lobster, tomato and wine. Only boiled potatoes or rice accompany, as if the concern is that nothing should detract from the central feature. The house dessert, coupe Mortimer, is straight out of the seaside café repertoire: vanilla ice-cream with chocolate and butterscotch sauces, whipped cream and chopped nuts. Bread attracts its own charge, but comes as satisfyingly large, ready-buttered rounds of brown granary. Service can be slow on a busy night, when hordes of the great unbooked may be turned away at the

door. Wines are predominantly white, of course, and offer a broad selection at prices that shouldn't cause upsets. House French is £7.45.

CHEFS: Kenneth Ambler and Carol Theobald PROPRIETORS: Kenneth Ambler and Michael Gooding OPEN: Mon to Fri L 12 to 2, Mon to Sat D 7 to 9 (6.30 to 8.15 Mon) CLOSED: 24 Dec to 5 Jan, 2 weeks Aug MEALS: alc (main courses £7.50 to £16) SERVICE: not inc CARDS: Access, Amex, Delta, Diners, Switch, Visa DETAILS: 60 seats. Private parties: 12 main room, 22 private room. Car park. Children's helpings. Smart dress preferred. Wheelchair access (1 step). No music

---

IXWORTH Suffolk map 6

Theobalds 🍷

68 High Street, Ixworth IP31 2HJ COOKING 2
TEL: (01359) 231707 COST £25–£46

A regular visitor notes that little changes here. Over the 14 years of the restaurant's existence the furniture has been replaced, but the beams and the atmosphere remain much the same. It is comfortable, generally full of locals and warmed by a big fire in winter. Staff are as attentive, and Geraldine Theobald as charming as ever. Although regulars might prefer the puddings to be revamped a little more often, the rest of the menu rings the changes well enough, with standbys of corn-fed chicken, roast Aylesbury duckling, a choice of two or three fish and a seasonal showing for pheasant and walnut terrine, or roast partridge.

The set meal price varies with the choice of main course, but includes tasty nibbles to begin, a starter, either sweet or cheese, and coffee to finish. Main courses tend to be fillets, and sauces may have an alcoholic component: sherry for lamb, white port for roast turbot. The à la carte lunch menu is a lighter and cheaper affair, but along similar lines: a salad of dressed crab, perhaps, a breast of corn-fed chicken wrapped in bacon and served with a tomato and tarragon sauce, or a twice-baked cheese soufflé. Iced Grand Marnier mousse with chocolate sauce, and caramelised lemon tart with strawberry sauce are among the puddings. The wine list is a manageable size, with about half the bottles being specially recommended. A fine selection of half-bottles from T&W Wines is particularly welcome. House Merlot and Chardonnay are £11.50 and £12.50. CELLARMAN'S CHOICE: Muscadet, Le Clos du Pont 1992, Dom. Marcel Guilbard, £20.80; Bordeaux, Notre Dame de Landiras 1990, £16.20.

CHEF: Simon Theobald PROPRIETORS: Simon and Geraldine Theobald OPEN: Tue to Fri and Sun L 12.15 to 1.30, Tue to Sat D 7.15 to 9.30 CLOSED: 1 week Aug MEALS: alc L (main courses £8). Set Sun L £16.95, Set D £20.50 (vegetarian) to £28.50 SERVICE: not inc CARDS: Access, Switch, Visa DETAILS: 36 seats. Private parties: 36 main room. Vegetarian meals. Children's helpings. No children under 8 D. Smart dress preferred. No smoking while others eat. No music

---

All details are as accurate as possible at the time of going to press, but chefs and owners often change, and it is wise to check by telephone before making a special journey. Many readers have been disappointed when set-price bargain meals are no longer available. Ask when booking.

JEVINGTON East Sussex map 3

Hungry Monk

Jevington BN26 5QF
TEL: (01323) 482178 FAX: (01323) 483989 COOKING 1*
off A22/A259, between Polegate and Friston COST £31–£50

'It is the only local restaurant we still visit after 20 years,' say a pair of loyalists who felt that the balance of comment in last year's *Guide* entry was on the negative side. The Monk is cloistered in a row of ancient flint cottages in a little Downland village, and the comforting domesticity is appreciated. Fixed-price lunch and dinner menus provide expansive choice, offering tastes of yesteryear alongside the thoroughly newfangled. So there may be rabbit and prune terrine, but also haddock and salmon with purée foie gras. Guinea-fowl with apples and calvados sounds like a normal Norman dish, but where does Barbary duck breast with passion-fruit and Marsala come from? Devotees have followed faithfully the development of the cooking over the years, as witness those regulars of two decades who enjoyed, among other things, spiced avocado with beansprout pancake: there can't have been much of that about in the 1970s. Others found koulibiac of salmon 'interestingly fancy but not gimmicky' and pronounced puddings 'very good' – particularly the stem ginger pudding with lavender ice-cream which was 'light, very sweet and intensely gingery'. You might prefer hot baby doughnuts with jam and cream or the house speciality of banoffi pie. The home-made bread is praised, as is good cafetière coffee that comes with chocolates and a glass of port. Service will always be appreciated by those who find their preferences remembered from visit to visit. The wine list majors in France, the selections from elsewhere tending to be brief compilations of familiar names. Prices are VAT-specific to the penny. House wines start at £8.90.

CHEFS: Claire Burgess and Thai Laroche PROPRIETORS: Nigel and Susan Mackenzie OPEN: Sun L 12 to 2.30, all week D 7 to 10 CLOSED: 24 to 26 Dec MEALS: Set L and D £21.90 SERVICE: not inc CARDS: Amex DETAILS: 42 seats. Private parties: 40 main room, 6 to 16 private rooms. Car park. Vegetarian meals. Children's helpings. No children under 3. Smart dress preferred. No smoking in dining-room. Music

KENDAL Cumbria map 8

Moon £

129 Highgate, Kendal LA9 4EN COOKING 1
TEL: (01539) 729254 COST £19–£28

The Moon, on the main street opposite the Brewery Arts Centre, aims for informality. Val Macconnell's monthly-changing blackboard menu is not entirely vegetarian, but leans heavily in that direction. The thrust is bold flavourings, whatever the dish, from garlic-flavoured hummus with tomato and chilli dip, to a filo-pastry parcel of goats' cheese, mango and red pepper with an apple, gooseberry and honey sauce. Borrowings are from around the world – pork loin with Moroccan fruit sauce, a spiced balti made from cauliflower and butterbeans, and a lamb and apricot bobotie from South Africa – and puddings can be as rich as steamed fruit suet pudding or a cheesecake of chocolate, apricot and stem ginger. The short under-£10 wine list is supplemented by a few bottled beers, of which Chimay, Duvel and Jenlain French Bière de Garde are the pick. House wine is £7.55 a litre.

CHEFS: Val Macconnell and Sharon Moreton PROPRIETOR: Val Macconnell OPEN: all week, D only 6.30 (6 Sat) to 10 CLOSED: 24, 25 and 31 Dec, 1 Jan MEALS: alc (main courses £7.50 to £8.50) SERVICE: not inc, card slips closed CARDS: Access, Switch, Visa DETAILS: 38 seats. Private parties: 10 main room, 35 private room. Car park. Vegetarian meals. Children's helpings. No smoking in dining-room. Wheelchair access. Music

KENILWORTH Warwickshire map 5

Restaurant Bosquet 🍷

97A Warwick Road, Kenilworth CV8 1HP
TEL: (01926) 52463, changing to (01926) 852463 in December 1995
COOKING 3*
COST £32–£48

Despite the name, little in the way of normal restaurant trappings has been applied here to what is basically still very much a private home. That thoroughly domestic feel is found entirely endearing by most. 'You go upstairs to the loo and see a little head peering out of a bedroom door, and then you wash your hands and find no towel. Just like home.' The house is small, Victorian and terraced, and eating takes place in the sitting-room. The modesty of it all, however, belies the great talent of Bernard Lignier.

While the style may be refined French classicism, it is brought off without pretentiousness or over-elaboration. Menus are kept sensibly short so that everything receives proper attention, and the *carte* is backed up by a three-course set-price menu on weekdays. Can there be any better way of being welcomed to table than by a bowl of plump green olives and a tartlet of onion and anchovy? 'What a kick-start to the taste-buds,' wrote one man, who then went on to a balsamically dressed salad of crayfish, pigeon breast, asparagus and wild mushrooms. The profundity of flavours, even in the tiny crayfish, made the dish memorable, the dressing adding mellow richness. A main course built around duck offered the breast sauced with a gently spicy reduction, with a confit of the leg shredded among salad leaves and orange segments – a neat idea. The generosity of the cooking is shown in a saddle of lamb given a crust of truffles and breadcrumbs, the sauce a reduction of the cooking juices lit up with sherry. Vegetables are good, though many in number, and puddings – including a gratin of rhubarb and strawberries – are well rendered. Coffee comes with a plethora of petits fours, including immaculate tiny apple tartlets. Everything adds up to tremendous value, served 'smoothly and unobtrusively' by Jane Lignier in calm, civil surroundings.

Fittingly, the cooking is given a serious wine list to accompany it, all French and none the poorer for that, so good are the selections. The overall price framework feels a shade high, but mark-ups are not excessive for the quality. Thoroughbred clarets and burgundies are supported by a great little list of south-western wines and there are a dozen or so halves. Four of the five house wines are £11. CELLARMAN'S CHOICE: Jurançon 1992, Dom. Cauhapé, £15; Madiran, Ch. Montus Cuvée Prestige 1990, Brumont, £32.

CHEF: Bernard Lignier PROPRIETORS: Bernard and Jane Lignier OPEN: Tue to Fri L (bookings only) 12 to 1, Tue to Sat D 7 to 9.30 CLOSED: 3 weeks in Aug MEALS: alc (main courses £14.50 to £15). Set L £21, Set D Tue to Fri £21 SERVICE: not inc CARDS: Access, Amex, Switch, Visa DETAILS: 26 seats. Private parties: 30 main room. Children's helpings. Smart dress preferred. Wheelchair access (1 step). No music

Simpson's ✱

NEW ENTRY

101–103 Warwick Road, Kenilworth CV8 1HL — COOKING 1*
TEL/FAX: (01926) 864567 — COST £22–£35

Simpson's brings all the style and flash of a cosmopolitan brasserie to the middle England spa town of Kenilworth. Vibrant green awnings shade the frontage (which is stencilled with images of chefs holding domed dishes), curtains are looped over rails and you can often hear the racket from the street. Inside, it is all bright lights, mirrors and floors of untreated wood; service is from young bloods of both sexes in waistcoats.

Andreas Antona and his team deliver the kind of food that some might call 'modern bistro': anything goes, influences and ideas are stacked up and fused into unlikely alliances. Confit of duck is paired with Irish colcannon, kleftiko lives with couscous or okra, and roast pheasant is married to 'pineapple sauerkraut'. Meals are fixed-price for two or three courses, the menu changes with the seasons, and the value for money is never in doubt. Reporters have praised a colourful tomato risotto topped with king prawns, and grilled fillet of cod wrapped in paper-thin slices of pancetta with flageolet beans and piles of chunky chargrilled vegetables. Sweets range from apple fritters with ginger ice-cream to orange soufflé gratin. Home-baked bread wins approval, the coffee sometimes does not; 'hippie' tea bags are brought to the table in a box that you might think contained cigars. The wine list includes some interesting drinking and – like the food – will not threaten the purse. House wine is £9.50.

CHEFS: Andreas Antona, Andrew Waters and Luke Tipping PROPRIETORS: Andreas and Alison Antona OPEN: Mon to Fri L 12.30 to 2, Mon to Sat D 7 to 10 (10.30 Sat) CLOSED: 25 and 26 Dec, bank hols MEALS: Set L £13.95, Set D £16.95 (2 courses) to £19.95 SERVICE: not inc, card slips closed CARDS: Access, Amex, Delta, Diners, Switch, Visa DETAILS: 80 seats. Private parties: 70 main room, 70 private room. Car park. Vegetarian meals. Children's helpings. Smart dress preferred. No smoking in 1 dining-room. Music. Air-conditioned

---

KESWICK Cumbria — map 10

▲ *Swinside Lodge* ✱

Newlands, Keswick CA12 5UE
TEL/FAX: (01768) 772948
off A66 Penrith to Cockermouth road, turn left at Portinscale and follow Grange road for 2m — COOKING 2 — COST £26–£36

This Victorian lodge enjoys a location close by Derwentwater that will appeal to 'serious fell-walkers', suggested a reporter, 'the kind of residents who go out after a good breakfast and do not reappear until late afternoon'. Then again, others may do no more than potter down to the lakeside, but all are reunited at 7 o'clock for a tot of sherry and perusal of the evening's menu.

The format is textbook Lakeland: a single sitting for a fixed-price dinner of five courses with coffee, choice necessary only at dessert. Meals kick off with leek and pesto flan with walnut salad, perhaps, or roasted red pepper soufflé, followed by a soup such as pea and mint. Main courses aim for safety, not a bad strategy when there isn't an alternative dish. A salmon fillet with white wine, tomato and dill butter shows sufficient skill in sauce-making. Roast local lamb with rosemary and a tartlet of shallot purée is the kind of thing done with meat. Desserts provide three choices. A brandy-snap basket of ginger syllabub had refreshing bite at one dinner, although a raspberry soufflé on one occasion disappointed. All are agreed that the offering of North Country cheeses – from Allerdale goats' to buttery Cotherstone – is extremely fine. Details such as the variety of home-made breads and the aromatic blend of coffee keep the edges nice and trim. One couple thought the atmosphere one of 'workmanlike efficiency rather than friendliness', but the rest of this year's weighty postbag on Swinside is united in challenging that view. The hotel has no licence, which means the aperitifs are complimentary, and you will need to furnish your own wine.

CHEFS: Chris Astley, Paul White and Graham Taylor PROPRIETOR: Graham Taylor OPEN: all week D only 7.30 (one sitting) CLOSED: mid-Dec to mid-Feb MEALS: Set D £24 to £27.50. Unlicensed, but bring your own: no corkage SERVICE: not inc CARDS: none DETAILS: 18 seats. Private parties: 6 main room. Car park. No children under 12. Smart dress preferred. No smoking in dining-room. No music ACCOMMODATION: 7 rooms, all with bath/shower. TV. D, B&B £60 to £135. Deposit: £20. No children under 12. Afternoon teas. Garden (*The Which? Hotel Guide*)

KEYSTON Cambridgeshire map 6

Pheasant Inn 🍷 ✻ £

CAMBS 1996 PUB

Keyston PE18 0RE
TEL: (01832) 710241 FAX: (01832) 710340 COOKING 2*
on B663, 1m S of junction with A14 COST £20–£46

'This is a very accessible place because of its informality and flexible menu,' commented one satisfied customer. There isn't a dining-room as such, just something called the Red Room, which has large tables, proper napkins, is smoke-free and needs booking. Otherwise, the same menu operates throughout the thatched, beamed country pub, and you can eat as much or a little as you like: altogether a simple, welcome and no-nonsense approach. The kitchen uses chargrilling and pan-frying – for saddle of venison or breast of woodpigeon respectively, for example – and throws in some good sausages, such as wild boar or sticky cotechino. 'Roger Jones certainly knows how to cook fish,' said one who enjoyed a 'succulent and stunningly fresh fillet of sea bass'.

An Italian theme runs through much of the food, with the use of salsas, pesto and pasta, and through the meatless options, such as a pancake filled with ricotta cheese and spinach, or baked goats' cheese with tapénade and herb grissini. In an attempt to allay fears about the trade in calves, the menu states that 'all veal is hand-reared, milk-fed and not mistreated in any way'. Choice is generous and prices fair. The home-made ice-creams are good. 'I can recommend the coconut ice-cream served with a wicked pancake covered in hot maple syrup,' writes one who tried it. 'We like the friendly service from the young team,' tells us someone who has become a regular. Three or four real ales are on tap, including perhaps Adnams Best, Flowers Original or London Pride. Huntsbridge (formerly part of Poste Hotels) has an enlightened wine policy, and the list includes some exciting bottles at very reasonable prices, all arranged by style. A dozen house wines, from £8.50 a bottle, are available by the glass (for around £2), as are a few interesting sweet ones. CELLARMAN'S CHOICE: Salice Salentino 1989, Candido, £10; Bourgogne Aligoté 1993, Goisot, £14.

CHEF: Roger Jones PROPRIETOR: Huntsbridge OPEN: all week 12 to 2, 6.30 to 10 CLOSED: D 25 and 26 Dec, D 1 Jan MEALS: alc (main courses £6.50 to £15) SERVICE: not inc, card slips closed CARDS: Access, Amex, Diners, Switch, Visa DETAILS: 100 seats. 5 tables outside. Private parties: 40 main room, 35 private room. Car park. Vegetarian meals. Children's helpings. No smoking in 1 dining-room. Wheelchair access (1 step; also WC). No music

KINGSBRIDGE Devon map 1

▲ *Buckland-Tout-Saints Hotel, Queen Anne* 

Goveton, Kingsbridge TQ7 2DS
TEL: (01548) 853055 FAX: (01548) 856261 COOKING 1
1½m off A381, 2m NE of Kingsbridge COST £24–£39

Built of handsome grey stone during the reign of Queen Anne, after whom the restaurant is named, the hotel sits at the end of a carriage sweep, seemingly 'designed to set off cars of distinction'. Good housekeeping keeps the interiors looking spruce, and the panelled dining-room feels cosy. The Taylors appointed David Newland head chef in March 1995, while the format of fixed-price three-course meals continues. Menus read well, from the modishness of warm pigeon salad with pickled cabbage to the more recognisable country-house idiom of poached paupiette of lemon sole filled with a mousseline of smoked salmon. Light, well-flavoured chicken terrine studded with ham and pistachios comes with a simple yoghurt and dill sauce, while 'admirably tender' rack of lamb is given a sweetish sauce of mixed berries and port.

A willingness to resort to the bottle is evident in desserts: Tia Maria goes into coffee soufflé, and a splash of whisky into an 'excellent, sinfully rich' chocolate torte served with cream cheese. An enterprising wine list covers most of its areas well, but mark-ups within the traditional French regions soon take off. Look elsewhere for relief. Half-bottles are liberally scattered throughout, though. House selections open at £9.75 for French white and Australian red.

CHEFS: David Newland, Richard Pinney and John Stevens PROPRIETORS: John and Tove Taylor OPEN: all week 12.30 to 1.45, 7.30 to 9.30 MEALS: Set L £14.50, Set D £25 SERVICE: not inc, card slips closed CARDS: Access, Amex, Delta, Diners, Switch, Visa DETAILS: 48 seats. 5 tables outside. Private parties: 38 main room, 14 private room. Car park. Children's helpings. Smart dress preferred. No smoking in dining-room. No music ACCOMMODATION: 13 rooms, all with bath/shower. TV. Phone. B&B £35 to £100. Children welcome. Baby facilities. Pets welcome. Afternoon teas. Garden (*The Which? Hotel Guide*)

KING'S LYNN Norfolk map 6

Riverside

27 King Street, King's Lynn PE30 1HA
TEL: (01553) 773134

COOKING 1
COST £17–£42

If you're fond of the spirit-level flatness of East Anglian waterscapes, with their mud flats, jetties and boats, the Riverside makes a delightful spot for a meal. Go at lunch-time or early on a summer's evening to enjoy the scene at its best. The restaurant is in a 500-year-old listed building overlooking the Ouse, with lots of exposed ships' timbers and bare brickwork contrasting with starched turquoise cloths and sparkling glassware in the dining-room. Alternatively, you can sit on the terrace. Lunch is aimed at casual callers and shoppers as well as those wanting a formal meal; choose between omelettes, pasta and other light dishes or opt for something more substantial, such as warm cauliflower salad with mustard vinaigrette, followed by pan-fried fillets of pink trout scattered with fresh tomato, big capers and pine-kernels. In the evening the kitchen moves into slightly more ambitious territory for avocado with smoked salmon pâté, and breast of Barbary duck with port and cherries. Desserts include a good wobbly version of apricot mousse with apricot coulis. Service is tidy, chatty and helpful. The revamped wine list runs to about 50 bins with a good showing of halves and plenty of dependable drinking from around the world. House wine is £8.25.

CHEFS: Dennis Taylor and Pat Isbill PROPRIETORS: Michael and Sylvia Savage OPEN: Mon to Sat 12 to 2, 7 to 10 MEALS: alc (main courses £5 to £17). Set L £7.50 (2 courses) to £10, Set D £16.95 SERVICE: not inc, card slips closed CARDS: Access, Visa DETAILS: 75 seats. 12 tables outside. Private parties: 80 main room. Car park. Vegetarian meals. Children's helpings. Smart dress preferred. Music

Rococo 🍷

11 Saturday Market Place, King's Lynn PE30 5DQ
TEL: (01553) 771483

COOKING 2
COST £20–£42

The Andersons achieve a harmony of style and content, of the feel of the place and the kind of food they serve, which speaks of a single-minded approach to the whole business of running a restaurant. The bold pictures that bring life to the bright green front parlour and the pale-washed dining-room are 'not the sort that people put up to decorate a restaurant, more the sort they love to have themselves'. This is a distinctly personal endeavour, built around food that is a lively modern amalgam of the broadly British and the frankly French.

Lunch is a light affair. The effort is concentrated on dinner, in dishes of sauté local wild mushrooms and a poached duck's egg on brioche, or in warm salad of crispy tongue with a herb dressing. Fish might appear in the form of grilled sea bass with aubergine crisps and tomato relish, and the vegetarian offering one night was Thai bean-cakes and fragrant rice with a blue-cheese sauce. This is seductive cooking that does not try to overpower with strong flavours, and keeps up the momentum in a banana steam sponge pudding with golden syrup and egg custard, or a sloe-gin parfait with a bitter plum sauce. The wide-ranging wine list is put together with one eye on quality and both eyes on value. A 'personal choice' section directs attention to a more manageable subset, with four of them available by the glass, and two dozen half-bottles provide back-up. CELLARMAN'S CHOICE: Staton Hills Chardonnay 1989, Yakima Valley, Washington State, £14.30; Parker Terra Rossa Cabernet Sauvignon 1991, Coonawarra, S. Australia, £17.23.

CHEFS: Nick Anderson and Tim Sandford PROPRIETORS: Nick and Anne Anderson OPEN: Tue to Sat L 12 to 2, Mon to Sat D 7 to 10 CLOSED: 25 to 31 Dec MEALS: alc L (main courses £5.50 to £7). Set L £9 (2 courses) to £12, Set D £19.50 (2 courses) to £24.50 SERVICE: not inc, card slips closed CARDS: Access, Amex, Delta, Switch, Visa DETAILS: 40 seats. Private parties: 40 main room. Vegetarian meals. Children's helpings. Smart dress preferred. No smoking during meals. Wheelchair access (also WC). Music

KINGSTON UPON THAMES Surrey map 3

Ayudhya

SURREY 1996 THAI

14 Kingston Hill, Kingston upon Thames
KT2 7NH COOKING 2
TEL: 0181-549 5984 and 546 5878 COST £21–£35

Ayudhya was the ancient capital of Siam, now best known to tourists for its traditional teak houses. The eponymous restaurant in well-heeled Kingston is both a great culinary ambassador and a fine neighbourhood eating-place. It occupies three floors and is suitably decked out with pictures of Thai grandees, solidly elegant furniture, winking fairy lights, artificial bamboo and a model Ayudhya-style house – although a reproduction of Constable's *Hay Wain* seems to have intruded from somewhere else. The set-up runs smoothly, thanks to a team of waiters who manage to be both charming and effortlessly professional.

Behind the scenes is an accomplished Thai kitchen capable of keeping up with the best of them; ingredients are top-quality, preparation is sharp, and there is no evidence of parsimony or short-cuts. The menu of around 80 dishes covers all the essentials, from chicken satay to roast duck curry, and descriptions are spot-on. 'Wonderful' bo taek (mixed seafood soup) comes loaded with big mussels, crab claws, carved squid and balls of cod in a subtly fragrant stock; somtum salad is the real thing made with long threads of green papaya, minced shrimps and crushed, roasted peanuts. Chef/proprietor Somjai Thanpho also produces a fine version of haw mok talay (a lightly curried seafood mousse), and comes up with a few specialities of her own: kung sawoy – prawns dipped in tempura batter, then stir-fried with red curry paste and Thai green beans. As an accompaniment ask for pak boong (water spinach) if it is available. The kitchen also copes impressively with Westernised desserts such as banana fritters. As an alternative to Singha Thai beer, peruse the well-considered wine list, which has plenty of award-winning stuff from good sources. House wine is £6.95.

CHEF/PROPRIETOR: Somjai Thanpho OPEN: Tue to Sun L 12 to 2.30 (12.30 to 3 Sun), all week D 6.30 (6 Sun) to 11 (11.30 Fri and Sat) CLOSED: 25 Dec, 1 Jan, Easter Sun MEALS: alc (main courses £5 to £9) SERVICE: not inc CARDS: Access, Amex, Delta, Diners, Switch, Visa DETAILS: 82 seats. Private parties: 42 main room, 30 private room. Vegetarian meals. Children's helpings. Smart dress preferred. No smoking in 1 dining-room. Wheelchair access (1 step). Music

KINGTON Hereford & Worcester map 5

▲ *Penrhos Court*

Kington HR5 3LH
TEL: (01544) 230720 FAX: (01544) 230754 COOKING 1*
on A44, 1m E of Kington COST £33–£40

The Elizabethan wing, housing the dining-room with its vast oak beams, is a mere youngster compared with the older sections of Penrhos, which were built around the time that Edward I snatched Kington from the Welsh. Daphne Lambert presides over the place with enthusiasm that remains undimmed after 20 years, running cookery courses and tending the herb and vegetable gardens. Her fixed-price menus raid the world's larder for dhal mung-bean soup with creamed coconut, Parmesan-glazed polenta with roasted aubergine and sun-dried tomatoes, and duck confit with potato and celeriac rösti and madeira sauce. Vegetarian dishes are a strong point: roasted vegetables with wholemeal spaghetti, or a buckwheat pancake encasing spinach, glazed onions and goats' cheese. Carrot cake, or orange and almond cake with honey yoghurt, keeps the calories under control, although a tempting ice-cream made from malt whisky, soured cream and raisins won't. Good, strong coffee comes in earthenware jugs with bitter chocolates. The compact wine list does its main business in France, the foreigners including an English pair and Trapiche Pinot Noir from Argentina. House wines start at £10.50.

CHEF: Daphne Lambert PROPRIETORS: Daphne Lambert and Martin Griffiths OPEN: all week D only 7.30 to 10 CLOSED: first 2 weeks Feb MEALS: Set D £19.50 (2 courses) to £23.50 SERVICE: not inc CARDS: Access, Amex, Diners, Switch, Visa DETAILS: 100 seats. Private parties: 100 main room, 70 and 100 private rooms. Car park. Vegetarian meals. Children's helpings. No smoking in dining-room. Wheelchair access (3 steps; also WC). Music ACCOMMODATION: 19 rooms, all with bath/shower. TV. Phone. B&B £80 to £100. Deposit: 50%. Rooms for disabled. Children welcome. Baby facilities. Garden

KINTBURY Berkshire map 2

▲ *Dundas Arms*

53 Station Road, Kintbury RG15 0UT
TEL: (01488) 658263 FAX: (01488) 658568 COOKING 1
1m S of A4, between Newbury and Hungerford COST £24–£46

David Dalzell-Piper took charge of this pub in 1967 and, over the years, has turned it into one of the most popular venues of its kind in the area. Part of its allure is the setting: the building stands at the junction of the River Kennet and the Kennet and Avon Canal, with a backdrop of towering trees and wildlife all around. In summer the tables laid out on the jetty and towpath are at a premium; in frosty weather you can soak up the scene from the warmth of the bar and dining-room. The restaurant menu is a short list of fairly priced dishes that are attuned to the needs of both die-hard traditionalists and those with an appetite for something more modern. On the one hand you might find home-cured gravlax and roast rib of beef with Stilton sauce, and on the other warm ratatouille with grilled Italian bread, breast of wild pigeon with honey and lentil sauce, and grilled spiced monkfish with tomato, ginger and olive oil. First-rate snacks and pints of real ale are served in the bar, but most people head straight for the idiosyncratic wine list with its pedigree Bordeaux and burgundies, most (apart from the white burgundy) from vintages in the 1980s. A wide spread of prices reflects the range from humble to first-class. The rest, minimal though the list may be, have been sensibly chosen. CELLARMAN'S CHOICE: Jackson Estate Chardonnay 1994, Marlborough, New Zealand, £18; Médoc, Ch. Ramage La Batisse 1989, £21.

CHEFS: David Dalzell-Piper, Sue Bright and Stuart Hall PROPRIETOR: David Dalzell-Piper OPEN: Mon to Sat L 12 to 1.30, Tue to Sat D 7 to 9.15 CLOSED: 25 Dec to 1 Jan MEALS: alc (main courses £11 to £15). Set L £17.50 SERVICE: not inc CARDS: Access, Amex, Switch, Visa DETAILS: 40 seats. 10 tables outside. Private parties: 22 main room. Car park. Vegetarian meals. Children's helpings. Smart dress preferred. No smoking in 1 dining-room. Wheelchair access. No music ACCOMMODATION: 5 rooms, all with bath/shower. TV. Phone. B&B £55 to £65. Rooms for disabled. Children welcome. Pets welcome (*The Which? Hotel Guide*)

KIRKHAM Lancashire map 8

Cromwellian 🍷

16 Poulton Street, Kirkham PR4 2AB COOKING 3
TEL/FAX: (01772) 685680 COST £23–£36

The restaurant is on a domestic scale, with low-beamed ceilings, three tables in the front room, two in the back, and a little lounge upstairs. 'Very bijou' is how it struck one reporter. The fact that the Fawcetts are on tap to look after customers is considered a plus: 'Mrs Fawcett pops out with a small dish of four hot and appetising canapés, and has a quick word before popping back into the kitchen.' After nine years of operating a fixed-price menu, they have switched to a short *carte* instead. It may be slightly against the national trend, but it makes sense to them and is welcomed by reporters. The restrictions of a fixed-price format meant that any special items that were impulse-bought from a supplier ended up with a price supplement, which 'became rather unwieldy'. The new method enables daily specials to slot in more easily, and makes the food that bit more responsive to the market.

Along with the menu change comes a penchant for naming dishes. 'The Local Hero' is a Lancashire black pudding served with mushy peas and a rich brown gravy, and 'Wild Thing' is a baked breast of pheasant with sage and onion stuffing and a port wine sauce. As before, a vegetarian main course is always on offer, although the Fawcetts note that 'vegetarian customers continue to be elusive in this part of Lancashire, and in the last six months we have seen a major resurgence in red meat sales'. Such protein might include Aberdeen Angus sirloin served with a pickled walnut sauce, or fillet steak with a Stilton and port sauce. 'Top marks for her potatoes,' writes an enthusiast of the thinly sliced King Edwards baked with cream and onions, 'and for Peter's management of the wine list'. Good burgundies front the French section, careful selection characterises the list, and the 20 half-bottles are welcome. House French is £9.50. CELLARMAN'S CHOICE: Marsannay 1993, Alain Guyard, £19.95; Crozes-Hermitage 1992, Dom. Bernard Chave, £16.95.

CHEFS: Josie Fawcett and Diane Rowe PROPRIETORS: Peter and Josie Fawcett OPEN: Tue to Sat D only 7 to 9 MEALS: alc (main courses £8.50 to £14). Minimum £12.50 SERVICE: not inc, card slips closed CARDS: Access, Amex, Diners, Visa DETAILS: 18 seats. Private parties: 10 main room, 10 private rooms. Vegetarian meals. Children's helpings. Smart dress preferred. Wheelchair access. Music

LANGAR Nottinghamshire map 5

▲ *Langar Hall*

Langar NG13 9HG
TEL: (01949) 860559 FAX: (01949) 861045 COOKING 1
between A46 and A52, 4m S of Bingham COST £25–£46

The attractive soft-stone building by the church dates from 1830: a modest and relaxed country house set in the tranquil Vale of Belvoir. It retains the feel of a private house, and various operatic and theatrical events take place after dinner on the last Friday of the month. Menus change daily but keep to a seasonal four- to six-week basic run, and tempting ideas include marrow and pesto soup, black pudding ravioli with a compote of split-peas and onion, and warm potato pancake with sauté duck liver and lentils.

A varied catch of fish might produce Norfolk crab-cakes with shellfish sauce, mackerel tempura, or salt-cod with chorizo in a spicy tomato-flavoured fish stock. A British thread runs through the enterprise, turning up beef and oyster pie, or potted tongue with home-made chutney. Chips are 'large, brown and yummy', while puddings range from an iced soup of summer berries, through hot chocolate pudding, to good home-made ice-creams. Canapés, home-made bread, vegetables and unlimited mineral water are included in the price. The 40 wines are largely French, including Maître d'Estournel at £13.50. House wines are around £10 to £12.

CHEF: Toby Garratt and Chris Ansell-Green PROPRIETOR: Imogen Skirving OPEN: Mon to Sat 12.30 to 2, 7 to 9.30 (10 Fri and Sat) CLOSED: 25 to 31 Dec MEALS: alc (main courses £9.50 to £17). Set L £17.50, Set D Mon to Fri £19.50 SERVICE: not inc, card slips closed CARDS: Access, Amex, Diners, Visa DETAILS: 50 seats. Private parties: 20 main room, 10 and 20 private rooms. Car park. Vegetarian meals. Children's helpings. No smoking in 1 dining-room. Music ACCOMMODATION: 12 rooms, all with bath/shower. TV. Phone. B&B £60 to £125. Deposit: £25. Children welcome. Pets by arrangement. Afternoon teas. Garden. Fishing (*The Which? Hotel Guide*)

LANGHO Lancashire map 8

▲ *Northcote Manor*

Northcote Road, Langho BB6 8BE
TEL: (01254) 240555 FAX: (01254) 246568 COOKING 3
on A59, 8½m E of M6 junction exit 31 COST £25–£64

Northcote has gone from strength to strength since it came into the joint ownership of Craig Bancroft and chef Nigel Haworth. Ancient history, both actual and mythic, lurks in the immediate environs, from the old Roman town of Ribchester to the witches of Pendle Hill. The manor is full of northern gravitas,

Edwardian-style, but the refurbishments have laid the emphasis on comfort, and the approach is both genial and informative.

There is a determined and commendable attempt to celebrate the best of Lancashire produce, which may be sampled on the *carte* or in the form of a fixed-price six-course gourmet menu. The starter dish of Lancashire specialities includes Bury black pudding and shrimps from Morecambe Bay, poultry comes from Goosnargh and lamb from Pendle.

That there is a palpable culinary intelligence at work in the transformation of these ingredients was evidenced by an inspection meal taken in the spring, when crisp-skinned sea trout formed the centrepiece of a substantial first course that included 'first-rate' potato purée with strands of leek, broad beans and peas. Hindle Wakes uses rhubarb and breadcrumbs to stuff corn-fed Goosnargh chicken, which is garnished with more rhubarb wrapped in bacon: a brave combination that works. 'Well-kept cheeses of good provenance' included local items as well as Cashel Blue from Tipperary, while the iced bread-and-butter pudding garnished with mixed fruit was 'a refreshing variation on the theme'. Incidentals such as vegetables and bread maintain a high standard, although espresso has been disappointingly weak. Wine advice is knowledgeably dispensed on request, and is worth heeding. There are some fine clarets and burgundies, but mostly at sinew-stiffening prices. Sadly, many of the other regions very soon scramble above £20 as well, although some relief may be found in Chile, Portugal and South Africa. Good German wine is given a fighting chance, and there are masses of halves. House burgundy is £9.25.

CHEF: Nigel Haworth PROPRIETORS: Craig Bancroft and Nigel Haworth OPEN: all week 12 to 1.30 (2 Sun), 7 to 9.30 (10 Sat, 9 Sun) MEALS: alc (main courses £13.50 to £24.50). Set L £17.95, Set D £35 SERVICE: 10% (optional), card slips closed CARDS: Access, Amex, Delta, Diners, Switch, Visa DETAILS: 80 seats. Private parties: 100 main room, 40 private room. Car park. Vegetarian meals. Children's helpings. Smart dress preferred. No smoking in dining-room. Wheelchair access (2 steps; also WC). Music ACCOMMODATION: 14 rooms, all with bath/shower. TV. Phone. B&B £75 to £100. Rooms for disabled. Children welcome. Afternoon teas. Garden (*The Which? Hotel Guide*)

LANGLEY MARSH Somerset map 2

▲ *Langley House Hotel*

Langley Marsh, Wiveliscombe TA4 2UF
TEL: (01984) 623318 FAX: (01984) 624573 COOKING 3
½m N of Wiveliscombe COST £35–£47

Langley House's plain white Georgian exterior belies a tendency to florid ornamentation within. If the comfortable sofas in the lounge don't lull you into slumber, the 'prettily rural' dining-room will charm the eye with sprays of dried flowers and flickering candles. Peter Wilson's cooking has achieved an enviable consistency over the past decade, largely because he takes care not to overreach himself with elaborately lengthy menus. Indeed, the four-course set dinners offer choice only at the final stage. While menus change from night to night, certain dishes turn up like old friends.

The style is one of honest simplicity, the descriptions of dishes sensibly plain, although a fish 'symphony' – that long-dead nouvelle metaphor – cropped up on a March menu. First courses as often as not use fruit to awaken the palate, as in immaculately carved avocado and orange salad or Comice pear sliced paper-thin with walnut oil and herbs. Fish follows and is generally sensitively treated: a fillet of sea bass had a 'non-belligerent' provençale crust of breadcrumbs, herbs and tomato, and was sauced with a brilliantly judged beurre blanc with steamed leeks. Well-trimmed meats may also be crisply topped, as in Aberdeen Angus fillet with rosemary, mustard and lemon, which impressed for flavour as well as tenderness. Local spring lamb came with fine ratatouille but a rather overpowering soupy tomato coulis. Belgian chocolate terrine made good use of 'superb, slightly bitter' dark chocolate with praline and almonds, and the vibrant flavours of mango and lemon sorbet were given focus by a 'very tart' strawberry coulis. Good, mainly local cheeses come with agreeably solid walnut and banana bread.

The wine list still majors in Bordeaux and Burgundy, the selections fine but very limited under £20. New Zealand whites and Australian reds afford some relief but more restricted choice. Real effort has been made with halves. House wines start at £9.75. CELLARMAN'S CHOICE: Jackson Estate Sauvignon Blanc 1994, Marlborough, New Zealand, £18.25 Morgon 1993, Drouhin, £17.25.

CHEF: Peter Wilson PROPRIETORS: Peter and Anne Wilson OPEN: all week D only 7.30 to 8.30 MEALS: Set D £24.50 to £28.50 SERVICE: not inc, card slips closed CARDS: Access, Amex, Visa DETAILS: 20 seats. Private parties: 20 main room, 20 private room. Car park. Children's helpings. No children under 7. Smart dress preferred. No smoking in dining-room. Wheelchair access (also WC). No music ACCOMMODATION: 8 rooms, all with bath/shower. TV. Phone. B&B £62.50 to £167. Children welcome. Baby facilities. Pets welcome in bedrooms only. Afternoon teas. Garden (*The Which? Hotel Guide*)

LAVENHAM Suffolk map 6

▲ *Great House*

Market Place, Lavenham CO10 9QZ COOKING 2
TEL: (01787) 247431 FAX: (01787) 248007 COST £23–£53

'With your eyes open you are very much in England; with them closed you could be very much in a French auberge or family-run restaurant.' So runs a report from visitors who dined at this patriotically Gallic venue in one of East Anglia's most attractive medieval towns. Wealth from the wool trade gave Lavenham its stature – and architecture to match: even the Georgian façade added on to the Great House does nothing to detract from its historical charge. Meals are served in a beamed dining-room that most people reckon is comfortable and well laid out, although one reporter felt that the tables were 'as cramped as Chelsea, the place lit only by one candle on each table'. Staff know how to play their part; they are friendly, attentive and 'a bit flighty' too. At lunch-time the menu is a mixed bag of old-school offerings that can be ordered as snacks or part of full meals: moules marinière, lamb casserole, breast of chicken bourguignon, frogs' legs. Dinner is a slightly more ambitious affair, but chef Regis Crépy knows his raw materials and knows how to make rich, intense sauces: witness braised pheasant breast with wild mushrooms, and pink lamb cutlets with basil. Elsewhere, reporters have enthused about leek and garlic cream soup, warm salad of chicken livers with avocado and flaked almonds, and tarte Tatin. The French cheeseboard is a splendid selection of precisely matured, ripe specimens, and the coffee is strong cafetière. The wine list covers a lot of ground in terms of price and quality, although France is – naturally – the main contributor. Ten wines are sold by the glass; house wines (not the cheapest on the list) are from £11.80 to £15.

CHEF/PROPRIETOR: Regis Crépy OPEN: Tue to Sun L 12 to 2.30, Tue to Sat D 7 to 9.30 (10.30 Sat) CLOSED: 3 weeks Jan MEALS: alc (main courses £6.50 to £17). Set L £16.95, Set D Tue to Fri £16.95 SERVICE: not inc CARDS: Access, Amex, Delta, Visa DETAILS: 45 seats. 7 tables outside. Private parties: 50 main room. Vegetarian meals. Children's helpings. Smart dress preferred. Music ACCOMMODATION: 4 rooms, all with bath/shower. TV. Phone. B&B £50 to £88. Deposit: £25. Children welcome. Baby facilities. Pets welcome exc in restaurant. Afternoon teas. Garden (*The Which? Hotel Guide*)

LEAMINGTON SPA Warwickshire map 5

Les Plantagenêts

15 Dormer Place, Leamington Spa CV32 5AA COOKING 2
TEL: (01926) 451792 FAX: (01926) 435171 COST £22–£38

'This is a very French restaurant,' observed one visitor, although the setting – a cellar below one of Leamington's Regency terraces – might seem to be the height of shires Englishness. Rémy Loth is a seasoned restaurateur and an accomplished cook who plies his trade within a rich seam of classic French cuisine, turning out such dishes as braised lambs' sweetbreads with a mirepoix of vegetables, or pavé of beef with black pepper sauce and cognac. He is also prepared to pull out all the stops for special occasions: one couple were delighted by the menu created for a fiftieth-birthday celebration – excellent seafood, 'superb rich sauces' and perfectly cooked vegetables were all given glowing accolades.

The cornerstones of the cooking are fixed-price menus for lunch and dinner, but these are augmented by a slate of specials (which may carry a supplementary charge), for M. Loth buys his seafood fresh from the market. There are some good ideas and well-handled ingredients here, although the practice of reciting dishes by waiters 'with a varying grasp of English' can sometimes lead to confusion over just what is available and what the final cost may be. Desserts may include 'light and very easy to eat' chocolate mousse, and 'melt-in-the-mouth' French apple tarts served with crème anglaise. The French cheeseboard earns full marks and is served by knowledgeable staff. The wine list has been described as 'handsome' and is not overpriced, with plenty from Alsace. House wine is £10.50.

CHEF/PROPRIETOR: Rémy Loth OPEN: Mon to Fri L 12.15 to 2.15, Mon to Sat D 7.30 to 10.15 MEALS: Set L £12.50, Set D £18.50 SERVICE: not inc CARDS: Access, Amex, Visa DETAILS: 40 seats. Private parties: 45 main room. Children welcome. Smart dress preferred. No smoking in 1 dining-room. Music. Air-conditioned

Net prices *in the details at the end of an entry indicates that the prices given on a menu and on a bill are inclusive of VAT and service charge, and that this practice is clearly stated on menu and bill.*

LECK Lancashire map 8

▲ *Cobwebs*

Leck, Cowan Bridge LA6 2HZ
TEL/FAX: (015242) 72141
2m SE of Kirkby Lonsdale on A65, turn left at Cowan Bridge

COOKING 3
COST £37–£45

John Ruskin was patriotically fond of the Lune Valley near Kirkby Lonsdale, and even today the northernmost reaches of Lancashire are the most uninterfered with in the whole county. The tiny hamlet of Leck is a swerve off the A65 just before the border with Cumbria. It has a Norman church, a couple of houses and Cobwebs: lavishly decorated with antique ornaments and 'hectic wallpapers'. Eating takes place in a spacious conservatory extension.

The fixed-price dinner menu of four courses with coffee offers a choice only for the opener, generally between a fish dish and the signature split soup-bowl, in which two soups meet without mingling. At an autumn dinner the soups were a sweet but balanced beetroot and apple next to a 'very creamy, pleasantly smoky and granular' celeriac and smoked chicken. Other reporters have enjoyed a 'delicate but delectable' first-course tartlet of smoked salmon and asparagus with a salad garnish containing Parmesan shavings and grapes, and 'excellent, tender' roast loin of local Herdwick lamb on parsnip purée. Puddings might include something along the lines of lemon mousse with a plentiful garnish of fresh fruit, or orange and almond sponge with Cointreau sauce. Dinners end with a patiently explained offering of excellent local cheeses. 'Paul Kelly makes you feel at home and enjoys chatting,' says one report. Others may not find this quite such a blessing, depending on how formal you like these occasions to be.

Wine is approached with evangelical fervour. A glance through the list shows the excitement is justified, from the New World through a run of Marqués de Murrieta Castello Ygay Riojas and Nebbiolos from Gaja, to good Rhônes, superlative Alsaces and vintage champagnes. Prices throughout are exceedingly fair, though a POA tag appears with irritating frequency. Bloody Good Red and White from California's Bonny Doon make fine house wines at £12. CELLARMAN'S CHOICE: St Andrews Chardonnay 1992, Napa Valley, California, £14; Buckleys Cabernet Sauvignon 1991, Coonawarra, S. Australia, £14.

CHEF: Yvonne Thompson PROPRIETORS: Paul Kelly and Yvonne Thompson OPEN: Tue to Sat D only 7.30 for 8 (one sitting) CLOSED: end Dec to mid-Mar MEALS: Set D £28 SERVICE: not inc, card slips closed CARDS: Access, Visa DETAILS: 30 seats. Private parties: 30 main room. Car park. No children under 12. Smart dress preferred. No smoking in dining-room. Wheelchair access (2 steps; also WC). Music ACCOMMODATION: 5 rooms, all with bath/shower. TV. Phone. B&B £45 to £60. Deposit: 10%. No children under 12. Afternoon teas. Garden. Fishing (*The Which? Hotel Guide*)

▲ *This symbol means accommodation is available.*

indicates that smoking is either banned altogether or that a dining-room is maintained for non-smokers. The symbol does not apply to restaurants that simply have no-smoking areas.

LEDBURY Hereford & Worcester map 5

▲ *Hope End*

Hope End, Ledbury HR8 1JQ
TEL: (01531) 633613 FAX: (01531) 636366 COOKING 3
2m N of Ledbury, just beyond Wellington Heath COST £34–£45

The setting is 'marvellous', hemmed in by hills on all sides, making the seclusion and quiet 'amazing'. A slight air of eccentricity owes something to the architecture's preponderance of curves, in round pillars, an arched gateway and of course the minaret. Inside, the house may give the impression of having seen better days, and if the colours are not bright, that may be due to mostly natural materials: pine tables and chairs, a carved wooden fireplace, a marble coffee table. A sense of the natural is fundamental to Patricia Hegarty's English country cooking too.

Everything is done in threes: three courses, three choices for each, three vegetables with the main dish, three cheeses for those who want to add an extra course, even three kinds of tea: China, Indian or herb. All for £30. A soup to start and a vegetarian main course are always on offer, though one reporter expected more choice for the price (there used to be more), and menus are not over-endowed with fish. Hope End certainly doesn't bother about fashion; indeed it is rooted in tradition, quite literally as far as the walled garden goes, which supplies sea kale, artichoke, cardoon, pumpkin, several fruits and umpteen herbs. Given that one of the fundamental principles of good cooking, and of healthy eating, is freshness of supply, Hope End gets off to a racing start.

Herefordshire beef olives, pork with prunes and cider, and wild salmon with sorrel sauce are among traditional offerings, but the kitchen also comes up with enterprising ideas such as carrot and hazelnut terrine, prawn and curd pancake with mild curry sauce, and ham and spinach hotpot with nutmeg sauce. Meals might finish with apple upside-down pudding (with apple ice-cream and butterscotch sauce), or demerara meringues with a fruit sauce such as loganberry. Tiptop claret – some bottles going back to the 1970s, many in halves – heads up an imposing list of mainly French wines. The point of the older vintages is that the wines are ready to drink: this is a considerate cellar that takes such matters seriously, as it does the provision of half-bottles throughout. Mark-ups are very fair, but if some prices appear high give thanks for Australia and New Zealand. House wine is £8.

CHEF: Patricia Hegarty PROPRIETORS: John and Patricia Hegarty OPEN: all week D only 7.30 to 8.30 CLOSED: mid-Dec to first weekend Feb MEALS: Set D £30 SERVICE: none, card slips closed CARDS: Access, Delta, Switch, Visa DETAILS: 24 seats. Private parties: 6 main room. Car park. Vegetarian meals. No children under 12. Smart dress preferred. No smoking in dining-room. No music ACCOMMODATION: 9 rooms, all with bath/shower. Phone. B&B £85 to £140. Deposit: £60. No children under 12. Garden (*The Which? Hotel Guide*)

LEEDS West Yorkshire map 8

Brasserie Forty Four

44 The Calls, Leeds LS2 7EW COOKING **2***
TEL/FAX: **0113-234 3232** COST **£22–£40**

Outside London the city brasserie is not the swinging success it might be. Fashionable food at reasonable prices is not such a bad idea, and the inhabitants of Leeds, at least, are grateful that Michael Gill has taken it on board. Joined at the hip to Pool Court next door (see entry), down by the Leeds-Liverpool Canal and the River Aire, the brasserie does the everyday business, and its menu is a compendium of modern items from spiced aubergine salad with coriander and minted yoghurt, by way of risotto of smoked fish and saffron, through sun-dried tomatoes and olive oil mash, to brioche-and-butter pudding.

With more attention being focused on Pool Court this year, there may be a feeling that the brasserie is not quite at the cutting edge – 'a lack of sparkle and direction' is how one reporter put it. Certainly the menu options have been trimmed; the set lunch and the special deals for early and late eaters have gone, but the value is still considered good, and the food skips from casserole of pork with black pudding and root vegetables, to roast Whitby cod with tapénade and garlic toasts, without ever becoming a jumble. The blend of British (roast sirloin of beef with Yorkshire pudding and horseradish), oriental (deep-fried duck pancakes with cucumber and plum sauce) and vaguely Mediterranean (sauté of lamb on a chickpea and garlic purée with red pepper sauce) gives it all the pizazz it needs. Three dozen wines from around the world are mostly priced between £10 and £20, and house vin de pays is £9.25.

CHEF: Jeff Baker PROPRIETOR: Michael Gill OPEN: Mon to Fri L 12 to 2, Mon to Sat D 6.30 (6 Sat) to 10.30 (11 Fri and Sat) MEALS: alc (main courses £6.50 to £12.50) SERVICE: not inc CARDS: Access, Amex, Delta, Diners, Switch, Visa DETAILS: 100 seats. Private parties: 60 main room, 55 private room. Vegetarian meals. Children welcome. Smart dress preferred. No cigars or pipes. Music. Air-conditioned (*The Which? Hotel Guide*)

▲ *Haley's*

Shire Oak Road, Headingley, Leeds LS6 2DE COOKING **2**
TEL: **0113-278 4446** FAX: **0113-275 3342** COST **£21–£41**

If the challenge is to see how near to a large urban centre a country house can get while maintaining its pastoral composure, then Haley's takes some beating. It is a large Victorian mansion, a mere couple of miles from the middle of Leeds, and the dining area is a long, gold-lit room of quiet elegance. A changing of the kitchen guard took place in early 1995, and while first reports suggest a bit of a wobble, the outlook none the less remains bright. Dinner menus are priced according to the choice of main course for the first two stages, with desserts and coffee extra.

Main courses tend to revolve around prime cuts rather than anything more challenging, so it was reassuring to see the care taken in the preparation of rabbit at an inspection meal. The leg had been cooked with bacon lardons in a salty meat reduction, while the lighter meat came in a 'wonderful light creamy mustard sauce' with tagliatelle. Al dente vegetables are served separately in a crisp shell of Yorkshire pudding. An iced Grand Marnier soufflé delivered strong flavours of both fresh citrus and spirit, and scarcely seemed to need the chocolate sauce that came with it. Most find the approach welcoming, and the willingness to cater for a vegan diner at Easter was commended as 'unprecedented in a non-ethnic restaurant'. The wine list, though mainly French, also has representatives from around the world. House wines start at £10.15, and are mostly available by the glass.

CHEF: Jon Vennell PROPRIETOR: John Appleyard OPEN: Sun L (winter only) 12.15 to 2, Mon to Sat D 7.15 to 9.45 CLOSED: 26 Dec to 30 Jan MEALS: Set L Sun £13.95, Set D £14.50 (2 courses) to £19.95 SERVICE: not inc, card slips closed CARDS: Access, Amex, Diners, Switch, Visa DETAILS: 45 seats. Private parties: 45 main room, 14 and 25 private rooms. Car park. Vegetarian meals. Children welcome until 8pm. Smart dress preferred. No cigars/pipes in dining-room. Music. Air-conditioned ACCOMMODATION: 22 rooms, all with bath/shower. TV. Phone. B&B £95 to £112. Children welcome. Baby facilities

Leodis 🍷

Victoria Mill, Sovereign Street, Leeds LS1 4BJ — COOKING 2
TEL: 0113-242 1010 FAX: 0113-243 0432 — COST £19–£43

Brasserie cooking has caught on emphatically in Leeds, and this converted riverside mill with cast-iron pillars and a vaulted brick roof exactly matches the mood of the moment. Glass partitions efficiently divide its expanse and, although a couple of hundred people may be catered for on the busiest nights, service seems well drilled enough to keep the operation streamlined. A monster menu of around 20 starters and 20 main courses indicates that the brasserie format is being taken seriously. Choosing will require a fair amount of concentration, but the kitchen is happy to vary or simplify dishes as you wish. Dead-straight options, like asparagus with hollandaise or avocado with prawns, mix with more recherché items among the starters: potato rösti is impregnated with pieces of salmon and served with a pimento relish and salad, for example.

Main course of sea bass is lightly grilled, and rack of lamb is 'juicy, sweet, superb' meat with an aubergine-wrapped parcel of moussaka and steamed spinach, while house bangers and mash with rich onion gravy met with approval from two junior critics. Puddings are an expansive sheet of shortcakes, cheesecakes, ice-creams and chocolate. Eat early and the place may feel as if everyone has 'just poured out of the office', but then that is one of the functions of a true brasserie. Like the food itself, wines come from all over the world in impeccably democratic array. There are 'fine wines from our cellars at Paris', but oceans of affordable fare besides. International house wines start at £7.95. CELLARMAN'S CHOICE: Goundrey Wines Langton Chardonnay 1993, Mount Barker, W. Australia, £12.95; St-Aubin *premier cru* 'Le Charmois' 1990, Olivier Leflaive, £24.45.

CHEFS: Steven Kendell and Nick Male PROPRIETORS: Martin Spalding and Steven Kendell OPEN: Mon to Fri L 12 to 2, Mon to Sat D 6 to 10 (11 Fri and Sat) MEALS: alc (main courses £6 to £14). Set L and D (exc Sat after 7.30) £11.95 SERVICE: not inc CARDS: Access, Amex, Delta, Diners, Switch, Visa DETAILS: 160 seats. 16 tables outside. Private parties: 160 main room. Car park. Vegetarian meals. Children's helpings. Smart dress preferred. Wheelchair access (also WC). Music. Air-conditioned

Pool Court

W. YORKS 1996 NEWCOMER

NEW ENTRY

42 The Calls, Leeds LS2 7EW — COOKING 3*
TEL: 0113-244 4242 FAX: 0113-234 3332 — COST £34–£60

'The transfer from Pool-in-Wharfedale has worked to the great advantage of Leeds,' maintains a supporter. The new site is near the Corn Exchange, in smartened-up sandblasted industrial premises, where it is difficult to tell the River Aire from the Leeds-Liverpool Canal. Michael Gill and his team opened Brasserie 44 first (see entry), then moved in next door with the revamped Pool Court. It is very much a smart city restaurant in both looks and ambition, briskly turned out in elegant creams, greys and dark blues, employing curved lines in '30s maritime genre, with a balcony overlooking the water (and the Tetley brewery). It is small and intimate, with pin-prick spotlights to give the food the sort of help it might get in a photographic studio.

The thrust of the menu is posh comfort food: tournedos Rossini with a truffled madeira sauce, for instance, or baked Jersey royal potatoes with smoked salmon, soured cream and Beluga caviare. It is not innovative food, but it does require a high degree of skill to accomplish well. An unctuous terrine of foie gras comes properly pink, with a tiny splodge of preserved fig and a glass of sweet Loupiac wine. A soup of langoustines is silkily creamy, velvety rich and wonderfully aromatic, 'with the taste of pulverised shells'. The foundation is French, but the food can hold its own alongside that of most modern practitioners. Local duckling comes in two parts: thick slices of breast twirled and piled on half-roasted potatoes (or, on another occasion, on black olives and polenta) with a separate plate for the crisp and 'brilliantly tasty' leg.

Minor quibbles surface, but the food speaks of confidence and assurance, and the money pays for prime ingredients cooked as they should be, without distraction or apprehension, including puddings such as pithiviers of dark chocolate with a milk chocolate sauce, or a simple lemon tart with the consistency of lemon curd, an ultra-thin glaze and good pastry. The seven-course 'gourmand menu' (for the whole table only) is aptly described but only makes sense if you are Desperate Dan hungry; there is nothing different about the dishes, just more of them. Wines are helpfully organised into a main body of youthful but interesting bottles, a short selection of current favourites and a few more expensive treats. A good spread of prices, ten half-bottles and a weekly-changing choice of wines by the glass add to the appeal.

CHEF: Jeff Baker PROPRIETORS: Michael and Hanni Gill OPEN: Mon to Fri L 12 to 2, Mon to Sat D 7 (6 Sat) to 10 (10.30 Fri and Sat) MEALS: Set L £17.50 (2 courses) to £22, Set D £22.50 (2 courses) to £37.50 SERVICE: 10%, card slips closed CARDS: Access, Amex, Delta, Diners, Switch, Visa DETAILS: 37 seats. 8 tables outside. Private parties: 38 main room. Children's helpings. Vegetarian meals. Smart dress preferred. No cigars/pipes in dining-room. Wheelchair access (also WC). No music. Air-conditioned

If a restaurant is new to the Guide *this year (did not appear as a main entry in the last edition),* NEW ENTRY *appears opposite its name.*

Sous le Nez en Ville £

The Basement, Quebec House, Quebec Street,
Leeds LS1 2HA — COOKING 2
TEL: 0113-244 0108 FAX: 0113-245 0240 — COST £19–£41

'Under your nose in town' may not be an over-helpful description if you are trying to find this trend-setting restaurant in the financial district of Leeds. Look for the discreet sign on the corner of the building, and the glass-cased menu. Inside is half-bar, half-eating area, both resonant with noises from tiled or wooden flooring and exposed brickwork. Service is brasserie-fashion, by long-aproned waiters without much to say.

The *carte* menus are bolstered by fish specials on a blackboard, and an early-evening set-price dinner offering noteworthy value for three courses with a half-bottle of wine per person. As the name implies, the cooking takes its cue from French modes, but not so single-mindedly that it can't also find room for sausage and bean gumbo, or tagliatelle with Thai-spiced spinach. An inspection took in a rich and moist terrine of pork, duck livers and prunes wrapped in smoked bacon, with Cumberland sauce, and a classic preparation of beef fillet, crusted with black peppercorns and stuffed with a mushroom purée, garlic and shallots. Franglais desserts include jam sponge and custard, chocolate marquise, and a thin apple tart with boldly flavoured cardamom ice-cream.

The wine list is admirably laid out and provides generous choice below £20. It avoids the tendency to go overboard for New World wines (although the Australian section is very good) and affords fair prominence to the old European wine lands. French country wines are well chosen, and the sheet of 'personal recommendations' displays a broad mind, as do the various house wines, which start with a pair of Australians at £8.50.

CHEF: Andrew Carter PROPRIETOR: C.R.C.R. Partnership OPEN: Mon to Fri L 12 to 2.30, Mon to Sat D 6 to 10.30 (11 Fri and Sat) CLOSED: bank hols MEALS: alc (main courses £7 to £13.50). Set D 6pm to 7.30pm £13.95 (inc wine) SERVICE: not inc, card slips closed CARDS: Access, Amex, Delta, Switch, Visa DETAILS: 90 seats. Private parties: 100 main room, 20 private room. Vegetarian meals. Children welcome. No cigars/pipes in dining-room. Music

---

LEICESTER Leicestershire — map 5

Welford Place

9 Welford Place, Leicester LE1 6ZH — COOKING 2
TEL: 0116-247 0758 FAX: 0116-247 1843 — COST £18–£49

This is one of the very few places in the *Guide* to be open 365 days a year, catering without a break for breakfast custom all the way through to the outflowing theatre and concert crowds in the evening. It is a high-ceilinged Victorian building with period pillars and chandeliers and 'every splinter of wood a genuine antique'. And although it can cater for over 200 customers, it does so with exemplary courtesy rather than conveyor-belt rush. The tone of most of the cooking is that of a contemporary brasserie built around a solid base of traditional English fare, though that doesn't stop the kitchen being able to produce a mightily impressive starter of penne with smoked mussels, prawns and green peppers in a 'wonderfully rich' saffron cream sauce. Black pudding crops up to partner light-tasting pigeon breast and three colours of pepper, while a main course of lamb fillet is popped into little cornets of filo along with some firm mushrooms, garlic and rosemary, the flavours together attaining an 'enjoyable corpulence'.

Puddings offer confections of toffee, banana and chocolate, and a dish of freshly baked shortbread with orange segments and a Cointreau cream. Cappuccino 'had a head on it that most brewers would be jealous of'. As for service, 'politeness reigns'. Sift through the cheerful jumble of the wine list and some good bottles emerge. There are few halves, but prices are mostly manageable. House burgundy is £9.70.

CHEFS: Lino Poli and Jamie Matts PROPRIETORS: Michael and Valerie Hope OPEN: all week 8am to midnight MEALS: alc (main courses £7.50 to £19.50). Set L £8.75 (2 courses) to £10.50, Set L Sun £14, Set D £11 (2 courses) to £14 SERVICE: not inc, card slips closed CARDS: Access, Amex, Diners, Visa DETAILS: 216 seats. Private parties: 60 main room, 16 to 60 private rooms. Vegetarian meals. Children's helpings. Wheelchair access (also WC). No music

LEWDOWN Devon map 1

▲ *Lewtrenchard Manor*

Lewdown EX20 4PN
off A30 Okehampton to Launceston road, turn left at Lewdown for ¾m

COOKING 2
COST £22–£46

The manor, built in 1600, retains a period feel with its mullioned windows, dark oak panelling, old portraits and candlelit dining-room. It has a sense of calm as well: 'It feels like a home rather than a hotel,' commented one couple. The *carte* has gone, leaving a fixed-price dinner menu of half a dozen choices per course, some with a supplement. Patrick Salvadori brings country-house cooking up to date without being sidetracked by the chargrill or exotic spices – apart, perhaps, from a fleck of coriander to chivvy up a first course of scallops and spinach under a layer of pasta. He is equally at home with humble fish-cakes, deep-fried and served with a lemon butter sauce, and with a veal terrine studded with asparagus and served with Cumberland sauce.

Sweetness occasionally appears in a savoury dish, as when quail are stuffed with fruit, or breast of duck is glazed with honey, but balance is maintained. Saucing can be as light as a warm dressing of olive oil and basil for a fillet of turbot (which also comes with marinated vegetables), or as rich as a port sauce that accompanies a rack of lamb with Roquefort ravioli. The sharp eye for a challenging yet workable combination continues in puddings of dark and white chocolate parfait with pistachio sauce, and a coconut and rum tart with clotted cream. The Murrays spend time with guests and make everyone feel welcome, while the rest of the service is polite, informed and quietly professional. South Africa figures prominently on the wine list, and what a delightful collection it is: some of the country's best producers are there, and most of the wines are under £20. Value permeates the whole list from France to Australia, a consequence of a fair pricing policy, and quality is high. House wine is £8.50. CELLARMAN'S CHOICE:Thelema Mountain Vineyards Chardonnay 1991, Stellenbosch, South Africa, £17.50; St-Emilion *grand cru*, Ch. Franc 'Grace Dieu', 1985, £10.75.

CHEF: Patrick Salvadori PROPRIETORS: James and Sue Murray OPEN: Sun L 12.15 to 1.45, all week D 7.15 to 9.30; Mon to Sat L by arrangement MEALS: Set L Sun £16, Set D £26 SERVICE: not inc, card slips closed CARDS: Access, Amex, Delta, Diners, Switch, Visa DETAILS: 30 seats. Private parties: 8 main room, 16 private room. Car park. No children under 8 D. Smart dress preferred. No smoking in dining-room. No music ACCOMMODATION: 8 rooms, all with bath/shower. TV. Phone. B&B £75 to £130. No children under 8. Pets by arrangement. Afternoon teas. Garden. Fishing (*The Which? Hotel Guide*)

LIDGATE Suffolk map 6

Star Inn NEW ENTRY

The Street, Lidgate CB8 9PP
TEL: (01638) 500275 COOKING 1
on B1063, 6m SE of Newmarket COST £20–£33

Lidgate is English through and through, with its pretty thatched cottages, and swans and ducks on the village pond. Its bucolic image is reinforced by the Star, a 500-year-old beamed building with brick fireplaces, tankards hung above the bar and wood-panelled bench seating. Greene King real ales are on tap, and the pub plays host to local cricket teams.

However, one glance at Maria Teresa Axon's *'carta'* tells a very different story. Her blackboard menu is a short, ever-changing selection of dishes with a sunny Mediterranean flavour and a noticeable Spanish slant. Fish soup is a wholesome brew packed with prawns, scallops, nuggets of lobster, squid and vegetables. Monkfish 'marinière' is forthrightly provençale, and lamb is roasted with garlic and wine. The summer-holiday feel of it all is bolstered by Catalan salad, paella, and prawns malaguena, although the kitchen assuages traditional appetites with smoked salmon and avocado salad, roast beef, and sirloin steak in Stilton sauce. Desserts range from homespun apple pie to a splendid home-made chocolate roulade. Service is chatty and genuinely enthusiastic. Like the menu, the wine list is constantly varying, with wines of the week complementing a handful of old favourites. House wine is £9.

CHEF/PROPRIETOR: Maria Teresa Axon OPEN: all week L 12.30 to 2, Mon to Sat D 7.30 to 10 MEALS: alc (main courses £7 to £10.50). Set L Sun £12.50 SERVICE: not inc CARDS: Access, Amex, Diners, Visa DETAILS: 52 seats. 5 tables outside. Private parties: 35 main room. Car park. Vegetarian meals. Children's helpings. Smart dress preferred. Music

LIFTON Devon map 1

▲ *Arundell Arms*

Lifton PL16 0AA
TEL: (01566) 784666 FAX: (01566) 784494 COOKING 2*
just off A30, 3m E of Launceston COST £25–£45

'This may be a sporting inn, but it deserves to attract a much wider clientele for its cooking.' Over the three decades of her ownership Anne Voss-Bark has seen the old village pub (complete with surviving cockpit) move with the times, sprouting wings, extra buildings and a conference centre as it went. But it still retains strong sporting links: fishing tackle in the flag-floored lounge, lessons for beginners, and 20 miles along the Tamar and tributaries to practise on. There is no need to wear thigh-length wellies to enjoy the food, though. Bar meals of Spanish omelette, salads or lambs' kidneys are popular, but lunch in the restaurant is 'excellent value for this quality of cooking'. The conference business has not dragged down the food into meaningless and tasteless frivolity, as can happen. Good buying, skill and care in the kitchen, and 'smiling, attentive, responsive service' combine to make this a delight.

Two reporters independently raved about their 'casserole' of fish, with a saffron sauce in one case, chive in the other. This is no jumble, but a classy mix of what is available – salmon, red mullet, sea bass, John Dory, hake, monk, scallops – all perfectly steamed, bouncy and tasty. Locally sourced ingredients include organic beef, which might turn up roasted with parsley tartlets, béarnaise sauce and baby vegetables. The food is accomplished but not showy, as in a rich milk chocolate ice-cream and dark chocolate sorbet served with a creamy nutmeg sauce, while incidentals from bread to petits fours keep up the standard. The good showing of mainly French wines includes a fair number of half-bottles and wines by the glass. Half a dozen house wines are around £11 a bottle.

CHEFS: Philip Burgess and Nick Shopland PROPRIETOR: Anne Voss-Bark OPEN: all week 12.30 to 2, 7.30 to 9.30 CLOSED: D 3 days Christmas MEALS: Set L £13 (2 courses) to £16, Set D £23 (2 courses) to £29 SERVICE: not inc CARDS: Access, Amex, Diners, Switch DETAILS: 70 seats. Private parties: 80 main room, 30 private room. Car park. Vegetarian meals. Children's helpings. Smart dress preferred. No smoking in dining-room. Wheelchair access (2 steps). Music ACCOMMODATION: 29 rooms, all with bath/shower. TV. Phone. B&B £57.50 to £93. Children welcome. Baby facilities. Pets welcome. Afternoon teas. Garden. Fishing (*The Which? Hotel Guide*)

LINCOLN Lincolnshire map 9

Jew's House

15 The Strait, Lincoln LN2 1JD COOKING 1*
TEL: (01522) 524851 COST £18–£49

The location is an enclosed short alley at the bottom of aptly named Steep Hill, the vertiginous plunge that leads down from the cathedral. In a house no less than 800 years old, with partially exposed interior stone walls, Richard and Sally Gibbs ply their trade. His cooking style is almost bistro, with a few nods to contemporary taste in the likes of grilled goats' cheese with bacon and croûtons, and tomato and pesto tartlet with herbed vinaigrette. Confidently rendered provençale fish soup has textbook tastes of fresh fish, garlic, tomato and pepper, the rouille good and pungent, the croûtons crisp. A main course of grilled salmon steak, carefully timed, comes in a very creamy sauce of pink peppercorns. Another main course of fillet of sea bass is served with a strong peppery purée of tomato, paprika and mixed peppers. Lemon tart has good zip to the filling, crème brûlée is well made, and there is an impressively varied cheeseboard. Home-made walnut bread is excellent, as are the chocolate truffles with coffee. Service has been described as 'very friendly and helpful'. The wine list is stylistically arranged, helpfully annotated, soundly chosen and reasonably priced. House wines start at around £9.50.

CHEF: Richard Gibbs PROPRIETORS: Richard and Sally Gibbs OPEN: Tue to Sat L 12 to 1.30, Mon to Sat D 7 to 9.15 CLOSED: 25 and 26 Dec, bank hol Mons MEALS: alc (main courses £11 to £15). Set L £11.95, Set D £19.95 SERVICE: not inc CARDS: Access, Amex, Delta, Diners, Switch, Visa DETAILS: 26 seats. Private parties: 30 main room. Vegetarian meals. Children's helpings. No smoking in dining-room. Music

Wig & Mitre £

29 Steep Hill, Lincoln LN2 1LU
TEL: (01522) 535190 and 523705 COOKING **2**
FAX: (01522) 532402 COST **£20–£37**

Food 'in perpetual motion' from eight in the morning to late in the evening is one of the selling points of this admirable venue in a converted medieval building close by the cathedral and castle. It finds favour with a happy-go-lucky assortment of young and old, locals and visitors alike: 'Here some American businessmen, there someone entertaining a German supplier, in the middle a couple enjoying a quiet evening out, and in the corner a lone management consultant reading a report on the truck industry,' commented one traveller. A mix-and-match policy applies to the frequently changing menus, and diners can jump between sandwiches and snacks, daily blackboard specials and the full printed *carte* – or call in for just a pint of beer.

The inspiration comes mainly from England, France and Italy, and there are some neat ideas tucked in among old favourites. A salad of chorizo with nuggets of black pudding and a strong mustard vinaigrette was reckoned to be an 'inspired combination', while strongly flavoured breast of wood pigeon with red wine sauce was perfectly balanced by a mushroom duxelles. Elsewhere you might find anything from venison sausages with spicy tomato sauce to chicken breast with lemon, pesto and cream. The cheeseboard is a selection from the pick of Britain's farmhouse producers, while sweets could take in cappuccino mousse as well as Bakewell tart. Service is 'solicitous and friendly'. Well-established names from France dominate the wine list, but there are also some thoughtfully chosen bottles from around the world, plus bin ends. House wine is £9.70.

CHEFS: Paul Vidic and Peter Dodd PROPRIETORS: Valerie and Michael Hope OPEN: all week 8am to 11pm CLOSED: 25 Dec MEALS: alc (main courses £5 to £14.50) SERVICE: not inc, card slips closed CARDS: Access, Amex, Diners, Visa DETAILS: 120 seats. 6 tables outside. Private parties: 60 main room, 40 private room. Vegetarian meals. Children's helpings. Wheelchair access (1 step; also WC). No music

£ *indicates that it is possible to have a three-course meal, including coffee, a half-bottle of house wine and service, at any time the restaurant is open (i.e. at dinner as well as at lunch, unless a place is open only for dinner), for £20 or less per person.*

The Guide *relies on feedback from its readers. Especially welcome are reports on new restaurants appearing in the book for the first time. All letters to the* Guide *are acknowledged.*

LINTON West Yorkshire map 8

▲ *Wood Hall*

Trip Lane, Linton, nr Wetherby LS22 4JA
TEL: (01937) 587271 FAX: (01937) 584353
from Wetherby take A661 N for ½m, turn left to Sicklinghall and Linton, then left to Linton and Wood Hall, and turn right in Linton opposite Windmill pub

COOKING 1
COST £21–£54

This Georgian house, set in 100 acres of parkland, is heavily furnished and provides a living for the local florist. With the departure of Andrew Mitchell, Stephanie Moon has been promoted to head chef. The reliance on conference and corporate business trade, plus weekend leisure breaks, probably accounts for the ambition of the large *carte* – over 30 dishes in total – which at an inspection meal produced bell pepper and onion frittata ('more or less an omelette') and poor roast leg of lamb. The short set-price 'house menu' seems to offer better cooking and fairer prices: one reporter enjoyed an 'exquisite' brochette of chicken livers wrapped in bacon, and 'tender, juicy breast of Barbary duck with a crisp skin' in a creditable madeira sauce, followed by crêpes filled with a warm berry compote and almond cream. The wine list is vast, and outside the half-dozen house wines (from £10.95) and a few others, prices rise steeply, although ten are normally available by the glass from £2.50.

CHEF: Stephanie Moon PROPRIETOR: Country Mansion Hotels Ltd OPEN: Sun to Fri L 12.30 to 2.30, all week D 7 to 10 MEALS: alc (main courses £15.50 to £18.50). Set L £15.95, Set L Sun £13.95, Set D £26.95 SERVICE: not inc CARDS: Access, Amex, Delta, Diners, Switch, Visa DETAILS: 70 seats. 5 tables outside. Private parties: 110 main room, 12 to 40 private rooms. Vegetarian meals. Children's helpings. Smart dress preferred. No smoking in dining-room. Wheelchair access (3 steps; also WC). Music ACCOMMODATION: 43 rooms, all with bath/shower. TV. Phone. B&B £90 to £155. Rooms for disabled. Children welcome. Pets welcome. Afternoon teas. Garden. Swimming-pool. Fishing

LITTLE SHELFORD Cambridgeshire map 6

Sycamore House

1 Church Street, Little Shelford CB2 5HG
TEL: (01223) 843396

COOKING 2
COST £27–£34

Michael and Susan Sharpe built up a loyal body of support when they were in Cambridge itself, so much so that some have followed their trail to this agreeable little village nearby, where they are now encamped in a converted pub. Some feel the décor is somewhat on the austere side, but any perceived lack of cosiness is soon dispelled by the good things on offer. The format is a four-course fixed-price menu which changes monthly, with salad of the day after the first course. Starters and mains are usually four choices each, with vegetarians always catered for. Soups are hearty country fare, sometimes drawing on Continental influences as in vegetable goulash or white bean with pesto.

Techniques are interesting: avocado may be deep-fried in wedges and given a provençale sauce, or black pudding may be cooked in a crêpe with sour cream and horseradish. Invigorating meat preparations may include lamb marinated in pomegranate and rice wine, with Greek yoghurt and mint, or pigeon breasts

flambé in armagnac, with a sauce of orange and cassis. Chocolate squidgy cake to finish may prove irresistible to some, but the îles flottantes, crêpes suzette and ice-creams such as ginger or Grand Marnier all inspire praise. Susan Sharpe works hard out front, although some sympathetic souls have suggested another pair of hands might not go amiss on occasion. Wines will provide plenty of excitement. The choices are mostly superb and prices are extremely reasonable, with even vintage champagne coming in at not much above retail. House French wines start at £7.95. CELLARMAN'S CHOICE: **Sancerre 1993, Vacheron, £15.50; Rockford Semillon 1989, Barossa Valley, S. Australia, £15.**

CHEF: Michael Sharpe PROPRIETORS: Michael and Susan Sharpe OPEN: Tue to Sat D only 7.30 to 9.30 (L by arrangement) CLOSED: Christmas MEALS: Set D £19.95 SERVICE: not inc, card slips closed CARDS: Access, Visa DETAILS: 24 seats. Private parties: 24 main room. Car park. Vegetarian meals. No children under 12. Smart dress preferred. No smoking in dining-room. No music

LITTLE WALSINGHAM Norfolk **map 6**

▲ *Old Bakehouse*

33 High Street, Little Walsingham NR22 6BZ
TEL: (01328) 820454 **COOKING 1**
on B1105, 4½m N of Fakenham **COST £28–£38**

The building dates from Tudor times, and during its term as a bakehouse must have supplied the staff of life to countless pilgrims to Little Walsingham. Pink and pine now dominate, and an open coal fire set into the brick wall is welcoming in cold weather. Chris Padley, formerly a teacher, is a self-taught cook who doesn't major in fish, despite the sea's proximity, although seafood pancake and smoked haddock in a creamy cheese sauce might feature among first courses. There is something else he doesn't do: 'In this part of Norfolk it is a relief not to find sun-dried tomatoes' – these the words of a seasoned reporter. Instead, there is a steady trickle of cream and alcohol in sauces, and the solid assurance of beef Wellington, pigeon breasts in a rich red wine sauce, and, by way of variety, a chicken breast stuffed with banana in a curry and almond sauce. Puddings tread a familiar path with banoffi pie, sticky toffee, and blackberry and apple crème brûlée, and a few good names appear on the varied and acceptably priced wine list.

CHEF: Christopher Padley PROPRIETORS: Christopher and Helen Padley OPEN: Sun L once a month 12.15 to 1.30, Tue to Sat D 7 to 8.45 CLOSED: Tue Nov to Easter, 1 week Nov, 2 weeks Jan and Feb, 1 week June MEALS: alc (main courses £13.50 to £15). Set D £12.50 (residents only) SERVICE: not inc, card slips closed CARDS: Access, Delta, Switch, Visa DETAILS: 40 seats. Private parties: 40 main room, 12 private room. Vegetarian meals. No smoking in dining-room. Wheelchair access (2 steps). Music ACCOMMODATION: 3 rooms, 1 with bath/shower. TV. B&B £22.50 to £40. Deposit: £5. Children welcome. Pets by arrangement (*The Which? Hotel Guide*)

Card slips closed ***in the details at the end of an entry indicates that the total on the slips of credit cards is closed when handed over for signature.***

LIVERSEDGE West Yorkshire map 9

▲ *Healds Hall Hotel, Harringtons* £ NEW ENTRY

Leeds Road, Liversedge WF15 6JA COOKING 1
TEL: (01924) 409112 FAX: (01924) 401895 COST £15–£37

Built in 1764, Healds Hall first gained fame through its association with the Brontë family. The Harringtons have developed the hotel into a valuable local asset: pinks, greys, maroons and cream set the tone in the restaurant, where guests sit at pale wooden chairs arranged around neatly laid tables. The set-price menus offer the best value, although there is also a short *carte* that mixes modern British with a few exotic flourishes.

First courses might include a Chinese-inspired appetiser consisting of slices of roast belly-pork arranged over bean sprouts and tiny pieces of chicken with a light soy dressing. Meat and game main courses are handled more robustly: fillet of beef with smoked bacon, shallots and a rich claret sauce, and loin of venison with sloe-gin sauce have both been capably executed. Fish-lovers might opt for steamed salmon with lime and dill, or pesto-coated sea bass with tomato and olive dressing. A generous wedge of glazed lemon tart finishes things off nicely, and the Anglo-Irish cheeseboard features some big names, such as Appleby's Cheshire, Bonchester and Cooleeney. At lunch-time you can get sandwiches and snacks in addition to the full menu. The wine list is a well-spread selection with plenty of halves and seven available by the glass. House wine is £7.95.

CHEF: Philip McVeagh PROPRIETORS: Thomas and Nora Harrington OPEN: Sun to Fri L 12 to 2, Mon to Sat D 6.30 to 9.30 CLOSED: bank hol Mons MEALS: alc (main courses £4 to £14). Set L £9.75, Set D £16.95 SERVICE: not inc, card slips closed CARDS: Access, Amex, Delta, Diners, Switch, Visa DETAILS: 50 seats. Private parties: 18 main room, 12 and 30 private rooms. Car park. Vegetarian meals. Children's helpings. Smart dress preferred. No smoking in dining-room. Wheelchair access (also WC). Music. Air-conditioned ACCOMMODATION: 25 rooms, all with bath/shower. TV. Phone. B&B £35 to £70. Rooms for disabled. Children welcome. Baby facilities. Pets welcome. Afternoon teas. Garden

LOCKINGTON Humberside map 9

Rockingham Arms

52 Front Street, Lockington YO25 9SH
TEL: (01430) 810607 COOKING 1
off A164, between Beverley and Driffield COST £29–£40

A former stable serves as the dining-room for this converted pub – a Grade II listed building – which achieves a pleasantly provençale atmosphere by dint of brick alcoves, fabrics and candlelight. The food is not Mediterranean, though: coconut milk, mango, and Malaysian curry sauce point to the east as a source of inspiration. Ingredients are above average, and the kitchen piles lots of ideas into a single dish: for example, a hotpot of mushrooms and smoked haddock with cider and cream in a filo 'nest', or lamb fillet sauté with strawberries, green peppercorns, coriander and gin. The fixed-price menu is supplemented by dishes from the board, and puddings range from a white chocolate mousse wrapped in a dark chocolate sponge on a coffee crème anglaise to a more down-to-earth ginger pudding with custard. Fifty-odd diverse wines are considerate to those wanting change from £20, and the blackboard also features wines of the month for around £10 a bottle, or £2.25 a glass.

CHEFS/PROPRIETORS: David and Susan Barker OPEN: Tue to Sat D only 7 to 10 CLOSED: bank hols, 2 weeks in summer MEALS: Set D £16.95 (2 courses) to £19.95 SERVICE: not inc CARDS: Access, Delta, Switch, Visa DETAILS: 60 seats. Private parties: 24 main room. Car park. Vegetarian meals. No children under 6. Smart dress preferred. Music

LONG CRENDON Buckinghamshire map 2

▲ *Angel Inn*

Bicester Road, Long Crendon HP18 9EE
TEL: (01844) 208268 FAX: (01844) 208652 COOKING 1
on B4011, 2m NW of Thame COST £24–£37

This converted sixteenth-century inn has evolved from village local into an up-market pub/restaurant with brasserie overtones. It still caters for those living nearby, although it is equally sought out by travellers from much further afield. Inside, it is a rabbit-warren of different rooms and areas: here a modest bar lounge with sofas and a warming fire, there a narrow conservatory festooned with wickerwork. Most customers home in on the blackboard of fish specials: deliveries arrive three times each week from Scotland, Cornwall and Billingsgate, and the kitchen delivers the goods in the shape of roast monkfish with tapénade and aubergine salad, halibut with spinach and tomatoes, chargrilled tuna with shellfish risotto, and hake en papillote with crab sauce, not to mention cod and chips. There is also a standard menu offering soups, pasta, salads, mixed crostini and old favourites such as bangers and mash, although confit of duck with provençale bean stew seems to stand head and shoulders above the rest. Staff are helpful and considerate, even though the pressure at peak times can be immense. The good-value wine list is arranged by 'weight' and style. There is also a collection of wines of the month, and you can even bring your own (corkage £1 per person). House wines are around £9 and £10.

CHEFS: Mark Jones and Wendy Shower PROPRIETORS: Mark and Ruth Jones OPEN: all week L 12 to 2.30, Mon to Sat D 6.30 to 10 CLOSED: Sun L Sept to Easter MEALS: alc (main courses £8 to £12) SERVICE: not inc CARDS: Access, Switch, Visa DETAILS: 80 seats. 4 tables outside. Private parties: 40 main room, 10 and 25 private rooms. Car park. Vegetarian meals. Children welcome. No smoking in 1 dining-room. Music ACCOMMODATION: 3 rooms, all with bath/shower. TV. Phone. B&B £35 to £50. Children welcome

LONG MELFORD Suffolk map 6

Scutchers Bistro

SUFFOLK 1996 BISTRO

Westgate Street, Long Melford CO10 9DP COOKING 1*
TEL/FAX: (01787) 310200 and 310620 COST £21–£35

The consensus seems to be that Nicholas Barrett's pleasant bistro opposite Melford Hall is keeping up its momentum. There is as much to divert attention on the up-to-the-minute menus as there is in the windows of the numerous antique shops nearby. Mediterranean influences have come to the fore in the cooking, not just the Italian axis of sun-dried tomatoes, balsamic vinegar, basil and Parmesan, but ratatouille and couscous as well. An engaging touch of Anglicism is apparent at the edges, though, as shown by duck confit that comes on mushy peas and a shallot gravy, while main courses are served with chips, new potatoes or rice. Thinly cut slices of smoked duck on a pile of lemony rocket was a supremely satisfying starter for one lunchtime visitor, and a top-quality lamb chop with potato galette and raisin gravy pleased another. Fish, too, is well handled: 'a most interesting way of presenting cod' is to roast it under a herbed breadcrumb crust and douse it with lemon, while monkfish is sliced into collops and served on a 'minestrone' of vegetables flavoured with coriander. Sticky toffee pudding with the obligatory butterscotch sauce is done well, as are apple fritters with apricot coulis. Extra charges for vegetables and salads will push up the bill, and putting a price on bread arouses 'intense irritation'.

Greater care has been taken over wines than the bistro context may lead one to expect. Although whites major in Sauvignon and Chardonnay, space is also found for Coche-Dury's benchmark Bourgogne Aligoté, and reds include some good Australian Shiraz, the little-known Tuscan Parrina and Depardon's stunning Fleurie. Halves are plentiful, and an international spread of house wines opens with Côtes de St-Mont at £7.90. CELLARMAN'S CHOICE: Santa Rita Chardonnay 1993, Chile, £10.50; Côtes du Rhône 1992, Guigal, £13.50.

CHEF/PROPRIETOR: Nicholas Barrett OPEN: Mon to Sat 12 to 2, 7 to 9.30 CLOSED: 25 and 26 Dec, 1 Jan, bank hol Mons MEALS: alc (main courses £7 to £11) SERVICE: not inc CARDS: Access, Amex, Delta, Switch, Visa DETAILS: 75 seats. 6 tables outside. Private parties: 75 main room. Car park. Vegetarian meals. Children welcome. No cigars/pipes in dining-room. Wheelchair access (also WC). Music

---

LONGRIDGE Lancashire map 8

Paul Heathcote's

104–106 Higher Road, Longridge PR3 3SY COOKING 4
TEL: (01772) 784969 FAX: (01772) 785713 COST £32–£82

The restaurant has four dining-rooms. If that sounds vast, it isn't. The scale is that of a large cottage, with exposed stone, good fabrics, and a homely yet businesslike feel. Meals usually begin in the comfortable lounge with a drink and a plate of appetisers: a tiny cottage pie, perhaps, or an excellent 'sausage roll' made from duck and gently flavoured with Middle Eastern spices.

One of the great Heathcote attractions is that humble, basic and earthy ingredients often play a starring role. Even when they are de-boned, polished and refined for a clientele that is not used to holding a trotter or a ham shank in two hands and gnawing away at it, the ingredients still retain an elemental stickiness, which is the essence of many of these northern dishes. Such cooking also happens to be very much in the swim, but that is by the by. What matters is the pleasure it gives. Pig's trotter is a case in point: boned, filled with diced meat in an eggy medium, on a dark translucent puddle of rich sauce flecked with herbs, the whole thing 'terrifically tasty, wonderfully sticky'. Black pudding gets the up-market treatment too, served with crushed potato, baked haricot beans and a thyme sauce.

The cooking also has a sunnier side to its nature. Fillet of tuna is served on a bed of new potatoes with green beans and a balsamic dressing, a variation on salade niçoise, while moist fillet of halibut with 'soft, succulent' scallops, both lightly browned, are served with shredded leeks. This is undeniably good cooking, although not done with quite the passion of the gutsy native stuff. Technique is never in question, as puddings confirm. A slice of firmly textured and intensely flavoured chocolate terrine, two dark layers enclosing a white one, comes with a pool of dark chocolate sauce and a honey ice-cream, while a pyramid of iced caramel with almond wafers would have impressed the pharaohs.

Lunch is available only on Friday and Sunday, but is considered a bargain. Breads invariably get a mention, and second offerings are gratefully received. Dining is 'lovely and leisurely', and service 'unobtrusively attends to every requirement'. The practice of adding ten per cent service up to a maximum of £15 is refreshing in this field, bringing relief to most parties of four or more. 'I wish they would stock some cheaper wines,' said one reporter. The general arguments are well rehearsed: customers enjoy the food and resolve to eat out more often, then get the bill and go off the idea; restaurants have to make a living. Suffice to say that although prices tend to be high, so is the quality; the range is broad, and able assistance from the wine waiter is worth a few bob. Four house wines are £2.50 a glass.

CHEFS: Paul Heathcote and Andrew Barnes PROPRIETOR: Paul Heathcote OPEN: Fri and Sun L 12 to 2.15, Tue to Sun D 7 to 9.30 MEALS: alc (main courses £15 to £20). Set L £22.50, Set D £35 to £55 SERVICE: 10% (optional; maximum £15), card slips closed CARDS: Access, Amex, Diners, Switch, Visa DETAILS: 55 seats. Private parties: 55 main room, 18 private room. Car park. Vegetarian meals. Children welcome. Smart dress preferred. No smoking in dining-room. Wheelchair access. Music

LONGSTOCK Hampshire **map 2**

Peat Spade Inn

Longstock, nr Stockbridge SO20 6DR
TEL/FAX: (01264) 810612 COOKING 1*
off A3057, 1m N of Stockbridge COST £25–£42

'Not a very 'pubby' pub, more an inn with [the] accent on eating' is how Julie Tuckett describes her converted Victorian house by the River Test. As owner and cook, she has to work within strict limits; her menu is short and seasonal, there is no leeway for outlandish risk-taking, and visitors are expected to be patient, because proper cooking – Julie's way – inevitably takes time. Guests are encouraged to mix and match from the menu: a starter and a pudding, two starters, a main course or the full works – anything goes. There are also good-value fixed-price menus for lunch and dinner. You can even choose where you want to eat: in the bar, the dining-room or the garden in summer. Julie's repertoire is a well-tried run through rillettes of pork, aubergine tart, chargrilled breast of Barbary duck, sauté pigeon breasts, and pheasant flamed in calvados and finished with champagne, cream and crushed livers. Fish dishes ring the changes with smoked haddock pie or roast monkfish with tomato and basil. Main courses come with plain steamed vegetables or salad, while desserts range from hot apricot brioche to sticky toffee pudding. Beer drinkers can look forward to an ever-changing line-up of brews that might include Fuller's London Pride or representatives from Gibbs Mew; wine buffs can take their pick from 16 wines by the glass or dip into the lively, well-chosen list. House wines start at £9.70.

CHEF/PROPRIETOR: Julie Tuckett OPEN: all week 12 to 2, 7.15 to 10 CLOSED: 25 and 26 Dec, 3 weeks Jan to Mar MEALS: alc (main courses £10 to £16). Set L £11.85 (2 courses) to £16.50, Set D £11.85 (2 courses) to £16.50 SERVICE: not inc, card slips closed CARDS: Amex, Diners DETAILS: 30 seats. 6 tables outside. Private parties: 24 main room, 14 private room. Car park. Vegetarian meals. Children's helpings. Smart dress preferred. Wheelchair access (also WC). No music

LOWER BEEDING West Sussex map 3

Jeremy's at the Crabtree

Brighton Road, Lower Beeding RH13 6PT COOKING 2
TEL: (01403) 891257 FAX: (01403) 891606 COST £20–£37

Inside the pretty Georgian building, with its façade of simple, classic proportions, is a huddle of flagstoned eating areas that create 'a marvellous atmosphere'. Jeremy's is probably best thought of as a roadside restaurant and pub where families enjoy eating together. The food dips in and out of different culinary traditions, turning up a terrine of duck livers with a sweet onion compote, grilled spiced chicken breast with coconut rice and a mango and coriander purée, and fillet of salmon with a pesto topping. Fish is particularly well handled.

'There is integrity in the cooking,' maintained one supporter, pointing to mussels in a creamy saffron sauce, lamb with garlic and rosemary sauce, and prune and armagnac ice-cream, dishes that were 'beautifully done' and 'tasting of themselves'. The basics are done well, including bread and 'the lightest pastry ever' for asparagus tart, and flavours stand out right through to puddings, such as an 'intensely flavoured rhubarb compote'. Service is by 'polite young staff', while wines give Old and New Worlds equal prominence and don't aim to break the bank. House French is £9.95.

CHEFS: Jeremy Ashpool, Pia Waters and Tom Clarke PROPRIETOR: Jeremy's Restaurant Ltd OPEN: all week L 12.30 to 2, Tue to Sun D 7.30 to 9.45 CLOSED: bank hol D MEALS: alc L Mon to Sat (main courses £6.50 to £8.50). Set L Sun £13.50, Set D Tue to Thur £11.50, Tue to Sat £21.50 SERVICE: not inc L, 10% D CARDS: Access, Delta, Switch, Visa DETAILS: 40 seats. 4 tables outside. Private parties: 26 main room, 26 private room. Car park. Vegetarian meals. Children welcome. No smoking in 1 dining-room. Wheelchair access. No music

▲ *South Lodge*

Brighton Road, Lower Beeding RH13 6PS
TEL: (01403) 891711 FAX: (01403) 891766 COOKING 2
on A281, 6m S of Horsham COST £29–£76

'As we swept up the drive I was not prepared for anything on this scale. In Scotland, perhaps, in Horsham, no.' The grounds are extensive, the beige-coloured mansion vast, with acres of corridors, and the number of people wearing name tags gives a clue that conference business takes up a lot of South

Lodge's attention. Panelled walls, big chandeliers and three elephantine heavily carved oak dressers in the dining-room are impressive if not daunting. Local lad Timothy Neal now heads the kitchen, and the food makes a stab at Anglo-French modernity, layering local goats' cheese between slices of potato with a sauce vierge, and topping brill with a basil crust and serving it with caramelised onions.

Ingredients and basic techniques are generally sound, from a salad of asparagus and other vegetables to a steamed fillet of sea bass, 'tender and cooked correctly', with crunchy samphire. Chargrilled scallops have been 'cooked to tender perfection', although if couscous was to be the partner then the dish needed more sauce. Given the conference trade, large portions are the norm, with high prices to match. Desserts were the high point for one pair of reporters who hesitated over iced aniseed parfait, and butterscotch soufflé with pistachio ice-cream, and then chose instead a bitter chocolate brûlée with white chocolate sorbet, and a delicate vanilla cream with poached fruits in a syrup of lemon and champagne. Staff are youthful and multinational, and service is smooth. Wines are pricey, with classical leanings. House wine is £13.50.

CHEF: Timothy Neal PROPRIETOR: Exclusive Hotels OPEN: all week 12.30 to 2 (3 Sun), 7.30 to 10 (10.30 Fri and Sat) MEALS: alc D (main courses £19.50 to £24). Set L Mon to Sat £16, Set L Sun £18.50, Set D £25 to £32 SERVICE: not inc, card slips closed CARDS: Access, Amex, Delta, Diners, Switch, Visa DETAILS: 40 seats. 4 tables outside. Private parties: 80 main room, 8 to 80 private rooms. Car park. Vegetarian meals. Children's helpings. Jacket and tie D. No smoking in dining-room. Wheelchair access (also WC). Music ACCOMMODATION: 39 rooms, all with bath/shower. TV. Phone. B&B £100 to £275. Rooms for disabled. Children welcome. Baby facilities. Afternoon teas. Garden. Fishing (*The Which? Hotel Guide*)

LOWER SLAUGHTER Gloucestershire **map 5**

▲ *Lower Slaughter Manor*

Lower Slaughter GL54 2HP
TEL: (01451) 820456 FAX: (01451) 822150 COOKING 3
off A429, at sign 'The Slaughters' COST £22–£53

The village is as pretty as any in the Cotswolds, with the regulation stream flowing through on its way to join the Windrush, and lots of pale honey-coloured buildings. Over a high wall lies the sixteenth-century Manor, a Grade II listed building rescued from the receivers by the Markses in 1992. 'Very Cotswolds,' said one reporter, noting the lush fabrics, Knowle sofas and a baby grand piano in support. It may look imposing and formal, as do the morning-suited waiting staff (mostly French), but the welcome is warm enough to dispel any idea that it might be fusty. The Markses have been in the business long enough to get the 'mine hosting' just right, and in December 1994 they installed Michael Benjamin (who used to work at Gidleigh Park with Shaun Hill) in the kitchen. One reporter describes the service as 'Rolls-Royce, but friendly'.

Comfortable country-house hotels tend to have comforting food. The emphasis is less on innovation, more on soothing and restful eating, but the assurance with which it is all done, the fine ingredients, the certainty that you will get good food properly served up, is worth a lot: definitely more than the

£17.95 charged for the standard lunch, or the £12.95 for a light lunch consisting of soup, a choice of about six lighter main courses, and a pudding off the normal lunch menu. Dinner is a more elaborate affair. The cooking is based on a loose amalgam of British, French and Italian notions that might translate into home-made noodles with smoked salmon, or a first-class puff pastry circle covered with thin slices of tomato, anointed at table with Provence olive oil.

Puddings tap the French classical vein with a plate of caramel desserts and hot apple tart with calvados ice-cream. Half a dozen breads are made on the premises, and salmon is locally smoked, although the Markses buy their lavender honey from Provence. The vast majority of wines are French, some very classy, some under £20, but the Californian section is well worth a look if money isn't too tight, and wines from Australia and New Zealand are good despite some expensive bottles. House wine is £16, or £4 a glass.

CHEF: Michael Benjamin PROPRIETORS: Audrey and Peter Marks OPEN: all week 12 to 2 (2.30 Sun), 7 to 9.30 (10 Fri and Sat) CLOSED: 3 weeks Jan MEALS: Set L £12.95 (light lunch) to £17.95, Set D £32.50 SERVICE: not inc CARDS: Access, Amex, Delta, Switch, Visa DETAILS: 36 seats. Private parties: 30 main room, 16 and 30 private rooms. Car park. Vegetarian meals. No children under 10. Jacket and tie D. No smoking in dining-room. No music ACCOMMODATION: 14 rooms, all with bath/shower. TV. Phone. DB&B £145 to £310. No children under 10. Afternoon teas. Garden. Swimming-pool (*The Which? Hotel Guide*)

LOWICK Cumbria map 8

▲ *Bridgefield House*

Spark Bridge, Lowick LA12 8DA
TEL: (01229) 885239 FAX: (01229) 885379
4m N of Ulverston, off A5084 on back road to Coniston, E of River Crake

COOKING 2
COST £27–£33

Regulars who have supported the Glister family's Victorian country-house hotel since its inception remember the time when 'dinner, bed and breakfast were £18'. Happy days, indeed. Thankfully, it has survived and prospered, despite the fact that it is on the fringes of the Lakeland tourist trail. Bridgefield House blossoms when it is full: no customers, no atmosphere is a state of affairs noted by more than one reporter. Rosemary Glister continues to beaver away in the kitchen, providing guests with a six-course dinner that can run long into the evening without forcing customers to throw in the towel before the finish.

A meal may begin with prawn and fennel fettuccine with Sambuca and cream sauce, then proceed to watercress and lettuce soup with a slice of sesame-topped toast. There's no choice for the main course: it may be strips of Barbary duck with kumquats and peppercorns, or poached fillet of wild salmon with a vermouth sauce, plus a splendid array of vegetables including perhaps roasted sweet potatoes and turmeric-spiced cauliflower. A water-ice precedes the pudding: maybe date and butterscotch, or strawberries in purée mango syllabub cream ('a most satisfying, voluptuous sweet'). Events drew to a savoury close with a choice between Chinese pear with crumbly Lancashire cheese, or sauté lambs' kidneys on toast. The concise and varied list of reliable wines, almost entirely under £20, does the job of partnering the food extremely well, and half-bottles are very fair. CELLARMAN'S CHOICE: Redwood Valley

Estate Sauvignon Blanc 1993, New Zealand, £15.10; Rioja Contina Reserva 1987, £17.84.

CHEF: Rosemary Glister PROPRIETORS: the Glister family OPEN: all week D only 7.30 for 8 (one sitting) CLOSED: 25 Dec MEALS: Set D £22.50 SERVICE: none, card slips closed CARDS: Access, Visa DETAILS: 24 seats. Private parties: 24 main room. Car park. Children's helpings. Smart dress preferred. No smoking in dining-room. No music ACCOMMODATION: 5 rooms, all with bath/shower. Phone. B&B £35 to £70. Deposit: £20. Children welcome. Baby facilities. Pets welcome in bedrooms only. Garden. Fishing (*The Which? Hotel Guide*)

LOW LAITHE North Yorkshire map 9

Dusty Miller

Low Laithe, Summerbridge HG3 4BU
TEL: (01423) 780837 FAX: (01423) 780065 COOKING 3
on B6165, 2m SE of Pateley Bridge COST £27–£53

This is not a converted mill but a solid stone house on the main road from Pateley Bridge. The door opens straight into the dark bar, where a log fire welcomes in winter and decorations range from an old lead-lined box for storing champagne to a fine collection of spirits. Candles on the tables are poked into expensive champagne bottles: no mere Mateus Rosé empties here. The whole place feels cared for and comfortable, and the fact that the hands-on Dennisons are involved in everything makes for tight control. Last orders at 11 means that theatre-goers in nearby Harrogate can pop in for a late meal, and there's a no-choice three-course menu as well as the *carte*.

The style is as straightforward as asparagus hollandaise, or a plate of Irish oysters, followed by roast fillet of beef with horseradish and parsnips, and the cooking impresses for its easy directness and lack of fuss. Fish is well handled, demonstrating not only excellent buying but confident technique. One reporter enjoyed a small pastry case piled high with chunks of steamed sole, monkfish and salmon – 'wonderfully fresh and perfectly done' – topped with a hairnet of leeks reaching several inches into the air, all surrounded by a gentle chive sauce. Rack of Nidderdale lamb understandably features: the 'eye' cut into six pink slices at one meal, served with a dark brown rosemary-infused stock-based sauce and two jellies – redcurrant and mint – to spoon on to the plate if desired.

The approach is traditional, but the cooking is accurate and uncluttered, and the effect of adding kumquats and alcohol to a bread-and-butter pudding serves to enrich rather than complicate it. Mrs Dennison has the service down to a fine art yet makes it all seem very natural. The short and largely French wine list includes four house wines at around £11 to £13 which are also available by the half-bottle, and by the glass from £3.

CHEFS: Brian Dennison and Ben South PROPRIETORS: Mr and Mrs Brian Dennison OPEN: Tue to Sat D only 6.30 to 11 MEALS: alc (main courses £10 to £20). Set D £24 SERVICE: not inc, card slips closed CARDS: Access, Amex, Visa DETAILS: 44 seats. Private parties: 14 and 30 mainroom. Car park. Vegetarian meals. No children under 9. Smart dress preferred. Wheelchair access (1 step). No music

LUDLOW Shropshire map 5

Merchant House

SHROPSHIRE 1996 NEWCOMER

NEW ENTRY

Lower Corve Street, Ludlow SY8 1DU COOKING 3*
TEL/FAX: (01584) 875438 COST £33–£40

Shaun Hill opened the tiny swing doors of this Jacobean house in January 1995 after nine years at Gidleigh Park (see entry, Chagford). The scale has gone from grand-country-house to domestic, and the move has brought much delight to those living within driving distance of Ludlow. Far from drawing attention to itself, the restaurant is more of a well-kept secret, or was, until the Hills had the bright idea of erecting a hanging sign 'so that customers might actually be able to find us'.

The setting is half a dozen bare-topped tables in two interconnected rooms, with a few modern paintings and some colourful crockery. Anja Hill and one assistant comfortably manage all the service between them, producing a calm and friendly feel. There is no big kitchen brigade, just Hill working at an accomplished level within his own logistic limitations. Meals are all one price (service included), which buys three courses with a choice of three or four items at each, and the food is shopping-based, whether from local contacts for game, or Birmingham market for fish. 'His fish is the very best: turbot, scallops, monkfish, all served simply with textbook sauces,' according to one reporter.

Earthier dishes work just as well, the flavours often spiked with something sharp or spicy: capers in the sauce with calves' sweetbreads and kidney, or mild horseradish with a thick fillet of hare, 'seared on the outside, rare inside, perfectly cooked, properly rested, moist and full of flavour'. Somloi is a Hungarian pudding, like a trifle with sponge, chocolate, walnuts and apricots; caramelised rice pudding is good; and 'my pear poached in red wine syrup, with two scoops of gingerbread ice-cream, is well worth a mention, for the texture of the fruit, and for the smooth ice-cream speckled with cinnamon'. Buttermilk bread is a gem. The wine list avoids clichés in favour of interesting bottles at affordable prices from California, the Rhône, Italy and Australasia, among others. House Italian is £11.50.

CHEF: Shaun Hill PROPRIETORS: Shaun and Anja Hill OPEN: Fri to Sat L 12.30 to 2.30, Tue to Sat D 7 to 9.30 MEALS: Set L and D £25 SERVICE: net prices CARDS: Access, Amex, Visa DETAILS: 20 seats. Private parties: 10 main room. No smoking in dining-room. No music

LYMINGTON Hampshire map 2

▲ *Gordleton Mill Hotel, Provence*

Silver Street, Hordle, nr Lymington SO41 6DJ COOKING 4
TEL: (01590) 682219 FAX: (01590) 683073 COST £25–£87

It is probably best to visit the seventeenth-century mill in daylight, the better to appreciate its watery setting, rustic bridges, sluice-gates, weir, lily pond and formal gardens. The comfortable lounge 'was the sort of room I could easily have lived in', wrote an inspector, while the dining-room is convincingly provençale, with white-painted beams, airily peachy pinks and beigey greys: a simple room dedicated to eating, which is just as well in view of what is in store. Toby Hill took control of the kitchen towards the end of 1994, and as soon as he did so favourable reports began to flow. 'A dream of clear, unsullied flavours,' said one.

The Mediterranean looms large and the style is mostly modern classic French. Anybody who does not like truffles, foie gras, caviare and a Japanese influence had better leave now. One couple, on reading the menu, 'knew we had struck gold'. They enjoyed starters of crisp layers of potatoes on foie gras ('pure melting decadence') with local wild mushrooms and caramelised turnips, and salmon done three ways: tartare with lemon, briefly poached in an emulsified tomato and olive oil coulis, and smoked with a softly poached egg. Sea bass with a firm, fresh texture was served with a lightly poached oyster and 'the best noodles I have ever eaten'. A chef who can make noodles exciting has talent indeed. He also goes in for different kinds of potato accompaniment, depending on the dish, and for one couple 'the vegetables were excellent, despite the baby sweetcorn'. Our inspector concluded that 'if Raymond Blanc keeps on training chefs to this standard we can all look forward to a happy future'. Puddings have included hot black cherry soufflé served with flambé cherries 'which practically everybody in the room seemed to be eating, with a lot of macho flambé action by the waiters', and a poached peach on vanilla ice-cream in a cracknel cup with a coulis of apricot and raspberry. Scrumptious titbits arrive with pre-dinner drinks and rich chocolate truffles with coffee. Waiters are 'sassy, slick, amusing, confident'. Try to pour your own water and a waiter materialises from nowhere before you can say 'Hildon'. 'No one asked us if everything was all right. They knew it was...A really terrific meal.'

France dominates the wine list, quality is high, prices even higher. A good range of vintages adds depth, and there are interesting corners to explore, such as the Hospices de Beaune range of burgundies, and Opitz wines from Austria. Half-bottles are generous in scope. CELLARMAN'S CHOICE Vin de pays d'Oc, Dom. de Capion 1993, Salasc, £19; Santenay *premier cru* 'Le Passetemps' 1987, Maufoux £24.50.

CHEF: Toby Hill PROPRIETOR: William Stone OPEN: all week 12 to 2.30, 7 to 9.30 CLOSED: first two weeks Jan MEALS: alc (main courses £17 to £27.50). Set L £15 (exc wine) to £21.50 (inc wine), Set D £24 to £45 (all inc wine) SERVICE: not inc CARDS: Access, Amex, Delta, Diners, Switch, Visa DETAILS: 55 seats. 4 tables outside. Private parties: 70 main room, 16 private room. Car park. No children under 7. Smart dress preferred. No smoking in dining-room. Wheelchair access (also WC). Music. Air-conditioned ACCOMMODATION: 7 rooms, all with bath/shower. TV. Phone. B&B £69 to £115. Deposit: £50. No children under 7. Afternoon teas. Garden. Fishing (*The Which? Hotel Guide*)

LYMPSTONE Devon map 1

▲ *River House*

The Strand, Lympstone EX8 5EY COOKING 1*
TEL: (01395) 265147 COST £26–£52

The house is blessed with splendid views over the Exe to Dartmoor, and watching the sun setting may be quite an experience. 'We were glad we took our binoculars in to dinner,' reported a resourceful couple. The upstairs dining-room is done in muted colours, the better to enjoy the prospect, and the approach is soothingly domestic.

Reports extol the attention to detail in Shirley Wilkes's cooking, which makes enthusiastic use of home-grown vegetables, salads, herbs and fruit. Starters such as smoked fish mousse, and ravioli of crab and asparagus have also been successful, as have some interesting main courses. Spanish treatments are favoured: Catalan chicken with orange and lemon surprised and pleased one diner, for example. Most reports comment on the imaginative preparation of vegetables: fennel breadcrumbed and baked with tomato; Savoy cabbage rolls filled with carrot on a bed of broccoli sprigs; cucumber and sugar-snaps sauté in soy sauce. Vegetarians are accordingly well looked after. Fine home-made ice-creams may be the thing to go for at dessert – one report praises the 'sharp and tangy' gooseberry number with blackcurrant purée – and alcoholic banana pancakes come flavoured with orange and cardamom. Because of limitations on staff, the Wilkeses prefer it if you book ahead, but a couple who arrived at an hour's notice wanting a room were none the less treated with great warmth. The wine list does its job unspectacularly, concentrating mainly on France, with shorter excursions elsewhere. Prices are not especially low, but there is a reasonable showing of halves. House wines start at £9.45.

CHEF: Shirley Wilkes PROPRIETORS: Michael and Shirley Wilkes OPEN: Tue to Sun L 12 to 1.30, Tue to Sat D 7 to 9.30 (10.30 Sat) CLOSED: 26 and 27 Dec, 1 Jan, bank hol Mons MEALS: Set L £12.50 (2 courses) to £29.50, Set D £25.95 (2 courses) to £29.50 SERVICE: not inc CARDS: Access, Amex, Visa DETAILS: 34 seats. Private parties: 100 main room, 14 private room. Car park. Vegetarian meals. No children under 6. Smart dress preferred. No smoking in dining-room. No music ACCOMMODATION: 4 rooms, all with bath/shower. TV. Phone. B&B £55 to £74. No children under 6

MAIDEN NEWTON Dorset map 2

Le Petit Canard

Dorchester Road, Maiden Newton DT2 0BE COOKING 2*
TEL: (01300) 320536 COST £31–£37

This small restaurant, lit by candles and fairy lights, has been run by the Chapmans since 1988 and is very much a personal enterprise. They think of their cooking as 'modern with a classic French base, Mediterranean flavours, North American boldness, and much chargrilling and fast wok cooking'. And that's before you get to the Australian ingredients: chargrilled kangaroo fillet, for example, is served with a Dijon and shallot sauce. The style is certainly bright, vivid and cosmopolitan, and a pity it is not matched by regular city habits: 'Here in rural Dorset, eating out three times a year is the norm: two birthdays and an anniversary.' Shame.

The basic ingredients (apart from kangaroo) are locally bought and common enough, and might include baked salmon or crispy roast duck, but the flavourings and spices bring welcome zest and vitality: a hoisin-Cabernet sauce for roast leg of lamb, for instance, or stir-fried woodpigeon served with sun-dried fruits, mushrooms and chilli-orange oil. 'Refreshingly uncomplicated and unpretentious, yet far from humdrum' was one reporter's view of charred marinated quail on confetti-pepper pasta, and a goats' cheese and tapénade soufflé with a sun-dried tomato vinaigrette. A chilli-fig-walnut tartlet with cinnamon ice-cream pursues the theme about as far as it will go, although other puddings, such as dark and white chocolate sorbets on a mango puddle, are more mainstream. West Country cheeses make a good alternative. Wines aim for a range of flavours from Viognier to Dolcetto, and the 30-strong list is supplemented by bargain bin-ends and a representative choice of half-bottles. House wine is around £11.

CHEF: Geoff Chapman PROPRIETORS: Geoff and Lin Chapman OPEN: Tue to Sat D only 7 to 9 CLOSED: 1 week Jan MEALS: Set D £21.50 SERVICE: not inc CARDS: Access, Visa DETAILS: 28 seats. Private parties: 34 main room. Vegetarian meals. No children under 7. No cigars/pipes in dining-room; and no smoking while others eat. Music

MALVERN WELLS Hereford & Worcester **map 5**

Croque-en-Bouche

221 Wells Road, Malvern Wells WR14 4HF
TEL: (01684) 565612 COOKING **4**
on A449, 2m S of Great Malvern COST £28–£49

The end-of-terrace Victorian house emphasises the domestic scale of the operation, which has seen some changes this year. Robin Jones feels that the five-course menu at £33.50 has led people to regard the Croque-en-Bouche as a 'special occasion restaurant' and, since mid-week has been 'woefully short of trade', has now decided to introduce greater flexibility and lower prices. It seems self-evident that this should bring benefits all round, and it is encouraging to see yet another restaurant paying attention to what customers want. Those who don't like change can still enjoy the old format on Fridays and Saturdays, though pressure from the separate wine business, which accounts for nearly half the turnover, has reduced winter opening to three evenings only. The style of food and standard of cooking remain as before, as does the choice on the menu itself: soup followed by one of three savoury items, then three main courses, and half a dozen desserts.

The highlights of one visit were a clear-tasting terrine of prawns, skate and creamy crab served with artichoke leaves and a tangy salsa; guinea-fowl with oriental cabbage and hoisin sauce; and a 'magic' strawberry tart with crème pâtissière and a 'rose geranium' ice-cream. Soups of smoked haddock, tomato and basil, or of butter-bean, leek and celeriac ('creamy and well balanced') are among successes, although it is usually at the next course that interest hots up, especially if the Japanese Selection is on. This offers an intriguing combination of tastes: a 'memorable and aesthetic collection of sushi and sashimi' on one occasion, and of teriyaki goose breast with vegetable rolls and mushrooms on another. Spicing is a feature that most enjoy, as are the dauphinois potatoes, although one reporter who was offered only potatoes in July felt that a greater variety of fresh vegetables might have been in order.

Praise for Italian desserts, including tiramisù and the simple partnership of cantucci biscuits and a glass of vin santo, is matched by that for salads and sorbets, and for the good variety of cheeses 'in superb nick'. The Joneses do everything themselves, and lack of help in both dining-room and kitchen can make arrival time critical, which no doubt contributes to the occasional difficulty of establishing a satisfactory rapport. Olives and baby vegetables keep reporters happy while they peruse the wine list, a job that can take some time. Advice is forthcoming about wines, which is a good job in view of the list's length: 1,500 bins of the great and the good, with enough room to accommodate the unusual and the unknown. A balanced selection of house wines simplifies choosing, and customers are left to pour their own wines. CELLARMAN'S CHOICE: Dashwood Sauvignon Blanc 1994, New Zealand, £14.50; Goundrey Cabernet/Merlot 1991, W. Australia, £14.

CHEF: Marion Jones PROPRIETORS: Robin and Marion Jones OPEN: Wed to Sat D only 7.30 to 9 (exc Wed Oct to May) CLOSED: Christmas, New Year MEALS: Set D Wed and Thur £21 to £25, Fri and Sat £33.50 SERVICE: net prices, card slips closed CARDS: Access, Delta, Visa DETAILS: 22 seats. Private parties: 6 main room, 6 private room. Children welcome. No smoking in dining-room. Wheelchair access (1 step). No music

Planters

191–193 Wells Road, Malvern Wells WR14 9HB
TEL: (01684) 575065 COOKING 1*
on A449, 3m S of Great Malvern COST £23–£34

A flower-festooned restaurant in a row of shops next to the local post office sounds as English as you can get, especially if you add the Malvern Hills as a backdrop. However, Planters is something different. Behind the maroon-painted frontage is a kitchen dealing in South-east Asian food. There is much pine in the dining-room, the colour schemes are pink and grey, and a few black and white ethnic drawings cover the walls. Most of the noise comes from conversation and from food orders being phoned through to the cooks. A new venture is the 'under a tenner' menu (available every day except Saturday), offering one-dish meals with coconut rice and stir-fried vegetables. Alternatively, select your main course, pick a starter from the *carte* and you will be offered a dessert on the house.

Reporters have been particularly impressed by the freshness and subtlety of the spicing, as in mixed satay with a trio of distinctive sauces (peanut, plum and chilli), and Singapore sweet-and-sour duck breast stir-fried with a curious melange of vegetables (young asparagus tips and aubergines in batter as well as the more usual bean sprouts *et al*). Elsewhere, the menu ranges from Sri Lankan chicken curry, and rump of beef with potatoes in a pepper and coconut sauce, to chana dhal, and nasi goreng. Ice-creams made locally give a lift to desserts such as tropical fruit pavlova. The wine list is a useful, modestly priced selection of around 30 bins with a few halves: note the representative from nearby Coddington Vineyard. House wine is £7.50.

CHEF: Chandra de Alwis PROPRIETOR: Sandra Pegg OPEN: Tue to Sat D only 7 to 9.30 CLOSED: Tue in winter MEALS: alc (main courses £7 to £8). Set D £9.25 (2 courses) to £19.95 SERVICE: not inc, card slips closed CARDS: Access, Visa DETAILS: 40 seats. Private parties: 40 main room. Vegetarian meals. Children welcome. No cigars/pipes in dining-room. Wheelchair access (1 step). No music

CELLARMAN'S CHOICE: *Wines recommended by the restaurateur, normally more expensive than house wine.*

MANCHESTER **Greater Manchester** map 8

Chiang Rai £

NEW ENTRY

16 Princess Street, Manchester M1 4NB
TEL: 0161-237 9511

COOKING 1*
COST £19–£31

'This must be the most stylish and pleasant oriental restaurant in Manchester,' concluded a well-seasoned Mancunian reporter after a visit to Chiang Rai. The restaurant is in a tastefully furnished basement in the ethnic heartland of the city. Thai artefacts abound, flower arrangements are everywhere, and the lighting is 'seductive'. In keeping with the mood of the place, the food looks elegant, particularly when plates are garnished with orchids. The menu runs to about 60 dishes, with a separate allocation for vegetarians. A handful of northern Thai specialities and curiosities, such as pla Samui (hot-and-sour fish with ginger and pineapple, made to a Samui Island recipe), lift the repertoire above the norm, and the results are 'refreshing, chilli hot and vivid'. Tempura prawns with vegetables, steamed mussels with a garlic and chilli dip, and somtum salad (green papaya with dried prawns) have been first-rate starters, while successful main courses have included curries, 'gutsy' stir-fried beef with lime leaves, and pla jian (deep-fried mackerel with shredded pork and mushrooms). Accompaniments are decent enough. Service is pleasant, and everyone smiles. House wine is £7.90.

CHEF: Mrs S. Klintaworn PROPRIETORS: Mr and Mrs P. Parkhouse OPEN: Mon to Sat L 12 to 2, all week D 6 to 11 MEALS: alc (main courses £5 to £8). Set L £5 to £9 (all 2 courses), Set D £17.20 to £21.40 SERVICE: 10%, card slips closed CARDS: Access, Amex, Delta, Diners, Switch, Visa DETAILS: 80 seats. Private parties: 80 main room, 60 private room. Vegetarian meals. Children's helpings. Smart dress preferred. Music

Koreana £

Kings House, 40A King Street West,
Manchester M3 2WY
TEL: 0161-832 4330 FAX: 0161-832 2293

COOKING 1
COST £11–£32

'Sheer Korean' is how the owners describe their pleasant restaurant just off Deansgate. The décor may be 'unmemorable', but reporters confirm that the food holds plenty of interest. A novel system of ordering operates here: the idea is to construct your own set-price, three-course meal from the full menu (individual dishes are not priced). Alternatively, you could play safe and settle for one of the more elaborate banquets, although a reporter thought that 'the dishes did not combine as well as a set banquet should' and that one ought to 'try to buck the system and pick and mix for oneself'. Appetisers are particularly well handled: kun mandoo (shallow-fried beef dumplings), marinated spare-ribs, and honghab jurn (potato-cakes with mussels) have been greatly appreciated. The repertoire also embraces soups, hotpots, stir-fries and that cornerstone of Korean cuisine, bulgogi (thinly sliced strips of marinated beef or chicken cooked at the table). There is also a modest 'vegetarian corner', although meatless dishes are also sprinkled throughout the menu. As a finale, try authentic Korean sweet cake or rice cake (an egg-shaped fritter with a hint of syrup). Korean Crown Super

Dry beer and jung-jong (Korean saké) are alcoholic alternatives to green tea and ginseng tea. House wine is £7.50.

CHEFS: Hyun-Suk Shin and Mrs Kim PROPRIETOR: Koreana Restaurant Ltd OPEN: Mon to Fri L 12 to 2, Mon to Sat D 6.30 to 11 CLOSED: 25 to 29 Dec MEALS: Set L £5 to £7.30, Set D £12.50 to £19.50 SERVICE: not inc, card slips closed; 10% on parties of 8 or more CARDS: Access, Amex, Delta, Diners, Switch, Visa DETAILS: 60 seats. Private parties: 70 main room. Vegetarian meals. Children's helpings. Smart dress preferred. No music

Kosmos Taverna £

248 Wilmslow Road, Manchester M14 6LD — COOKING 1
TEL: 0161-225 9106 FAX: 0161-256 4442 — COST £17–£32

Wilmslow Road is an ethnic melting-pot that bubbles with restaurants and cafés from countless cultures; this long-serving Greek taverna fits in perfectly, and continues to serve a faithful band of regulars, newcomers, young and old, 'smart and scruffy' with equal good humour. Loulla Astin's menu evolves slowly. Mainstays such as hearty hortosoupa (a country soup with purée vegetables in a meat-based stock), dips, salads and casseroles continue to win approval, while the quality of the mixed grill (chicken, minced kebab and lamb chop) suggests that there is a good butcher behind the scenes. Daily specials are varied enough to keep the regulars interested. One reporter enjoyed a Valentine's Day special of salmon in pink champagne; elsewhere you might find grilled baby squid with chilli, and stamna (Athenian-style rump steak with red wine and baby potatoes served in an earthenware dish). Three versions of meze (including one for vegetarians) are also worth sampling. The short wine list is notable for its low prices and gutsy Greek and Cypriot bottles. House wine is £9.

CHEF: Loulla Astin PROPRIETORS: Stewart and Loulla Astin OPEN: Sun all day 1 to 11.30, Mon to Sat D 6.30 to 11.30 (12.30 Fri and Sat) CLOSED: 25 and 26 Dec, 1 Jan MEALS: alc (main courses £5.50 to £11). Set L and D £11 to £14 SERVICE: not inc CARDS: Access, Visa DETAILS: 90 seats. Private parties: 40 main room. Vegetarian meals. Children's helpings. Smart dress preferred. No pipes in dining-room. Wheelchair access. Music. Air-conditioned

Lime Tree

8 Lapwing Lane, West Didsbury,
Manchester M20 8WS — COOKING 1
TEL: 0161-445 1217 — COST £15–£37

This aptly named bistro is on the edge of a leafy lane in a lively student quarter of the city. It attracts a young crowd who make lots of noise and set the casual mood of the place – although they are helped along admirably by an enthusiastic band of waiting staff. Once the pace hots up in the evening, the kitchen responds with a high level of activity and some very competent cooking. Lamb is British, game is seasonal, but the menu strikes out to foreign parts for much of its inspiration. One reporter found the terrine of chicken, lambs' sweetbreads and wild mushrooms 'a rare and dramatic experience for the tastebuds'. He was equally bowled over by 'mouth-wateringly moist' roast guinea-fowl (also with wild mushrooms), followed by strongly flavoured chocolate and orange terrine with almonds and walnuts. The cooking extends to Thai cod fritters with yoghurt, mint and cucumber dressing; Caesar salad; roast spiced duck breast with honey and soy sauce; and Cajun-style monkfish tails with raw-tomato sauce. France is the main contributor to the short wine list, although bin-ends and specials are drawn from further afield. House wine is £8.95.

CHEFS: Damian Kay and Nick Barnie PROPRIETOR: Patrick Hannity OPEN: Tue to Fri and Sun L 12 to 2.30, all week D 6 to 10.30 CLOSED: bank hols exc Good Fri MEALS: alc (main courses £3 to £14). Set L Sun £10.95, Set L Tue to Fri £8.95 (2 courses), Set D 6pm to 7pm £8.95 (2 courses) SERVICE: not inc CARDS: Access, Amex, Switch, Visa DETAILS: 80 seats. 7 tables outside. Private parties: 40 main room. Vegetarian meals. Children welcome. Music

Little Yang Sing

17 George Street, Manchester M1 4HE — COOKING 2
TEL: 0161-228 7722 FAX: 0161-237 9257 — COST £15–£38

Be warned: this is an extremely busy restaurant. If you want to book a table for dinner, expect to be given a slot, told when to arrive and when to leave. That kind of pressure is not to everyone's liking, although most agree that the food is worth the regimented approach. The dining-room is a crowded basement with duck-egg blue damask cloths on the elbow-to-elbow tables. Occasional lapses have been noted, but the consensus is that the kitchen generally delivers Cantonese food of a high order. A reporter of long standing sums it up thus: 'Cooking techniques are assured and there is a freshness and a willingness to experiment with East/West crossover which recalls the heady days when Big Yang Sing occupied these premises.'

The short list of dim-sum has produced some 'impeccable' items, such as steamed beefballs in 'paper-thin pasta', spare-ribs heavily laced with garlic, and ungreasy deep-fried king prawns with a 'mayonnaise' dipping sauce. Juicy steamed scallops served in the shell and topped with a few garlicky crumbs have also hit the button. Among the list of main dishes are powerful casseroles loaded with top-drawer ingredients, a strong showing of one-plate rice and noodle dishes, plus authentic offerings such as fish fillet topped with shredded pork, and chicken with green peppers and black-bean sauce. Vegetarians are particularly well looked after with a line-up that includes crispy coconut milk balls, spicy yam twists and bean curd with chilli. The fixed-price 'daytime menu' is an affordable deal, and there is also a mini-version for children. Service is welcoming and friendly. The short wine list has a fair selection from reliable sources around the globe. House French is £9.50.

CHEF: Ting Chung Au PROPRIETOR: L.Y.S. Ltd OPEN: all week 12 to 5.30, 7 to 11.15 CLOSED: 25 Dec MEALS: alc (main courses £7 to £12.50). Set L £8.95, Set D £15 SERVICE: 10% CARDS: Access, Amex, Switch, Visa DETAILS: 90 seats. Private parties: 90 main room. Vegetarian meals. Children's helpings. Smart dress preferred. Music. Air-conditioned

The Guide *relies on feedback from its readers. Especially welcome are reports on new restaurants appearing in the book for the first time. All letters to the* Guide *are acknowledged.*

▲ *Moss Nook*

Ringway Road, Manchester M22 5NA
TEL: 0161-437 4778 FAX: 0161-498 8089
on B5166, 1m from Manchester Airport, M56 junction 5

COOKING 3
COST £23–£62

This cosy nook is not so much beside a babbling brook as a mere mile away from Manchester International Airport. The garden, however, is well laid out, and the outdoor tables will tempt when the sun shines. Inside, all is suave formality, the dining-room upholstered in warm crimson, the service punctilious but not overbearing. The undoubtedly serious prices on the *carte* are written in words for that final touch of poshness.

Kevin Lofthouse has clocked up over a decade at Moss Nook and has reached a high degree of accomplishment in that time. The style is extremely classic, but enlivened with plenty of diverting ideas. A mousse of turbot is filled with prawns and served with sauté scallops. Gastronomic swords are crossed in a pairing of Bury black pudding with boudin noir, mustard sauce playing the role of mediator. Duckling breast is sauced with redcurrant and elderflower, and the strawberries in a sablé are marinated in Amaretto. Those who can't choose may opt for the seven-course menu surprise, on which 'Kevin [will] take you through an adventure of flavours and textures'. One who embarked on the adventure had a pretty good time. Things began with a pastry shell filled with creamy chicken and mushrooms, giving way to a fruit plate of melon and mango. The stride was hit with a soufflé of Swiss cheese and chives sauced with red pepper – 'an imaginative and successful dish' – and then a well-rendered classic of poached salmon with asparagus and a béarnaise. The mid-meal sorbet can be eschewed in favour of a soup served in tiny quantity, 'a mere sip', in this case of fine minestrone. Rack of lamb with mushrooms in a madeira sauce was brought off with aplomb, and the pudding was an agreeably light raspberry mille-feuille. Breads are interesting and coffee good and strong. Here is a well-oiled operation that exudes both care and skill.

The main run of wines is not outlandishly priced, although value is concentrated outside France. Those with money to spend will find some dazzlers among the page of fine clarets, New World wines are reasonably sound, and there are just enough halves. House wines start at £9.50.

CHEF: Kevin Lofthouse PROPRIETORS: Pauline and Derek Harrison OPEN: Tue to Fri L 12 to 1.30, Tue to Sat D 7 to 9.30 CLOSED: 2 weeks Christmas MEALS: alc (main courses £18 to £19.50). Set L £16.50, Set D £29.95 SERVICE: not inc, card slips closed CARDS: Access, Amex, Diners, Visa DETAILS: 65 seats. 8 tables outside. Private parties: 60 main room. Car park. No children under 12. Smart dress preferred. No pipes in dining-room. No music ACCOMMODATION: 1 room in cottage, with bath/shower. TV. Phone. D, B&B £70 to £140.

Pearl City £

33 George Street, Manchester M1 4PH
TEL: 0161-228 7683 FAX: 0161-237 9173

COOKING 1*
COST £13–£48

Pearl City is highly valued for its long opening hours (until 3.30am on Saturdays) and its robust Cantonese cooking. The setting might seem rather inauspicious – functional dining-rooms on two floors – but flavours are not watered down to suit Western palates, and prices are competitive. The long list of dim-sum is the main daytime attraction, while the monster 250-dish menu majors in seafood, barbecued meats and one-plate rice and noodle specialities. Steamed duck is done four ways, and the repertoire also takes in such things as sauté king prawns with baked ham, steamed chicken with Chinese sausage, and pork chop with salt and chilli. The section devoted to flambé specialities (including fillet steak satay, and eel with honey sauce) is something of a novelty. Banquets are a neat way of sampling what the kitchen has to offer. House wine is £7.90 a bottle.

CHEF/PROPRIETOR: Chi Ming Cheung OPEN: all week noon to 1.30am (3.30am Sat, 11.30pm Sun) MEALS: alc D (main courses £5 to £19.50). Set L £4.70 (2 courses) to £9.50, Set D £15.50 to £19.50 SERVICE: 10%, card slips closed CARDS: Access, Amex, Delta, Switch, Visa DETAILS: 400 seats. Private parties: 200 main room, 100 private room. Vegetarian meals. Children welcome. Smart dress preferred. Music. Air-conditioned

Siam Orchid £

54 Portland Street, Manchester M1 4QU — COOKING 1
TEL: 0161-236 1388 FAX: 0161-236 8830 — COST £19–£42

Despite the waitresses in Thai costume, the pictures of Thailand on the walls and the Thai music in the background, Siam Orchid's long menu is written in matter-of-fact English. It is mostly conventional stuff – the kind of thing offered by an ever-growing number of similar restaurants across the land – but results are satisfying. Satays, curries, stir-fries and noodles form the backbone of the repertoire, and vegetarians are well catered for. Reporters have enthused about superb deep-fried fish-cakes, dim-sum dumplings scattered with nuts, a salad of chargrilled beef with 'plenty of zip' in the dressing, and green chicken curry in a wonderfully rich, creamy coconut sauce. Lively dips help to perk up the cooking, spicing is accurate and the whole experience represents value for money. The short, reasonably priced wine list features quite a few drinkable bottles. House wine is £8.90. There is a sister branch, called Royal Orchid, at 36 Charlotte Street, Manchester M1 4DF, Tel: 0161-236 5183.

CHEF: C. Sirisompan PROPRIETORS: C. Sirisambhand and K. Sirisompan OPEN: Mon to Fri 11.30 to 2.30, 6.30 to 11.30, Sat and Sun noon to 11.30pm MEALS: alc (main courses £6 to £10). Set L £5 (2 courses), Set D £16 to £27 SERVICE: 10% CARDS: Access, Amex, Delta, Diners, Switch, Visa DETAILS: 55 seats. Private parties: 50 main room. Vegetarian meals. Children welcome. Smart dress preferred. Music. Air-conditioned

That Café

1031 Stockport Road, Levenshulme,
Manchester M19 2TB — COOKING 1
TEL: 0161-432 4672 — COST £19–£37

Back in the early 1980s, Joe Quinn ran an antique shop here, before taking over the building next door and turning the whole place into a restaurant. The interior still has echoes of its former incarnation, with old advertising signs, sepia photographs and old, dark fireplaces imbuing it with a distinctly 1930s feel.

Despite some quibbles about 'bland' flavours and poorly cooked vegetables, at its best the cooking offers good value and plenty of global interest, whether you choose from the *carte* or the fixed-price three-course menu. Home-made soups (such as lentil and red wine) are 'original and well balanced', and readers have also approved of mushrooms in Pernod and cream sauce, braised shoulder of lamb, and paupiettes of plaice prettily wrapped around sliced red peppers. Desserts such as marmalade bread-and-butter pudding, and banana and cream cheesecake with toffee sauce ('I need to steal the recipe,' said one reporter) have been heartily endorsed. Regulars find the service ever-attentive; first-timers have described it as 'friendly but rudimentary'. The wine list is a short run through most of the major styles and familiar names, with three organic 'country wines' from Hugh Rock also on show. House Australian is £8.50.

CHEF/PROPRIETOR: J. Quinn OPEN: Sun L 12 to 3.30, Tue to Sun D 7 to 11 MEALS: alc (main courses £8 to £14). Set L Sun £11.95, Set D Tue to Fri £14.95 SERVICE: not inc, card slips closed CARDS: Access, Amex, Delta, Switch, Visa DETAILS: 80 seats. Private parties: 50 main room, 35 private room. Vegetarian meals. Children's helpings. Music

▲ *Woodlands*

33 Shepley Road, Audenshaw,
Manchester M34 5DJ
TEL: 0161-336 4241

COOKING 2
COST £23–£41

Dennis Crank and his wife have been in residence at this Victorian villa for a decade and have sustained its sound reputation as a stronghold of French cooking on the outskirts of Manchester. Travellers regularly make the seven-mile trip out of the city to sample the likes of smoked chicken and chicory salad, calf's liver with bacon, and medallions of venison flamed in whisky and served with tarragon cream sauce. Fish is a strong suit: expect anything from terrine of lobster and lemon sole to herb-crusted fillet of turbot with lemon butter sauce. A good-value table d'hôte (not available Saturday night) focuses on more robust offerings, such as Lancashire black and white pudding with mustard sauce, and fillet of cod on a bed of spinach with white wine sauce. 'Safe and sound' might sum up the place. The short, reasonably priced list of around 40 wines is resolutely Franco-German, with a token trio of Australians. House wine is £8.25.

CHEF: William Jackson PROPRIETORS: Mr and Mrs Dennis Crank OPEN: Tue to Fri (and last Sun of month) L 12 to 1.45, Tue to Sat D 7 to 9.30 (10 Sat) MEALS: alc (main courses £12.50 to £13.50). Set L and D £15.95 (exc Sat D) SERVICE: not inc, card slips closed CARDS: Access, Visa DETAILS: 40 seats. Private parties: 24 main room, 17 and 24 private rooms. Car park. Children's helpings. Smart dress preferred. Music ACCOMMODATION: 3 rooms, all with bath/shower. TV. Phone. B&B £40 to £60. Rooms for disabled. Children welcome. Garden

Yang Sing £

34 Princess Street, Manchester M1 4JY
TEL: 0161-236 2200 FAX: 0161-236 5934

COOKING 2
COST £16–£45

Yang Sing's flashy full-colour brochure is a reminder that this restaurant is a bullish, high-profile venue in the heart of Manchester's Chinatown. It demands accolades and expects crowds. Book one hour in advance and you might end up with 'the worst table in the place, next to the window looking into the kitchen through the hanging corpses of ducks'. The basement dining-room is smartly done out in red, with high-backed chairs, damask cloths on closely packed tables and lots of lacquered dragon artefacts. The mood is lively, and almost everyone agrees that the army of waiting staff is exceptionally pleasant and 'comparatively knowledgeable'.

Part of Yang Sing's reputation hinges on its dim-sum, which are dispensed from two trolleys parked in the centre of the room. On a good day the kitchen can deliver 'technically impeccable' examples of the genre: steamed beef balls with ginger and spring onion; fried prawn dumplings in crisp, ungreasy pastry; and steamed spare-ribs laced with garlic, red chilli and black beans. Otherwise, the menu is a long trawl through the Cantonese repertoire, taking in hotpots, casseroles, rice and noodle dishes and a few creations fashioned from ox-tripe, chicken gizzards and fish lips. Over the years, chef Harry Yeung has also developed a number of East–West crossover specialities, although these tend to be confined to special banquets. Duck is regularly endorsed (sliced with a pungent black-bean sauce, or steamed and smothered in slithery fungi, greens and assorted vegetables), and reporters have also enjoyed 'precisely steamed' scallops in the shell, fried prawns with ham, and crisp vermicelli noodles. At its best, the cooking is unrivalled in Manchester, but regular complaints about bland flavours, glutinous sauces and dubious ingredients ('flaccid' lobster, 'jelly-like' beef) – not to mention mistakes about orders and an obligatory ten per cent service charge (plus credit card slips left open) – have set alarm bells ringing once again. The wine list is 'well above the Chinatown norm, without being sensational', noted one knowledgeable reporter. House wines start at £8.70.

CHEF: Harry Yeung PROPRIETOR: Yang Sing Restaurant Ltd OPEN: all week noon to 11 CLOSED: 25 Dec MEALS: alc (main courses £5 to £14). Set D £14 to £30 SERVICE: 10% CARDS: Access, Amex, Switch, Visa DETAILS: 140 seats. Private parties: 30 to 220 private rooms. Vegetarian meals. Children welcome. Smart dress preferred. Music. Air-conditioned

MANNINGTREE Essex map 6

Stour Bay Café

39–43 High Street, Manningtree CO11 1AH COOKING 1*
TEL: (01206) 396687 FAX: (01206) 395462 COST £20–£39

The Bay in question is an inlet of the River Stour, although the style of the food may evoke sharper affinities with San Francisco than Essex. Uncovered floors and closely crowded tables set the tone. The dazzle arrives on the plate.

Chef Sherri Singleton hails from Los Angeles, and in true West Coast – and indeed now thoroughly British – style, the menu describes a broad culinary trajectory. New England is the inspiration for a bowl of mussel chowder, Italy provides bresaola with rocket, Parmesan and white-truffle oil, and Japan contributes ginger-marinated salmon with cucumber and wasabi. Fish is always given a goodly share of the menu, and is appreciably fresh and accurately cooked – a soup of seafood with fennel, tomato and saffron delivers 'lots of strong flavour' – and vegetarian dishes are imaginative: polenta gratin with Gorgonzola sauce is filled with roasted aubergine, pine-nuts and peppers. Desserts bring some arresting ideas into play. Nutty cheesecakes receive enthusiastic approval, and there may be Key lime pie with a mango coulis, or crème caramel spiked with orange and rosemary. Service on one busy Saturday night was 'friendly but fully stretched'. The enterprising wine list majors in top-drawer wines from Australia, California, New Zealand and Chile. An expanded selection of mainly white French wines takes in burgundies from Olivier Leflaive and Natter's Sancerre. Prices are fair, and a good range is offered by the glass. House wines from Fetzer – a good choice – are £8.75.

CHEF: Sherri Singleton PROPRIETORS: David McKay and Sherri Singleton OPEN: Fri and Sat Sun L 12 to 2.30, Tue to Sat D 7 to 10 CLOSED: 2 weeks Jan, 2 weeks Sept MEALS: alc (main courses £8 to £14). SERVICE: not inc CARDS: Access, Amex, Delta, Visa DETAILS: 65 seats. Private parties: 65 main room, 20 private room. Vegetarian meals. Children's helpings. No smoking in 1 dining-room. No music

MARSDEN West Yorkshire map 8

Olive Branch

NEW ENTRY

Manchester Road, Marsden HD7 6LU
TEL: (01484) 844487
on A62, 7m SW of Huddersfield

COOKING 1
COST £20–£35

John Lister has transformed this dark-stone pub into something rather special. The setting draws poetic jottings from some visitors: 'Nice Pennine view of fields and dry-stone walls, and the summer rain cascading into the valley below.' Inside, it is done out with Gerald Scarfe wine cartoons, and china figures of Punch and Judy on the mantelpiece. The impression is of an up-and-coming bar/brasserie, although one reporter confirmed that the place still sells a decent pint. Most of the time, food centres on an impressive blackboard of eclectic dishes ranging from game and pistachio 'terrain' (*sic*) with lavender jelly, and smoked haddock Basque-style, to roast monkfish in curry oil, and casserole of English lamb. Soups, such as tomato and pesto, are the genuine article – sometimes subtle, sometimes robust. Confit of duck is perfectly prepared so that the flesh almost falls off the bone, while a dish of garlicky tagliatelle with olive oil, tomato, mushrooms and nuts drew unexpectedly ecstatic praise from a vegan reporter. Desserts are equally impressive: 'a commonplace-looking treacle tart was rendered extraordinary by the texture of oats and the zest of lime', wrote one satisfied customer. Arrive for Saturday dinner and you will be offered a fixed-price menu drawn from the same repertoire. All in all, it represents excellent value. The list of around 80 wines keeps prices firmly in check while offering plenty of dependable drinking across the board. House wine is £8.95.

CHEF: John Lister PROPRIETORS: John and Ann Lister OPEN: Tue to Sun 12 to 1.45, 7 to 9.30 (10 Sat, 8.45 Sun) CLOSED: first 2 weeks Feb, last week July MEALS: alc all week L, Sun to Fri D (main courses £6.50 to £11.50). Set D Sat £12.75 (2 courses) to £15.50 SERVICE: not inc, card slips closed CARDS: Access, Switch, Visa DETAILS: 65 seats. Private parties: 36 private room. Car park. Vegetarian meals. Children welcome. Smart dress preferred. Wheelchair access. Music

MARY TAVY Devon map 1

▲ *Stannary*

Mary Tavy PL19 9QB
TEL: (01822) 810897 FAX: (01822) 810898
on A386 Tavistock to Okehampton road,
4m NE of Tavistock

COOKING 1
COST £38–£52

Michael Cook and Alison Fife would no doubt agree with one reader's comment that 'they are very committed and strict vegetarians (unlike 95 per cent of their clientele!)'. Their comfortable restaurant-with-rooms is dramatically done out in Victorian-Gothic style, which is perhaps an over-zealous attempt to banish the stripped-pine 1960s image of most comparable eating-places. Computer-generated colour images of carrots, brassicas and aubergines add a touch of life to the menu, which is full of lively inventions based on seaweeds, fungi, edible flowers and hedgerow gleanings as well as more usual fruit and vegetables: organic produce is used where possible, and the whole enterprise is sustained by self-sufficient endeavour.

Excellent speciality breads set the ball rolling. Starters could include hummus garnished with herbs and seaweed, Moroccan nut soup, which the menu states is 'infused with orange and lime oils', or black olive and sun-dried tomato tart. The eclectic touch also shows in main dishes: a trio of colourful curries (mild mango, medium green vegetable, and red-hot hazelnut), artichoke hearts and brown lentils wrapped in vine leaves, and pancakes stuffed with a purée of beetroot and lemony couscous, for example. To finish, try delicate rose-petal ice-cream or a dessert based on crab-apples. Myriad coffees, teas, infusions and juices are listed alongside Newquay Steam Bitter, elderberry stout or pineapple and gooseberry lager. The wine list is long and serious with a global outlook and a strong bias towards organics. Stannary-made house wine is £8.50, organic French £9.20.

CHEF: Alison Fife PROPRIETORS: Michael Cook and Alison Fife OPEN: Tue to Sat D only 7 to 9.30 CLOSED: Christmas; Tue and Wed Jan to Mar MEALS: Set D £24 (2 courses) to £35 SERVICE: not inc, card slips closed CARDS: Access, Amex, Visa DETAILS: 20 seats. Private parties: 30 main room. Car park. Vegetarian meals. No children under 12. Smart dress preferred. No smoking in dining-room. Music ACCOMMODATION: 3 rooms, 1 with bath/shower. TV. D,B&B £70 to £120. Deposit: £20. No children under 12. Garden

MASHAM North Yorkshire map 9

N. YORKS 1996 BARGAIN LUNCH

Floodlite

7 Silver Street, Masham HG4 4DX
TEL: (01765) 689000
off A6108, 9m NW of Ripon

COOKING 3
COST £16–£42

'We returned here a year after our previous visit and were delighted to find it as good as before,' wrote two satisfied reporters, who went back again the next day and confirmed the consistency of the cooking. The ground-floor dining-room still looks like the shop it once was, and given the plastic flowers and glass cabinets 'you just pray that the taste in food is better than the décor', confided a first-timer, who discovered that 'fortunately, it is'. The setting may be unlikely, but Charles Flood is a knowledgeable cook who does not try to impress with empty gestures. Taste is paramount, and the value – at lunch-time particularly – is excellent.

A lunching inspector was impressed with a salmon and pike terrine, 'a perfectly produced example of its kind', flecked with herbs and studded with diced and slightly crunchy vegetables, tasting fresh and fishy, with a dill-flecked sauce of soured cream. At other meals watercress soup, foie gras, tender and succulent grouse, fillet steak, and sea bass have stood out from the generous *carte* of over a dozen items per course. Fish varies by the day, and game – thick slices of roe-deer with wild mushrooms in a rich wine gravy, for example – is a particular Flood favourite. A fricassee of pheasant for one reporter 'must have contained the best part of a pheasant (the flesh, har har)' chopped into four or five pieces, all accurately cooked and perfectly integrated with a sauce that was 'not self-consciously reduced but strongly flavoured. It all spoke of naturalness, of self-effacing good cooking. What a delight.'

Fresh and appetising vegetables accompany, and puddings include a bit of everything, from crème caramel to lemon tart, from white and dark chocolate mousses to an unusual blackberry and apple bread-and-butter pudding, 'rather like a warm, steamed summer pudding'. Nibbles in the bar are 'basic packet peanuts', but otherwise the package pleases from start to finish, including the concise but wide-ranging list of affordable wines, with half-bottles to match. House wine is from £1.50 a glass.

CHEF: Charles Flood PROPRIETORS: Charles and Christine Flood OPEN: Fri to Sun L 12 to 1.30, Tue to Sun D 7 to 9.30 CLOSED: 2 weeks Jan MEALS: alc D (main courses £9 to £17). Set L £10.50 SERVICE: not inc, card slips closed CARDS: Access, Amex, Visa DETAILS: 40 seats. Private parties: 30 main room, 10 and 30 private rooms. Vegetarian meals. Children's helpings. Smart dress preferred. Wheelchair access. Music

MATLOCK Derbyshire map 5

▲ *Riber Hall*

Matlock DE4 5JU
TEL: (01629) 582795 FAX: (01629) 580475 NEW CHEF
1m off A615 at Tansley COST £25–£54

The experience of both staying and eating at this romantic Elizabethan country house inspires some reporters to wax lyrical: tucked away down a long, winding lane, it is 'a vision of beauty – weathered grey stone with roses climbing and falling all over it'. The whole place exudes comfort and elegance rather than ostentation, and the mood is sustained by 'quietly friendly' staff.

After eight years here, Jeremy Brazelle left in the summer of 1995 and his sous-chef took over the reins: too late for us to receive any reports or send along an inspector, hence no cooking score. Menus have offered a generous choice – there is a full vegetarian menu, for example – along the lines of asparagus tart, guinea-fowl with lyonnaise potatoes, and monkfish with lentils, perhaps followed by a hot coffee and Amaretto soufflé. The wine list is a substantial read, with champagnes, heavyweight clarets and burgundies rubbing shoulders with youthful vintages from the New World. Chilean house wine is £12.50.

CHEF: Russell Archer PROPRIETOR: Alex Biggin OPEN: all week 12 to 1.30, 7 to 9.30 MEALS: alc D (main courses £12.50 to £17.50). Set L £11 (2 courses) to £14.50, Set D £25.50 SERVICE: not inc, card slips closed CARDS: Access, Amex, Delta, Diners, Switch, Visa DETAILS: 60 seats. Private parties: 40 main room, 16 and 24 private rooms. Car park. Vegetarian meals. Children's helpings. Smart dress preferred. No smoking in 1 dining-room. No music ACCOMMODATION: 11 rooms, all with bath/shower. TV. Phone. B&B £79.50 to £143. Deposit: £35. No children under 10. Pets welcome by arrangement. Afternoon teas. Garden (*The Which? Hotel Guide*)

MAWGAN Cornwall map 1

Yard Bistro

Trelowarren, Mawgan TR12 6AF
TEL: (01326) 221595 COOKING 1
off B3293, 3m SE of Helston COST £13–£34

'I want people who like eating, are adventurous in taste and are not in a hurry,' writes Trevor Bayfield. If you think that sounds like you, go for it. The Bistro is a large-windowed room looking on to a courtyard that is part of Trelowarren's old carriage house. It is a 'comfortable atmosphere' in which the cooking moves assiduously with the times. Sea bass pickled with lime juice and coriander should wake up the tastebuds. Other starters sound substantial enough to be main courses: for example, roast pigeon breast with wild mushrooms and a madeira sauce. Red mullet, a main course, is steamed en papillote with a fennel and herb butter, while its grey cousin was served one lunch-time on a simple (though 'over-abundant', thought one reporter) sauce of chopped tomatoes and garlic. Pork tenderloin is given a honey glaze and offset with a sauce of raspberry vinegar and soured cream. Puddings show a light touch in apple sorbet on a biscuit, or chocolate and honey parfait, though bread-and-butter pudding comes with the regulation clotted cream. The sanely priced short wine list is more interesting in the southern hemisphere than it is in Europe. House red and white are £7.50, and there is rosé from Fonscolombe at £9.

CHEF/PROPRIETOR: Trevor Bayfield OPEN: Tue to Sun L 12 to 2, Wed to Sat D 7 to 9 MEALS: alc (main courses £3 to £12.50). Set L Sun £7.50 SERVICE: not inc CARDS: none DETAILS: 50 seats. 4 tables outside. Private parties: 100 main room. Car park. Vegetarian meals. Children's helpings. Wheelchair access (also WC). Music

---

MAWNAN SMITH Cornwall map 1

CORNISH 1996 BUSY BEE

▲ *Nansidwell*

Mawnan Smith TR11 5HU
TEL: (01326) 250340 FAX: (01326) 250440
off A494 Helston road, take left fork at Red Lion in village COOKING 2
COST £22–£56

The stern creeper-covered façade of this grey-stone house belies both the brightly airy rooms within and the surrounding luxuriant gardens of subtropical flora. There can't be many English chefs with instant access to banana trees. A Canadian visitor, describing Antony Allcott's cooking as 'comforting but not modern', proceeded to praise roast beef with all the trimmings and had no complaints. This is a ferociously industrious kitchen: there is much smoking of mollusc, fish and flesh, as well as pickling, preserving and baking. It all ends up on the imaginative fixed-price menus in the form of some thoughtful and stimulating cooking. Thin slices of sea bass and brill come on a vermouth cream sauce with grapes and cucumber duxelles. Hake is baked with prawns and Cornish Yarg. Meats are treated to layers of flavour, as in beef fillet baked with Stilton and smoked ham on a sauce of horseradish and madeira. The same intricacy is evident in puddings, such as a timbale of tropical fruits with an iced soufflé of coconut and raspberry. Dark chocolate and black cherry torte might have been Black Forest gâteau in another era. Good strong coffee is accompanied by home-made petits fours, and National Trust coastal tracks await the post-prandial walker.

The wine list is pretty compact in most areas and – with the exception of an Australian pair and a Chilean trio – confines itself to Europe. Halves are a bit thin on the ground, but prices throughout are sensible. House wines start with Spanish red and white at £10.

CHEF: Antony Allcott PROPRIETORS: Jamie and Felicity Robertson OPEN: all week 12.30 to 1.30, 7 to 9 CLOSED: 2 Jan to 1 Feb MEALS: Set L £14.75, Set D £25 SERVICE: not inc, card slips closed CARDS: Access, Delta, Switch, Visa DETAILS: 40 seats. Private parties: 45 main room. Car park. Children's helpings. No children under 7 D. Smart dress preferred. No cigars/pipes in dining-room. Wheelchair access. No music ACCOMMODATION: 12 rooms, all with bath/shower. TV. Phone. B&B £85 to £154. Deposit: £100. Rooms for disabled. Children welcome. Pets welcome in bedrooms only. Garden (*The Which? Hotel Guide*)

MELBOURN Cambridgeshire map 6

Pink Geranium $*

Station Road, Melbourn SG8 6DX
TEL: (01763) 260215 FAX: (01763) 262110 COOKING 3
just off A10, 2m N of Royston COST £30–£74

Think pink when you venture out to the Saunders' cottage restaurant near Royston. Everything, from the chairs you sit on to the bill you pay, is in more or less glowing shades of the colour. High sophistication is the declared aim of the cooking, and the set-price dinner menu of three courses with coffee is buttressed by an ambitiously costed *carte*. Conceptions are nothing if not bold: one spring starter was a 'pot-au-feu' of king scallops and baby fennel poached in Barsac served with black tagliatelle. Dishes give the impression of having received much time and attention, as in a first course of 'moist, fresh and flavoursome' John Dory bedded on fondant leeks in a puff pastry tart, surrounded by a coriander-strewn beurre blanc with new potatoes. One reporter found a navarin of seafood as a main course extraordinarily generous, comprising a variety of carefully cooked fish and shellfish in a shellfish velouté infused with lemon grass; with small portions of green noodles and spinach adding contrasting flavours. Saddle of venison on 'hongroise' potatoes – a sort of semi-mash spiked with tomatoes and onions – is accompanied by a pink peppercorn sauce of great intensity. Caramelised apples, sage risotto and mustard sauce support main-course saddle of rabbit, and equal pains are taken with vegetarian dishes.

Complexity continues at dessert stage, where a baked apple in puff pastry comes with plum-flavoured mascarpone and an Amaretto sabayon. A soufflé of Grand Marnier and chocolate with a brandy-snap cup of lime sorbet on the side was well worth the wait for an inspector, the sharpness of the sorbet refreshingly cutting the eggy richness of the soufflé. Should you decide not to drive, a chauffeur-driven Bentley may convey you there and back. If you're overcome with impatience on the way, the driver carries the menu and is a dab hand at opening champagne. There's posh. House wines from Languedoc-Roussillon are £11.95.

CHEFS: Steven Saunders and Paul Murfitt PROPRIETORS: Steven and Sally Saunders OPEN: Tue to Fri and Sun L 12 to 2, Tue to Sat D 7 to 9.30 (10 Sat) MEALS: alc (main courses £19 to £27). Set L Tue to Fri £13.95 (2 courses) to £18.95, Set L Sun £18.95, Set D £29.95 SERVICE: not inc CARDS: Access, Amex, Delta, Visa DETAILS: 75 seats. Private parties: 50 main room, 8 to 16 private rooms. Car park. Vegetarian meals. Children's helpings. Smart dress preferred. No smoking in dining-room. Wheelchair access. Music

MELKSHAM Wiltshire map 2

▲ *Toxique*

187 Woodrow Road, Melksham SN12 7AY
TEL: (01225) 702129
off A3102 Calne road, turn left after ¾m and follow Forest Road, on left-hand side after 1m

COOKING 2
COST £23–£43

Toxique is a brave name to give to a place devoted to feeding people, but then there is much that is bold and idiosyncratic about this restaurant-with-rooms. It was once a farmhouse and the relatively calm exterior does nothing to prepare you for the visual dramatics within. One dining-room is in brooding indigo, the other in simmering primrose, and both are adorned by Peter Jewkes's demonstrative artwork, pine cones, chic candles and contemporary flower arrangements. The bedrooms are also fashionably decorated.

Helen Bartlett works from a bold enough palette herself, marshalling some strong flavours in her resourceful fixed-price menus. Starters explore the piquant and the pungent, as in a Thai-style soup with dumplings of lemon grass, coriander and chilli, or smoked eel fish-cakes with sour cream. Fish receives uninhibited treatment all round: one meal began well with a 'stunningly fresh, exceptionally interesting' salad of scallops with their corals, finely shredded raw leek and orange zest. Trelough duck, while over-trimmed, was good breast meat perched on rösti potato, accompanied by spiced red cabbage. A penchant for aromatic spices continues through to desserts: witness rhubarb parfait with fragments of ginger, and apple strudel. The home-made breads (olive or walnut), simple petits fours and decent coffee indicate proper concern at the margins of the operation. Wines are an intelligently chosen and comprehensive range. There are four clarets and one red burgundy under £20, and not much relief elsewhere in France. The rest of the world, though, looks better value. Try one of the quartet of Pays d'Oc house wines at £9.75.

CHEF: Helen Bartlett PROPRIETORS: Peter Jewkes and Helen Bartlett OPEN: all week L 12.30 to 2, all week D 7 to 10; booking essential CLOSED: 2 weeks winter, 2 weeks summer MEALS: Set L Sun £14.50 (2 courses) to £17.50, Set D £26.50 SERVICE: net prices, card slips closed CARDS: Access, Amex, Delta, Switch, Visa DETAILS: 30 seats. Private parties: 24 main room. Car park. Vegetarian meals. Children's helpings. Smart dress preferred. No smoking in dining-room. Wheelchair access (1 step). Music ACCOMMODATION: 4 rooms, all with bath/shower. B&B £60 to £84. Deposit: £50. Children welcome. Baby facilities. Garden (*The Which? Hotel Guide*)

MELMERBY Cumbria map 10

Village Bakery £

Melmerby CA10 1HE
TEL: (01768) 881515 FAX: (01768) 881848 COOKING 1
on A686, between Penrith and Alston COST £15–£21

Lis and Andrew Whitley's showpiece organic enterprise (with a craft gallery upstairs) goes from strength to strength. Its 'green' credentials are impeccable, and it is run like a working blueprint for the ecologically minded country restaurant of the future. At its core are the brick-built, wood-fired ovens where breads, pizzas and cakes are baked using organic stone-ground flour. Beyond is a five-acre smallholding that provides fruit and vegetables and enough space for pigs to range freely. Breakfast (served until 11am) spells out the ideology: the full fry-up contains not only free-range eggs, mushrooms, tomatoes and fried bread, but also Waberthwaite's home-cured bacon and Cumberland sausage. There are also oak-smoked Inverawe kippers, raspberry porridge, croissants with home-made jam, and pots of organic tea. Lunches are a similar mix: shouraba (a Libyan soup of lamb and chickpeas), main courses of spicy pork casserole, root-vegetable crumble, or brown lentil moussaka, with Cumberland rum Nicky among the puddings as well as North Country cheeses with hunks of bread. Drinks range from teas and juices of all kinds to organic Golden Promise beer, Pinkus lager and a few wines. House wine is £6.95.

CHEF: Diane Richter PROPRIETOR: Andrew Whitley OPEN: all week daytime only 8.30 (9.30 Sun) to 5 (2.30 Mon to Fri Jan and Feb) CLOSED: Christmas MEALS: alc (main courses £5 to £6.50) SERVICE: not inc, card slips closed CARDS: Access, Delta, Diners, Switch, Visa DETAILS: 50 seats. Private parties: 40 main room. Car park. Vegetarian meals. Children's helpings. No smoking in dining-room. Wheelchair access (1 step). No music

MERLEY Dorset map 2

Les Bouviers

Oakley Hill, Merley BH21 1RJ COOKING 1*
TEL: (01202) 889555 COST £19–£56

'Les bouviers' means 'the cowherds', which might be construed as a punning reference to the name of chef/proprietor James Coward. There's no doubting that he is an industrious fellow, and this set-up is developing and evolving all the time: extensions to the dining-room are his latest venture. The building is housed in a rambling low-ceilinged cottage that has seen service as a private residence, a baker's and a post office. Inside, it is all frills, pastel colour schemes and 'lady-like touches'. Guests have the daunting task of taking their pick from a long *carte* or settling for either the four-course set meal or the menu surprise of six courses. There is even a full menu for vegans.

The cooking has a French stamp on it, and the kitchen is fond of herbs. A 'light nage of lemon grass and vegetable consommé with pearls of cucumber, beetroot and avocado' sounded 'weird' to a reporter, who found that this well-balanced, many-layered broth was 'a real delight'. In simpler vein, orange and ginger soup has been equally well received. Reporters have also praised grey mullet with caper meunière sauce, venison with chocolate and juniper, and apple Bakewell tart. Vegetables are elaborately contrived medleys, bread is 'decent', and the coffee is good. Service is friendly in a formal sort of way. The wine list is a hefty 30-page document with a wide spread, a strong California contingent and some intriguing Loire reds. House wines start at £9.95.

CHEF/PROPRIETOR: James Coward OPEN: Sun to Fri L 12 to 2, all week D 7 to 10 MEALS: alc (main courses £14 to £18). Set L £8.95 (2 courses) to £18.95, Set D £23.95 to £38 (inc wine) SERVICE: not inc, card slips closed CARDS: Access, Amex, Delta, Diners, Switch, Visa DETAILS: 70 seats. Private parties: 24 main room, 40 private room. Car park. Vegetarian meals. Children's helpings. Smart dress preferred. No smoking in 1 dining-room. Music. Air-conditioned

MIDDLE WALLOP Hampshire **map 2**

▲ *Fifehead Manor*

Middle Wallop SO20 8EG COOKING 2*
TEL: (01264) 781565 FAX: (01264) 781400 COST £26–£39

Fifehead is an ancient manor house in extensive well-tended grounds not far from Winchester. Its venerable interiors have seen the centuries pass, and in spring and summer are awash with flowers, ensuring that a visit 'gives one a great lift'. It changed hands in June 1995, but the new owner aims to ensure continuity and has sensibly opted to retain the services of chef Mark Robertson, not the least of Middle Wallop's assets.

The cooking style has refused to settle into the country-house time warp, and has instead absorbed influences from all over the Mediterranean. Dinner is a set-price affair of three courses with coffee, and shows a nice balance of robust and lighter dishes so that all scales of appetite are catered for. Red peppers and anchovy dressed with vinaigrette is a palate-sharpening opener, warm salad of smoked duck with creamed lentils and garlic a more substantial one. At inspection, main-course meats were well accompanied: parsley-crusted lamb with flageolets and a madeira sauce, and duck breast glazed with honey and soy in a sesame sauce with spinach. Citrus addicts might lap up a dessert of three-ways-with-lemon – tart, mousse and sorbet – while chocolate mousse on coffee-bean sauce, two 'smooth, rich and buttery' slabs, has induced ecstasy. Service is both polite and friendly. Wines are a largely French selection at reasonable prices, backed up by a good showing of halves. House French is £9 (red) and £10 (white).

CHEF: Mark Robertson PROPRIETOR: Mrs Bishop-Milnes OPEN: all week 12 to 2, 7 to 9.30 MEALS: Set L £19, Set D £25 SERVICE: not inc CARD: Access DETAILS: 46 seats. 5 tables outside. Private parties: 40 main room, 16 private room. Car park. Children's helpings. No smoking in dining-room. Wheelchair access (also WC). Music ACCOMMODATION: 16 rooms, all with bath/shower. TV. Phone. B&B £45 to £85. Rooms for disabled. Children welcome. Pets welcome. Afternoon teas. Garden

MIDHURST West Sussex map 3

▲ *Angel Hotel*

North Street, Midhurst GU29 9DN COOKING 2*
TEL: (01730) 812421 FAX: (01730) 815928 COST £24–£52

Peter Crawford-Rolt says the aim of his old coaching-inn is 'to bridge the gap between town-house thrift and country-house cosseting'. To that end, three eating areas are offered: wooden tables in the bar, a brightly painted brasserie and the 'subdued luxury' of the Cowdray Room restaurant. Although the menus in the last two may be identical, there is a surcharge for the luxury.

The immediate environs provide much for the kitchen partnership to get their knives into. Abundant wild fungi, freshwater fish as well as their saltier cousins from Brixham, and South Downs lamb all make an appearance. Menus are as extensive as ever, marshalling vivacious flavours to mostly good effect. First-course favourites such as salmon fish-cakes with cucumber and lemon butter are joined by modish touches like a salad of black-eyed beans dressed with chilli and coriander to accompany grilled scallops. One couple praised the cooking of medallions of pork with red cabbage, apples, sultanas and red wine, while another less-than-contented patron mourned the 'quite ordinary' chocolate and mango ice-creams, and coffee that was 'much too weak'. Although service does its level best, there is still a feeling, as waiters scurry through the dining-room with bar food, that everybody is taking too much on. The extensive wine list offers some good bottles but mark-ups are very high. Basic house wine is £9.95.

CHEFS: Peter Crawford-Rolt and Andrew Stephenson PROPRIETORS: Peter Crawford-Rolt and Nicholas Davies OPEN: all week 12 to 2.30, 6.30 to 10 MEALS: alc (main courses £10 to £17.50). Set L £12.50 to £14.50, Set D £17.50 SERVICE: not inc CARDS: Access, Amex, Diners, Visa DETAILS: 90 seats. 6 tables outside. Private parties: 100 main room, 40 to 70 private rooms. Car park. Vegetarian meals. Children welcome. No cigars/pipes in dining-room. Wheelchair access. Music ACCOMMODATION: 21 rooms, all with bath/shower. TV. Phone. B&B £65 to £130. Rooms for disabled. Children welcome. Baby facilities. Afternoon teas. Garden (*The Which? Hotel Guide*)

Maxine's £✗

Elizabeth House, Red Lion Street, Midhurst GU29 9PB COOKING 2*
TEL: (01730) 816271 COST £19–£34

Next to the pub in the heart of old Midhurst, the de Jagers' reassuringly informal little restaurant in a narrow timbered house is into its fourteenth year of business. Its success has been built on an atmosphere of genuine warmth in which not just regulars but intermittent customers too find themselves recognised and welcomed, and the consistent quality of Robert de Jager's cooking wins converts.

The fare is essentially that of a bistro, but brought off with disarming flair. Starters run a familiar gamut of fish soup with rouille and the trimmings, king prawns fried in garlic butter, Gruyère soufflé, duck liver pâté and gravad lax. Ethnic techniques are occasionally utilised for main courses like crispy duck or pork satay with fried rice; otherwise, madeira and tarragon join forces to complement fillet of lamb, poached salmon comes with sorrel sauce, and calf's liver is trendily citrified with orange and grapefruit. A fixed-price menu may offer the likes of boeuf bourguignonne alongside dishes such as chicken breast with banana in a curry sauce – a glimpse of the nouvelle after-life if ever there was one. Vegetables are accorded proper respect. Pears in chocolate sauce sprinkled with almonds, hazelnut parfait with coffee sauce, and well-loved Dutch apple pie are typical desserts. Contentment radiates through the tiny room and 'Mrs de Jager is a dear'. House wines from southern France are £7.95.

CHEF: Robert de Jager PROPRIETORS: Robert and Marti de Jager OPEN: Wed to Sun L 12 to 1.30, Wed to Sat D 7 to 9.30 CLOSED: 2 weeks Jan MEALS: alc (main courses £9 to £14). Set L £13.95, Set D Wed to Fri £13.95 SERVICE: net prices, card slips closed CARDS: Access, Visa DETAILS: 24 seats. Private parties: 30 main room. Children's helpings. Smart dress preferred. No smoking in dining-room. No music

MILFORD ON SEA Hampshire map 2

Rocher's

69–71 High Street, Milford on Sea SO41 0QG
TEL: (01590) 642340 COOKING 2*
on B3058, 3m SW of Lymington COST £21–£38

In this quiet seaside town, Rocher's looks as if it might house a little gift shop or similar. Inside it feels like somebody's living-room: 'cosy but not crowded'. The aim is fairly classic French bistro cooking within a set-price framework, often of an accomplished order. Alain Rocher writes a new menu every day according to market availability, although certain old favourites crop up regularly. Sauté chicken livers with diced tomato, shallots and capers, and a puff pastry case filled with spinach and shallots on a cream sauce are first-course stalwarts.

A summer evening began memorably for one reporter with a generous serving of 'perfectly chilled and delicious' gazpacho. Main courses are divided equally between fish and meat, and may offer sea bass with a sauce of Noilly Prat, or guinea-fowl with a grain mustard sauce. You need to leave room for desserts, as most contain cream: crème brûlée, caramel bavarois, or passion-fruit mousse with strawberry sauce set the tone. If there is a feeling that the Rochers are idling somewhat at the moment, it is as well to remember that loyal customers return for what they know best, more than out of a desire to be startled by novelty. Service is 'very charming'. The exhaustive French wine list is supplemented by two pages of wines from other countries. Prices can seem a touch fierce, but there is relief in the Loire, the Mâconnais and Beaujolais, and an enormous selection of halves. House wines start at £8.50.

CHEF: Alain Rocher PROPRIETORS: Alain and Rebecca Rocher OPEN: Sun L 12.15 to 1.45, Wed to Sat D and bank hol Sun D 7.15 to 9.30 CLOSED: 2 weeks Jun MEALS: Set L Sun £14.50, Set D Wed to Fri and Sun bank hols £16.50 to £22.90, Set D Sat £22.90 SERVICE: not inc, card slips closed CARDS: Access, Amex, Diners, Switch, Visa DETAILS: 24 seats. Private parties: 30 main room. No children under 10 L, 13 D. Smart dress preferred. No cigars/pipes in dining-room. Wheelchair access. No music

MINCHINHAMPTON Gloucestershire map 2

Markey's Restaurant

The Old Ram, Market Square,
Minchinhampton GL6 9BW
TEL: (01453) 882287

COOKING 1
COST £12–£31

'The Old Ram' was once a village pub, but Ian and Ann Markey have transformed this seventeenth-century stone building into a relaxed country restaurant stuffed with cottagey paraphernalia. It is a place that wins approval from readers who like the fact that the food is 'in plentiful supply' and dishes are elegantly served, French-style, on 'huge grass-green plates'. The kitchen looks to France for inspiration and ideas, although the Markeys are keen to make the best use of what the Cotswolds can offer: in particular, they have had a 'magnificent response' to requests for supplies of game, such as venison and wild boar. One favourably reported meal began with a tartlet of scallops with creamed leeks and chives, moved on to roast monkfish with spring onion and ginger sauce, and finished off with chocolate and coffee mousse in a tuile basket with coffee-bean sauce. Other items from the dinner menu might range from twice-baked cheese soufflé with onion marmalade to breast of duck with a creamy sauce of cracked pepper and mustard. Set lunches are excellent value. Service is described as 'really intelligent'. Eight wines are served by the glass, and the short list is thoughtfully chosen and keenly priced. House wine is £7.50.

CHEF: Ian Markey PROPRIETORS: Ian and Ann Markey OPEN: Tue to Sat 12 to 1.30, 7 to 9.30 CLOSED: 2 weeks Jan, 2 weeks end July/Aug MEALS: alc (main courses £7.50 to £11). Set L £5.25 (2 courses) to £6.50 SERVICE: not inc, card slips closed CARDS: Access, Amex, Delta, Switch, Visa DETAILS: 26 seats. Private parties: 34 main room. Vegetarian meals. Children's helpings. Smart dress preferred. No smoking in dining-room. No music

MINSTER LOVELL Oxfordshire map 2

▲ *Lovells at Windrush Farm*

Old Minster Lovell OX8 5RN
TEL/FAX: (01993) 779802
off B4047, 3m NW of Witney, on S bank of River Windrush

COOKING 1
COST £24–£48

Eighty acres of park and woodland surround the sixteenth-century stone farmhouse, just across the River Windrush from ruined Minster Lovell Hall. Walking, fishing and horse trials count among local diversions, although the small, tastefully decorated dining-room feels more cosmopolitan than you might expect from all this. As the last *Guide* appeared, Robert Marshall-Slater left and

Marcus Ashenford arrived, the change-over causing barely a ripple. The pattern remains the same: three-course lunches and seven-course dinners, with beef or lamb generally forming the centrepiece. There is no choice.

The reporter who wrote 'nicely spaced out' was referring to the seven-course dinner itself, not his feelings after eating it. Portions are well judged, and his spring meal was 'full of flavour', beginning with confit of duck with a balsamic-dressed salad, followed by cream of Jerusalem artichoke soup, then fillet of cod on a bed of spinach in a cream and leek sauce. The main-course fillet of beef, strewn with vegetables, came in a madeira sauce, and was followed by a selection of six cheeses. Just dessert to go, then? Not quite. First comes a pre-dessert – in this case a warm chocolate tart with passion-fruit sorbet and raspberry coulis – then three more 'real' ones: plum soufflé, strawberry ripple ice-cream, and lemon ravioli. Naturally, there are petits fours with the coffee. Apart from a handful, the wines are French and not short on quality, with some particularly juicy clarets and tempting burgundies. Three wines are available at £3 a glass.

CHEF: Marcus Ashenford PROPRIETOR: Lovells Windrush Farm Ltd OPEN: Tue to Fri and Sun L 12.30 to 1.30, Tue to Sat D 7.45 to 9 CLOSED: Jan MEALS: Set L £14.50, Set D £29.50 SERVICE: not inc CARDS: Access, Amex, Delta, Diners, Visa DETAILS: 18 seats. Private parties: 18 main room. Car park. No children under 12 D. Smart dress preferred. No smoking in dining-room. Wheelchair access (1 step). No music ACCOMMODATION: 2 rooms, both with bath/shower. TV. Phone. D,B&B £95 to £160. Children welcome. Baby facilities. Pets welcome. Garden. Fishing

MOLLINGTON Cheshire map 7

▲ *Crabwall Manor* 🍷

Parkgate Road, Mollington CH1 6NE
TEL: (01244) 851666 FAX: (01244) 851400 COOKING 3
off A540, 3m N of Chester COST £24–£50

Crabwall leads a double life. During the week it caters for corporate business and is proud of its conference facilities. Weekends are about looking after people who are there purely for pleasure. It takes great managerial dexterity for a hotel to keep both plates spinning at once, but Crabwall appears to be bringing it off. The setting is an endearingly sleepy village a couple of miles out of Chester.

Michael Truelove cooks a wide-ranging menu that aims to please everybody, cleverly interspersing some brave ideas amid the more familiar country-house productions. Délices of salmon on a warm tomato and basil salad, and Mediterranean vegetable terrine will appeal to those of gentler tastes. For the more adventurous, oysters on tagliatelle with a red wine reduction, or duck leg confit on shredded cabbage with an anise-flavoured sauce, may stir the imagination. As so often, it is in offal and game that the more daring turns are tried: venison comes with a Jerusalem artichoke purée on a liquorice sauce. Liquorice crops up again as an ice-cream paired with blackcurrant sorbet, while the sharpness of lemon tart is emphasised with an orange syrup. Sunday lunch sees bread-and-butter pudding and crème brûlée brought on. Service is capable of a high degree of professionalism, and seems genuinely interested.

The encyclopedic wine list provides generous choice. An excellent selection of Alsace, good growers of burgundy, thoroughbred clarets and a more than perfunctory choice of German wines should whet the appetite. Prices are high, but there are lots of halves. Last year's *Guide* offered the advice that Asti Spumante is not made by the champagne method, as somebody at Crabwall still seems to think. It still isn't. House burgundy is £12.50. CELLARMAN'S CHOICE: Bourgogne Aligoté de Bouzeron 1992, De Villaine, £22; Côtes du Rhône 1991, Guigal, £16.75.

CHEF: Michael Truelove PROPRIETOR: Carl Lewis OPEN: Sun to Fri L 12 to 2, all week D 7 to 9.30 MEALS: alc (main courses £11.50 to £19). Set L Sun £15.50 SERVICE: not inc, card slips closed CARDS: Access, Amex, Delta, Diners, Switch, Visa DETAILS: 100 seats. Private parties: 90 main room, 30 to 100 private rooms. Car park. Vegetarian meals. Children's helpings. Jacket and tie. No cigars/pipes in dining-room. Wheelchair access (2 steps; also WC). Music. Air-conditioned ACCOMMODATION: 48 rooms, all with bath/shower. TV. Phone. B&B £70 to £125. Rooms for disabled. Children welcome. Baby facilities. Garden (*The Which? Hotel Guide*)

MONTACUTE Somerset map 2

▲ *Milk House*

The Borough, Montacute TA15 6XB — COOKING 1
TEL: (01935) 823823 — COST £27–£39

One couple who arrived at Montacute during the filming of *Sense and Sensibility* were much taken with the fun atmosphere of a National Trust village transformed into the set of a TV drama. By contrast, they found the Milk House a touch serious in style and intent. The house itself is a gem: five centuries old, built of honeyed stone and full of polished antiques ('You may sit at a Georgian table on a carved rosewood chair,' the owners tell us.) In fine weather there are tables on the lawn and terrace; otherwise, meals are taken in a 'charming' dining-room with mullioned windows and a showpiece 'safely covered' well. Lee Dufton's cooking is based on ecologically sound principles: bread is home-baked, main dishes are served with a harvest festival of home-grown vegetables, and cold-pressed oils are often used instead of butter. Organic produce comes to the fore whenever possible, and the kitchen has no truck with farmed game and fish.

The four-course menu leaves you in no doubt that 'wholefood' and 'French provincial' are the main sources of inspiration. Subtly pungent sunflower-seed soup is based on really good stock, daube of lamb is cooked for hours to create something 'truly delicious', while cod and prawns are served in a delicate asparagus sauce. Desserts have drawn a mixed response (astringent sorbets, and a blackcurrant tart with heavy wholemeal pastry ended one inspection meal on a down note); the cafetière could also do with a lift. Service is friendly in a leisurely kind of way. The wine list includes some award-winning organics, and prices are kept in check. House wines start at around £10.

Restaurateurs justifiably resent no-shows. If you quote a credit card number when booking, you may be liable for the restaurant's lost profit margin if you don't turn up. Always phone to cancel.

CHEF: Lee Dufton PROPRIETORS: Lee and Bill Dufton OPEN: Wed to Sat D only 7.30 to 9; Sun L by arrangement CLOSED: 2 weeks Christmas and New Year, 3 weeks June to July MEALS: alc (main courses £12.50 to £14). Set D £22.90. Minimum £14.40 D SERVICE: none, card slips closed CARDS: Visa; 3.5% surcharge on credit card transactions DETAILS: 40 seats. 3 tables outside. Private parties: 40 main room, 6 and 24 private rooms. Vegetarian meals. Children's helpings. No children under 2. Smart dress preferred. No smoking in dining-room. Wheelchair access. No music ACCOMMODATION: 2 rooms, both with bath/shower. B&B £40 to £58. Deposit: £20. No children under 8. Pets welcome in bedrooms only. Garden (*The Which? Hotel Guide*)

MORETON-IN-MARSH Gloucestershire map 5

Marsh Goose ⁂

High Street, Moreton-in-Marsh GL56 0AX COOKING 3
TEL: (01608) 652111 COST £21–£42

The old stone frontage in this Cotswold village hides a labyrinth of comfortable and pleasantly furnished rooms dotted with paintings by local artists. Although Marsh Goose is not run like a commune, staff are 'encouraged to develop their own ideas and skills', which results in a less-doctrinaire approach to the food. The benefit is that ideas are continually refreshed, while the drawback is that both cooking and service may appear to lack direction. Menus are rewritten for each meal. Turning out the same dishes every day would obviously send this team round the bend; they thrive on daily deadlines. The simple no-choice set lunch is considered good value, while dinner adds on a few supplements.

The food covers a wide range, from grilled tuna with a salad of broad beans, capers and beetroot, to braised oxtail. 'Good-quality ingredients, nicely assembled' might apply to several dishes, including scallops with avocado and green salad, and guinea-fowl with potato cake. Proper care is taken with butchering, stock-making, bread-baking, and most dishes work, although, given the pace of activity in the kitchen, a few seem to escape the drawing-board prematurely. Even then the problems are rarely to do with technique or quality of ingredients, but come down to whether the pancetta and cream sauce overwhelm the pan-fried cod, why certain things need to swim in oil, or, in one case, whether vegetarians get a fair deal.

Puddings – 'a class above the previous courses' for one reporter – might include rhubarb fool with shortbread biscuit, or terrine of blackberry and ginger. Black coffee jelly with butterscotch sauce is a regular favourite. The wine list is full of interest and helpfully organised around styles, from 'oaked whites' to 'classic reds', and there is ample choice under £20. Wine service is generally, but not always, good, but one or two prices (£5.50 for a glass of Elysium, for example, which sells retail for £5.99 a half-bottle) seem out of step with the rest of the operation. House red or white from Navarra is £9.50.

CHEF: Sonya Kidney PROPRIETORS: Sonya Kidney, Leo Brooke-Little and Gordon Campbell Gray OPEN: Tue to Sun L 12.30 to 2.30, Tue to Sat D 7.30 to 9.45 MEALS: alc L Tue to Sat (main courses £11.50 to £14). Set L Tue to Sat £13.50. Set L Sun £18, Set D £24 SERVICE: not inc CARDS: Access, Amex, Delta, Switch, Visa DETAILS: 70 seats. Private parties: 20 main room, 15 private room. Vegetarian meals. Children's helpings. Smart dress preferred. No smoking in dining-room. Wheelchair access (also WC). No music

MORSTON Norfolk map 6

▲ *Morston Hall*

Morston NR25 7AA
TEL: (01263) 741041 FAX: (01263) 740419 COOKING 2*
2m W of Blakeney, on A149 COST £20–£36

Morston Hall is certainly in an isolated location. A couple who motored up to nearby Blakeney Point to savour the 'large empty views' discovered an eerily deserted prospect, despite a fine June evening. The Hall itself is a modestly proportioned building of grey flint with brick facings and a trim garden complete with pond and fountain. A surprising degree of formality in an atmosphere of reverential hush pervades the dining-room, although the chef does a perambulation around the room at some point. Dinners follow the Lakeland formula (Galton Blackiston used to be at Miller Howe; see entry, Windermere): one sitting, 7.30 for 8, with a set menu of four courses, the last either a dessert or cheese.

The cooking style has strayed a little outside the Cumbrian model, however, to take account of present-day preoccupations. Fresh tagliatelle forms a good backdrop for powerfully rich wild mushrooms with bacon in a cream sauce with dill. The second course may be thickly sliced smoked salmon served on a kind of rösti containing onion with sour cream, before roast loin of lamb – described as 'quality meat, pinkly cooked' – set off by the appealing sweetness of a redcurrant and caper jelly. Vegetables are served ready-plated. Desserts on the 'Morston Hall assiette' take in a 'superbly textured, intense and fudge-like' caramel parfait, a slice of 'pleasantly sharp' lemon tart and a poached peach. The imaginatively chosen wine list is arranged by grape type, and has good notes for a comprehensive selection of bottles from all over. Around ten house recommendations are available by the glass, including a pair of wines of the month. Prices throughout are very fair, starting at £8.95.

CHEFS: Galton Blackiston and Lorna Powell PROPRIETORS: Galton and Tracy Blackiston, and Justin Fraser OPEN: Sun L 12.30 for 1, all week D 7.30 for 8 (one sitting) CLOSED: Jan to Feb MEALS: Set L Sun £14, Set D £23 SERVICE: not inc, card slips closed CARDS: Access, Amex, Visa DETAILS: 40 seats. Private parties: 40 main room. Car park. Children's helpings. Smart dress preferred. No smoking in dining-room. Wheelchair access (1 step; also WC). No music ACCOMMODATION: 6 rooms, all with bath/shower. TV. Phone. D,B&B £80 to £140. Children welcome. Baby facilities. Pets welcome. Afternoon teas. Garden (*The Which? Hotel Guide*)

MOULSFORD Oxfordshire map 2

▲ *Beetle & Wedge*

Ferry Lane, Moulsford OX10 9JF
TEL: (01491) 651381 FAX: (01491) 651376 COOKING 3
off A329, down Ferry Lane to river COST £30–£70

The hotel is on the upper reaches of the Thames, close by the stretch of riverbank that provided the inspiration for *The Wind in the Willows*. 'A very pretty garden with pergola and seating leads down to the water's edge, where swans do their best to look decorative,' reads one report. Once a simple inn, the Beetle & Wedge has, under the experienced tutelage of Richard and Kate Smith, long outgrown its humble origins and is now an ambitious operation.

The Boathouse is the informal venue for brasserie-style eating, with its own menu and its own chef, Robert Taylor. The tone of the conservatory Dining Room is one of elegant refinement, and Richard Smith's cooking strives for similar effect. Lunches are fixed-price, dinner à la carte. The style is a thoughtful mixture of classicism – artichoke heart with mushrooms and hollandaise, for example – and today's magpie tendency that can bring on a stir-fry of spicy squid with bean sprouts, scallops, coriander and tomato. At inspection hot Stilton soufflé was well risen, if strangely reticent in flavour for a blue-cheese dish, but came with a copper saucepan of 'creamy wild mushroom sauce'. Loin of hare was 'the roughest and best textured and wildest, most mature and well hung that I've eaten', served in caramelised cooking juices with a goodly quantity of foie gras and morels. Rösti is served on the side, as it is with all main courses. Others speak well of chargrilled Dover sole with 'fruity olive oil and roughly chopped herbs', and 'beautiful-looking' poached apricots and plums with an apricot coulis and vanilla ice-cream. Iced desserts are reported as lacking intensity of flavour.

Wines have long been a strength. Formidable quality is evident at every turn, with a French bias. Mark-ups may occasion the odd sigh of regret – £20 for Sancerre gives a rough idea – and more could be done for those who wish to drink for less than this, but the 'dipstick' policy continues, whereby you can order a full bottle and drink half or more of it and pay pro rata with a £1.25 supplement. Four house wines are £11.50. CELLARMAN'S CHOICE: Alsace Muscat 1992, Dom. Schlumberger, £18.50; Devils Lair Cabernet Sauvignon 1991, Margaret River, W. Australia, £24.50.

CHEF: Richard Smith (Dining Room), Robert Taylor (Boathouse) PROPRIETORS: Richard and Kate Smith OPEN: Tue to Sun 12.30 to 2, Tue to Sat 7.30 to 10 MEALS: alc (main courses £19 to £23). Set L Tue to Sat £17.50 (2 courses) to £21.50, Set L Sun £27.50 SERVICE: not inc CARDS: Access, Amex, Delta, Diners, Switch, Visa DETAILS: 35 seats. Private parties: 40 main room, 60 private room. Car park. Vegetarian meals. Children welcome. Smart dress preferred. No smoking in Dining Room. Wheelchair access. No music ACCOMMODATION: 10 rooms, all with bath/shower. TV. Phone. B&B £75 to £125. Rooms for disabled. Children welcome. Baby facilities. Pets by arrangement. Garden (*The Which? Hotel Guide*)

MOULTON North Yorkshire map 9

Black Bull Inn

Moulton DL10 6QJ
TEL: (01325) 377289 FAX: (01325) 377422 COOKING 2
1m SE of Scotch Corner, 1m from A1 COST £21–£47

First choose your room in this old whitewashed pub. Apart from the bar, which serves snacks for under £5, the same menu holds throughout. In the conservatory, pots of geraniums sit on the windowsill, an old vine grows out through the ceiling, and a display of railway insignia covers one wall. A panelled restaurant is reserved for those who have not booked ahead, another is for private parties, while outside sits a 1930s Pullman carriage salvaged from the Brighton Belle, which provides another dining area.

The main business is a wide variety of fish and shellfish, Aberdeen Angus beef, and game in season. Oysters, scallops and prawns are served variously hot or cold, while halibut, sole, monkfish and sea bass are poached, steamed, roasted, or pan-fried. Fish-cakes, pancakes and soups are natural diversions, but even here frills are kept to a minimum. Tried and tested Anglo-French saucing – wine and shallots, madeira and tarragon – is the kitchen's favoured way of dealing with meat. Portions (including vegetables) are average by Yorkshire standards, which is to say generous. If you have appetite left, there are puddings such as pear tart with chocolate and sabayon. Wines run the gamut from Liebfraumilch to Guigal's Côte Rôtie, by way of a strong burgundy section, and prices are generally fair. House wines (Picpoul de Pinet white and Duboeuf red) are £7.75 and £7.50.

CHEF: Stuart Birkett PROPRIETORS: G.H. and A.M.C. Pagendam OPEN: Mon to Fri L 12 to 2, Mon to Sat D 6.45 to 10.15 CLOSED: 24 to 27 Dec MEALS: alc (main courses £13.50 to £19.50). Set L £13.75 SERVICE: not inc, card slips closed CARDS: Access, Amex, Delta, Switch, Visa DETAILS: 100 seats. 4 tables outside. Private parties: 30 main room, 10 to 30 private rooms. Car park. No children under 7. No music

NAILSWORTH Gloucestershire map 2

William's Bistro

3 Fountain Street, Nailsworth GL6 0BL COOKING 2
TEL: (01453) 835507 FAX: (01453) 835950 COST £24–£47

'Very relaxed atmosphere. Come as you are!' proclaims the handout. William Beeston is a busy man: he not only runs a splendid delicatessen, but he is also at the helm of a cheerful, good-value bistro housed in an extension at the back of the shop. There is no stuffiness or fussiness here: roller blinds hang at the windows, pictures of French scenes decorate the terracotta walls, the doors are painted bottle-green. An aroma of garlic wafts from the hubbub of the kitchen.

The hand-written menu, with its jokey doodles of smiling crabs, molluscs and anthropomorphic sea creatures, leaves you in no doubt that fish is what William's is all about. The latest addition to the menu is a dish of squat lobsters from the Isle of Skye, but there is much more besides. Fish soup slightly disappointed one reporter, but fillet of wild salmon was beautifully tender and served with a tart, spicy sauce of rhubarb and ginger. Other reporters have praised sea bream with poached oysters, and halibut with tomato vinaigrette. Alternatives to fish appear in the form of risotto of chorizo and wild mushrooms, a warm salad of pigeon breast, and roast duck on a bed of spring onions and thyme. Desserts might include tangy passion-fruit tart and crème brûlée (complete with 'wafer rolls' stuck into it). The place can get packed in the evening, but service never seems to wane. William Beeston says his wine list is 'a movable feast': bottles come and go, but prices are very fair and there is precious little above £15 unless you want to dip into the fizz. House wine is £7.

CHEFS: Clive Gawlick and William Beeston PROPRIETORS: William and Rae Beeston OPEN: Tue to Sat D only 7 to 9.45 CLOSED: Christmas, Easter, Tues after bank hols MEALS: alc (main courses £9.50 to £22.50) SERVICE: not inc, card slips closed CARDS: Access, Visa DETAILS: 45 seats. Private parties: 50 main room. Children's helpings. No music

NANTWICH Cheshire map 5

Churche's Mansion

Hospital Street, Nantwich CW5 0RY COOKING 2*
TEL: (01270) 625933 FAX: (01270) 524256 COST £24–£45

Having survived a conflagration that consumed the rest of Nantwich six years after it was built, this four-gabled Elizabethan mansion has weathered the centuries stoutly. Nervous guests may like to know that hauntings appear to be ten a penny, with evanescent white figures traipsing the stairs and ghostly presences hovering in the dining-room. A more welcome appearance there is Graham Tucker, whose accomplished cooking continues to elicit loud bravos from readers.

A sliding scale of prices operates according to the number of courses eaten. Choice is bewilderingly wide, and inspiration is drawn from many culinary sources offering seared skate with pickled lemons, chillies, ginger, lemon grass and deep-fried noodles; or an intriguing-sounding 'dartois of falafel in a salad of confited aubergine dressed with yoghurt and tahini'. For one reporter, the 'exquisite flavours of a wild mushroom sauce compensated for slightly overdone tagliatelle', while the 'super' banana fritters with caramel sauce and 'good selection and very generous helping' of British farmhouse cheeses made successful endings. Service, even when stretched, remains calm and efficient.

The carefully annotated wine list offers much to chew over but is strongest in classical France. Half-bottles are plentiful, and prices are reasonable to a fault. If youngish claret is not your bag, cast an eye over the good Australian reds. House selections start with burgundy at £9.75. CELLARMAN'S CHOICE: Morgan Winery Chardonnay 1993, Monterey, California, £23.50; Riddoch Estate Shiraz 1991, Coonawarra, S. Australia, £16.75.

CHEF: Graham Tucker PROPRIETORS: Robin Latham and Amanda Latham OPEN: Tue to Sun L 12 to 2.30, Tue to Sat D 7 to 9.30 CLOSED: second week Jan MEALS: Set L £12.50 (2 courses) to £15.50, Set D £24 SERVICE: not inc, card slips closed CARDS: Access, Delta, Diners, Switch, Visa DETAILS: 58 seats. 4 tables outside. Private parties: 48 main room, 24 and 48 private rooms. Car park. Vegetarian meals. Children's helpings. No children under 10 D. Smart dress preferred. No smoking in dining-room. Wheelchair access (through kitchen). Music

NAYLAND Suffolk map 6

Martha's Vineyard

18 High Street, Nayland CO6 4JF
TEL: (01206) 262888 COOKING 3
off A134, 5m N of Colchester COST £26–£32

American-born Larkin Rogers explains the set-up: 'If we were parents, our business would be described as "mom 'n' pop" – we do it all ourselves. Christopher is the sommelier, maître d', front-of-house cleaner, trash man and shopper; I am the executive chef, chef tournant, main potato-peeler and lettuce-washer, kitchen cleaner, baker and herb gardener.' Martha's Vineyard runs to its own rules. This tiny place on a village street corner cut its opening to two evenings a week, but badgering requests led the owners to expand a little. It remains a 'brilliantly vibrant venue', with closely packed tables, cheeky fabric table-mats with different colours on each side, new linen napkins and eye-dazzling technicolour curtains ('Habitat meets Matisse').

The cooking has been described as 'maverick with transatlantic overtones', although evangelical when it comes to procuring local ingredients. Rare breeds (Norfolk horned sheep, Essex saddleback pigs, black turkeys) are used regularly, although Larkin Rogers writes that 'the English free-range chicken continues to elude our grasp'. The menu is short, hand-written, fixed price for two or three courses and amazing value. Meals begin with 'marvellously squidgy' slices of thick-cut cornmeal and raisin bread. Black-bean chilli with avocado salsa and soured cream is 'as subtle as a shot from a six-gun', but it goes straight to the heart with no holding back on flavour or intensity.

Larkin Rogers admits that her talents also lie with fish stews: her Brazilian version is laced with lime, coconut, coriander and ancho chillies, while cioppino (from California) dazzled one reporter with its sheer freshness. Elsewhere, the kitchen has delivered impeccably timed chicken breast, sliced thick to allow a buttery blackberry and coriander sauce to seep though the fibres. Vegetables might include New Zealand spinach – curious little sprigs of leaf and delicate stem that one reporter reckoned were 'out of this world' – while the bowlfuls of green salads may contain herb leaves and marigold petals. In the words of one convert, 'This is cooking that makes you sit up and take notice. It is inspired, risky and dazzling when it works – which is most of the time.' Desserts have been less applauded. Around 40 wines (mostly young) are sharply chosen and sensibly priced. Flavour is their common characteristic. Those from North America are worth serious consideration. French country house wine is £10.95. CELLARMAN'S CHOICE: Mâcon-Clessé 1992, Dom. Guillemot-Michel, £14.95; Madiran, Ch. Montus 1991, Brumont, £16.95

CHEF: Larkin Rogers PROPRIETORS: Christopher Warren and Larkin Rogers OPEN: Sun L 12.30 to 2, Tue to Sat D 7.30 to 9.30 CLOSED: 2 weeks summer, 2 weeks winter MEALS: Set L and D £15 (2 courses) to £18.50 SERVICE: not inc; 10% for parties of 6 or more CARDS: Access, Visa DETAILS: 41 seats. Private parties: 8 main room. Vegetarian meals. Children's helpings. No smoking in dining-room. Wheelchair access. No music

NEAR SAWREY Cumbria map 8

▲ *Ees Wyke*

Near Sawrey LA22 0JZ
TEL: (01539) 436393 COOKING 2
on B5286 from Hawkshead COST £25–£30

The house is around the corner from the Beatrix Potter museum at Hill Top, just up the road from the car ferry to Windermere. A modern dining-room at the back overlooks Esthwaite and the Old Man of Coniston. John and Margaret Williams do everything themselves, and adopt the standard Lakeland format: assemble at 7 for drinks, eat at 7.30. The atmosphere of the dining-room owes much to Margaret Williams, who juggles several bright and cheery conversations at once, which pleases some more than others. There is certainly no reverential hush.

The five-course menu ploughs a traditional furrow, from sirloin steak with blue-cheese sauce to sticky toffee meringue. Course number two is a no-choice item, perhaps soup or salad, and the fifth is cheese. One of the delights of a spring meal was a filo pastry tartlet containing a set savoury custard 'tasting mildly and delightfully of goats' cheese', with chopped spears of asparagus for crunch. Some dishes, such as fricassee of veal with mushrooms, are more in the mould of 'dinner-party cooking', but the kitchen works comfortably within its own compass. A first course of crispy duck, for example, although partnered by a powerfully spicy and acetic sauce, had been properly dried so that the skin was light and free of excess fat. Vegetables are piled on rather indiscriminately, puddings tend to be rich, and the three dozen diverse wines are commendably priced. Breakfasts are highly rated, and the overnight package is considered good value.

CHEF: John Williams PROPRIETORS: Margaret and John Williams OPEN: all week D only 7 for 7.30 (one sitting) CLOSED: Jan and Feb MEALS: Set D £12 residents, £18 non-residents SERVICE: not inc, card slips closed CARDS: Amex DETAILS: 16 seats. Private parties: 20 main room. Car park. No children under 8. Smart dress preferred. No smoking in dining-room. Wheelchair access (1 step). No music ACCOMMODATION: 8 rooms, all with bath/shower. TV. B&B £38 to £76. Children welcome. Pets welcome. Afternoon teas. Garden (*The Which? Hotel Guide*)

NEW ALRESFORD Hampshire map 2

▲ *Hunters*

32 Broad Street, New Alresford S024 9AQ COOKING 1*
TEL/FAX: (01962) 732468 COST £20–£43

Hunters is a restaurant with a river on its doorstep, always an attraction. The Georgian building has allure too, the entrance reached via a passageway to the rear that would once have resounded to the clatter of horses' hooves. Michael Greenhalgh's culinary style is an assertive one. A warm salad of duck, mushrooms and Stilton should stiffen the sinews at the outset of lunch, and may be succeeded by the likes of black pudding and bacon with mash and a mustard cream sauce, or wild boar and apple sausages with leeks and onions. At dinner, a starter of spaghetti with langoustines and Parma ham may be followed by pork fillet stuffed with a single stalk of asparagus accompanied by onion compote and a 'sweet but not sickly' sauce of prunes and kümmel. Summer fruits are accorded prominence in desserts, either gratinated with ice-cream or heaped luxuriantly in a summer pudding. More fashionable is rhubarb crumble tartlet with its own ice-cream. Service at inspection was thought 'friendly but sloppy'. The wine list confines itself to short, serviceable selections in the areas it covers. Prices are mostly within reason. House wines start at £8.95.

CHEF: Michael Greenhalgh PROPRIETOR: Martin Birmingham OPEN: all week L 12 to 2, Mon to Sat D 7 to 10 CLOSED: 1 week Christmas; Sun May to Sept MEALS: alc (main courses £5.50 to £16). Set D Mon to Fri £13.95 (2 courses) to £15.95 SERVICE: not inc; 10% on parties of 6 or more CARDS: Access, Amex, Diners, Visa DETAILS: 110 seats. 8 tables outside. Private parties: 30 main room, 80 private room. Vegetarian meals. Children's helpings. Wheelchair access (also WC). Music ACCOMMODATION: 3 rooms, all with bath/shower. TV. B&B £37.50 to £47.50. Deposit: £10. Children welcome. Garden

NEWARK Nottinghamshire map 5

Gannets Bistrot

35 Castlegate, Newark NG24 1AZ COOKING 3
TEL: (01636) 610018 COST £17–£40

'We were very sorry indeed when Colin White left Lincoln some years ago to open a restaurant in Cricklade in Wiltshire,' began our first report on this venture. 'He opened the bistro today and we were his first lunchtime customers.' That was just before the *Guide* came out last year, since when the Whites have been welcomed back to what some consider their home territory. The setting – opposite the castle – is plain, clean and simple, though one reporter felt it could do with brightening up. The Whites lease the first floor from the Bowers, who still run the ground-floor lunchtime-only café, though the bistro is accessed via a separate side entrance.

The food is responsive, tasty and varied, and the informality of a bistro format ties in well with the simple and direct flavours, sometimes with a bit of heat emanating from salsas, rouille and the like: fillet of sea bass, for example, arrives on a bed of pulses, with a spicy tomato sauce. This is not typical bistro cooking – Colin White is in a class of his own as far as that's concerned – it is just that the two seem made for each other. For a start the materials are impeccable: fish comes from Brixham three times a week, and links with local organic suppliers have produced Trudy Potter's excellent pork steaks, served with apples and cider, and Peter Onions's chickens (which won a National Organic Poultry award) chargrilled and served with polenta and parsley pesto. Vegetables, including tarragon mash, have also come in for praise.

Cheeses are excellent, though desserts were the high point for one reporter: creamy, sharp lemon tart with good pastry and a lightly caramelised top, coffee ice-cream with hot chocolate sauce, and hazelnut pudding with a poached pear and crème fraîche. 'A very enthusiastic lady met us and welcomed us to the restaurant.' That would be Gwen White, whose friendly, polite and relaxed approach could not be bettered. Wine service is matter-of-fact: 'We were not asked to taste the wine and had to serve ourselves,' with which there is nothing wrong at all. The short, ultra-sharp list of three dozen bottles stays under £20 (apart from Cornas and champagne) yet manages to include Jermann's Vinnae, and Cabernet Sauvignons from Vasse Felix and Stag's Leap. Six house wines between £8 and £10 are available by the glass from £1.40.

CHEF: Colin White PROPRIETORS: Colin and Gwen White OPEN: Tue to Sat 12 to 2, 6.30 to 9.30 MEALS: alc (main courses £7 to £14.50). Set L Mon to Sat £7.50 (2 courses) to £10 SERVICE: 10%, card slips closed CARDS: Access, Delta, Switch, Visa DETAILS: 40 seats. Private parties: 32 main room. Vegetarian meals. Children's helpings. No smoking in dining-room. Music

Several sharp operators have tried to extort money from restaurateurs on the promise of an entry in a guidebook that has never appeared. The Good Food Guide *makes no charge for inclusion.*

NEWCASTLE UPON TYNE Tyne & Wear map 10

Courtney's

5–7 The Side, Newcastle upon Tyne NE1 3JE COOKING 2
TEL: 0191-232 5537 COST £22–£43

If you want to check Newcastle's gastronomic pulse, head for the Quayside. This is where most of the action is, and where the restaurant scene is at its most cosmopolitan. Michael and Kerensa Carr's brasserie has been part and parcel of things since 1990, and it continues to court regulars and first-timers alike. The split-level dining-room looks every inch the part, from the modern posters on the walls, black chairs and swags of dried flowers to the bottles of herb-flavoured olive oil on each table. The blackboard has been replaced by a weekly-changing printed *carte*, and there's also a set-price menu at lunch-time.

Modernity is the theme, and the kitchen goes boldly into the big-city world of blackened chicken with tomato and coriander salsa, risotto of leeks and morels, and darkly lacquered salmon teriyaki with stir-fried vegetables, as well as keeping faith with classics such as eggs Benedict, and veal fillet served 'chop-house style' with grilled tomatoes and mushrooms. Desserts are well-tried confections, including îles flottantes, chocolate marquise, and strawberry and passion-fruit tuile. The cooking is consistent and successful, although some reporters have hoped for a little more dazzle. A lively New World contingent steals the limelight on the short but thoroughly modern wine list. House wine is £10.

CHEF: Michael Carr PROPRIETORS: Michael and Kerensa Carr OPEN: Mon to Fri L 12 to 2, Mon to Sat D 7 to 10.30 CLOSED: 1 week Christmas, 2 weeks May, bank hols MEALS: alc (main courses £10.50 to £15.50). Set L £13 (2 courses) to £15 SERVICE: not inc CARDS: Access, Amex, Switch, Visa DETAILS: 26 seats. Private parties: 26 main room. Vegetarian meals. Children welcome. Smart dress preferred. No cigars/pipes in dining-room. Music. Air-conditioned

Fisherman's Lodge ★

Jesmond Dene, Jesmond,
Newcastle upon Tyne NE7 7BQ COOKING 3
TEL: 0191-281 3281 FAX: 0191-281 6410 COST £24–£75

Lord Armstrong, founder of the engineering firm, lived in this stone Victorian house, which stands within the large expanse of parkland known as Jesmond Dene. The Cetolonis opened their restaurant here in 1979, and over the years it has become securely established as one of the best addresses on Tyneside, for the smooth professionalism with which it is run and for some consistently impressive cooking.

The current incumbent in the kitchen, Steven Jobson, has been here for seven years, enough time to have consolidated a reputation. There is a high gloss to the cooking, displayed in a comfortable balance of 'Chef's classics' and constantly changing specialities. As the name suggests, fish is a strong point, and may be as simple as deep-fried monkfish with a garlic mayonnaise, or as opulent as turbot on a puff pastry nest with creamed leeks and a mustard sauce. Otherwise asparagus might be lightly chargrilled and dressed with olive oil, cayenne and

Parmesan, and meat has included well-timed and 'beautifully tender' Northumberland lamb served with a 'slightly heavy' leek pudding and assertive sage and onion sauce. Eton mess makes the most of June strawberries, while 'smooth, creamy' chocolate fondant comes in a layer of sponge with feathered crème anglaise. Cheeses are tip-top, good breads and well-made petits fours offer classy support to the main business, and the service is commended as 'prompt, courteous and efficient'. The wine list performs its function capably in most regions. Many of the choices are pretty standard, but there is a sense of value and a good range of halves. House French is £10.

CHEFS: Steven Jobson and Poul Amer PROPRIETORS: Franco and Pamela Cetoloni OPEN: Mon to Fri L 12 to 2, Mon to Sat D 7 to 11 CLOSED: bank hols MEALS: alc (main courses £16.50 to £27). Set L £16.70, Set D Mon to Fri £26.50 SERVICE: not inc CARDS: Access, Amex, Delta, Diners, Switch, Visa DETAILS: 65 seats. 9 tables outside. Private parties: 16 main room, 14 and 43 private rooms. Car park. Vegetarian meals. No children under 10 D. Smart dress preferred. No smoking in dining-room. Wheelchair access (1 step; also WC). Music

Leela's *

20 Dean Street, Newcastle upon Tyne NE1 1PG — COOKING 2
TEL: 0191-230 1261 — COST £23–£40

It would be hard to imagine this restaurant without its eponymous owner, Leela Paul. She is the star of the show and the action revolves around her: she can be either 'charming, personable and motherly' or 'pushy', depending on your viewpoint. Essentially, these rather elegant premises near the Theatre Royal are an extension of her own kitchen, which means that the menu is used as the jumping-off point for themes and variations dictated by what is in the larder. The result is 'excellent' South Indian home cooking from Leela's native Kerala and the adjacent region of Tamil Nadu.

Vegetarian and non-vegetarian specialities have equal billing. Packavadas (another name for vegetable pakoras) are grease-free nuggets served with minty yoghurt, sambar is the real thing with lentils and exotic vegetables including 'drumstick' seed-pods, while chera varalan appears as a crisp, delicate mixture of spinach and potatoes stir-fried with sesame seeds. Among the meat dishes, reporters have praised marinated high-range beef (melt-in-the-mouth meat in a lush sauce that 'left an aromatic afterglow in the mouth'), and chicken pappas (a whole breast in a lightly spiced cream sauce). Basmati rice is described as 'whiter than white and fluffier than swans'-down'. To finish, try home-made kulfi or payasamu ('temptingly moreish' roasted vermicelli in a soothing milky sauce with cashew-nuts and sultanas). A buffet is offered in addition to the full menu at lunch-time. Leela is keen to promote the virtue of wine with Indian food, and her list is promising. House wine is £8.95.

CHEF: Kuriakose Paul PROPRIETORS: Leela and Kuriakose Paul OPEN: Mon to Sat 11.30 to 2.30, 5.30 to 11.30 CLOSED: first 2 weeks Jan, bank hols MEALS: alc (main courses £8 to £13). Buffet L £5.95, Set D £13.95 (2 courses) to £16.95 SERVICE: not inc CARDS: Access, Amex, Diners, Visa DETAILS: 50 seats. Private parties: 35 main room. Vegetarian meals. Children welcome. Smart dress preferred. No smoking in dining-room. Music

21 Queen Street 🍷

19–21 Queen Street, Princes Wharf, Quayside,
Newcastle upon Tyne NE1 3UG — COOKING 3*
TEL: 0191-222 0755 FAX: 0191-221 0761 — COST £25–£52

Elsewhere it might have been called Laybourne's, but modesty suits the surroundings. Under the lee of the great bridge, in a water-front area full of restaurants and bars, number 21 has a discreet frontage, with dark green paint, buff-coloured blinds, and no sign save a small brass plaque. Redecoration has brought a light, uncluttered, ultra-modern feel: Arctic-white walls are relieved by modern watercolours, much as the waiters' white shirts are by their jazzy ties. 'Relaxed, cool, unfussy' is how it feels, and it is populated at lunch-time by suits and briefs (the courts are nearby), who may not look quite as trendy as the décor.

The menu spans a range of genres as wide as the Tyne itself. A strong oriental streak shows in tempura-fried prawns with crisp cabbage and lobster cream. Classics – ribeye steak, or poached Tweed salmon with asparagus, Jersey potatoes and hollandaise sauce – run alongside a homage-to-roots section: ham knuckle and foie gras terrine with pease-pudding is described as 'the gastronomic equivalent of a Geordie miner winning the lottery'. Then there are novelties (fricassee of asparagus with morel mushrooms and roast chicken wings), and fashionable Newcastle upon Med items such as grilled snapper with chorizo and fennel, or red mullet with roasted vegetables and tapénade cream. 'The menu makes a good read – and a hard choice.'

An inspector visiting in May enjoyed a 'beautifully butchered and prepared' fillet of 'fabulous-tasting new season's lamb' that came with a sandwich of roasted aubergines, courgettes and red peppers topped with baked garlic cloves: 'judiciously composed...a colourful, bold dish fashioned with verve and confidence.' It was the highlight of a meal that began with a generous piece of smoked salmon on warm, sliced Jersey potatoes tossed in olive oil, herbs and 'the teensiest dribble of balsamic', and finished with an exceptionally light yet creamy vanilla mousse ringed with wrinkled and chewy slices of dried fruits. A simple and unadorned wedge of 'impeccable' lemon tart with a caramelised topping was distinguished by its 'sharp, clean, vivid taste'.

Apart from a few French country wines, the utterly sound and reliable list stays with the mainstream, offering a good choice of styles and prices within the major regions. Mark-ups on the whole are fair, and there are 20 half-bottles. CELLARMAN'S CHOICE: Mâcon-Clessé, Dom. de la Bon Gran 1991, Thévenet, £30; Châteauneuf-du-Pape, Dom. de Beaurenard 1991, P. Coul et Fils, £24.

CHEF/PROPRIETOR: Terence Laybourne OPEN: Mon to Fri L 12 to 2, Mon to Sat D 7 to 10.45 MEALS: alc (main courses) £14.50 to £17.50. Set L £13 (2 courses) to £15 SERVICE: not inc CARDS: Access, Amex, Visa DETAILS: 70 seats. Private parties: 60 main room. Vegetarian meals. Children's helpings. Smart dress preferred. No pipes in dining-room. Wheelchair access. Music

Restaurateurs justifiably resent no-shows. If you quote a credit card number when booking, you may be liable for the restaurant's lost profit margin if you don't turn up. Always phone to cancel.

NEW MILTON Hampshire map 2

▲ *Chewton Glen, Marryat Restaurant*

Christchurch Road, New Milton BH25 6QS
TEL: (01425) 275341 FAX: (01425) 272310
from A35 follow signs to Walkford and Highcliffe, take second turning on left after Walkford down Chewton Farm road

COOKING 3
COST £33–£67

The Skans have gone to great lengths to provide just about every facility you can think of: gardens with a croquet lawn, indoor and outdoor tennis courts, ditto swimming-pools, a nine-hole golf course, gymnasium, treatment rooms and so on. The hotel is like a small Olympic village, with a restaurant attached for those with any strength left to eat. The house has consequently grown, the old red brick and green and white paint of the Captain Marryat era supplemented by newer bits. The setting is as restful as any, the welcome is warm, and service as good as you'll get. What Chewton Glen does as well as anywhere is to provide a complete and enveloping experience (the word 'package' is too vulgar to describe it) which works because all the details are carefully orchestrated.

Meals are a fixed price with generous choice, taken in the restaurant or in the light, airy conservatory with its billowing white-tented ceiling. Many of the ingredients are local – braised Hampshire hog is served on a bed of crushed potato – fish is a strength, seasonality is respected, and ostentatious flourishes are kept to a minimum. Many items are cooked simply (roasting, grilling and pan-frying apply equally to meats and fish) and perhaps given a jus, a flavoured butter or a gently flavoured sauce. The result is satisfyingly clear flavours. The hotel has a well- deserved worldwide reputation, and perhaps customers on that kind of circuit tend to favour a rather conservative style. An inspector wondered if the food might have backed away from a forceful identity of its own so as not to give offence. 'Polite food,' she called it, in no way disparaging the quality, merely attempting to convey the style. It is as comforting as the squishy sofas in the lounge, from a double-baked Emmental soufflé through grilled Dover sole to a hot chocolate fondant served with mint chocolate ice-cream.

Aristocratic claret and burgundy head up the wine list, and champagne is given star billing, but lesser regions of France, including Languedoc-Roussillon and Provence, get a look-in too. The New World figures prominently, half-bottles are a bit uneven, and despite many high prices (even some in Italy and Iberia) there are nearly 60 wines under £20. House Bordeaux red and New Zealand Chardonnay are £13 and £14.15 respectively. CELLARMAN'S CHOICE: Borro della Sala 1992, Antinori, £18.90; Volnay *premier cru* 'Les Chevrets' 1985, Dom. Jean Boillot, £40.65.

CHEF: Pierre Chevillard PROPRIETORS: Martin and Brigitte Skan OPEN: all week 12.30 to 2, 7 to 9.30 MEALS: Set L £18.50 (2 courses) to £23.50, Set D £39.50 SERVICE: not inc, card slips closed CARDS: Access, Amex, Diners, Switch, Visa DETAILS: 180 seats. 10 tables outside. Private parties: 70 and 120 private rooms. Car park. Vegetarian meals. No children under 7. Jacket and tie. No smoking in dining-room. Wheelchair access (also WC). Music ACCOMMODATION: 57 rooms, all with bath/shower. TV. Phone. B&B £185 (double room) to £375. Rooms for disabled. No children under 7. Afternoon teas. Garden. Swimming-pool (*The Which? Hotel Guide*)

NORTH CHEAM **Greater London** map 3

Partners Brasserie £

23 Stonecot Hill, North Cheam, nr Sutton SM3 9HB
TEL: 0181-644 7743 COOKING 1*
on A24, 1m SW of Morden (nr Woodstock pub) COST £18–£31

This is the cheaper, simpler version of Partners West Street in Dorking (see entry) but has charm enough of its own to win local converts. Set in an unprepossessing shopping arcade, it is attractively decorated and sharply lit, and the feel is 'informal without clatter or histrionics'. Chairs may look 'somewhat orthopaedic' but are none the less comfortable. Rebecca Jones became head chef at the end of 1994, and her menus happily plunder the known culinary world for inspiration. Most things seem to work. A dish of tagliatelle with field mushrooms and Parmesan has been impressive, the sauce a 'big fungal creamy concoction' which also contains olive oil, while seared tuna on a potato and black olive salad presents neatly charred fish and a well-seasoned salad. Equally sensitive fish cookery is evident in a thick chunk of salmon fillet roasted to retain 'the right amount of springiness' and in four fillets of red mullet on radicchio with a fresh basil dressing. More olive oil goes into the 'smoothest possible' mashed potato that accompanies lambs' liver and smoked bacon. 'Very crisp, short, buttery' pastry characterises a strawberry and clotted cream tart with feathered raspberry coulis, though bread-and-butter pudding has been described as 'a little bit solid'. Bread rolls and cappuccino contribute to people's enjoyment, as does 'effortless' service. A short, serviceable wine list keeps everything under £20, including champagne. House burgundy from Lupé-Cholet is £7.95.

CHEFS: Rebecca Jones and Claire Atkinson PROPRIETOR: Partners Restaurants plc OPEN: Tue to Fri L 12 to 2, Tue to Sat D 7 to 9.30 CLOSED: 1 week Christmas MEALS: alc (main courses £7 to £10). Set L and D £8.45 (2 courses) to £10.95 SERVICE: 10%, card slips closed CARDS: Access, Amex, Diners, Switch, Visa DETAILS: 30 seats. Private parties: 33 main room. Children's helpings. Wheelchair access (1 step). Music. Air-conditioned

NORTHLEACH **Gloucestershire** map 2

Old Woolhouse

Market Place, Northleach GL54 3EE COOKING 3
TEL: (01451) 860366 COST £50–£59

In the gastronomic Mecca that is Market Place, Northleach, you can feast in either English or French mode, depending on whether you choose Wickens (see entry, below) or the Old Woolhouse. Jacques and Jenny Astic's little restaurant declares that it is 'not a follower of fashion', and indeed a deep vein of classicism runs through much of the elegant cooking. The set-price menus impress for the conscientious quality of ingredients used, and an inspector's admiration for the combined 'subtlety and strength of the flavours' indicates that M. Astic certainly knows what to do with such ingredients.

Sauces, pastry-work and overall timing of dishes are all excellent. Rolled fillets of sole may be accompanied by a mound of 'intensely flavoured' mussels and sauced traditionally without being overwhelmed with white wine and cream. Similarly, a Burgundian sauce of red wine, button mushrooms and lardons with turbot showed 'amazing self-assurance'. Veal kidneys are briefly sauté, strewn with more of those exquisite little mushrooms, and the pan juices fired up with mustard. As this is French cooking, no side-plate of six vegetables is offered, just a slice of dauphinois potatoes and a salad. Apple tart was 'superbly light' but full of flavour, while a prune and almond tart was garnished with whole prunes whose stones had been replaced with cylinders of marzipan. The pastry in both was 'the most admirable' sweet shortcrust. Petits fours are equally 'delicious', but the fine French butter is let down by boring bread. When Astic is on song – as he mostly is – this is a jewel of a restaurant.

Once again, we have been unable to persuade the Astics to send in menus or wine list, but tales are told of a hand-written selection of champagnes, Burgundies and Bordeaux (nothing else) at prices to induce a hot flush. There are half-bottles, but no house wines.

CHEF: Jacques Astic PROPRIETORS: Jacques and Jenny Astic OPEN: Tue to Sat D only from 8.15; other times by arrangement CLOSED: 1 week Christmas MEALS: Set D £35 SERVICE: not inc DETAILS: 18 seats. Private parties: 18 main room. Children welcome. Smart dress preferred. No music

Wickens

Market Place, Northleach GL54 3EJ — COOKING 3
TEL: (01451) 860421 — COST £19–£31

Times have not been easy in the past few years for small restaurateurs off the beaten track, but Christopher and Joanna Wickens have managed to keep their heads while others might have panicked. Northleach exercises a powerful gastronomic pull: one reporter's 'ideal location for a quiet, escapist dinner'. Notwithstanding that, the cooking remains firmly rooted in reality, somewhat simplified of late, in the opinion of a visitor, who thought the trend beneficial.

Fixed-price menus are the order of the day, supplemented at lunch-time by an open sandwiches on thick granary bread. Soups are imaginative amalgams along the lines of cannellini beans and apple infused with thyme, while now-traditional modern British themes are given a gentle twist, as in black pudding with bacon and apple with a raspberry vinaigrette – 'an unusual but effective combination'. Salmon fish-cakes, wrote a Londoner, 'were the finest I've ever had, with chunks of fresh rosy salmon and waxy potatoes, held together without "glue", just a thin coating of crunchy breadcrumbs, and baked rather than fried'. Vegetarian main courses aim for lightness and flavour, as in lentil rissoles seasoned with cumin accompanied by raita. The most robust carnivorous appetites are catered for with slowly braised pigeon in Yorkshire brown ale with flageolet beans and spinach.

Meals usually end on a lighter note, whether it be strawberry and cream cheese tartlet in almond pastry, or gooseberry jelly with elderflower syrup, impeccably seasonal desserts enjoyed in scorching July. Chocolate mint slices are offered with cafetière coffee. The unobtrusive front-of-house approach is generally appreciated, though the atmosphere can sometimes seem a little 'hushed'. The largely New World wine list sets a standard. Where European wines do pop up, there is a feeling that they have earned their place on it, instead of being included in bland homage to tradition. Ch. Tahbilk Marsanne and Brokenwood Cabernet Sauvignon are just a couple of good Australians, and there is a patriotic listing of 14 of the best English wines. The house selections – from England, Chile, Spain and France – are £8.75 and £9.75. CELLARMAN'S CHOICE: Pilton Manor Medium Dry 1992, Somerset, £11.75; Three Choirs Estate Reserve Red 1992, Gloucestershire, £9.95.

CHEFS/PROPRIETORS: Christopher and Joanna Wickens OPEN: Tue to Sat 12.30 to 1.30, 7.20 to 9; L Nov to Apr by arrangement MEALS: Set L £9.95 (2 courses), Set D £19.50 SERVICE: net prices, card slips closed CARDS: Access, Amex, Delta, Switch, Visa DETAILS: 36 seats. Private parties: 22 main room. Vegetarian meals. Children's helpings. No smoking in dining-room. Music

NORWICH Norfolk map 6

Adard's

79 Upper St Giles Street, Norwich NR2 1AB COOKING 4
TEL: (01603) 633522 COST £25–£53

Behind the dark green façade, up the hill from the market square towards the inner ring road, works one of East Anglia's most talented chefs. The street is a cul-de-sac, the building eighteenth-century and Grade II-listed, the feel cool, relaxed, unhurried, with 'a nice contented hum'. Just about everything is green, apart from the modern paintings. Lighting is discreet, but you can see what you are eating. As like as not, David Adlard will put in an amiable appearance and wander about a bit. The low snoot factor is crucial. One 10-year-old, used to eating out, claims it is her favourite restaurant in England, 'because nobody made her feel like a child or talked down to her'. Naturally, she keeps wanting to go back. 'Things don't change much here,' reported an older diner, and there is little reason to alter things when they work so well.

The commitment to fresh food and locally grown produce – no strawberries or asparagus out of season, for example – comes on top of an accomplished style with its roots in the classic French repertoire. But the food is not staid. There is a liveliness about pressed lamb terrine with mint dressing served with chargrilled focaccia, or oxtail rissole, or a mille-feuille of Jerusalem artichokes and onion marmalade with a basil and balsamic vinaigrette. There may even be a jokiness about fillet of beef with onion rings and chips, but the execution is serious enough: according to a senior inspector, it was 'one of the finest fillets I have eaten – large, pink and soft' and accompanied by 'four light, dry, deep-fried onion rings, six little chips, and a rich red wine sauce'. What also impressed at this meal was a first course of a slice of perfectly cooked foie gras with nutty Puy lentils in a rich duck sauce cut with sherry vinegar, and a main course of pink duck breast with a pastry parcel of minced leg that came with 'Brussels sprout-sized footballs of dense and beautifully cooked spinach'. Anyone who doubts the trouble the kitchen takes might care to sample the assiette of chocolate – white mousse flavoured with cardamom, dark mousse, a hot chocolate pudding with sauce, a tart, and ice-cream – served in 'tiny portions, all with distinct and wonderful flavours'.

Service is cheery, fairly knowledgeable, but not necessarily quick, and at this level the synchronised appearance of dishes at a table should be standard procedure. The lack of ceremony is commendable when it comes to wine. 'There is no wine service. The bottle is on your table.' And what bottles: immense choice, very high quality, especially under £30, and with a fair selection under £20, plentiful halves and short, helpful notes. House wines are £9. CELLARMAN'S CHOICE: Mâcon-Clessé Quintaine 1992, Dom. Guillemot-Michel, £17.50; Rosemount Estate Shiraz 1992, Hunter Valley, New South Wales, £16.

CHEFS: David Adlard and Aiden Byrne PROPRIETORS: David and Mary Adlard OPEN: Tue to Sat L 12.30 to 1.45, Mon to Sat D 7.30 to 10.30 MEALS: Set L £13.50 (2 courses) to £16.50, Set D £27.50 (2 courses) to £34 SERVICE: not inc, card slips closed CARDS: Access, Amex, Switch, Visa DETAILS: 40 seats. Private parties: 40 main room. Children's helpings. No smoking until after main course. No music

Brasted's

8–10 St Andrews Hill, Norwich NR2 1AD
TEL: (01603) 625949 FAX: (01603) 766445

COOKING 1
COST £26–£47

Although Brasted's boasts a central Norwich location, the little cobbled lane in which it stands can be difficult to find. Dark green woodwork, prints and watercolours greet the persevering pathfinder, as does the jovial hail-fellow of John Brasted. Adrian Clarke's cooking may be thought to have a 'reasonably dated' feel, but there are many who welcome that while fashion rages elsewhere. Five filo purses filled with cheese, on an 'addictively sweet' apple and thyme jelly, or smoked haddock baked in a savoury custard, are alternative beginnings. Native steak and kidney pudding, and loin of wild boar with an apple purée, take their place beside Gallic lobster américaine, cassoulet and braised lamb shank with garlic and lentils. Accurate cooking of medallions of beef fillet on creamed spinach impressed an inspector. Poached pear and mascarpone is a good way to finish, with a sweet biscuit filling that 'gave something to bite on'. Vegetarian dishes may not be so hot, but the cafetière coffee is 'decent'. A confidently chosen wine list centres on classic burgundies and clarets, but has sound choices from all over. House wines start at £9.75.

CHEF: Adrian Clarke PROPRIETOR: John Brasted OPEN: Mon to Fri L 12 to 2, Mon to Sat D 7 to 9.30 CLOSED: bank hols MEALS: alc (main courses £9 to £18) SERVICE: not inc CARDS: Access, Amex, Delta, Diners, Switch, Visa DETAILS: 24 seats. Private parties: 24 main room. Vegetarian meals. Children's helpings. Smart dress preferred. Music

▲ *By Appointment*

27–29 St Georges Street, Norwich NR3 1AB
TEL: (01603) 630730

COOKING 1
COST £26–£43

This former merchant's house dates from the fifteenth century, and in the silk-swagged pink sitting-room the silver and glass antiques and the elaborately written blackboard menu fight for maximum impact. When a place has a solid local following, outsiders can find the programme bemusing at first; here the menu is recited to each table in turn: guaranteeing in this small space that you will hear it several times of an evening. Timothy Brown makes his own breads, ice-creams and chocolates, and marinates and smokes fish and meat on the premises. The dominant style is florid: filo baskets of smoked duckling with a gooseberry vinaigrette; baked fillets of Dover sole stuffed with prawns and red sea bream mousse and sauced with seafood and champagne. An inspection meal found too many dishes striving for complexity, thus losing out on flavour. Higher praise has gone to simpler family-style dishes such as steak, kidney and oyster pudding, and spotted dick and custard. Wines, arranged by price, offer a conscientiously broad international selection to suit most pockets. Prices open at £8.35.

CHEF: Timothy Brown PROPRIETORS: Timothy Brown and Robert Culyer OPEN: Tue to Sat D only 7 to 9.30 MEALS: alc (main courses £10.50 to £15) SERVICE: not inc, card slips closed CARDS: Access, Delta, Switch, Visa DETAILS: 40 seats. Private parties: 36 main room, 5 to 36 private rooms. Car park. Vegetarian meals. No children under 12. Smart dress preferred. No smoking in dining-room. Wheelchair access (also WC). Music ACCOMMODATION: 3 rooms, all with bath/shower. TV. D,B&B £88 to £115. Deposit 10%. No children under 12

Marco's

17 Pottergate, Norwich NR2 1DS — COOKING 1*
TEL: (01603) 624044 — COST £23–£46

From the outside it looks like a converted pub. Once inside the pillared doorway all is spruce, well kept, modern and as clean as a new pin, with expensive-looking sofas and a primrose-yellow dining-room. Marco Vessalio has celebrated 25 years at these premises, nearly all of them in the *Guide,* and has obviously found a style that consistently pleases. The food is Italianate, combining gnocchi or bresaola of boar with British saddle of venison in red wine sauce.

Pasta (like bread) is made in-house and ranges from cannelloni with spinach and ricotta to a sea bass ravioli. Fish is ever-present: grilled sardine on the good-value fixed-price lunch menu, or a mixture of halibut, sea bass, monkfish and king prawns in a sauce of tomato, garlic, herbs and white wine from the *carte.* The cooking is simple but effective, in the best Italian tradition, and the core repertoire remains more or less constant, right down to the bread-and-butter pudding Italian-style, and classic zabaglione. Espresso coffee is a fine way to finish. Wines do justice to the Italian regions, listing top producers from Puiatti, Pieropan and Tedeschi in the north to Mastroberardino and De Bartoli in the south. House Settesoli is £9.50.

CHEF/PROPRIETOR: Marco Vessalio OPEN: Tue to Sat 12 to 2, 7 to 10 CLOSED: 3 weeks Sept to Oct MEALS: alc (main courses £14.50 to £16.50). Set L £14 SERVICE: not inc, card slips closed CARDS: Access, Amex, Diners, Switch, Visa DETAILS: 22 seats. Private parties: 12 main room. Vegetarian meals. Children's helpings. Smart dress preferred. No smoking in dining-room. Wheelchair access. No music

St Benedicts

9 St Benedicts Street, Norwich NR2 4PE — COOKING 1
TEL/FAX: (01603) 765377 — COST £21–£35

The layout is bistro through and through, with bare pews for the larger tables and simple chairs for the rest. Dark blue is the prevailing colour scheme, unless you count the white/beige paintwork on the walls. Trappings and paraphernalia are kept to a minimum. Lunch is a particularly good bet, 'especially if you like venison sausages', notes a regular visitor. Nigel Raffles makes them himself, and customers can sample the results with 'splendid' chips or mash. He also invests in east coast fish for a modern-sounding menu that could include salmon with Chinese five-spices and home-made noodles, or chargrilled fillets of sea bream with fondant fennel and a champagne sauce. Slow-cooked crispy duck is a permanent fixture, as is iced praline parfait. Vegetables, which are charged extra, include such things as a gratin of turnips with Gruyère, and leeks in sweet-and-sour sauce. Meals are rounded off with unlimited cups of coffee. The wine list has modest mark-ups and provides plenty of dependable drinking, especially from Spain and Australia. House wine is £7.25.

CHEF: Nigel Raffles PROPRIETORS: Nigel and Jayne Raffles OPEN: Tue to Sat 12 to 2, 7 to 10 (10.30 Fri and Sat) CLOSED: 25 to 31 Dec MEALS: alc (main courses £7 to £11) SERVICE: not inc CARDS: Access, Amex, Delta, Diners, Switch, Visa DETAILS: 42 seats. Private parties: 42 main room, 24 private room. Vegetarian meals. Children welcome. No cigars/pipes in dining-room. Wheelchair access. No music

NOTTINGHAM Nottinghamshire map 5

Saagar

473 Mansfield Road, Sherwood,
Nottingham NG5 2DR
TEL: 0115-962 2014 and 969 2860 COOKING 1
on A60, 3m from city centre COST £13–£37

'More Indian restaurants should be like this one,' commented one couple after a visit to this long-serving establishment in the Nottingham suburb of Sherwood. The fact that it has had the same owner and chef since it opened in 1984 has obviously helped to maintain consistency through the years. The menu trawls its way through Punjabi tandooris, Kashmiri kormas, Hyderabadi chicken and a few South Indian ideas, including several versions of kaallan (meat or prawns cooked with mangoes, yoghurt and coconut). Reporters have given the thumbs-up to many dishes, including prawn poori, 'gorgeously flavoured' rogan josh, balti chicken and dhansaks. King prawns – 'truly king-size' – are the kitchen's speciality. Portions are 'hugely generous'. Prices of most main courses might seem on the high side, but rice, poppadum and chutney are included. Coffee is 'real and tasty', while alcoholic refreshment comes in the form of beer or wine from the short, everyday list. House wine is £8.50 a litre.

CHEF: Amjaid Habib PROPRIETOR: Mohammed Khizer OPEN: all week 12 to 2.15, 6 to 12.15 CLOSED: 25 Dec MEALS: alc (main courses £8 to £11). Set L £7, Set D £28 SERVICE: not inc CARDS: Access, Amex, Delta, Switch, Visa DETAILS: 75 seats. Private parties: 45 main room, 45 private room. Car park. Vegetarian meals. No children under 7 after 7pm. Smart dress preferred. No pipes in dining-room. No music. Air-conditioned

The Guide is totally independent, accepts no free hospitality, and survives on the number of copies sold each year.

London round-ups listing additional restaurants that may be worth a visit can be found after the main London section.

Sonny's

3 Carlton Street, Hockley, Nottingham NG1 1NL — COOKING 1
TEL: 0115-947 3041 FAX: 0115-950 7776 — COST £17–£40

From a long white room with deep windows, Sonny's commands diverting views of one of Nottingham's more fashionable precincts, a pedestrianised area of chic shops. The interior is split-level: a raised area offering a 'café menu' is distinguished from the rest by its undressed tables. There you may eat bang-bang chicken or goats'-cheese focaccia with onion marmalade. Graeme Whatson cooks in contemporary vein, and the style is similar to the London Sonny's in Barnes (see entry). A characteristic dish that may be had as starter or main is sweet potato gnocchi with roasted cherry tomatoes, basil and smoked mozzarella. One satisfied customer was impressed by an 'interesting combination' of monkfish with mildly chillied haricot beans. Other stimulating ideas have been blackened salmon with coriander and spring onion butter, leek and cheese sausage with fennel dauphinoise, and loin of lamb with couscous and rosemary aïoli. The 'uniformly good' desserts at a March dinner included chocolate polenta cake; in summer there may be gooseberry crème fraîche tart with elderflower ice-cream, and hot peppered strawberries with a sorbet. Exhaustive notes flesh out the carefully chosen wine list, although the very finest wines are presented as a prefatory jumble, unordered as to region or price. The price average may feel a trifle higher than the context dictates, but house wines, a California white and a red from Ardèche, are both £8.95.

CHEF: Graeme Watson PROPRIETOR: Rebecca Mascarenhas OPEN: all week 12 to 12.30, 7 to 10.30 (11 Fri and Sat, 10 Sun) CLOSED: 25 and 26 Dec, 1 Jan, Easter MEALS: alc (main courses £8 to £13). Set L Sun £10.95 SERVICE: not inc; 10% for parties of 6 or more CARDS: Access, Amex, Visa DETAILS: 90 seats. Private parties: 90 main room. Vegetarian meals. Children welcome. Smart dress preferred. No cigars/pipes in dining-room. Music

---

OLD BURGHCLERE Hampshire — map 2

Dew Pond

Old Burghclere RG15 9LH
TEL: (01635) 278408 — COOKING 2*
off old A34, 3m W of Kingsclere — COST £22–£48

Old Burghclere was established in Saxon times, but the pair of drovers' cottages that this restaurant occupies date from the sixteenth century. All the rooms are tiny, with a smartly decorated dining-room that retains a pleasingly domestic feel. Staff do their job 'quietly and unobtrusively'.

Keith Marshall's cooking has taken on an air of refinement over the past six years. Menus, fixed-price for three courses, follow a fairly classical theme. Twice-baked Gruyère soufflé, seared scallops with coconut and lemon grass, and honey-roast quail with bacon and pine-nuts indicate the range of techniques on offer. An aficionado of Mediterranean fish soup was demonstrative in her approval of the Marshall rendition: 'very smooth, wonderfully rich and full of flavour', sprinkled with croûtons and with a blob of good aïoli. 'Superb' meat dishes have included a pair of maturely flavoured fillet steaks on garlicky rösti with plenty of wild mushrooms and a good madeira sauce. Toffee pudding with fine vanilla ice-cream is impressive, or there might be an elaborately constructed terrine of dark and white chocolates and hazelnut biscuit. Simple, well-made petits fours come with cafetière coffee that has been thought 'rather too weak for after dinner'. An attractive, well-priced wine list that offers an uncommonly generous choice of half-bottles is led by 11 house wines starting at £11.

CHEF: Keith Marshall PROPRIETORS: Keith and Julie Marshall OPEN: Sun L 12 to 2, Tue to Sat D 7 to 9.30 CLOSED: 2 weeks Jan, 2 weeks Aug MEALS: Set L £14.50, Set D £23 SERVICE: not inc CARDS: Access, Delta, Switch, Visa DETAILS: 44 seats. Private parties: 32 main room, 20 and 32 private rooms. Car park. Vegetarian meals. No children under 5. Smart dress preferred. No smoking in dining-room. Wheelchair access (also WC). No music

OSWESTRY Shropshire map 7

Sebastian

45 Willow Street, Oswestry SY11 1AQ — COOKING 2
TEL: (01691) 655444 FAX: (01691) 653452 — COST £15–£45

The atmosphere of an authentic French bistro has been painstakingly re-created in the improbable setting of a Shropshire market town. Although the exterior is English enough in its half-timbered way, inside is a monument to a timeless Gallic ideal: champagne advertising posters decorate the walls, flowers in Perrier bottles are on the tables and French pop music plays without cease. As the *Guide* went to press, plans were afoot to enlarge the restaurant and to introduce accommodation.

The large *carte* is supplemented by a set-price menu of the month, and the seriously determined (in a party of at least six) may opt for Le Grand Bouffe – six courses at £17.95. The evidence is that Mark Fisher is good at what he does. French onion soup is absolutely correct: a deep, steaming pot of satisfying stock filled with sweetly soft sliced onion and two cheese croûtons. Main-course duck magret, in a sauce of green peppers and foie gras, has been declared 'a huge success, the meat of superb quality and beautifully cooked'. There is good fish, which the proprietors collect personally from the North Wales coast. Classic desserts might include strawberry vacherin and crêpes suzette. This is good-value food of considerable panache. The wine list is predominantly French, with an adequate selection, but space is found for an Argentinian white among the house recommendations, and there's a page of New World wines. House French is £8.95.

CHEF: Mark Sebastian Fisher PROPRIETORS: Mark Sebastian and Michelle Fisher OPEN: Wed to Fri L 12 to 2, Tue to Sat D 6.30 to 10.30 CLOSED: 25 and 26 Dec, 1 Jan MEALS: alc (main courses £3.50 to £19). Set D £14.95 to £17.95 (latter needs booking 24 hours in advance and is for a minimum of 6) SERVICE: not inc, card slips closed CARDS: Access, Amex, Delta, Switch, Visa DETAILS: 40 seats. 4 tables outside. Private parties: 20 main room, 6 private room. Vegetarian meals. Children welcome. Smart dress preferred. Wheelchair access. Music

Not inc *in the details at the end of an entry indicates that no service charge is made and any tipping is at the discretion of the customer.*

OXFORD Oxfordshire map 2

▲ *Al-Shami* £

25 Walton Crescent, Oxford OX1 2JG COOKING 1
TEL: (01865) 310066 FAX: (01865) 311241 COST £20–£36

'Al-Shami is my favourite Oxford ethnic restaurant,' observes a regular visitor. Al-Shami (the name apparently means 'from Damascus') is on the corner of a residential street within walking distance of the city centre. Inside, it is compact, with minimalist décor, tiled floors and large mirrors on bare brick walls. All-day opening and authentic, excellent-value food mean that it can get packed. The cover charge pays for olives, chillies and a huge bowl of vegetables that look as if they are dewy fresh from the garden. Despite the geographical implications of the restaurant's name, the cooking is described as Lebanese. You could eat well without straying from the long list of hot and cold meze: one reporter plumped for a quartet of cold appetisers, including 'foul moukala' (broad beans with citrus juice), moutabel, stuffed vine leaves, and loubieh bzeit (French beans cooked in olive oil with tomatoes, onion and garlic). Grills and kebabs dominate the main courses, although there are a few possibilities for fish-lovers and vegetarians. Shish taouq (boneless marinated chicken) has been particularly successful. Accompanying pitta bread and rice are as they should be, and the Lebanese desserts are authentically sweet. Coffee is strong, mint tea refreshing. If you fancy wine, the rudimentary list includes a good run of lush, spicy Ch. Musar of different vintages. House wine is £9.99.

CHEF/PROPRIETOR: Mimo Mahfouz OPEN: all week noon to 11.50pm MEALS: alc (main courses £6 to £12). Set L and D £15. Cover £1 SERVICE: not inc; 10% on parties of 6 or more CARDS: none DETAILS: 80 seats. Private parties: 50 main room, 30 private room. Vegetarian meals. Children welcome. Smart dress preferred. Wheelchair access (also WC). Music ACCOMMODATION: 12 rooms, all with bath/shower. TV. Phone. B&B £30 to £45

▲ *Bath Place Hotel* 🍷 £*

4–5 Bath Place, Oxford OX1 3SU COOKING 2*
TEL: (01865) 791812 FAX: (01865) 791834 COST £28–£72

A cobbled path opposite the Holywell Music Rooms leads to the bijou cluster of seventeenth-century weavers' cottages which the Fawsitts converted to a hotel and restaurant in 1989. 'I had digs here in 1942,' writes an old-timer, 'and they were among the best in Oxford at the time, at a rather dear £2 12s 6d a week, bed and breakfast.' The bits of exposed stone in the dining-room go back further still – they are part of the original city wall – and the room itself allows for a happy blend of conviviality and privacy.

There must be a lot going on in the kitchen, judging by the number of menus: a seasonal three-course lunch, a five-course dinner, with a *carte* at both, plus supplementary daily dishes, plus the 'menu surprise' of eight courses, not to mention the vegetarian menu. Set dinners are good value 'provided you want a five-course meal'. The style is along 'modern European' lines, and cosmopolitan Oxford is perfectly at home with confit of belly-pork (in a salad of green beans), gâteau of lambs' sweetbreads and provençale vegetables, or a whole English pigeon on a bed of shredded Savoy cabbage.

There can also be a lot going on in the dishes themselves, which means they may not always live up to expectation, but sauces are generally good, making use of truffle oil, the inevitable sun-dried tomatoes, and a range of vinegars from sherry through raspberry to balsamic. Reductions are just right, not overdone, and game appears in season. A trio of crèmes brûlées (vanilla, orange and cardamom) or a gratin of fruits in zabaglione are the sort of desserts to expect. Wines are wide-ranging, carefully selected and fairly priced, with brief but apposite annotation. Four house wines are £10.75. CELLARMAN'S CHOICE: Menetou-Salon 1994, Clément, £14.50; Cape Charlotte Shiraz 1992, Barossa Valley, S. Australia.

CHEF: Jeremy Blake O'Connor PROPRIETORS: the Fawsitt family OPEN: all week 12 to 2 (12.30 to 2.30 Sun), 7 to 10 (10.30 Fri and Sat, 9.30 D Sun) MEALS: alc (main courses £17.50 to £24.50). Set L Mon to Sat £14.50 (2 courses) and £17.50, Set L Sun £21.50, Set D £17.50 (Sun and Mon only) to £49.50 SERVICE: not inc CARDS: Access, Amex, Delta, Visa DETAILS: 32 seats. 4 tables outside. Private parties: 40 main room. Vegetarian meals. Children's helpings. Smart dress preferred. No smoking in dining-room. Music. Air-conditioned ACCOMMODATION: 10 rooms, all with bath/shower. TV. Phone. B&B £70 to £100. Deposit: £25. Children welcome. Baby facilities. Pets by arrangement

Cherwell Boathouse

Bardwell Road, Oxford OX2 6SR — COOKING 2
TEL/FAX: (01865) 52746 — COST £22–£27

The Boathouse is well worth punting to for those who happen to be drifting down river, or just wandering through this agreeably tranquil part of Oxford. Diverting watercolours and discarded boaters adorn the walls. Although, notes one visitor, there are 'no intimations of luxury whatsoever, only a snob could fail to find eating here a pleasurable experience'. More outdoor tables have been provided to enhance that pleasure.

Fixed-price menus, sensibly limited to three choices in the first two courses, are the drill at both lunch-time and in the evening. The aim of the cooking is to find exciting combinations while avoiding over-elaboration. First courses usually include a soup, such as red pepper with chives, or mussel with saffron and garlic, and a fish or game terrine. Main courses mix old Eastern classics, such as cod plaki and imam bayaldi, with modern British ideas like mackerel fillets in oatmeal with rhubarb sauce. Sharp accompaniments bring dishes to life: sweet mustard mayonnaise with seafood terrine, or shallots and plums with loin of pork, for example. Maple spice cake with maple cream will satisfy the sweetest tooth at dessert, and there is usually a steamed pudding and an ice-cream. Incidentals, particularly the 'delicious and wholesome' pumpkin-seed bread, keep the Boathouse watertight. 'The Australian-accented waiters are amiable and caring.'

Any wine list put together by wine merchants Morris and Verdin is going to have plenty going for it. The selections are impeccable, from Ostertag's Alsace wines and Rion's burgundies to the Selvapiana Chianti and Qupé California Syrah. No matter that the list is stronger in some areas than in others; what it offers is illustrious and good, and the prices are so generous that choosing will be hard indeed. House wines from the South of France are £6.50.

CHEF: Gerard Crowley PROPRIETOR: Anthony Verdin OPEN: Wed to Sun L 12 to 2, Tue to Sat D 6 to 10.30 CLOSED: 24 to 30 Dec MEALS: alc L (main courses £9). Set L £10.50 (2 courses) to £16.50, Set D £17.50 SERVICE: not inc CARDS: Access, Amex, Delta, Diners, Switch, Visa DETAILS: 60 seats. 5 tables outside. Private parties: 50 main room, 120 private room. Car park. Vegetarian meals. Children's helpings. No smoking before 2 L, 10 D. Wheelchair access (1 step; also WC). No music

15 North Parade

15 North Parade, Oxford OX2 6LX — COOKING 1*
TEL: (01865) 513773 — COST £21–£42

Georgina Wood's North Oxford restaurant has changed its tone quite a bit in the last few years. Where once it may have seemed a little shy and retiring, it now strides out in bold modern attire, a high-tech open kitchen the latest evidence of contemporaneity. Sean Wood's cooking has also helped to keep it in the spotlight, with some vivid flavours drawn from southern Spain and North Africa, perhaps via North America. Boston crab-cakes with mayo, stewed Andalusian squid, and tagine of rabbit, honey, almonds and dates with a timbale of three rices, sit in comfortable cohabitation. Moroccan rice-pudding with tangerine confit, and peach tarte Tatin make a change from the usual sticky toffee and brûlée. Those bored with coffee may opt for mint tea with crystallised pecans. A short but fine, ultra-modern wine list is arranged stylistically in best wine writer-speak (the 'complex balsamic and earthy aroma' section lists no fewer than eight bottles). Prices are near the top end. House recommendations start at £9.75.

CHEF: Sean Wood PROPRIETOR: Georgina Wood OPEN: Tue to Sun L 12 to 2, Tue to Sat D 7 to 10.30 CLOSED: last 2 weeks Aug MEALS: alc (main courses £9 to £12). Set L Mon to Sat £10 (2 courses) to £12, Set L Sun £13.75, Set D £15 SERVICE: not inc CARDS: Access, Delta, Switch, Visa DETAILS: 90 seats. 15 tables outside. Private parties: 70 main room, 30 private room. Vegetarian meals. Children's helpings. Smart dress preferred. No smoking in 1 dining-room. Wheelchair access (1 step). Music. Air-conditioned

Gee's

NEW ENTRY

61A Banbury Road, Oxford OX2 6PE — COOKING 1
TEL: (01865) 53540 FAX: (01865) 310308 — COST £22–£39

A large conservatory built at the end of the last century, Gee's was for 80 years a greengrocer's and florist's shop. Converted to a restaurant in the mid-1980s it is now in the same ownership as the Old Parsonage Hotel (see entry, below) just up the road. With its scrolled wrought iron and potted plants, it makes a 'delightful' venue in an area of Oxford 'where town and gown rub shoulders'.

Graham Corbett cooks an up-to-the-minute menu heavily influenced by the Mediterranean doings of recent times, from 'robustly flavoured' leek and potato soup with croûtons and mozzarella, through a single, sliced scallop on a heap of buttery leeks, to chargrilled salmon steak, served with a pile of mussels, spinach, and a 'clumsy' hollandaise. Individual tarte Tatin is authentic and served with thick cream, and a pair of regulars insist that 'the puddings are quite magnificent'. Service is slick. The wine list fits nicely with the air of cool modernity of the whole operation, its prices manageable and the choices intelligent. Touraine Sauvignon from Marcadet, Riesling Halbtrocken from Matuschka-Greiffenclau and Jean-Luc Colombo's Côtes du Roussillon will stimulate the most demanding of palates. Prices open at £9.50.

CHEF: Graham Corbett PROPRIETOR: Jeremy Mogford OPEN: all week 12 to 2.30, 6 to 11 MEALS: alc (main courses £7.50 to £13). Set L Mon to Sat £11.50 (2 courses) SERVICE: not inc; 10% on parties of 5 or more CARDS: Access, Delta, Switch, Visa DETAILS: 90 seats. Private parties: 90 main room. Vegetarian meals. Children welcome. Music. Air-conditioned

▲ *Old Parsonage Hotel, Parsonage Bar*

1 Banbury Road, Oxford OX2 6NN COOKING 1
TEL: (01865) 310210 FAX: (01865) 311262 COST £27–£50

The seventeenth-century building, at the top end of St Giles north of the city, is embroidered with plants and creepers. Enter through a pleasant courtyard into the bar – more of a lounge really – with dark polished tables, comfortable chairs and squashy sofas. It feels like a country house in town, all peace and civilised seclusion, although it can get packed too. The menu is a short, modern mix of up-market pub grub and bistro fare, based on chargrilling of steak, chicken and fish, on fishy things with mayonnaise, and on pasta.

At one meal fresh flavours and light cooking characterised a warm salad of monkfish, scallops and prawns with a pungent oily dressing on a pile of leaves, while chargrilled brochette of lamb produced two skewers of good meat, with a noticeable hint of marinating, on a bed of mint-and-lemon couscous. Chocolate tart with vanilla sauce, or treacle pudding with butterscotch sauce may follow, though don't dismiss the passion-fruit sorbet: three smooth, fruity blobs of 'just the right texture and temperature' for one reporter. Decent, fashionable breads are offered freely and replenished, though service has been slow at times. Wines are well suited to the job in hand: a good range of youthful fruity flavours packed into a 50-strong list with a handful of halves and eight wines by the glass from £2.85.

CHEF: Alison Watkins PROPRIETOR: Jeremy Mogford OPEN: all week 12 to 3, 6 to 11 CLOSED: 25 and 26 Dec MEALS: alc (main courses £9.50 to £17) SERVICE: not inc, card slips closed CARDS: Access, Amex, Diners, Switch, Visa DETAILS: 37 seats. 8 tables outside. Car park. Vegetarian meals. Children welcome. Smart dress preferred. No cigars/pipes in dining-room. Wheelchair access. Music. Air-conditioned ACCOMMODATION: 30 rooms, all with bath/shower. TV. Phone. B&B £110 to £190. Children welcome. Pets by arrangement. Afternoon teas. Garden (*The Which? Hotel Guide*)

Restaurant Elizabeth 🍷

82 St Aldate's, Oxford OX1 1RA COOKING 1
TEL: (01865) 242230 COST £22–£44

Down a little alleyway opposite Christ Church, the Elizabeth occupies the upper storey of a house next to the shop that Lewis Carroll featured in *Through the Looking Glass*. Nothing much changes from year to year, which is precisely what its supporters appreciate. Salvador Rodriguez cooks the sort of French haute cuisine that Escoffier would have recognised, since many of the dishes were his.

Quenelles de saumon sauce Nantua sits alongside snails, chicken liver pâté, and avocado prawns with intriguing-sounding Alabama sauce among the starters, while main courses bring on chateaubriand, Stroganov and canard à l'orange. One report particularly commends the 'superb quality' of the fillet of beef, which, was cooked 'precisely as requested'. Crème brûlée – 'still an Elizabeth classic after 30 years' – and 'sharp, creamy' raspberry sorbet are recommended puddings. Coffee is heated at the table in a lovely old Cona contraption that makes for a diverting ritual.

The wine list is as classic as the food. It deserves an award for its formidably exhaustive showing of French stars, including a fine selection of Sauternes, and for an uncommonly good run of red Riojas. The top breeding of many of the bottles pushes up the prices, but there is an acceptable degree of choice below £20. House French is £8.25. CELLARMAN'S CHOICE: Mâcon Lugny 'Les Genièvres' 1992, Latour, £15.70; Rioja, Imperial Reserva 1986, £20.35.

CHEF: Salvador Rodriguez PROPRIETOR: Antonio Lopez OPEN: Tue to Sun 12.30 to 2.30, 6.30 to 11 (7 to 10.30 Sun) CLOSED: 24 to 30 Dec, Good Fri MEALS: alc (main courses £13.50 to £18). Set L £15. Cover £1. Minimum £12.50 SERVICE: net prices CARDS: Access, Amex, Diners, Visa DETAILS: 40 seats. Private parties: 40 main room, 20 and 40 private rooms. Vegetarian meals. Children's helpings. Smart dress preferred. No music. Air-conditioned

Whites

16 Turl Street, Oxford OX1 3DH — COOKING 2
TEL: (01865) 793396 FAX: (01865) 200303 — COST £30–£58

A more scholastic location would be difficult to find, even in Oxford. Whites is next to Jesus, in the temporal rather than spiritual sense, and is a wine merchant as well as a restaurant, so drinking is taken seriously, to the extent of a selected glass of wine being offered with each of the courses on the two set-price dinner menus. Some inventive cooking is going on here, from duck rillettes with a crunchy coriander-flavoured muffin, to a smoked salmon parcel containing 'mild and creamy' Jerusalem artichoke purée. A main-course fillet of brill, the portion seemingly geared to half-starved students, comes plainly baked and 'glamorised' by a garnish of vegetable julienne and rösti, while best end of lamb is marinated in honey and thyme, stuffed with almonds and spinach and sauced with mustard. The execution of most things shows skill. Save some appetite for desserts, which tend to the richness of baked vanilla cheesecake, and caramel mousse with pear and butterscotch sauce.

Wines are as fine as they should be from a specialist. France is most conspicuous, supplemented by a short, productive canter into the southern hemisphere. Prices are near the top, but the quality is very sound. House wines from the Vallée de l'Aude are £9.50.

CHEFS: Christopher Lennox-Bland, Bertrand Fachaux and David Owens PROPRIETOR: Whites Restaurant (Oxford) Ltd OPEN: all week 12.30 to 2, 6.30 to 10 CLOSED: 1 week Christmas; Sun D in summer MEALS: alc D (main courses £12 to £18). Set L Mon to Sat £12.95 (2 courses), Set L Sun £15.95, Set D £29.50 to £38.50 (inc wine) SERVICE: not inc CARDS: Access, Amex, Delta, Diners, Switch, Visa DETAILS: 45 seats. Private parties: 40 main room. Vegetarian meals. Children's helpings. Smart dress preferred. No smoking in 1 dining-room. Wheelchair access. Music

PADSTOW Cornwall map 1

Bistro Margot Thomas

NEW ENTRY

11 Duke Street, Padstow PL28 8BE COOKING 1*
TEL: (01841) 533441 COST £25–£30

In this unpretentious single-room bistro serving a fixed-price blackboard menu, Victorian *objets* and sepia photographs are the chosen adornments, and the free-floating culinary style is in keeping with the times. Fried halloumi and mountain ham might start you off in style – and be succeeded by a goulash of monkfish and hake, or boeuf en daube. A starter of Thai prawn tartlets is three 'crisp little pastry cases, the shellfish redolent of subtle spices and lemon grass'. Crab-cakes fried to order have a generous ratio of crabmeat, and roast poussin with a stuffing of coriander and feta comes with cubed potatoes roasted with garlic to lend weight to the impact. Desserts look familiar enough and are well rendered: a slice of lemon tart 'full of lemon zest in a lovely sweet crisp pastry', for instance, or a bread-and-butter pudding with a passion-fruit coulis. Mike Meredith is a practised host who heaves to with a will and is good at making friends. The short, low-priced wine list is pretty basic and could do with a few more whites. House Italian is £7.95.

CHEFS: Elaine Meredith and Alexander Dudfield PROPRIETORS: Mike and Elaine Meredith OPEN: Tue to Sat D only 7 to 9.30 CLOSED: Tue and Wed in winter, Jan to Feb MEALS: Set D £17.50 SERVICE: not inc, card slips closed CARDS: Access, Visa DETAILS: 32 seats. Children's helpings. Smart dress preferred. No smoking in dining-room. Music

▲ *St Petroc's*

4 New Street, Padstow PL28 8EA COOKING 1
TEL: (01841) 532700 FAX: (01841) 533344 COST £22–£26

St Petroc's is, of course, owned and run by Rick Stein of the acclaimed Seafood Restaurant (see entry, below), but is not a clone. 'The feeling was of relatively quickly and easily cooked rather than thoughtfully and lengthily produced food' was one reporter's impression, neatly summing it up. The attractive period house has white walls, cane furniture and pictures by local artists, some for sale. Closely packed tables and fast turnover are the order of the day, with a short menu that deals in familiar moules marinière, chargrilled grey mullet with chips, and chocolate mousse, all for a fixed price. That's about it, really, except for sirloin steak with salsa verde, or boeuf bourguignonne with a big dollop of mashed potato, for non-fish-eaters, and ice-creams. The two dozen or so sensibly chosen wines are mostly under £20, with house Sauvignon Blanc from Haut-Poitou at £2 a glass.

CHEF: Paul Hearn PROPRIETOR: Richard Stein OPEN: Tue to Sun 12.30 to 2.15, 7 to 9.30 CLOSED: 3 to 30 Dec MEALS: Set L and D £13.95 SERVICE: not inc CARDS: Access, Amex, Delta, Switch, Visa DETAILS: 38 seats. Private parties: 38 main room. Vegetarian meals. Children's helpings. No smoking in dining-room. Wheelchair access. Music ACCOMMODATION: 8 rooms, 7 with bath/shower. TV. Phone. B&B £25 to £77. Deposit: 25%. Children welcome. Pets welcome. Garden

▲ *Seafood Restaurant*

Riverside, Padstow PL28 8BY — COOKING 3*
TEL: (01841) 532485 FAX: (01841) 533344 — COST £32–£78

'The visit here was a long-awaited treat, and it came up to expectations,' began one report, while another concluded that 'it is not cheap, but is worth every penny'. The airy dining-room is a converted warehouse, on the sea-front overlooking the harbour; it feels cool and relaxed, clean and welcoming, a 'wonderful dining environment', and the atmosphere is friendly and lively. Meals begin with olives in the conservatory and progress to the dining-room, with its colourful prints on bright white walls and crisp white linen on the tables. Rick Stein is a seafood missionary, gathering converts from all over the country for his simple, good fresh fish and shellfish. It is cooked only as much as it needs to be, and accompanied by a straightforward sorrel or hollandaise sauce, or perhaps an emulsion of olive oil, garlic and lemon juice.

The excellence of the cooking elicits praise: for mouclade with leeks, 'one of the best dishes we have eaten anywhere in this country', for a 'truly superb' bourride of John Dory, brill and salt-cod, and for soft-shell crab, chargrilled squid, beautifully textured steamed brill with a beurre blanc, and grilled mackerel with lemon grass and coriander. Even the dishes that have to be 'mucked about with' work well, thanks to freshness and distinctive flavours: a rich hot tureen of tan-coloured shellfish soup, and crawfish ravioli with basil and spinach that was judged 'sublime, a truly fantastic dish'. One pair of reporters confessed that 'until this meal we had never realised how truly memorable lobster can be'.

Lemon tart, Bakewell tart, hot bread pudding and apricot crumble are among desserts that have found favour, and there is a well-kept and well-served selection of cheeses. The restaurant continues to divide reporters, though. Some feel it is on the up, others think it is slipping. An absence of taste in some dishes, or simply 'tired' fish that could have been better, or could have been fresher, have disappointed. Service, too, has been described as 'impeccable', 'professional', 'friendly', 'helpful' and 'relaxed', as well as 'supercilious', 'offhand', 'rushed', and 'sullen'. The predominantly white wine list is as enthusiastic about interesting wines of humble origin as it is about the big guns from Burgundy, which results in a fair spread of grape varieties and some good-value bottles: under £20 are François Sack's white cassis, de Villaine's Bourgogne Aligoté, Brumont's Pacherenc du Vic-Bilh, and many others. The one-page 'selection' is the first place to look, but don't neglect the rest. House wines start at £10.50. CELLARMAN'S CHOICE: Gaillac Blanc, Les Greilles 1993, Dom. Causse Marines, £16; Fixin 'Les Chenevrières' 1988, Moncaut, £27.50.

CHEF: Richard Stein PROPRIETORS: Mr and Mrs C.R. Stein OPEN: Mon to Sat 12.30 to 2.15, 7 to 9.30 (10 in high season) MEALS: alc (main courses £13.50 to £37). Set L £21.50, Set D £29.30 SERVICE: not inc CARDS: Access, Delta, Switch, Visa DETAILS: 70 seats. Private parties: 15 main room. Car park. Vegetarian meals. No children under 2 L, 5 D. No music. Air-conditioned ACCOMMODATION: 10 rooms, all with bath/shower. TV. Phone. B&B £38 to £115. Deposit: 25%. Children welcome. Pets welcome (*The Which? Hotel Guide*)

PAINSWICK Gloucestershire map 2

Country Elephant

NEW ENTRY

New Street, Painswick GL6 6XH
TEL: (01452) 813564

COOKING 2
COST £21–£48

Just up the road from Painswick's old churchyard, with its 99 yew trees, lurks the Elephant, a seventeenth-century beast in grey Cotswold stone. Acquired in 1994 by John Rees, it has been redecorated in pale neutral tones, and the interior thus looks lighter and more spacious – just as well for an elephant – than hitherto. The new chef is the proprietor's brother Robert, formerly of Splinters in Christchurch (see entry). Indications are that a promising first year has been chalked up; 'some terrific ideas' were noted at an inspection dinner.

As the name of the place suggests, this is first and foremost rustic cookery, but artfully conceived for all that. Full vent is given to contrasts of texture and flavour, as in a fine risotto of peas, broad beans and laverbread cooked in port. Colour is used to great effect in a sauté of John Dory fillets on a mound of samphire with a saffron cream sauce garnished with tomato. Creamed fennel and a tarragon jus support beef medallion, while truffled mash lends class to lemon sole. Vegetables are not offered separately, and their presence in the main dishes may be quite nugatory: deep-fried threads of mixed vegetables have little more than visual impact, all the elements reduced to homogeneity. They came in a mound on roast duck breast, together with a couple of slices of very rare sauté foie gras. Lemon tart is served with a creamy orange sauce with macerated strawberries and blueberries, another colourful dish served on a giant plate; other desserts make use of seasonal fruits. Coffee for one reporter could have been stiffened up considerably. Service has been described as 'disarmingly charming, observant'. An inspired modern wine list offers fairly priced drinking from most corners of the globe, with seven available by the glass. House wines are £9.60 (a South African white) and £10.25 (an Australian red).

CHEF: Robert Rees PROPRIETOR: John Rees OPEN: Wed to Sun 12 to 2, 7 (6.30 June to Aug) to 10 CLOSED: first 2 weeks Jan MEALS: alc (main courses £6.50 to £16). Set L Wed to Sat £10 (2 courses; not served June to Aug), Set L Sun £13 SERVICE: 10%, card slips closed CARDS: Access, Diners, Switch, Visa DETAILS: 34 seats. 7 tables outside. Private parties: 34 main room. Vegetarian meals. Children's helpings. No smoking in dining-room. Music

PAULERSPURY Northamptonshire map 5

▲ *Vine House*

100 High Street, Paulerspury NN12 7NA
TEL: (01327) 811267 FAX: (01327) 811309
off A5, 2m SE of Towcester

COOKING 2
COST £22–£40

Relaxation sets in as soon as you enter the quiet village, and doesn't seem to stop until you leave. The small seventeenth-century limestone house has been sympathetically modernised, and meals begin in the lounge with drinks and a taste of, perhaps, salmon mousse on toast, or duck terrine with apricot chutney. Home-made non-alcoholic ginger beer or lemonade are more than just a sop to drivers; would that more places offered drinks like these.

There is no shortage of intriguing dishes – a savoury bread-and-butter pudding of smoked salmon and leeks to begin, or a cod and marrowfat pea pie, for example – and much of the time they work well. 'Marcus Springett is adventurous in his dishes and good at presentation,' writes a seasoned reporter. 'Interesting food at reasonable prices,' is how another summed it up. Terrines include one made from Scotch broth with a garlic dressing, another from home-smoked cod and red peppers which was judged 'subtly flavoured with a delightful array of textures'. The food follows the seasons, and ingredients are good, although there is a view among reporters that some items lack a 'distinctive harmony', as for example when the sweetness of a fruit accompaniment to venison takes over the whole dish. Meals end in fine form with sticky toffee pudding, or perhaps a summer dish of strawberries marinated in sweet rose petal syrup with rhubarb ice. Service is informal and obliging. Wines include a short selection from the New World, but France fills most of the list, with rather a lot of bottles from négociants. House wines are £9.95.

CHEF: Marcus Springett PROPRIETORS: Marcus and Julie Springett OPEN: Tue to Fri L 12 to 2.30, Mon to Sat D 7 to 10 CLOSED: 1 week Christmas MEALS: Set L £13.95, Set D £19.50 (Mon to Thur) to £23.50 (Fri and Sat) SERVICE: not inc CARDS: Access, Visa DETAILS: 45 seats. Private parties: 45 main room, 12 private room. Car park. Children's helpings. Smart dress preferred. No smoking in 1 dining-room. Wheelchair access (3 steps). No music ACCOMMODATION: 6 rooms, all with bath/shower. TV. Phone. B&B £39 to £61.50. Children welcome. Garden (*The Which? Hotel Guide*)

PENZANCE Cornwall map 1

Harris's

46 New Street, Penzance TR18 2LZ COOKING **2**
TEL: (01736) 64408 COST **£29–£48**

A tip-off during a lobster-buying session on Newlyn quay led a pair of reporters to Roger and Anne Harris's 'charming' restaurant opposite the Humphrey Davy statue in the centre of Penzance. They were not disappointed – and are not alone in their enjoyment of 'the most delicious lunch' (from one Londoner). There is in addition a light lunch menu which makes for good-value grazing. Others have raved about the evening experience which shows off the freshness of the Newlyn fish, and takes advantage of locally reared meat and seasonal game. Roger Harris has delighted visitors with smoked salmon cornets and crab mayonnaise, 'nice and pink' rack of lamb with crab apple-flavoured jus, and stuffed breast of pheasant in a filo pastry case with glazed apple. Elsewhere he might offer roast monkfish with cep risotto, steamed John Dory with saffron sauce, grilled guinea-fowl with lemon and basil, and hot apple strudel. Mrs Harris and local helpers run the pink-painted, ground-floor dining-room most efficiently. The short wine list has France as its major contributor, but the New World also has its say, and halves are plentiful. House wine is £10.50.

CHEF: Roger Harris PROPRIETORS: Anne and Roger Harris OPEN: Tue to Sat L 12 to 2, Mon to Sat D 7 to 10 CLOSED: 2 weeks Nov, 1 week Feb, Mon D Nov to May MEALS: alc (main courses £10.50 to £16). Light L menu SERVICE: 10%, card slips closed CARDS: Access, Amex, Visa DETAILS: 40 seats. Private parties: 20 main room, 20, 20 private rooms. Children welcome. Smart dress preferred. Music

PITTON Wiltshire map 2

Silver Plough 🍷 NEW ENTRY

Pitton SP5 1DZ
TEL: (01722) 712266 COOKING 1*
on A30, 5m E of Salisbury COST £21–£39

A pair of ancient ploughs stands outside this white village pub. The beamed interior is done in red plush and decorated with drinking vessels of all kinds. The cooking scores some palpable hits: baked goats' cheese with roast beetroot, an elderflower-dressed salad of avocado with mozzarella and strawberries, and baked salmon with a Cajun crust and lime butter are several notches above the pub norm, and one reporter enjoyed a bowl of green-lipped mussels with a 'very rich, yet interestingly acid and tangy' sauce of wine, herbs and cream. Desserts are chalked on the blackboard and take in Bakewell tart, brandy-snap baskets of strawberries, and chocolate biscuit cake, the last turning out to be a 'gorgeous' agglomeration of chocolate, dried fruit, nuts and smashed biscuit. The fine international wine list has been put together by somebody with a good knowledge of the subject. For its catholicity, helpful notes and very generous pricing, it deserves commendation. There are no house wines as such, but ten are available by the glass at £1.70. CELLARMAN'S CHOICE: Aotea Sauvignon Blanc 1993, Gisborne, New Zealand, £11.94; Te Mata Cabernet/Merlot 1993, Hawkes Bay, New Zealand, £13.95.

CHEF: Dawn Wieland PROPRIETOR: Michael Beckett OPEN: all week 12 to 2, 7 to 9.30 (10 Sat, 9 Sun) MEALS: alc (main courses £8 to £14) SERVICE: not inc, card slips closed CARDS: Access, Amex, Diners, Visa DETAILS: 60 seats. 10 tables outside. Private parties: 40 main room. Car park. Vegetarian meals. Children's helpings. Smart dress preferred. Music

PLUMTREE Nottinghamshire map 5

Perkins Bar Bistro £

Old Railway Station, Plumtree NG12 5NA
TEL: 0115-937 3695 FAX: 0115-937 6405 COOKING 2
off A606, 2m S of Nottingham COST £20–£34

In 1982 Tony and Wendy Perkins had the bright idea of converting Plumtree's railway station into a bistro. Since then they have worked up a good head of steam: the old booking hall and adjacent rooms have been turned into pleasant dining areas and a small conservatory stands where the original platform used to be. 'A single-track line still exists,' observed one visitor, and 'although rusting, the state of the rails indicates that there are still some trains running.'

You can come here for a drink and a mug of prawns, but most people opt for the full menu – a daily slate of dishes with clear French overtones. Classics such as poached eggs Benedict, salade niçoise and entrecôte steak béarnaise might share the billing with vegetable and chicken broth with coriander and goats' cheese dumplings, or grilled fillet of cod on a bed of butter-beans with pistachio and watercress sauce. Pheasant – a gamey, well-hung bird – might be served old-style with bread sauce and game chips, or roasted off the bone and paired with lemon and thyme stuffing and apple sauce, while vegetarians have been well pleased with a vol-au-vent of creamed eggs with grilled vegetables, pine-kernels and 'oriental vinaigrette'. Chocolate roulade has been a good choice from the long list of puddings. Service is unhurried and 'mature'. Half a dozen French country wines offer excellent value, and the full list holds plenty of interest at prices that will not empty the wallet. House wine is £7.80.

CHEF: Tony Perkins PROPRIETORS: Tony and Wendy Perkins OPEN: Tue to Sat 12 to 2, 6.45 to 9.45 CLOSED: bank hols MEALS: alc (main courses £8 to £10.50) SERVICE: not inc CARDS: Access, Amex, Delta, Diners, Switch, Visa DETAILS: 73 seats. 6 tables outside. Private parties: 14 main room, 30 private room. Car park. Vegetarian meals. Children welcome. Smart dress preferred. No smoking in 1 dining-room. Wheelchair access (1 step). Music

PLYMOUTH Devon map 1

Chez Nous 🍷

13 Frankfort Gate, Plymouth PL1 1QA COOKING 3*
TEL/FAX: (01752) 266793 COST £39–£47

The restaurant doesn't draw attention to itself, but behind the discreet dark blue frontage it makes no bones about its French leanings. The colour scheme is the red, white and blue of the tricolour, and adverts for Pernod and Gauloise confirm the tone, while the reproduction menus on the walls point to Troisgros and Roger Vergé as Jacques Marchal's culinary heroes. *Cuisine spontanée* is the message on cards and napkin covers. The place looks and feels like a smart bistro, the menu is chalked on a board, and frogs' legs are thrown to the gallery, but this is no casual set-up. The unassuming yet high-quality French cooking is not tricksy or trendy, just sound and confident.

Duck with lentils or beef with oyster mushrooms are typical offerings: in place of risks and showmanship we get simple and often familiar items properly cooked. Onion soup is made with well-browned onions, good bread, and cheese that stretches out like telephone wires when scooped up. The spontaneity manifests itself in the dodging and weaving between ingredients. Today is chicken breast with leeks, and turbot with saffron; tomorrow the turbot takes the leeks while the chicken moves on to ginger sauce. It is a manageable repertoire kept on the move by what the market provides, from mackerel (with white wine) through scallops (with garlic butter) to ravioli filled with whatever takes the kitchen's fancy. Saucing is subtle but leaves the main item centre stage. Puddings, recited by the staff, avoid stodginess. Even a chocolate praline dish with chocolate sauce manages to be a light and comparatively refreshing change from the rich buttery versions that abound.

The wine list is as French as the *ouvert* and *fermé* signs on the door, with only a token New World presence, and the quality is high. House Merlot and Sauvignon Blanc are around £10.50, or £3 per glass. CELLARMAN'S CHOICE: Villette 1993, Henri Contesse S.A. Gully, Vaud, Switzerland, £19.50; St Aubin *premier cru*, Les Murgers des Dents de Chiens 1990, Dom. Roland Maroslavac-Léger, £22.

CHEF: Jacques Marchal PROPRIETORS: Suzanne and Jacques Marchal OPEN: Tue to Sat 12.30 to 2, 7 to 10.30 CLOSED: 3 weeks Feb, 3 weeks Sept MEALS: Set L and D £28.50 SERVICE: not inc CARDS: Access, Amex, Diners, Switch, Visa DETAILS: 28 seats. Private parties: 32 main room. Children welcome. Smart dress preferred. Music

POLPERRO Cornwall map 1

Kitchen

The Coombes, Polperro PL13 2RQ
TEL: (01503) 272780 COOKING 1
on A387, 3m SW of Looe COST £23–£42

The Batesons' restaurant is a tiny little gem that caters for the seasonal influx of tourists to Polperro. It is not a place for an intimate tête-à-tête or even a big celebration – unless, of course, you decided to reserve all ten tables in the cramped dining-room. People come here to eat: it's as simple as that. The day's catch from the local boats is the backbone of the menu, but Ian Bateson likes to jazz things up with a liberal dose of spices and exotic flavours. Swordfish steak is chargrilled and served with provençale sauce, crab is cooked with coconut and coriander, breast of chicken is fired with piri-piri sauce, lamb is braised Moroccan-style with apricots. You could start with locally made pork and garlic sausages, or roasted vegetable and noodle salad, and finish off with mango fruit ice or banoffi pie. The wine list offers the prospect of sound, affordable drinking. House wine is £8.90.

CHEFS/PROPRIETORS: Ian and Vanessa Bateson OPEN: Mon to Sat D only 7 to 9.30 CLOSED: Nov to Easter; Mon and Tue Mar to May and Oct, Mon June and Sept MEALS: alc (main courses £8.50 to £16.50). Minimum £8.50 SERVICE: not inc, card slips closed CARDS: Access, Visa DETAILS: 24 seats. Private parties: 6 main room. Vegetarian meals. No children under 12. Smart dress preferred. No smoking in dining-room. Music

PONTELAND Northumberland map 10

Café 21

NORTHUMBERLAND 1996 CAFE

NEW ENTRY

35 The Broadway, Darras Hall,
Ponteland NE20 9PW COOKING 1*
TEL: (01661) 820357 COST £20–£37

The urban tendency for conspicuously successful restaurants to spawn smaller progeny has not passed the Newcastle area by. Hard on the heels of Terence and Susan Laybourne's 21 Queen Street (see entry, Newcastle) comes this no-bookings café spin-off, set at the end of a shopping parade. The green frontage betokens understated décor within, the tiled floors and paper table-cover giving the place a not disagreeable 'subdued and clinical' feel. The menu explores modern modes, first courses revolving around bruschetta, Caesar salad, roast tomato soup, and deep-fried wun-tuns, while main courses go for unapologetic bulk; a satisfying dish of cod with cannellini beans and red peppers, say, or navarin of 'extremely tender and flavourful' lamb with spring vegetables. Otherwise, expect roast rabbit on olive butter, or oxtail braised in red wine. Sticky toffee pudding has been lighter than usual, and nougat glacé with raspberries, and pear and almond tart also make an appearance. Service is sufficiently attentive and well paced. The imaginatively chosen wine list does a good job at keeping prices for everything well within £20. House wines are £7.

CHEF: David Kennedy PROPRIETORS: Terence and Susan Laybourne OPEN: Tue to Sat 11.30 to 3, 6 to 10.30 CLOSED: bank hols MEALS: alc (main courses £7 to £14.50). Set L £11 (2 courses) to £13.50 SERVICE: not inc CARDS: Access, Amex, Delta, Diners, Switch, Visa DETAILS: 36 seats. Private parties: 48 main room. Vegetarian meals. Children's helpings. Music

POOLE Dorset map 2

▲ *Mansion House*

Thames Street, Poole BH15 1JN COOKING 1*
TEL: (01202) 685666 FAX: (01202) 665709 COST £24–£40

This very singular operation is a hotel, restaurant and dining club. Non-members may eat here for a premium of 15 per cent, but that is waived if you are staying at the hotel. A plush, comfortable dining-room with light wood panelling on the lower ground level is where the action takes place. The atmosphere is indeed clubby, but not oppressively so. 'White tablecloths and good lighting prevent a basement feel,' comments one visitor.

Running down the centre of the room is a buffet table, from which a selection of hors d'oeuvre may be chosen as one of the starter options on any of the fixed-price menus. There are, for example, well-herbed mushrooms, king prawns, fat asparagus cooked *à point*, carpaccio and celery rémoulade. A bowl of mussel and garlic soup at an inspection lunch was 'chockfull of mussels', and daily specials have included a 'satisfying and unfussy' brochette of monkfish, salmon, prawns and bacon. On some days roasts are carved from a trolley, and one or two trendy notes creep in, such as pot-roasted pigeon breasts on a bed of black pudding with a red wine sauce. Desserts offer something for everyone, from lemon and raspberry crème brûlée, to warm banana and hazelnut cheese-cake with white chocolate ice-cream. Service is 'absolutely first-rate – courteous but also very friendly'. The bipartite wine list includes a showing of expensive French classics alongside a more catholic selection of international wines arranged by style. Choice below £20 is ample enough. Prices start at £9.50.

CHEF: Gerry Godden PROPRIETOR: Robert Leonard OPEN: Sun to Fri L 12 to 2, Mon to Sat D 7 to 9.30 CLOSED: L bank hol Mons MEALS: Set L £13.25 (2 courses) to £19.50 (inc wine), Set D £16 (2 courses) to £22.25; 15% surcharge on these prices for non-members and non-residents SERVICE: not inc CARDS: Access, Amex, Delta, Diners, Switch, Visa DETAILS: 100 seats. Private parties: 100 main room, 14 to 40 private rooms. Car park. Vegetarian meals. No children under 5. Smart dress preferred. Music. Air-conditioned ACCOMMODATION: 28 rooms, all with bath/shower. TV. Phone. Air-conditioned. B&B £55 to £110. Children welcome. Baby facilities. Pets by arrangement. Afternoon teas (*The Which? Hotel Guide*)

PORTHLEVEN Cornwall map 1

▲ *Critchards*

The Harbourside, Porthleven TR13 9JA COOKING 1
TEL: (01326) 562407 COST £21–£42

A restored former mill-house set slightly back from Porthleven harbour is the setting for Steve and Jo Critchard's ambitious seafood restaurant, which is open for dinner only. The à la carte menu is supplemented by nightly-changing specials and a vegetarian menu that borrows productively from ethnic sources. Meals start simply enough with platters of smoked fish, Cantonese scallops in black-bean sauce, or 'beautifully crisp' deep-fried squid with garlic dip. Main courses are where imagination comes into play. Monkfish medallions are rolled in crushed peppercorns, fried and given a relish of grilled sweet peppers. Crab claws and prawns come in Indian guise with freshly ground spices and lemon rice. Mackerel is grilled and sauced with rhubarb and ginger. Those of a non-fish disposition may opt for fillet steak with a variety of traditional sauces, or butterfly lamb chop with mint, rosemary and garlic. Banana baked in foil with Strega, mint and vanilla and served with whipped chocolate cream sits alongside Italian-inspired confections that manage to avoid today's dessert clichés. Service is willing enough. Wines are a fairly stolid bunch of reasonable range and price. House French is £8.60.

CHEF: Jo Critchard PROPRIETORS: Steve and Jo Critchard OPEN: Mon to Sat D only 6.30 to 9.30 CLOSED: Jan MEALS: alc (main courses £7 to £16) SERVICE: not inc, card slips closed CARDS: Access, Delta, Switch, Visa DETAILS: 44 seats. Private parties: 34 main room. Vegetarian meals. No children under 5. Smart dress preferred. No smoking in 1 dining-room. Wheelchair access. Music ACCOMMODATION: 1 room, with bath/shower. TV. B&B £42 (double room). Deposit: 25%. Children welcome. Baby facilities

PORTHOUSTOCK Cornwall map 1

Volnay

Porthoustock, nr St Keverne TR12 6QW
TEL: (01326) 280183
from Helston take A3083, then B3293 and continue for
1m E of St Keverne to Porthoustock (opposite red phone box)

COOKING 2
COST £22–£34

The setting is a whitewashed fisherman's cottage on an out-of-the-way beach in a 'rugged' Cornish cove, and the name conjures up thoughts of Burgundy, but Steven Chapman's lively establishment looks mainly to the Mediterranean for culinary inspiration. He is reckoned to be 'a great showman' and the whole set-up is driven along by the very enthusiastic team out front. Entry is through a small bar to the low-ceilinged room seating only 20 people. Smoke can sometimes be a problem. Colin Rye's cooking works to a sensibly tight menu that might take in marinated anchovy and radicchio salad, roast confit of duck with borlotti beans, bacon and garlic, and poached pears with mascarpone cheese and chocolate sauce. Casting his net wider, Colin can also deliver Tuscan toasts with chicken livers, ragoût of lamb with red wine and plums, and tarte au citron. 'Delightful' and 'delicious' are typical verdicts from reporters' pens. The wine list is a mere fistful of adequate bottles at reasonable prices. House wines are £8.50 a litre.

CHEF: Colin Rye PROPRIETOR: Steven Chapman OPEN: Tue to Sat (also bank hols Sun and Mon) D only 7.30 to 9 MEALS: alc (main courses £8 to £11) SERVICE: not inc CARDS: none DETAILS: 20 seats. Private parties: 20 main room. Vegetarian meals. Children welcome. No cigars in dining-room. Music

POULTON-LE-FYLDE Lancashire map 8

▲ *River House*

Skippool Creek, Thornton-le-Fylde,
Poulton-le-Fylde FY5 5LF
TEL: (01253) 883497 and 883307 COOKING 2*
FAX: (01253) 892083 COST £27–£56

The house, built in 1830, is on the River Wyre four miles from Blackpool. The Scotts list the attractions as 'boats, birds, tides, mud, sand, wind, trees, dogs, wood fires, wellies, good food, fine wine and happy, funny people'. Mr Scott takes the order, 'pinny on, glass of wine in hand', and meals are eaten in the spacious dining-room off bare polished tables. The menu is not ambitious, but is built around prime cuts of steak, lamb fillet and venison, with duck breast and suckling pig for variety. Fish is from Fleetwood. A 'full-flavoured, beautifully tender, rare chateaubriand' is not the only thing to be served with béarnaise sauce: ostrich, roasted rare, gets the same treatment.

First courses are straightforward too, perhaps sauté scallops in wine and cream sauce, or chicken livers with mushrooms and marjoram. Soufflé suissesse ranks among the better ones, and soups use good stock. 'Here is a man who knows good ingredients and what to do with them,' sums up one visitor. The menu talks of the 'chaotic supply situation' that leaves some dishes unavailable, which disappointed one reporter, and service doesn't seem to be as sharp as it was. Puddings might include Bramley apple and cinnamon tart, or dark chocolate mousse. For students of who-did-it-first? the ticky-tacky pudding with butterscotch sauce and vanilla ice-cream specifies 1958 as the date of its first appearance at the River House. For some reason erratic supplies seem to afflict the wine list too, which may explain the absence of vintages and producers against some bottles, but there is no doubting the quality where those details are available. Mature German wines seem to be a hobby. House wine is £12.50.

CHEF: Bill Scott PROPRIETORS: the Scott family OPEN: Mon to Sat D only 7 to 10; L by appointment MEALS: alc (main courses £16 to £20). Set L and D £18.50 SERVICE: not inc CARDS: Access, Visa DETAILS: 40 seats. 4 tables outside. Private parties: 40 main room, 14 private room. Car park. Children's helpings. Smart dress preferred. Music ACCOMMODATION: 5 rooms, all with bath/shower. TV. Phone. B&B £50 to £80. Children welcome. Pets welcome. Garden (*The Which? Hotel Guide*)

POWBURN Northumberland map 10

▲ *Breamish House* £✱

Powburn NE66 4LL COOKING 1
TEL: (01665) 570266 FAX: (01665) 578500 COST £21–£36

Travellers taking the scenic, cross-country route from the east coast often set their compasses for this imposing Georgian house surrounded by five acres of woodland and glorious formal gardens (complete with a resident kingfisher and red squirrel). As a result, Doreen and Alan Johnson's hotel attracts a 'somewhat eclectic bunch' of walkers, birdwatchers and tourists (one guest appeared for dinner 'in a bow tie and carpet slippers and no socks', according to an amused reporter). Four-course menus are served more or less in one sitting, and take their cue from local produce and the output of the hotel's own vegetable patch. The style is unadorned domestic cooking, which could mean terrine of pheasant with hazelnuts, cream of tomato and basil soup, then loin of pork with calvados and Bramley apples, or poached fillet of salmon with dill. Desserts might range from pavlova to bread-and-butter pudding. The latter is a fixture: 'Bookings for '96 already request [it] to be served at least once during their stay,' the Johnsons told us in spring '95. The wine list is well-spread and prices shouldn't raise too many eyebrows. House wine is £11.50.

CHEFS: Doreen and Alan Johnson, and Debbie Lowrie PROPRIETORS: Doreen and Alan Johnson OPEN: Sun L 12 to 12.30, all week D 7 to 7.30 CLOSED: 30 Dec to mid-Feb MEALS: Set L Sun £13.50, Set D £21.50 SERVICE: not inc, card slips closed CARDS: Access, Delta, Switch, Visa DETAILS: 30 seats. Private parties: 25 main room, 10 and 15 private rooms. Car park. No children under 12. Smart dress preferred. No smoking in dining-room. Wheelchair access (1 step; also WC). No music ACCOMMODATION: 11 rooms, all with bath/shower. TV. Phone. B&B £54 to £106. Deposit: £25 per person. No children under 12 except by prior arrangement. Pets welcome by prior arrangement, in bedrooms only. Afternoon teas. Garden (*The Which? Hotel Guide*)

PRESTBURY Cheshire map 8

▲ *White House*

New Road, Prestbury SK10 4DG
TEL: (01625) 829376 FAX: (01625) 828627 COOKING 1
on A538, 2m N of Macclesfield COST £19–£54

A few minutes' walk from White House Manor, the hotel part of the operation, the White House Restaurant is a stylish, up-market venue much favoured by the residents of the south Manchester stockbroker belt. Ryland Wakeham and his team deliver food that is spiked with ideas and ingredients from the gastronomic encyclopedia of the 1990s. Fish from Fleetwood might appear in the shape of roast monkfish with pancetta, tarragon and spinach, or lemon sole with wilted greens and Parmesan; venison is from Tatton Park ('exceptionally good, very tender, yet full of flavour as well'), and cheeses come from a specialist in Chester. Vegetables are 'cooked to perfection', and salads are reckoned to be minor works of art. You might start with Caesar salad and hot, locally smoked chicken, and finish with steamed sponge pudding with plum compote, or mille-feuille of dark and white chocolate with whisky mousse (the essential ingredient is specially blended by a local chocolatier). Service is generally professional and friendly, although one dissatisfied customer found it 'rude'. The 80-strong wine list has some good, fairly priced drinking from the New World; ten wines are served by the glass. House Duboeuf is £11 a litre.

CHEFS: Ryland Wakeham and Mark Cunniffe PROPRIETORS: Ryland and Judith Wakeham OPEN: Tue to Sun L 12 to 2, Mon to Sat D 7 to 10 MEALS: alc (main courses £9 to £13). Set L £11.95, Set D Mon to Fri £13.50 (2 courses) to £16.50 SERVICE: not inc CARDS: Access, Amex, Delta, Diners, Switch, Visa DETAILS: 75 seats. 3 tables outside. Private parties: 60 main room, 5 to 40 private rooms. Car park. Vegetarian meals. Children's helpings. Smart dress preferred. No cigars/pipes in dining-room. Wheelchair access (1 step). Music ACCOMMODATION: 9 rooms, all with bath/shower. TV. Phone. B&B £45 to £127. Rooms for disabled. Children welcome. Baby facilities. Pets welcome. Garden (*The Which? Hotel Guide*)

PRESTON Lancashire map 8

Heathcote's Brasserie

LANCS 1996 NEWCOMER

NEW ENTRY

23 Winckley Square, Preston PR1 3JJ
TEL: (01772) 252732 COOKING 2
FAX: (01772) 203433 COST £18–£45

Is Paul Heathcote bidding to become the Marco Pierre White of the North West? An empire is born, as his elegant Longridge restaurant (see entry) is now joined by a sleek modern brasserie that created an immediate splash when it opened in May 1995. It occupies two floors of a house in a leafy square of Georgian terraces, the basement serving Loch Fyne oysters, prawns with garlic aïoli, and grilled Goosnargh chicken 'with really good chips'. The ground floor buzzes with life and stimulates visually with its sinuous walls, jazzy mural, and polished wood floor: Philippe Starck's white bucket chairs are more comfortable to sit in than they look. Menus combine Mediterranean and favourite British food in the approved contemporary manner, giving Preston plenty to chew over.

Lightly cooked warm mackerel fillets with 'juicy little mussels' and piquant celeriac rémoulade make a 'simple but classy' starter, while fillet of baked cod comes with both new potatoes and a Caesar salad. Two reporters praised what might be a quintessential Heathcote dish of ox-cheek and oxtail braised in red wine with mashed potato spiked with horseradish: 'really big-boy stuff.' Creamy, smooth and 'satisfyingly boozy' prune and armagnac parfait, 'great' lemon tart, and 'exquisite' melting chocolate tart have come off the dessert menu, and the well-selected cheeses are treated with respect. Bread and vegetables are charged extra, although main dishes are already generously garnished. Staff, though a bit nervy to begin with, have been full of enthusiasm. A compact up-to-the-minute and imaginative wine list offers ten each of white and red, plus a couple of sparklers, at perfectly sensible prices, and all available by the glass. House vin de pays d'Oc is £10.25.

CHEF: Max Gnoyke PROPRIETOR: Paul Heathcote OPEN: all week 11.45 to 2.15, 6 to 10.30; seafood bar Mon to Sat 11 to 11, Sun 12 to 3, 7 to 10.30 MEALS: alc (main courses £7.50 to £14.50). Set L £8.50 (2 courses) to £10.50 SERVICE: not inc CARDS: Access, Amex, Switch, Visa DETAILS: 90 seats. Private parties: 20 main room. Vegetarian meals. Children's helpings. Smart dress preferred. No cigars/pipes in dining-room. Music

PULBOROUGH West Sussex map 3

Stane Street Hollow

Codmore Hill, Pulborough RH20 1BG
TEL: (01798) 872819 COOKING 2
on A29, 1½m NE of Pulborough COST £23–£43

'Unpretentious and homely, rather like a Swiss tavern,' is how René and Ann Kaiser's restaurant comes across, thanks partly to the collection of sundry patriotic items. 'The chisels, planes and cowbells are not upsetting.' In fact the cowbells – rows of them – are there for a very good reason: 'to keep the chef from home-sickness.' It seems to have worked, because the Kaisers are now in their twentieth year, and with an enviable track record. Highlights include first-class fish, and unusually good vegetables: the Kaisers grow their own, along with soft fruit and herbs. They also keep ducks and chickens for their eggs, and smoke their own salmon, chicken and duck on the premises, showing the kind of commitment that too few country restaurants indulge in. It allows them to exploit the seasons well – the menu changes monthly – and to keep the quality of the food under their own control.

The French influence on the cooking is stronger than the German. Tartelette jurassienne is made with onions and bacon, topped with a Swiss cheese soufflé mixture; braised ham comes with sauerkraut; and apple fritters are tossed in cinnamon sugar. The welcome is warm, staff are helpful, and reporters come away with a feeling of having eaten well and paid a fair price. Wines are predominantly French, well chosen at all levels, and reasonably marked up, with a good selection of half-bottles, and half a dozen varied sweet wines by the glass. House Chardonnay from Piedmonte is £2.50 per glass, and a dry white from the Pyrenees £2. CELLARMAN'S CHOICE: Pinot Gris d'Ardon 1992, Switzerland, £13.50; Châteauneuf-du-Pape 1986, Clos St Jean, £16.75.

CHEF: René Kaiser PROPRIETORS: René and Ann Kaiser OPEN: Wed to Fri and Sun L 12.30 to 1.15, Wed to Sat D 7.15 to 9.15 CLOSED: 2 weeks end May, 2 weeks end Oct MEALS: alc (main courses £9.50 to £12.50). Set L £10.50 (2 courses) to £13.50 SERVICE: not inc CARDS: Access, Delta, Switch, Visa DETAILS: 30 seats. Private parties: 20 main room, 14 private room. Car park. Vegetarian meals. Children's helpings. Smart dress preferred. No smoking in dining-room. Wheelchair access (3 steps). No music

RAMSBOTTOM Greater Manchester map 8

Village Restaurant

16–18 Market Place, Ramsbottom BL0 9HT
TEL: (01706) 825070 COOKING 1
off A56/M66, 4m N of Bury COST £16–£29

It's all change again for Chris Johnson and Ros Hunter. The bistro style with a blackboard full of choices didn't work out as well as expected, although a vestige remains in the two- and three-course lunches of pasta, salads, cured meats and a few more substantial items, starting at £5 for a first course and pud with a cup of tea or coffee. This seems ideal for anybody popping into the well-stocked delicatessen, which is full of oils, cheese, olives, smoked salmon, bread, chocolates, wines and so forth.

In the evening they have reverted to their tried-and-tested dinner-party format, the one they feel most comfortable with: five courses (the second soup, the third dressed salad leaves) starting at 7.30 and ending at around 11. Organic materials figure prominently, 'cooking is minimalist' (to quote Chris Johnson) and salt-free, and most items on the menu are marked with a V for vegetarians, along the lines of English asparagus with hollandaise, for example. Even when the main course is roast rib of well-hung Galloway beef, or breast of Barbary duckling, vegetarian alternatives and a fish option are available. Puddings range from apple crumble to Cheshire strawberries with a balsamic dressing.

Wines continue to delight and astound, with 300 regular lines and a similar number in the 'fine and rare' section. The pattern is (or soon will be) to browse the cellar before dinner (arrive in good time) and pay for the wine at shop prices;

or, alternatively, to choose from the list at table and add a corkage charge. An idea of the detail may be gleaned from the 17 Alsace Rieslings or the 30 German wines from Max Ferd Richter, though the net is spread wide and catches a lot of exceptionally good wine at all price levels. House vin de pays (shipped direct) is £8.95. CELLARMAN'S CHOICE Alsace, Edelzwicker 1991, Rolly-Gassmann, £14.50; Madiran, Ch. Peyros, 1989, £14.50.

CHEF: Ros Hunter PROPRIETORS: Ros Hunter and Chris Johnson OPEN: Wed to Sun L 12 to 2.30 (1 for 1.30 Sun; one sitting) Wed to Sat D 7.30 for 8 (one sitting) MEALS: Set L Wed to Sat £5 (2 courses) to £10, Set L Sun £17.50, Set D £17.50 SERVICE: not inc, card slips closed CARDS: Access, Amex, Delta, Diners, Switch, Visa DETAILS: 40 seats. Private parties: 30 main room, 10 and 30 private rooms. Vegetarian meals. Children welcome. Smart dress preferred. No smoking in dining-room. No music

REIGATE Surrey map 3

Dining Room

59A High Street, Reigate RH2 9AE COOKING 2
TEL: (01737) 226650 COST £34–£47

Paul Montalto's desire to create a plush dining-club ambience in this first-floor restaurant in the centre of Reigate has paid off. The kind of place that could easily be overlooked in London, it has found in the suburbs a constituency appreciative of Anthony Tobin's well-crafted cooking. Both set-price and à la carte eating offer earthy flavours and plenty of substance, as in guinea-fowl and pistachio sausage in pastry with mustard and tarragon, salad of red tilapia (a warm-water fish) with gazpacho sauce, and duck breast on rösti with deep-fried beetroot. One reporter felt that 'the desire to present everything looking beautiful results in some dishes being a little over-wrought' but couldn't fault the skill. Another's lunch began well with 'good, pink-in-the-middle' chicken livers on brioche, and salmon and crab sausage with ginger on a bed of scrambled egg.

Simple puddings, such as chocolate and orange mousse, and blackberry and apple tart with 'excellent' vanilla ice-cream, have been very sound. Espresso and petits fours both win approval, and there is a good choice of breads. Wines are a concise international selection from Bibendum, and our complaint last year about missing vintages has been properly addressed. House vins de pays d'Oc are £7.50, and the list also features Albert Beerens champagne – one of the best producers in the Aube.

CHEF: Anthony Tobin PROPRIETOR: Paul Montalto OPEN: Mon to Fri L 12 to 2, Mon to Sat D 7 to 10 CLOSED: 2 weeks Christmas, 1 week Easter, 1 week end Aug MEALS: alc (main courses £13 to £15). Set L and D £13.95 (2 courses) SERVICE: not inc CARDS: Access, Amex, Diners, Switch, Visa DETAILS: 50 seats. Private parties: 50 main room. Vegetarian meals. Children welcome. Smart dress preferred. No smoking in dining-room. Music

The Guide *office can quickly spot when a restaurateur is encouraging customers to write recommending inclusion – and sadly, several restaurants have been doing this in 1995. Such reports do not further a restaurant's cause. Please tell us if a restaurateur invites you to write to the* Guide.

RICHMOND Surrey map 3

▲ *Petersham Hotel, Nightingales*

Nightingale Lane, Richmond TW10 6UZ COOKING 1*
TEL: 0181-940 7471 FAX: 0181-940 9998 COST £28–£49

The Victorian hotel overlooks a particularly inviting stretch of the Thames as it meanders its way towards central London, just eight miles away. Plain English cooking, the thrust of Tim Richardson's menus, asserts itself in watercress soup, cod and salmon fish-cakes, Lancashire hotpot, or, on a Sunday, 'three large slices of rare roast beef with potato croquettes and a light Yorkshire pudding'. More elaborate ideas include duck and Parma ham roulade with fresh figs, or terrine of ox-tongue and globe artichoke, although it is the simple and accurate cooking of 'a flavoursome pair of lamb noisettes stuffed with a purée of mushrooms and chestnuts' that appealed to one reporter more than the 'unfortunate gelatinous saucing'. The fare is not all red-blooded, though: other options include a tart of onion, spinach and wild mushroom, and vegetable kedgeree or risotto. Crème brûlée is very rich, steamed ginger pudding comes with honey custard, and pastry-work, in apple flan for instance, is good. Service is rather uninvolved. More than half the wine list is taken up with pedigree Bordeaux and burgundies, but other sections are more affordable. House Bordeaux is £12.50.

CHEF: Tim Richardson PROPRIETOR: Colin Dare OPEN: all week 12.15 to 2.15 (2.45 Sun), 7 to 9.45 (8.45 Sun) CLOSED: 25 and 26 Dec MEALS: Set L £17.50 to £23, Set L Sun £20, Set D Mon to Sat £23, Set D Sun £20. Minimum £19 SERVICE: not inc CARDS: Access, Amex, Diners, Visa DETAILS: 70 seats. Private parties: 12 main room, 10 to 30 private rooms. Car park. Vegetarian meals. Children's helpings. Smart dress preferred. No smoking in 1 dining-room. Wheelchair access (4 steps; also WC). Music ACCOMMODATION: 54 rooms, all with bath/shower. TV. Phone. B&B £103 to £160. Children welcome. Afternoon teas. Garden

RIDGEWAY Derbyshire map 8

Old Vicarage

Ridgeway Moor, Ridgeway S12 3XW
TEL: 0114-247 5814 FAX: 0114-247 7079 COOKING 3*
off A616, on B6054 nearly opposite village church COST £29–£57

The house is a Victorian vicarage in two acres of lawned and wooded grounds, overlooking green-belt land, yet only ten minutes from Sheffield city centre and junction 30 of the M1. Its stylish décor appeals in a 'pleasantly un-designerish way', and meals are taken either in the blue-walled dining-room or in the conservatory surrounded by greenery. 'We like to visit the Old Vicarage in summer in order to take advantage of the produce from the garden,' write one couple. Fruit, vegetables, herbs and crisp salad leaves are grown by the Bramleys, or come from nearby farms, and their dashing flavours play an important role.

'The menu changes monthly and reflects the seasons – part of the *raison d'être* of a country restaurant,' writes Tessa Bramley. It also reflects an interest in things beyond Sheffield. But although salsas, corn-cakes, crab-cakes, ceps and pancetta make an appearance, the cooking is not just a frantic scramble for exotic ingredients; it is as carefully judged as couscous mixed with cumin seeds and cashew-nuts to provide a 'stunning' accompaniment to roasted fennel with a 'cake' of aubergine. A lack of seasoning, though, has been noted on more than one occasion, 'which is a pity because the impact of the fine ingredients was lessened'. While the food can be exceptionally good, it does not always seem to be firing on all cylinders, and some meal-times (Sunday lunch, for example) do not show the kitchen off to best advantage.

Desserts that have shown up well include a shortbread tart, and a beautifully light chocolate sponge with custard and fudge sauce. Excellent marinated green olives and pistachios arrive with drinks, and good wholemeal bread rolls are provided. Service, whether the Bramleys are there or not, is invariably welcoming and friendly, and while it may be slightly formal it is also very pleasant and informative. Wines adopt a pedigree approach, and quality oozes from every page of the list. France accounts for the lion's share, and, although prices can be high, at least the wines under £20 are chosen with care. A few Spanish, German and New World wines add interest, and 'oddities' are lumped with Italy. A shorter list abstracts some 45 wines for at-a-glance choosing, and house wine is £12. CELLARMAN'S CHOICE: St-Joseph Blanc, Clos de l'Arbalestrier 1987, Florentin, £29; Vega Sicilia 1985, Valbuena, £39.

CHEF: Tessa Bramley PROPRIETORS: Tessa and Andrew Bramley OPEN: Tue to Fri and Sun L 12.30 to 2 (12 to 2.30 Sun), Tue to Sat D 7 to 10.45 (11 Sat) MEALS: Set L and D £18.50 (exc Sat) to £35 SERVICE: not inc, card slips closed CARDS: Access, Amex, Delta, Switch, Visa DETAILS: 50 seats. 8 tables outside. Private parties: 44 main room, 10 and 30 private rooms. Car park. Vegetarian meals. Children's helpings. Smart dress preferred. No smoking in dining-room. Wheelchair access (3 steps). Music

RIPLEY North Yorkshire map 9

▲ *Boar's Head*

Ripley HG3 3AY COOKING 2
TEL: (01423) 771888 FAX: (01423) 771509 COST £21–£51

One reporter described this re-vamped coaching-inn as a 'grand patrician country-house hotel in the real tradition': the Ingilby family has been incumbent here since the Middle Ages and still maintains stewardship of the nearby castle and its glorious gardens, as well as the Boar's Head. Family portraits and antiques from the castle are reminders of the time-honoured connections between the two.

Plentiful use is made of produce from the estate for a menu that has hardly a whisper of Olde English about it. Chilled poached pear with lemon dressing is served with rocket and mizuma leaves, grilled medallions of venison come with Savoy cabbage and celeriac purée, while roasted monkfish is paired with braised celery and a grain-mustard and tarragon sauce. Sweets are immaculate conceptions, such as a pyramid of iced nougatine filled with dark rum ganache served on a crushed raspberry sauce. The lunch menu features some more workaday dishes, such as leek and asparagus soup, and Cumberland sausage with onion gravy. Sir Thomas Ingilby's personally assembled wine list is a magisterial tome running to more than 200 bins, with realistic prices and plenty of choice from sources around the world. House wine is £8.95.

CHEFS: David Box, Alan Hunter and Kevin Schofield PROPRIETOR: Sir Thomas Ingilby OPEN: all week 12 to 1.45, 7 to 9.30 MEALS: alc (main courses £13.50 to £19.50). Set L Sun £14.95 SERVICE: not inc, card slips closed CARDS: Access, Amex, Switch, Visa DETAILS: 40 seats. Car park. Vegetarian meals. No children under 10. Smart dress preferred. No smoking in 1 dining-room. Wheelchair access (also WC). Music ACCOMMODATION: 25 rooms, all with bath/shower. TV. Phone. D,B&B £75 to £105. Rooms for disabled. Children welcome. Baby facilities. Pets welcome. Afternoon teas. Garden. Fishing (*The Which? Hotel Guide*)

RIPLEY Surrey map 3

Michels'

13 High Street, Ripley GU23 6AQ
TEL: (01483) 224777 and 222940 COOKING 3*
off A3, 4m SW of Cobham COST £28–£61

The dining-room of this Georgian house has been repainted and the chairs replaced. The Michels' discrimination, as displayed in the design, furnishing and decoration of their restaurant, is the legacy of an artistic background, and yet they have managed to retain an appealingly homely feel. The food looks good too, and a streak of tasteful invention runs through the menus. The *carte* changes seasonally, the set menus more frequently, and although an overseas visitor wondered if the chef might be trying too hard, it is difficult to take exception to the gentle innovation and playful pairings in Erik Michel's cooking. Just look at these dishes: a pot of warm set custard with sea urchins; ravioli filled with pig's trotter; or loin of Hampshire hog lightly smoked, served with a pea purée. There is nothing truly exotic here; rather the dishes are thinking man's classic cooking, done with élan and enthusiasm, paying due regard to texture as well as taste.

The freshness of fish and the proper hanging of beef can be taken for granted, as can the timing of their cooking. The menu at £28 for four set courses, including a different glass of wine with each, is considered good value. One spring version consisted of a quenelle of seafood with langoustine sauce and broccoli spears before a mille-feuille of asparagus with wild rice and orange sauce, then a cassoulet with duck and wild boar sausages, and finally cinnamon blancmange with caramelised apples. Other puddings might include a warm honey and orange soufflé served between orange pancakes, or slices of crystallised pineapple with a mousse of coconut. The alternative savoury puts ordinary Welsh rarebit in the shade: a pastry case filled with goats'-milk curd, flavoured with rose-water and served with a blueberry salad. Wines span a good range of quality and styles at fair mark-ups. Half-bottles and the house selection are helpful, with Côtes de Duras white at £9.25 and Costières de Nîmes red at £9.95.

CHEF: Erik Michel PROPRIETORS: Erik and Karen Michel OPEN: Tue to Fri and Sun L 12.30 to 1.30, Tue to Sat D 7.30 to 9 CLOSED: first week Jan MEALS: alc (main courses £16 to £20). Set L £19.50, Set D £21 to £28 SERVICE: not inc, card slips closed CARDS: Access, Amex, Delta, Visa DETAILS: 50 seats. Private parties: 18 main room, 12 private room. Car park. Children welcome. Smart dress preferred. Wheelchair access (2 steps). No music

RIPON North Yorkshire map 9

▲ *Old Deanery*

Minster Road, Ripon HG4 1QS COOKING 2
TEL: (01765) 603518 COST £21–£50

Pudding fetishists do their thing at the Old Deanery, with a Pudding Club menu offered every other month. After a light main course, they can indulge in a cornucopia of cobblers, fools and pies, marking them on a rating system to show which they enjoyed the most. This cosy restaurant opposite the cathedral caters for savoury tastes too, putting on themed French evenings on the last Friday of every month, as well as offering the normal business of a *carte* and set-price menus. The culinary style has a strong British input in lambs' kidneys with a mustard and calvados sauce, or a first course of asparagus wrapped in smoked salmon. Then, after a sorbet, it's on to the likes of 'symphony of fish' – three species in a puff pastry lattice on a champagne and chive sauce – or venison fillet with a smoked venison sausage and leek tagliatelle on a wine and peppercorn reduction. A French night in December produced at least one thoroughly satisfied customer who polished off wild mushroom and chicken liver tart, calvados sorbet, pheasant breast with apples, potatoes and bacon, and a dessert called Utopia, which turned out to be a chocolate mousse gâteau. Iced Grand Marnier soufflé and cassata also feature. The familial approach of the Dooleys is warmly appreciated: 'attention to detail is excellent'. A solidly based wine list is broad-minded enough not to accord special prominence to France, and contains plenty of drinking below £20. Eight house wines start at £9.25.

CHEFS: Daphne and Jon Dooley PROPRIETORS: Graham, Daphne and Jon Dooley OPEN: Tue to Sat L 12 to 2, Tue to Sat D 7 to 9.30 MEALS: alc (main courses £16.50 to £18). Set L Tue to Sat £10.50 (2 courses) to £12.95, Set L Sun £11.50, Set D Tue to Fri £10.50 (2 courses) to £12.95, Set D Sat £19.95 SERVICE: not inc, card slips closed CARDS: Access, Amex, Delta, Diners, Switch, Visa DETAILS: 60 seats. 4 tables outside. Private parties: 80 main room, 15 to 35 private rooms. Car park. Vegetarian meals. Children welcome. Smart dress preferred. No smoking in dining-room. Wheelchair access. No music ACCOMMODATION: 2 rooms, both with bath/shower. TV. D,B&B £55 to £150. Children welcome. Afternoon teas. Garden

ROADE Northamptonshire map 5

Roadhouse Restaurant

16 High Street, Roade NN7 2NW
TEL: (01604) 863372 COOKING 3
off A508, 4m S of Northampton COST £21–£38

This is a small restaurant, formerly a pub, that feels spacious thanks to its open-plan design. 'There is always a pleasant lightness about the atmosphere that tells you you're going to enjoy the evening,' writes one reporter, while another describes it as 'homely'. The positive vibes continue more or less without interruption to the food, which is 'always more interesting than it sounds, and always pleases'. Christopher Kewley's food is above all comfortable, partly because of the certainty that nothing will ever be badly timed or half-finished, which is reassuring to know, and partly because the food itself satisfies rather than surprises.

There is usually something fishy among first courses, and a feuilleté of asparagus with smoked salmon, poached egg and butter sauce was 'classic Kewley' for one reporter, while another enjoyed a filo pastry tart containing sauté onion 'with a little binding gunge of some delicious flavour', topped with pieces of dark field mushroom. Roasting is applied to fish and meat alike, but fish are also steamed and meats grilled. Sauces are generally stock reductions with an occasional splash of alcohol, and sometimes a vinaigrette or emulsion will ring the changes. One reporter in spring savoured the tender, sweet, delicate flavour of young lamb, cooked pink, rested and sliced, and served on a bed of lentils with garlic sauce. Simplicity on the plate relies on craft in the kitchen, and the latter's effectiveness is evident from the consistency noted by regular reporters. Vegetables appear in serve-yourself hot dishes and are usually plain, apart from cheese sauce, perhaps, with cauliflower.

Sticky toffee pudding is a relatively light version, while the trio of chocolates incorporates a particularly good mousse. Susan Kewley manages to chat while keeping an eye on everything and checking the wines, and there are 'plenty of young attentive staff on hand to provide swift and friendly service'. The view on value is unanimous: 'a fair price for a good meal', helped by the fact that service is included, and by 60 reasonably priced wines with house red and white at £9.50.

CHEF: Christopher Kewley PROPRIETORS: Christopher and Susan Kewley OPEN: Tue to Fri L 12.30 to 1.45, Tue to Sat D 7 to 9.30 CLOSED: 2 weeks Christmas MEALS: alc (main courses £12 to £16). Set L £15 SERVICE: net prices, card slips closed CARDS: Access, Amex, Delta, Switch, Visa DETAILS: 45 seats. Private parties: 50 main room. Car park. Children's helpings. Smart dress preferred. No cigars/cigars in dining-room. No music

---

ROMALDKIRK Co Durham map 10

▲ *Rose and Crown*

Romaldkirk DL12 9EB
TEL: (01833) 650213 FAX: (01833) 650828 COOKING 1
on B6277, 6m NW of Barnard Castle COST £17–£35

A couple who stayed at this thoughtfully updated eighteenth-century coaching-inn during the 'deadest' week of the year found much to praise and enjoy: the atmosphere was eminently warm and comfortable and the staff were exceptionally welcoming and dutiful. Much of the credit must go to Christopher and Alison Davy, who have cultivated the place as a country hotel without stripping it of its distinctiveness as the village local. Christopher's cooking continues to evolve: he tells us that he is 'moving more to regional cookery as local supplies develop', and his daily-changing, four-course dinner menu might feature the likes of Cotherstone cheese fritters, sauté chicken livers on pan haggerty, breast of grouse with juniper, and bramble and apple posset. Otherwise, he looks further afield for strips of beef fillet with green peppercorns and Puy lentils, baked fillet of Scotch salmon in vermouth with julienne of braised leeks, and iced meringue parfait with preserved strawberries. Bread and ice-creams are made on the premises. The cheaper bar menu is of a similar standard and Theakston beers are kept in good condition. The wine list is a realistically priced selection starting with the New World and ending in Europe. House wine is £8.50.

CHEFS: Christopher Davy and Dawn Stephenson PROPRIETORS: Christopher and Alison Davy OPEN: Sun L 12 to 1.30, Mon to Sat D 7.30 to 9 CLOSED: 25 and 26 Dec MEALS: Set L Sun £11.50, Set D £22 SERVICE: not inc, card slips closed CARDS: Access, Visa DETAILS: 24 seats. Private parties: 30 main room. Car park. Children's helpings. Smart dress preferred. No smoking in dining-room. No music ACCOMMODATION: 12 rooms, all with bath/shower. TV. Phone. B&B £54 to £75. Deposit: £30. Rooms for disabled. Children welcome. Pets welcome (in bedrooms only). Afternoon teas (*The Which? Hotel Guide*)

ROMSEY Hampshire map 2

HANTS 1996 KITCHEN

Old Manor House

21 Palmerston Street,
Romsey SO51 8GF
TEL: (01794) 517353

COOKING 3
COST £27–£49

The house is a delightful and well-preserved Tudor building in the town centre, with wooden beams, old bricks and a log fire. The score for cooking dropped to 2 last year following unfavourable reports. Somebody who visited soon afterwards concluded that 'the *Guide* has made an ass of itself'. But this year's inspector recommended the above score, which we are confident is right. Mauro Bregoli's Italian approach is more than skin-deep; it has direct links to the raw materials – he shoots deer and collects wild mushrooms – and treats them intelligently, and of course he makes his own pasta.

The collecting pays dividends in tagliatelle with gloriously tasty porcini, while thin strips of briefly seared venison are given extra point by a red onion confit. Sometimes the food has an obvious Italian connection – pasta e fagioli soup, gnocchi in a rustic Bolognese sauce, and tiramisù – and sometimes not. Either way, the results are impressive: slices of sticky and gelatinous cotechino sausage with lentils, or very fresh fillet of brill 'of exquisite texture' wrapped in ultra-thin slices of potato (no thicker than filo pastry), which kept the fish beautifully moist, accompanied by strips of roasted red pepper in oil.

Bregoli doesn't shout from the rooftops – one couple had to ask to establish that he makes his own cotechino; instead he quietly gets on with the job of cooking real food to a high level, which includes an exceptionally good crème brûlée, 'the consistency of a rich mayonnaise and with a perfect wafer-thin crust', flavoured with fennel and herbs and considered 'inventive without being outrageous'. Bread and vegetables may not quite match the standard of the rest of the operation, but service is clued up, which is helpful when it comes to choosing from the generous collection of high-quality wines on the list. France is the strong suit (claret is trumps, with a royal flush of first growths) and quality doesn't come cheap, but there should be enough affordable and interesting bottles for most people. House Italian is £9.95. CELLARMAN'S CHOICE: Perusai 1992, Azienda Barbarossa, £19.50; Carignano del Sulcis Riserva 'Rocca Rubia' 1990, Cantina Sociale Santadi, £16.

CHEF/PROPRIETOR: Mauro Bregoli OPEN: Tue to Sun L 12 to 2, Tue to Sat D 7 to 9.30 CLOSED: 1 week Christmas and New Year MEALS: alc (main courses £12.50 to £17.50). Set L and D £13.50 (2 courses) to £17.50 SERVICE: not inc, card slips closed CARDS: Access, Amex, Switch, Visa DETAILS: 45 seats. Private parties: 22 private room. Car park. Vegetarian meals. Children welcome. Smart dress preferred. No cigars/pipes in dining-room. No music

ROSS-ON-WYE Hereford & Worcester map 5

▲ *Pheasants*

52 Edde Cross Street, Ross-on-Wye HR9 7BZ COOKING 2*
TEL: (01989) 565751 COST £25–£50

Eileen Brunnarius's smartly converted seventeenth-century tavern/restaurant somehow got described as a 'bistro' in last year's *Guide* – a definition that, as a couple of readers have pointed out, was somewhat wide of the mark. Walls are ragged in soft red, the antique chairs have been replaced with modern Italian designer numbers, and the wine is now poured into Riedel glasses.

The combination of idiosyncratic but accomplished cooking and the highly polished wine service by Adrian Wells represents a strong formula. Four or five choices are offered at each course, sufficient to provide a good range without stretching the limited resources unrealistically. Marinated salmon with cucumber spaghetti in a dressing of soy and sherry makes a palate-sharpening starter. Beef fillet poached in red wine with shallots received enthusiastic endorsement at an autumn dinner, while a spring menu featured poached halibut in a luxurious sauce of shrimps and champagne with pickled samphire. Occasionally, reports of pallid flavours surface, though a rendition of sticky toffee pudding was 'impossible to criticise'. Prune and almond tart comes with crème fraîche; citrus fans should try the trio of lemon desserts. The pace of an evening here is very measured, perhaps even slow to those who want to get on, but an impressed reporter commented with regard to the cooking, 'how Eileen Brunnarius does it all herself is a miracle'.

Look at the first page of the wine list to get an idea of its scope: 17 fine fortified wines, including two dry Marsalas as suggested accompaniments to the starters. The rest of the list gathers inspired selections from all over the world, and then proceeds to tell you about them in an evocative and accessible way. Prices are extremely fair, with extensive options below £20, and many of the wines may be tried by the glass. Here is a model for others. Prices open at £9.50. CELLARMAN'S CHOICE: Grauer Burgunder Spätlese Trocken 1989, Schales, Rheinhessen, £15.20; Uva Rara, Oltrepò Pavese 1990, Angelo Ballabio, £21.40.

CHEF/PROPRIETOR: Eileen Brunnarius OPEN: Tue to Sat (L bookings only) 12.30 to 2, 7 to 10 CLOSED: 25 Dec to 2 Jan MEALS: alc (main courses £12 to £18). Set L £12 (2 courses) to £15, Set D Tue to Fri £16 (2 courses) to £19.50 SERVICE: not inc CARDS: Access, Amex, Diners, Switch, Visa DETAILS: 22 seats. Private parties: 30 main room. Vegetarian meals. Children's helpings. Smart dress preferred. No smoking in dining-room. Wheelchair access. Music ACCOMMODATION: 2 rooms. D,B&B £45 to £100. Children welcome

ROWDE Wiltshire map 2

George & Dragon

High Street, Rowde SN10 2PN COOKING 3
TEL: (01380) 723053 FAX: (01380) 724738 COST £17–£45

A reporter sets the scene: 'The first thing we saw as we entered was a huge ginger cat, Ralph by name, in prime position by the roaring fire. White paws, white bib, white whiskers, good solid head – the archetypal pub cat. Looking at the special fish menu on the blackboard, we could understand that Ralph was on to a winner by deigning to stay here. How many cats get leftover monkfish, gurnard, sea bass heads?' All of which sums up the style, intentions and special attraction of this unassuming village pub. Chef/landlord Tim Withers manages to pull off a near-perfect balancing act here, satisfying the needs of drinkers looking for pints of Wadworth real ale and plates of local ham, and attracting others who crave 'upper-class' pub food served without frippery or formality.

Meals can be eaten in the bar, the garden or the dining-room, where the wood-panelled walls are decorated with 'a positive agglomeration' of paintings, prints and plates; autumnal harvest-festival displays hang from the ceiling, the tables are laid with raffia mats and paper napkins and the mood is chatty. Fish specials are the stars of the show and the freshness of the catch is never in doubt: scallops are flash-fried and assembled into a salad with bacon, leaves and a 'tangy' walnut and pine-kernel dressing; 'terrific' squid is confidently paired with an ink and orange sauce; and fillet of swordfish is jazzed up with a tomato salsa. The printed menu covers a lot of territory, moving beyond seafood and taking in everything from spinach and watercress soup and asparagus risotto to lamb korma, chicken savoyarde and pan-fried rib of beef in wild mushroom sauce.

Puddings could include pavlova ('the size of a pillow'), fruity sorbets that look like a designer's dream, and brown sugar meringues with unpasteurised Jersey cream. Otherwise, there are British cheeses to round things off. The wine list is a sound collection with some notable French country wines, Rhônes and a New World selection. Plenty of interesting bottles can be had for under £12, and 14 wines are available by the glass.

CHEF: Tim Withers PROPRIETORS: Mr and Mrs T. Withers OPEN: Tue to Sat 12 to 2, 7 to 10 CLOSED: 25, 26 and 31 Dec MEALS: alc (main courses £6 to £17.50). Set L £8.50 (2 courses) to £10 SERVICE: not inc, card slips closed CARDS: Access, Delta, Switch, Visa DETAILS: 35 seats. 4 tables outside. Private parties: 30 main room. Car park. Vegetarian meals. Children's helpings. No young children after 9pm. No music

RYE East Sussex map 3

Landgate Bistro

5–6 Landgate, Rye TN31 7LH COOKING 2*
TEL: (01797) 222829 COST £19–£34

Funds have not been wasted on extraneous frills here – though 'the new plastic tablecloths are very pleasant', commented one – and there is quite an assortment of chairs. The achievement, though, lies in refusing to cook traditional bistro dishes, and given the Landgate's location this standpoint 'verges on heroism'.

The business is dinner only, in the form of either a good-value set-price three courses with coffee or a reasonably adventurous *carte*. The latter offers the likes of leek and Roquefort tart, or chickpea fritters with tomato and chilli sauce to start, followed maybe by cod with ginger and spring onions, or lambs' kidneys with a grain-mustard sauce. 'Strong and well-balanced flavours' characterised one reporter's first course of squid and tomato stew; others speak warmly of main courses of mallard in a red wine sauce, and beef fillet en croûte with an accomplished rosemary béarnaise. Good desserts have included Jamaican cream

– 'like a strongly rum-flavoured crème brûlée topped with crisp bitter chocolate' – and pear sorbet in 'two squashed scoops of remarkable smoothness and strong fruit flavour'. A couple of reporters have referred to weak coffee, but the Landgate by and large maintains a high standard overall. The wine list has a good run of well-chosen bottles from around the world at generous prices. Chartron et Trébuchet's Bourgogne Chardonnay and Ch. Carras, a Bordeaux-style blend from Greece, show imaginative buying. Seven wines are available by the glass. House French is £7.90.

CHEF: Toni Ferguson-Lees PROPRIETORS: Nick Parkin and Toni Ferguson-Lees OPEN: Tue to Sat D only 7 to 9.30 (10 Sat) CLOSED: 1 week Christmas, 2 weeks June, 1 week autumn MEALS: alc (main courses £8.50 to £12.50). Set D Tue to Thur £15.50 SERVICE: net prices, card slips closed CARDS: Access, Amex, Delta, Diners, Switch, Visa DETAILS: 30 seats. Private parties: 30 main room. Children welcome. Music

ST IVES Cornwall map 1

Pig 'n' Fish

Norway Lane, St Ives TR26 1LZ COOKING 2*
TEL: (01736) 794204 COST £26–£45

'We were enchanted by the building, a former pilchard shed.' That may sound an improbable rhapsody, but Cornwall has its own ways of delighting the senses. Mount the wooden staircase to the old net loft above, and the view over rooftops to the bay as the sun sets is an arresting one indeed. This little restaurant, done out in dignified dark greens, not far from the St Ives Tate, is full of pottery and paintings, and the people who made them may well turn up at the next table.

The name of the place announces the twin gastronomic concerns, although the owners have not been sufficiently satisfied of late with the quality of pork products available, so those have taken a back seat. The lure these days is exceptionally good fish, and that should be enough. Ravioli of lobster and spinach uses fresh, thickly rolled pasta to encase its generous filling, and sits in a pool of intense lobster sauce. Thai seasonings of coriander, lemon grass and chilli add piquancy to filo pancakes of crab, while at the other end of the spectrum monkfish, John Dory and 'plump juicy mussels' go into a ragoût with a dill-perfumed, light creamy sauce. Vegetables are plain and sensible, and avoid overload.

Even the simple-sounding desserts are thoughtfully worked, including lemon delicious: a three-layered triumph of 'syrupy sauce, dense mousse and foamy froth' of great citric intensity. Home-made walnut bread, chocolate truffles and almond biscuits show an uncommon attention to detail in such a modestly framed restaurant. Service is agreeable. The predominantly white wine list has some fine choices, particularly among burgundies, and a reasonable spread of prices. House wines are from £9.50.

CHEFS: Paul Sellars and Grant Nethercott PROPRIETORS: Debby and Paul Sellars OPEN: Tue to Sat L 12.30 to 1.30, Mon to Sat D 7 to 9.30 CLOSED: Nov to Mar MEALS: alc D (main courses £11 to £16.50). Set L £15.20 (2 courses) to £17.50, Set D £17.50 SERVICE: not inc CARDS: Access, Visa DETAILS: 30 seats. Private parties: 20 main room. Children's helpings. No cigars/pipes in dining-room. Music

ST KEYNE Cornwall map 1

▲ *Well House*

St Keyne PL14 4RN
TEL: (01579) 342001 FAX: (01579) 343891 COOKING 3*
on B3254, 3m S of Liskeard COST £32–£45

'This is a good restaurant in a delightful spot and offers remarkably good value for money,' summed up one reporter. Nicholas Wainford is a natural hospitable host, 'as urbane as ever', and Well House seems to be an extension of his own home. It is peaceful, timeless, elegant, with an atmosphere of 'unhurried comfort', and is 'unexpectedly perfect in all the important little ways', according to one. Everything appears effortless, though of course it is the result of relentless attention to detail. The bar, the only room without a view of the garden, is 'very cocktail hour', with low lighting around the velvet wall-seating, while the sitting-room is chintzy, and the dining-room light, airy and hung with good watercolours.

Wayne Pearson's menu is flexible enough, offering two to four courses (if the latter, one of them will be cheese), with four or five dishes per course to choose from. Soup is a fixture, and so is smoked salmon, although it may be served with cucumber noodles and a honey dressing. This is country cooking of a high order which relies on freshness and flavour for impact, not on twiddles and garnish. 'How wonderful to find a place not afraid of offal,' rejoiced one reporter who chanced upon sweetbreads, although calf's liver is a more likely option, pan-fried and served with tarragon potatoes and caramelised shallots, perhaps.

Fish is particularly well handled, and might range from salmon, filled with a crab mousse and baked in filo pastry, to large medallions of firm-fleshed monkfish with intensely flavoured pesto and tomato coulis, which was 'a real masterpiece of subtlety' for an inspector. What impressed overall at a test meal was that 'the balance of flavours and textures had been well planned and carefully executed', a judgement that applies equally to puddings. Chocolate marquise is given an orange and cardamom sauce, while iced lemon parfait benefits from a red berry coulis. Presentation is good in all departments, and the home-made bread includes crusty rolls and 'wonderful walnut bread'. Eighty-odd wines are sensibly chosen and mostly French, with good value at the lower end of the scale and some impressive heights for those with no price limit. House wine is £8.50, or £1.75 a glass.

CHEF: Wayne Pearson PROPRIETOR: Nicholas Wainford OPEN: all week 12.30 to 1.30, 7 to 9 MEALS: Set L and D £19.95 (2 courses) to £29.70 SERVICE: not inc, card slips closed CARDS: Access, Delta, Switch, Visa DETAILS: 32 seats. 5 tables outside. Private parties: 32 main room. Car park. No children under 8 D. Smart dress preferred. Wheelchair access (1 step; also WC). No music ACCOMMODATION: 7 rooms, all with bath/shower. TV. Phone. B&B £60 to £120. Deposit: £50. Children welcome. Baby facilities. Pets welcome. Garden. Swimming-pool (*The Which? Hotel Guide*)

All entries in the Guide *are rewritten every year, not least because restaurant standards fluctuate. Don't rely on an out-of-date* Guide.

ST MARGARET'S AT CLIFFE Kent map 3

▲ *Wallett's Court*

West Cliffe, St Margaret's at Cliffe CT15 6EW
TEL: (01304) 852424 FAX: (01304) 853430
on B2058, off A258 Dover to Deal road, 3m NE of Dover

COOKING 2
COST £30–£44

Reporters may think of this as a useful stopping-off point before crossing the Channel, although originally it was a handy base for those who had made the journey the other way. William the Conqueror gave the manor to his brother-in-law, Bishop Odo of Bayeux, since when the generations have left a legacy of oak beams, seventeenth-century wall-paintings, Adam fireplaces and a carved staircase. This is a family operation – the Oakleys celebrate 20 years here in 1996 – and the pattern is a set menu of three courses during the week, bumped up to five on Saturday with the addition of a fish course and a sorbet.

The kitchen has a liking for fish and game, the latter producing wild rabbit terrine and jugged hare on a spring menu. Apart from Hebridean salmon (baked with lemon, butter and rosemary), the seafood is mostly local, perhaps combining cockles, mussels, squid, scallops and shrimps in a saffron-flavoured cream sauce. Alcohol is a favourite saucing ingredient, from madeira with a brace of quail to green Chartreuse with turbot or monkfish in a lobster sauce. Apples from the family's own orchard might turn up, alongside pears and whipped cream, or between shortcake biscuits, and there are generous helpings of bread-and-butter pudding, Eton mess and chocolate orange tarlets. The fairly priced wines major on France but also include Australian Verdelho and Marsanne. House Haut-Médoc and Côtes de Duras are £10 a bottle, £3 a glass.

CHEF: Chris Oakley PROPRIETORS: the Oakley family OPEN: Mon to Sat D only 7 to 9 CLOSED: 4 days Christmas MEALS: Set D Mon to Fri £21 to £26.50 SERVICE: not inc CARDS: Access, Visa DETAILS: 50 seats. Private parties: 40 main room, 20 private room. Car park. Vegetarian meals. Children's helpings. No smoking in dining-room. Wheelchair access. No music ACCOMMODATION: 11 rooms, all with bath/shower. TV. Phone. B&B £30 to £75. Rooms for disabled. Children welcome. Baby facilities. Garden (*The Which? Hotel Guide*)

ST MICHAEL'S ON WYRE Lancashire map 8

Mallards

Garstang Road, St Michael's on Wyre PR3 0TE
TEL: (01995) 679661

COOKING 1
COST £16–£32

This converted smithy has a comfortable lounge, with 'modern but harmonious decoration and friendly yet courteous service'. Menus rely on a small core of items, such as Bury black pudding, served hot with a grain-mustard and cream sauce, or pasta with salmon and prawns. Reporters have enjoyed hot cheese tartlets (in effect mini-soufflés) and omelette Arnold Bennett to begin, and main courses of pork fillet in orange sauce, and 'well-hung mallard breast cooked blue'. Puddings are standard. Dinner is a choice of two, three or four courses – with chicken, steak, lamb and fish as the backbone – and if Sunday lunch is not a bargain (it even includes coffee), we wonder what is. Reliable producers pepper the wine list, which is considerately priced, and the choice of half-bottles is impressive. House vin de table is £8.50.

CHEF: John Steel PROPRIETORS: John and Ann Steel OPEN: Sun L 12 to 2.30, Mon to Sat D 7 to 9.30 CLOSED: 1 week Jan, 2 weeks Aug, MEALS: Set L Sun £10.50, Set D £14.50 (2 courses) to £17.95 SERVICE: not inc, card slips closed CARDS: Access, Delta, Switch, Visa DETAILS: 30 seats. Private parties: 40 main room. Car park. Children's helpings. Smart dress preferred. No smoking while others eat. Music

SANDIWAY Cheshire map 7

▲ *Nunsmere Hall*

CHESHIRE 1996 HOTEL

Tarporley Road, Sandiway CW8 2ES
TEL: (01606) 889100 FAX: (01606) 889055 COOKING 3*
off A49, 4m SW of Northwich COST £28–£63

Built around the turn of the century for the indomitable shipping magnate Sir Aubrey Brocklebank, Nunsmere has had a heroic history. It was here in the 1920s that the plans for the *Queen Mary* were pored over, with 16 successive models bobbing in the simulation tank under Sir Aubrey's critical gaze. He didn't live to see the launch. Another big launch took place in 1989, when the McHardys opened the newly converted Nunsmere as a top-drawer country-house hotel. The interior décor is of a high order, with elegant Chinese figurines of cats and horses popping up everywhere. Reports still comment on the youthfulness of all visible staff – yet the operation usually runs on rails.

The cooking, led by Paul Kitching, is described as 'modern French'. Presentational skills figure highly, there are delicate touches of Provence, and many dishes discreetly buoy up their main ingredients with luxuries. A poached egg may sound a little abstemious to start, but it is surrounded by truffled cream sauce, deep-fried spinach and morels. Sauté red mullet from Cornwall is sauced with orange and butter, and further enriched with foie gras. Though braised leg of duckling with black pudding and creamed potatoes is only a first course, the restraint dispels all doubts about culinary judgement. Main courses, offering more meats than fish, continue to impress. Whole pigeon is roasted with veal sweetbreads and served with tarragon ravioli, or there may be Gressingham duck breast fashionably treated with a white truffle sauce and a balsamic vinegar glaze. A December pudding plate that paired a tuile full of orange mousse with a chocolate cup of tangerine ice-cream managed to outdo all that had gone before. Vegetarians have their own richly varied menu that wisely leaves it to the diner to decide which shall be starter and which main course. Some grumble a little about portion sizes, but the consensus is that this is a seriously accomplished kitchen that does Cheshire proud.

If you have only £20 for wine, the list won't do you many favours. Perhaps the assumption is that if you have only £20 you probably wouldn't be here. The house selections are good, though, and the small set of halves offers a wide stylistic range. Italians are less expensive than most, so it's all the more regrettable that none of the reds owns up to its producer. House French is £13.15.

CHEF: Paul Kitching PROPRIETORS: Malcolm and Julie McHardy OPEN: all week 12 to 2, 7 to 10 MEALS: Set L £16.95 (2 courses) to £19.50, Set D £28.50 to £34.50. Minimum £20 D SERVICE: not inc, card slips closed CARDS: Access, Amex, Diners, Switch, Visa DETAILS: 50 seats. 6 tables outside. Private parties: 60 main room, 22 to 42 private rooms. Car park. Vegetarian meals. Children's helpings. No children under 10 D. Smart dress preferred. No smoking in dining-room. Wheelchair access (3 steps; also WC). Music ACCOMMODATION: 32 rooms, all with bath/shower. TV. Phone. B&B £95 to £120. Rooms for disabled. Children welcome. Afternoon teas. Garden (*The Which? Hotel Guide*)

SAXTON North Yorkshire map 9

Plough Inn £

Headwell Lane, Saxton LS24 9PB
TEL: (01937) 557242 COOKING 2
off A162, between Tadcaster and Sherburn in Elmet COST £15–£29

'From the outside the Plough looks no more than the average village local, but once you step into the bar, you know that you have found somewhere special,' comments a reporter. The building is a converted Victorian farmhouse in a tiny hamlet within striking distance of the Wars of the Roses battlefields. It is run as a family affair, and the Treanors have resisted the temptation to tart up the place. A fire blazes in the bar when the Yorkshire weather closes in, and an easy-going atmosphere pervades the warm dining-room. Dishes are listed on blackboards hung over the fireplace, and the same *carte* operates in both bar and dining-room. (Sunday lunch is a set menu.)

Simon Treanor's cooking is modern by inclination, although he is equally at home in the comforting world of black pudding and roast beef. Recent highlights have included warm goats' cheese and shallot tart served with a blob of tomato pickle; rabbit and pork terrine inlaid with pieces of soft carrot; and salmon with chive and butter sauce. But there is much more, from rack of lamb with green peppercorn crust and chickpea cake, to a vegetarian galette with Thai vegetables. Puddings – and limitless coffee – receive fulsome praise: beautifully presented sticky toffee pudding with butterscotch sauce; chocolate and almond ice-cream in a brandy-snap basket surrounded by three pools of colourful coulis. The wine list is a lively, catholic selection of interesting stuff at down-to-earth prices. House wines are £7.65 and a further half-dozen are also available by the glass.

CHEF: Simon Treanor PROPRIETORS: Simon and Nicola Treanor OPEN: Tue to Sun L 12 to 2, Tue to Sat D 6.30 to 10 MEALS: alc (main courses £7.50 to £9). Set L Sun £9.95 SERVICE: not inc CARDS: Access, Delta, Switch, Visa DETAILS: 65 seats. 4 tables outside. Private parties: 65 main room. Car park. Vegetarian meals. Children's helpings. Smart dress preferred. No smoking in dining-room. Wheelchair access (also WC). Music. Air-conditioned

---

The Good Food Guide *is a registered trade mark of Which? Ltd.*

Card slips closed *in the details at the end of an entry indicates that the total on the slips of credit cards is closed when handed over for signature.*

SEAFORD East Sussex map 3

Quincy's £✱

42 High Street, Seaford BN25 1PL — COOKING 2*
TEL: (01323) 895490 — COST £30–£36

'Passengers for the 10.30pm sailing from Newhaven could do a lot worse than take an early dinner at Quincy's; they open at 7.15' – although it would also be a pleasure to spend the whole evening here. Two rooms have been knocked into one in this shop conversion. Cookery and wine books fill the shelves, confirming that the Dowdings' interest in food and drink is more than skin deep.

Dinner is two or three courses, with a wide spread of dishes from beetroot soup with savoury duck patties, through stir-fried squid with black beans, to rabbit cooked in Barolo with wild mushrooms and polenta. Although it calls on several culinary traditions, this is more than just 'ip-dip-dip' cooking: genuine skill underpins it, and there is consistency in execution and firm control over flavourings. It is diligent, and not in the least complacent. Vegetarian options run to spinach soufflé stuffed with goats' cheese and tomato with an anchovy sauce, or roast aubergine with peppered couscous and coriander relish. Occasionally a savoury – hot onion tart with melted goats' cheese, for example – may appear as an alternative to warm damson frangipane with calvados custard, or hot lime soufflé with passion-fruit ice-cream.

Ian Dowding explains that more breads are now on offer, including 'onion, wild mushroom, peanut and sesame, pimento and poppy seed. At the end of the session we are usually left with just the plain bread.' A warm welcome, friendly and efficient service, and a lack of pretension all heighten the pleasure. The serviceable list of wines perhaps lacks the zest of the food, but there are some good bottles, a fair showing of half-bottles, and mark-ups are reasonable. Half a dozen house wines start at £8.25, with three by the glass.

CHEF: Ian Dowding PROPRIETORS: Ian and Dawn Dowding OPEN: Sun L 12 to 2.30, Tue to Sat D 7.15 to 10 MEALS: Set L and D £17.95 (2 courses) to £21.45. Minimum £17.95 SERVICE: not inc CARDS: Access, Amex, Visa DETAILS: 28 seats. Private parties: 20 main room. Vegetarian meals. Children welcome. Music

SEATON BURN Tyne & Wear map 10

▲ *Horton Grange* £✱

Seaton Burn NE13 6BU
TEL: (01661) 860686 FAX: (01661) 860308 — COOKING 2*
off A1, at Stannington, 3m N of Newcastle upon Tyne — COST £41–£49

The solid, grey-stone house is within the Newcastle city boundary yet in the middle of open farmland. It once belonged to a farming family, and is now elegantly furnished but not designerish, with comfortable sofas and smartly laid tables. 'A delightful place,' summed up one contented visitor who was addressed as 'Ma'am' though she wasn't the Queen. The Shiltons run the place 'very much in a hands-on way', so there is no question about informed advice on the food. They are cheerful hosts who preside over a professional organisation and take pains to do the right things.

It is not a place to drop into for a quick snack. Five courses are the pattern, six if you count coffee and chocolates, which come as part of the deal, although 'it would be nice to be able to choose to eat less for less outlay', maintained one. Water-ice or soup constitute the second course – a rather unusual lamb consommé on one occasion – and a cheese selection slots in after pudding: perhaps Lancashire, Leicester and Stilton. Rich chicken liver parfait is in classical vein, though the general leaning is towards more modern touches: vinegars to brighten up sauces and added to warm dressings, or an onion compote with medallions of venison. Fresh fish and good-quality meats underpin the operation, though the food can be just a little bit fancy when simpler ideas might work better. Around two dozen wines stay mostly between £10 and £20, with house Navarra at £10.90. All the wines on the list can be had by the glass.

CHEF: Stephen Martin PROPRIETORS: Andrew and Susan Shilton OPEN: Mon to Sat D only 7 to 8.45 CLOSED: 25 and 26 Dec, 1 Jan MEALS: Set D £32 SERVICE: not inc CARDS: Access, Delta, Switch, Visa DETAILS: 30 seats. Private parties: 35 main room, 10 private room. Car park. Children's helpings. Smart dress preferred. No smoking in dining-room. Wheelchair access (also WC). Music ACCOMMODATION: 9 rooms, all with bath/shower. TV. Phone. B&B £59 to £80. Rooms for disabled. Children welcome. Garden (*The Which? Hotel Guide*)

SEMINGTON Wiltshire map 2

▲ *Highfield House, Edward's Dining Room*

Semington BA14 6JN
TEL: (01380) 870554 COOKING 1
on A350, 2m S of Melksham COST £23–£28

Take an eighteenth-century Grade II listed farmhouse, turn it carefully into a sumptuous restaurant with a couple of guest-rooms, pack it with teddy bears, and you may have a winning formula. At least Highfield House has, and there has been no stinting on the teddies. They lord it over table-tops, and colonise the loo. Their namesake, Edward Street, manages to cook some unflashy but accomplished food in the middle of all this. A large cheese scone filled with mushrooms simmered in garlic cream may be a comforting way to start, 'escalope' of pink trout with a crab and lobster sauce a more opulent one. Prawns turn up in some out-of-the-way combinations, either in a first course of sliced pineapple with cocktail sauce, or stuffed into chicken breast and served with a mushroom and tarragon cream sauce. Loin of pork with an apple and cranberry *jus* is more recognisably English, while kumquats give a sharp twist to the duck with orange theme. Finish with the likes of crème brûlée with raspberries, chocolate roulade, or coffee toffee pie. Service aims to make you feel at home. Somebody has spent a deal of time sourcing drink-related literary quips for the wine list, which is a fairly priced if limited collection. House wines are £9.50.

CHEF: Edward Street PROPRIETORS: Edward and Philippa Street OPEN: Sun L 12 to 3, Wed to Sat D 7 to 9.30 (10 Sat) MEALS: Set L Sun £7.50 (2 courses), Set D £16.50 SERVICE: not inc CARDS: Access, Amex, Visa DETAILS: 40 seats. 3 tables outside. Private parties: 40 main room. Car park. Children's helpings. Wheelchair access (1 step; also WC). Music ACCOMMODATION: 2 rooms. B&B £20 to £30. Children welcome

SHAFTESBURY Dorset map 2

La Fleur de Lys

25 Salisbury Street, Shaftesbury SP7 8EL — COOKING 2
TEL: (01747) 853717 — COST £25–£46

A bare quarter of a mile away from Gold Hill, scene of the famous Hovis advert (and you thought that was set in Yorkshire!), is this small neighbourhood restaurant overlooking the Blackmoor Vale. It is run by a dedicated trio who have carefully sized up the local constituency and tempted it in with a range of fixed-price and à la carte menus of dishes that soothe rather than shock. Combinations may be unusual but always logical, as in a starter of smoked chicken, asparagus and apple with toasted pine-nuts in a honey dressing, or a main course of fillet of brill with accompaniments of scallops, langoustines and mange-tout in a pink champagne sauce. Artistry is let rip at pudding stage, with constructions such as caramel and pecan meringue with coffee and Tia Maria mousse on a dark chocolate sauce. Coffee and petits fours are generally up to the mark, and service is commended as 'friendly and unobtrusive' – the perfect mix.

An enthusiastic mind is evident in the extensive wine list that has plenty of top-value choice in the southern hemisphere, as well as a fine slate of Washington State wines and an impressive list of mature clarets. Burgundies are less good. The intrepid may like to try their luck with the Turkish demi-sec. House Spanish is £9.95. CELLARMAN'S CHOICE: Cooks Sauvignon Blanc 1991, Fernhill Vineyard, New Zealand, £18; Nederburg Chardonnay 1993, Paarl, South Africa, £13.

CHEFS: David Shepherd and Marc Preston PROPRIETORS: David Shepherd, Mary Griffin and Marc Preston OPEN: Tue to Sun L 12 to 12.45, Mon to Sat D 7 to 10 CLOSED: Mon to Wed during last 3 weeks Jan MEALS: alc (main courses L £11 to £13.50, D £14 to £16). Set L Tue to Fri £12 (2 courses), Set L Sun £14.95 (2 courses) to £17.95, Set D Mon to Thur £15.95 (2 courses) to £19.45. Minimum £9 L, £15 D SERVICE: not inc CARDS: Access, Amex, Delta, Diners, Visa DETAILS: 40 seats. Private parties: 36 main room, 12 private room. Vegetarian meals. Children's helpings. Smart dress preferred. No smoking in 1 dining-room. Music. Air-conditioned

SHEFFIELD South Yorkshire map 9

Greenhead House

84 Burncross Road, Chapeltown, Sheffield S30 4SF — COOKING 2
TEL: 0114-246 9004 — COST £36–£46

Neil and Anne Allen have started to make speciality soups and other products as a sideline at their restaurant on the northern fringes of Sheffield; otherwise, it is business as usual. The setting is a small stone-built house with a pleasing garden and an attractive dining-room done out in subdued colours. Neil's four-course dinner menu (priced according to the main course) has noticeable French overtones and acknowledges the Mediterranean to boot.

Commended dishes have included mussels with Roquefort, quail with fennel and rosemary, and calf's liver with aubergines and tomato. On the menu you might find anything from cod fillet topped with slices of smoked cod roe wrapped in puff pastry, to Aberdeen Angus sirloin steak and scallops thermidor.

One satisfied couple also praised the vegetables, which were 'not grossly undercooked as is so fashionable'. Moving on to desserts, you could choose between poached pear tart, 'wet' chocolate cake soaked with brandy, or berry fruits with lemon cream. French and New World wines jostle for the limelight on the short, affordably priced list. Australian house wine is £9.95.

CHEFS: Neil Allen and Christine Roberts PROPRIETORS: Neil and Anne Allen OPEN: Wed to Sat D only 7 to 9 CLOSED: Christmas to New Year, 2 weeks Easter, 2 weeks mid-Aug MEALS: Set D £27.50 to £29.95 SERVICE: not inc, card slips closed CARDS: Access, Visa DETAILS: 34 seats. Private parties: 34 main room. Car park. No children under 7; children's helpings. Smart dress preferred. No smoking in dining-room. No music

Le Neptune

141 West Street, Sheffield S1 4EW — COOKING 1
TEL: 0114-279 6677 — COST £22–£46

'If you blink in West Street,' comments one familiar with the upheavals, 'there is a danger of losing yourself. Sheffield is transforming itself at a pace.' The expanding university is one of the prime motivators, and the Neptune – like much else – has a sense of suspended anticipation. The cooking takes a fundamentally French line, with fish the main business, offering scallops grilled in the shell with herbs, cod baked on Breton potatoes, and chicken breast stuffed with St Agur cheese and served with roast garlic and shallots. A main course of monkfish casserole, more 'prissy' than robust, nevertheless produced strong flavours. Coffee and walnut ice is an 'expertly and cleanly flavoured marriage of the two ingredients'; other desserts include baked tamarillo, passion-fruit crème brûlée, and pear and raisin tart. Service is 'pleasant enough'. The wine list, short and to the point, is not excessively priced. House French starts at £8.95.

CHEF: Nick Wilks PROPRIETOR: William Glossop OPEN: Mon to Fri L 12.30 to 2, Mon to Sat D 6.15 to 10 (11 Sat) CLOSED: 7 days at New Year MEALS: alc Mon to Fri L, Mon to Thur D (main courses £8 to £16). Set L £10 (2 courses) to £17.95, Set D £14.25 to £17.95 SERVICE: not inc, card slips closed CARDS: Access, Amex, Visa DETAILS: 70 seats. Private parties: 50 main room, 22 private room. Vegetarian meals. Children's helpings. Smart dress preferred. No pipes in dining-room. Wheelchair access (also WC). Music

SHELF West Yorkshire — map 8

Bentley's £

12 Wade House Road, Shelf HX3 7PB — COOKING 1
TEL: (01274) 690992 — COST £12–£43

The full title is Bentley's Food and Wine Company – a reminder that this restaurant is housed in a converted wine shop. Descend a stone staircase to reach the main dining-room, an impressive conversion with rough walls, a stone-flagged floor, polished tables and fresh flowers. Starters vary from day to day, and the kitchen copes equally well with warm salad of black pudding, dressed crab, and scallops with mash, spinach and garlic sauce. Ideas are up to the minute and classic by turns – witness main courses of loin of venison with oyster mushrooms and damson wine sauce, confit of duck with boulangère potatoes, and roast salmon with hollandaise and crispy leeks. You might even notice that rare and unclassifiable speciality 'freshly baked-to-order Yorkshire puddings with foie gras and onion gravy'. Home-made orange ice-cream, cherry Bakewell tart and sticky toffee pudding are typical desserts. The wine list is notable for its low prices. Six house wines start at £8.50.

CHEFS: Paul Bentley and Anthony Bickers PROPRIETORS: Paul and Pam Bentley OPEN: Tue to Fri and Sun L 12 to 2, Tue to Sat D 6.30 to 9.30 CLOSED: 26 to 31 Dec, 2 weeks Aug MEALS: alc D (main courses £7.50 to £13.50). Set L Tue to Fri £4.25 (2 courses) to £5.95, Set L Sun £8.50. Licensed, but you may also bring your own: corkage £2 SERVICE: not inc, card slips closed CARDS: Access, Visa DETAILS: 44 seats. Private parties: 25 main room, 24 and 25 private rooms. Car park. Vegetarian meals. Children's helpings. Smart dress preferred. No smoking in dining-room. Music

SHEPTON MALLET Somerset map 2

Blostin's

29 Waterloo Road, Shepton Mallet BA4 5HH COOKING 2
TEL: (01749) 343648 COST £22–£34

The style is somewhere between a restaurant and a bistro: small, rustic, but very friendly. Diners, crammed in, don't seem to mind the lack of space, but they are grateful for the value. Nick Reed's cooking is moving away from the heavier cream sauces towards more natural jus liaisons – not perhaps a startling revelation these days, but welcome none the less. A three-course meal might take in fish soup with rouille and croûtons, breast of chicken with oyster mushrooms and a mustard sauce, and iced ginger meringue with coffee sauce. Fish from Newlyn appears in the form of pan-fried skate, steamed mussels, or poached monkfish with a saffron sauce and parsnip chips, and freshness and accurate cooking combine to elicit praise for a dish of griddled scallops with samphire and lemon-butter sauce. Winter brings grilled pigeon with rocket salad and sun-dried tomatoes, perhaps followed by loin of venison with wild mushrooms. Vegetarians are offered a separate menu that might include grilled goats' cheese with toasted brioche and endive salad, and aubergine fritters with oyster mushrooms and braised lentils. The 40-bottle wine list is arranged by grape variety. Most bottles are under £15, with house French at £7.95.

CHEF: Nick Reed PROPRIETORS: Nick and Lynne Reed OPEN: Tue to Sat D only 7 to 9.30 (10 Sat) CLOSED: 2 weeks Jan, 2 weeks June MEALS: alc (main courses £11.50 to £12.50). Set D £13.95 (2 courses) to £14.95 SERVICE: not inc, card slips closed CARDS: Access, Delta, Switch, Visa DETAILS: 32 seats. Private parties: 32 main room. Vegetarian meals. Children's helpings. No cigars/pipes in dining-room. Wheelchair access (2 steps). Music

▲ *Bowlish House* 🍷

Wells Road, Shepton Mallet BA4 5JD
TEL/FAX: (01749) 342022 COOKING 2*
on A371, ¼m from town centre COST £19–£35

'After five lonely years of hard times,' write the Morleys in response to last year's *Guide* entry, 'a pat on the head is worth more to us than a new car.' Heads are not, of course, patted out of sheer sympathy, but in acknowledgement of consistent, and improving, performance. The Morleys achieved that in the teeth of the recession – no mean feat in itself – and their restaurant-with-rooms has once more garnered a healthy customer base. It is a well-maintained Palladian house just outside the town centre.

Linda Morley's cooking, presented in the form of a set-price meal of three courses with coffee, is careful not to go off at tangents. Variations on cheese soufflés include Cheddar with spring onions, or Stilton with celeriac. Filo purses of smoked chicken and apple on a mint mayonnaise is an inventive, well-established starter, and duck breast with pink peppercorns, strawberries and balsamic vinegar one of the signature main courses. At a family birthday outing grilled goats' cheese yielded up its textures in strict sequence – 'crunchy on the outside, then melty, then chewy'. Succulent entrecôtes were 'perfectly cooked as requested, but needed more tang in the sauce until the girls were told to squeeze the roasted garlic', and were grateful for the advice. Piquancy as well as richness comes into play for desserts, such as banana meringue with a lime zest sauce. Thoughtfully balanced vegetables and good chocolate truffles with coffee play their supporting roles well.

The wine list is a monument to vinous enthusiasm. Painstaking consideration has been applied to every section, from the flight of vintages of Ch. Musar through the very sound Italian and Spanish bottles to the fine wines of the big French regions, many of them at complete maturity. Prices throughout are demonstrably kind, and the list offers a good selection of halves. The ten house wines are all at one price just as they should be: £8.25. CELLARMAN'S CHOICE: Hollick Chardonnay 1992, Coonawarra, S. Australia, £14.95; Nebbiolo delle Langhe, Monprivato 1991, Giuseppe Mascarello, £13.75.

CHEF: Linda Morley PROPRIETORS: Bob and Linda Morley OPEN: L first Sun of month 1.30 (one sitting; L other days by arrangement), all week D 7 to 9.30 CLOSED: 1 week spring, 1 week autumn MEALS: Set L Sun £12.95, Set D £22.50 SERVICE: not inc, card slips closed CARDS: Access, Visa DETAILS: 24 seats. Private parties: 36 main room. Car park. Vegetarian meals. Children welcome. No smoking while others are eating. No music ACCOMMODATION: 3 rooms, all with bath/shower. TV. B&B £48 (double room). Children welcome. Baby facilities. Pets welcome in bedrooms only. Garden (*The Which? Hotel Guide*)

SHINFIELD Berkshire map 2

L'Ortolan

The Old Vicarage, Church Lane, Shinfield RG2 9BY
TEL: (01734) 883783 FAX: (01734) 885391 COOKING **4***
off A33, S of M4 junction 11 COST £40–£93

In contrast to the wallowing luxury of some places, and the claustrophobic tweeness of many a country-house hotel, this old red-brick vicarage is refreshingly modest. Indeed, it is the domestic scale and lack of grandeur that brings full focus to what is on the plate. There are conservatories for drinking and eating in, and the doors are flung open on warm days. Several menus offer lots of choice, and descriptions give a clear picture of what to expect. After a slightly wobbly patch in 1994 the food seems to be back on course. 'Dazzling' was how one reporter rated it. 'Brilliant!' wrote another, several times. 'Our meal became a testament to the chef's fanatical sense of detail and purposeful single-mindedness,' added an inspector.

The food can be complicated, but it is also balanced. The impact of component tastes – sweet, sour, salty and bitter – is carefully controlled from a humble sorbet to the most complicated sauce. The food uses, but doesn't hide behind, luxury ingredients and, like his one-time mentor Raymond Blanc, John Burton-Race is an exponent of layering elements in a dish. 'The flavours were completely distinct and well developed,' wrote a reporter of roasted scallops with artichoke hearts, and a mousse of white fish with warmed oysters. Beef fillet with a tartlet of bone-marrow, and venison in a garlic and herb crust are about as close to being robust as the cooking gets, and although some flavours are fugitive, an inspector gave 'delicacy' the benefit of the doubt.

Even at these heady prices 'value for money' is not in question, according to one reporter. From one of the set lunch menus, three small fillets of just-cooked and 'deliberately lukewarm' skate wing were followed by roast duck legs; in each case acidity was carefully considered and finely judged. Vegetables are first-rate, and the cheeseboard 'was simply beyond praise'. Among desserts, an inspector's assiette framboisier 'scaled the Himalayan heights', with uniform excellence displayed in a light foamy soufflé with a crisp, sugary crust; an impressively silky sorbet; and a jelly sitting next to a luscious vanilla mousse topped with tiny raspberries, its sides wrapped in an extraordinarily bitter casing of chocolate. 'A virtuoso display of brilliant technique, led by an inventive mind, and finished with a feather-light touch' was one inspector's summing up of a summer lunch. Shortcomings, such as the rather impersonal service by young French staff, pale into the background. Wine quality on the French list (with just a few Australians and Californians) is good, but prices can be heart-stoppingly high. Look to the lesser French regions for a little relief, or ask the sommelier, who seems to know his stuff. House wines are around £15, and wines by the glass begin at £2.95.

CHEF: John Burton-Race PROPRIETOR: Burton-Race Restaurants plc OPEN: Tue to Sun L 12 to 2.15, Tue to Sat D 7 to 10 CLOSED: last 2 weeks Feb, last 2 weeks Aug MEALS: Set L £25 to £35, Set D £35 to £59 SERVICE: not inc CARDS: Access, Amex, Diners, Switch, Visa DETAILS: 65 seats. Private parties: 45 main room, 10 and 30 private rooms. Car park. Children's helpings. Smart dress preferred. No pipes in dining-room. Music

SHOTLEY Suffolk map 6

Old Boot House

Main Road, Shotley IP9 1EY
TEL: (01473) 787755 COOKING 1
10m SE of Ipswich on B1456 COST £19–£37

This old boot is certainly out on a limb: a mile or so from the Orwell estuary, surrounded by cornfields. The Chamberlains have none the less forged themselves a style that shows they are not entirely cut off from the outside world. Deep-fried squid sauced with orange and ginger, and chicken with its livers cooked with prunes, bacon and cognac suggest a restless culinary intelligence. Technique does not let the side down either. Crunchy vegetable spring rolls come with strips of lamb and a soy and sesame oil sauce for dipping. Lavender and honey are used in a gravy to accompany a 'succulent' duck breast sliced and interleaved with fig – a brave conception that works.

The floral tendency recurs in puddings, such as a 'gorgeous' tartlet of strawberries and crystallised rose-petals on sour cream. Sourness has been marshalled again to good effect in a black cherry sauce with rice-pudding fritters. Coffee comes with 'luscious little chocolate croissants'. The cooking is 'always imaginative and flexible', writes one who has followed Ian Chamberlain's career for several years. 'Service with a smile' helps to ensure return visits. Wines are a resourceful selection from around the world offered at prices that won't break the bank. House French is £7.35.

CHEF: Ian Chamberlain PROPRIETORS: Ian and Pamela Chamberlain OPEN: Tue to Sun L 12 to 1.45, Tue to Sat D 7 to 8.45 (9.30 Sat) MEALS: alc (main courses £7 to £15). Set L Sun £12.95 SERVICE: not inc, card slips closed CARDS: Access, Visa DETAILS: 45 seats. Private parties: 45 main room. Car park. Children welcome. Smart dress preferred. No smoking in dining-room. No music

SHURDINGTON Gloucestershire map 5

▲ *Greenway*

Shurdington GL51 5UG
TEL: (01242) 862352 FAX: (01242) 862780 COOKING 1
on A46, 2½m S of Cheltenham COST £27–£48

Now under the new ownership of David White, one-time manager of the Lygon Arms in Broadway (see entry), the sixteenth-century manor-house of weathered stone set against a backdrop of green hills provides one of the most beautiful tableaux that even the Cotswolds can come up with. Dinner is in the conservatory overlooking the fish pond, and the menu makes sure to list its up-to-the-minute ingredients of morels, red onion marmalade, gremolata, baby capers, pearl barley risotto, and so on. It prides itself, rightly, on fine sourcing of Severn salmon, Scottish beef and Cotswold venison. Among fish dishes enjoyed at a May meal was a warm salad of sweet, fresh, succulent seared skate wing paired with some tasty smoky ham in a split-pea dressing.

At an inspection meal, however, rich sauces tended to unbalance the food and 'detracted from the finesse', though venison 'came in slices pink and juicy' and beef fillet had 'superb' texture. Commendable cheeses might include unpasteurised English ones, such as Montgomery Cheddar or Harbourne Blue, or Irish Cashel Blue, Gubbeen and Mileens. Service at inspection left a lot to be desired: 'I have not said 'Excuse me!' so many times to gain attention in a restaurant for years.' Wines match the elegant setting, with a wide-ranging choice and some country-house mark-ups. House wine is £12.50.

CHEF: Christopher Colmer PROPRIETORS: David and Valerie White OPEN: Sun to Fri L 12.30 to 2 (Sat by arrangement), all week D 7.30 to 9.30 (9.45 Sat) MEALS: Set L £12.50 (2 courses) to £16, Set L Sun £16, Set D £27.50 SERVICE: not inc, card slips closed CARDS: Access, Amex, Diners, Switch, Visa DETAILS: 60 seats. 5 tables outside. Private parties: 65 main room, 14 and 24 private rooms. Car park. Vegetarian meals. No children under 7. Smart dress preferred. No cigars/pipes in dining-room. Wheelchair access (also WC). Music ACCOMMODATION: 19 rooms, all with bath/shower. TV. Phone. B&B £77.50 to £160. Deposit: 1 night's stay. Rooms for disabled. No children under 7. Afternoon teas. Garden (*The Which? Hotel Guide*)

SISSINGHURST Kent map 3

Rankins' Restaurant

The Street, Sissinghurst TN17 2JH COOKING 1*
TEL: (01580) 713964 COST £29–£39

Framed watercolours by Hugh Rankin decorate the walls of this family-run restaurant, a weatherboarded cottage with a slate roof and wooden beams, in the centre of Sissinghurst. The food is modern and British, which is to say it picks up ingredients and ideas from the north of Scotland to the southern Mediterranean and builds them into an attractive menu of about four choices per course. An early-summer menu included Hastings smokie, a lamb 'burger' with lemon, mushrooms and green olives, and coffee fudge pudding with toffee ice-cream. Fish and vegetables are as prominent as meat, prompting good reports of tiger prawns with Thai spices, herb-crusted cod, and a spinach and roasted red-pepper terrine with mushroom sauce. Cheese is 'a finger of the cheese of the week', and 'the chocolate terrine with strawberries is a *must*'. The short wine list is sympathetically priced, with house red at £8.50, white £7.80, with both at £2.20 a glass.

CHEF: Hugh Rankin PROPRIETORS: Hugh and Leonora Rankin OPEN: Sun L 12.30 to 1.30, Wed to Sat D 7.30 to 9 CLOSED: bank hols MEALS: Set L Sun £20.95, Set D £19.95 (2 courses) to £23.95 SERVICE: not inc CARDS: Access, Delta, Visa DETAILS: 26 seats. Private parties: 30 main room. Vegetarian meals. Children's helpings. Smart dress preferred. No smoking until 2 L, 10 D. No music

SLAIDBURN Lancashire map 8

▲ *Parrock Head*

Woodhouse Lane, Slaidburn BB7 3AH
TEL: (01200) 446614 FAX: (01200) 446313 COOKING 1
1m NW of Slaidburn COST £21–£30

'Few restaurants can have such a breathtaking setting,' writes a well-travelled reporter of the Umberses' farmhouse hotel in rugged Lancashire moorland. In contrast to the surrounding bleakness, all is comfort within, from the dining-room in the former milking shed to Vicky Umbers's thoughtful set-price menus. Some daring turns are essayed in accompaniments, but the balance seems to hold. Scallops come in a vermouth and tarragon cream sauce on chillied spaghetti, while a soup that combined peas, pears and cinnamon had 'interesting' flavours. Sea bass, so often given the Chinese treatment, is here sauced with gooseberry and nutmeg and garnished with a tagliatelle of carrot. Seared sirloin steaks are from properly matured beef, and may be peppered and accompanied by snails in a filo boat on Shropshire Blue.

Vegetables are out of the ordinary – perhaps butter-nut squash, salsify and cauliflower in a lovage sauce – and good pastry-work is demonstrated in a tartlet of strawberries on crème pâtissière. Despite the complexity, the cooking still manages to seem 'uncluttered'. Friendliness and efficiency typify the service. The well-spread wine list keeps prices briskly in check, with house wines at £7.50.

CHEFS: Vicky Umbers and Dale Thornber PROPRIETORS: Richard and Vicky Umbers OPEN: Sun L (bookings only) 12 to 1.30, D all week 7 to 8.30 MEALS: Set L Sun £13.50, Set D £17.50; light L available Mon to Sat SERVICE: not inc, card slips closed CARDS: Access, Amex, Diners, Switch, Visa DETAILS: 35 seats. Private parties: 40 main room. Car park. Children's helpings. Smart dress preferred. No smoking in dining-room. Wheelchair access (also WC). Music ACCOMMODATION: 9 rooms, all with bath/shower. TV. Phone. B&B £40 to £69. Deposit: £10. Rooms for disabled. Children welcome. Baby facilities. Pets welcome. Afternoon teas. Garden (*The Which? Hotel Guide*)

SOUTHALL Greater London map 3

Brilliant £ **NEW ENTRY**

72–74 Western Road, Southall UB2 5DZ COOKING 2
TEL: 0181-574 1928 FAX: 0181-574 0276 COST £16–£37

Brilliant by name and brilliant by nature – so indicate reports received this year. Opened in 1975, and laying claim to being Southall's original culinary star, this is – according to the owners – 'a restaurant run by a family for families'. The Anands (who also maintain Madhu's Brilliant, see below) have created 'a phenomenally successful operation', according to one who is seriously hooked on the place. Plans are afoot to refurbish the upstairs (used as an overspill area) into a fully fledged dining-room; 'if only he'd change the music and do something about the décor while he was at it,' adds a reporter. The cooking is North Indian and is reckoned to be among the best of its kind in the UK. Recommendations speak for themselves: masala egg ('for the princely sum of 60p'), mixed vegetable bhajias ('the best I have ever eaten'), aloo chollay, methi chicken 'bursting with spicy flavour', chilli chicken ('no complaints under the Trade Descriptions Act here'), king prawn masala that actually tastes of crustacea, and methi paneer (a variation on mater paneer that includes fenugreek) have received unqualified praise. Other visitors have waxed enthusiastic about butter chicken and the karahi dishes. The kitchen has no tandoor (Mr Anand Senior never believed there was any culinary mileage in such devices), so nan bread is made in a novel way: a searingly hot griddle is used to cook one side and then the other side is grilled, mimicking the effect of the clay oven. Rice and kulfi are both superb. 'It is difficult to eat in ordinary Indian restaurants after this,' concludes a devotee. To drink, there is lassi by the pint, Indian lagers by the bottle and a handful of cheap and cheerful wines, with house red and white at £7.

CHEF: D.K. Anand PROPRIETORS: K.K. and D.K. Anand OPEN: Tue to Fri L 12.15 to 2.45, Tue to Sun D 6 to 11.15 (midnight Fri and Sat) MEALS: alc (main courses £4.50 to £7.50) SERVICE: 10% CARDS: Access, Amex, Delta, Diners, Switch, Visa DETAILS: 120 seats. Private parties: 40 main room, 40 private room. Vegetarian meals. Children's helpings. Smart dress preferred. No smoking in 1 dining-room. Wheelchair access (also WC). Music. Air-conditioned

Not inc *in the details at the end of an entry indicates that no service charge is made and any tipping is at the discretion of the customer.*

indicates a change of chef since last year's Guide.

Madhu's Brilliant £

39 South Road, Southall UB1 1SW
TEL: 0181-574 1897 and 571 6380 COOKING 2
FAX: 0181-813 8639 COST £16–£34

The story goes that Madhu's was set up by Sanjay and Sanjeev Anand (sons of the owner of the original Brilliant; see above) because in 1980 they believed that tandoori chicken would be the next Indian culinary trend in Britain. Their oven not only delivers definitive versions of marinated and fiercely cooked chicken, lamb chops and kebabs, but also spectacularly good breads – fluffy nans with a perfect texture, and bhatura 'puffed up like a balloon', for example. Reporters claim that vegetable dishes often outshine meat and fish: aloo tikka (deep-fried mashed potato rissoles with fenugreek) are in a class of their own, bhindis are excellent, and aloo chollay makes its impact with 'perfectly tender chickpeas'. Otherwise, butter chicken and chilli chicken are high points, and rice is reckoned to be 'remarkable'. Even when the place is full to bursting with a lively mixture of Indian families and non-Indian aficionados, service remains knowledgeable and friendly: there is genuine politeness and concern that things should be enjoyed to the full. Like the Brilliant, Madhu's has the power to put most other Indian restaurants in the shade. Drink lassi, lager or one of the basic wines: house wine is £7.

CHEFS: Sanjeev Anand and Satpal Gill PROPRIETORS: Jagdish Kumar Anand, Krishna Kumari Anand, Sanjay Anand and Sanjeev Anand OPEN: Wed to Fri and Mon L 12.30 to 2.30, Wed to Mon D 6 to 11.30 (midnight Fri and Sat) MEALS: alc (main courses £3.50 to £7.50) SERVICE: 10%, card slips closed CARDS: Access, Amex, Delta, Diners, Switch, Visa DETAILS: 104 seats. Private parties: 60 main room, 60 private room. Vegetarian meals. Children welcome. Smart dress preferred. Wheelchair access. Music. Air-conditioned

SOUTH MOLTON Devon map 1

▲ *Whitechapel Manor* 🍷

South Molton EX36 3EG
TEL: (01769) 573377 FAX: (01769) 573797 COOKING 3
1m off A361 at roundabout 1½m E of South Molton COST £28–£61

The house is a delight, a Grade I listed building dating from 1572, with a Jacobean carved oak screen, William and Mary plasterwork, and big fireplaces in which logs burn slowly. It has the feel of having been lived in since it was built. Seafood and game figure prominently – this is on the edge of Exmoor and people come for pheasant shoots – and the cooking style is fairly conservative but utterly correct and displays the kitchen's obvious sense of confidence in its own abilities. Occasional excursions into a lemon grass sauce (for scallops) or a sweet-and-sour sauce (for steamed fillet of sea bass) do not divert the kitchen from its main business of serving roast saddle of venison or fillet of Devon beef with roasted root vegetables and red wine sauce. This is not a place for vegetarians.

It is a place, however, that gives ingredients a spotlit stage on which to shine. Sauté fillet of turbot is a single fat piece, as well timed as you could ask for. Neither the aubergine purée on which it sits nor the fennel and cardamom sauce tries to upstage it. Salmon is home-smoked, and home-made ravioli might be filled with Brixham crab. At one meal a gamey mix of minced meat in a pithiviers casing came with roast parsnips and port sauce. Cheeses may include Jersey Blue, Sharpham from Devon or Yarg from Cornwall, and puddings range from a dark chocolate mousse, layered with puff pastry and served with coffee-bean sauce, to a poached pear served with honey sauce and vanilla ice-cream, the pear studded with 'intriguingly subtle' cloves.

Service is charm itself, well informed, affable yet concerned that everything goes right. The wine list offers some delightful bottles at generally fair prices, although mark-ups are variable. The New World in particular is worth exploring. Half-bottles on the other hand are mostly French. House wine is around £12.50. CELLARMAN'S CHOICE: Goldwater Estate Chardonnay 1992, Marlborough, New Zealand, £17.50; C.J. Pask Cabernet Merlot 1992, Hawke's Bay, New Zealand, £18.25.

CHEFS: Patricia Shapland and Martin Lee PROPRIETORS: John and Patricia Shapland OPEN: all week 12 to 1.45, 7 to 8.45 MEALS: Set L £19.50 to £28, Set D £28 to £40 SERVICE: not inc, card slips closed CARDS: Access, Amex, Delta, Diners, Switch, Visa DETAILS: 30 seats. Private parties: 36 main room, 6 private room. Car park. Children welcome. Smart dress preferred. No smoking in dining-room. No music ACCOMMODATION: 10 rooms, all with bath/shower. TV. Phone. B&B £65 to £165. Children welcome. Baby facilities. Afternoon teas. Garden (*The Which? Hotel Guide*)

SOUTHSEA Hampshire map 2

Bistro Montparnasse

103 Palmerston Road, Southsea PO5 3PS COOKING 1*
TEL/FAX: (01705) 816754 COST £21–£40

A favoured pit-stop for travellers *en route* to France and well supported by South Coast regulars, the Scotts' likeable town-centre restaurant continues to fulfil its aims. What it offers is competent cooking in pleasant surroundings, although one reporter thought that it was neither 'bistro' nor particularly 'Montparnassien'. Arches divide up the two dining areas on different levels, chintz curtains are draped at the windows, and floral prints decorate the terracotta walls.

The dinner menu is bolstered by a blackboard of specials, and Gillian Scott's cooking has its heart in the Anglo-French tradition. Ham and smoked haddock chowder goes down well as a starter, prosciutto with sauté greens and balsamic vinegar is a neat idea, and a skilfully made spinach, pine-nut and olive tart comes with a jug of caramelised onion sauce. Elsewhere you might find hefty rump of lamb with thyme stuffing, and confit of pork with Puy lentils. Vegetables are 'a star turn', salads are impeccably dressed, while puddings are mostly rich confections such as rum-soaked savarin with gingered fruit compote. A trio of home-made breads, served with olives and olive oil, is worth the supplement, and dark chocolate truffles with coffee round things off. The short wine list is a knowledgeable selection of well-chosen bottles at realistic prices. House wine is £9.90.

CHEF: Gillian Scott PROPRIETORS: Peter and Gillian Scott OPEN: Tue to Sat D only 7 to 10 CLOSED: bank hols, Tue after bank hols MEALS: alc (main courses £10.50 to £15). Set D Tue to Fri £12.50 SERVICE: not inc CARDS: Access, Amex, Visa DETAILS: 50 seats. Private parties: 40 main room, 25 private room. Vegetarian meals. Children's helpings. Smart dress preferred. No cigars/pipes in dining-room. Wheelchair access. No music

SOUTHWATER West Sussex map 3

Cole's

Worthing Road, Southwater, nr Horsham RH13 7BS COOKING 2
TEL: (01403) 730456 COST £22–£42

Having started out in lean economic times, the Coles have now clocked up four years as restaurateurs in this picturesque Sussex village. The setting is a barn conversion, made as handsome as can be with elegant tableware and candlelight at dinner. Passing trade is pretty thin on the ground when you are as far off the beaten track as this, but a solid bedrock of regulars seems to have been established.

Elizabeth Cole's cooking is simple in style, essentially English with gentle inflections of French, shrewdly enough targeted to entice people to travel. Starters of lentil and mushroom pâté flavoured with garlic and thyme, or smoked chicken salad with asparagus and mustard vinaigrette, set the tone. Fish is treated delicately, so that fillets of sea bass may simply be steamed and served on a watercress underlay with chive sauce. Bolder flavours are marshalled for meats: cranberries and ginger go with sauté pork, and apple and Cointreau with venison. Vegetarian options are based on filo pastry or pasta. Pudding people will find a bewilderingly wide choice, from the familiar crème brûlée and sticky toffee to the more inventive orange and lemon roulade filled with grated chocolate. Cole's has found its niche, as our correspondents attest. 'The service was superb,' adds one, 'and contributed to a memorable evening out.' The wine list is serviceable without being electrifying, its main focus of France being supported by regulation pairs from other countries. Trapiche Reserve Chardonnay from Argentina is worth a go, as are the Piper's Brook wines from Tasmania. House French is £9.75.

CHEF: Elizabeth Cole PROPRIETORS: the Cole family OPEN: Tue to Sun 12 to 2, 7 to 9 (Sun D by arrangement) MEALS: alc (main courses £10.50 to £16). Set L £12.95 (2 courses) to £15 SERVICE: not inc CARDS: Access, Amex, Diners, Visa DETAILS: 36 seats. Private parties: 36 main room, 10 private room. Car park. Vegetarian meals. Children's helpings. Smart dress preferred. No smoking in dining-room. Wheelchair access (2 steps; also WC). Music

SOUTHWOLD Suffolk map 6

▲ *The Crown*

High Street, Southwold IP18 6DP COOKING 2*
TEL: (01502) 722275 FAX: (01502) 724805 COST £21–£31

First-time visitors to this seaside East Anglian town may be forgiven for thinking they have arrived in Adnamsville, UK. The portfolio takes in hotel, pub, restaurant, retail and brewing operations, and an internationally renowned wine business. At the head of the empire sits the Crown, a whitewashed eighteenth-century posting-inn that functions as a good bustling local pub, has a recital room for concerts and a serious restaurant.

Into that last, in 1994, came Richard Pye with a brief to continue the daily-changing, innovative cooking of his various predecessors. Fresh fish remains an emphasis, and many readers' letters (and there are many) insist on the flawless quality of the prime materials. King prawn salad with a Thai dressing of coconut and coriander, gravad lax with sweetly marinated herrings, and gingered seafood chowder indicate the versatility of the approach. A witty variant on fish and chips with a dollop of ketchup sees a grilled fillet of catfish sauced with fresh tomato butter and served with parsnip chips. One reporter praised a main course of guinea-fowl cooked in madeira for being 'as good as anything I have ever eaten away from home', and roast quail with crispy noodles, pistachios and redcurrants has also scored highly. There are some tales of dissatisfaction, whether for pallid flavours or experiments that don't seem to have clear rationale, but the overwhelming consensus is positive. Desserts include challenges, like strawberry gratin with balsamic syrup and mascarpone, but also more familiar items, such as orange tart with chocolate sauce, and tiramisù. The absence of formality about it all usually gratifies.

The supremely authoritative wine list does the Crown proud. While the choice of producers is very sound, notes on the less great vintages for the French regions are refreshingly frank. Selections from Italy and all the non-European areas are inspiring. Prices throughout are exceptionally fair, and start from £6.75. CELLARMAN'S CHOICE: Shaw & Smith Sauvignon 1993, Adelaide Hills, S. Australia, £12.88; Côtes du Rhône, Ch. Grand Moulas 1993, Ryckwaert, £8.40.

CHEF: Richard Pye PROPRIETOR: Adnams Hotels OPEN: all week 12.15 to 1.30, 7.30 to 9.30 CLOSED: 1 week Jan MEALS: Set L £12.95 (2 courses) to £15.50, Set D £17.95 (2 courses) to £19.95; bar meals available SERVICE: not inc, card slips closed CARDS: Access, Amex, Delta, Diners, Switch, Visa DETAILS: restaurant 22 seats, bar 56 seats. 3 tables outside. Private parties: 22 main room. Car park. Vegetarian meals. Children's helpings. Smart dress preferred. No smoking in dining-room. No music. Air-conditioned ACCOMMODATION: 12 rooms, all with bath/shower. TV. Phone. B&B £41 to £68. Children welcome. Baby facilities (*The Which? Hotel Guide*)

STADDLEBRIDGE North Yorkshire map 9

▲ *McCoy's Restaurant* 🍷

The Tontine, Staddlebridge DL6 3JB
TEL: (01609) 882671 FAX: (01609) 882660 COOKING 3
6m NE of Northallerton, at junction of A19 and A172 COST £26–£53

To be fair, although this solid stone former coaching-inn is invariably described as being beside the A19, it is also, if you look the other way, on the edge of thousands of acres of National Park. Traffic whizzes past, but the rooms are quiet and breakfast is worth staying for. As to the décor, nothing matches, except that everything looks like odds and ends from the 1930s – beaten-up sofas, Art Deco lamps, log fires – and the dark dining-room is lit only by candles. 'We were hemmed in by plants, rather like a garden centre' was the view of one party. But if the place looks off-beat and higgledy-piggledy, that merely serves to disguise the professionalism with which it is run.

The restaurant is on the ground floor, the bistro, which is open all week for lunch and dinner, is in the basement. Normally a bistro would be the cheaper, less formal alternative, but in this case it is impossible for anywhere to be more relaxed than the restaurant, and prices are about the same anyway. A wide-ranging repertoire is common to both, taking in leek and potato soup, crab with a ramekin of mayonnaise 'tasting strongly of olive oil', charcoal-grilled steaks, and sweet discs of scallop arranged around a 'pesto' of chopped raw vegetables flavoured with basil and spiked with chilli. Luxury ingredients crop up but are used sparingly and sensibly. High-quality meat is the foundation of main courses, in loin of lamb with olive-oil mashed potatoes, or in a Bresse pigeon cut into four, served in a bowl with white haricot beans, green flageolets and Puy lentils, in a spicy, gamey sauce enriched with foie gras. Occasionally technique might not quite match the ambition, but above all dishes taste good, seasoning is spot-on and flavour comes first.

A plate of strawberries, puff pastry and crème pâtissière seemed rather unseasonal to one reporter 'even though this [was] the warmest November since 1659'. Staff are young, welcoming, competent, cheerful, and Peter McCoy is personable. Wines are served matter-of-fact, and the list is tightly organised, with little room for dead wood. We could wish for more under £20, but non-French wines are well worth exploring. House wine is £12.65. CELLARMAN'S CHOICE: Cloudy Bay, Pelorus 1989, Marlborough, New Zeleand, £26.50; Saumur Champigny 'Vieilles Vignes' 1989, P. Filliatreau, £27.

CHEF: Tom McCoy PROPRIETORS: the McCoy brothers OPEN: restaurant Tues to Sat D only 7 to 10.30, bistro all week 12 to 2, 7 to 10.30 CLOSED: 25 and 26 Dec and 1 Jan MEALS: alc (main courses restaurant £14 to £18, bistro £9 to £17) SERVICE: not inc CARDS: Access, Amex, Diners, Switch, Visa DETAILS: 70 seats. Private parties: 12 main room, 30 private room. Car park. Vegetarian meals. Children's helpings. Music. Air-conditioned ACCOMMODATION: 6 rooms, all with bath/shower. TV. Phone. Air-conditioned. B&B £79 to £99. Children welcome. Pets welcome. Garden

---

STAITHES North Yorkshire map 9

▲ *Endeavour*

1 High Street, Staithes TS13 5BH — COOKING 1
TEL: (01947) 840825 — COST £24–£43

A trip to Lisa Chapman's 'delightful' quayside restaurant involves plenty of walking, up or down the steep hill that dominates the centre of Staithes. Fish from local boats is the backbone of her daily-changing menu, and reporters have spoken highly of moules marinière and lobster with garlic butter. There are some nice touches and bags of enthusiasm here: pan-fried cod roe is spiced up with Indian aubergine salad, fillet of brill gets a rhubarb butter sauce. Lisa also scours the hedgerows for ingredients such as hawthorn and elderflowers (the former goes into cucumber soup, the latter provides the syrup for a peach and melon starter). Carnivores might be offered pot-roast partridge or sauté lambs' liver, while vegetarians should be well pleased with colourful ideas such as a crisp tart of tomatoes, aubergines and Gruyère with yellow pepper sauce. Crème brûlée with raspberries remains the best-selling dessert, and you might find steamed orange sponge with home-made marmalade ice-cream, or iced Drambuie mousse. The wine list puts the emphasis firmly on variety and value for money. House wine is £7.95.

CHEF/PROPRIETOR: Lisa Chapman OPEN: Mon to Sat 12 to 2, 6.45 to 9.30; Sun D bank hols and July to Sept CLOSED: 25 and 26 Dec, mid-Jan to mid-Mar SERVICE: not inc CARDS: none DETAILS: 45 seats. Private parties: 30 main room, 12 to 18 private rooms. Vegetarian meals. Children welcome. No smoking in 1 dining-room. Music ACCOMMODATION: 3 rooms, 1 with bath/shower. TV. B&B £18 to £42. Children welcome

STAMFORD Lincolnshire map 6

▲ *George of Stamford*

St Martins, Stamford PE9 2LB COOKING 2
TEL: (01780) 55171 FAX: (01780) 57070 COST £25–£50

Stamford is a picturesque market town with some fine Georgian architecture and a steady flow of tourists on the 'We saw it on TV' trail. The George, a sixteenth-century coaching-inn, has adapted well to its mix of casual eaters and business customers, and the conference centre round the back adds to the bustle. Businessmen with mobile phones, 'ladies who lunch' and a sprinkling of international travellers are the sort of folk who might turn up in the cobbled courtyard among the hanging baskets to sample the light lunch menu on a fine day: two savoury dishes (choose from spicy Thai crab-cake, buttered haddock fingers, or cannelloni, for example) plus dessert or cheese for £16.50. Variously flavoured cream sauces appear regularly.

In old-hotel fashion a silver carving-wagon of roast sirloin of beef trundles round the panelled dining-room, and other red-blooded dishes constitute the heart of the *carte*: roast rack of lamb, or fillet of venison with spätzli. Portions are generous. There are trolleys for cheese, puddings and drinks too, all adding to the impression of the George as a modest and provincial version of the Connaught. Service varies, but at its best is exemplary. 'These people know what service is about. They seemed to be mind readers and approached just as you were mentally formulating your next need.' Wines are staggeringly good, wonderfully varied, intelligently chosen, briefly annotated, enthusiastically recommended and benefit from the Poste Hotels' sensible mark-up policy. Half-bottles, big bottles, bin ends and 20 house wines (a dozen of them available by the glass) add to the fun. CELLARMAN'S CHOICE: Alan Scott Sauvignon Blanc 1994, Marlborough, New Zealand, £16.75; Carignano del Sulcis Riserva 'Rocca Rubia' 1990, Cantina Sociale Santadi, £15.75.

CHEFS: Chris Pitman and Matthew Carroll PROPRIETOR: Poste Hotels Ltd OPEN: all week 12.30 to 2.30, 7.15 to 10.30. Light menu available all day MEALS: alc (main courses £13 to £18.50). Set L Mon to Sat £16.50 (light lunch menu) to £19.50 SERVICE: net prices, card slips closed CARDS: Access, Amex, Delta, Diners, Switch, Visa DETAILS: 200 seats. 30 tables outside. Private parties: 100 main room, 8 to 100 private rooms. Car park. Vegetarian meals. Children's helpings. Smart dress preferred. Wheelchair access (also WC). Music ACCOMMODATION: 47 rooms, all with bath/shower. TV. Phone. B&B £72 to £160. Children welcome. Baby facilities. Pets welcome. Afternoon teas. Garden (*The Which? Hotel Guide*)

STANTON Suffolk map 6

Leaping Hare Café **NEW ENTRY**

Wyken Vineyards, Stanton IP31 2DW COOKING 2
TEL: (01359) 250287 FAX: (01359) 250240 COST £20–£34

The proprietors are a Conservative Member of Parliament and an American-born civil rights campaigner. They are among England's finest wine-makers, with awards to prove it, and in 1992 the barn on their estate was opened as a restaurant. Carla Carlisle used to cook at the ground-breaking Chez Panisse in Berkeley, San Francisco, so what we have here is a little patch of California within wine-spitting distance of Bury St Edmunds.

East Anglian chef Dean Simpole-Clarke is charged with capturing the Cal-Ital style and does so with considerable aplomb. From the moment the bread arrives – rosemary focaccia with olive oil for trickling over – there is no doubt about the culinary orientation. Wine and vine play their part in much that comes on to the menu, including the bresaola, home-cured in Wyken Vineyards' red and partnered with ricotta, Parmesan and lime – 'a happy marriage of flavours'. Reuben sandwich of grilled salt-beef is a quintessential Stateside starter, while Petaluma duckburger with red pepper mayo offers a meat patty highly spiced with cumin ('tasting very similar to merguez') on a good bun with 'pleasantly mild' mayonnaise. Vegetarians might try tagliatelle with basil and tomato pesto, or risotto of leeks and butternut squash. Chunky desserts use Wyken Auxerrois for poaching peaches with a zabaglione of the same wine, and whole almonds in a Berkeley version of almond tart with crème fraîche. Note the very restricted opening times, and go with an open mind. Wines are essentially the vineyard's own, not unexpectedly, together with their own cider. A California red and a claret are included for those who want to be awkward. Everything is available by the glass. Bottle prices start at £6.95.

CHEF: Dean Simpole-Clarke PROPRIETORS: Kenneth and Carla Carlisle OPEN: Thur, Fri and Sun L 12 to 3, Fri D 7 to 9.30 (open Sat mid-Nov to Christmas) CLOSED: Christmas to 10 Feb MEALS: alc (main courses £7 to £11) SERVICE: not inc, card slips closed CARDS: Access, Delta, Switch, Visa DETAILS: 45 seats. 3 tables outside. Private parties: 50 main room. Car park. Vegetarian meals. Children's helpings. No smoking in dining-room. Wheelchair access (also WC). No music

STOKE BRUERNE Northamptonshire map 5

Bruerne's Lock

5 The Canalside, Stoke Bruerne NN12 7SB
TEL: (01604) 863654 COOKING 1
off A508, 3½m from A5 at Towcester COST £24–£48

Considering it is only three or four miles from the M1 and A5, the setting is remarkably peaceful, beside the Grand Union Canal next to a waterways museum. The car park – shared with the museum – is free to Bruerne's Lock customers (the charge is reimbursed by the restaurant). One couple visiting in summer sat on the narrow terrace among the roses and watched people wander along the towpath while Gavin – or was it Nigel? – read out the first courses, embellishing them as he went. 'Twinning' with a restaurant in Lucca brings a few Italianate dishes on to the menu, along the lines of Tuscan ravioli with a smoky-flavoured oyster mushroom sauce, but the kitchen generally weaves a path across several national boundaries, taking in ale and onion soup, and braised duck in a jasmine and sultana sauce on a bed of cabbage.

The kitchen is into garnish, decorating pot-roast shank of lamb with diced tomato, for example, while leaving some cooking times, and hence textures, to look after themselves. It would all benefit from a clearer sense of direction, though the food's basic obligation to be tasty is fulfilled. Lunch is considered good value, with a choice of three or four items at each stage, and cheese is 'not a bad selection'. Meals can be very leisurely indeed, and considering it is the owners who work front-of-house, one reporter felt that 'it would be so much better if the question of tips did not arise'. Nigel – or is it Gavin? – brings round the wine from a 50-strong, mostly French and fairly priced list, beginning with house South African at £11.95.

CHEFS: Glenn Barrable and Alun Franklin PROPRIETORS: Gavin Caldwell, Nigel Hollick and Michael Ross Collins OPEN: Tue to Fri and Sun L 12.30 to 2, Tue to Sat D 7.30 to 9.45 MEALS: alc D (main courses £14 to £17). Set L £16 SERVICE: not inc CARDS: Access, Amex, Visa DETAILS: 30 seats. 4 tables outside. Private parties: 32 main room. Car park. Children's helpings. Smart dress preferred. Wheelchair access (2 steps). Music

STOKE-BY-NAYLAND Suffolk map 6

▲ *Angel Inn*

Stoke-by-Nayland CO6 4SA
TEL: (01206) 263245 FAX: (01206) 337324 COOKING 2
on B1068 5m SW of Hadleigh COST £21–£39

'Pubby but sophisticated' is a fair summary of this sixteenth-century village inn in Constable country. Like many converts which concentrate on food, it has ceased to function strictly as a pub, but the sympathetic furnishings – beams, cottagey furniture, log fires in winter, comfortable armchairs and sofas – make it more successful than the usual hybrid. A well and a gallery add to the character. The blackboard menu is a mix of commonplace offerings, from fish and chips with salad to rissoles on a tomato coulis, and trickier dishes, such as lamb chops in pastry, or ballottine of duck, all of which work well. Fish might include grilled plaice or wing of skate, and vegetables are simple but enticing.

'Our chalkboard enables us to continually vary the menu and avoid kitchen fatigue,' writes Richard Wright, which may explain the bright flavours and accurate seasoning in chicken and mushroom terrine, or in baked Mediterranean vegetables, and account for the appeal of chocolate cup with bananas and coffee caramel. Reporters are impressed by the friendly atmosphere and prices, not least on the well-chosen wine list. Vintages are often split, but grape varieties run from Australian Riesling and Semillon to Chilean Cabernet Sauvignon and Californian Zinfandel. House wine is £7.40.

NEW CHEF *is shown instead of a cooking mark where a change of chef occurred too late for a new assessment of the cooking.*

CHEF: Mark Johnson PROPRIETORS: Richard Wright and Peter Smith OPEN: all week 12 to 2, 6.30 (7 Sun) to 9 CLOSED: 25 and 26 Dec MEALS: alc (main courses £6 to £15). Cover £1 SERVICE: not inc CARDS: Access, Amex, Delta, Diners, Switch, Visa DETAILS: 80 seats. 4 tables outside. Private parties: 28 main room. Car park. Vegetarian meals. No children under 8. Wheelchair access (1 step). No music ACCOMMODATION: 6 rooms, all with bath/shower. TV. Phone. B&B £44 to £57.50. No children under 8 (*The Which? Hotel Guide*)

STOKESLEY North Yorkshire **map 10**

▲ *Chapters*

27 High Street, Stokesley TS9 5AD COOKING 2
TEL: (01642) 711888 FAX: (01642) 713387 COST £18–£42

Business is now firmly bistro-style at the Thompsons' converted Georgian coaching-inn close to the River Leven. Guests can still eat in the original restaurant (where the cover charge pays for the table-linen), although most are encouraged to opt for the informal buzz of the stone-floored bistro with its 'foodie watercolours' on cream and green stencilled walls, exposed brickwork, and waiters in long white aprons.

The food revolves around an extensive menu that globetrots with abandon, plundering Catalonia for a casserole of squid, other seafood and chorizo, then zooming off to Indonesia for chicken satay, before coming home for bread-and-butter pudding. Daily deliveries ensure that fish remains the major attraction, be it huge portions of plump rope-grown mussels, crab-cakes with curry sauce, 'expertly cooked' halibut in herb butter sauce, or king scallops baked in their shells with ginger and soy. Elsewhere there is much use of filo pastry and spicy accompaniments (rhubarb and ginger compote for grilled goats' cheese, pickled kumquats with chicken liver pâté), and the kitchen goes back to the classic textbooks for steak au poivre, chicken with wild mushroom sauce, and pork fillet casseroled with root vegetables and cider. Desserts might include strawberry ice-cream as well as white and dark chocolate terrine or peach schnapps cheesecake. The short list of around 30 lively wines is augmented by a few premier bins. Georges Duboeuf house wine is £8.95.

CHEF: Richard West PROPRIETOR: Alan Thompson OPEN: Mon to Sat 12 to 2, 7 to 9.30 (10 Sat) CLOSED: 25 Dec MEALS: alc (main courses £5 to £15) SERVICE: not inc CARDS: Access, Amex, Delta, Diners, Switch, Visa DETAILS: 80 seats. 10 tables outside. Private parties: 65 main room. Vegetarian meals. Children's helpings. Smart dress preferred. No smoking in 1 dining-room. Music ACCOMMODATION: 13 rooms, all with bath/shower. TV. Phone. B&B £44 to £62. Children welcome. Baby facilities. Pets welcome. Afternoon teas. Garden (*The Which? Hotel Guide*)

The 1997 Guide *will be published before Christmas 1996. Reports on meals are most welcome at any time of the year, but are particularly valuable in the spring (no later than June). Send them to* The Good Food Guide, *FREEPOST, 2 Marylebone Road, London NW1 1YN. Or e-mail your report to guidereports@which. co. uk.*

STON EASTON Somerset map 2

▲ *Ston Easton Park*

Ston Easton BA3 4DF
TEL: (01761) 241631 FAX: (01761) 241377 COOKING 3*
on A37, 12m S of Bristol COST £33–£65

This stark, imposing Palladian mansion, set in an eighteenth-century landscape (the work of Humphry Repton) in the Mendips between Bath and Wells, is 'a beautiful house in which to relax', thanks to the informal approach of the Smedleys, whose home it is. Carved plasterwork, pediments and *trompe-l'oeil* paintings of classical subjects decorate the house, although the dining-room is lighter and more garden-like. The cooking's foundation, almost as classical as the house, shows itself in lobster consommé, or a confit of duckling with Puy lentils and roast galette of celeriac. One reporter found the styles on offer – 'from traditional English to French bistro to Italian' – a bit confusing, but most observers would now accept such a mix to be part of the British way of doing things. Why stick to one tradition when you can benefit from several?

The kitchen deploys the usual range of techniques, from roasting (of partridge) to pan-frying (of lamb) to chargrilling (of Dover sole or breast of Hereford duckling), and the results are impressive. Richness – in the form of wild mushrooms, foie gras, and truffle butter sauce – is balanced by simply baked fillet of sea bass or a tartlet of feta cheese, artichoke and sun-dried tomatoes. Mark Harrington also injects vitality in the form of lightly acidulated dressings, relishes (a beetroot chutney to accompany toasted goats' cheese) and is likely to throw in celeriac chips to add crunch to a warm quail salad, or spiced black olives to counter the sweetness of honey-roasted veal sweetbreads. 'Carefully chosen and precisely cooked vegetables' are an integral part of main-course dishes.

There may well be sticky toffee pudding on the menu, but caramelised rice condé served with banana fritters and fudge ice-cream is more interesting and 'absolute heaven' into the bargain. 'Dull bread' lets the side down, but reports of 'good coffee' perhaps reflect the outlay on 'a wonderful Italian coffee machine', to quote the manager, that dispenses espresso and cappuccino. 'I pulled down the roller blind because I noticed the sun was in your eyes' is typical of the ever-attentive service, and 'the fact that staff don't want gratuities just adds the final perfect touch'. The grand setting obviously demands grand wines, and gets them, with France to the fore. Quality is impeccable. A dozen wines under £20 head up the aristocratic list, which otherwise rarely strays below this financial Plimsoll line. Penfolds Bin 707 1989 at £56 is just one example of what a couple of years in the cellar can do to a mark-up: the 1992 sells in Oddbins for £17.49. CELLARMAN'S CHOICE: Pacherenc du Vic-Bilh, Ch. Bouscassé 1992, Brumont, £18; Capello di Prete Rosso Salentino 1990, Candido, £15.50.

The Guide *office can quickly spot when a restaurateur is encouraging customers to write recommending inclusion – and sadly, several restaurants have been doing this in 1995. Such reports do not further a restaurant's cause. Please tell us if a restaurateur invites you to write to the* Guide.

CHEF: Mark Harrington PROPRIETORS: Peter and Christine Smedley OPEN: all week 12.30 to 2, 7.30 to 9.30 (10 Fri and Sat) MEALS: alc D (main courses £19 to £25). Set L £26, Set D £38.50 SERVICE: none, card slips closed CARDS: Access, Amex, Diners, Switch, Visa DETAILS: 40 seats. 4 tables outside. Private parties: 8 main room, 24 private room. Car park. Vegetarian meals. No children under 7. Jacket and tie. No smoking in dining-room. Wheelchair access (2 steps). No music ACCOMMODATION: 21 rooms, all with bath/shower. TV. Phone. B&B £93.50 to £337. No children under 7. Pets by arrangement. Afternoon teas. Garden (*The Which? Hotel Guide*)

STONHAM Suffolk map 6

Mr Underhill's

Stonham IP14 5DW
TEL: (01449) 711206 COOKING 4
on A140, 300 yards S of junction with A1120 COST £34–£52

The Bradleys celebrate 15 years here in 1996, and continue to impress with their straightforward but accomplished country cooking. Bar and dining-room share one split-level space, with a token division of beams between them. The effect of deep pink walls, red carpet and colourful pictures is 'luxurious and in the best of taste', and 'there is something about the place which breaks down the traditional English reserve', helped no doubt by the charm and efficiency with which Judy Bradley manages front-of-house.

The unadorned style is a sign of Christopher Bradley's well-placed confidence in his materials, and dishes might not stray beyond a compote of roasted peppers on chargrilled Tuscan bread, or Thai-style pickled vegetables with a parfait of chicken livers and foie gras. A winter meal ran as follows: salmon on a bed of spinach with tomato and sherry vinegar, loin of beef with essence of tarragon and white truffle, and chocolate parfait. The menu offers no choice before pudding, which leads some reporters to expect a trade-off for what they perceive as the kitchen's easy time of it: either a lower bill, or food that knocks them for six. 'After all, they can pour all their creative energies into just a few dishes. We thought an extra spark of imagination would have been in order,' commented one visitor.

The appeal, though, is in correct execution rather than innovative flavours. The menu is telephoned in advance to customers who have reserved a table, then typed out and customised for each party. Since different tables may well be eating different dishes, the kitchen is not necessarily having an easy time of it, but that is by the by. An early summer meal began with a warm and very green salad of chopped asparagus, purée broad beans and a basil-flavoured dressing, followed by crisp-skinned leg of Barbary duck on a bed of tangy shredded cabbage and carrot, with runner beans and a 'heavenly' gratin dauphinoise. 'We could find no fault in the cooking, and all the ingredients were excellent,' concluded the reporter.

If the price for two courses seems a lot (as it does to some), then the deal improves with the addition of puddings – there is a choice of six, perhaps including smooth, coffee-flavoured iced parfait, or mild lemon tart – and cheese: a plate of eight arrives, varied to include a mix of Otley goats', soft Chaource, creamy blue Langres, ripe Epoisses, Wigmore, Milleens, Cashel Blue and

Vacherin. The wine list is for the enthusiast, which is to say it is packed with interest, and with as much attention devoted to less-expensive and lesser-known wines as to more aristocratic ones. House wines, a short 'special selection' and 'latest finds' are highlighted. CELLARMAN'S CHOICE: Kumeu River Sauvignon/Semillon 1993, New Zealand, £19.95; Collioure, Les Clos de Paulilles 1990, £14.50.

CHEF: Christopher Bradley PROPRIETORS: Christopher and Judy Bradley OPEN: Sun L 12.30 to 1.45 (Tue to Fri by arrangement), Tue to Sat D 7.30 to 8.45 MEALS: Set L £21 (2 courses) to £29.25, Set D £26 (2 courses) to £34.25 SERVICE: not inc CARDS: Access, Visa DETAILS: 24 seats. 6 tables outside. Private parties: 24 main room. Car park. Children's helpings. Smart dress preferred. No smoking in dining-room. Wheelchair access. No music

STONOR Oxfordshire map 2

▲ *Stonor Arms* 🍷

Stonor RG9 6HE
TEL: (01491) 638345 and 638866
FAX: (01491) 638863
on B480, 5m N of Henley-on-Thames

COOKING 1*
COST £23–£45

'We go there regularly for lunch in the middle of a day's walking,' wrote one reporter. Part of the charm of Stonor Arms is that 'it copes effortlessly with a clientele half of whom come in Mercedes and half in walking-boots', which it does by dint of having two dining-rooms: a flagstoned bar called Blades, and a carpeted restaurant; both have a conservatory section overlooking the carefully laid-out garden. The walker enjoyed a lunch of 'three starters, a pudding, a pint and a cappuccino – no hassle'. Blades' free-ranging *carte* takes in baked aubergine with pesto, and smoked cod fish-cakes, along with weightier matters such as a mixed grill of lambs' liver, bacon and black pudding with mashed potato and onion gravy.

The restaurant offers more comfort and less choice, and dishes can take on a slightly more genteel air – pan-fried Cornish scallops on a fennel marmalade with dill vinaigrette, for instance – although there is still a basic country heartiness in braised ox-tongue, or in roast squab pigeon on a cake of potato and cabbage served with a juniper sauce. Ingredients are good, and 'portions are decidedly generous', which may explain why few make it to puddings of chilled rhubarb mousse, or pear tart with caramel sauce. Historic vintages of Ch. Batailley, and a dozen Leflaive burgundies are typical of the quality and enthusiasm that underpin this broad, considered list. The selection and prices are approachable, with a decent spread of half-bottles. House French is £8.95.

CHEFS: Stephen Frost and Amanda Beeden PROPRIETOR: Stonor Hotels Ltd OPEN: Blades all week 12 to 2, 7 to 9.30 (9 Sun); restaurant Mon to Sat D only 7 to 9.30) CLOSED: restaurant bank hols MEALS: alc Blades (main courses £8 to £11). Set D restaurant £29.50 SERVICE: not inc CARDS: Access, Amex, Switch, Visa DETAILS: Blades 40 seats, restaurant 20 seats, 6 tables outside. Private parties: 24 main room, 14 private room. Car park. Vegetarian meals. Children's helpings. Smart dress preferred. Wheelchair access (also WC). Music ACCOMMODATION: 9 rooms, all with bath/shower. TV. Phone. B&B £82.50 to £137.50. Rooms for disabled. Children welcome. Afternoon teas. Garden (*The Which? Hotel Guide*)

STORRINGTON West Sussex map 3

▲ *Manleys* 🍷

Manleys Hill, Storrington RH20 4BT COOKING 3*
TEL: (01903) 742331 COST £29–£60

Here, in a pair of Queen Anne houses at the foot of the South Downs, may be encountered one of the more tenacious campaigners of the Home Counties. Karl Löderer has been running Manleys since 1978, building success on a foundation of great formality that some may see as verging on camp ('even the *bread* was domed') and nailing his colours to a loftily classical mast. Many of the dishes rely on sauces of the old school, painstaking stock bases enriched with 'unbelievably gorgeous' butter. The method is, of course, essentially French, but there is a gentle leavening of earthier elements in there too, reflecting the chef's Austrian provenance and occasionally nodding to other food cultures.

'Where are the dabs of Far Eastern spicing?' last year's *Guide* asked rhetorically. The answer is that they are here, in a first course of scallops – corals intact – on an underlay of shredded and stir-fried oriental vegetables topped with a frizz of deep-fried leek. First courses mobilise many components but still seem to achieve harmony, as in crabmeat and prawns parcelled in smoked salmon and served with asparagus, crème fraîche and some fresh horseradish for piquancy. Main courses may be similarly complex but never lose sight of culinary logic. Dover sole fillets are poached in a Riesling reduction and garnished with langoustines, while duck breast is seasoned with Chinese spices, its skin 'completely black, the meat remaining pink', and laid on shredded white cabbage mildly spiced with ginger. Desserts rely on cream, perhaps thanks to a Central European strain that shows itself in a cream-stuffed meringue cornet with butterscotch sauce of unctuous smoothness scattered with walnuts. It all takes place in an atmosphere of refined calm, against a background of classical music, with every propriety duly observed.

The wine list doesn't have much truck with anything outside France, Germany or, naturally, Austria, but the quality is very high. Burgundy growers are impeccable, and the German Rieslings have been thoughtfully selected too. While prices are not exactly low, nor are the mark-ups ridiculous. House French is £13.80. CELLARMAN'S CHOICE: Pinot Blanc Kabinett 1988, Ried Kuchelviertel, £15.50; St-Julien, Ch. Gloria 1983, £26.80.

CHEF/PROPRIETOR: Karl Löderer OPEN: Tue to Sun L 12 to 1.45, Tue to Sat D 7 to 9.15 CLOSED: first 10 days Jan MEALS: Set L Tue to Sat £19.60, Set L Sun £23.50, Set D £28.50 to £36.30 SERVICE: not inc, card slips closed CARDS: Access, Amex, Delta, Switch, Visa DETAILS: 48 seats. Private parties: 34 main room, 14 and 22 private rooms. Car park. Children's helpings. Smart dress preferred. No cigars/pipes in dining-room. Wheelchair access (also WC). No music. Air-conditioned ACCOMMODATION: 1 apartment, with bath/shower. TV. Phone. B&B £50 to £85

Old Forge

6A Church Street, Storrington RH20 4LA COOKING 1*
TEL: (01903) 743402 FAX: (01930) 742540 COST £21–£42

Clive and Cathy Roberts succeeded in acquiring the property adjoining the Old Forge at the end of 1994; as a result they now have more tables and additional space for pre-prandial drinks. Otherwise, it is business as usual in their 500-year-old beamed building. The Robertses bake their own bread and cook with a dutiful eye on the seasons. A typical dinner from a February menu could begin with mushroom and dry sherry soup or gratin of mussels and fennel, before braised ox tongue, or steamed fillet of hake on a bed of creamed cabbage fired up with wholegrain mustard. As a finale you might choose between home-made ice-creams and an elaborately constructed chocolate caramel mousse with poached pears layered between chocolate sponge and hazelnut meringue. Meals kick off with 'delicious savouries hot from the oven' and finish with coffee and home-made petit fours. The fixed-price lunch menu is an affordable prospect, offering the likes of whole boned trout with mushroom and herb stuffing followed by lemon tart with elderflower and lemon ice-cream. Bottles from trustworthy New World producers loom large on the wine list, although France and Germany are not neglected. House wines are £9.

CHEFS/PROPRIETORS: Clive and Cathy Roberts OPEN: Wed to Fri and Sun L 12.30 to 1.30, Tue to Sat D 7.15 to 9 CLOSED: 1 week spring, 3 weeks autumn MEALS: alc (main courses £10.50 to £14). Set L £12 (2 courses) to £14.50, Set D £16 (2 courses) to £20.50 SERVICE: not inc, card slips closed CARDS: Access, Amex, Delta, Diners, Switch, Visa DETAILS: 36 seats. Private parties: 18 main room, 12 private room. Vegetarian meals. Children welcome. Smart dress preferred. No smoking while others eat. Music

STOW-ON-THE-WOLD Gloucestershire map 5

▲ *Wyck Hill House*

Burford Road, Stow-on-the-Wold GL54 1HY
TEL: (01451) 831936 FAX: (01451) 832243
on A424, 2m SE of Stow-on-the-Wold

COOKING 2
COST £23–£63

This lavishly upholstered Cotswold house within sweeping grounds aims for grandeur. Everything is orchestrated to impress, from the gargantuan floral displays to the correctly attired tables and lush drapes. Ian Smith has a decade under his belt in the Wyck Hill kitchen, but has resisted the temptation to coast along and gone on developing. Dishes bear the hallmarks of a creative faculty working at high rev, so much so that even first courses sound awesomely complex. Chargrilled tuna sits on a purée of roasted aubergine seasoned with garlic and rosemary, accompanied by a further assemblage of artichoke, sun-dried tomatoes and lime. Wild rabbit and sweetbreads are made into a boudin that comes on creamed cabbage and bacon with a sage-infused jus. Main courses are easier to visualise, and the counterpoints of flavour more obvious. Red mullet is chargrilled and set on fennel with a warm pesto dressing, while duck is orientalised with shiitakes, spring onion and ginger. Simpler dishes are available, from salmon with hollandaise to grilled lamb cutlets with mint and apple jelly. Vegetarians have their own menu with a reasonable spread of assertive flavours. Desserts may include an Italian-influenced pine-nut torte with Cointreau-soaked oranges, or rhubarb and cinnamon soufflé with calvados cream. If prices seem high, note that the fixed-price lunch offers excellent value. Do not expect bargains on the wine list. The range is extensive and expensive, although the selections are good for those with the means. House French is £11.95.

CHEF: Ian Smith PROPRIETOR: Lyric Hotels OPEN: all week 12 to 2, 7.30 to 9.30 MEALS: alc (main courses £13 to £23). Set L Mon to Sat £9.50 (2 courses) to £11.95 (light alc menu also available), Set L Sun £17.50 SERVICE: not inc CARDS: Access, Amex, Diners, Visa DETAILS: 70 seats. 5 tables outside. Private parties: 30 main room, 40 private room. Car park. Vegetarian meals. Children's helpings. Smart dress preferred. No smoking in dining-room. Wheelchair access (also WC). Music. Air-conditioned ACCOMMODATION: 31 rooms, all with bath/shower. TV. Phone. B&B £78 to £140. Children welcome. Baby facilities. Pets welcome in bedrooms only. Afternoon teas. Garden

---

STRETE Devon map 1

Laughing Monk

Strete TQ6 0RN
TEL: (01803) 770639 COOKING 1
5m from Dartmouth on coast road to Kingsbridge COST £17–£34

The Rothwells intended the name of their little south Devon restaurant to reflect an atmosphere of unrestrained cheer. Perhaps once upon a time there was a tinge of gloom in the air to exorcise, as it started life as a Victorian school; nowadays, says a reporter, 'you get a very warm impression...subdued lighting, comfortable seats...very welcoming approach'. The cooking is countrified and homely, making good use of classic techniques and local materials, including fish from Brixham and Plymouth and plenty of Devon cream. Poached pear is filled with a herby cheese pâté and coated with curried mayonnaise, while a Stilton soufflé, for one reporter, was 'quite outstanding'. Salmon may be bedded on spinach and sauced with vermouth and cream, and rack of lamb is herb-crusted and comes with a rosemary and redcurrant jus. Desserts, according to one visitor who tried three, are 'a great delight'. This is an unaffectedly friendly and hospitable place. Even a waiting taxi-driver got invited in for coffee and a home-made bitter chocolate mint. A concise wine list offers a brisk international choice, including the little-known but impressive Bouché champagne. House French is £7.95.

CHEF: David Rothwell PROPRIETORS: David and Trudy Rothwell OPEN: Sun L 12.15 to 1.45, Tue to Sat (and Sun and Mon bank hols) D 7 to 9.30 MEALS: alc (main courses £9.50 to £13). Set L Sun £10.95 SERVICE: not inc, card slips closed CARDS: Access, Diners, Visa DETAILS: 50 seats. Private parties: 60 main room. Car park. Vegetarian meals. Children's helpings. Smart dress preferred. No smoking in 1 dining-room. Wheelchair access (2 steps; also female WC). Music

---

STUCKTON Hampshire map 2

Three Lions

Stuckton Road, Stuckton SP6 2HF
TEL: (01425) 652489 FAX: (01425) 656144 COOKING 1*
off A338, 1m SE of Fordingbridge COST £25–£53

Take one brilliant chef, put him in a pub restaurant of his own, and the results should be stupendous. Michael Womersley moved from Lucknam Park at Colerne (see entry) and took over from the Wadsacks, who have retired to Sweden. The place looks bright and fresh, the bar fireplace is opened up and knocked through to the dining-room, though pine tables and chairs remain, and the blackboard is still there, perched in a rather awkward waiting area and written in cryptic shorthand ('sc' apparently means 'sauce', not 'served cold'). The entire operation does a good job of getting as far away as possible from the grandiose style of Lucknam Park.

Womersley has scaled down his food to suit the circumstances, and is the beneficiary of some good local supplies, including fish, although at a very early inspection the timing went slightly awry, perhaps owing to a new and unfamiliar kitchen. Seared tuna and mussels in white wine were on offer, but meat was more successful: pigeon salad with juicy pleurotte mushrooms; thick, pink duck magret with crispy skin and a strewing of blackcurrants; and grilled lamb, also with crisp skin and an intense sauce, or rather 'sc'. Indeed, any lamb dish is probably a good bet. Chocolate pudding in raspberry sauce, and lemon parfait are good ways to finish. Service might have been sharper, but given Womersley's enthusiasm, materials and evident skill, the signs are that the Three Lions is one to watch. A new wine list is being compiled. More reports, please.

CHEF: Michael Womersley PROPRIETORS: J.M. and S.J. Womersley OPEN: Tue to Sun L 12.30 to 2 (2.30 Sun), 7.30 to 9.30 (10 Fri and Sat) CLOSED: 23 Jan to 12 Feb MEALS: alc (main courses £8.50 to £15) SERVICE: not inc CARDS: Access, Switch, Visa DETAILS: 60 seats. Private parties: 12 main room. Car park. Vegetarian meals. No children under 8. Wheelchair access. No music

STURMINSTER NEWTON Dorset map 2

▲ *Plumber Manor*

Hazelbury Bryan Road, Sturminster
Newton DT10 2AF
TEL: (01258) 472507 FAX: (01258) 473370
A357 to Sturminster Newton, take first left to Hazelbury Bryan, on left-hand side after 2m

COOKING 1
COST £21–£36

A Jacobean manor house in Thomas Hardy's Dorset, Plumber has been home to generations of the Prideaux-Brune dynasty since the 1600s, and Brian of that ilk has manned the stoves since it became a country-house hotel. Despite the tranquil setting, the ambience is cheering; a couple dining while March winds blew made glad use of the lounge bar's 'roaring fire and labradors to keep one's feet warm'. Two set-price menus are on offer, with a fish course added for an extra £2.50. The menus keep things uncomplicated and make conscientious use of local fare. Crab tartlets are thermidored, while a boned-out quail is stuffed with wild rice and parcelled in filo. On one evening, brill had a good sauce of ginger and white wine, and peppered steak an even better one of garlic, mustard, tarragon and brandy. Although presentation can, on occasion, be a weak point, puddings have been described as the best part of the meal: both lemon ginger crunch and chocolate torte are described as light and not over-sweet. Friendly and welcoming service makes for further contentment. The mainly French wine list has some mature clarets at very reasonable prices, a smattering of good New World bottles and a healthy stock of halves. House wine is £10.

CHEF: Brian Prideaux-Brune PROPRIETOR: Richard Prideaux-Brune OPEN: Sun L 12.30 to 2, all week D 7.30 to 9 MEALS: Set L Sun £17.50, Set D £12.50 (2 courses) to £25 SERVICE: net prices, card slips closed CARDS: Access, Amex, Diners, Switch, Visa DETAILS: 60 seats. 4 tables outside. Private parties: 50 main room, 15 to 50 private rooms. Car park. Vegetarian meals. Children's helpings. Smart dress preferred. Wheelchair access (also WC). No music ACCOMMODATION: 16 rooms, all with bath/shower. TV. Phone. B&B £65 to £115. Rooms for disabled. Children welcome. Baby facilities. Pets welcome. Garden (*The Which? Hotel Guide*)

SUDBURY Suffolk map 6

Mabey's Brasserie

47 Gainsborough Street, Sudbury CO10 7SS
TEL/FAX: (01787) 374298 COOKING 1
next to Gainsborough House Museum COST £21–£33

The décor is pure provincial brasserie, the prevailing colour blue, and many of the seats are church pews arranged in partitioned alcoves. Menus are chalked on boards above the cooking area, but a printed version is brought to table, and the food is mostly simple stuff, a mixture of something old, something new, something borrowed, something blue: tuna, for instance (blue-fin variety), grilled and served with coriander and walnut pesto. Much of the preparation and assembly is done beforehand – chicken and sweetbread terrine, for example – and salads and pizzas can be put together at a moment's notice. At dinner, two sittings seem to happen quite spontaneously at 7 and 9. Simple grills of beef and bakes of salmon work well. Puddings may include a dip-your-own chocolate fondue with seasonal fruits. Prices are fair for both food and wine, the latter on a short but lively and modern list, beginning with house wine at £7.50. Robert Mabey now appears to be cooking here as well as at Regatta (see entry, Aldeburgh).

CHEF: Robert Mabey PROPRIETORS: Robert and Johanna Mabey OPEN: Tue to Sat 12 to 2, 7 to 10 MEALS: alc (main courses £8 to £12) SERVICE: not inc, card slips closed CARDS: Access, Amex, Visa DETAILS: 60 seats. Private parties: 60 main room. Vegetarian meals. Children's helpings. No smoking in 1 dining-room. Wheelchair access (2 steps). No music. Air-conditioned

Red Onion Bistro £ NEW ENTRY

57 Ballingdon Street, Sudbury CO10 6DA COOKING 1*
TEL: (01787) 376777 COST £13–£24

'The Fords are back in town!' exclaimed a reporter when Gerry and Jane returned after working their way through several of East Anglia's favourite eating-places. They have converted an old barn-like garage on the outskirts of town into a cheap, cheerful and lively bistro with polished floorboards, colourful pictures on the walls and partitions dividing up the eating area. Tiny tables for two have board games printed on them, larger ones are covered with 'American cloth' and there is a monster communal table for walk-ins occupying the centre of the room. Business is brisk, and all ages and all comers frequent the place.

The Fords buy locally, change their menus each day and make as much as possible in-house – including regular batches of the eponymous red onion bread. Recommendations have come in thick and fast: crab bisque, smooth duck parfait with rhubarb chutney, thick spears of asparagus with a 'technically impeccable' butter sauce, cassoulet as good as anything from Toulouse, pigeon breasts in juniper gravy, salmon rösti fish-cakes with chive sauce – the list says it all. Then there are the puddings: treacle and walnut tart with an 'outstanding filling', steamed treacle and lemon sponge pudding, 'stunning' butterscotch ice-cream. There's no wine list as such, but you are invited to choose from a display of about 80 bins in a small room just off the restaurant. A 75-centilitre jug of red or white is £5.75.

CHEFS: Gerry and Jane Ford, and Stuart Mott PROPRIETORS: Gerry and Jane Ford OPEN: all week L 12 to 2 (12.30 to 1.45 Sun) Mon to Sat D 6.30 to 9.30 CLOSED: Christmas to New Year MEALS: alc L Mon to Sat (main courses £3.50 to £8.50). Set L Sun £9.75, Set D £9.75 SERVICE: not inc, card slips closed CARDS: Access, Delta, Switch, Visa DETAILS: 60 seats. 6 tables outside. Private parties: 22 main room. Car park. Vegetarian meals. Children's helpings. No cigars/pipes in dining-room. Wheelchair access (1 step). No music

SWAFFHAM Norfolk map 6

▲ *Stratton House* $*

4 Ash Close, Swaffham PE37 7NH COOKING 2
TEL: (01760) 723845 FAX: (01760) 720458 COST £28–£34

This eighteenth-century Palladian villa has made all manner of people comfortable in its time. Lady Hamilton stayed here in 1806, and the Surrey slow bowler 'Razor' Smith lived in the house up to his death just after the war. Les and Vanessa Scott took up residence in 1990, and whether you are staying in one of their lavishly appointed rooms or just popping in for the fixed-price dinner, you will experience the same feeling of being welcomed into the most hospitable private house.

A recognisable English country-house style runs throughout, although dishes are not over-elaborate. Crab from Cromer is given robust treatment with port and mushrooms, while soups centre on apposite pairings of wild mushroom with walnut, or parsnip and Bramley apple with curry seasoning. A Pyrenean recipe involving pastis, mushrooms and cream was unearthed for rainbow trout, and Vanessa's vegetarian repertoire is accomplished. Finish with British farmhouse cheeses in full ripeness, or perhaps raspberry and rose-petal crumble tart, ginger cake ice-cream, or port and prune fool. A couple who stayed in March enjoyed everything from the fluffy white towels to the last petit four and thought their visit 'excellent value for money'. An exhaustively annotated wine list is categorised by style and offers small but canny selections from around the world, including England. The emphasis throughout is on value. House French starts at £8.50.

denotes an outstanding wine cellar; denotes a good wine list, worth travelling for.

CHEF: Vanessa Scott PROPRIETORS: Les and Vanessa Scott OPEN: all week D only 7 to 10; L by arrangement CLOSED: 25 and 26 Dec MEALS: Set D £23.50 SERVICE: net prices, card slips closed CARDS: Access, Amex, Visa DETAILS: 20 seats. 2 tables outside. Private parties: 22 main room. Car park. Vegetarian meals. Children's helpings. Smart dress preferred. No smoking in dining-room. Music. Air-conditioned ACCOMMODATION: 7 rooms, all with bath/shower. TV. Phone. Air-conditioned. B&B £79 to £128. Deposit: £20. Children welcome. Baby facilities. Pets welcome. Afternoon teas. Garden (*The Which? Hotel Guide*)

SWANAGE Dorset map 2

Galley

9 High Street, Swanage BH19 2LN COOKING 1
TEL: (01929) 427299 COST £24–£29

The Storers have been in residence at their converted estate agent's office on the corner of the high street for more than eight years, but expansion is in the air: a move to larger premises a few yards down the road is planned for late 1996. This is a seaside fish restaurant without a deep-fat frier. What it offers, according to Nick Storer, is 'dead-simple food'. The simplest items are, in fact, grilled sole, sea bass, lobster and scallops that receive little more than a brushing of clarified butter. Exoticism flourishes in the shape of Thai fish soup with chilli and lemon grass, while meat and game are represented by steaks, breast of chicken with spicy salsa sauce, and duck with chestnuts, apple sauce and calvados gravy. A gardener now produces most of the vegetables and herbs, plus hop shoots, required by the kitchen. Rounding things off are old favourites such as crème caramel, chocolate liqueur mousse and steamed fruit sponge with Muscat sauce. A strong showing of well-chosen wines is backed up by some intriguing 'country wines, bin-ends and old French masters', as the wine list describes them. House wines start at £8.50.

CHEF: Nick Storer PROPRIETORS: N. D. and M. G. Storer OPEN: all week D only 6.45 to 9.30 (10 Sat) CLOSED: 2 weeks Nov, 1 Jan to 14 Feb MEALS: Set D £16.50 SERVICE: not inc, card slips closed CARDS: Access, Amex, Delta, Diners, Visa DETAILS: 36 seats. Private parties: 36 main room. Vegetarian meals. Children's helpings. Wheelchair access (2 steps). Music. Air-conditioned

TADWORTH Surrey map 3

Gemini

28 Station Approach, Tadworth KT20 5AH COOKING 2
TEL: (01737) 812179 COST £20–£38

The setting is a Tudor tea-room, the food's foundation is French. Few cooks in Britain, unless they were born and raised in France, stick exclusively to the traditional repertoire, and the lure of other ideas and ingredients has proved too much for Robert Foster too. He is happy to put his own stamp on things: hence marinated loin of marlin comes with a stir-fry of mung beans and snow peas, while smoked haddock and poached egg rest on squid-ink pasta.

Venison and beef get the stir-fry treatment too, plus a sweet chilli and garlic sauce, while more mainstream dishes include a tartlet of crab, mussels and prawns in a white wine sauce with chives and morel mushrooms, and pan-fried calf's liver with garlic and olive oil mash. Plentiful vegetables accompany, while puddings include rhubarb crème brûlée, and a choux pastry filled with praline cream and surrounded by a warm butterscotch sauce. Debbie Foster does a good job of meeting, greeting and taking orders. Fifty tasty and reasonably priced wines from around the world are headed by a short house selection starting at £8.50.

CHEF: Robert Foster PROPRIETORS: Robert and Debbie Foster OPEN: Tue to Fri and Sun L 12 to 2, Tue to Sat D 7 to 9.30 CLOSED: 2 weeks after Christmas, 2 weeks June MEALS: Set L Mon to Fri £11.50 (2 courses) to £13.50, Set L Sun £14.50, Set D Tue to Thur £18.50 (2 courses) to £22.50, Set D Fri and Sat £22.50 SERVICE: not inc, card slips closed; 10% for parties of 8 or more CARDS: Access, Delta, Switch, Visa DETAILS: 40 seats. Private parties: 38 main room. Vegetarian meals. Children's helpings Sun L. No children under 10 D. Smart dress preferred. No cigars/pipes in dining-room. Wheelchair access (1 step). Music

TAPLOW Berkshire **map 3**

▲ *Cliveden, Waldo's*

Taplow SL6 0JF
TEL: (01628) 668561 FAX: (01628) 661837 COOKING 3*
on B476, 2m N of Taplow COST £56–£93

Cliveden appears to have everything: centuries of history, pots of cachet, tons of period furniture, as well as tennis, swimming, squash, boating, beauty treatments, and bedrooms the like of which you've never seen. It is both a hotel and a stately home, in 376 acres of National Trust private gardens, for the upkeep of which a contribution of £2.50 per meal is levied. The present building is nineteenth-century, designed by Sir Charles Barry, architect of the Houses of Parliament. It has been home to royalty, and has entertained both the great and the good, plus a large number of politicians. The entire place is stunning from top to bottom, inside and out. Of the three eating areas, the Pavilion puts on light buffet lunches by the pool, the Terrace dining-room overlooks the parterre, and Waldo's is in what we mistakenly referred to last year as the 'basement'. It is, of course, on the 'lower ground floor', and we have the brochure to prove it.

Not surprisingly, Ron Maxfield makes unfettered use of luxuries from wild mushrooms and caviare to truffles and foie gras. Waldo's set-price dinners are the showpiece for modern dishes along the lines of gnocchi with Gruyère cheese and wild mushrooms in a light cream sauce with a shaving of white truffle, or a fillet of red mullet with chorizo on a tomato and chive vinaigrette with an oil scented with lemon grass and lime leaves. These artful constructions have had enough practice to make them near-perfect. The menu doesn't change much, which is unusual given the talent required to make the dishes work: most such chefs would be bursting to try new ideas.

Reporters justify the cost to themselves by mentally allocating a portion of the bill to the views and surroundings; what remains then makes the food seem good value. You would not expect cheap wine here, and you will not be disappointed. An upper limit of £20 buys very little from a wide-ranging list that takes in 'North America Blanc' and 'Australia Rouge'.

CHEF: Ron Maxfield PROPRIETOR: Cliveden plc OPEN: Tue to Sat D only 7 to 10.30 MEALS: Set D £45 to £60 SERVICE: not inc, card slips closed CARDS: Access, Amex, Delta, Diners, Visa DETAILS: 30 seats. 9 tables outside. Private parties: 12 to 54 private rooms. Car park. Vegetarian meals. Children welcome. Jacket and tie. No smoking in dining-room. Wheelchair access (also WC). Music. Air-conditioned ACCOMMODATION: 37 rooms, all with bath/shower. TV. Phone. 6 rooms air-conditioned. B&B from £210. Rooms for disabled. Children welcome. Baby facilities. Pets welcome. Garden. Swimming-pool. Fishing

---

TAUNTON Somerset map 2

▲ *Castle Hotel*

Castle Green, Taunton TA1 1NF COOKING 4
TEL: (01823) 272671 FAX: (01823) 336066 COST £28–£60

This town-centre landmark is 'all wonderfully country-like', wrote one reporter, eyeing the Norman garden and wistaria-covered façade. 'Taunton is lucky to have it,' said another. If first impressions count, then the Castle gets off to a flying start. The reception is suave and efficient, while fresh flowers are 'beautiful' and napery and glass 'immaculate'. 'We were struck by the pristine condition of everything.' The bar 'is one of the nicest in southern England', while the dining-room is comfortable enough, with fine-patterned wallpaper, big brass chandeliers and swagged curtains.

The set-up is two parallel menus, each offering three or four courses, with a £10 difference between them. The less-expensive alternative is simpler and plainer, less ambitious but perfectly good. At one meal a mild curried parsnip soup was followed by steamed fillets of plaice with spring onions and creamed potatoes, then baked rice pudding with caramel and oranges. For the extra tenner you get more choice, taller towers (dishes are 3-D constructions) and perhaps sea bass instead of pollack, or saddle of venison instead of chicken breast, that sort of thing. Braised shoulder of lamb from this menu is a circular chunk of meat wrapped in caul fat, 'meltingly tender and very tasty', sitting on a disc of fondant potato with shredded cabbage and other vegetables, in a rather dark and pungent sauce.

Phil Vickery's food is modern and British without being tub-thumpingly so. The quality of ingredients and level of execution are not generally in doubt, although not all reporters have been happy with their experiences. 'Have they changed the chef?' asked one, while another complained of tough and tasteless steak. But the kitchen can turn out a delightful first course of potted pigeon and duck, and an assured pudding of poached pear with lemon grass sabayon and hazelnut shortbread. What it seems a bit short on is a spark of gastronomic inspiration that makes reporters go 'Wow!' Marinated olives come with aperitifs, and breads include a popular bacon and onion version.

Burgundy and Bordeaux get more serious treatment than anywhere else on the wine list, but the spread throughout the world is good, including a dozen Italians and four from Somerset. The Castle is one of the few restaurants to take sherry seriously, and malt whiskies are mouth-watering. The list of two dozen wines under £15 is useful, and all are available by the glass at £2. CELLARMAN'S CHOICE: Sauvignon Blanc 1993, Klein Constantia, South Africa, £14.45; Rouge Homme Cabernet Sauvignon 1989, Coonawarra, S. Australia, £21.25.

CHEF: Phil Vickery PROPRIETORS: the Chapman family OPEN: all week 12.30 to 2, 7.30 to 9 MEALS: Set L £17.90 to £35, Set D £20.90 to £35 SERVICE: not inc, card slips closed CARDS: Access, Amex, Delta, Diners, Switch, Visa DETAILS: 65 seats. Private parties: 110 main room, 16 and 25 private rooms. Car park. Vegetarian meals. Children's helpings. Smart dress preferred. No smoking in dining-room. Wheelchair access (also WC). Music ACCOMMODATION: 35 rooms, all with bath/shower. TV. Phone. B&B £70 to £170. Rooms for disabled. Children welcome. Baby facilities. Pets welcome in bedrooms only. Afternoon teas. Garden (*The Which? Hotel Guide*)

TAVISTOCK Devon map 1

▲ *Horn of Plenty*

Gulworthy, Tavistock PL19 8JD
TEL/FAX: (01822) 832528
3m W of Tavistock on A390, turn right at Gulworthy Cross

COOKING 3
COST £27–£51

The 'plenty' in the name given to this handsome Georgian house on the western fringe of Dartmoor could refer to the copious flora that brighten the gardens from early spring, or to the lush views across the Tamar Valley from bedrooms and dining-room. The latter is pleasingly decorated with bold floral wallpaper and elegant table-settings. Ian and Elaine Gatehouse have this year introduced a cheaper 'pot luck' menu on Monday evenings to bolster their usual set-price menus; it offers a more restricted choice but has proved deservedly popular.

Chef Peter Gorton seems to be gaining in authority year by year. That notional world-cookery encyclopedia that so many chefs today appear to be working from is employed to telling effect in beetroot ravioli filled with a mousse of spinach and ricotta, in monkfish grilled and served with a sauce of coconut and spring onion to which are added fried shallots and coriander, and in roast pigeon on saffron couscous. A slice of terrine that combines duck confit and 'slightly woody' wild mushrooms is given majestic finish by a light garlic cream spread under it. The accuracy of all elements in a main dish of venison adds up to a *tour de force*: the tender meat itself, slices of caramelised apple on top, a show-stopping potato galette, and a 'strong and dark, slightly sweet' sauce of cider and black pepper. Vegetable accompaniments for one inspector 'were at least 50 per cent responsible for our state of advanced well-being'.

Fine lemon tart is given extra point by garnishes of orange, while light, indeed 'fluffy', toffee pudding is anointed – this being Devon – with clotted cream. Service is 'assiduous rather than intrusive'. The wine list provides plenty of choice, but remains rather old-fashionedly focused on France, though the affordable bottles mostly crop up elsewhere. There is a good showing of halves, however, and six of the house wines come by the glass. Bottle prices start at £10.75.

The Guide *always appreciates hearing about changes of chef or owner.*

All main entries are fully indexed at the back of the Guide.

CHEF: Peter Gorton PROPRIETORS: Elaine and Ian Gatehouse OPEN: Tue to Sun L 12 to 2, all week D 7 to 9.30 MEALS: Set L £10.50 (2 courses) to £17.50, Set D Mon £18.50, Tue to Sun £28.50 SERVICE: not inc CARDS: Access, Amex, Switch, Visa DETAILS: 50 seats. 5 tables outside. Private parties: 50 main room, 12 private room. Car park. No children under 13 (exc Sun L). Smart dress preferred. No smoking in dining-room. Wheelchair access (also WC). No music ACCOMMODATION: 7 rooms, all with bath/shower. TV. Phone. B&B £68 to £98. Deposit: 20%. Rooms for disabled. No children under 13. Pets welcome in bedrooms only. Garden (*The Which? Hotel Guide*)

Neil's ⁜

27 King Street, Tavistock PL19 0DT — COOKING 2
TEL: (01822) 615550 — COST £25–£39

The scale is small, with room for only twenty people, five nights a week, but regulars continue to return to the stone walls and oak beams of this sixteenth-century house for more of Janet Neil's careful cooking. The style is considered, Francophile rather than straight French, and the repertoire evolves slowly. Apart from the odd bit of pasta, there are no borrowings from Italy, and the exotic is generally avoided. Rather, the food is a gentle interpretation of some of the classics, along the lines of Swiss cheese soufflé, or roast breast of goose with apples, cream and calvados. The idea of the provençale fish tart with rouille, olives and sun-dried tomatoes, Janet Neil tells us, came from bourride.

An April version of the fixed-price three-course menu, with a choice of two items per course, produced courgette and lettuce soup, plaice fillets in puff pastry, and banana sorbet in a coconut tuile basket. Puff pastry makes a regular appearance, as a container for eggs and hollandaise with poached salmon, or for chicken livers with shallots in a marsala cream sauce. The richness is no more than is typical for French provincial dishes. Main-course meats favour fillet or tenderloin of locally farmed venison, guinea-fowl in a mustard sauce, or roast duck breast with lentils and cep sauce. A concise list of around 30 wines is very well sourced and sensibly priced, with interesting house wine at £8.95, or £1.75 a glass.

CHEF/PROPRIETOR: Janet Neil OPEN: Tue to Sat D only 7 to 9 CLOSED: 24 to 26 Dec MEALS: alc (main courses £13 to £15). Set D £17 SERVICE: not inc CARDS: Access, Amex, Visa DETAILS: 20 seats. Private parties: 25 main room. Vegetarian meals. Children welcome. Smart dress preferred. No smoking in dining-room. No music

TEFFONT EVIAS Wiltshire — map 2

▲ *Howard's House* ⁜

Teffont Evias SP3 5RJ
TEL: (01722) 716392 FAX: (01722) 716820 — COOKING 2*
off B3089, W of Dinton, signposted Chicksgrove — COST £27–£49

The house has been owned by the same family since the late seventeenth century. An extension put on in the year Victoria acceded to the throne was inspired by architecture seen on the Swiss leg of the Grand Tour, but otherwise all remains much as it was. The dining-room resounds to Mozart in the evenings, and an enterprising menu is offered. Paul Firmin has carved out quite a reputation for himself over the last few years, with raw materials and presentation of a high order. The cooking moves with the times, invoking most of today's culinary talismans with panache. Boudin noir with red onions, apples and calvados sits happily among the first courses alongside mussels steamed with lemon grass, star-anise and coriander. 'Imaginative and entirely successful' accompaniments add interest to main courses, so that brill is partnered with artichokes, broad beans and a shellfish sabayon, saddle of venison has a mushroom and celeriac lasagne, and grilled beef sirloin combines two classic ingredients in a béarnaise sauce given bite with horseradish. Desserts too may stimulate the senses: grilled plums were served one night in almond milk with a praline ice-cream; another night produced an 'excellent' mango mousse. Some people have found the coffee and petits fours 'unexceptional', others 'superb'. House wines are £10.75 (white) and £12.95 (red).

CHEF: Paul Firmin PROPRIETORS: George Ford, Jonathan Ford and Paul Firmin OPEN: Sun L 12.30 to 2, all week D 7.30 to 10 MEALS: alc (main courses £13 to £17). Set L Sun £19.50 SERVICE: not inc CARDS: Access, Amex, Delta, Switch, Visa DETAILS: 40 seats. 3 tables outside. Private parties: 40 main room. Car park. Vegetarian meals. Children's helpings. No smoking in dining-room. Wheelchair access (also WC). Music ACCOMMODATION: 9 rooms, all with bath/shower. TV. Phone. B&B £87.50 to £107.50. Children welcome. Pets welcome. Garden (*The Which? Hotel Guide*)

TETBURY Gloucestershire map 2

▲ *Calcot Manor*

nr Beverston, Tetbury GL8 8YJ
TEL: (01666) 890391 FAX: (01666) 890394 COOKING 2
on A4135, 4m W of Tetbury COST £25–£42

Changes are afoot at Calcot as the Stone family has tried to ease the whole operation gently out of the limiting country-house mould of the 1980s. A new wing was opened in late 1994 to house the Gumstool Inn, a self-contained pub with flagged floor and chunky oak furniture offering simpler food (reports, please). The latter has been refurbished in muted shades, the better perhaps to emphasise the vista of Cotswold hills it enjoys.

Edward Portlock returned to the kitchens in spring 1995. Previously understudy to other Calcot chefs, he subsequently cooked at the Royal Crescent Hotel in Bath (see entry) and at L'Ortolan and Hambleton Hall (see entries, Shinfield and Hambleton). The style retains aspects of the country-house mode, and though some things might strain too hard for effect, accompaniments on the whole are carefully considered. Grey mullet on roasted ratatouille vegetables and chopped olives is a top-quality combination, and the fish itself 'stood up amazingly well to the strong-tasting vegetable mixture'. Similarly, the tartness of apple and apricot with roast duckling offsets both the fattiness of the confit of leg and the sweetness of a translucent stock sauce flavoured with cinnamon. Desserts go for gentle flavours in caramel mousse with Amaretto, or honey parfait, although summer saw an orange tart served with marinated straw-berries. At inspection breads and petits fours showed up well, vegetable side-plates less so. There is potential enough here to make the new regime worth watching.

Good suppliers have resulted in an authoritative wine list that is unashamedly strong in classical France but which also embraces thoughtful selections from Australia and the USA. Prices are not giveaway, but there is enough choice under £20 for decency's sake, and the house offerings – starting at £11 – represent a wide spread. CELLARMAN'S CHOICE: Pouilly Fumé 'Les Loges' 1992, Guyot, £19; Collioure 1991, Dom. du Mas, £18.

CHEF: Edward Portlock PROPRIETORS: the Stone family OPEN: all week 12.30 to 2, 7.30 to 9.30 MEALS: Set L £17, Set D £26 SERVICE: not inc, card slips closed CARDS: Access, Amex, Delta, Diners, Switch, Visa DETAILS: 50 seats. 4 tables outside. Private parties: 60 main room, 12, 15 and 60 private rooms. Car park. Vegetarian meals. Children's helpings. Smart dress preferred. No smoking in dining-room. Wheelchair access (also WC). No music ACCOMMODATION: 20 rooms, all with bath/shower. TV. Phone. B&B £75 to £165. Rooms for disabled. Children welcome. Baby facilities. Afternoon teas. Garden. Swimming-pool (*The Which? Hotel Guide*)

THORNBURY Avon map 2

▲ *Thornbury Castle*

Castle Street, Thornbury BS12 1HH
TEL: (01454) 281182 FAX: (01454) 416188
off B4061, at N end of town

COOKING 2
COST £27–£47

'Only in England can we be so casual about something so stunning,' thought one reporter who liked to consider herself unfazed by dining in a 450-year-old castle yet found it 'rather a magical experience'. The whole place is 'achingly beautiful, very English, and very understated'. Inside the crenellated walls the mood turns from Tudor to mid-nineteenth-century Victorian Gothic, a decorative mix of the old and the new, 'the fake and the true' – although the suit of armour still looks 'intimidatingly original' – complete with 25-foot-high ceilings, and plenty of paintings to cover the walls. It is a hard act for anybody's food to follow.

Steven Black took over the kitchen in March, and his daily-changing three-course menus – similar in scope at both lunch and dinner – are in the familiar mould of contemporary country-house cooking, taking in duck liver parfait, a salad of sauté potatoes with black pudding and poached egg, and main courses of poached salmon or roast lamb with a mint crust. Two dishes at one meal – boned woodpigeon and roasted monkfish – came with mangold, the large, dark-green leaf of the mangel-wurzel that one reporter considered 'vastly superior to those anorexic, pre-pubescent spinach leaves, and which tasted as if it was injecting iron straight into my bloodstream'.

Desserts run from tart summer pudding to rich treacle tart with Cornish clotted cream, and service is from a very jolly and smart head waiter who is 'a mine of information'. The wine list includes 'burgundy and Bordeaux to dream of', which is as close as some of us will ever get, given some of the prices, though venerable vintages from the 1920s perhaps warrant their three figures. Wines under £20 include Hamilton Russell's Pinot Noir from South Africa, and Thornbury Castle's own wine, made from the Müller-Thurgau vines you pass on the way in.

CHEF: Steven Black PROPRIETORS: Baron and Baroness Portlethen OPEN: all week 12 to 2, 7 to 9.30 (10 Fri and Sat, 9 Sun) CLOSED: 2 days Jan MEALS: Set L £18.50, Set D £31 SERVICE: none, card slips closed CARDS: Access, Amex, Diners, Switch, Visa DETAILS: 60 seats. Private parties: 26 main room, 12 and 28 private rooms. Car park. Vegetarian meals. No children under 12. Jacket and tie. No smoking in dining-room. Music ACCOMMODATION: 18 rooms, all with bath/shower. TV. Phone. B&B £75 to £205. No children under 12. Afternoon teas. Garden (*The Which? Hotel Guide*)

THORNTON-CLEVELEYS Lancashire map 8

▲ *Victorian House*

Trunnah Road, Thornton-Cleveleys FY5 4HF
TEL: (01253) 860619 FAX: (01253) 865350 COOKING 1
off A585, 3m N of Blackpool COST £17–£35

Antiques and period furnishings populate this Victorian house not far from the windmill. Dinner is a serious four-course affair, served on lace tablecloths by keen staff 'who are ready to swoop at the drop of a knife'. The food is old-style French, if the snails in garlic and parsley butter are anything to go by. This inexhaustible seam also yields moules marinière and seafood crêpe to begin, followed by poached salmon with hollandaise sauce, or roast fillet of pork served with a grand veneur sauce. Lunch in the conservatory is a more informal affair that might include a soup of asparagus with strips of smoked salmon, or on one occasion a simple plate of thinly cut ham impressively combining charcoal smokiness with the sweetness of a honey coating and the sharpness of the cider it was cooked in. Ice-creams, sorbets, meringues, and tarts of lemon or pecan bring up the rear. Three dozen French wines are helped along by ten from the New World. French house wine is £9.50 a bottle or £1.70 a glass.

CHEF: Didier Guérin PROPRIETORS: Louise and Didier Guérin OPEN: Tue to Sat L 12 to 1.30, Mon to Sat D 7 to 9.30 CLOSED: first 2 weeks Feb MEALS: alc L (main courses £5 to £6). Set D £21 SERVICE: not inc, card slips closed CARDS: Access, Visa DETAILS: 60 seats. Private parties: 44 main room, 20 private room. Car park. Children's helpings. No children under 6. Smart dress preferred. Music ACCOMMODATION: 3 rooms, all with bath/shower. TV. Phone. B&B £35 to £80. Pets welcome in bedrooms only. Garden (*The Which? Hotel Guide*)

THUNDRIDGE Hertfordshire map 3

▲ *Hanbury Manor*

Thundridge SG12 0SD
TEL: (01920) 487722 FAX: (01920) 487692 COOKING 2*
off A10, 1½m N of Ware COST £32–£78

The mock Jacobean mansion was built in 1890 for Edmund and Amy Hanbury, though most of its 200 acres now seem to be taken up with golf, while a swimming-pool and gymnasium also lend credence to its 'country-club resort' tag. Ten conference rooms indicate the corporate pitch. Cars are valet-parked, and the entrance to the Zodiac restaurant is through an oak-panelled lounge with a high ceiling, big fireplace, tapestries and large sofas and chairs. A pianola plays in the background, and 'unlike a real pianist, it doesn't take a break'. Gentlemen

are required to wear a tie, even on the hottest days, which one reporter (unable to order a drink until he complied) felt strongly about: 'Any place that puts its own little rituals above the comfort of guests is plainly in the wrong business. This is not my idea of hospitality.' Another summed it all up as 'pretentious and overpriced'. But the food is good.

The dining-room is painted white, though not blindingly so – stare hard at the barrel-vaulted ceiling for signs of the zodiac – and looks out on to mature trees and golf buggies. 'Douze livres cinquante' intones the menu for a first course of roast mullet surrounded by wedges of artichoke heart, tomato flesh and olive paste with a dribble of good olive oil: an impeccably Mediterranean gesture that only a tastier piece of fish would have improved. An inspector, however, was bowled over by a flavourful chicken cooked in the style of bouillabaisse, in a 'brilliant' saffrony stock-based sauce, even though its accompanying aïoli and oily bread were under par, if we may borrow a golfing term. Whatever else, though, the food looks good, especially a raft of thin sticks of rhubarb surmounted by a tuile cage cleverly enclosing a yoghurt ice-cream. Service is a bit stiff, wines are good but expensive, with house wine £13. Two other dining areas – the Conservatory and Vardon's – serve simpler and less expensive food.

CHEF: Rory Kennedy PROPRIETOR: Poles Ltd OPEN: all week 12 to 3, 6.30 to 10 MEALS: alc (main courses £13 to £32). Set L £19.50 to £26, Set D £25 SERVICE: net prices, card slips closed CARDS: Access, Amex, Diners, Visa DETAILS: 40 seats. 10 tables outside. Private parties: 100 main room, 10 to 100 private rooms. Car park. Vegetarian meals. No children under 8. Jacket and tie. No smoking in dining-room. Wheelchair access (3 steps; also WC). Music ACCOMMODATION: 96 rooms, all with bath/shower. TV. Phone. B&B £103 to £376. Deposit: 1 night's stay. Rooms for disabled. Children welcome. Baby facilities. Pets welcome. Afternoon teas. Garden. Swimming-pool

TORQUAY Devon map 1

Table

135 Babbacombe Road, Babbacombe,
Torquay TQ1 3SR COOKING 3*
TEL: (01803) 324292 COST £35–£42

Fashioned from two rooms of a converted end-of-terrace shop, the restaurant is on a small scale – Trevor Brooks cooks while Jane manages front-of-house single-handedly – and feels more informal than one might expect for sharp modern cooking of this kind. Despite only four choices per course, there are no doubts about variety or balance, or about the bright flavour combinations that produce crab broth with pickled ginger and lemon grass, or black pudding with potato galette and mustard dressing.

Fish and shellfish understandably play a central role. One dish at a May meal paired seared sweet scallops with satisfyingly bitter asparagus, while another set two crab-cakes, coated with brioche crumbs and Parmesan, on a saffron risotto, and surrounded them with a thick dark red sauce of smoked tomato with a well-judged splash of chilli oil: 'quite a bite, but not enough to overpower the crab'. Red wine sauces with fish are something of a trade mark, served at one autumn meal with steamed halibut that rested on a bed of pasta and a profusion of wild mushrooms, including chanterelles, trompettes-de-mort, cauliflower fungus and hedgehog fungus.

It is the three-dimensional effect of this attention to tastes and textures that sets Trevor Brooks apart, and applies equally to desserts of rhubarb tartlet with ginger ice-cream, or torrone parfait with a milk chocolate sauce and coconut sorbet. Cheese might be a selection of six local varieties, while incidentals, from olives in garlicky oil to excellent home-made bread full of nuts and seeds, maintain the standard. Wines are arranged by style, appropriately varied, and kind to the pocket. There are twenty half-bottles, and house wine is from £9.50. CELLARMAN'S CHOICE: Sancerre, Clos du Roy 1993, Millerioux, £16; Côtes du Luberon, Ch. La Verrerie 1989, £14.

CHEF: Trevor Brooks PROPRIETORS: Trevor and Jane Brooks OPEN: Tue to Sat 7.30 to 9.30 CLOSED: 1 to 18 Feb, 1 to 18 Sept MEALS: Set D £30.50. Minimum £30.50 SERVICE: none, card slips closed CARDS: Access, Visa DETAILS: 20 seats. Private parties: 20 main room. No children under 10. Smart dress preferred. No smoking in dining-room. Wheelchair access. No music

TRUSHAM Devon map 1

▲ *Cridford Inn* £ **NEW ENTRY**

Trusham TQ13 0NR
TEL: (01626) 853694
off B3193 Chudleigh to Exeter road, 3m NW of Chudleigh

COOKING 1
COST £18–£37

Once you have negotiated the winding road to the village itself, you will see the pub set back in all its splendour. Built in Saxon times and modernised as a 'hall house' in 1081, it ranks as the oldest domestic dwelling in Devon. The evidence of its antiquity is everywhere: from the mosaic of a date-stone embedded in the floor of the dining-room to the earliest example of a domestic stained-glass window in the bar. One menu (plus a blackboard of specials) is served throughout, and you can eat in the massively beamed bar or in the dining-room (the latter open only on Friday and Saturday).

David and Sally Hesmondhalgh take full advantage of reliable local supplies: fish comes from Brixham, cheese from the Ticklemore cheese shop, game from a neighbouring estate, ice-creams from Langage Farm, while salmon is cured in the pub's own smokehouse. The cooking is unpretentious and sauces are handled judiciously. Dry-cured Denhay ham is served with green figs, 'excellent' cream cheese terrine is studded with walnuts and chives. Main courses stay with the same theme: rump steak is a decent hunk of cooked-to-order meat from a good butcher, while roast duckling is a proper crisp-skinned bird with plenty of flavour on a bed of sage and onion stuffing with an orange and port sauce. Desserts are pleasing offerings along the lines of tipsy trifle and spicy apple strudel. The short, sensible wine list (from Christopher Piper) is fleshed out with an excellent selection of wines by the glass. House wines start at £9.50.

CHEF: David Hesmondhalgh PROPRIETORS: David and Sally Hesmondhalgh OPEN: all week 12 to 1.45, 7 to 8.45 CLOSED: 25 Dec MEALS: alc (main courses £5.50 to £13) SERVICE: not inc, card slips closed CARDS: Access, Visa DETAILS: 50 seats. 10 tables outside. Private parties: 20 main room. Car park. Vegetarian meals. No children under 8 after 8.30. Smart dress preferred. No smoking in dining-room. No music ACCOMMODATION: 4 rooms, all with bath/shower. TV. B&B £37.50 to £55. Deposit: 10%

TUNBRIDGE WELLS Kent map 3

Cheevers

56 High Street, Tunbridge Wells TN1 1XF COOKING 2
TEL: (01892) 545524 FAX: (01892) 535956 COST £26–£39

A little way up the hill on the high street is this converted shop where Tim Cheevers has been cooking for a decade now. The approach is very much steady-the-buffs, and all the more appreciated for that. Crowd-pleasing dishes of quail's eggs in a flaky pastry case with mushrooms and hollandaise gratify because they are at a level of technicality just above the domestic. Seafood is gently treated in mussel and fennel broth, or crab mousse wrapped in spinach. Main courses tend to support their principal ingredients with one apposite flavour: Pernod with sauté monkfish, or apple with roast guinea-fowl. The signature roast duckling with ginger and spring onions has been 'first-rate – the outside crisp and unfatty, the flesh tender and tasty'. A sauté of beef fillet in yoghurt and coriander is a more novel idea that succeeds. Desserts will either soothe the taste-buds with banana ice-cream in a brown sugar meringue and fudge sauce, or keep them buzzing with gin and grapefruit sorbet. 'Excellent and unobtrusive' service keeps its head at the busiest times.

A cosmopolitan wine list takes in Kent as well as Chile, though the base line is France. Price order is not observed, so you will have to concentrate. Half-bottles are in generous proportion to the list overall. House vin de pays is £8.95 the bottle, £2.25 the glass.

CHEF: T. J. Cheevers PROPRIETORS: T. J. Cheevers, M. J. Miles and P. D. Tambini OPEN: Tue to Sat 12.30 to 2 (1.45 Sat), 7.30 to 10.30 MEALS: alc L Tue to Sat, D Tue to Thur (main courses £9.50). Set D Fri and Sat £25 SERVICE: not inc CARDS: Access, Amex, Delta, Switch, Visa DETAILS: 32 seats. Private parties: 20 main room. Children welcome. No pipes in dining-room. Wheelchair access (1 step). No music. Air-conditioned

Sankeys

39 Mount Ephraim, Tunbridge Wells TN4 8AA COOKING 1
TEL: (01892) 511422 FAX: (01892) 536097 COST £23–£51

Sankey's occupies a Victorian villa on Mount Ephraim, a preserved historic quarter of Royal Tunbridge Wells: about as dignified a situation as is possible to achieve. The ambience is not in the least reverential, though. This is a lively and well-supported venue offering uncomplicated cooking of impeccably fresh seafood. Gratinated first courses work well, as in avocado with crab under a cheese glaze, or scallops with a mushroom and white wine sauce. Main courses offer classic treatments, such as a generous plateau de fruits de mer and bouillabaisse, as well as fashionable forays into garlicky roasted monkfish, or an accompaniment of spring onion, soy and ginger for steamed sea bass. Agreeably rich chocolate mousse seems a better dessert option than the workaday version of French apple tart. 'Unrushed' service allows everybody to relax. The basement wine bar has a shorter menu and cheaper prices. The wine list offers a comprehensive range at prices that won't alarm, and provides a far more generous selection of reds than you might expect in a fish restaurant. House French is £8.

CHEF: Eleutorio Lizzi PROPRIETORS: Guy and Amanda Sankey OPEN: restaurant Mon to Sat 12 to 3, 7 to 10; wine bar all week 12 to 3, 7 to 10 CLOSED: 25 and 26 Dec; restaurant bank hol Mons MEALS: restaurant alc (main courses £9 to £21). Set L £10 (2 courses inc wine); wine bar alc (main courses £5 to £8) SERVICE: not inc CARDS: Access, Amex, Diners, Switch, Visa DETAILS: 60 seats. 8 tables outside. Private parties: 16 main room. Vegetarian meals. Children's helpings. Smart dress preferred. No smoking in 1 dining-room. Music. Air-conditioned

Thackeray's House 🍷

85 London Road, Tunbridge Wells TN1 1EA — COOKING 3
TEL/FAX: (01892) 511921 — COST £27–£68

Bruce Wass oversees a basement bistro and a 'most attractive' ground-floor dining-room set with Victorian furniture, next door to the Conservative Association. If the lunchtime menu in the dining-room seems rather more low-key than dinner, the price difference does enough to explain it, and in any case there is no stinting. A three-course midday meal of pike and salmon mousseline with lobster sauce, lamb sweetbreads with broad beans, and an apricot, walnut, ginger and toffee pudding, of this quality, at this price, seems very fair.

Indeed, fairness is a hallmark of the operation. Choice at dinner is extremely generous – some first courses can also be upgraded to mains – and much effort has been made to make the combinations appealing. The style is modern but restrained, in the sense that it goes in for onion marmalade (with a salad of preserved duck) but not for anything as dazzling as, say, a lime, chilli and coriander salsa. Fresh Kent asparagus gratiné with wild mushrooms is more its bag, along with chicken breast with wood blewits, or guinea-fowl with morels. Any earthiness comes from such simple wild ingredients.

Fish and shellfish get serious treatment in dishes of grilled skate fillets with crab vinaigrette, and in the crispy fried oysters and laverbread sauce that come with roast monkfish and scallops. Simplicity rules at dessert stage, among the îles flottantes and exemplary lemon brûlée tart. Some mature vintages pop up in the major French regions, variety is provided by Italy, Spain, Australia and New Zealand, some mark-ups are high, but a short selection of characterful wines up to £20 is helpful, and there are so many half-bottles that they need a separate list.

CHEF/PROPRIETOR: Bruce Wass OPEN: Tue to Sun L 12.30 to 2, Tue to Sat D 7 to 10 MEALS: alc (main courses £10 to £18.50). Set L £12 (2 courses), Set L Sun £18.50, Set D Tue to Thur £22 to £42 SERVICE: not inc CARDS: Access, Delta, Switch, Visa DETAILS: 50 seats. 6 tables outside. Private parties: 50 main room, 12 to 22 private rooms. Vegetarian meals. Children's helpings. No cigars/pipes in dining-room. Wheelchair access (1 step). No music

TWICKENHAM Greater London map 3

McClements

2 Whitton Road, Twickenham TW1 1BJ COOKING 2*
TEL: 0181-744 9610 COST £24–£50

Last year John McClements ran a main restaurant and a bistro. This year he is doing exactly the same, except that the main restaurant is now to be found in what was the bistro, and the shop next door to it has been bought for conversion into a bistro. Simple really, though the transition has thrown up a few difficulties, not to mention different sorts of menus. But when McClements himself is cooking it can be very good indeed; and by having both outlets on one site he will presumably be able to keep a close watch on everything. His personal tastes include offal and seafood, which is a rare enough combination to mark this out as an unusual venue, and one to be cherished by lovers of either.

A first course of Yorkshire pudding with foie gras and onion gravy shows a welcome playfulness, while boned pig's head, served with cabbage and a piquant sauce, makes a satisfying main course. Meals might begin with an amuse-gueule of a coffee-cup of chilled gazpacho, followed by a 'perfect' open ravioli of roasted langoustines in a cream sauce, then crisp breast of guinea-fowl with the leg minced and made into an accompanying shepherd's pie. Saddle of lamb or venison, and beef bordelaise, indicate that there is no need to share either of the McClements' passions. Pear Tatin, though it may not be a strictly accurate designation, is very good, with caramelised pear halves, caramel sauce and custard. 'No room for dessert,' wrote one, 'but the petits fours more than made up for it.' House wine is £10.

CHEF/PROPRIETOR: John McClements OPEN: Mon to Sat 12 to 2.30, 7 to 11 MEALS: alc D (main courses £12.50 to £16). Set L £15 SERVICE: 10%, card slips closed CARDS: Access, Visa DETAILS: 45 seats. Private parties: 50 main room. Children welcome. Wheelchair access (also WC). Music. Air-conditioned

UCKFIELD East Sussex map 3

▲ *Horsted Place*

Little Horsted, Uckfield TN22 5TS
TEL: (01825) 750581 FAX: (01825) 750240 COOKING 2*
2m S of Uckfield, on A26 COST £24–£55

The Victorian Gothic mansion, set in seven acres of listed gardens designed by Sir Geoffrey Jellicoe, became a country-house hotel in 1986, and no expense seems to have been spared. As well as the gardens it boasts a terrace, croquet lawn, golf course and swimming-pool. The setting is 'wonderful' and the rooms 'hugely opulent', including the bright pink dining-room and an attractive library laid out with a few well-spaced tables.

The kitchen smokes its own salmon, makes preserves and pays due regard to the season. The *carte* may go in for an occasional lavish gesture, such as ballotine of warm foie gras, but in general it avoids the more obvious country-house clichés. In their place we might find roasted guinea-fowl filled with halloumi cheese, or osso buco. The menu insists on offering us 'pouding aux pommes' at 'four pounds and fifty pence', which is not a good sign – it sounds far better in translation as steamed apple sponge with fudge sauce – but the kitchen delivers the goods, which is what matters. A typical three-course set lunch might take in asparagus soup, pan-fried skate wing, and chocolate marquise, while the vegetarian *carte* has included a salad of Jerusalem artichokes with a 'tapénade' of olives and figs. Rich and squidgy fruit puddings are highly rated and might include figs glazed with mascarpone and served with a blackberry sauce, or Liwanzau, a pancake filled with mango and banana and served with clotted cream. The heavyweight wine list offers some choice under £20. House French is £10.

CHEF: Allan Garth PROPRIETOR: Granfel Holdings Ltd OPEN: all week 12 to 2, 7.30 to 9.30 MEALS: alc (main courses £18 to £20). Set L £10 (2 courses) to £14.95, Set D £28.50 SERVICE: not inc CARDS: Access, Amex, Delta, Diners, Switch, Visa DETAILS: 40 seats. 6 tables outside. Private parties: 12 main room, 18 and 26 private rooms. Car park. Vegetarian meals. No children under 7. Jacket and tie. No smoking in dining-rooms. Wheelchair access (also WC). No music ACCOMMODATION: 20 rooms, all with bath/shower. TV. Phone. B&B £100 to £325. Deposit: £50. Rooms for disabled. No children under 7. Pets welcome in bedrooms only. Afternoon teas. Garden. Swimming-pool (*The Which? Hotel Guide*)

ULLSWATER Cumbria map 10

▲ *Sharrow Bay*

Ullswater CA10 2LZ
TEL: (01768) 486301 FAX: (01768) 486349
2m from Pooley Bridge on E side of lake, signposted Howtown and Martindale

COOKING 3*
COST £31–£56

'Sharrow Bay is an institution. It bows to no fashion, keeps rigidly to the same format, and fills the place all the time,' writes one visitor. 'The experience and pleasure are worth the quite reasonable expense' is a common conclusion. While many country-house hotels, especially in the south, cater for expense-account visitors riding the international circuit, Sharrow Bay retains its charm as a place where most people come to enjoy themselves and spend their own money. There are three 'holding areas' to begin: the conservatory, an 'over-the-top 1930s' lounge, and the lakeside room. The dark wood and heavy curtains of the dining-room frame the spectacular view down Ullswater towards Helvellyn.

This is not a place for casual eating. Sharrow Bay has cornered the special-occasion market, and its food is both rich and plentiful. It has always been English in character, long before this became fashionable. Starters and main courses offer plenty of alternatives, while a no-choice sorbet and fish course are slotted in between: the soufflé suissesse and creamy sauce served with the fish are greatly comforting. Few reporters make it through to the puddings or English cheese, so generous are the quantities. Vegetables have a small but culpable role in this: there are seven, three of which are different kinds of potato.

Taken by themselves, individual items please, from a creamy soup of tomato with mushroom, orange and chopped walnuts, to one of the lighter and more refreshing puddings, such as an upturned jelly in which were embedded lychee, orange, strawberries and raspberries. Several reporters have remarked on subdued, indistinct, even 'bland' flavours, notably among fish dishes, which rather spoils the point of their elaborate presentation. But the more robust flavours of venison, grouse or calf's liver generally get through, even in the teeth of a fresh mango and cassis sauce in the latter case. Sweetness and fruitiness are not uncommon with main-course meats.

'Waiters are dressed like civil servants, for some reason,' but are super-attentive. 'It struck us as a well-oiled machine, stimulating and theatrical,' wrote one. For the most part the stage-managing is done with tact and grace, and is responsive to individual quirks: 'old-fashioned courtesy' is a fair description. The wine list is varied and very much on the ball, taking delight in a number of interesting bottles that might escape the notice of other country-house hotels. Quality is high, yet there is no heavy-handedness. A separate list of Before and After drinks, including wines by the glass, is particularly useful. Wine service is good too. CELLARMAN'S CHOICE: Béarn Blanc, Dom. Guilhemas 1993, Lapeyre, £13.95; Faugères 1992, Dom. Alquier, £13.50.

CHEFS: Johnnie Martin, Colin Akrigg, Philip Wilson and Chris Bond PROPRIETORS: Francis Coulson and Brian Sack OPEN: all week 1 to 1.45, 8 to 8.45 CLOSED: end Nov to end Feb MEALS: Set L £25 to £30.75, Set D £40.75 SERVICE: net prices DETAILS: 65 seats. Private parties: 15 main room. Car park. No children under 13. Smart dress preferred. No smoking in dining-room. Wheelchair access (1 step). No music ACCOMMODATION: 28 rooms, 24 with bath/shower. TV. D, B&B £90 to £310. Rooms for disabled. No children under 13. Afternoon teas. Garden (*The Which? Hotel Guide*)

ULVERSTON Cumbria map 8

▲ *Bay Horse Inn*

Canal Foot, Ulverston LA12 9EL
TEL: (01229) 583972 FAX: (01229) 580502
off A590, just before centre of Ulverston, follow signs to Canal Foot

COOKING 2*
COST £23–£41

The view over Morecambe Bay across to Cartmel and the Leven viaduct is glorious, enough to make you forget the 'depressing drive past the Glaxo works' to get there. But industry is not to be shunned, and the factory probably provides quite a few customers for this joint pub and restaurant. The two parts are linked but separate; indeed, each has its own Muzak, with a clash near the join. Bar snacks are served among the beams and horse brasses of the pub, while the restaurant offers a short *carte* plus a two-choice set-price lunch.

'Rich and joyful' is how one reporter described the cooking's impact. Soups tend to be thick and vegetable-based: rich artichoke in winter, perhaps, or refreshing pea, mango and lime, served cold in late spring, accompanied by a small loaf of bread, with butter carved into swan shapes. Fillet or sirloin steak, hung for a month, is served with baked potato and salad. There is much stuffing and wrapping of ingredients – breast of chicken stuffed with a tasty herb and cheese pâté, for example, but the original idea can get lost. At an inspection lunch two fillets of plaice, lacking bouncy texture and real taste, were swamped by a stuffing of mushroom and onion pâté. Vegetables are in the Miller Howe mould (John Tovey is a joint owner – see entry, Windermere) which is to say full of interesting and unusual flavours, but having little to do with the food they accompany, and garnish occasionally gets the upper hand. For pudding, brown-sugar meringue (another swan shape) is filled with fresh fruit, and sticky toffee pudding is 'soft and delicious'. Service is all it should be from Peter McKinnon, the restaurant manager, and the New World wine list is just the ticket for taste and value.

CHEFS: Robert Lyons and Esther Jarvis PROPRIETORS: Robert Lyons and John Tovey OPEN: Tue to Sat L 12 to 1.30, all week D 7.30 for 8 MEALS: alc (main courses £13 to £16). Set L £14.50. Minimum £10 SERVICE: 10% (optional), card slips closed CARDS: Access, Visa DETAILS: 50 seats. Private parties: 50 main room. Car park. Vegetarian meals. No children under 12. Smart dress preferred. No smoking in dining-room. Wheelchair access (also WC). Music. Air-conditioned ACCOMMODATION: 7 rooms, all with bath/shower. TV. Phone. D,B&B £65 to £160. No children under 12. Pets welcome in bedrooms only. Afternoon teas

UPPER SLAUGHTER Gloucestershire map 5

▲ *Lords of the Manor*

Upper Slaughter, nr Bourton-on-the-Water GL54 2JD
TEL: (01451) 820243 FAX: (01451) 820696 COOKING 3
turn W off A429, 3m S of Stow-on-the-Wold COST £32–£61

Upper Slaughter is little more than a collection of Cotswold stone buildings, of which this seventeenth-century former rectory – in eight acres of walled gardens and parkland – is the grandest. More recent extensions retain the style and character of the old house, which likes to think of itself as a 'home from home' for visitors. Anybody with a home this size must be green with envy at the staff, who come out to valet-park the car and generally smooth things along. In the dining-room large paintings hang from yellow walls, and a fire rages at one end 'with a little help from the gas board'. Starched white tablecloths on well-spaced tables confirm the serious intent for anybody still in doubt.

The kitchen, though perfectly at home with traditional fillet of beef or a creamed mushroom and Jerusalem artichoke soup, seems to revel more in the possibilities afforded by a free-ranging approach to ingredients and ideas. It proclaims its up-to-the-minute credentials in a warm couscous salad that accompanies pan-fried cannon of lamb, and in a curry-flavoured pearl barley risotto which, together with a home-made apple and lime chutney, did unexpected wonders for pink breast and crispy leg of Trelough duckling. The Mediterranean tendency, meanwhile, shows itself in roast chump of lamb with grilled provençale vegetables and olive jus. In the annals of prince-and-pauper cooking, the Manor may have clocked up a first by serving grilled foie gras with mushy peas.

Seven or eight desserts might include a hot plum soufflé or baked figs with cinnamon ice-cream, but if the chocolate and rosewater mousse with orange blossom brûlée and praline is on, take it. Dinner begins with a complimentary cup of soup and ends with petits fours. Since the quality doesn't drop at lunch, it is considered something of a bargain, especially on a fine day out on the patio. But reporters do complain about the habit of leaving the credit card slip open after a 12.5% service charge has already been levied, and also about some of the wine prices. When Ch. de Sours Rosé 1993 was selling for £4.99 a bottle in the shops, it was going for £5.25 a glass here. Plus 12.5% of course. Nevertheless the

Manor is to be congratulated on serving around 15 wines by the glass, and in having put together a splendid collection of bottles from around the world.

CHEF: Clive Dixon PROPRIETORS: James Gulliver, J.G Gulliver Jnr, A.G. Gulliver and E.P. Good OPEN: all week 12.30 to 2 (2.30 Sun), 7.30 (7 Fri and Sat) to 9.30 CLOSED: 2 to 11 Jan MEALS: Set L £14.95 (2 courses) to £17.50, Set D £29.50 (2 courses) to £34.50 SERVICE: not inc L, 12.5% D CARDS: Access, Amex, Delta, Diners, Switch, Visa DETAILS: 50 seats. 12 tables outside. Private parties: 60 main room, 8 and 22 private rooms. Car park. Children's helpings. Jacket and tie. No smoking in dining-room. Wheelchair access (also WC). Music ACCOMMODATION: 27 rooms, all with bath/shower. TV. Phone. B&B £80 to £190. Rooms for disabled. Children welcome. Baby facilities. Afternoon teas. Garden. Fishing (*The Which? Hotel Guide*)

WALKINGTON Humberside map 9

▲ *Manor House*

Northlands, Walkington HU17 8RT
TEL/FAX: (01482) 881645 COOKING **1***
off B1230 towards Beverley from Walkington COST **£35–£47**

Plumb in the heartland of the old East Riding is this Victorian country house that furnishes classical comfort on a human scale. Derek Baugh was once at the Dorchester (see entry, London), and the training shows in the elaborate presentation of the food and the somewhat florid writing of the menu. A 'knapsack' of prawns turns out to be prawns wrapped in a crisp pancake and served with a creamy lobster and sherry sauce. Main courses are richly classic in inspiration, though the classicism isn't always French. Honey-roast duck breast of great tenderness is given a vaguely Pekinese twist with spring onion, cucumber and shredded duck meat in filo, the sauce made from roasting juices lightly flavoured with plum.

Bread-and-butter pudding and crème brûlée are competently rendered, the latter laden with fruit. Service was found wanting on two occasions, 'excellent' on another. The wine list takes in some pedigree names in France, though at stiffish prices. Better value is to be found in the rest of the world, where most things are under £20. High rollers may like to explore the list of fine clarets, stepping gingerly over a 1937 Cos d'Estournel that may be falling apart at the seams. House wines are £8.95.

CHEFS: Derek Baugh and Gareth Bendle PROPRIETORS: Derek and Lee Baugh OPEN: Mon to Sat D only 7.30 to 9.15 CLOSED: 25 and 26 Dec, 1 Jan MEALS: Set D Mon to Fri £15 to £27.50 SERVICE: not inc, card slips closed CARDS: Access, Switch, Visa DETAILS: 58 seats. Private parties: 44 main room, 24 and 44 private rooms. Car park. Vegetarian meals. No children under 12. Smart dress preferred. No cigars/pipes in dining-room. Music ACCOMMODATION: 7 rooms, all with bath/shower. TV. Phone. B&B £69.50 to £117. No children under 12. Small dogs welcome. Garden

CELLARMAN'S CHOICE: *Wines recommended by the restaurateur, normally more expensive than house wine.*

▲ *This symbol means accommodation is available.*

WAREHAM Dorset map 2

▲ *Priory Hotel*

Church Green, Wareham BH20 4ND — COOKING 1
TEL: (01929) 551666 FAX: (01929) 554519 — COST £26–£60

The conversion of the Tudor Priory of Lady St Mary into an impeccable country hotel has been a triumph. The gardens running down to the river provide the perfect setting for tea on a summer afternoon, while the interior is seductively comfortable. No wonder the Priory is a favourite venue for wedding receptions. You can eat in either the ground-floor dining-room overlooking the lawns or in the converted wine cellars.

Chef Michael Rust makes good use of fish from the Dorset boats, game from local estates and vegetables grown by gardeners in the Purbeck Hills. His cooking stays in touch with current trends, although he also pleases traditionalists with flambées and beef Wellington carved at the table. The *carte* is bolstered by fixed-price menus that offer courgette soup with nan bread, crisp roast duck breast accompanied by a confit of the leg in a ginger and orange jus, and raspberry and lime syllabub with almond shortbread.

The list of British farmhouse cheeses must rank as one of the most impressive in the area, as does that for wines, which takes its claret particularly seriously: the 1970 vintage is well represented, for example. Elsewhere, the mix should suit most pockets, with Germany and the New World both showing initiative, although it is France, as usual, that furnishes the half-bottles. Dom. Laroche house vin de pays is £10.50, or £3.50 for a large glass. CELLARMAN'S CHOICE: Médoc, Ch. La Tour St-Bonnet 1990, £18.50; St Véran 1993, Luquet £15.50.

CHEF: Michael Rust PROPRIETORS: John and Stuart Turner OPEN: all week 12.30 to 2, 7.30 to 10 MEALS: alc (main courses £18 to £21). Set L Mon to Sat £12.95 (2 courses) to £14.95, Set L Sun £17.95, Set D Mon to Fri £24.50, Set D Sat £28.50 SERVICE: not inc, card slips closed CARDS: Access, Amex, Diners, Visa DETAILS: 68 seats. 10 tables outside. Private parties: 44 main room, 24 and 44 private rooms. Car park. Vegetarian meals. Children's helpings. Smart dress preferred. Wheelchair access (also WC). Music ACCOMMODATION: 19 rooms, all with bath/shower. TV. Phone. B&B £70 to £185. Rooms for disabled. Children welcome. Afternoon teas. Garden. Fishing (*The Which? Hotel Guide*)

WARMINSTER Wiltshire map 2

▲ *Bishopstrow House*

Warminster BA12 9HH
TEL: (01985) 212312 FAX: (01985) 216769 — COOKING 2
on B3414, SW of Warminster — COST £24–£62

Two guests who swept up the curving drive of Bishopstrow to the pillared entrance resplendent with wallflowers (the entrance, not the guests) reported that they encountered a gentleman waiting on the steps to greet them by name. The country-house professionalism also runs to ostentatious displays of spring flowers and encouragingly hearty glasses of Tio Pepe. Chris Suter's cooking is founded on classic French principles, yet maintains a degree of flexibility. A three-course set lunch consisting of langoustine terrine with saffron vinaigrette, salmon cooked in duck fat and served with a fresh tomato sauce, and bread-and-butter pudding for £12.50 looks like pretty good value.

A foie gras parfait with grape and apple chutney at a dinner in May was 'outstanding – real melt-in-the-mouth stuff', while salmon mousse was as 'light as a feather with bags of taste', and a nicely charred rump of lamb came with chargrilled vegetables provençale and an olive-flecked tapénade sauce. A selection of four ice-creams in a 'beautifully crisp' tuile tulip seems a good bet for dessert, or there may be caramelised lemon and banana tartlet with apricot and citrus jus. Trimmings are mostly fine, the nibbles 'gorgeous'. Wines are sound if unexciting, the list informative, but the mark-ups press hard – £55 for 1990 *grand cru* Chablis – and halves are thin on the ground. Head for the New World. House wines from Bordeaux and Australia are £12.50.

CHEF: Chris Suter PROPRIETOR: Blandy Brothers & Co Ltd OPEN: all week 12.30 to 2, 7.30 to 9.30 MEALS: Set L £12.50 to £25, Set D £33 to £38; light L available SERVICE: not inc, card slips closed CARDS: Access, Amex, Delta, Diners, Switch, Visa DETAILS: 60 seats. 6 tables outside. Private parties: 30 main room, 20 private room. Car park. Vegetarian meals. Children's helpings. Smart dress preferred. No smoking in dining-room. Music ACCOMMODATION: 30 rooms, all with bath/shower. TV. Phone. B&B £98 to £125. Deposit: £100. Rooms for disabled. Children welcome. Baby facilities. Pets welcome. Afternoon teas. Garden. Swimming-pool. Fishing (*The Which? Hotel Guide*)

WATERHOUSES Staffordshire map 5

▲ *Old Beams*

Waterhouses ST10 3HW
TEL: (01538) 308254 FAX: (01538) 308157 COOKING 3
on A523, 7m SE of Leek COST £22–£47

'A cosy, likeable place which, when on form, produces food of exemplary quality,' summed up one experienced reporter of this restaurant-with-rooms. In summer begin with drinks in the small sheltered garden at the back and progress to the conservatory with 'fairy-tale-like' murals that cover everything that is not glass (including the door marked 'loos'); in winter the darker restaurant with its endlessly cited beams beckons. This is a professionally run enterprise with a repertoire based on classic French techniques, yet very modern in its outlook. The 'bold and imaginative' food makes a colourful and artistic splash, and comes up with some original combinations.

The strong identity of flavours impresses, from the main ingredients themselves down to simple infusions in olive oil that bring dishes to life: for example, one of saffron, forming a thin yellow moat around a 'beautifully textured, wobbly' twice-baked soufflé of scallops and lobster, making it clear 'exactly what saffron tastes like'. 'Very complex but totally fascinating' was how a main-course pastry tart of lightly roasted pigeon was described, indicating Nigel Wallis's power to intrigue with both flavours and textures. Vegetables are adapted to individual dishes, and even the chives in a potato dish tasted 'incredibly, essentially chivey'. Others have endorsed very good cheeses, and 'divine' soufflés of chocolate or strawberry. A duet of caramelised mangoes and bananas with spicy Indian ice-cream was 'one of the most gorgeous dishes' one inspector had ever eaten. 'Absolutely bowled me over.'

Lunch may not quite match the ambition of dinner, but then look at the price difference. 'Meals mostly satisfy but occasionally lack impact,' maintained another inspector, although incidentals are all tip-top, including good olives, home-made potato crisps, excellent appetisers and bread rolls. Ann Wallis is a 'charming, exuberant, friendly and informative hostess', now joined by her son. The wine list keeps up with developments, and concentrates on bankable quality, pushing the balance of prices above £20, although there are intriguing bottles below that, including an Irouléguy from south-west France. Blanket coverage is not the style, making the list manageable, and half-bottles are generous. CELLARMAN'S CHOICE: Meursault 'Les Chevalières' 1992, Boisson-Vadot, £27; St-Joseph 1992, Trollat, £20.75.

CHEF: Nigel Wallis PROPRIETORS: Nigel and Ann Wallis OPEN: Tue to Fri and Sun L 12 to 2, Tue to Sat D 7 to 9.30 MEALS: Set L Tue to Fri £10.95 (2 courses) to £17.50, Set L Sun £17.50, Set D Tue to Fri £18.50 to £35 SERVICE: none, card slips closed CARDS: Access, Amex, Delta, Diners, Switch, Visa DETAILS: 40 seats. 2 tables outside. Private parties: 20 main room, 12 and 20 private rooms. Car park. Children welcome. No smoking in dining-room. Wheelchair access (also WC). Music ACCOMMODATION: 5 rooms, all with bath/shower. TV. Phone. B&B £55 to £89.95. Rooms for disabled. Children welcome. Baby facilities. Garden. Fishing (*The Which? Hotel Guide*)

WATERMILLOCK Cumbria map 10

▲ *Rampsbeck Country House Hotel*

Watermillock, Ullswater CA11 0LP
TEL: (01768) 486442 FAX: (01768) 486688
on A592, Penrith to Windermere road

COOKING 3
COST £29–£51

This is an elegant eighteenth-century house on the shores of Ullswater, on the opposite side of the lake from Sharrow Bay. A long gravel drive leads up to luxuriant flower-beds, an immaculate yew hedge, and a dining-room with a view. 'You feel welcome the moment you enter.' Lunch in the dining-room needs to be booked 24 hours in advance, while simpler unbooked meals are available in the bar. Dinner is four courses, one of them a sorbet such as elderflower or lemon grass.

The enterprise is discreet, not showy, and impresses for the consistency of its accomplishment. Andrew McGeorge adopts a modern approach to the country-house style; he is generous with prime cuts, occasionally indulgent, and adept at working up a dish into something you would think twice about preparing at home. Fish turned out well at inspection: a first course of red snapper attractively presented, with a crisp potato topping, on a warm salad with pesto, and a main course of 'fresh-tasting, firm yet tender' roast wild salmon on tasty noodles with tomato and basil dressing. Another main course of sauté steak of new season's lamb was accompanied by roasted vegetables and a rich jus that made this 'a most satisfying dish'. What takes three lines to describe (on the menu) emerges on the plate as precisely as it reads. Side plates of vegetables are keyed to the choice of main course and are served 'in a sensible amount'. Symphonies, sabayons and soufflés are the stuff of desserts, among which might be a hot raspberry soufflé served in a copper pan, 'as light as a feather' (the soufflé, not the pan) and accompanied by that old stalwart, a raspberry ripple ice-cream. The 'impeccable' service is by 'people who obviously enjoy their work, have pride in what they were putting before you, and then leave you to enjoy it'.

Wines are arranged by style (subdivided for greater clarity), and skilfully chosen for flavour and character. Add some demonstrably keen pricing, and here we have one of the friendliest lists in the area. House wines start at £9.50. CELLARMAN'S CHOICE: Delegat's Chardonnay 1992, Hawkes Bay, New Zealand, £13.75; Coteaux du Tricastin, Dom. le Vieux Micocoulier 1990, £12.75.

CHEF: Andrew McGeorge PROPRIETORS: T.I. Gibb and Mrs M.M. Gibb, and Mrs M.J. MacDowall OPEN: all week 11.45 for 12, 12.45 for 1.15 (two sittings), 6.30 for 7, 8 for 8.30 (two sittings) CLOSED: 4 Jan to mid-Feb MEALS: Set L £22, Set D £26 to £34; bar L available SERVICE: not inc, card slips closed CARDS: Access, Visa DETAILS: 40 seats. Private parties: 60 main room, 16 private room. Car park. Vegetarian meals. Children's helpings. Smart dress preferred. No smoking in dining-room. No music ACCOMMODATION: 21 rooms, all with bath/shower. TV. Phone. B&B £48 to £150. Deposit: £15. Children welcome. Pets welcome by arrangement. Afternoon teas. Garden (*The Which? Hotel Guide*)

WATH-IN-NIDDERDALE North Yorkshire map 8

▲ *The Sportsman's Arms*

Wath-in-Nidderdale, Pateley Bridge HG3 5PP
TEL: (01423) 711306 FAX: (01423) 712524
take B6156 or B6265 to Pateley Bridge, follow signs by village, 2m NW of Pateley Bridge

COOKING 2*
COST £20–£39

Fields full of lambs caught one springtime visitor's eye as she crossed the narrow bridge over the River Nidd to reach this seventeenth-century stone building. Tranquillity defines the setting; there are magnificent views of Nidderdale all around and Gouthwaite Reservoir (famous for its bird life) is a stroll away. Inside, guests chat and enjoy themselves in the comfortably upholstered lounges and the restaurant, where service is 'pleasant and informed'. Velvet curtains hang at the windows, mirrors and Art Nouveau prints line the walls, and flowers fill the room.

Ray Carter and his kitchen team make exemplary use of local produce for their fixed-price menus, although North Country ingredients are often jazzed up with some lively accompaniments. A salad of chorizo and baby French black pudding is an unexpected starter, while breast of duck comes with blackcurrants and mango. Meat dishes have been mightily impressive: particularly 'beautifully tender' roast best end of Dales lamb, adorned with garlic, tomato, olives and spring onion in a natural jus. To finish, there are some interesting local and French cheeses, a Welsh rarebit savoury and big portions of desserts such as pear and almond tart and summer pudding. Bar meals are available when the restaurant is closed. The wines are wide-ranging in scope, and good value is the motivating force. French regional wines and nine house recommendations are all helpfully priced around £10. Half-bottles are exclusively French. CELLARMAN'S CHOICE: Jackson Estate Sauvignon Blanc 1993, New Zealand, £17.65; Pauillac, Ch. Batailley 1979, £28.50.

CHEF: Ray Carter PROPRIETORS: Ray and Jane Carter OPEN: all week L 12 to 2.15, Mon to Sat D 7 to 9.30 CLOSED: 25 Dec, 1 Jan MEALS: alc bar meals (main courses £5.50 to £10). Set L Sun £13.50, Set D £19.75 to £25 SERVICE: not inc, card slips closed CARDS: Access, Visa DETAILS: 90 seats. 6 tables outside. Private parties: 60 main room, 10 private room. Car park. Children's helpings. Smart dress preferred. No smoking in dining-room. Wheelchair access. No music ACCOMMODATION: 7 rooms, 2 with shower. All with TV. B&B £20 to £58. Children welcome. Afternoon teas. Garden. Fishing (*The Which? Hotel Guide*)

WELLS Somerset map 2

Ritcher's

SOMERSET 1996 VALUE

5B Sadler Street, Wells BA5 2RR COOKING 2
TEL/FAX: (01749) 679085 COST £13–£32

This friendly little restaurant and bistro not far from the cathedral certainly doesn't declaim its presence to the world. Less formal eating goes on in the ground-floor bistro, but an agreeable air of relaxation also pervades the upper-level restaurant, reached by a spiral staircase. Nicholas Hart cooks in essentially Gallic mode and keeps a beady eye on London trends, changing the menus daily. Reporters are all agreed on the extraordinary value of the fixed-price menus, especially downstairs.

A weekday lunch in the bistro may consist of leek and Stilton flan with sauce béarnaise, ragoût of pheasant with smoked bacon and mushrooms, and a dessert of the day, all for £6.95. Grilled banana wrapped in bacon on curried mayonnaise may not be what Wells is used to, but the bedrock repertoire is sound enough. Restaurant dishes have included spinach and Brie dumpling on saffron cream to start, followed by breast of guinea-fowl parcelled in air-dried ham and served with noodles and a sweetcorn sauce. Traditional French desserts of soufflés, crêpes and crème brûlée are joined by the odd interloper like sticky toffee tart. 'It deserves to be full every day,' says a reader. The mainly French wine list is sensibly priced, and there is a reasonable selection of Spanish bottles too. Vintage port is taken seriously, and there are around ten half-bottles. House French is £7.95.

CHEFS: Nicholas Hart and Sarah Walklett PROPRIETORS: Nicholas Hart and Kate Ritcher OPEN: bistro all week 12 to 2, 7 to 9 (9.30 Sat, 12 to 9.30 Sat in summer); restaurant Tue to Fri L 12 to 2 (bookings only), Tue to Sat D 7 to 9 CLOSED: 26 Dec, 1 Jan MEALS: bistro Set L Mon to Sat £4.95 (2 courses) to £6.95, Set L Sun £5.95 (2 courses) to £7.95, Set D Sun to Fri £11.50 (2 courses) to £13.50, Set D Sat £12.50 (2 courses) to £14.50; restaurant Set L £12.50 (2 courses) to £14.50, Set D £15.50 (2 courses) to £18.50. Minimum £4.95 bistro SERVICE: not inc, card slips closed CARDS: Access, Delta, Switch, Visa DETAILS: bistro 18 seats, restaurant 14 seats. 3 tables outside. Private parties: 24 main room. Children's helpings in bistro. No children under 10 in restaurant. Smart dress preferred. No cigars/pipes while others are eating. Wheelchair access bistro (also WC). Music

See inside the front cover for an explanation of the symbols used at the tops of entries.

An asterisk (*) after the 1 to 5 cooking mark at the top of an entry signifies that the Guide *and its readers think that the restaurant is a particularly fine example within its rating.*

WELLS-NEXT-THE-SEA Norfolk map 6

Moorings 🍷

6 Freeman Street, Wells-next-the-Sea NR23 1BA COOKING 3
TEL: (01328) 710949 COST £26–£38

Just near the quay in 'semi-picturesque' Wells-next-the-Sea, the Moorings is a small industry on its own. Norfolk is rich in produce, and the Phillipses have their feet firmly planted in the soil and along the coastline. 'As far as possible, we use locally raised, grown or caught ingredients,' writes Bernard Phillips, pointing out that many apparently exotic items now fall into these categories. Certainly, seasonal treasures such as samphire, artichokes and wild mushrooms grow hereabouts, and woods and hedgerows yield other materials. Then there is the shoreline, providing cockles, mussels, whelks, clams, razor fish, lobsters, oysters, shrimps and hermit-crabs, and a range of fish from sole and dabs to cod and monk.

Carla Phillips writes out the long menu by hand twice a day, with dishes grouped together in three sections: meat, fish and vegetables. Much pickling, marinating and smoking goes on to produce vigorous flavours, particularly among the fish, and she has a New Yorker's willingness to demolish gastronomic boundaries in the search for attention-grabbing tastes. The 'exceptional hedgerow herrings' marinated in home-made blackberry vinegar are a case in point, as are Louisiana crab-cakes with tomato tartare sauce and salsa. Reporters have also enjoyed a dish of cod cooked 'stockfish-style' with garlic, potatoes, parsley and walnut oil. Among the 'mountains of vegetables' might be hot beetroot, ratatouille, red cabbage, broccoli or the widely acclaimed mashed potatoes.

Worries surface from time to time, fuelled by a sad salad, 'overcooked' vegetables or a 'heavy-handed sauce', and one reporter was surprised, with treacle pudding on the menu, that the kitchen 'refused to do custard'. It does, however, produce a light butterscotch pie with walnut crust, and an impressive and unusual dish of hunza apricots with pistachio baklava and halva ice-cream. The wide-ranging wine list 'covers all needs and most interests', and does so at encouragingly low prices, offering both security and a chance to explore the byways. A dozen house wines under £10 are also available by the half-bottle and glass. CELLARMAN'S CHOICE: Thelema Mountain Vineyards Sauvignon Blanc 1994, Stellenbosch, South Africa, £13; Thelema Mountain Vineyards Chardonnay 1993, Stellenbosch, South Africa, £13.

CHEF: Carla Phillips PROPRIETORS: Bernard and Carla Phillips OPEN: Fri to Mon L 12.30 to 1.45, Thur to Mon D 7.30 to 8.45 CLOSED: 2 weeks early Dec, 2 weeks mid-June MEALS: Set L and D £10.20 (1 course) to £18.20 SERVICE: not inc CARDS: none DETAILS: 35 seats. Private parties: 35 main room. Vegetarian meals. Children's helpings. No smoking in dining-room. Wheelchair access (also WC). No music

The text of entries is based on unsolicited reports sent in by readers, backed up by inspections conducted anonymously. The factual details under the text are from questionnaires the Guide *sends to all restaurants that feature in the book.*

WEST BAY Dorset map 2

Riverside £

West Bay DT6 4EZ
TEL: (01308) 422011
off A35, ¾m S of Bridport

COOKING 1*
COST £20–£59

Walk the plank over the water to reach the Riverside, decked out in nautical blue and white and standing cheek by jowl with the local post office. The setting is a delight – boats bobbing about, birds and holidaymakers everywhere – and there are great views of the River Brid from almost every window in the place. Not surprisingly, it gets chock-a-block in season, so book well ahead.

Fish and shellfish from West Bay boats provide the kitchen's stock-in-trade: select what you want, order a full or half-portion and have it grilled, baked, poached or deep-fried with chips (although these were 'pallid and tasteless' on one occasion); otherwise, opt for one of the more ambitious sauced specialities. Brill, done the Greek way with 'robust herbs and garlic', is well worth the 40-minute wait, and the same fish is also filleted and served with sorrel sauce and crispy spinach (during May and June they pick and use local wild sea spinach) You may also find red mullet with saffron sauce and black olives, plus a token showing of meat and vegetarian dishes. Desserts are mostly cream-laced confections of the rice-pudding and knickerbocker glory variety. Young waitresses in Breton-style tops serve efficiently. The list of around 70 wines has an abundance of reasonably priced whites from France and the New World. House wine is £10.95 a litre.

CHEFS: Janet Watson, Neil Fanous and Michael Mills PROPRIETORS: Arthur and Janet Watson OPEN: bank hol Mon and Tue to Sun L 11.30 to 2.30, bank hol Mon and Tue to Sat D 6.30 to 9, Mon and Sun D 6.30 to 9 in peak season; times may vary in early and late season CLOSED: early Dec to early Mar MEALS: alc (main courses £5 to £25) SERVICE: not inc, card slips closed CARDS: Access, Delta, Switch, Visa DETAILS: 75 seats. 6 tables outside. Private parties: 100 main room. Vegetarian meals. Children's helpings. No cigars/pipes in dining-room. Music

WEST MERSEA Essex map 3

▲ *Blackwater Hotel, Le Champenois*

20–22 Church Road, West Mersea CO5 8QH
TEL: (01206) 383338 and 383038
just off B1025 from Colchester, turn right at West Mersea church

COOKING 1*
COST £22–£42

'More backwater than Blackwater,' joked one visitor to West Mersea, who enjoyed this 'charming' restaurant in the creeper-covered hotel just one minute from the sea. Fishing, sailing and pottering around the island are among local leisure pursuits. Old timbers, check tablecloths and 'loads of ornaments' contribute to the bistro atmosphere, and the food follows suit, unashamedly dishing up hallowed favourites from the French repertoire. Chicken liver pâté, snails in garlic butter and trout with almonds are the stock-in-trade, helped along by daily specials of pork dijonnaise, navarin of lamb or 'delicately succulent' Dover sole. The seaside location also throws up oysters (which might be grilled), mussels (stuffed with herbs and garlic butter), wing of skate and monkfish. Vegetables are up to snuff, and puddings run to lemon tart, oeufs à la neige, and nougat glacé in a caramel sauce covered with caramel tracery. The wine list is a collection of labels, largely French, with house Vin de Pays du Gers red and white at £8.25.

CHEF: R. Roudesli PROPRIETOR: Mrs M. Chapleo OPEN: Wed to Mon L 12 to 2, Mon to Sat D 7 to 10 CLOSED: first 3 weeks Jan MEALS: alc (main courses £9.50 to £13.50). Set L £15.50, Set D (exc Sat) £18.80 SERVICE: not inc, card slips closed CARDS: Access, Amex, Delta, Visa DETAILS: 46 seats. 3 tables outside. Private parties: 55 main room, 25 private room. Car park. Vegetarian meals. Children's helpings. Smart dress preferred. No cigars/pipes in dining-room. Wheelchair access (1 step; also WC). No music ACCOMMODATION: 7 rooms, 4 with bath/shower. TV. B&B £25 to £62. Deposit: £10. Children welcome. Baby facilities. Pets by arrangement. Afternoon teas. Garden (*The Which? Hotel Guide*)

WETHERSFIELD Essex map 6

ESSEX 1996 FLAVOUR

Dicken's 🍷

The Green, Wethersfield CM7 4BS COOKING 3
TEL: (01371) 850723 COST £21–£38

'If we want to give our friends a memorable meal, Dicken's is where we head for,' write a pair of reporters, vigorously seconded by another couple who regularly travel from Bedfordshire for Sunday lunch. If its pastoral setting in one of the leafier parts of Essex is one lure, the attractive, mostly seventeenth-century building with a minstrels' gallery is another. The strongest draw, though, must be John Dicken's culinary talents.

People understand and admire the way the cooking here effects a graceful compromise between metropolitan fashion and traditional classics. There may be bruschetta laden with with roasted peppers, plum tomatoes and basil, but there will also be Mediterranean fish soup, or scrambled eggs with smoked haddock and chives. Roasted monkfish on spiced bean shoots is a nod in the direction of oriental modishness, while impeccable French credentials are evident in a dish of beef fillet with a sauté of mushrooms, potatoes, shallots and garlic and a jus containing ceps. Vegetables served separately are considered 'exemplary'. A thorough report analyses the appeal thus: 'John Dicken's cooking is very precise, with a delicacy and lightness hard to find elsewhere, even when he is turning out some of the more solid English dishes.' Puddings are of the comforting variety, including chocolate brownies with ice-cream, bread-and-butter pudding and a version of crème brûlée with stewed plums and ginger. 'Service, spearheaded by Maria Dicken, is impeccable.' This place has firm devotees.

The wine list harbours some excellent bottles. The choice of French growers displays a keen eye for quality and, although clarets and burgundies inevitably stretch the range, prices are generally on the moderate side. There is a fine selection of half-bottles, the quartet of Wines of the Month is worth a look, and the whole list is intelligently annotated. Six house wines start at £7.95. CELLARMAN'S CHOICE: Frog's Leap Sauvignon Blanc 1993, California, £16.95; St-Emilion, Ch. St-Christophe *grand cru* 1989, £16.95.

CHEF/PROPRIETOR: John Dicken OPEN: Wed to Sun L 12.30 to 2, Wed to Sat D 7.30 to 9.30 MEALS: alc (main courses £11 to £14.50). Set L £15 SERVICE: not inc CARDS: Access, Delta, Switch, Visa DETAILS: 60 seats. 6 tables outside. Private parties: 36 main room, 10 and 18 private rooms. Car park. Vegetarian meals. Children's helpings. Smart dress preferred. Wheelchair access (1 step; also WC). No music

WHIMPLE Devon map 1

▲ *Woodhayes*

Whimple EX5 2TD
TEL: (01404) 822237 FAX: (01404) 822337 COOKING 2
off A30, 9m E of Exeter COST £30–£36

Frank, Katherine and Michael Rendle all help in the running of this white-painted Georgian residence in an alluring apple-orchard setting less than a mile from the A30. Visitors love it. The combination of genuinely personable atmosphere and consistently rewarding food is what brings people back year after year. The Rendles are noticeably house-proud, and they know how to satisfy their customers. Their daily-changing dinner menu runs to six carefully balanced courses, but there's no sense of being faced by unmanageable quantities of food. The only choice you have to make is at the pudding stage, although the Rendles are happy to provide an alternative to any dish if required.

A typical meal might begin with a salad of spinach, bacon and croûtons, before a clear soup of chicken and vegetables. Fish comes next: perhaps monkfish with saffron and peppers or salade niçoise with fresh tuna. Centrepieces are traditional: roast fillet of venison on celeriac purée with red wine and port sauce, or pan-fried fillet of beef with tomatoes, mushrooms and tarragon, for example. Crème brûlée and home-made ice-creams are ever-present desserts, or you might choose pear and almond tart. Cheese is generally Quicke's unpasteurised Cheddar and Long Clawson Stilton with grapes and walnuts. The overall results draw unqualified praise. A new wine list was in the pipeline as we went to press, but it is likely to remain very much in line with the old one – namely, a dozen house wines keenly priced at £9.90 backed up by plenty of halves and a varied selection drawn from around the world.

CHEFS: Katherine Rendle and Michael Rendle PROPRIETORS: Frank and Katherine Rendle OPEN: all week D only 7.30 to 9; L residents only MEALS: Set D £25 SERVICE: net prices, card slips closed CARDS: Access, Amex, Delta, Diners, Switch, Visa DETAILS: 18 seats. Private parties: 14 main room. Car park. Vegetarian meals. No children under 12. Smart dress preferred. No smoking in dining-room. Music ACCOMMODATION: 6 rooms, all with bath/shower. TV. Phone. B&B £65 to £90. No children under 12. Garden (*The Which? Hotel Guide*)

WHITBY North Yorkshire map 9

Magpie Café £

N. YORKS 1996 SEASIDE CAFE

14 Pier Road, Whitby YO21 3PU COOKING 2
TEL: (01947) 602058 COST £14–£32

'Splendid of its kind' is a typical response to this great seaside café. The Robsons and the McKenzies have been running the show for more than 30 years and visitors still descend on the place by the coachload. Such is the café's popularity that the owners have extended the opening times and hope to keep going right through the year (apart from six weeks in deepest winter). The restaurant is a converted Georgian merchant's house by the quay, and the prospect of tucking into utterly fresh fish from the local boats is the reason most people come here. Expect anything from a mixed seafood platter of 'monumental proportions' to 'delicate and beautifully prepared' halibut. Meat eaters and vegetarians are also well looked after, and the Magpie deserves a round of applause for its attitude to families: children's meals are available (there is even a 'baby' version with boiled eggs, jelly and custard); and toys, high-chairs and a changing room are fixtures. As befits a café, afternoon tea is a big occasion, and the menu has a prodigious list of cakes and puddings, ranging from sherry cake with Wensleydale cheese to fruit crumble. Service is as pleasant as can be. Drinks include pots of tea, freshly squeezed orange juice and glasses of champagne. House wine is £6.25.

CHEF: Ian Robson PROPRIETORS: Ian Robson and Alison McKenzie-Robson, Sheila and Ian McKenzie OPEN: all week 11.30 to 6.30 (9pm Fri and Sat, and all week mid-July to mid-Sept) CLOSED: 6 weeks Jan to mid-Feb MEALS: alc (main courses £4.50 to £9). Set L and D £8.45 to £13.45 SERVICE: not inc, card slips closed CARDS: Access, Delta, Switch, Visa DETAILS: 100 seats. Private parties: 50 main room. Vegetarian meals. Children's helpings. No smoking in 1 dining-room. Music. Air-conditioned

WHITLEY BAY Tyne & Wear map 10

Le Provençale

179–183 Park View, Whitley Bay NE26 3RE COOKING 1
TEL: 0191-251 3567 COST £12–£42

The citizens of Whitley Bay and beyond regularly fill this family-run restaurant near the centre of town and seem to enjoy themselves thoroughly in the process. 'North-easterners favour a good dose of red meat if the menu is anything to go by,' noted a traveller from the West Midlands. Steaks come in various guises and the emphasis is firmly on a mixture of classic and nouvelle French, although portions are far from tiny. Dinner is an elaborate affair, and reporters have enjoyed wild mushrooms in puff pastry, and stuffed breast of pheasant with red wine sauce. Desserts continue the theme: French apple tart, home-made shortbread with strawberries and fruit coulis, or pancakes with orange and bitter chocolate sauce. Michel Guijarro in summer 1995 introduced some additional fixed-price menus (the Monday night option is particularly good value) and as we went to press was fleshing out his repertoire with a few more fashionable ideas: fillet of lamb with green lentils, barley and smoked bacon, for example. Lunches are mostly one-dish meals of omelettes, coq au vin, or beef bourguignon. Staff are pleasant and courteous. The wine list offers fair-priced drinking from a mostly French selection. House wine is £7.90.

CHEF: Michel Guijarro PROPRIETORS: Mr and Mrs Michel Guijarro OPEN: Wed to Fri and Sun L 12 to 1.45, Mon and Wed to Sat D 7 to 9.45 MEALS: alc (main courses L £3.50 to £5, D £12.50 to £15). Set Sun L £8.95, Set D £11.95 (Mon) to £16.95 SERVICE: not inc CARDS: Access, Amex, Delta, Diners, Switch, Visa DETAILS: 52 seats. Private parties: 52 main room. Vegetarian meals. Children's helpings. Smart dress preferred. Music. Air-conditioned

WHITSTABLE Kent map 3

▲ *Whitstable Oyster Fishery Co*

Royal Native Oyster Stores, The Horsebridge,
Whitstable CT5 1BU
TEL: (01227) 276856 FAX: (01227) 770666

COOKING 1
COST £24–£42

'A place to really 'slurp' your oysters,' commented one reporter about this Victorian warehouse conversion right by the beach. Whitstable's only cinema is housed upstairs and, as a result, the Fishery plays to full houses right through the year. Visitors have described the décor as '*faux*-French scruffiness', but attractive with it. However, native and rock oysters, cock crab, bowls of mussels and grilled plaice are good and couldn't be simpler, and the kitchen also succeeds when it tackles pan-fried squid with garlic, baked cod with soured cream and chives, poached sea bass, and grilled mackerel with gooseberries. Boiled potatoes are the standard accompaniment, although one customer observed that most people seem to leave them. There are puddings, too, if you have room: ginger ice-cream or old-fashioned bread-and-butter pudding. To wash it all down, try a bottle of Shepherd Neame porter or something from the short wine list. House Chardonnay is £9.95.

CHEFS: Nikki Billington and Chris Williams PROPRIETOR: Whitstable Oyster Fishery Co OPEN: Tue to Sun L 12 to 2.30 (3 Sun), Tue to Sat D 7 to 9 (12 to 10 Sat May to Sept, 12 to 3, 6 to 10 Sat Oct to Apr) CLOSED: 25 and 26 Dec MEALS: alc (main courses £9 to £15) SERVICE: not inc CARDS: Access, Amex, Delta, Diners, Switch, Visa DETAILS: 160 seats. 20 tables outside. Private parties: 100 main room, 100 private room. Car park. Vegetarian meals. Children's helpings. Wheelchair access (also WC). No music ACCOMMODATION: 8 rooms, all with bath/shower. Room only £45 to £75. Deposit: 50%. Children welcome

WICKHAM Hampshire map 2

Old House

The Square, Wickham PO17 5JG
TEL: (01329) 833049 FAX: (01329) 833672
2½m N of Fareham, at junction of A32 and B2177

COOKING 2
COST £37–£44

Over the past 25 years, Richard and Annie Skipwith have turned their Georgian house into a most attractive establishment that has the charm of a well-maintained private residence. The setting may be rural English, but Annie Skipwith hails from Bordeaux and her cooking has a strong Gallic accent. Menus are fixed-price for two or three courses and the style is classic provincial, coloured with a few ideas from the Mediterranean and beyond. Fish is from the Portsmouth boats, game is local and the repertoire could embrace anything from grilled skate served on slices of aubergine candied in sherry vinegar and honey, to wild rabbit pot-roasted with red onions, sun-dried tomatoes, white wine, balsamic vinegar and grain mustard. Fillet of beef and noisettes of lamb have been timed to perfection.

Home-made ice-creams are alternatives to desserts such as crème brûlée with honeyed apricots, or chocolate tart with caramelised blackberry coulis. Visitors confirm that the cooking is 'of a very high standard'; the value for money and the helpful but unobtrusive service are plus-points. An added bonus for a couple who stayed overnight was 'the small but pretty garden and the peace and quiet of a delightful bedroom in this country town hotel'. The serviceable list of around 40 wines includes a brace from the local Wickham Vineyard, as well as sound drinking from France and the New World. House wine is £12.

CHEF: Nicholas Harman PROPRIETORS: Richard and Annie Skipwith OPEN: Tue to Fri L 12.30 to 1.45, Mon to Sat D 7.30 to 9.30 CLOSED: bank hols, 2 weeks Christmas, 1 week Easter, 2 weeks Aug MEALS: Set L and D £20 (2 courses) to £25 SERVICE: net prices, card slips closed CARDS: Access, Amex, Diners, Visa DETAILS: 40 seats. Private parties: 40 main room, 14 private room. Car park. Children's helpings. Smart dress preferred. No cigars/pipes in dining-room. Wheelchair access. No music ACCOMMODATION: 12 rooms, all with bath/shower. TV. Phone. B&B £72 to £98. Children welcome. Baby facilities. Garden (*The Which? Hotel Guide*)

WILLINGTON Co Durham map 10

Stile

97 High Street, Willington DL15 0PE
TEL: (01388) 746615 COOKING 1
on A690, 4m N of Bishop Auckland COST £22–£37

Stile is a yellow house with a hanging sign on the main road through this quiet mining village, and you enter through an attractive back garden. The interior might seem a little cheerless in a dimly lit sort of way, but Mike Boustred is a good host and dispenses plenty of bonhomie. He and Jenny James insist that their cooking 'leans heavily towards France', but an inspector thought otherwise: 'It is much more sound British home-cooking – nothing too fancy but using good ingredients.' A starter salad of avocado, orange and watercress displays care in the preparation, though main courses are considerably more inspired: baked sole with a cheese and parsley crust is brought off with aplomb, while a breast of duckling of abundant flavour, cooked pink, with a crispy-skin and a good layer of fat, comes with an 'excellent winey, fruity sauce' containing blackcurrants. Competently cooked vegetables may include carrot and swede purée and crumbed and herbed cauliflower.

Staple puddings take in fruit crumbles and profiteroles, 'impeccably light' syrup and ginger sponge that is full of crystallised ginger, and 'zingy' orange liqueur pancakes. The extensive wine list has been put together by a true enthusiast, as the notes clearly show. Although it majors in France, it is also thoroughly sound in other parts, even extending to a good Argentinian Malbec. Prices are extremely considerate, with house French £7.30.

CHEF: Jenny James PROPRIETORS: Mike Boustred and Jenny James OPEN: Tue to Sat 7 to 9.15 CLOSED: 2 to 6 Jan, 2½ weeks Sept MEALS: alc (main courses £10 to £13). Set D £15 to £19.50 SERVICE: not inc, card slips closed CARDS: Access, Visa DETAILS: 45 seats. Private parties: 36 main room, 18 and 36 private rooms. Car park. Vegetarian meals. Children's helpings. Smart dress preferred. No smoking in dining-room. No music

WILLITON Somerset map 2

▲ *White House*

Williton TA4 4QW COOKING 3
TEL: (01984) 632306 and 632777 COST £39–£47

Not the least reason for the sustained success of the White House is that Dick and Kay Smith know when to take time off. Rather than flog themselves to a standstill, they prefer to open seasonally and make the most of the summer months. Even at the peak period, the serenity of the hotel is unruffled, its gleaming white exterior enhanced with hanging baskets and wildly climbing clematis, while the absence of clutter within extends to the simplest of table-settings.

The Smiths share the cooking, and present the results in the form of a fixed-price dinner menu. Their style is finely balanced between the deep French classicism of soufflé suissesse, or roast loin of lamb with sauce paloise, and the earthier side of modern British cooking along the lines of haggis stuffed into quail and served warm in a salad. Other items receive a little ethnic tweaking, as in seared escalope of Scottish salmon bedded on couscous with a chive and crème fraîche accompaniment. Mulberries make a sharp variant on the traditional fruity sauce with roast duck, in this case a local Gressingham bird. Desserts aim for lightness, perhaps in the form of a simple orange and strawberry salad with strawberry sorbet, but there is also a richer hazelnut and chocolate tart with clotted cream. The Smiths make their own oatmeal biscuits to go with the good English cheeses. Extras, from palate-whetting nibbles to caramel fudge with coffee, are of uniformly high quality.

Nor does the wine list let the side down. Overhauled again in 1995, it seems to go from strength to strength, a combination of the pedigree of the various suppliers and Dick Smith's canny eye for a bargain. Here is one of the very few lists prepared to accord due respect to German Rieslings, the world's most neglected fine wines. Good growers in Burgundy, great clarets and a revamped Italian section all impress. An extensive range of halves adds depth to the choice. House wines start at £11.80.

CHEFS/PROPRIETORS: Dick and Kay Smith OPEN: all week D only 7.30 to 8.30 CLOSED: Nov to May MEALS: Set D £27.50 SERVICE: not inc CARDS: none DETAILS: 26 seats. Private parties: 10 main room. Car park. Children's helpings. No smoking in dining-room. Wheelchair access (also WC). No music ACCOMMODATION: 12 rooms, 9 with bath/shower. TV. Phone. B&B £32 to £84. Deposit: £50. Rooms for disabled. Children welcome. Baby facilities. Pets by arrangement (*The Which? Hotel Guide*)

WILMINGTON East Sussex map 3

▲ *Crossways* NEW ENTRY

Lewes Road, Wilmington, nr Polegate BN26 5SG COOKING 1
TEL: (01323) 482455 FAX: (01323) 487811 COST £31–£41

David Stott and Clive James (no, not that one) have established a loyal band of supporters in this white-fronted Georgian hotel in an East Sussex village, many of whom followed them here from Brighton eight years ago. The Long Man of

Wilmington, an imposing gentleman carved into the South Downs chalk, overlooks the village. The formula is a set-price four-course dinner with coffee, the second course soup of the day. Menus change monthly.

The cooking is sound and gently inventive with a faintly Lakeland accent. 'Light and very skilfully flavoured' was the verdict on a dauntingly proportioned wedge of leek and hazelnut cake, while a Stilton soufflé with a gingered cream sauce showed confident technique. Soup may be curried parsnip, discreetly spiced. Accurate timing is evident in a dish of calf's liver, 'moist with just a hint of pinkness', accompanied by a sauce of perhaps gin and lime or avocado and sage. Vegetables come in a robust quantity. Regulars anticipate the recitation of puddings with scarcely contained glee: perhaps an accomplished parfait of three citrus fruits, or an apricot and Amaretto ice-cream. This is considered cooking that doesn't set out to amaze, served with capably paced enthusiasm. The modest wine list majors in France, with prices kept on a firm leash, and there are half a dozen English wines, including the house white. That and the Australian house red are £8.95.

CHEFS: David Stott and Juliet Anderson PROPRIETORS: David Stott and Clive James OPEN: Tue to Sat D only 7.30 to 8.45 MEALS: Set D £23.95 SERVICE: not inc CARDS: Access, Amex, Delta, Diners, Switch, Visa DETAILS: 24 seats. Private parties: 6 main room. Car park. No children under 12. Smart dress preferred. No smoking while others are eating. Wheelchair access (2 steps). Music ACCOMMODATION: 7 rooms, all with bath/shower. TV. Phone. B&B £36 to £68. No children under 12. Garden

WINCHCOMBE Gloucestershire map 5

▲ *Wesley House*

High Street, Winchcombe GL54 5LJ
TEL: (01242) 602366 FAX: (01242) 602405 COOKING 1*
on B4632, Cheltenham to Broadway road COST £21–£45

'Wesley House was highly recommended to us by the Vicar of Winchcombe,' noted a couple who have since made the restaurant a regular haunt. The fifteenth-century, half-timbered house was visited by John Wesley during one of his evangelical jaunts; later it became a teashop, and in its present guise continues to exude warmth and casual informality. The interior is unfussy, with beams everywhere and a narrow, split-level dining area overseen by friendly young staff. From the terrace you can gaze across the Cotswold Edge towards Studeley Castle.

Jonathan Lewis is a thoroughly modern cook with a fondness for fish and exotic gestures. Layered terrines – smoked chicken with braised red cabbage, for example – are one of his trademarks, and many dishes are gilded with vivid accompaniments. Salad of hot chicken livers comes with grape chutney and redcurrants in olive oil; grilled fillets of red mullet get an orange and turmeric dressing; the inherent richness of roast duckling is cut through with kumquat and greengage relish. Soups such as white onion and apple are well reported and desserts draw heaps of praise: baked apple and blackberry crumble, strawberry meringue in butterscotch sauce, and figgy pudding with cranberries are examples. On Tuesdays Jonathan Lewis's minions take over the reins and the menu often has an 'Old English' theme. The short wine list may be bereft of

halves, but ten wines are available by the glass. Good-value house recommendations start at £8.95.

CHEF: Jonathan Lewis PROPRIETORS: Matthew Brown and Jonathan Lewis OPEN: all week L 12 to 2.30, Mon to Sat D (also Sun before bank hols) 7 to 9.30 (10 Sat) CLOSED: 16 Jan to 12 Feb MEALS: Set L £12.50, Set D £21.50 SERVICE: not inc CARDS: Access, Amex, Delta, Switch, Visa DETAILS: 50 seats. Private parties: 65 main room. Vegetarian meals. Children's helpings. Smart dress preferred. No smoking in restaurant until after 10pm. Wheelchair access. Music ACCOMMODATION: 6 rooms, all with bath/shower. TV. Phone. B&B £39 to £65. Afternoon teas

WINCHESTER Hampshire map 2

HANTS 1996 STORMER

▲ *Hotel du Vin & Bistro*

NEW ENTRY

14 Southgate Street, Winchester SO23 9EF COOKING 2*
TEL: (01962) 841414 FAX: (01962) 842458 COST £25–£41

Robin Hutson and Gerard Basset have taken Winchester by storm. They were previously, and respectively, managing director and sommelier at Chewton Glen (see entry, New Milton) – as good a training ground as any – and have completely renovated this fine Georgian house, giving wine and food equal billing. The laudable aim is not too many frills, and sensible prices, the latter point appreciated by reporters with murmurs of 'excellent value for money'. The lack of a cover charge and hidden extras is considered a fair exchange for the absence of amuse-gueules and petits fours. Bedrooms take up the wine theme, each sponsored by and decorated with memorabilia from a wine producer, while the restaurant is spread over two rooms and has simple wooden tables that accommodate Savile Row suits, jeans and leather jackets alike.

It says much for the well-placed confidence of this pair that they need nothing more than a humble 'bistro' tag on which to hang their own and James Martin's talents. He uses good-quality prime cuts, often subjected to the standard bistro technique of chargrilling, which makes a particularly good foil for the wines. 'Bistro food at its best,' wrote one, and the list of commended dishes bears this out, from 'obscenely buttered' chargrilled asparagus with chunks of rock salt scattered about, to rack of lamb 'rather on the young side of juvenile', with parsnip chips, to chargrilled tuna seared on the outside, 'with an almost raw nugget in the middle, oozing juiciness, quite terrific', with a pool of coriander salsa by its side.

Service 'could not have been better or more friendly'. It is also knowledgeable when it comes to the nub of the operation, recommending wines to go with food. Advice is worth taking. The wine list is an eagle-eyed collection that pays as much attention to vin de pays as it does to fine claret and burgundy, by way of Savoie, Israel and Argentina. Fair mark-ups and plenty of half-bottles add to the appeal. In addition, a shorter list changes daily, allowing matchings and pairings to suit the day's food. The entire approach to wine, not just the list of bottles, is what makes this place so special. CELLARMAN'S CHOICE: Auxey-Duresses 1992, Jean Pascal, £18.60; Haut-Médoc, Ch. Magnol 1988, £15.50.

CHEF: James Martin PROPRIETORS: Robin Hutson and Gerard Basset OPEN: all week 12 to 2, 7 to 9.45 MEALS: alc (main courses £6 to £13) SERVICE: not inc, card slips closed CARDS: Access, Amex, Delta, Diners, Switch, Visa DETAILS: 50 seats. 8 tables outside. Private parties: 12 main room, 40 private room. Car park. Vegetarian meals. Children's helpings. No cigars/pipes in dining-room. No music ACCOMMODATION: 19 rooms, all with bath/shower. TV. Phone. B&B £60 to £95. Children welcome. Garden (*The Which? Hotel Guide*)

Hunters £

5 Jewry Street, Winchester SO23 8RZ COOKING 2
TEL: (01962) 860006 FAX: (01962) 877707 COST £18–£42

David Birmingham, owner of Hunters, writes that, in a year that has seen the local competition stiffen, he has continued to benefit from a happy band of regulars: 'barristers, accountants and ladies who lunch'. If that sounds a trifle staid, do not be deceived. The atmosphere is infectiously jovial at most sessions, service 'endearing and eager'. Whatever Frenchness there is about the place is confined to posters celebrating the golden age of ballooning, and the odd staple such as moules marinière or steak au poivre.

Alan Stubbington, who took over as head chef towards the end of 1994, has retained the modern British feel with lemon sole and crab roulade on mash, chicken breast with leek mousse in filo and an asparagus cream sauce, and a carrot, leek and Gruyère pithiviers on chervil butter. An inspector thought too many starters relied on fruit for impact, but enjoyed a first course of duck livers on a 'hefty' croustade with a madeira sauce. Another reporter heartily approved the 'lovely, fresh' sea bream with a spaghetti of vegetables and a pink sauce tasting like the 'essence of bouillabaisse'. Crème brûlée is brought off with great dash, flavoured either with coffee or with strawberries and champagne, and lemon tart with raspberry coulis is as pleasantly tart as it should be. A brisk, no-nonsense wine list offers good-value drinking to suit most tastes. House wines start at £8.95.

CHEF: Alan Stubbington PROPRIETOR: David Birmingham OPEN: Mon to Sat 12 to 2, 6.30 to 10 CLOSED: 24 to 31 Dec MEALS: alc (main courses £5 to £16). Set L £7.50 (2 courses), Set D £9.95 (2 courses) to £13.50 SERVICE: not inc CARDS: Access, Amex, Delta, Diners, Switch, Visa DETAILS: 65 seats. Private parties: 20 main room, 25 private room. Vegetarian meals. Children's helpings. Smart dress preferred. No smoking in 1 dining-room. Wheelchair access. Music

Old Chesil Rectory

NEW ENTRY

1 Chesil Street, Winchester SO23 8HU COOKING 2
TEL: (01962) 851555 COST £23–£45

This particular rectory has character to spare. Built in the mid-fifteenth century, it lays claim to being the oldest building in Winchester. Entry is through a head-bumping low doorway down some steps. 'Owing to the age of the place,' noted a reporter, 'the floors are far from flat, and our table sloped disconcertingly.' It is simply decorated, with crisp white damask, flowers and candles making the tables pretty, lead-paned windows giving views of passing ankles outside.

The food, say the Ruthven-Stuarts, is aiming for 'gutsy, punchy flavours', to which end the menus make all the right modern noises. Spinach and mascarpone crespolini (pancakes) or a pasta dish of ratatouille with fresh anchovies, pesto and Parmesan get things off to a bright start. Main courses go for tried and true combinations, such as calvados, prunes and apple with pork, or port and juniper with pigeon. A fish 'symphony' introduces brill, monkfish and salmon to each other, the last 'terrifically tender' with a layer of subcutaneous fat that 'slithered around the tongue – divine'. Prune and armagnac parfait has been described as 'well presented, light and delicious', while summer pudding has been made with too much bread, though it benefited from the acidity of red- and blackcurrants. Good strong cafetière coffee will set you up for wandering round the cathedral. The wine list is predominantly French and has some fine bottles, but for much choice below £20 it is necessary to explore the southern hemisphere. The international house selection is good, though, and starts at £9.50.

CHEFS: Nicholas Ruthven-Stuart and Nicola Saunders PROPRIETORS: Nicholas and Christina Ruthven-Stuart OPEN: Tue to Sat 12 to 2, 7 to 9.30 CLOSED: 1 week Christmas, 2 weeks July to Aug MEALS: alc (main courses £5.50 to £15). Set L £9.95 (2 courses) SERVICE: not inc, card slips closed CARDS: Access, Switch, Visa DETAILS: 60 seats. Private parties: 40 main room, 10 and 14 private rooms. Vegetarian meals. Children's helpings. No smoking in 1 dining-room. Wheelchair access (3 steps). Music

▲ *Wykeham Arms* £ *

75 Kingsgate Street, Winchester SO23 9PE — COOKING 1
TEL: (01962) 853834 FAX: (01962) 854411 — COST £17–£33

Anyone looking for old Winchester might find this pub the ideal location: it is 250 years old itself, on a corner between college and cathedral. For years it has maintained an astonishing collection of tankards – 'there must be a thousand at least' – made of pewter, glass and china, strung from beams and hung around pictures. The warm welcome and buzz of people augurs well – it is a meeting-place for bell-ringers and cathedral lay clerks, among others – and service 'couldn't be nicer'. Three cooks devise menus and prepare the food two days a week each, which means, firstly, there is variety and, secondly, if there is one cook whose food appeals particularly, then it may be difficult to plan a subsequent visit to coincide with her turn in the kitchen.

The food ranges from simple gravad lax, or beef and venison casserole with juniper, to more involved duck breast marinated in plum sauce served with a confit of onion and orange in a bitter orange sauce. The reporter who ate this felt that 'after all that attention, it just tasted like duck breast with a slightly orangey sauce', which is perhaps all to the good, since competition between the ladies seems to result in 'too much going on' in some dishes. Carrot and ginger pudding or raspberry trifle may be among the desserts. Consider one of the cask ales as an alternative to the short but sympathetically priced wine list.

An asterisk (*) after the 1 to 5 cooking mark at the top of an entry signifies that the Guide *and its readers think that the restaurant is a particularly fine example within its rating.*

CHEFS: Vanessa Booth, Belinda Watson and Helen Brooks PROPRIETORS: Graeme and Anne Jameson OPEN: Mon to Sat 12 to 2.30, 6.30 to 8.45 MEALS: alc (main courses £4.50 to £11) SERVICE: not inc, card slips closed CARDS: Access, Amex, Delta, Switch, Visa DETAILS: 90 seats. Private parties: 8 main room. Car park. Vegetarian meals. No children under 14. Smart dress preferred. No smoking in dining-room. No music ACCOMMODATION: 7 rooms, all with bath/shower. TV. Phone. B&B £65 to £75. No children under 14. Pets welcome. Afternoon teas. Garden (*The Which? Hotel Guide*)

WINDERMERE Cumbria map 8

▲ *Gilpin Lodge*

Crook Road, Windermere LA23 3NE
TEL: (015394) 88818 FAX: (015394) 88058 COOKING 2
on B5284, 2m SE of Windermere COST £20–£46

It is a busy time for John and Christine Cunliffe, owners of this Lakeland lodge set in 20 acres of secluded gardens, woodland and moorland. Refurbishment seems to be an ongoing process, and there are plans to alter and expand many of the public areas as well as part of the dining-room. There have also been changes in the kitchen: Mrs Cunliffe now takes a back seat, allowing Christopher Davies full rein as head chef. Last but not least, the menus were being completely restructured as we went to press.

The aim is to limit dinner to four courses (rather than five) with a sorbet as a second-course option and a choice of cheese or a savoury in place of dessert. Vegetarians have their own menu of main courses. The kitchen's loyalty to local produce is unchanged: Cumberland ham finds its way into a terrine with leeks and asparagus, and roast rack of Herdwick lamb is served with a roasted garlic and thyme sauce. Kentmere beef is hung to the Cunliffe's specifications, venison is culled from Holker Hall. The weekday lunch *carte* is equally suited to a snack in the lounge or a full meal in the restaurant. Service continues to draw murmurs of discontent: 'Efficient but a little distant,' said one; 'No smiles,' commented another. Like everything else, the wine list has undergone change, with an injection of interest from Italy and the New World. It is full of stylish bottles, carefully selected, of which eight are offered by the glass from £3.10. CELLARMAN'S CHOICE: Groot Constantia Estate Sauvignon Blanc 1993, South Africa, £17.65; Concha y Toro Cabernet Sauvignon 1989, Don Melchor, Maipo, Chile, £21.85.

CHEFS: Christopher Davies and Christine Cunliffe PROPRIETORS: John and Christine Cunliffe OPEN: all week 12 to 2.30, 7 to 8.45 MEALS: alc L (main courses £4.50 to £8.50). Set L Sun £14, Set D £26 SERVICE: not inc CARDS: Access, Amex, Delta, Diners, Switch, Visa DETAILS: 45 seats. 3 tables outside. Private parties: 25 main room, 14 and 16 private rooms. Car park. Vegetarian meals. Children's helpings. No children under 7. Smart dress preferred. No smoking in dining-room. Wheelchair access. Music ACCOMMODATION: 9 rooms, all with bath/shower. TV. Phone. B&B £50 to £160. Deposit: £20. No children under 7. Afternoon teas. Garden

NEW CHEF *is shown instead of a cooking mark where a change of chef occurred too late for a new assessment of the cooking.*

▲ *Miller Howe* 🍷 £✱

Rayrigg Road, Windermere LA23 1EY
TEL: (01539) 442536 FAX: (01539) 445664 COOKING 2*
on A592, between Windermere and Bowness COST £26–£45

Miller Howe has a wonderful lakeside setting, and both conservatory and dining-room make the most of the view; total privacy prevails. The menu is printed in flamboyant script, lists the canapés (served by John Tovey if he is in residence) and bread, and indicates whether Chris Blaydes or Susan Elliott is at the stoves that evening. Confirmation of this comes later when he or she does a turn round the dining-room while you are eating pudding.

The format has altered little over the years. Gather for drinks at 7.30 and begin the synchronised eating of four courses at around 8pm. There is, in time-honoured Lakeland fashion, no choice before the pudding, and main courses come with five vegetables: at one meal a purée of Jerusalem artichoke, scrunchy mange-tout with walnut oil dressing, potatoes sliced thin, cooked crisp and flavoured with cumin, a slice of aubergine with a smear of pesto, braised fennel with calvados, and provençale tomatoes – in the middle of which sat a first-class piece of beef, cooked medium-rare and properly rested, as well as some caramelised shallots and cheese-flavoured puff pastry. All the individual components of this dish were excellent, but there is a division of opinion as to whether or not such an ensemble works. The debate is not just about style, but about flavours and culinary judgement. The overall conception of a dish matters to some people, and to them Miller Howe doesn't work as well as it should. To others, if the individual components are good, as they undoubtedly are here, then that is all that matters.

To give the cooking its due, it is not stuck in a rut. The style has lightened perceptibly, and there are interesting ideas, some more successful than others. Among those that have worked is a golden-yolked and perfectly poached egg on nutmeggy spinach, covered in thin wisps of shaved foie gras, and a pile of deep-fried strands of leek. Lunch, by the way, is a much lighter affair. 'The excellent breads, – many of them innovative, such as onion, orange and macadamia (that's just one) – deserve a mention'. Butter is sculpted into little swan shapes, and the bread-and-butter pudding is good. The New World wines, almost entirely from Australia, New Zealand and South Africa, are top-notch and reasonably priced. Wines by the glass (two per evening) are £3.50.

CHEF: Chris Blaydes and Susan Elliott PROPRIETOR: John Tovey OPEN: all week 1 and 8 (one sitting at each meal) CLOSED: early Dec to early March MEALS: Set L £12.50 (inc glass of wine), Set D £26 SERVICE: 12.5% (optional), card slips closed CARDS: Access, Amex, Diners, Visa DETAILS: 70 seats. Car park. No children under 8. Smart dress preferred. No smoking in dining-room. Music. Air-conditioned ACCOMMODATION: 12 rooms, all with bath/shower. TV. Phone. D,B&B £95 to £250. No children under 8. Pets welcome in bedrooms only. Afternoon teas. Garden (*The Which? Hotel Guide*)

All entries in the Guide *are rewritten every year, not least because restaurant standards fluctuate. Don't rely on an out-of-date* Guide.

Miller Howe Café

Lakeland Plastics Ltd, Alexandra Buildings, Station Precinct, Windermere LA23 1BQ
TEL: (015394) 46732

COOKING 1
COST £16–£24

This popular in-store café is due to be extended and refitted ready for 1996, which may relieve pressure on both kitchen and service. The style is pleasantly informal, and orders are taken at the counter. Find cheese and herb pâté, jacket potatoes with various fillings and bobotie, a South African dish of spicy minced lamb with apricots, almonds and an egg custard topping. Cumberland sausage comes with apple sauce and date chutney, and Waberthwaite sugar-baked ham is served with local mustard. Sticky toffee pudding is obligatory for most people. Drinks include tea, coffee, hot chocolate, lager, and house wine at £7.50 a litre.

CHEFS: Ian Dutton and Steven Kirkbride PROPRIETORS: Ian and Annette Dutton OPEN: all week 9 (10 Sun) to 5 CLOSED: 25 and 26 Dec, 1 Jan MEALS: alc (main courses £5 to £7) SERVICE: not inc, card slips closed CARDS: Access, Switch, Visa DETAILS: 45 seats. 5 tables outside. Private parties: 50 main room. Car park. Vegetarian meals. Children's helpings. Smart dress preferred. No smoking in dining-room. Wheelchair access (also WC). No music. Air-conditioned

Roger's

4 High Street, Windermere LA23 1AF
TEL: (01539) 444954

COOKING 2*
COST £23–£43

Roger's is easy to find. Set a course for Windermere's high street, and it's opposite the Tourist Information Centre. It is a small, terrace-end house run with warmth and brio by the Pergl-Wilsons, opening for candlelit evenings that are sometimes themed to the culinary regions of France. If your knowledge of the cuisine of the Jura is a little rusty, this is the place at which to brush it up.

On non-themed evenings, the extensive *carte* is joined by a good-value set-price menu of four courses with coffee. The food moves gently with the tide of current tastes, but is careful not to strain the loyalty of regulars, who may expect to see certain dishes. Warm vegetable mousses are a favourite way of starting, followed by a hearty soup such as leek and potato. Main courses marry their principal ingredients with well-established partners, such as black-currants with honey-glazed Gressingham duck, or port and cranberries with venison. Roger's Special is a goulash of pork with spätzli. One reporter was full of praise for devilled crab en croûte, cod with spinach and a light cheese sauce, and 'particularly good' chocolate marquise – cooking of 'sophistication and variety'. Desserts weave a Lakeland spell of steamed white chocolate pudding with hot fudge sauce, and walnut meringues with bananas and a ginger and coffee cream. For one couple the balance is clearly right: 'This is our favourite restaurant in the Lake District.' The cleverly constructed wine list starts in New Zealand and works its way outwards, finding good things in most departments and offering them at agreeable prices. House Duboeuf is £9.50.

CHEF/PROPRIETOR: Roger Pergl-Wilson OPEN: Mon to Sat, and Sun bank hols, D only 7 to 9.30 CLOSED: 1 week Jan, 1 week summer MEALS: alc (main courses £5.50 to £13). Set D £15.75. Minimum £10 SERVICE: not inc, card slips closed CARDS: Access, Amex, Diners, Visa DETAILS: 44 seats. Private parties: 30 main room, 30 private room. Vegetarian meals. Children's helpings. Smart dress preferred. Wheelchair access (2 steps). Music

WINKLEIGH Devon map 1

Pophams £

Castle Street, Winkleigh EX19 8HQ COOKING 2*
TEL: (01837) 83767 COST £15–£31

Behind the bow-windowed shop-front in the middle of sleepy Winkleigh, Melvyn Popham and Dennis Hawkes cook and serve respectively for no more than ten people at a time. A modest, unassuming, open-plan café it may be, but it is also 'a little gem', according to a reporter who was 'delighted with the quality of the food and the splendid service'. A blackboard lists the daily dishes and, lunch being the only business, salads are much in evidence: warm pear and Cambazola, or avocado and crispy bacon. Main courses run to a more substantial poached salmon with hollandaise, or fillet of beef with oyster mushrooms and madeira sauce. Everybody can watch the food being cooked, which promotes an air of domesticity and relaxation. 'When we asked for our duck to be well cooked instead of pink, our request was met with gracious acquiescence.' Bacardi and lime jelly, which takes its place alongside sticky toffee pudding and chocolate roulade, was so good that a reporter 'had two goes'. There is no drinks licence, but no corkage charge either, and white wine is taken away to be cooled if necessary.

CHEF: Melvyn Popham PROPRIETORS: Melvyn Popham and Dennis Hawkes OPEN: Mon to Sat L only 12 to 3 CLOSED: Feb MEALS: alc (main courses £7.50 to £12). Unlicensed, but bring your own: no corkage SERVICE: not inc, card slips closed CARDS: Access, Delta, Visa DETAILS: 10 seats. Private parties: 10 main room. Vegetarian meals. No children under 14. No smoking in dining-room. Music. Air-conditioned

WINTERINGHAM Humberside map 9

▲ *Winteringham Fields*

Winteringham DN15 9PF COOKING 4*
TEL: (01724) 733096 FAX: (01724) 733898 COST £29-£71

The restaurant is a warren of oak-beamed rooms with a conservatory at one end, and a 'marvellous collection of Victoriana' that reminded one reporter of his grandmother's home. It is not grand, but welcoming. The smart dining-room (soon to be extended, along with the kitchen) has been refurbished with slate-blue walls, shot silk drapes, capacious upholstered chairs, and mirrors that discreetly make the best of the L-shaped space. Germain Schwab is cooking up a storm. 'I think he is just getting better and better,' wrote an off-duty inspector. 'It is confident, daring and powerful, within the context of a neo-classical European style, and done with total integrity.' Schwab takes a standard idea and gives it a new twist, producing dishes that are founded in familiar territory and yet have a capacity to surprise and delight.

The unsuspecting might need to prepare themselves for 'wave after wave of impeccable dishes shooting out of the kitchen', beginning perhaps with a soup of mussel bisque, or carrot and cardamom, served in a 'doll's house bowl', or 'terrific' pastry cubes of oxtail and tongue, or 'stunning' boned quail stuffed with foie gras. This is all while you are still reading the menu, which offers a three-course no-choice daily option, a six-course surprise, a *carte* and a couple of specials. If there was a lacuna, felt one reporter, it was the lack of vegetarian options.

A crusted salmi of woodpigeon with black truffles was considered 'classicism triumphant' by one reporter: a white dish covered in a puff pastry pithiviers hat 'so light it could have floated away had it not been anchored to the side', under which lurked dark, boldly flavoured pieces of game and root vegetables in an earthy, aromatic and well-reduced sauce. Another praised a 'gateau' – looking like a quiche made of fine filo pastry – filled with pieces of perfectly cooked quail, delectably rich duck liver and lightly crunchy asparagus, in a just-set herby egg mixture, with a deeply flavourful sauce around it: 'an unusual, inventive main course with just the right degree of complexity.'

Fish – always a strength – might include an exquisite darne of brilliantly fresh and tasty hake served skin side up on a bed of perfectly timed and slithery black ink noodles, in a charcoal-coloured sauce. What was odd about this dish was that it contained two kinds of pasta – the other was a simple square covering some clams – yet 'what could so easily have become a dog's dinner was quite faultless', thanks to subtle saucing and harmonious flavours. Other fishy successes have included scallops wrapped in home-made filo pastry with a wild mushroom sauce, and a rich and velvety soup of North Sea fish, given a Mediterranean twist with rouille and toast.

The cheese trolley is a magnificent array, all perfectly kept – 'you don't see many like this any more' – while 'magical' crème brûlée has fought for attention against 'fabulous' wafer-thin slices of pineapple spiked with a little white rum, together with a small mound of 'gorgeous' soured cream ice-cream, or a beignet de carnival, straight from the pan, dusted with icing sugar: a 'French market' idea done in style with verve and confidence. Impressive service combines precision with unflagging attentiveness. The Schwabs are 'outstandingly kind and welcoming', which cuts refreshingly through any formality; reporters are tolerant of the training of younger staff. Classy French wines form the backbone of the list, backed up by interesting Italians, good-value Australians, a few from Germain Schwab's native Switzerland, and a fair choice of half-bottles. The monthly selection is worth a squint, and four house wines are £12. CELLARMAN'S CHOICE: Merryvale Cabernet Sauvignon 'Hillside' 1992, Napa, California, £33; Mâcon-Fuissé, Dom. de Fussiacus 1993, Jean Paul Paquet, £19.

CHEF: Germain Schwab PROPRIETORS: Germain and Annie Schwab OPEN: Tue to Fri L 12 to 1.30, Mon to Sat D 7.15 to 9.30 CLOSED: 2 weeks Christmas, first week Aug MEALS: alc (main courses £18.50 to £22). Set L £17.50, Set D £28 to £43 SERVICE: not inc, card slips closed CARDS: Access, Amex, Switch, Visa DETAILS: 46 seats. Private parties: 10 main room, 10 private room. Car park. Smart dress preferred. No smoking in dining-room. Wheelchair access. Music ACCOMMODATION: 7 rooms, all with bath/shower. TV. Phone. B&B £60 to £95. Children welcome. No children under 8. Garden (*The Which? Hotel Guide*)

WITHERSLACK Cumbria map 8

▲ *Old Vicarage*

Church Road, Witherslack LA11 6RS
TEL: (01539) 552381 FAX: (01539) 552373 COOKING 2
off A590, take first left in village to church COST £22–£42

Witherslack is off the Barrow road near Grange-over-Sands, not far from the M6 but seemingly a world away once you get there. Two families have run this country-house hotel for 15 years (no prizes for guessing its previous incarnation), steering a steady course through hazardous economic times and emerging in fine fettle.

One sight of the menu will tell you this is Lakeland, with Swaledale and Wensleydale cheeses, pork from Waberthwaite and, of course, Cumberland sauce. The daily-changing fixed-price four-course dinner usually comprises a single main course with a choice of four starters, a pair of desserts and individual cheeseboards to finish. One couple who enjoyed a summer idyll at the Vicarage ate 'superb' chicken liver pâté with Cumberland sauce and a plate of fine mixed charcuterie with apple and mint dressing to start. Their main course was excellent stuffed roast loin of pork with apricot sauce. Vegetables tend to come in generous amounts, and each has had something different done to it. To finish, try chocolate and vanilla mousse or steamed nectarine pudding. Coffee arrives with home-made chocolates as well as Kendal mint cake. The staff appear as 'relaxed and happy' as the customers.

The wine list is a model of compact intelligence. Choices have been made in every section, and number almost as many half-bottles as full. Pask from New Zealand, Casablanca from Chile and Graillot in Crozes-Hermitage are all fine producers, and there is an intriguing selection of Italian specialities. Good fortified wines of the calibre of Hidalgo sherries and Blandy's madeiras come by the glass. There are no house wines as such, but prices start at £12. CELLARMAN'S CHOICE: Vernaccia di San Gimignano 1993, Conti G. Strozzi, £12.50; Cabernet-Merlot 1991, Conti Bossi Fedrigotti-Foianeghe, £13.50.

CHEF: Stanley Reeve PROPRIETORS: the Burrington-Brown and Reeve families OPEN: Sun L 12.30 for 1, all week D 7.30 for 8 MEALS: Set L Sun £13.50, Set D £25. Min £25 D SERVICE: not inc, card slips closed CARDS: Access, Amex, Delta, Diners, Switch, Visa DETAILS: 35 seats. Private parties: 18 main room, 12 private room. Car park. Children's helpings. Smart dress preferred. No smoking in dining-room. Wheelchair access (3 steps). Music ACCOMMODATION: 14 rooms, all with bath/shower. TV. Phone. B&B £59 to £170. Children welcome. Baby facilities. Pets by arrangement. Afternoon teas (*The Which? Hotel Guide*)

WOBURN Bedfordshire map 6

Paris House

Woburn Park, Woburn MK17 9QP
TEL: (01525) 290692 FAX: (01525) 290471 COOKING 2
on A4012, 1¾m E of Woburn in Abbey grounds COST £33–£57

The setting is a joy 'even in January', and there can be few grander entrances in the county. The black and white timbered building, relocated from the Paris

Exhibition of 1878, stands in the deer-strewn grounds of the Duke of Bedford's estate. Judging by a feuilleté of lambs' tongues and wild mushrooms in tarragon, or entrecôte chasseur, the French connection in Peter Chandler's cooking is strong too. But he is also happy preparing seafood tagliatelle, sweet-and-sour chicken with pineapple, and, after a trip to the USA, a salad of Cajun prawns or a pudding of hot bananas with chocolate-chip cookie ice-cream. Variety extends to treatments, flavours and textures.

Most reporters are happy with the food. Lunch is pricey for some, good value for others, while service, although it can be 'gracious and attentive', also comes in for some criticism. The general feeling seems to be that if prices were reduced and service improved this would be an altogether more attractive package. Menus might be more user-friendly too. The £25 lunch menu has limited choice, while the so-called *carte* is a set £38 with no individual prices. Peter Chandler can obviously cook, but the organisation required to turn his talent into a satisfactory experience for the customer needs an overhaul. A few New World wines pad out the largely French list. Wines under £20 exist but are thin on the ground, and mark-ups are high. House wine is £10.

CHEF/PROPRIETOR: Peter Chandler OPEN: Tue to Sun L 12 to 2, Tue to Sat D 7 to 9.30 CLOSED: Feb MEALS: Set L £25, Set D £38 SERVICE: not inc, card slips closed CARDS: Access, Amex, Delta, Diners, Switch, Visa DETAILS: 45 seats. Private parties: 45 main room, 16 private room. Car park. Vegetarian meals. Children's helpings. Smart dress preferred. Wheelchair access (3 steps; also WC). No music

WOLTERTON Norfolk map 6

▲ *Saracen's Head* £ NEW ENTRY

Wolterton NR11 7LX
TEL: (01263) 768909
off A140 Aylsham to Cromer road, through Erpingham and Calthorpe

COOKING 1
COST £17–£32

It may be on the North Norfolk B-roads – a stone's throw from Wolterton Hall – but Robert Dawson-Smith's inn-cum-eating-house really brings in the crowds. It is a place that serves all comers, although you are advised to book for meals at weekends. One couple who turned up for Sunday lunch found the bars humming with 'parties of pensioners, thirtysomethings nursing hangovers or small children – or both – family groups, a solo man with a pint and, upstairs, a christening party of 40 just winding down'. Mr Dawson-Smith has tried to emulate the style of a 'Tuscan inn', as he puts it, with log fires ablaze during the winter, a pretty courtyard for al fresco eating, pleasant accommodation and monthly feasts that are a regular sell-out.

The menu is chalked on blackboards, and promises robust country cooking based on sound Norfolk ingredients – venison from nearby Gunton Park, fish from the coast and meat from an 'old-fashioned' butcher. Chips and peas are outlawed. You might be offered crispy fried aubergines with garlic mayonnaise, and braised local pigeon in a rich fruity sauce, as well as Morston mussels with cider, and pot-roast leg of lamb. Puddings cover everything from upside-down apple tart to sorbets. In addition to well-kept real ales, the Saracen's Head has a promising wine list, assembled with help from Adnams and Barwell & Jones. House wine is £8.25.

CHEF/PROPRIETOR: Robert Dawson-Smith OPEN: all week 12.30 to 2.15, 7.15 to 9.30 CLOSED: 25 Dec MEALS: alc (main courses £5.50 to £10.50). Set L Mon to Fri £4.75 (2 courses), Set D Sun £5.95 (2 courses) SERVICE: not inc, card slips closed CARDS: Access, Amex, Visa DETAILS: 60 seats. 8 tables outside. Private parties: 26 main room, 60 private room. Car park. Vegetarian meals. Children's helpings. No music ACCOMMODATION: 4 rooms, all with bath/shower. TV. B&B £35 to £50. Deposit: 20%. Children welcome. Pets welcome in bedrooms only. Garden

WOODSTOCK Oxfordshire map 2

▲ *Feathers Hotel*

Market Street, Woodstock OX20 1SX COOKING 2*
TEL: (01993) 812291 FAX: (01993) 813158 COST £39–£63

Woodstock is one of the jewels in Oxfordshire's crown, a bit of heritage England that has done very well without themed repackaging. It is a rewarding trot from Blenheim Palace to this seventeenth-century town-house hotel where all manner of contentment may be found. 'I know of few better experiences,' writes a reporter, 'than a walk round Woodstock Park on a fine autumn morning among the golden beeches and the pheasants flying, followed by lunch in the bar at the Feathers, which you can do in your walking-boots without feeling embarrassed.'

David Lewis's cooking is packed with character. Despite the resolute Englishness of the setting, he has intelligently absorbed some of the recent Mediterranean trends without ending up with an unseemly hodgepodge. Watercress soup has a poached hen's egg and chorizo in it, while goats' cheese is baked in oats and comes with lentils and smoked bacon. Straightforward grills supplement more ingenious main courses such as fillet of red mullet with aubergine and garlic confit. Vegetables are charged for separately and do not always appear to be offered. Desserts do some exotic things with favourite flavours: witness white chocolate and ginger mousse with local rhubarb, or hot cinnamon fritter with banana jam and custard. The 'voluntary gratuity' of 15 per cent still causes grumbles, though the service is 'pleasant and adequate'. If you have a mere £20 to spend on wine, you will find little for your comfort – even outside France – unless you can make do with a half-bottle. For all that, there are some good bottles to choose from. The house selection starts at £11.60.

CHEF: David Lewis PROPRIETORS: Andrew Leeman, Simon Lowe and Howard Malin OPEN: all week 12.30 to 2.15 (2.30 Sun), 7.30 to 9.15 (9.30 Sat) MEALS: alc (main courses £15.50 to £19.50). Set L and D £19.50 (2 courses) to £24.50 SERVICE: 15% (optional), card slips closed CARDS: Access, Amex, Diners, Visa DETAILS: 60 seats. Private parties: 60 main room. Children's helpings. Smart dress preferred. No cigars/pipes in dining-room. Music. Air-conditioned ACCOMMODATION: 17 rooms, all with bath/shower. TV. Phone. B&B £78 to £150. Children welcome. Baby facilities. Pets welcome. Afternoon teas. Garden (*The Which? Hotel Guide*)

WOOLTON HILL Hampshire map 2

▲ *Hollington House*

Woolton Hill RG15 9XR
TEL: (01635) 255100 FAX: (01635) 255075 COOKING **2**
off A343, 3m S of Newbury COST £28–£70

The Edwardian house, built in 1904, is set in 25 acres of gardens and woodland which are 'worth a visit in themselves'. Furnishings may be 'a bit over the top', but are impressive none the less, from the oak-panelled galleried entrance hall to the comfortable dining-room with views from its mullioned windows. David Lake arrived in the kitchen shortly after the last edition of the *Guide* went to press, and his varied menu requires quite a bit of work to put together, with only a little help from luxury ingredients. Lamb sweetbreads, for example, are interleaved with filo pastry, Savoy cabbage and a slice of foie gras. 'Highly competent cooking' was the verdict of one satisfied reporter.

Ambition is high and the food covers the spectrum from a tian of provençale vegetables to braised oxtail (boned, filled with cabbage and bacon) to hot coconut soufflé with nougatine ice-cream. Fish, from salmon and sea bass to baked red mullet, have been endorsed, along with goats' cheese soufflé, and loin of local venison, tender from marinating, served with braised cabbage, though some dishes have lacked punch and vitality. English cheeses are 'perfectly kept, and generously allocated'. Chocolate terrine comes with raspberry sorbet, thin apple tart with cinnamon ice-cream, and one reporter enjoyed a Mont Blanc 'of sizeable proportions', which was a 'beautiful' creation of chestnut, chocolate, meringues and cream. Service by smartly dressed staff is 'charming, with an ideal mix of informality and high standards that is rarely seen'.

Australia takes pride of place on the wine list, with examples from lesser-known regions of Bendigo, Pyrenees, Geelong and Gippsland (all in Victoria) taking their place alongside Margaret River, Coonawarra and Hunter Valley. Highlighted producers include Henschke and Penfolds, and vintages go back to 1962. France is treated equally seriously, and the United States includes intriguing oddities from Maryland and Virginia. Mark-ups can be high, although good dessert wines and a fair selection of half-bottles add to the appeal. House South African is £12. CELLARMAN'S CHOICE: Moss Wood Pinot Noir 1990, Margaret River, W. Australia, £30; Pipers Brook Chardonnay 1990, Tasmania, £28.50.

CHEF: David Lake PROPRIETORS: John and Penny Guy OPEN: all week 12 to 2.30, 7 to 9.30 MEALS: alc (main courses £17 to £25). Set L £13.75 (2 courses) to £16.75, Set D £28 SERVICE: not inc CARDS: Access, Amex, Diners, Visa DETAILS: 50 seats. 6 tables outside. Private parties: 30 main room, 14, 20 and 70 private rooms. Car park. Vegetarian meals. Children's helpings. Smart dress preferred. No smoking in dining-room. Wheelchair access (also WC). Music ACCOMMODATION: 20 rooms, all with bath/shower. TV. Phone. B&B £90 to £350. Deposit: 50%. Rooms for disabled. Children welcome. Baby facilities. Afternoon teas. Garden. Swimming-pool (*The Which? Hotel Guide*)

indicates that smoking is either banned altogether or that a dining-room is maintained for non-smokers. The symbol does not apply to restaurants that simply have no-smoking areas.

WORCESTER Hereford & Worcester map 5

Brown's

24 Quay Street, Worcester WR1 2JJ
TEL: (01905) 26263

COOKING 2
COST £21–£42

This converted grain mill overlooks the River Severn near the bridge carrying the main road out of Worcester. 'In the hands of another designer it might have been cavernous' but instead has turned out 'elegant and airy'. Girders remain, brick walls are painted cream, and Parisian café posters don't look out of place. The welcome is inviting, and drinks arrive with a bowl of olives and the menu. Customers 'like what they know, and are only willing to experiment so far', write the Tansleys, perhaps feeling it necessary to justify a conservative-sounding menu in this day and age. But there is no need to apologise for devilled herring roes on brioche toast, charcoal-grilled fillet of beef or ginger treacle sponge.

The thrust is British, but that still leaves room for monkfish with a Japanese dressing, or fabada: a Spanish dish of white beans with poached beef, pork, ham and chicken. Lunch is considered a bargain, with a choice of five first and main courses plus pudding, while the dinner menu adds a cheese course. Service is 'smooth and unobtrusive', and the fact that all prices are fully inclusive is welcomed. Good French wines form the backbone of the list, and half-bottles are generous. House French or Australian is £9.90.

CHEFS: W.R. Tansley and K. Powles PROPRIETORS: W.R. and P.M. Tansley OPEN: Mon to Fri and Sun L 12.30 to 2.45, Mon to Sat D 7.30 to 9.45 CLOSED: 1 week Christmas, bank hol Mons MEALS: Set L £16, Set D £30 SERVICE: net prices, card slips closed CARDS: Access, Amex, Delta, Diners, Switch, Visa DETAILS: 100 seats. Private parties: 100 main room. Vegetarian meals. No children under 8. Smart dress preferred. No smoking in 1 dining-room. Wheelchair access (also WC). No music

Il Pescatore

34 Sidbury, Worcester WR1 2HZ
TEL/FAX: (01905) 21444

COOKING 1
COST £19–£46

Wooden beams and an old brick fireplace in this timber-framed building near the cathedral confirm its venerable age. The food is in Anglo-Italian mould, and the menu is long enough to cover the repertoire from minestrone to zuppa inglese by way of veal kidneys and fillet of pork with Stilton. The combination of a light lunch, other set menus, a *carte* and daily or seasonal specials brings welcome flexibility. Fresh fish is one of the strengths, with good reports of sardines, grilled hake and seafood tagliatelle. Home-made pasta is another forte, from lasagne to trenette with olive oil, garlic and chillies.

Dishes are substantial enough to satisfy, in one case, an appetite honed by 'working a narrowboat along the canals for five days'. Presentation is not a strong point, and vegetables, garnishes, petits fours and service could all do with a face-lift, but the main business convinces, not least in puddings such as tiramisù or hot passion-fruit soufflé. Apart from 'guest wines' from France, the list is Italian, with a varied and interesting showing of good-value bottles. Last year we noted the absence of vintages; this year they are almost universally

listed, a big improvement. Next year it may be the producers' turn. Half a dozen house wines under £10 are available by the glass at £1.75.

CHEF: Kevin Capper PROPRIETOR: Giuliano Ponzi OPEN: Tue to Sat L 12 to 2, Mon to Sat D 6.45 to 10 MEALS: alc (main courses £8 to £16.50). Set L £7.50 (2 courses) to £11.50, Set D £16.50 SERVICE: not inc CARDS: Access, Switch, Visa DETAILS: 40 seats. Private parties: 45 main room. Vegetarian meals. Children welcome. Smart dress preferred. Music

WORFIELD Shropshire **map 5**

▲ *Old Vicarage Hotel*

Worfield WV15 5JZ
TEL: (01746) 716497 FAX: (01746) 716552 **COOKING 2**
1m N of A454, 3m E of Bridgnorth **COST £25–£57**

This Edwardian parsonage in two acres has a view over the Shropshire countryside, good Victorian furniture and a comfortable and homely atmosphere. Lunch has disappeared, perhaps a casualty of the recession, and Sundays are different (lunch is every other week, and dinner is either roast beef or a vegetarian dish), but weekday dinner offers a choice of six items per course, with nine British cheeses making up the fourth. Modern British input shows itself in the red onion marmalade, balsamic lentils, and horseradish dressing that are used to sharpen up chicken and bacon terrine, breast of duck, or salad of smoked salmon with avocado and mango.

The same vitality applies to mainstream dishes such as an innovative warm duck pudding ('a sort of terrine and full of flavour') served with beetroot chutney. Cornish fish often gets a lift from citrus and herbs – brill and red mullet with a lemon and chive sabayon – while goats' cheese has made an appearance in a main-course tartlet with creamed leeks, and (together with lemon) in a sweet tart with raspberry syrup and vanilla ice-cream: 'an absolutely inspired blend of delicious flavours in perfect harmony'. Indeed, puddings seem to have crept up a notch, with special mention for orange tart with honey and rose-water ice-cream, and the notably light sticky toffee. Stylish wines from around the world embrace the best of traditional and modern wine-making. The choice from France is as good outside Burgundy and Bordeaux as in, the list has its finger on the pulse, and prices are fair. CELLARMAN'S CHOICE: Mâcon-Clessé 1992, Dom. Guillemot-Michel, £18.50; Fleurie La Madone 1993, Dom. Chantreuil, £18.50.

CHEF: John Williams PROPRIETORS: Peter and Christine Iles OPEN: Sun L 12 to 1.45 (not every Sunday – phone to check), all week D 7 to 8.45 CLOSED: 22 Dec to 14 Jan MEALS: Set L Sun £13.95, Set D Sun to Thur £24 to £28.50. Set D Fri and Sat £29.50 to £35 SERVICE: not inc CARDS: Access, Amex, Diners, Visa DETAILS: 50 seats. Private parties: 16 main room, 14 and 16 private rooms. Car park. Vegetarian meals. No children under 8. Smart dress preferred. No smoking in dining-room. Wheelchair access (2 steps; also WC). Music ACCOMMODATION: 14 rooms, all with bath/shower. TV. Phone. B&B £65 to £120. Deposit: £50. Rooms for disabled. Children welcome. Baby facilities. Pets welcome in bedrooms only. Afternoon teas. Garden (*The Which? Hotel Guide*)

WRIGHTINGTON Lancashire map 8

High Moor

High Moor Lane, Wrightington WN6 9QA
TEL: (01257) 252364 FAX: (01257) 255120
off A5209, between M6 junction 27 and Parbold, take Robin Hood Lane at crossroads W of Wrightington Hospital, then next left

COOKING 2
COST £17–£35

One of the themes running through our correspondence concerns restaurants that aim high and miss. You know the sort of thing: chef offers a tian of aubergines with tomatoes, bell peppers and seared scallops dressed in balsamic vinegar, makes a decent fist it, but no more, and the customer is charged £20 for two courses. 'Cut out the pretence!' reporters write; 'just cook something simpler, charge less, and we would be much happier.' Now, the High Moor has done just that.

The dish above came from the previous menu, which the High Moor now considers 'a tired product and a tired formula'. The proprietors closed the restaurant, refurbished it and started again from scratch. Now look at it: Caesar salad, Thai crab-cakes, deep-fried fish and chips, or breast of chicken on a split-pea purée. The place is open every meal-time, and prices have come down too. It may be argued that yet another Caesar salad, or more fish and chips, in Lancashire of all places, is hardly progress. But rather these done well than yet another tarted-up dish of salmon that tries to be something it isn't. Oak beams and tables, York-stone flags and 'plenty of atmosphere' are the background to braised oxtail with bubble and squeak, and hot cinnamon apples with a strudel lid. There is a directness and heartiness about the food that was not there before. The wine list has been trimmed a bit too. A few of the more expensive clarets and burgundies have gone, and the emphasis has shifted more towards affordability and approach- ability, with nearly 20 wines now available by the glass from £1.50.

CHEFS: Darren Wynn and Lee Conroy PROPRIETORS: James Sines and John Nelson OPEN: all week 12 to 2 (4 Sun), 5.30 to 10 (8.30 Sun) CLOSED: 1 Jan MEALS: alc (main courses £5.50 to £13). Set L £9 (2 courses) to £11, Set D £5.30 to 7 £9.50 (2 courses) to £11.50 SERVICE: not inc CARDS: Access, Amex, Delta, Diners, Switch, Visa DETAILS: 100 seats. 6 tables outside. Private parties: 85 main room. Car park. Vegetarian meals. Children's helpings. Smart dress preferred. Music. Air-conditioned

WYE Kent map 3

▲ *Wife Of Bath*

4 Upper Bridge Street, Wye TN25 5AW
TEL: (01233) 812540 and 812232
FAX: (01233) 813630
just off A28, Ashford to Canterbury road

COOKING 1*
COST £25–£39

The Wife of Bath was once home to the doctor of Wye, and a reporter notes that it still feels pleasingly homely today. Good humour prevails, and refuses to flag even when the staggered bookings on a packed-out Easter evening somehow arrived all together on the dot of 8pm. Robert Hymers cooks set-price menus at both lunch-time and in the evening, with a *carte* coming into play, unusually, at lunch-time only. Although one or two voguish notes are sounded – for example, in a starter of tagliatelle with roasted tomatoes, basil and shaved Parmesan – the style is essentially in line with modern British cooking of recent years.

First courses may take in a warm mille-feuille of smoked salmon and spinach, or scallop ceviche with lime and chervil, followed by roast local duckling with kumquats, and a mighty rack of lamb encased in pastry. Apple frangipane tart was 'a tiny delicious portion with excellent crème anglaise'. The cheese choice may include Ireland's Cashel Blue, and there is usually a selection of home-made ice-creams. The feeling is that, despite one or two lapses, everything represents good value. The mainly French wine list has some classy names among the clarets, with prices to match, although the overall spread is democratic enough and there's a small range from the New World. House wines start at £9.75.

CHEF: Robert Hymers PROPRIETOR: John Morgan OPEN: Tue to Sat 12 to 2.30, 7 to 10 CLOSED: first week Jan, first 2 weeks Sept MEALS: alc L (main courses £10 to £14). Set L £8.50 (2 courses), Set D £19.95 SERVICE: not inc CARDS: Access, Delta, Switch, Visa DETAILS: 55 seats. Private parties: 60 main room, 15 private room. Car park. Vegetarian meals. Children's helpings. Smart dress preferred. No pipes in dining-room. Wheelchair access (1 step). No music ACCOMMODATION: 6 rooms, all with bath/shower. TV. Phone. B&B £25 to £60. Rooms for disabled. Children welcome. Garden

YARM Cleveland map 10

CLEVELAND 1996 LIVE WIRE

D.P. Chadwick's

NEW ENTRY

104B High Street, Yarm TS15 9AU COOKING 2
TEL: (01642) 788558 COST £17–£43

Yarm didn't know what had hit it when Daryl Chadwick moved into town in 1992 and opened his self-styled 'continental café'. The young ex-army parachutist from Darlington meant business and set about disturbing the peace in the nicest possible way. Go at lunch-time and you will be knocked backwards by the blast of noise, the heat and the sheer cosmopolitan vitality of his brilliant venture. Waiters in long aprons rush around between marble-topped tables, swerving around burnt-umber faux marble pillars, dodging terracotta plant-pots and an upright piano piled with silver serving-domes. The action continues well into the afternoon as the crowds continue to pour in: no bookings are taken, but the long queues are fast-moving.

The menu is on a blackboard – if you can manage to see it without binoculars – and its tone is brasserie rather than café, with lots of Italian/French cross-overs propped up by pasta and charcuterie. During the day you can order trendy sandwiches (pastrami and Provolone in pain rustique) or anything from Cullen skink and a Caesar salad of imperial proportions to hunky Italian sausages with true-Brit mash, or spaghetti with cauliflower, spring onion and flecks of chilli. In the evening there are also more elaborate inventions, such as crab-crusted cod with shellfish sauce, honey-roast duck with cinnamon and wild cherry sauce, bourride, and medallions of lamb with lentils and a thyme jus. Desserts feature a better-than-average tiramisù as well as lemon and sultana pudding with hot lemon sauce. The wine list is a short, sharp collection favouring youthful vigour rather than maturity. House wine is £8.50.

CHEF: David Brownless PROPRIETOR: D.P. Chadwick OPEN: Tue to Sat 11.30 to 9.30 CLOSED: Second week Oct MEALS: alc (main courses £3.50 to £13) SERVICE: not inc CARDS: none DETAILS: 70 seats. 4 tables outside. Vegetarian meals. Children's helpings. No smoking in 1 dining-room. Music

YATTENDON Berkshire map 2

▲ *Royal Oak* NEW ENTRY

The Square, Yattendon RG16 0UF
TEL: (01635) 201325 FAX: (01635) 201926 COOKING 1
off B4009, 5m W of Pangbourne COST £30–£43

Chef Robbie Macrae joined the Royal Oak in 1994 after a year at The Restaurant at the Hyde Park Hotel (see entry, London). From bustling London to a red-brick sixteenth-century inn with a walled garden and a beamed bar is quite a transition. Food is served in both bar and restaurant. Inevitably, the former may be characterised as simpler, but that doesn't preclude dishes such as squid risotto, artichoke à la grecque with couscous, or rabbit confit with mushroom tagliatelle. In the restaurant, a starter of tomato and herb salad with 'UFO-shaped' shellfish ravioli uses a good mixture of seafood and 'lots of shredded basil'. Another reporter was glad of a dish of 'pungent' Yattendon sausages and lentils one winter's evening. Poached pear with caramel and ginger, or marbled chocolate terrine may be safer than a 'somewhat dull' raspberry soufflé. Fine home-made chocolate truffles go some way to making up for 'thin and tasteless' coffee. The wine list offers good drinking from around the world, the house selections alone a commendably catholic range beginning at £8.95 and stopping just short of £20.

CHEF: Robbie Macrae PROPRIETOR: Regal Hotel Group OPEN: restaurant Sun to Fri L 12 to 2 (2.30 Fri to Sun), Mon to Sat D 7.30 to 9.30; bar all week breakfast 7 to 9.30 (8.30 to 10.30 Fri to Sun), all week L 12 to 2 (2.30 Fri to Sun), Mon to Sat D 7 to 9.30 MEALS: restaurant Set L £15.50 (2 courses) to £19.50, Set D £19.50 (2 courses) to £25; bar alc (main courses £7.50 to £11.50) SERVICE: not inc CARDS: Access, Amex, Delta, Diners, Switch, Visa DETAILS: 64 seats. 6 tables outside. Private parties: 24 main room. Vegetarian meals. Children's helpings. Smart dress preferred. Wheelchair access. No music ACCOMMODATION: 5 rooms, 3 with bath/shower. TV. Phone. B&B £60 to £85. Children welcome. Pets welcome. Afternoon teas. Garden (*The Which? Hotel Guide*)

YORK North Yorkshire map 9

Kites

13 Grape Lane, York YO1 2HU COOKING 1
TEL: (01904) 641750 FAX: (01904) 640121 COST £25–£43

Although right in the city centre, down a cobbled back street, Kites is 'a welcome escape from the tourist traps', with a 'pleasant, simple and unpretentious' feel about it. Forget the décor (try your best) and concentrate instead on the plain, simple food in this pair of upstairs rooms. It is an informal mix along the lines of

Thai crab-cakes, fillet of hare in a juniper-scented cream, and rice-pudding brûlée, backed up with a selection of Dales cheeses. Cheese also crops up in the brace of boozy fondues for two people: Cheddar with Theakston, or Stilton with cider.

All this is supplemented by daily specials, such as steak sandwich – flavoursome pink steak with béarnaise sauce in a slice of French bread – or creamy chicken casserole. Vegetarian dishes change by the day too, and vegetables with main courses are well treated. One reporter found ye olde banoffi pie 'traditionally made', while bread-and-butter pudding served with caramel sauce and cream was 'the highlight of the meal'. Service is willing and friendly. Thirty varied wines stay mostly below £15, with house French £10, or £1.95 a glass.

CHEF: Oliver Bell PROPRIETOR: C. Wright OPEN: Mon to Sat 12 to 2, 6.30 to 10.30 CLOSED: 25 and 26 Dec, 1 Jan MEALS: alc (main courses £8 to £14) SERVICE: not inc, card slips closed CARDS: Access, Amex, Diners, Switch, Visa DETAILS: 52 seats. Private parties: 28 main room, 16 and 28 private rooms. Vegetarian meals. Children's helpings. Music

Melton's

7 Scarcroft Road, York YO2 1ND — COOKING 3
TEL: (01904) 634341 FAX: (01904) 629233 — COST £19–£40

'I felt I had to write and let you know about the remarkable quality of food at this unassuming restaurant,' enthused one reporter, confirming its popularity. Melton's attracts all ages, but is not easy to find despite the clear directions: ten minutes' walk from the Castle Museum and Clifford's Tower, over Skeldergate Bridge, third road on the right, opposite a public car park. Sandwiched between a couple of shops, it has the rather neutral décor of a suburban living-room decorated with homely pictures, which does not always prepare reporters for the high quality of the food.

The menus are flexible, with set-price and à la carte options at both lunch and dinner. A set dinner, offered all evening, is reduced in price for those prepared to leave by 7.45pm. The repertoire is broad enough to encompass escabèche of mackerel, and caldo verde soup (with cabbage, sausage and garlic) as well as gnocchi, risotto, mutton steaks and rhubarb. Tuesdays are especially good for vegetarian dishes, Wednesdays for puddings and Thursdays for fish and shellfish. The fact that coffee, mineral water and service are included in the price receives unanimous praise. 'Incredible value for money,' said one reporter, who particularly enjoyed the coconut and aubergine loaf with hot red pepper sauce, and the pan-fried cod with saffron mashed potatoes. Another meal began with a basket of caramelised onions, followed by moist red mullet on a bed of potatoes and crisp vegetables, and finished with white chocolate parfait that was cut with a sharp lime syrup.

Service is friendly and unpretentious. The maximum wine mark-up is £10, which is particularly good news for those who buy the more expensive bottles, and the widely spread selection is generally as sound as the cooking. Highlights include an Australian Verdelho, and 'Rocca Rubia' (made from Carignan grapes in Sardinia). CELLARMAN'S CHOICE: Menetou-Salon 'Morogues' 1993, Henry Pellé, £13.90; Coteaux du Languedoc, Pic St-Loup 1992, Dom. L'Hortus, £13.70.

CHEF: Michael Hjort PROPRIETORS: Michael and Lucy Hjort OPEN: Tues to Sun L 12 to 2, Mon to Sat D 5.30 to 10 CLOSED: 3 weeks from 24 Dec, last week Aug MEALS: alc (main courses £9.50 to £17). Set L £13.90, Set D Mon to Sat before 7.45pm £13.90, Mon to Thur £19.50, Fri and Sat Gourmet menu £28.50 SERVICE: net prices, card slips closed CARDS: Access, Delta, Switch, Visa DETAILS: 44 seats. Private parties: 30 main room, 14 private room. Vegetarian meals. Children's helpings. No smoking in 1 dining-room. Wheelchair access (1 step). Music

▲ *Middlethorpe Hall*

N. YORKS 1996 NEWCOMER

NEW ENTRY

Bishopthorpe Road, York YO2 1QB — COOKING 3

TEL: (01904) 641241 FAX: (01904) 620176 — COST £20–£55

Middlethorpe is one country house that knows how to pile on the style. A short trot from the city centre, and adjacent to the racecourse, it is a beautifully restored William and Mary house with a walled garden, lavender walk and pleasant courtyard. The interiors have been decorated to a very high standard, and the enveloping hush that often deadens this sort of place is leavened a little by the unstarchy approach of the staff. Andrew Wood returned after a very uneven period in the kitchen, and a sigh of relief is heard. 'Whatever he is costing them,' opined a reporter, 'he is worth every penny.' The format is fixed-price, according to the number of dishes you want, with a dearer gourmet option and a full vegetarian menu. Recognisable country-house modes surface in dishes such as chicken terrine with spiced apple chutney, and codling meunière with creamed potato and ratatouille dressing. Inspectors who decided to go for the gourmet menu found the higher outlay more than justified in the quality of what they ate. Tortellini of crab and black pepper came with 'delicately sweet' sugar-snaps and a red pepper and ginger cream. Breast of duckling was coated in honey and five spices, cooked very rare, and accompanied by the crisply roasted leg, with an interesting garnish of tempura vegetables and a 'superb, delicious' reduction of cooking juices and red wine. Attention to detail does not flag at dessert stage. A hot plum soufflé is served with a sorbet of the plums in a chocolate cup, and a mille-feuille of poached pear arrives with well-rendered butterscotch parfait and a caramel sauce like 'sticky toffee pudding times a million'. Middlethorpe is back on track.

The classical wine list is full of gravitas and greatness. Clarets from the best vintages, burgundies from growers such as Lafarge, Michelot-Buisson and Sauzet, serious German wines and a fine spread from Australia and New Zealand exert a powerful pull. Prices, inevitably, strain in the opposite direction. None the less there are plenty of halves, and the selection of house French opens at £11.50. CELLARMAN'S CHOICE: Savennières 1990, Ch. de la Bizolière, £20; Malbec 1992, Bodega Norton, Argentina, £16.

CHEF: Andrew Wood PROPRIETOR: Historic House Hotels Ltd OPEN: all week 12.30 to 1.45, 7.30 to 9.45 MEALS: Set L £12.50, Set D £25.95 to £36.95 SERVICE: net prices, card slips closed CARDS: Access, Amex, Switch, Visa DETAILS: 50 seats. Private parties: 50 private room. Car park. Vegetarian meals. No children under 8. Jacket and tie. No smoking in dining-room. Wheelchair access. No music ACCOMMODATION: 30 rooms, all with bath/shower. TV. Phone. B&B £97 to £220. Deposit: 1 night's stay. Rooms for disabled. No children under 8. Afternoon teas. Garden (*The Which? Hotel Guide*)

19 Grape Lane $✻

19 Grape Lane, York YO1 2HU — COOKING 2
TEL: (01904) 636366 FAX: (01904) 702120 — COST £21–£42

Grape Lane is one of the little network of cobbled medieval thoroughfares that make up the centre of York, and a short trot from the Minster for those on the tourist circuit. The Alexanders run a comfortable bistro-style operation exactly in keeping with their surroundings. Michael Fraser's cooking is appreciated for the honesty of its intentions and its refusal to aim for needless elaboration. Both the lunchtime and evening *cartes* offer plenty of choice of a fairly rustic nature, as in broccoli and goats' cheese tart, baked cod topped with Cheddar and sauced with tomato, and wild boar sausages with mash. A visitor from Massachusetts admired the 'understated' blackcurrant vinaigrette with a starter of smoked pheasant, and approved of the rareness of medallions of hare with field mushrooms and madeira sauce. He was not sure about the grapes, though these now seem to be standard with hare. Chocolate, toffee and treacle may predominate on the pudding list when there isn't much fruit in season. The Stilton is judged 'first-rate'. A pleasing international jumble of wines is arranged by price, with most bottles below £20, and there is a very generous selection of halves. House Duboeuf is £8.95.

CHEF: Michael Fraser PROPRIETORS: Gordon and Carolyn Alexander OPEN: Tue to Sat 12 to 1.45, 6 to 9 (10 Sat) CLOSED: 25 to 27 Dec, 30 Jan to 19 Feb, last 2 weeks Sept MEALS: alc (main courses £6 to £14) SERVICE: not inc CARDS: Access, Visa DETAILS: 40 seats. Private parties: 12 main room, 22 private rooms. Vegetarian meals. Children welcome. No children under 8 D. Smart dress preferred. No smoking in 1 dining-room. Wheelchair access (1 step). Music

Scotland

ABERDEEN Grampian map 11

Courtyard on the Lane

1 Alford Lane, Aberdeen AB1 1YD COOKING 1*
TEL: (01224) 213795 FAX: (01224) 212961 COST £22–£44

When the Courtyard moved into town from Elrick in 1993, it cleverly hedged its bets with a bistro on the ground floor and a more serious restaurant upstairs. The bistro (Martha's Vineyard) is all hustle and bustle, with cheek-by-jowl eating from a blackboard menu with a transatlantic slant: smoked haddock chowder New England-style, or a schizophrenic-sounding bouillabaisse of chargrilled chicken breast Rhode Island-style. Upstairs is calmer, with quieter food, such as herb-crusted rack of lamb, or turbot with asparagus and gratin potatoes, as well as occasionally more direct and robust flavours – in a roast breast of pigeon on wild mushroom risotto, for example. The same vitality that pervades Mediterranean ideas is also a characteristic of Australian cooking, with which the kitchen feels some affinity, although there is no kangaroo on the menu as yet. Traditional crème brûlée, or caramelised apple tart with caramel sauce return the cooking to base. The up-to-date wine list crams in a variety of styles, a wide range of prices and a fair number of halves. House wines start with vin de pays at £11.

CHEFS: Tony Heath and Glen Lawson PROPRIETOR: Balgownie Restaurants Ltd OPEN: Tue to Sat 12 to 2.15, 6.30 to 9.45 CLOSED: 2 weeks mid-July MEALS: alc (main courses £7.50 to £15.50) SERVICE: not inc, card slips closed CARDS: Access, Amex, Delta, Switch, Visa DETAILS: 30 seats. Private parties: 30 main room. Children's helpings. Smart dress preferred. No cigars/pipes in dining-room. Music

Faraday's

2–4 Kirk Brae, Cults, Aberdeen AB1 9SQ
TEL/FAX: (01224) 869666 COOKING 1
on A93, 2m from city centre COST £18–£46

Restaurants are housed in a great variety of buildings, none more unusual than this converted hydro-electric station, which has somehow managed to acquire a minstrels' gallery and runs on candlepower. Lunch combines plain wholesome cooking, along the lines of steak casserole with doughballs, and bread-and-butter pudding, with salads and light dishes of pickled herring, all from a *carte*. Dinner, on the other hand, divides into two formats: three courses from

Monday to Thursday, five on Friday and Saturday when the white linen cloths and napkins are given an airing. The chef has to work a bit harder in the evening, turning out seafood tart, rabbit in white wine with chappit tatties and Jerusalem artichokes, and 'choc-o-block' with warm coffee sauce. Oriental flavours usually put in an appearance, from kofta curry to Chinese stir-fry, and scampi tails seem to be a fixture. The 40 wines are mostly French with a spread of styles and prices from demi-sec Vouvray to Ch. Margaux 1978. House wine is £12.90 a litre.

CHEFS: John Inches and Roger Ross PROPRIETOR: John Inches OPEN: Tue to Sat L 12 to 1.45, Mon to Sat D 7 to 9.45 CLOSED: 26 Dec to 6 Jan MEALS: alc L (main courses £4.50 to £6.50). Set D Mon to Thur £14.95, Fri and Sat £19.95 SERVICE: 10%, card slips closed CARDS: Access, Delta, Switch, Visa DETAILS: 40 seats. Private parties: 40 main room. Car park. Vegetarian meals. Children's helpings. Smart dress preferred. No smoking until 2 L, 10 D. Wheelchair access (also WC). Music. Air-conditioned

Silver Darling

Pocra Quay, North Pier, Aberdeen AB2 1DQ — COOKING 2
TEL: (01224) 576229 FAX: (01224) 626558 — COST £28–£47

The advice for those who have not been here before is to take a city map or an Aberdonian with you to find this quayside spot. Or look for the lighthouse at the harbour entrance; the restaurant is next to it, and feels a little like an old-fashioned schoolroom. 'Not surprisingly, in an establishment where a passing trawler could throw a herring through the front door, the menu is based on fish.' A herring is, of course, a silver darling to those who make a living from it, and it is a shame that no fisherman has thought fit to lob any herrings in Didier Dejean's direction: they don't feature in the repertoire. The kitchen concentrates instead on the swankier turbot, sea trout, sole and monkfish, variously grilled, poached, braised, but mostly barbecued, and partnered by rather more sophisticated sauces than barbecuing normally attracts – witness plum tomato and pesto compote, and wild mushroom and sorrel sauce.

One reporter was delighted with his choices that were 'brimming with cream and butter', happy with the generous but not gross portions, and with the 'gesture of accompanying vegetables'. Orkney oysters, crab mousse or a salad of scallops and prawns with blueberry vinegar provide an upbeat start, and puddings are taken as seriously as the rest. Finish with 'good and unlimited' coffee. The short wine list unsurprisingly majors on French whites, half-bottles are scarce and house wine is £9.50.

CHEF: Didier Dejean PROPRIETORS: Didier Dejean, Norman Faulks and Catherine Wood OPEN: Mon to Fri L 12 to 2, Mon to Sat D 7 to 10 CLOSED: 23 Dec to 6 Jan MEALS: alc D (main courses £15.50 to £17). Set L £15.80 (2 courses) to £17.50 SERVICE: not inc CARDS: Access, Amex, Diners, Switch, Visa DETAILS: 35 seats. Private parties: 35 main room. Children welcome. Smart dress preferred. Wheelchair access (1 step; also WC). Music

The 1997 Guide *will be published before Christmas 1996. Reports on meals are most welcome at any time of the year, but are particularly valuable in the spring (no later than June). Send them to* The Good Food Guide, *FREEPOST, 2 Marylebone Road, London NW1 1YN. No stamp is needed if posted in the UK.*

ABERFELDY Tayside map 11

▲ *Farleyer House*

by Aberfeldy PH15 2JE
TEL: (01887) 820332 FAX: (01887) 829430

COOKING 2*
COST £20–£48

There has been some alteration to Farleyer recently, with the addition of more bedrooms, a new kitchen and more places in which to eat and drink, not all of it complete as we go to press. Essentially, there are two eating options: the Menzies restaurant, and the Scottish bistro with its adjoining lounge – Pipers – for drinks, light snacks and live music.

The racing-green bistro conforms to type, making do without tablecloths and listing dishes on a blackboard: home-cured bresaola or gravad lax, grilled breast of duck or guinea-fowl, and strawberry and vanilla vacherin or chocolate marquise. An April visitor, knowledgeable about fish, had a 'memorable' dish of wild Tay salmon, 'steamed to perfection', while another enjoyed 'perfectly grilled rump steak'. Small medallions of dark, dense venison in a reduced red wine sauce were impressive too. 'Really good food at even better prices' was the conclusion.

The no-smoking Menzies restaurant works to a no-choice set-price dinner format of three or four courses: typically a centrepiece meat preceded by two fish courses and followed by either cheese or pudding. Lobster salad and pan-fried halibut with truffle sauce have been among the first options, while Tayside black-faced lamb with a basil and mustard sauce has been followed by orange and crêpe terrine or chocolate marquise. One couple dining in May began with a bonne bouche of guinea-fowl mousse wrapped in filo pastry, then enjoyed a green-pea soup with 'perfectly cooked scampi, just arrived that morning from the Isle of Skye', followed by 'exemplary' fillet of sea bass, and finished with a chilled lemon mousse with a caramelised topping. Service is cheerful. Wine prices are geared more towards a posh restaurant than a bistro, though there are drinkable bottles under £20, about 15 of which are available by the glass from £1.95.

CHEF: Richard Lyth PROPRIETORS: Farleyer House Hotel OPEN: restaurant all week D only 7.30 for 8 (one sitting); bistro all week 12 to 2.30, 6 to 9.30 CLOSED: restaurant Mon to Thur Nov to Apr MEALS: restaurant set D £27.50 to £32; bistro alc (main courses £6 to £17) SERVICE: not inc, card slips closed CARDS: Access, Amex, Diners, Switch, Visa DETAILS: restaurant 22 seats, bistro 56 seats. 26 tables outside bistro. Private parties: restaurant 34 main room, 25 private room, bistro 40 main room, 15 private room. Car park. Vegetarian meals bistro. Children's helpings. Smart dress preferred in restaurant. No smoking in restaurant; smoking permitted in bistro. Music ACCOMMODATION: 11 rooms, all with bath/shower. TV. Phone. D, B&B £95 to £190. Deposit: £85. Children welcome. Baby facilities. Pets by arrangement. Afternoon teas. Garden (*The Which? Hotel Guide*)

'White tablecloths, linen napkins, Villeroy and Boch plates, two candles in a brass sconce, and a large display of ivy and daffodils made the table a crowded place, and it was difficult to lean over without risking immolation on the candles or becoming entwined in the ivy.' (On eating in Wiltshire)

ABERFOYLE Central map 11

Braeval Old Mill

by Aberfoyle FK8 3UY
TEL: (01877) 382711 FAX: (01877) 382400 COOKING 4
on A81, 1 mile from Aberfoyle COST £28–£46

The mill seems tiny in view of its large reputation. Stone walls and a concrete slab floor feel pleasantly cool in summer, although a visitor in winter longed for more brightly coloured fabrics to look at between courses, to take his mind off the snow outside. Staff make up for any perceived lack of warmth, however, in amiability and attentiveness. The menu is recited, but doesn't tax the brain too much because there is no choice for the first three courses.

The no-choice meal is a simple trade-off, from which we hope to benefit by having the chef's undivided attention focused on one dish at a time. The downside is that some excitement may be lost: what chef is going to risk putting on unusual dishes with exotic flavours under those circumstances? But Nick Nairn manages to breathe life and interest into the food, in soups of artichoke with seared scallops, or watercress and potato with duck confit, for example, and in second courses of crab and Parmesan soufflé, or baked fillet of halibut with coriander and pickled ginger butter sauce. And there is nothing apologetic about an avocado salsa and a sauce of chilli, mint and lime to accompany a roast salmon main course. As to the quality, 'Nick Nairn is on top form,' writes a regular. It was the 'best meal in Scotland' for another who travels and knows his Onions. Textures are carefully judged too, as in roast salmon, crisp on the outside, barely cooked in the middle, on a bed of roasted vegetables and mussels. Puddings are perhaps less subject to change than the rest of the repertoire, and are likely to include chocolate soufflé pudding with chocolate sauce and cinnamon ice-cream, or armagnac ice-cream with prunes and a delicate Earl Grey sauce.

Wines are carefully chosen across the board, and make up in quality what they may lack in extent. There are no passengers on the list, just plenty of high-quality drinking at all levels, a generous choice of half-bottles, and a helpful house selection of a dozen wines under £16. CELLARMAN'S CHOICE: Pommard 1991, Boillot, £28.50; Henschke Semillon/Chardonnay 92, Tilly's Vineyard, S. Australia, £14.50.

CHEF: Nick Nairn PROPRIETORS: Nick and Fiona Nairn OPEN: Sun L 12.30 to 1.30, Tue to Sat D 7.30 to 9.30 CLOSED: 1 week Oct/Nov, 1 week Feb, 1 week June MEALS: Set L Sun £18.95, Set D £28.50 SERVICE: not inc, card slips closed CARDS: Access, Switch, Visa DETAILS: 34 seats. Private parties: 30 main room. Car park. No children under 10. Smart dress preferred. No cigars/pipes in dining-room; no smoking while others eat. Wheelchair access (1 step; also WC). No music

Prices quoted in the Guide *are based on information supplied by restaurateurs. The prices quoted at the top of each entry represent a range, from the lowest meal price to the highest; the latter is inflated by 20 per cent to take account of likely price rises during the year of the* Guide.

ACHILTIBUIE Highland map 11

▲ *Summer Isles Hotel*

Achiltibuie IV26 2YG
TEL: (01854) 622282 FAX: (01854) 622251 COOKING **2**
off A835 at Drumrunie, 10m N of Ullapool COST £38–£45

The hotel is one of the west coast's more remote outposts, in a village at the end of a long and winding road. People come to get away from everything except birds, the sea, moorland, sunsets and good food and drink. The Irvines (father Robert, then son Mark and wife Geraldine) have together clocked up a quarter of a century in the *Guide*, and they run 'a hotel of individual distinction' that struck one reporter, despite its isolation, as 'slightly Home Counties in feel'. It is simple yet comfortable and well run. The heart of its culinary success lies in the combination of fish and shellfish from up and down the coast, and in-house production of bread, marmalade, cheese biscuits and so on. Dinner begins at 8pm with soup the first of five courses – oxtail with madeira, perhaps, or minted pea and lettuce – with a loaf of oatmeal, or olive and buckwheat.

If the main course is fish, the intermediate one will be meat – a mousse of chicken livers with chutney and brioche toast, for example, or carpaccio of Aberdeen Angus beef with a horseradish relish – and vice versa. Treatments are commendably straightforward. Summer Isles prawns and spiny lobsters are served with hollandaise sauce and lemon, roast haunch of roe deer comes with creamed parsnips and port gravy, while roast leg of black-faced lamb is studded with garlic and served with capers and Savoy cabbage.

Then come the trolleys: Mark Irvine pushing cheese with the zeal of a knowledgeable enthusiast, Geraldine at the wheel of a pudding-mobile that might include steamed spiced fig pudding with custard, tangy lemon flan, or cranberry and apple suet pudding, as well as ice-creams, cheesecakes, tarts and pavlovas. Time spent flicking through the wine list (orders are expected by 7pm) is well spent. Classic Bordeaux and burgundy dominate, but the rest of France is very well treated and the New World is perfectly sound. Half-bottles are plentiful, and house wines are around £11, with extra ones by the glass to accompany particular first courses. CELLARMAN'S CHOICE: Sauvignon Blanc 1994, Scott, New Zealand, £16.50; Pinotage 1991, Viterwyk, Stellenbosch, S. Africa, £14.

CHEF: Chris Firth-Bernard PROPRIETORS: Mark and Geraldine Irvine OPEN: all week D only 8 (one sitting) CLOSED: 10 Oct to Easter MEALS: Set D £33 SERVICE: net prices DETAILS: 26 seats. Private parties: 12 main room. Car park. Children's helpings. No children under 5. No smoking in dining-room. No music ACCOMMODATION: 12 rooms, all with bath/shower. Phone. B&B £44.50 to £95. Deposit: £50. Children welcome (high tea served 5.30pm). Baby facilities. Pets welcome in bedrooms only. Fishing (*The Which? Hotel Guide*)

indicates that smoking is either banned altogether or that a dining-room is maintained for non-smokers. The symbol does not apply to restaurants that simply have no-smoking areas.

ALEXANDRIA Strathclyde map 11

▲ *Cameron House Hotel, Georgian Room*

Loch Lomond, Alexandria G83 8QZ
TEL: (01389) 755565 FAX: (01389) 759522
off A82, ½m N of Balloch roundabout, ½m N of Dumbarton

COOKING 3
COST £22–£61

This Loch Lomond-side hotel has bagged a mile-long stretch of bonny bank for itself and its leisure pursuits. It started life in the fifteenth century as a stone keep, has been variously modified and added to as the centuries have passed, survived the requisite major fire in Victorian times, and now emerges triumphant with golf course, marina and highly ambitious kitchen.

Jeff Bland's cooking is supremely confident: everything, including the home-made breads, which may feature mustard and black peppercorn loaves, aims to impress. The elaborately written *carte* is accompanied by a set-price 'Market Menu' of four courses plus coffee; only the second course offers no choice, but it is always something more involved than soup or sorbet. An inspector's first course of saffron-dressed langoustines with warm Parma ham and pine-kernels showed a nerveless approach to combinations. Quantity in the second course may seem a little daunting immediately before the main business, but the technique of a feuilleté involving 'crisp light pastry, succulent chicken and tender leeks' with a tarragon sauce could not be faulted. The complexity stakes are raised in main courses such as guinea-fowl with lentils served with a ballottine made from the leg meat and a rich port sauce. Casseroles of mixed seafood, generally perfumed with saffron, are a favoured presentation, while on the *carte* a brace of quail stuffed with foie gras, apple and chestnuts is partnered with stir-fried cabbage and pimentos and a chive butter sauce.

Inventiveness permeates puddings too: malt whisky bavarois with a praline sauce demonstrated 'real artistry and flair'. From the à la carte menu a tart of chocolate, almond, apple and pistachio is served warm with a madeira sabayon, while orange spikes the dark chocolate sauce that goes into a hot raspberry soufflé. All the dishes are served with a will by 'attentive and efficient' staff, who do not accept the indignity of gratuities. There are some very fine wines on the carefully chosen list, but prices within each section rocket quickly, restricting choice. If the budget is tight, Dom. Talmard's Mâcon-Uchizy, Ch. Sénéjac Haut-Médoc or Saintsbury Pinot Noir from California should well suffice. Vins de pays from the Vaucluse set the ball rolling at £11.65.

CHEF: Jeff Bland PROPRIETOR: Craigendarroch Group OPEN: Mon to Fri L 12.30 to 2, all week D 7 to 10 MEALS: alc (main courses £19 to £20). Set L £13.95 (2 courses) to £16.50, Set D £32.50 to £38.50 SERVICE: none, card slips closed CARDS: Access, Amex, Delta, Diners, Switch, Visa DETAILS: 44 seats. Private parties: 58 main room, 60 private rooms. Car park. Vegetarian meals. Children's helpings. Smart dress preferred. No smoking in dining-room. Wheelchair access (also WC). Music ACCOMMODATION: 68 rooms, all with bath/shower. TV. Phone. B&B £125 to £190. Deposit: £50. Rooms for disabled. Children welcome. Baby facilities. Afternoon teas. Garden. Swimming-pool. Fishing

ALYTH Tayside map 11

▲ *Drumnacree House*

St Ninians Road, Alyth PH11 8AP
TEL/FAX: (01828) 632194
off A926, Blairgowrie to Kirriemuir road

COOKING 2
COST £26–£34

The small country-house hotel, set in one and a half acres, is relaxed and informal in both feel and in its approach to cooking. Allan Cull is not one to let schools and styles restrict his free-ranging ideas: the temptation of Scandinavian gravad lax, Chinese-spiced confit of duck leg, and Cajun gumbos is too much. According to the menu, blackened dishes served with 'dirty rice' are 'not for delicate palates'. At the same time a British thread runs through in the form of devilled lambs' kidneys on toast, poached fillet of Tay salmon, or best end of lamb with a leek tart and a herb sauce.

All this provides variety for guests who stay a few days, and whose likes and dislikes are soon sussed out by the Culls. More than that, however, the kitchen follows the seasons and uses local produce to good effect. A warm salad of pigeon breast is as likely in spring as is roast grouse in autumn, and wild mushrooms, including chanterelles, ceps and blewits, which are plentiful round about, appear in soups or risotto, as an accompaniment to venison, or preserved in oil and served with a selection of cold cooked meats. A standard list of three dozen largely French wines includes house French and German at £9, or £1.60 a glass.

CHEF: Allan Cull PROPRIETORS: Allan and Eleanor Cull OPEN: Tue to Sat D only (all week for residents) 7 to 9.30 CLOSED: 15 Dec to 31 Mar MEALS: Set D £18.50. Minimum £19.50 SERVICE: not inc CARDS: Access, Visa DETAILS: 50 seats. Private parties: 50 main room, 12 and 30 private rooms. Car park. Children's helpings. Smart dress preferred. No smoking in dining-room. Wheelchair access (also WC). Music ACCOMMODATION: 6 rooms, all with bath/shower. TV. B&B £35 to £65. Deposit: £20. Children welcome. Pets welcome in bedrooms only. Garden

ANSTRUTHER Fife map 11

Cellar

24 East Green, Anstruther KY10 3AA
TEL: (01333) 310378 FAX: (01333) 312544

COOKING 3*
COST £22–£57

The Cellar occupies the site of a former smokehouse in this once-busy fishing village. 'The décor is a bit plain, but who cares?' asks one reporter. Attention is concentrated on the food, which makes a virtue of locally sourced fish and shellfish. Flavours are usually on course, thanks to ultra-fresh supplies and the confidence of the kitchen in letting them make their own splash on the plate. There are, for example, no fish mousses, which would take the ingredients too far from their origins. Instead, there are grills and roasts, with perhaps a marinade for the tuna beforehand, and equally direct treatment for shellfish – crab is served simply dressed and cold, lobster is boiled – while saucing is along the lines of flavoured butter or hollandaise. Exceptions to this might be a trio of

Shetland salmon – hot smoked, cold smoked, and gravlax – or an omelette along the lines of Arnold Bennett, filled with creamy smoked haddock.

The style doesn't change, and with good reason. Plainly served fresh fish is universal and eternal. A fillet of Perthshire beef with wild mushrooms and Dijon sauce is consolation for non-fish-eaters, and meals might end with terrine of chocolate or a vanilla ice-cream floating in a butterscotch sauce. 'The value for money is excellent,' writes a regular. 'I keep going back.' Peter Jukes describes the operation as 'relaxed but correct', a view that finds sympathy and support. Although red wines are not neglected, whites understandably have the edge. This is a list full of interest and class, with good showings in Alsace and Burgundy, and with more whites from Bordeaux and New Zealand on the way. A decent spread of vintages, impeccable producers and fair mark-ups add to the appeal. House white is £12.50. CELLARMAN'S CHOICE: Mâcon Uchizy 1992, Dom. Talmard £16.50.

CHEF/PROPRIETOR: Peter Jukes OPEN: Tue to Sat 12.30 to 1.30, 7.30 to 9 CLOSED: Christmas, New Year MEALS: alc L (main courses £6.50 to £10.50). Set D £20 (2 courses) to £30 SERVICE: not inc, card slips closed CARDS: Access, Amex, Delta, Switch, Visa DETAILS: 32 seats. Private parties: 36 main room. No children under 8. Smart dress preferred. No smoking in dining-room. Music

ARISAIG Highland map 11

▲ *Arisaig House*

Beasdale, by Arisaig PH39 4NR
TEL: (01687) 450622 FAX: (01687) 450626 COOKING **2***
on A830, 3m E of Arisaig village COST £27–£47

The granite house on the road to the isles is set in 20 acres of gardens, with rhododendrons, roses and giant sequoia trees; the gardens are a delight to walk around, as well as a source of fruit and vegetables for the kitchen. Inside is a splendid oak staircase, a formal drawing-room, a jauntier bar and a spacious dining-room with tall windows giving on to the lawns. Lunch is a relatively light affair of sandwiches, Loch Moidart mussels or grilled fish of the day.

Dinner is where the kitchen swings into a four-course trot, along the lines of warm salad of pigeon breast, creamy-textured watercress soup, rack of lamb with chanterelles, and a sablé of strawberries. Neither repertoire nor choice is extravagant, and the cooking is generally as straightforward as cheese soufflé or marinated venison with Puy lentils. Dishes rarely get more exotic than poached breast of corn-fed chicken with tarragon quenelles, or quick-fried scallops with soy sauce, but they are all cooked ably and accurately. Sticky toffee pudding and crème brûlée are likely desserts. Service is friendly and efficient. Wines are a conservative and high-class collection almost entirely from France (nothing at all from the New World), with prices not for the budget-conscious. House wine is £14.50.

CHEF: David Wilkinson PROPRIETORS: Ruth, John and Andrew Smither OPEN: all week 12.30 to 2, 7.30 to 8.30 CLOSED: 31 Oct to 31 Mar MEALS: alc L (main courses £7 to £12). Set D £29.50 SERVICE: none, card slips closed CARDS: Access, Amex, Switch, Visa DETAILS: 36 seats. 5 tables outside. Private parties: 10 main room. Car park. No children under 10. Smart dress preferred. No smoking in dining-room. Wheelchair access (1 step). No music ACCOMMODATION: 14 rooms, all with bath/shower. TV. Phone. B&B £65 to £210. Deposit: £50. No children under 10. Afternoon teas. Garden (*The Which? Hotel Guide*)

AUCHENCAIRN Dumfries & Galloway map 11

▲ *Collin House*

Auchencairn, Castle Douglas DG7 1QN
TEL: (01556) 640292 FAX: (01556) 640276
off A711, 1m E of Auchencairn

COOKING 2
COST £36–£44

'Delightfully situated and peaceful', Collin House dates from around 1750. Stone-built and painted pale pink, in some 20 acres of grounds, the property looks across the Solway Firth to Cumbria. The domestic scale appeals, as does the simplicity, directness and freshness of the food. John Wood draws heavily on local produce, from scallops and crabs to Galloway beef, but flies south for ideas such as risotto with smoked venison and ceps, or fillet of Scottish lamb with a caper and olive-scented juice. Five-course dinners are the form, and the pattern is a choice between two first and two main courses, with a soup in between – mussel and saffron, perhaps, or tomato and mint – followed by a choice of three or four puddings and cheese.

All this is a manageable size for the kitchen, and perfectly satisfactory for diners, one of whom enjoyed a meal of smoked salmon parcels with scallops, then red pepper soup, followed by turbot with sorrel sauce, and 'a boozy ice-cream' to finish. The pudding list might include bread-and-butter, mango fool, or chocolate parfait. Service normally goes without a hitch, although one reporter found that the advertised time for ordering and eating didn't allow much leeway: 'a little less drill might help relaxation.' The fairly priced list of wines covers a good variety of styles without amassing a bewildering number of bins, and encourages experiment. Four house wines are from £6.75 a bottle, and are available by the glass from £1.75.

CHEF: John Wood PROPRIETORS: Pam Hall and John Wood OPEN: all week D only 7.30 for 8 CLOSED: Jan to Mar MEALS: Set D £28 SERVICE: not inc, card slips closed CARDS: Access, Visa DETAILS: 24 seats. Private parties: 24 main room. Car park. No children under 11 D. Smart dress preferred. No smoking in dining-room. No music ACCOMMODATION: 6 rooms, all with bath/shower. TV. Phone. B&B £42 to £84. Deposit: 20%. Children's high teas. Pets welcome by arrangement. Garden (*The Which? Hotel Guide*)

The Guide *office can quickly spot when a restaurateur is encouraging customers to write recommending inclusion – and sadly, several restaurants have been doing this in 1995. Such reports do not further a restaurant's cause. Please tell us if a restaurateur invites you to write to the* Guide.

AUCHMITHIE Tayside map 11

But 'n' Ben £

Auchmithie DD11 5SQ
TEL: (01241) 877223 COOKING 1
on coast, 3m NE of Arbroath, off A92 COST £12–£30

Auchmithie is an old fishing village perched on a rugged stretch of hilltop, three miles from Arbroath. Both places have a stake in the 'smokie' industry, past and present. 'You can't miss the But 'n' Ben. There is only one road into and out of the village.' It is a small, family-run restaurant occupying two old fishermen's cottages knocked into one, cosy enough in winter when just the locals eat here, but big enough to cope with a summer influx of visitors.

The foundation is traditional cooking and baking, with an emphasis on fish and shellfish, and on good value. It is 'a firm family favourite' for one reporter, whose party one lunch-time enjoyed smokie and potato soup ('I would call this Cullen Skink'), bacon and egg pie ('I would call this a quiche'), a dish of 'about 30 mussels in a fine liquor', lobster salad, and scallops with bacon. Arbroath smokies might appear just hot and buttered or in a pancake, alongside big local prawns or fried haddock in oatmeal. Availability varies with the season. High tea is presumably for those who missed lunch or can't wait for the slightly more substantial dinner. All meals offer meaty alternatives, from haggis with tatties and neeps or peppered liver with tomato sauce, to game pie or grilled steak. Service is as homely as the food, and the wine list is brief, with house French at £7.50.

CHEFS: Margaret and Angus Horn PROPRIETORS: Margaret, Iain and Angus Horn OPEN: Wed to Mon L 12 to 2.30, and high tea 4 to 5.30, Mon and Wed to Sat D 7 to 9.30 MEALS: alc (main courses £4.50 to £11) SERVICE: not inc, card slips closed CARDS: Access, Switch, Visa DETAILS: 36 seats. Private parties: 40 main room. Vegetarian meals. Children's helpings. No smoking in dining-room. Wheelchair access (also WC). No music

AUCHTERARDER Tayside map 11

▲ *Auchterarder House* NEW ENTRY

Auchterarder PH3 1DZ COOKING 2
TEL: (01764) 663646 FAX: (01764) 662939 COST £23–£74

Described by the owners as 'a magnificent Victorian mansion', the house pre-dates the accession of Victoria by about five years or so but does have all the grandeur of the Victorian age. A long drive through fine rhododendrons and finer trees leads to an imposing entrance with a huge stone porch and giant bell-pull. This produces an instant response from one of the staff, whose pride in the place shows. 'Housekeeping is superb.' 'You could build a ship out of the library doors', while massive sculpted wooden ceilings glower some 30 feet above the heads of diners. Relief comes from bright contemporary paintings, cheerful fires and Mrs Brown's impressive flower arrangements.

Lunch is three courses, with two choices for each, and might produce tomato and mint soup, saddle of Perthshire lamb stuffed with garlic and herbs, and lemon tart with a dill and lemon sorbet. At dinner two menus are offered: a three-course 'taste of Auchterarder House' with no choice (for £27.50), and another of three, four or five courses for £37.50, £45 and £50 respectively. It costs £5 to swap any dish between the two menus. Scottish produce features – Shetland salmon, or a generous fillet of Aberdeen Angus served with bone-marrow and oatmeal – and butter and alcohol account for much of the saucing. Dishes such as artichoke soufflé with curried sabayon, or scallops with a smoked haddock mousseline bring welcome variety. 'Conventional but excellent' sweets have included dark and light chocolate bavarois with a coffee-bean sauce, and a timbale of steamed chocolate pudding. Claret forms the backbone of the rather traditional but appealing wine list, vintages are varied, prices on the whole are fair, and there is plenty of interest under £20, even though it is a minority interest. Wine by the glass 'depends on what is available on that day'. CELLARMAN'S CHOICE: St-Aubin premier cru 1992, Thomas, £26; St-Julien, Les Fiefs de Lagrange 1990, £21.50.

CHEF: Kieran Darnell PROPRIETORS: Mr and Mrs Ian Brown OPEN: all week 12 to 3, 6 to 9.30 MEALS: Set L £15 to £18.50, Set D £27.50 to £50 SERVICE: not inc, card slips closed CARDS: Access, Amex, Diners, Switch, Visa DETAILS: 30 seats. Private parties: 23 main room, 20 private rooms. Car park. No children under 10. Jacket and tie. No smoking in dining-room. Wheelchair access (3 steps). No music ACCOMMODATION: 15 rooms, all with bath/shower. TV. Phone. B&B £70 to £195. Rooms for disabled. Children by arrangement. Pets welcome in bedrooms only. Afternoon teas. Garden (*The Which? Hotel Guide*)

BALLATER Grampian map 11

▲ *Balgonie Country House*

NEW ENTRY

Braemar Place, Ballater AB35 5RQ — COOKING 2
TEL/FAX: (01339) 755482 — COST £25–£47

'I have spent 20 years searching for somewhere to stay on Deeside for my annual fishing trip, and this new hotel is a real gem.' Its appeal to fishermen may have something to do with the fact that 'rooms are named after individual salmon pools on the Dee'. Technically one might query the country-house designation since the hotel is within the Ballater town boundary, but it certainly qualifies in terms of large grounds and the view of sweeping lawns, towering beeches and beyond to the hills of Glen Muick, with not another house in sight. The beautifully maintained Edwardian house is uncluttered, and 'John and Priscilla Finnie make you welcome, warmly but without fuss'. 'Witty and primitive pictures' decorate the light, white, spacious dining-room.

Dinners are four courses, with no choice at the second and three or four options otherwise. A summer meal for two began with venison and pork terrine, and marinated salmon and smoked monkfish, before a 'simple but good filo packet of smoked haddock with cream'. David Hindmarch has experience of royal kitchens, including Balmoral down the road, and so must be no stranger to Aberdeen Angus beef, or to game birds such as roast woodpigeon, served traditionally in a red wine and game jus with spring cabbage and smoked bacon. Scottish cheeses in good condition offer an alternative to warm blackcurrant and apple tart, or steamed chocolate pudding. 'The service must have been good as we scarcely noticed it.' The wine list has the same forthright appearance as the rest of the establishment: not overpriced and with a fair representation from the New World. House wine is £13.

CHEF: David J. Hindmarch PROPRIETORS: John and Priscilla Finnie OPEN: all week 12.30 to 2, 7 to 9 (booking essential) CLOSED: mid-Jan to mid-Feb MEALS: Set L £16.50, Set D £27.50 SERVICE: not included, card slips closed CARDS: Access, Amex, Delta, Switch, Visa DETAILS: 25 seats. Private parties: 30 main room. Car park. Children's helpings. No children under 7. Jacket and tie. No smoking in dining-room. No music ACCOMMODATION: 9 rooms, all with bath/shower. TV. Phone. B&B £47.50 to £50. Children welcome. Baby facilities. Dogs welcome in bedrooms only and if attended. Afternoon teas; high teas available for young children. Garden (*The Which? Hotel Guide*)

▲ *Darroch Learg*

Braemar Road, Ballater AB35 5UX
TEL: (01339) 755443 FAX: (01339) 755252 NEW CHEF
on A93, ½m W of town centre COST £18–£43

Perched on a thickly wooded hillside overlooking Ballater, Darroch Learg is a Victorian country residence that became a hotel just after the war. The best way of viewing the surrounding countryside may be to take to the hang-glider, if you have time between riding your mountain bike, shooting clay pigeons and trekking on your pony. There's plenty to do.

On a summer's evening, the conservatory that forms the dining-room is a pleasant place in which to eat, though as we go to press we learn that Robert MacPherson is leaving and a successor has not yet been appointed. If the previous style is anything to go by, the new incumbent will be catering for healthy appetites, and will have anything from smoked salmon to oxtail, saddle of roe deer, rabbit and pigeon to call on. Service meanwhile has been warm and welcoming enough, and the wine list does a brisk canter through the French regions before venturing out into the big wide world. The selections are brief and adequate to the task, and prices are generous to a fault. House vin de pays d'Oc is £11 for Chardonnay and £11.50 for Merlot.

PROPRIETORS: the Franks family OPEN: Sun L 12.30 to 2, all week D 7 to 8.30 (9 Sat) CLOSED: Jan MEALS: Set L Sun £11.75, Set D £21.75 SERVICE: net prices, card slips closed CARDS: Access, Amex, Diners, Visa DETAILS: 48 seats. Private parties: 48 main room. Car park. Children's helpings. Smart dress preferred. No smoking in dining-room. No music ACCOMMODATION: 20 rooms, all with bath/shower. TV. Phone. B&B £40 to £100. Deposit: £40. Children welcome. Baby facilities. Pets welcome. Afternoon teas. Garden

▲ *Green Inn*

9 Victoria Road, Ballater AB35 5QQ COOKING 2*
TEL/FAX: (01339) 755701 COST £18–£41

The two-storey granite building, formerly a temperance hotel, overlooks the village green and parish church. Wall mirrors and a general redecoration have brightened the feel of the restaurant, and the effect is comfortable but not formal. The food is at times so proudly Scottish that you may need a Gaelic phrase-book to find out what syboes, bridies or clapshot are, and to decipher howtowdie wi' drappit eggs. Cheeses have never been south of the border either, and a selection of six is normally served from a list that includes Lochaber smoked, Brodick Blue (made from ewes' milk) and full-fat St Andrews. At the same time, though, Jeff Purves is not above incorporating such items as barley risotto and onion marmalade (served with lamb), grilled polenta with a ragoût of Mediterranean vegetables, and a rich Sauternes and foie gras sauce to accompany underdone fillet of Aberdeen Angus beef. The style is a personal interpretation of Scottish food, generally with common sense on its side.

Game is as easy to come by here as anywhere in the British Isles, and fish is abundant too. Braised haunch of venison comes with a red wine and mushroom sauce, and baked salmon is served equally simply on a bed of creamed leeks. Main courses arrive with appropriate vegetables already on the plate: saffron potatoes and a timbale of courgette and cucumber with the salmon, for example, or rösti potatoes and a stir-fry of vegetables with peppered duck. Prune and armagnac tart, and chocolate flan are among the puddings. Service is friendly and efficient, and wines are perfectly adequate for the job, including house French at £9.95.

CHEF: Jeff Purves PROPRIETORS: Carol and Jeff Purves OPEN: Sun L 12.30 to 2, all week D 6 to 9 CLOSED: 2 weeks Dec, Sun Nov to Mar MEALS: alc (main courses £13 to £15). Set L Sun £8.25 (2 courses) to £10.25 SERVICE: not inc CARDS: Access, Amex, Visa DETAILS: 32 seats. Private parties: 32 main room. Vegetarian meals. Children's helpings. Smart dress preferred. Wheelchair access (also WC). Music. Air-conditioned ACCOMMODATION: 3 rooms, all with bath/shower. TV. D, B&B £51.50 to £90. Deposit: 10%. Children welcome. Baby facilities. Pets welcome. Garden

▲ *Tullich Lodge*

Ballater AB35 5SB
TEL: (01339) 755406 FAX: (01339) 755397 COOKING 2
off A93, 1½m E of Ballater COST £32–£39

This is not a typical country-house hotel. 'The Lodge has human, talkative staff, but not scripted service,' writes Neil Bannister, and the only reason it is not listed among the *Guide*'s longest-serving restaurants is that it missed two years, one of them when Neil Bannister was seriously ill: 'I think they thought I'd gone.' Other than that, it has appeared annually since 1973, a good record by any standards. The 1975 edition avers that 'they keep prices low by offering little choice but a good balance in their meals', a strategy that remains in force. The turreted house is of pink granite, the bar a collectors' corner of tools and bottles of all kinds, while the mahogany-panelled dining-room is the setting for dinner.

Take any menu at random and the balance is apparent. One evening it was Finnan haddock, followed by watercress soup, then roast rib of Highland beef, and a choice between raspberry frangipane or Scottish cheeses. A week before it had been pigeon breast with kidney beans, then beef broth, crisp-skinned cod, and either bread-and-butter pudding or Scottish cheeses, the last a fixture. Despite the fact that a no-choice menu has to have wide appeal, the food does not shirk its obligation to be tasty and distinctive. Among the offerings have been mountain hare on a warm salad, smoked eel, pike dumplings, lamb hotpot, seared scallops and poached halibut, while Shetland lamb with a barley risotto indicates not only that provenance matters, but also that the kitchen is able to incorporate a few ideas along the way. The 40 wines, plus bin-ends and 20 half-bottles, are mostly French, with house Bordeaux at £9, and there is a good choice of malt whiskies.

CHEF: Neil Bannister PROPRIETORS: Hector Macdonald and Neil Bannister OPEN: all week D only 7.30 to 9 CLOSED: end Oct to end Mar MEALS: Set D £25; bar L available SERVICE: not inc, card slips closed CARDS: Access, Amex, Delta, Diners, Switch, Visa DETAILS: 25 seats. Private parties: 20 main room. Car park. Children's helpings D. Jacket and tie. No smoking in dining-room. Wheelchair access (2 steps). No music ACCOMMODATION: 10 rooms, all with bath/shower. TV on request. Phone. B&B £95 to £200. Children welcome. Baby facilities. Pets welcome in bedrooms only. Garden (*The Which? Hotel Guide*)

BLAIRGOWRIE Tayside map 11

▲ *Kinloch House*

by Blairgowrie PH10 6SG
TEL: (01250) 884237 FAX: (01250) 884333 COOKING 2
on A923, 3m W of Blairgowrie towards Dunkeld COST £20–£48

The setting is beautiful, with views south over Loch Marlee to the Sidlaw Hills. Comfortable rooms, friendly staff and good breakfasts bring people back for more. The Shentalls make good management look easy, and their unobtrusive professionalism accounts for the way everything fits seamlessly together. An 'airy, unsmoky and un-Muzaked bar' leads to a panelled dining-room with well-spaced tables. 'Good ingredients uncluttered by coulis clichés and strawberry garnishing' is how the food struck one reporter. A generous choice is offered through a combination of a set-price menu with supplements, and a daily-changing Scottish menu that might include potted hough (beef), parten bree (a thick crab soup), fillet of rabbit with mustard dough balls, and Atholl brose. All items on the Scottish menu are interchangeable with those on the main menu. Exotic touches (such as a starter of bananas coated in breadcrumbs, wrapped in bacon and topped with curried mayonnaise) are kept to a minimum, and the main business revolves around outstandingly fresh fish, including Kyle of Lochalsh scallops, and salmon in all its guises, as well as Aberdeen Angus beef and venison, grouse, pheasant, partridge and woodcock in season. Vegetables are varied, colourful and properly cooked. An 'awe-inspiring' sweets trolley is trundled round with immense meringues, crème brûlée, fruit salad and many more, after which 'it would take a hero to pronounce on the fudge and truffles' served with coffee. The malts (nearly 150) are served in a silver-plated quaich. The long wine list is strongest on France, with a good spread of claret vintages in particular, is not greedy when it comes to prices, and has a fair choice of half-bottles. A dozen house wines range from £10.90 to £17.90.

CHEF: Bill McNicoll PROPRIETORS: David and Sarah Shentall OPEN: all week 12.30 to 2, 7 to 9.15 MEALS: Set L £14.75, Set D £27.90 SERVICE: none, card slips closed CARDS: Access, Amex, Delta, Diners, Switch, Visa DETAILS: 55 seats. Private parties: 12 main room, 25 private room. Car park. Children welcome. No children under 7 at D. Jacket and tie. No smoking in dining-room. Wheelchair access (also WC). No music ACCOMMODATION: 21 rooms, all with bath/shower. TV. Phone. D,B&B £79.50 to £195. Rooms for disabled. Children welcome. Baby facilities. Pets welcome in bedrooms only. Afternoon teas. Garden. Fishing (*The Which? Hotel Guide*)

CAIRNDOW Strathclyde map 11

Loch Fyne Oyster Bar

Clachan Farm, Cairndow PA26 8BH
TEL: (01499) 600236 FAX: (01499) 600234 COOKING 1
on A83, at head of Loch Fyne COST £23–£49

The building is an old cattle byre on the shores of the loch, simply converted, with tables and alcoves made from home-grown larch and Scots pine. Food is served throughout the day, with no set pattern of eating. 'You are welcome to select any dish or selection of dishes from the menu and in whatever order you choose,' says the menu. The flexibility pleases readers enormously, as does the relaxed and pleasant service. A basket of bread arrives with the menu, which is a large sheet of paper with food listed on one side and drinks on the other. An asterisk picks out the lighter dishes and starters – shellfish soup or smoked eel and horseradish are typical – and a few daily specials are chalked on a board. 'There was a stamp of confidence about the simply served food, and no wonder – it was so fresh.' That goes for oysters especially: 'it's the only way to eat them, straight out of the water.' As one reporter put it: 'One does not go to the Loch Fyne Oyster Bar for the cooking, one goes for the ingredients.' This perceptive reporter – who, by the way, is all of 16 years old – continues: 'What they do, they do well, and most of what they do, they do very, very simply', a conclusion with which older reporters and inspectors absolutely concur. A trio of gravlax, for example, cold-smoked salmon and hot-smoked Bradan Rost was 'moist and flavoursome', and four different types of pickled herring were 'superb'. The couple of dozen wines are reasonably priced, with about a quarter of them available by the glass from £2.45, and house Gros Plant is £9.95.

CHEF: Morag Keith PROPRIETORS: Andrew Lane and John Noble OPEN: all week 9am to 9pm (6pm Mon to Thur 1 Oct to end Mar) CLOSED: 25 Dec and 1 Jan MEALS: alc (main courses £5 to £16) SERVICE: not inc CARDS: Access, Delta, Switch, Visa DETAILS: 80 seats. 6 tables outside. Private parties: 40 main room. Car park. Vegetarian meals. Children's helpings. No smoking in 1 dining-room. Wheelchair access (also WC). Music

CANONBIE Dumfries & Galloway map 11

▲ *Riverside Inn*

Canonbie DG14 0UX
TEL: (01387) 371295 and 371512 COOKING 2
off A47, 12m from M6, just over the border COST £29–£35

Canonbie is just a wee hop over the border, a little off the Carlisle to Edinburgh road that now gratifyingly bypasses the village. This handsome black and white inn stands near a bridge over the River Esk: a resort for the weary traveller, the serious gastronome and the wine-lover alike. Homeliness pervades the décor, from the sewing-machine tables in the bar to the plunger-like copper utensils on the dining-room hearth, and the cooking.

First-class ingredients are bought from a plethora of local suppliers, old books are raided for atavistic recipes, and bread is a particular pride. This year's boast is of the mastery of hot-water pastry for 'wonderful pork pies, etc.'. In the lounge bar a blackboard menu announces individually priced soups, pâtés, casseroles and chargrilled dishes with 'fat chips and salad'. A set-price menu of five courses plus coffee offers exemplary value in the dining-room, where a starter might be tomatoes stuffed with a cheese and herb mixture, before a main course of chargrilled corn-fed chicken with a fine tarragon hollandaise. One dinner ended on the high note of a light brandy-snap case filled with coffee ice-cream. The lack of pretentiousness is what is most appreciated at the Riverside, as well as Susan Phillips's personable approach and, for those who stay over, the ravishing breakfast cornucopia. In the relatively modest context, the wine list is a fine achievement. Each region is represented by a small cluster of the best producers, and the prices are heart-warmingly kind. An eye to the better vintages is apparent too. House wines from the Côtes de St-Mont are £7.95. CELLARMAN'S CHOICE: Vins de pays d'Oc, Ozidoc Sauvignon 1993, £8.95; Mitchell Shiraz 'Peppertree Vineyard' 1992, Clare Valley, S. Australia, £12.95.

CHEFS/PROPRIETORS: Robert and Susan Phillips OPEN: restaurant Mon to Sat D only 7.30 to 8.30; bar meals Mon to Sat 12 to 2, 7.30 to 8.30 CLOSED: 2 weeks Nov, 25 and 26 Dec, 1 Jan, 2 weeks Feb MEALS: restaurant Set D £22.50; bar alc (main courses £5 to £15) SERVICE: not inc, card slips closed CARDS: Access, Switch, Visa DETAILS: 26 seats. Private parties: 24 main room. Car park. Vegetarian meals. Children's helpings. Smart dress preferred. No smoking in dining-room. No music ACCOMMODATION: 6 rooms, all with bath/shower. TV. B&B £55 to £84. Deposit: £20. Rooms for disabled. Children welcome. Pets by arrangement. Garden

COLBOST Highland map 11

Three Chimneys

Colbost, by Dunvegan, Isle of Skye IV55 8ZT
TEL: (01470) 511258 COOKING 2*
on B884, 4m W of Dunvegan COST £21–£60

'Sometimes I think we do more here than you can cope with in our description,' writes Shirley Spear from this remote cottage restaurant beside the sea on Skye's north-west coast. She is referring to a range of daily activities that takes in morning coffee, afternoon tea and light meals as well as lunch and dinner. Good baking of scones and cakes underpins the teas, while hot kipper tart with lemon sauce, or potted wild duck pâté are offered until 4.30pm. Lunch is a flexible arrangement of soup, cheese salad with chutney, herring in oatmeal, or smoked venison, but also offers seafood specialities, from oysters to split langoustines or lobster salad, culminating in the Grand Seafood Platter at £45 for two people.

The evening version is even grander, preceded (for another £10 a head) by squat lobster bisque and baked scallops, and followed by cheese or pudding. Freshness and simple cooking are paramount, and the combination ensures that the Spears, and their customers, get the best out of the location. They are diligent about supplies and well placed to find the best. There is a vegetarian menu too, and meat is not neglected. Fillet of Highland lamb, venison, and wild mallard are likely at dinner, and there is an interpretation of surf 'n' turf in a sirloin steak filled with peat-smoked salmon. There is lots more too – we haven't even mentioned the sauces – but we can't possibly include everything. There is just room to note that the wine list is equally kind to reds and whites, that the shorter New World section is particularly astute, and that prices are very fair indeed.

Half a dozen wines are available by the glass from £2.75. CELLARMAN'S CHOICE: Mâcon-Villages Blanc 1993, Leflaive, £12.75; Crozes-Hermitage 1991, Graillot, £17.75.

CHEF: Shirley Spear PROPRIETORS: Eddie and Shirley Spear OPEN: Mon to Sat 12.30 to 2, 7 to 9 (10.30 to 12, 2 to 4.30 for light meals and afternoon tea) CLOSED: Nov to late Mar MEALS: alc (main courses £6 to £25.50). Set D £27.50 to £32.50. Minimum £3.50 L SERVICE: not inc CARDS: Access, Switch, Visa DETAILS: 30 seats. 2 tables outside. Private parties: 18 main room. Car park. Vegetarian meals. Children welcome. Smart dress preferred. No smoking in dining-room. Music

CRINAN Strathclyde map 11

▲ *Crinan Hotel* 🍷

Crinan PA31 8SR

TEL: (01546) 830261 FAX: (01546) 830292 **COOKING 1**

off A816, 6m NW of Lochgilphead **COST £36–£59**

This large white-painted hotel stands at the northern end of the Crinan Canal, 200 years old, family run and with wonderful views (weather permitting). There are two restaurants and a 'sensibly unsophisticated bar where oilskinned fishermen or wet yachtspeople can roister'. Lock 16 has recently undergone a refit which has benefited from Frances Ryan's artistic skills. Its business is nothing but shellfish, landed a few yards from the hotel shortly before dinner. If the weather is poor the boats don't go out, so 'check the weather before you commit yourself, and save yourself a journey if Lock 16 is not fully functioning with Loch Crinan jumbo prawns and all', advises one visitor.

The deal in Lock 16 is £40 for five courses that will probably incorporate a choice of Loch Craignish mussels or charcoal-grilled Sound of Jura king clams, then a plate of smoked wild salmon, then the jumbo prawns, followed by lemon tart, Stilton with oatcakes, and coffee. The Westward restaurant offers four courses of a more general fishy nature, as well as roast leg of Kintyre lamb or Aberdeen Angus fillet steak. The annotated wine list is put together by an enthusiast, makes quality its top priority, and is as kind to modest tastes as to expensive ones. House wine is £9.95. CELLARMAN'S CHOICE: Chablis premier cru Vaillons 1992, Collet £30; Sancerre Rouge 'Les Bruyères' 1992, Thomas, £22.

CHEF: Nicolas Ryan (Lock 16) and Angela Burns (Westward) PROPRIETORS: Nicolas and Frances Ryan OPEN: Lock 16 Tue to Sat D only 8 (one sitting); Westward all week D only 7 to 9 CLOSED: Lock 16 Oct to May; Westward 1 week Christmas MEALS: Lock 16 Set D £40; Westward Set D £27.50 SERVICE: not inc, card slips closed CARDS: Access, Amex, Switch, Visa DETAILS: 20 seats (Lock 16); 45 seats (Westward). Private parties: 25 main room (Lock 16), 45 main room (Westward). Car park. Vegetarian meals. Children welcome. Jacket and tie (Lock 16). No smoking while others eat in Lock 16; no smoking in Westward. Wheelchair access (also WC). No music ACCOMMODATION: 22 rooms, all with bath/shower. TV. Phone. B&B £75 to £115. Deposit: £50. Rooms for disabled. Children welcome. Baby facilities. Pets welcome. Afternoon teas. Garden (*The Which? Hotel Guide*)

▲ *This symbol means accommodation is available.*

CULLEN Grampian map 11

▲ *Bayview Hotel* £

57 Seafield Street, Cullen AB56 2SU
TEL: (01542) 841031 COOKING 1*
on A98 Fochabers to Banff road COST £17–£34

The house is at the end of a street overlooking the harbour, 'with a glorious view over the Moray Firth'. Pine tables and chairs in the bar give it 'a general aura of polish and uncluttered cleanliness'. Cullen skink apears on the short regular menu, along with prawn cocktail, first-rate fisherman's pie, and a few steaks, but there are other 'Cullen-ary delights', including roll mops and monkfish tails provençale, and one reporter reckons 'the real goodies are displayed on the blackboard'. Fish supplies are sound and the cooking hearty yet careful enough to bring out the best in a soup packed with crab, prawns, turbot, ling and more, or in grilled halibut with parsley sauce. Meals are 'beautifully presented and served', and might finish with Cranachan, iced Inchgower soufflé or butterscotch and almond ice-cream. Two dozen straightforward wines begin at £8.90 and stay mostly under £15.

CHEF: Jim Drury PROPRIETOR: David Evans OPEN: all week 12 to 1.45, 6.30 to 9 (phone to check in winter) MEALS: alc (main courses £6 to £12) SERVICE: not inc, card slips closed CARDS: Access, Visa DETAILS: 40 seats. Private parties: 20 main room, 20 private room. Vegetarian meals. Children welcome. No music ACCOMMODATION: 6 rooms, all with bath/shower. TV. Phone. B&B £27.50 to £60. Children welcome

CUPAR Fife map 11

Ostlers Close 🍷

25 Bonnygate, Cupar KY15 4BU COOKING 3
TEL: (01334) 655574 COST £22–£44

The ambition behind the Grahams' operation is exemplary: one that many aspire to but too few achieve. The restaurant is a manageable size that fits in comfortably with supply lines and with the kitchen's capabilities. It is all of a piece, enabling them to use local produce – including asparagus, sea kale and samphire in season – and even to have free-range ducks and corn-fed chickens bred especially for them. The Grahams pick and preserve their own mushrooms, have good suppliers of game, and naturally take advantage of local seafood: in broths or soups, or roasted and served with a gently acidulated butter sauce.

Given all this, it is understandable that although menus change daily the core repertoire remains much the same. Once on to a good thing, the Grahams stick with it. The elements come together in breast of chicken with preserved mushrooms, or a first course of west coast scallops and Pittenweem langoustines on a bed of sea kale in a shellfish stock flavoured with anise. The aim is clear-cut flavours, using stocks and herbs, and not crowding the plate with too many differing components. It is the kind of cooking that looks easier to achieve than it actually is. Lunch may be less expensive than dinner, but the food can still be as substantial as smoked haddock in a cream sauce with mashed potato, or as rich as roast breast of woodpigeon with goose confit in a game sauce.

Dinner begins with a 'complimentary offering' and might finish with baked lemon tart served with a lemon sorbet, or chocolate mousse with caramel sauce. The view is that food prices are reasonable for standards that are consistently high, and wines keep the bill on target. The list has just enough choice to provide interest and variety without being confusing, and mark-ups are kind. Australians are well worth considering, including David Wynn Riesling and Shiraz at £12.25, or £2.40 a glass. CELLARMAN'S CHOICE: Jacksons Sauvignon Blanc 1993, Marlborough, New Zealand, £13.95; Montes Alpha Cabernet Sauvignon 1989, Chile, £16.95.

CHEF: James Graham PROPRIETORS: Amanda and James Graham OPEN: Tue to Sat 12.15 to 2, 7 to 9.30 MEALS: alc (main courses £8.50 to £16.50) SERVICE: not inc, card slips closed CARDS: Access, Amex, Delta, Switch, Visa DETAILS: 28 seats. Private parties: 20 main room. Children's helpings. No children under 6 at D. No smoking during meals. No music

DERVAIG Strathclyde map 11

▲ *Druimard Country House* NEW ENTRY

Dervaig, Isle of Mull PA75 6QW
TEL: (01688) 400345 and 400291 COOKING 1
FAX: (01688) 400345 COST £25–£33

The world's smallest (43-seat) professional theatre, the Little Theatre of Mull, stands within the grounds of this Victorian country house, eight miles from Tobermory, on a hillside with stunning views across the River Bellart and surrounding hills and glens. Pre-theatre dinners are the lifeblood during the season. Rooms are simply furnished, with well-thumbed books, comfortable sofas, and games for wet days when walkers and twitchers are confined to quarters. Tables in the dining-room are 'a bit tea-room style', but what matters is the homely feel of the place. Haydn Hubbard is 'gentle and charming', and Wendy Hubbard 'has a smile that would light up the National Grid'.

Local seafood, including crab, lobster, prawns and dived scallops, are well used, along with Argyll lamb (with onion sauce), and local venison (with a partnering of blaeberries and sloes). One meal began with a refreshing cocktail of melon with grapes and tart orange plus a pear sorbet. Alcohol and cream trickle through the menu, and the cumulative effect of rich dishes, such as a bubbling hot mixture of prawns and mushrooms under a hat of melted local cheese, led one visitor to conclude that 'you need stamina to cope with this cooking'. On Sunday evening the main couse is roast beef, cooked beyond pink 'but still with good taste and texture', served with Yorkshire pudding and a cream sauce. Vegetables are first-rate. Isle of Mull and other Scottish cheeses are an alternative to raspberries on cinnamon shortbread, or apple frangipane tart with a 'wonderful' butterscotch sauce. The 40-strong roving list of wines rarely breaks through the £15 ceiling. House Côtes de Duras is £8.60.

indicates that smoking is either banned altogether or that a dining-room is maintained for non-smokers. The symbol does not apply to restaurants that simply have no-smoking areas.

CHEF: Wendy Hubbard PROPRIETORS: Haydn and Wendy Hubbard OPEN: Mon to Sat D only 6 to 8.30 (Sun for residents) CLOSED: end Oct to 1 Apr MEALS: Set D £16.50 SERVICE: not inc CARDS: Access, Visa DETAILS: 25 seats. Private parties: 20 main room. Car park. Vegetarian meals. Children's helpings. Smart dress preferred. No smoking in dining-room. Music ACCOMMODATION: 6 rooms, 4 with bath/shower. TV. Phone. B&B £44.55 to £85. Deposit: £75. Children welcome. Baby facilities. Pets welcome in bedrooms only. Garden (*The Which? Hotel Guide*)

DRYBRIDGE Grampian map 11

Old Monastery

Drybridge AB56 2JB
TEL: (01542) 832660 COOKING 1
2½m S of Buckie, at junction of A98 and A942 COST £20–£42

'The position is superb, with views across the whole expanse of Spey Bay with the Sutherland mountains in the distance,' writes an awestruck reporter. The owners add that even the spring water that supplied the Benedictine monks 'still provides us with our entire water needs'. The chapel is now the main dining-room, and the cloisters have been incorporated into the bar and lounge area. The Old Monastery is not, by the way, the size of a large cathedral, more that of a small church. The abundance of venison, Aberdeen Angus beef, fish (including wild salmon) and shellfish, as well as soft fruits in season, provides a solid foundation for Douglas Gray's traditional kind of cooking.

Meals might begin with caramelised onion quiche or fish roulade or, in winter, a miniature steak and kidney pudding. Treatments are all the better for being plain – Cumberland sauce for duck breast, redcurrant and port sauce for the medallions of venison – although puddings can be more inventive, as in a choux pastry case containing both pineapple poached in crème de cacao syrup and coconut ice-cream. Lunch is lighter. Seventy-five varied wines, with many good names among them, are backed up by decent halves. House Bordeaux is around £11 a bottle, or about £2 a glass.

CHEF: Douglas Gray PROPRIETORS: Douglas and Maureen Gray OPEN: Tue to Sat 12 to 1.30, 7.45 to 9.30 CLOSED: 3 weeks Jan, 2 weeks Nov MEALS: alc (main courses L £6 to £11, D £11 to £16) SERVICE: not inc, card slips closed CARDS: Access, Amex, Visa DETAILS: 50 seats. Private parties: 45 main room. Car park. Vegetarian meals. No children under 8. Smart dress preferred. No smoking in dining-room. Music

DUNKELD Tayside map 11

▲ *Kinnaird*

Kinnaird Estate, by Dunkeld PH8 0LB
TEL: (01796) 482440 FAX: (01796) 482289
from A9 2m N of Dunkeld, take B898, signposted COOKING 4
Kinnaird, for 4½m COST £35–£62

Kinnaird is for the country set. The 9,000-acre estate offers fishing on the Tay (which you can see from the dining-room window), grouse- and pheasant-shooting, deer-stalking, and a choice of various hideaway cottages for rent.

Needless to say, you are never far from a golf course in this part of the world either. A stay is like an Edwardian house party brought up to date. It is 'comfortable and welcoming', and luxury is taken for granted: wood is polished, brass gleams, log fires blaze in the public rooms, even the dogs' kennels are heated.

The cooking is grand country-house style (with prices to match), but thanks to John Webber it is a cut above most. Formerly at Gidleigh Park (see entry, Chagford), among other places, he has been at Kinnaird's stoves since 1989, and is keenly in touch with the best of British culinary thinking. Given the location, smoked salmon and poached fillet of salmon are inevitable, but dishes are by no means predictable. They are carefully managed, and evolve slowly rather than test new ground; they are classy without relying too much on country-house staples of lobster and foie gras; and they derive their richness from a variety of sources: olive oil with fish, gelatinous stickiness in braised and boned oxtail, or the combination of pastry and hot chocolate in a pithiviers served with rum sauce.

The re-working of ingredients, at times simple, at others ingenious, is never overdone, despite being indebted to more than one culinary tradition, as in grilled red mullet on a red pepper confit with a lemon grass sauce, or ravioli of rabbit and morel mushrooms with a madeira sauce. Ravioli is a favoured device, perhaps enclosing Toulouse sausage (to accompany a terrine of duck cassoulet), as are herb crusts for lamb or fish. Dishes ring the changes, too, by making use of couscous with roast rack of lamb, or polenta with fillet steak.

Puddings can vary from delicate elderflower sorbet to robust pear and sultana pie with hot custard, and a soufflé of some sort is normally on offer: raspberry on one occasion, banana and Galliano on another. Service is very proper, and the cellar could withstand a long siege: its scope is broad, its resources deep, especially among clarets. The serious attempt to offer good drinking under £20 is welcome, and the supply of half-bottles is very generous. House vin de pays d'Oc is £15-£16. CELLARMAN'S CHOICE: Haut-Médoc, L'Ermitage de Chasse Spleen 1990, £23; Jackson Estate Chardonnay 1993, Marlborough, New Zealand, £21.

CHEF: John Webber PROPRIETOR: Constance Ward OPEN: all week 12.30 to 1.45, 7 to 9.30 CLOSED: Mon to Wed from Jan to Mar MEALS: Set L £19.50 (2 courses) and £24, Set D £39.50 SERVICE: not inc, card slips closed CARDS: Access, Amex, Delta, Switch, Visa DETAILS: 28 seats. Private parties: 28 main room, 6 and 20 private rooms. Car park. No children under 12. Jacket and tie. No smoking in dining-room. Wheelchair access (also WC). No music ACCOMMODATION: 9 rooms, all with bath/shower. TV. Phone. B&B £175 to £250. Rooms for disabled. No children under 12. Pets welcome. Afternoon teas. Garden. Fishing (*The Which? Hotel Guide*)

'The special menu changes four times a year, but is not written down. I don't know why they don't duplicate the thing as this would spare the excellent manager the task of going through a description of the six courses rather like an army sergeant doing gun drill.'
(On eating in Cheshire)

DUNVEGAN Highland map 11

▲ *Harlosh House*

Dunvegan, Isle of Skye IV55 8ZG
TEL/FAX: (01470) 521367 COOKING 2
off A863, 3m S of Dunvegan COST £33–£40

Harlosh sounds a bit like the noise the waves make as they cascade against the nearby rocks. Views to the Cuillin Hills are magnificent, and wildlife abounds. The eighteenth-century house is remote, although the bridge linking Skye to the mainland may well bring more business to the whole island. In a place where so little changes, it is major news to note that Peter Elford has altered the format from a *carte* to a set-price, no-choice, four-course dinner. This is a sensible idea, and one to which customers seem to have taken well. With fewer distractions, the cook is better able to keep up the standard. Since the menu is posted up well before dinner, guests, who usually stay for a few days, have every opportunity to express dislikes or to ask for a lighter alternative.

It is quite properly assumed, however, that you don't come here unless you have some fondness for eating fish and shellfish, around which most meals are organised. One typical spring meal began with local langoustines and mayonnaise, before a soup of pea, mint and lettuce, then poached halibut with dill butter sauce, and finally a choice of three puddings or Scottish cheeses. Apart from fish, venison is a likely main course, or lamb, or a duck breast 'with crispy skin and succulent pink flesh. We have had many duck breasts and these are the best.' Peter Elford's enthusiasm impresses reporters, but fortunately doesn't lead him on elaborate detours. Saucing is simple and technique sound. Wines are sensibly chosen and priced, covering the essentials without going to extremes. House South African is £8.50.

CHEF: Peter Elford PROPRIETORS: Peter and Lindsey Elford OPEN: all week D only 7 to 8.30 CLOSED: mid-Oct to Easter MEALS: Set D £24.50 SERVICE: not inc, card slips closed CARDS: Access, Delta, Switch, Visa DETAILS: 16 seats. Private parties: 6 main room. Car park. Children's helpings. No smoking in dining-room. Wheelchair access (1 step). Music ACCOMMODATION: 6 rooms, all with bath/shower. B&B £44 to £90. Deposit: £50. Children welcome. Baby facilities. Afternoon teas (*The Which? Hotel Guide*)

EDINBURGH Lothian map 11

Atrium

10 Cambridge Street, Edinburgh EH1 2ED COOKING 3
TEL: 0131-228 8882 COST £25–£43

How long the décor will remain fashionable is anybody's guess. Stravinsky once remarked that his *Rite of Spring* might be raised by a semitone every decade in order to reinstate the freshness and shock of its first performance. So far, the impact of Atrium's bold décor has not been diminished by familiarity, and might well last a decade before needing a refit. In the same block as the Traverse Theatre, the restaurant sports a glass lift, visible ventilation ducts, tables made from railway sleepers, twisted wire sculptures, and white canvas seats that look too fragile to sit on. The room is lit by candles and is 'too dark for a solitary diner to read a book'.

The breezy menus are short, and rather assume that you like pesto, goats' cheese, toasted bread, courgettes, fish and fowl. The food is light enough to make lunch a good proposition, perhaps taking in pan-fried venison liver with champ and grilled bacon, followed by a rather precious-sounding 'salmon, spinach and hot things', and finishing with banana torte made with caramelised sun-dried banana. The beauty of this kind of food is that a lunchtime snack of paesano sausage with mash and lentil gravy can also double as a first course for dinner. Another advantage is that vegetarian dishes are not, as so often, consigned to the also-rans. A Parmesan tart of Irish Blue and leek is just as integral to the style as a dish of baked cod with Parma ham and pesto courgettes. All the cooking works as a lively and forthright interpretation of modern brasserie food, although it is 'not as good as it thinks it is', according to one reporter, and the prices have been questioned.

The lightness is helped partly by the preponderance of vegetables and fish – grilled brown (not rainbow) trout, or crab-cake with pesto and courgette – and partly by a reliance on fowl rather than the standard beef, lamb and pork – hence woodpigeon with roast roots and juniper, or guinea-fowl with mushrooms and Parma ham. Puddings have included steamed fig with custard, a partnering of baked banana (this year's fashionable fruit?) with espresso sorbet, and a boozy-sounding Grand Marnier and champagne sorbet. A sharp, compact but varied list of wines as modern as the food – with good producers from Alsace and the Rhône to Italy and California – is well priced, with a dozen by the glass from £2.25. CELLARMAN'S CHOICE: Wairau River Sauvignon Blanc 1993, Marlborough, New Zealand, £17.50; Bonny Doon 'Le Cigare Volant 1991, California, £19.75.

CHEF: Andrew Radford PROPRIETORS: Andrew and Lisa Radford OPEN: Mon to Fri L 12 to 2.30, Mon to Sat D 6 to 10.30 (11 during Edinburgh Festival) CLOSED: 1 week Christmas MEALS: alc (main courses £8 to £15.50); light L available SERVICE: not inc CARDS: Access, Amex, Switch, Visa DETAILS: 70 seats. Private parties: 100 main room. Vegetarian meals. Children's helpings. Wheelchair access (also WC). No music. Air-conditioned

Crannog NEW ENTRY

14 South St Andrew Street, Edinburgh EH2 2AZ COOKING 1
TEL: 0131-557 5589 FAX: 0131-558 3067 COST £15–£42

This is the third branch of Crannog to open its doors (see entries, Fort William and Glasgow), and the food follows the style of the others. The blackboard of daily specials is manhandled around the tables, a practice that mystifies reporters, but the essential appeal is fresh langoustines, either cold with mayonnaise or (the preferred option) hot with garlic butter, plus skate in dark butter, mussels in white wine, and numerous ways with salmon: smoked, of course, cured with dill and mustard, or baked and given a crab sauce. Dover sole and shark occasionally swim into view, and one reporter enjoyed monkfish with a mustard cream sauce. Smoking of mussels, oysters, mackerel, trout and salmon is done in Fort William; salads, new potatoes and chunky bread are standard; and puddings are missable. A similar wine list furnishes all three branches: fairly priced and well suited to the food.

CHEF: François Huguet PROPRIETOR: Crannog Ltd OPEN: all week 12 to 2.30, 6 to 10.30; closes later during Edinburgh Festival CLOSED: Sun and Mon in winter MEALS: alc (main courses £8.50 to £15). Set L £8.50 (2 courses) to £10 SERVICE: not inc, card slips closed CARDS: Access, Amex, Delta, Switch, Visa DETAILS: 70 seats. Private parties: 20 main room, 50 private room. Vegetarian meals. Children welcome. Music. Air-conditioned

Denzler's 121

121 Constitution Street, Leith, Edinburgh EH6 7AE COOKING 1
TEL: 0131-554 3268 FAX: 0131-467 7239 COST £20–£35

Given the Swiss obsession with banks, it may be no accident that the Denzlers ended up in these ornately marble-fronted vaults. There is no ordering by numbers, though. The modern room is done out in peach and apricot, with new wood and mirrors to lighten it further. Contemporary Scottish pictures hang on the walls, and the food whistles straight down from the Alps. Bündnerplättli is thin slices of air-dried beef and ham, while veal zurichoise comes in a mushroom and cream sauce with spätzli. But given rump steak with béarnaise sauce, and melon and prawns in a marie-rose sauce, it becomes clear that Sämi Denzler is no purist. 'An amazing combination of food,' is how one reporter described it. Lunch, for those with an afternoon's work ahead, can be as light as a glass of freshly squeezed orange juice followed by goujons of sole with tartare sauce. The usual accompaniment to main courses, when it's not spätzli, is potatoes cooked with onion, bacon and stock. There are more New Zealand than Swiss wines on the list, but quality throughout is generally high and prices are fair. Wines of the month may be more interesting than the French house wine at £10.35.

CHEFS: Sämi Denzler and Ian Gordon PROPRIETORS: Sämi and Pat Denzler OPEN: Tue to Fri L 12 to 2, Tue to Sat D 6.30 to 10 CLOSED: Christmas and 1 week Jan, 2 weeks end July MEALS: alc (main courses £7 to £12). Set L £7.75 (2 courses) SERVICE: net prices, card slips closed CARDS: Access, Amex, Delta, Diners, Switch, Visa DETAILS: 75 seats. Private parties: 75 main room. Children's helpings. Smart dress preferred. No music

Indian Cavalry Club ⁎ £

3 Atholl Place, Edinburgh EH3 8HP COOKING 1
TEL: 0131-228 3282 and 2974 FAX: 0131-225 1911 COST £16–£41

As the name suggests, this Indian restaurant takes as its theme a rosy-glowed vision of the old colonial days when officers of the Indian Cavalry regiment gathered in the mess and dined on 'the kind of cuisine favoured in the exclusive circles of Bombay and Delhi'. The ground-floor dining-room is appropriately fitted out with billowing drapes, luxuriant plants and lances on the walls. Even when the mood is frenetic and it is virtually impossible to hold a conversation, a brigade of waiters stays calm and kindly. At its best the kitchen offers a wide range of dishes full of subtle flavours and 'lovely, fragrant, spicy tastes'. Each item is listed with a recommended accompaniment and a suitable style of wine: for example, mightily impressive chicken Katmandu (with a cinnamon, spring onion and lentil sauce) is paired with pineapple sambar and a Chardonnay. North Indian chilli garlic lamb goes with Kashmiri raita (spicy yoghurt with fruits) and a bottle of Cabernet Sauvignon or Shiraz. Fish is adventurously handled, and vegetables and vegetarian dishes are also well worth exploring. Lunches revolve around a help-yourself buffet. To perk up the palate, try a glass of zeera-pani ('freshly spiced appetising spring water', explains the menu); otherwise, drink lassi, lager or something fitting from the short, reasonably priced wine list. House wine is £8.50.

CHEFS: Bilquis Chowdhury, Mukhtar Miah and Salim Haider PROPRIETORS: Mr Shahidul, Alam and Bilquis Chowdhury OPEN: all week 12 to 2, 5.30 to 11.30 MEALS: alc (main courses £6 to £12). Set L £6.95 (2 courses), Set D £9.95 (2 courses) to £16.95. Minimum £7 SERVICE: not inc CARDS: Access, Amex, Delta, Diners, Switch, Visa DETAILS: 120 seats. Private parties: 80 main room, 40 private room. Vegetarian meals. Children welcome. Smart dress preferred. No smoking in 1 dining-room. No music

Kalpna £

2–3 St Patrick Square, Edinburgh EH8 9EZ
TEL: 0131-667 9890

COOKING 1*
COST £10–£28

Kalpna has sustained a special place in the Edinburgh restaurant scene since 1982, attracting hordes from the nearby university and beyond with its distinctive brand of South Indian vegetarian cooking. Lunchtime buffets (and a more extensive evening version on Wednesdays) are one of the best deals in the city. Kachoris (deep-fried lentil balls with coconut) rate highly, and the list of starters also runs to 'very pleasant' pakoras, bhel pooris and dosas. From the selection of specialities and vegetable dishes, reporters have mentioned baingan bharta (mashed, roasted aubergine with nuts, spices and yoghurt) and phool aloo (steamed potatoes and cauliflower). Four thalis provide an affordable way of sampling dishes across the range, although breads have impressed more than rice. The cooking is still sound, but some supporters feel that standards have slipped slightly: 'Let's hope that in the coming year [co-owner] Mr Jogee can positively re-affirm it,' commented one who remembers the restaurant's heyday. The wine list deserves more than a cursory glance: Indian Veena and Omar Khayyam (sparkling Chardonnay) are tucked away among the French, Chilean and New World bottles. House wine is £6.95.

CHEF: Ajay Bhartdwaj PROPRIETORS: A. Bhartdwaj, M. Jogee, Mrs Mehta and Dr E. Barton OPEN: Mon to Fri L 12 to 2, Mon to Sat D 5.30 to 11 CLOSED: 25 and 26 Dec, 1 Jan MEALS: alc (main courses £3.90 to £6). Buffet L £4.50, Set D £7 to £9, Set buffet D Wed £8.50 SERVICE: not inc L, 10% D, card slips closed CARDS: Access, Visa DETAILS: 65 seats. Private parties: 70 main room, 30 private room. Vegetarian meals. Children's helpings under 6. Smart dress preferred. No smoking in dining-room. Wheelchair access. Music

Kelly's

46 West Richmond Street, Edinburgh EH8 9DZ
TEL: 0131-668 3847

COOKING 2
COST £20–£41

Although small, the restaurant feels intimate rather than crowded and is a comfortable place for quiet, civilised conversation. Jacqueline Kelly's cooking has modern leanings and an interesting way with soups: cream of leek and potato is flavoured with coriander, while tomato broth contains spinach dumplings. Among meat dishes, lamb cutlets are topped with tarragon mousse, wrapped in pastry and baked, and served with an aubergine, courgette and pepper charlotte, which seems a lot of trouble to go to. Other things are wrapped up too: a halibut bavarois inside smoked salmon, while a mixture of mushrooms, bacon and pine-nuts is used to stuff a chicken breast, which is served with a creamy onion timbale and a madeira sauce.

There are easier ways to fill a plate, as when roast monkfish and langoustines appear with baby vegetables in a lime and ginger sauce. For anybody wanting fewer than three courses, dishes are priced individually, with main courses £14, for example. Service is sharp and aware of the pressure on pre-theatre diners: the Festival Theatre is nearby. Smokers should be aware that lighting up is not permitted before 9.30pm. The 50-strong wine list is lively and up to date, considerately priced, with a dozen house wines available at £10 a bottle, and £2 a glass.

CHEF: Jacqueline Kelly PROPRIETORS: Jeffrey and Jacqueline Kelly OPEN: Wed to Sat D only 6 to 10.30 CLOSED: Oct, first week Jan MEALS: Pre-theatre Set D 6 to 7 £10 (2 courses) to £13.50, Set D £22. Minimum £10 SERVICE: not inc CARDS: Access, Amex, Delta, Switch, Visa DETAILS: 34 seats. Private parties: 34 main room. Vegetarian meals. No children under 6. Smart dress preferred. No smoking in dining-room until 9.30. Wheelchair access (1 step; also WC). Music

Le Marché Noir

2–4 Eyre Place, Edinburgh EH3 5EP — COOKING 2
TEL: 0131-558 1608 FAX: 0131-556 0798 — COST £29–£35

David Connell was promoted to head up the kitchen during 1995, and the French style continues. Dinner is three courses that might begin with a warm salad of goats' cheese with coriander dressing, or haggis dumplings with a turnip purée, followed by pan-fried lambs' liver with a confit of onion, or roast fillet of pork with bacon. Cheeses, pavé of chocolate, or lemon tart bring up the rear.

Fish is well treated, pork has come highly recommended in a creamy sauce, and a salad of avocado and smoked chicken for one reporter was 'well bought, neatly prepared and prettily arranged'. One May meal began with vigorously flavoured black pudding and ended with a terrine of white chocolate and orange, and a light bread-and-butter pudding. Mr Duck and his staff are welcoming and friendly. Phenomenally good value is a characteristic of the predominantly French wine list, which offers, for example, Ch Talbot 1978 at £24. The New World chips in with 20 wines under £20, while house French begins at £8.50.

CHEF: David Connell PROPRIETOR: Malcolm Duck OPEN: Mon to Fri L 12 to 2.30, all week D 7 to 10 (10.30 Fri and Sat) MEALS: Set L £10.50 (2 courses) to £12.50, Set D £19.50 SERVICE: not inc, 10% for parties of 6 or more CARDS: Access, Amex, Visa DETAILS: 45 seats. Private parties: 35 main room. Vegetarian meals. Children welcome. Smart dress preferred. No smoking D. Wheelchair access (1 step; also WC). No music

Martin's

70 Rose Street North Lane,
Edinburgh EH2 3DX
TEL: 0131-225 3106

COOKING 2
COST £23–£51

Martin's hides itself well – 'in a back alley between Princes Street and George Street' being about the best description. Despite the unprepossessing locale, Martin and Gay Irons are energetic hosts, 'smiling, welcoming and dashing around'. The décor may be on the basic side, but the cooking, by Messrs Stott and Banks, more than makes up for it in culinary panache.

The little *carte* of four starters and four main courses changes daily, and there is also a set-price lunch menu, although you may have to ask to see it, according to one reporter. Fish is used in variously inventive ways, as in a first course of monkfish and scallops sauté with asparagus and served with a tomato salsa, or in a main dish of grilled sea trout with sun-dried tomatoes and a basil vinaigrette. Meat draws high praise. One man's seared venison loin served on rösti with braised lentils and bacon, was 'simply the best that I've ever tasted'. Roast Barbary duck breast with juniper berries, cabbage and star anise was a roaring success at a summer dinner, while loin of lamb was given the Japanese treatment with shiitake and oyster mushrooms, mirin and soy. Desserts such as a light pastry case of raspberries and cream that comes with caramel ice-cream have been praised, although on one occasion a praline meringue with the same ice-cream was less successful. The cheeseboard is 'an experience not to be missed', advises a canny reporter. It is hard to imagine the subject taken more seriously than it is here: Martin Irons even knows the names of the cows that produce the milk for some items. The prime Scottish and Irish specimens are described in passionate detail and choices may include Ballindalloch goats' cheese, Lanark and Dunsyre Blues, nutty Ardrahan and pungent Milleens.

France, Australia and the US are the strongest suits on the intelligently chosen wine list, with Edinburgh merchant Raeburn Fine Wines supplying many of the gems. Prices are not low but quality is assured, as a glance at the burgundies alone will confirm. French and Italian house wines are £9.95. CELLARMAN'S CHOICE: Savennières, Clos de Coulaine 1991, Roussier, £17.05; Margaux, Dom. de Cure-Bourse 1979, Lurton, £17.35.

CHEFS: Forbes Stott and Peter Banks PROPRIETORS: Martin and Gay Irons OPEN: Tue to Fri L 12 to 2, Tue to Sat D 7 to 10 CLOSED: 4 weeks from 24 Dec, 1 week Jun, 1 week Sept/Oct MEALS: alc (main courses £17 to £18), Set L £11.95 (2 courses) to £15 SERVICE: not inc CARDS: Access, Amex, Delta, Diners, Switch, Visa DETAILS: 28 seats. Private parties: 28 main room, 8 private room. No children under 8. No smoking in dining-room. Music

Rendezvous

24 Deanhaugh Street, Stockbridge,
Edinburgh EH4 1LY
TEL: 0131-332 4476

COOKING 1
COST £14–£40

'Nothing better in Edinburgh for £8.20!' exclaimed a local academic. He was referring to the three-course set lunch (coffee included) on offer in this tiny 'semi-basement' decorated with bird paintings and ornithological sculptures.

But be warned: parking in the centre of Stockbridge is murder at midday, so you may have to walk or take a cab. The lunchtime menu is short and sweet, taking in such items as 'robust' carrot and orange soup, chicken stuffed with apples and walnuts, Bakewell tart, or poached oranges in warm caramel sauce. Visitors in the evening can choose from a more ambitious repertoire featuring 'Auld Alliance' centrepieces such as spring lamb with caramelised onions, baked fillet of Loch Fyne salmon with crab and lemon grass sauce, or roast breast of mallard with port and plum sauce. Fillet steak might be served with thyme and Guinness sauce or stuffed with haggis. Service is efficient and unobtrusive. The short list of around 20 wines puts its faith in good value and quality. House wine is £8.50.

CHEF: Richard Easton PROPRIETOR: Harry Anderson OPEN: Wed to Sun L 12 to 2.30, Tue to Sun D 6.30 to 10.30 MEALS: alc D (main courses £9 to £15). Set L £6.25 (2 courses) to £8.20, Set D £18.50 SERVICE: 10%, card slips closed CARDS: Access, Amex, Visa DETAILS: 24 seats. Private parties: 30 main room. Vegetarian meals. Children's helpings. Smart dress preferred. No smoking in dining-room while others eat. Music. Air-conditioned

Shore ✱ £

3–4 Shore, Leith, Edinburgh EH6 6QW
TEL/FAX: 0131-553 5080 COOKING 1*
off A199 on Firth of Forth, 2m E of city centre COST £18–£34

Overlooking the Water of Leith, the river that flows out into the Firth of Forth, this lively bar-restaurant appears 'fairly timeless' despite retaining some eighteenth-century features such as the tongue-and-groove panelling on ceiling and walls. Menus change at every sitting, but the emphasis is on fish cooked à la mode, with Mediterranean and oriental borrowings bolstering more traditional renderings such as Arbroath smokie served hot with a poached egg. Kicking off an inspection meal was grilled herring of fine quality that came with an oatmeal and herb mayonnaise. Sea wolf, a regular item, bemused the reporters as to its precise identity. By linguistic association, it was probably *loup de mer* (sea bass), its firm texture and good flavour enhanced by grilling, the accompaniments of coconut milk and coriander adding just the right touch. Similarly, the smoked bacon and garlic that came with roasted monkfish 'had an aroma and flavour that permeated the fish' with impressive subtlety. Desserts offer a pretty straightforward selection. Sticky toffee pudding was a masterly rendition – 'moist, rich and aromatic' – and a former pâtissier confessed herself awed by lemon tart that had 'excellent pastry and a sharp filling'. In an area where competition is hotting up, the Shore remains deservedly popular. Wines are a brisk international selection, with everything except champagne below £20. House French is £7.95.

CHEFS: Kevin O'Connor and Innes Gibson PROPRIETOR: Stuart Linsley OPEN: all week 12 (12.30 Sun) to 2.30 (3 Sun), 6.30 to 10.15 CLOSED: 25 and 26 Dec, 1 and 2 Jan MEALS: alc (main courses £7 to £12). Set L Sun £9.50 (2 courses) to £11.50, Set L Mon to Sat £6.95 (2 courses) SERVICE: not inc (10% for parties of 8 or more) CARDS: Access, Amex, Visa DETAILS: 36 seats. 4 tables outside. Private parties: 36 main room. Vegetarian meals. Children welcome. No smoking in dining-room. Wheelchair access (1 step). Music

Siam Erawan £

48 Howe Street, Edinburgh EH3 6TH — COOKING 1*
TEL: 0131-226 3675 — COST £13–£32

This sizeable basement restaurant, in effect two arched cellars, is the pick of Edinburgh's Thai specialists, at least on a par with some of the longer-established ones in London's Soho. It is simple, tasteful, attractive and relaxing, with friendly staff dressed in traditional Thai costume, and as well as the usual run of standard Thai dishes – tom yum soups 'with plenty of flavour and aroma', generous and skilfully marinated satays using good-quality meat, a variety of curries, minced meats with toasted rice, wok dishes, noodle dishes and hot-and-sour dishes – it also runs to more individual steamed rice tarts stuffed with spiced white fish, or prawns wrapped with a spiced vegetable mixture and cooked in rice flour. Ingredients are good. Local seafood is variously chargrilled or steamed and subjected to a range of treatments, from squid with Thai basil and chilli to goong nung – a dish of king prawns steamed with lemon grass, lime leaves, white wine and leaf coriander, served with a hot green chilli and garlic dip. Banana fritters, and coconut ice-cream with jack fruit and rambutan, are among the puddings. Wines are basic and reasonably priced.

CHEF/PROPRIETOR: Miss W. Chinnapong OPEN: all week 12 to 2, 6 to 10.45 CLOSED: 25 and 26 Dec, 1 and 2 Jan MEALS: alc (main courses £5 to £8.50). Set L £5.95 (2 courses) to £10, Set D £15.95 to £19.95 SERVICE: 10%, card slips closed CARDS: Access, Switch, Visa DETAILS: 50 seats. Private parties: 28 main room. Vegetarian meals. Children welcome. Smart dress preferred. Music

Spices ✱

110 West Bow, Grassmarket, Edinburgh EH1 2HH — COOKING 1
TEL: 0131-225 5028 — COST £12–£30

The carnivorous alternative to Kalpna (see entry, page 567) is entrenched firmly in the regal cuisine of Delhi, although the kitchen makes regular forays into Kashmir, Hyderabad and Goa. Out front, the doorway is guarded by a cigar-store 'Injun' effigy and the interior is a surprising mix of plum-coloured Rennie Mackintosh chairs, pink tablecloths and terracotta walls with dark olive drapes and swags – although the Indian paintings will remind you of what this place is really about. The menu is quite a read: raunaq-e-seekh 'dons a colourful summer garb with the singing flavours of corriander [sic]'; degh-e-delhi (a princely biryani) is 'the pluperfect rice delicacy', and so on. Ironically the kitchen seems to be at its best when it cooks without meat: witness bhindis 'with a roasted flavour and creamy texture that lifted it right out of the ordinary' and a dish of new potatoes in a 'cumminy, chillified tomato sauce'. Elsewhere you might find a curious fruit chaat served in a hollowed-out pineapple boat, cubes of paneer cheese 'glazed in the tandoor', and East African kuku paka (barbecued chicken cooked with coconut milk, ginger, garlic and lemon juice). Roti bread has been a perfectly textured example of the genre. Drink cardamom tea, Cobra beer or something from the modest, good-value wine list. House wine is £6.95.

CHEFS: Ajay Bhartdwaj and Faqira Rawat PROPRIETORS: Moussa Jogee and Ajay Bhartdwaj OPEN: Mon to Sat 12 to 2, 6 to 11 MEALS: alc (main courses £6 to £7.50). Set Buffet L £5.50, Set D £15 SERVICE: 10%, card slips closed CARDS: Access, Diners, Visa DETAILS: 60 seats. Private parties: 30 main room, 30 private room. Children's helpings. Smart dress preferred. No smoking in dining-room. Music

Vintners Rooms

The Vaults, 87 Giles Street, Leith, Edinburgh EH6 6BZ COOKING 3
TEL: 0131-554 6767 FAX: 0131-467 7130 COST £30–£45

During the height of Anglo-Caledonian rancour, when Scotland did brisk trade with France, this dockland area of Edinburgh was where the claret flowed in. The elegantly plastered room where it was sold now houses one of the city's most justly celebrated restaurants. Decoration is on the exotic side, with oriental hangings and stuffed animals on view, and there is also a large wine bar where the set-price lunches constitute exemplary value.

Tim Cumming's cooking works at the sharp end of the spectrum, marshalling some vibrant flavours into often improbable but usually successful combinations. Scallops, for example, may receive a 'beautifully delicate' trade-mark sauce of cream and Pernod or they may be sauté with plums and ginger. Boudin blanc is grilled and accompanied by apples and a sauce made from Muscat wine. Main-course influences are drawn from the best sources. Salmon baked in filo pastry with ginger and currants has long starred at the Carved Angel (see entry, Dartmouth), while the bitter chocolate in a casserole of venison may owe something to Pierre Koffmann. Sesame-seeded halibut with a sorrel sauce, and turbot with lobster in a lobster broth are typical fish preparations. A reporter praised the 'very good pastry' in an apricot and almond tart, and white chocolate parfait with a coffee sauce also led to contented sighs. Brandy-snap baskets of tropical fruits come with patriotic Drambuie syllabub. Details such as the top-notch breads and olives suggest that great pains are being taken in all the right places.

Evidence of that is further provided by the list of impeccably chosen wines. The French regions are all handsomely served, Alsace in particular offering good value. Prices are generally fair, with even the older, rarer wines not being too heavily marked up. A thorough selection of half-bottles rounds the list off. The page of house wines starts at £9. CELLARMAN'S CHOICE: Mercurey 1989, Juillot, £23; Gigondas 1989, Amadieu, £16.50.

CHEFS: Tim Cumming and James Baxter PROPRIETORS: Tim and Sue Cumming OPEN: Mon to Sat 12 to 2.30, 7 to 10.30 CLOSED: 2 weeks Christmas MEALS: alc (main courses £13 to £16) SERVICE: not inc CARDS: Access, Amex, Visa DETAILS: 66 seats. 3 tables outside. Private parties: 36 main room. Children's helpings. Smart dress preferred. No smoking in dining-room. Wheelchair access (2 steps). No music

Not inc *in the details at the end of an entry indicates that no service charge is made and any tipping is at the discretion of the customer.*

ERISKA Strathclyde map 11

STRATHCLYDE 1996 HIDEAWAY

▲ *Isle of Eriska*

Ledaig, Eriska PA37 1SD
TEL: (01631) 720371 FAX: (01631) 720531 COOKING 2
off A828, 12m N of Oban COST £43–£52

'Scots baronial' is the style of this late Victorian manor house of grey granite with red sandstone facings. The Buchanan-Smiths – Robin, Sheena, Beppo and Chay – have been at the hotel helm for over 20 years now, facilities blooming all around them as time has passed. Eriska has 'a magnetism of its own', and much to divert the receptive visitor: the island itself teems with wildlife, while one couple, returning year after year, derive 'much pleasure from observing the carelessly wealthy residents in their infinite variety'.

The daily-changing fixed-price dinner menus involve a fair bit of eating. First courses light the fuse with items like leek and Stilton tartlet or smoked chicken salad with ginger mayonnaise and pink grapefruit. Then comes a choice of soup or fish, maybe green pea soup or devilled whitebait, and then three options for the main course. Salmon is treated as royally as any roast, sliced from the trolley, 'lightly cooked and succulent'. Haunch of venison has been 'absolutely sensational', while king scallops on a spring menu were fried in butter with ginger, rosemary and cream. Desserts keep within the simple bounds of chocolate ice-cream in a brandy-snap basket with raspberry coulis, or apple strudel with crème anglaise. Then there's an old-fashioned savoury, such as devils on horseback or Ayrshire bacon, before a selection of Scottish cheeses and Stilton. If you still have a spare corner, coffee is served with miniature pastries. 'Service in the hotel and restaurant is outstanding,' attested a reporter up from Kent, while a Scots pair staying over noted that 'the porridge is excellent'. Modest runs of wine are offered across an international spectrum. Burgundies rely heavily on Louis Latour but there are fine Alsaces from Trimbach, as well as Cloudy Bay. House wines are £8.20.

CHEFS: Sheena Buchanan-Smith and Craig Roger PROPRIETORS: the Buchanan-Smith family OPEN: all week D only 8 to 9 CLOSED: Jan to end Feb MEALS: Set D £35 SERVICE: not inc, card slips closed CARDS: Access, Amex, Switch, Visa DETAILS: 40 seats. Private parties: 20 main room. Car park. No children under 10. Jacket and tie. No cigars/pipes in dining-room. Wheelchair access (also WC). No music ACCOMMODATION: 17 rooms, all with bath/shower. TV. Phone. B&B £135 to £195. Deposit: £50. Rooms for disabled. Children's high teas. Baby facilities. Pets welcome in bedrooms only. Garden. Swimming pool. Fishing (*The Which? Hotel Guide*)

FORT WILLIAM Highland map 11

Crannog ✱ £

Town Pier, Fort William PH33 7NG COOKING 1
TEL: (01397) 705589 FAX: (01397) 705026 COST £16–£39

The views over Loch Linnhe from this converted bait store are 'stunning' and the place serves some of the finest and freshest langoustines in the land, caught from the proprietor's own boat. They might appear on the plate 'perfectly cooked' in garlic butter or cold with a trio of mayonnaises (garlic, spicy and parsley rémoulade). The output of the Crannog smokehouse ranges from salmon to mussels, gravlax is cured on the premises, and the kitchen can also turn its hand to anything from punchy fish soup 'packed with wonderful bits of crustacea', or a salad of avocado and squat lobster, to whole trout baked with ginger and spring onions. Puddings such as cranachan and walnut tart are fine enough, although such sparklingly fresh seafood is a difficult act to follow. The whole enterprise is refreshingly unstuffy: 'Some people wore suits and ties, while others wore jeans and shorts.' No one feels uncomfortable or out of place here. Good-value whites are the mainstays of the short wine list. House wine is £8.95. Other branches are in Edinburgh and Glasgow (see entries).

CHEF: Susan Trowbridge PROPRIETOR: Crannog Ltd OPEN: all week 12 to 2.30, 6 to 10 (9pm winter) CLOSED: 25 Dec, 1 Jan MEALS: alc (main courses £5.25 to £13.50) SERVICE: not inc, card slips closed CARDS: Access, Delta, Switch, Visa DETAILS: 60 seats. Private parties: 30 main room. Vegetarian meals. Children's helpings. No smoking in 1 dining-room. Wheelchair access (also WC). Music

▲ *Inverlochy Castle*

Torlundy, Fort William PH33 6SN
TEL: (01397) 702177 FAX: (01397) 702953 COOKING 3
3m N of Fort William on A82 COST £31–£55

Visitors to Inverlochy should prepare to be dwarfed by its colossal scale. A glorious backdrop of mountains, among them Ben Nevis, peers magisterially on to the acres of parkland that form the estate. Gilded cherubs fight the massive chandelier for the focus of an upward gaze as you trek across the entrance hall, enormous oils adorn the walls, and the vast swagged windows in the lounge and dining-rooms afford fitting frames for the view. Seated on a 'somewhat disciplinarian' chair for dinner, you may now feel about three inches tall, but then the 'wonderfully attentive' staff will soothe you back to a sense of yourself and prepare you for Simon Haigh's cooking.

The set menus command a high price for four courses with coffee, the second course a soup. The question has to be whether the level of culinary achievement can justify the price. Inspectors have turned up much to suggest that it can. Rarely cooked and 'potent' woodpigeon was the centrepiece for a colourful and well-dressed salad dotted with apple and celeriac. Isle of Skye crab was 'superbly fresh and sweet' and very competently dressed, but with perhaps too many garnishes – new potatoes with a horseradish sauce 'strong enough to bring tears to your eyes', and blinis. Soups, such as a 'near perfect' bisque of Loch Linnhe prawns containing tiny prawn ravioli, or a gamey consommé of duck and rabbit, make powerful impressions on the palate. Halibut sauté on the bone was 'wonderfully delicate', with a hollandaise sauce garnished with orange segments and a hint of star-anise. Braised oxtail, with properly glutinous meat, is the product of long and gentle cooking, but a reporter felt 'the dish cried out for some really good mashed potato'. Palates that tend to droop at dessert stage will be shocked back into life by the tartness of the sauce with crêpes suzette and its 'very alcoholic' Grand Marnier ice-cream. The tang of fresh raspberries, similarly, is cleverly used to offset the enveloping richness of otherwise classic crème brûlée. Coffee arrives with a 'splendid array' of chocolates, and the whole evening has been summed up as 'theatre on a grand scale'.

Drinkers on a budget may feel a little humbled by the deeply serious wine list. A nice bottle of 1966 claret will cost you £170 (not bad, perhaps, compared with London), but Tuscany, Chile, Australia and South Africa offer some relief. The layout is such that, when a column of gentler prices suddenly flashes before you, they are quite likely to be half-bottles. House French is £12.50.

CHEF: Simon Haigh PROPRIETOR: Grete Hobbs OPEN: all week 12.30 to 1.45, 7 to 9.30 CLOSED: Dec to Feb MEALS: Set L £25, Set D £40 to £47.50 SERVICE: none, card slips closed CARDS: Access, Amex, Switch, Visa DETAILS: 50 seats. Private parties: 10 main room, 14 private room. Car park. Children's helpings. Jacket and tie. No smoking in dining-room. Wheelchair access (also WC). No music ACCOMMODATION: 17 rooms, all with bath/shower. TV. Phone. B&B £130 to £260. Rooms for disabled. Children welcome. Baby facilities. Afternoon teas. Garden. Fishing (*The Which? Hotel Guide*)

GLASGOW Strathclyde map 11

Buttery

652 Argyle Street, Glasgow G3 8UF COOKING 1*
TEL: 0141-221 8188 FAX: 0141-204 4639 COST £20–£48

The Buttery is not located in Glasgow's prettiest district, but its interior, graced by antique wooden cabinets, trophies, cricketing prints and red plush, quickly displaces any misgivings about the address. The approach can seem initially as crisply formal as the starched white tablecloths, but underneath is a warmth that can make an evening here a pleasure. Stephen Johnson cooks, and menus suggest a culinary philosophy that likes to set itself challenges. Grilled goats' cheese with a bramble dressing, or a tartlet of sauté rabbit with a ginger sauce and crème fraîche are typical starters. If chicken breast wrapped in smoked bacon on banana cream sounds a touch alarming, note that some complex-sounding dishes are actually reworkings of classic combinations, as in the pan-fried lamb cutlets that come with a compote of lentils and onions and mint beignets. Some reporters have felt that a few of these ideas are not sufficiently thought through; for example, on one occasion sweetbreads seasoned delicately with mint were smothered by their casing of buttery puff pastry and then overwhelmed by a soupy sauce made with kidneys. On the other hand, salmon in a brioche crust with a sweet-pepper coulis does succeed. Puddings tend to be over-complex as well: a reporter found that the crème brûlée underneath its chocolate coating, orange segments and sour cream was actually 'high-class and would have been fine on its own'. Good coffee comes with many and varied petits fours. The wine list may or may not have some good wines on it – hard to tell when nothing is marked with vintage or producer, so it is probably best to stick to the house Loire at £10.95.

CHEF: Stephen Johnson PROPRIETOR: Alloa Pubs and Restaurants Ltd OPEN: Mon to Fri L 12 to 2.30, Mon to Sat D 7 to 10.30 CLOSED: bank and local hols MEALS: alc (main courses £12 to £14). Set L £14.85 SERVICE: 10%, card slips closed CARDS: Access, Amex, Delta, Diners, Switch, Visa DETAILS: 50 seats. Private parties: 12 main room, 8 private room. Car park. Vegetarian meals. Smart dress preferred. No cigars/pipes in dining-room. Music. Air-conditioned

Café Gandolfi £

64 Albion Street, Glasgow G1 1NY — COOKING 1
TEL: 0141-552 6813 — COST £16–£29

'It feels like a sophisticated café – could be European,' writes a seasoned reporter, drinking in the surroundings of Tim Stead furniture, stylish stained glass and candles. The Gandolfi is open all day, serving good breakfasts and a range of authentic brasserie food with daily specials to an enthusiastic youngish crowd. The approach is 'relaxed, even slap-happy', the food variable but extremely pleasing when it hits the spot. Stornoway black pudding with mushrooms and pancakes did just that, with 'crumbly, spicy, ungreasy pud, ethereal pancakes, and mushrooms palely loitering amid onions and white wine'. A main-course Roquefort tart at one meal had a generous, satisfyingly salty filling and crisp pastry, or there are Mexican marinated fish, New York pastrami with Swiss cheese, Finnan haddock, and Polish hams with potato salad and pickled red cabbage. Finish with Scottish cheeses or desserts such as orange tea-cake, walnut tart or chocolate pot, and 'decent' cappuccino. Thirteen wines are offered, forming a contemporary international selection. House French is £9.

CHEF: Maggie Clarence PROPRIETORS: Iain Mackenzie and Seumas MacInnes OPEN: all week 9am (12 Sun) to 11.30pm CLOSED: 25 and 26 Dec, Easter Sun, bank hol Mons MEALS: alc (main courses £6.50 to £8.50) SERVICE: not inc, 10% on parties of 6 or more and on bookings; card slips closed CARDS: Access, Switch, Visa DETAILS: 60 seats. Private parties: 14 main room. Vegetarian meals. Children 's helpings. Wheelchair access (2 steps). Music

Crannog — NEW ENTRY

28 Cheapside Street, Glasgow G3 8BH — COOKING 1
TEL/FAX: 0141-221 1727 — COST £15–£34

Crannog is a small chain of three fish restaurants. The simple design of the Fort William original (see entry) – white walls and pine tables – is perpetuated in this branch off Anderston Quay, as is the reliance on west coast fish and shellfish. The Crannog enterprise (see also Edinburgh) is self-sufficient in langoustines and prawns from its own boats, and in salmon, mussels and trout from its own smokery. Throw in some gravad lax and a bowl of 'superb bouillabaisse loaded with chunks of fish', and you just about have the menu wrapped up.

The first-floor restaurant is a large, low-ceilinged room, light and relaxed, with a dozen tables that get booked up quickly. A blackboard of daily specials is trundled around. Langoustines come with three mayonnaises – spicy, garlic and more successful parsley – or else hot with garlic butter. In the opinion of an inspector, the more pretentious, flashy dishes do no one any favours', so it may be best to stay with straightforward and carefully cooked wings of skate in black butter, or scallops ('a generous helping, tender, juicy and sweet') with mushrooms and garlic. Reasonable prices and civilised service add to the appeal, and three dozen wines cope perfectly well with the down-to-earth style of the place. House wine is from £7.95.

CHEF: Paul Laurie PROPRIETOR: Crannog Ltd OPEN: Tue to Sat 12 to 2.30, 6 to 9.30 (10.30 Fri and Sat) CLOSED: Christmas and New Year MEALS: alc (main courses £9 to £12). Set L £8.50 (2 courses) to £10 SERVICE: not inc CARDS: Access, Delta, Switch, Visa DETAILS: 52 seats. Private parties: 60 main room. Vegetarian meals. Children's helpings. Music

Killermont Polo Club

2022 Maryhill Road, nr Bearsden, Glasgow G20 0AB COOKING 1
TEL: 0141-946 5412 COST £15–£40

'It's like dining in a Ralph Lauren advertisement,' commented a visitor to this converted manse that doubles as a restaurant and polo club (complete with its own mini-pitch and competing teams). The décor is a seriously themed assemblage of sporting references and mementoes with 'heavy Raj-appeal' although the same reporter felt there ought to be 'more art in the cooking and less in the window dressing'. Even so, there is much to enjoy from a menu that leapfrogs from authentic Indian regional specialities to 'home and colonial' throwbacks. The tandoori oven is used to telling effect, not only for 'magical, meltingly tender' chicken malai tikka but also for duck (marinated in orange and lemon) and salmon (cooked crisp with roasted peppers). Elsewhere you might notice Goan-style steamed mussels, fruity 'bahr' lamb with mangoes and apricots, and Parsee fish parcels wrapped in spinach, tucked up alongside such unlikely bedfellows as sirloin of beef or even haddock and chips. The vegetable contingent makes interesting reading and the lively assortment of relishes and chutneys is a plus point. Lunch is a set-price deal, and fixed-price buffets are served Sunday to Tuesday evenings. Three dozen wines offer the prospect of affordable drinking from around the globe. House wine is £8.25.

CHEF: Jas Sagoo PROPRIETORS: Kal Dhaliwal, Pami Dhaliwal and Jas Sagoo OPEN: Mon to Sat L 12 to 2, all week D 5 to 10.30 CLOSED: 25 Dec, 1 Jan MEALS: alc D (main courses £7 to £12). Set L £6.95 (2 courses) to £7.95, Set D Sun to Tue £9.95 SERVICE: not inc, card slips closed CARDS: Access, Amex, Diners, Switch, Visa DETAILS: 90 seats. 25 tables outside. Private parties: 50 main room, 24 to 50 private rooms. Car park. Vegetarian meals. Smart dress preferred. No smoking in dining-room. Wheelchair access. Music

Mitchell's West End £

31–35 Ashton Lane, off Byres Road, Glasgow G12 8SJ COOKING 1
TEL: 0141-339 2220 FAX: 0141-204 1818 COST £20–£38

Competition is stiff here – the Ubiquitous Chip (see entry, page 581) is across the road – but Mitchell's survives on a breezy diet of well executed bistro cooking. The compact, light room with bright colours and terracotta walls shows Mediterranean leanings, but the food is from all over. This being Scotland, salmon appears more than once on the menu, although anything from chump of lamb served with aubergine purée and a basil and tomato concassé to medallion of Angus fillet with a pickled walnut and crème fraîche sauce may draw up alongside. There are no surprises among puddings of bread-and-butter, chocolate fudge cake or sticky toffee. It should be noted that meals are available from 5.15pm. A licence has been applied for, but in the meantime you can Bring Your Own for a corkage charge of £1.95. A second branch, Mitchell's Charing

Cross is at 157 North Street, Glasgow G3 7DA, Tel: 0141-204 4312, is licensed and is open for meals all day.

CHEFS: Scott Baxter and Sean Ward PROPRIETORS: Angus Boyd and Sean Ward OPEN: Mon to Sat D only 5.15 to 10.30 MEALS: alc (main courses £7 to £14). Unlicensed, but bring your own; corkage £1.90 SERVICE: not inc CARDS: Access, Amex, Delta, Diners, Switch, Visa DETAILS: 44 seats. Private parties: 44 main room. Vegetarian meals. Children's helpings. Smart dress preferred. Music

▲ *One Devonshire Gardens*

1 Devonshire Gardens, Glasgow G12 0UX **COOKING 2***
TEL: 0141-339 2001 FAX: 0141-337 1663 **COST £36–£60**

Glasgow's West End has none of the hurly-burly of its London equivalent; it is a place of wide avenues and spreading trees, an enclave of unexpected serenity in this thoroughly vibrant city. One Devonshire Gardens was once three buildings, whose elegant restoration provides the setting for one of the city's most enjoyable hotels and for Andrew Fairlie's reliable and polished cooking.

The format is set price for both lunch and dinner, the former for three courses, the latter adding 'potage du jour' after the starter. Although luxuries like truffles and foie gras crop up regularly, the overall impression people seem to come away with is one of lightness. This can be cause for either relief or sulks, depending on your appetite. It is heartening, though, to find that most dishes are based on readily understandable culinary logic rather than the hectic piling on of whatever is to hand. Thus, smoked salmon is accompanied simply by a cream of horseradish, radishes and chives, while a delicately oriental treatment of scallops brings into play bean sprouts, crisp-fried vegetables and Thai spices. Main courses of chicken breast with flageolets and mushrooms, Aberdeen Angus fillet with creamed beetroot and red wine sauce, and roast cod with bacon and mashed potatoes display an instinct for safety. However, puddings deliver some invigorating flavours in the likes of aniseed parfait with blackberries, or a razor-sharp orange coulis to mitigate the richness of chocolate marquise. A pre-Christmas stay made a group from South Wales extremely happy, right down to the 'perfect ambience and excellent breakfasts'.

The expansive wine list offers plenty of geographical choice, although mark-ups throughout are fairly energetic and a £20 ceiling will prove very restrictive. House wines, including a Pinot Blanc from Austria, are £16.

CHEF: Andrew Fairlie PROPRIETOR: Ken McCulloch OPEN: all week (exc Sat L) 12.30 to 2, 7.15 to 10.15 MEALS: Set L £25, Set D £37.50 SERVICE: not inc, card slips closed CARDS: Access, Amex, Diners, Switch, Visa DETAILS: 50 seats. Private parties: 50 main room, 10 to 32 private rooms. Vegetarian meals. Children welcome. Smart dress preferred. Music ACCOMMODATION: 27 rooms, all with bath/shower. TV. Phone. B&B £137.50 to £185. Children welcome. Baby facilities. Pets welcome by arrangement. Afternoon teas. Garden (*The Which? Hotel Guide*)

Card slips closed *in the details at the end of an entry indicates that the total on the slips of credit cards is closed when handed over for signature.*

La Parmigiana £

447 Great Western Road, Glasgow G12 8HH — COOKING 1*
TEL: 0141-334 0686 FAX: 0141-332 3800 — COST £12–£41

This light and airy Italian restaurant manages to be 'cool, green and relaxing' as well as busy and lively thanks to a loyal local following. One packed Friday lunch-time a reporter was shoehorned into a tiny table at the top of the restaurant near the bar: 'It was ten past twelve, just before the rush.' The set-price lunch offers a three-course meal that might run from minestrone soup through lasagne or goujons of sole to crème caramel or fresh fruit: hardly ambitious cooking, but then look at the price. The *carte* may not raise any eyebrows with its familiar canter through a standard Italian repertoire of seafood salad, carpaccio, or veal with Parma ham and mozzarella, but the results are good.

Pasta is available in either large or small portions, and the pesto sauce ('our own blend') for spaghetti is rated highly for its 'full basil, oil and Parmesan flavours'. And full marks for ingenuity in serving a boiled egg deep-fried in breadcrumbs, a sort of Scotch egg without the meat. At one meal a 'massive plateful' of langoustines, simply grilled with butter and lemon, were 'fresh, full of flavour, sweet and truly wonderful'. White wine is a common cooking medium for fish, chicken and veal, with herbs and vegetables tossed in as appropriate. Puddings of tiramisù and strawberry mousse with kirsch have had the thumbs-up. Espresso is good, and service is friendly and willing to chat. Forty-odd largely Italian wines range from humble to exalted, and most are agreeably priced. House wine is £8.90 a litre.

CHEF: Sandro Giovanazzi PROPRIETORS: Angelo, Sandro and Stefano Giovanazzi OPEN: Mon to Sat 12 to 2.30, 6 to 11 CLOSED: 25 and 26 Dec, 1 and 2 Jan, bank hol Mons MEALS: alc (main courses £6 to £14). Set L £6.80 SERVICE: not inc CARDS: Access, Amex, Diners, Switch, Visa DETAILS: 55 seats. Private parties: 60 main room. Vegetarian meals. Children's helpings. Smart dress preferred. No pipes in dining-room. Music. Air-conditioned

Puppet Theatre

11 Ruthven Lane, Glasgow G12 9BG — COOKING 2
TEL: 0141-339 8444 FAX: 0141-339 7666 — COST £22–£46

Glasgow's West End now yields up a fair number of good eating places to choose from, but they don't come any more idiosyncratic than this one. In an old farmhouse and dairy that once upon a time were near a puppet theatre, a series of individually themed rooms has been designed, the star attraction of which is the Gaudi-esque conservatory looking out on to the courtyard.

The cooking, led by Iain McMaster, draws some inspiration from the Mediterranean vogue of latter years, but not to the exclusion of all else. Set-price menus at lunch-time make way for a *carte* of around seven choices per course in the evenings, and non-carnivores have their own 'menu of vegetables and spices'. Crinan scallops are paired with 'seared' potatoes in a trendy salad of sun-dried tomatoes, basil and olive oil, while smoked salmon, spinach and Gruyère go into a soufflé which is served with lemon hollandaise. A reporter at Christmas thought that a livery parfait lacked nothing in flavour and had 'excellent jelly'. Traditional treatments are often given a presentational twist, as in parcels of vegetable risotto with new season's lamb, or horseradish pancakes with Aberdeen Angus fillet.

The dessert list uses as much fruit as the kitchen can get its hands on for options poached figs with strawberry ice-cream and port syrup, mango and raspberry parfait with pistachio biscuit, and apricot beignets with rice-pudding and chocolate sauce. Even the crème brûlée is served in a baked apple. Some fine Scottish cheeses are offered, and 'first-rate' coffee comes with good chocolates. Service is reliable. The wine list is short and predominantly French. House burgundy is £11.50.

CHEF: Iain McMaster PROPRIETORS: Ron McCulloch and George Swanson OPEN: Sun to Fri L 12 to 2.30, Tue to Sun D 7 to 10.30 CLOSED: 25 and 26 Dec, 1 and 2 Jan MEALS: alc (main courses £13.50 to £15). Set L £9.95 (2 courses) to £12.50 SERVICE: not inc CARDS: Access, Amex, Switch, Visa DETAILS: 68 seats. Private parties: 26 main room, 12 and 26 private rooms. Car park. Vegetarian meals. No children under 12. Smart dress preferred. Wheelchair access (1 step; also WC). Music

Rogano

11 Exchange Place, Glasgow G1 3AN — COOKING **2**
TEL: 0141-248 4055 FAX: 0141-248 2608 — COST £24–£66

Rogano is an extraordinary period piece that sails on through the years oblivious to fashion. Opened in 1935, it was deliberately fitted out in Art Deco style to resemble the great Clyde-built liner the *Queen Mary*. Push open the portholed doors and walk past the atmospheric long bar to reach the main restaurant, a beautifully lit 'gem' of a room with 'blond-grained wood panels' and smoked-glass mirrors. A swirly brown and orange carpet maintains the '30s mood, while maritime and arboreal reliefs line the walls.

Fish and seafood from Scottish waters predominate, and new chef Derek Marshall has made a promising start, although a few details (especially vegetables, salads and coffee) seem to need some attention. Reporters have been well pleased with 'sweet' Oban mussels with garlic and tomato concassé, 'accurately steamed' medallions of monkfish with a creamy pink peppercorn sauce, and superb grilled langoustines served in the shell on a herb and a lemon butter ('simple perfection, requiring only knowledgeable buying and considerate timing,' was one verdict). Those with a taste for meat might be offered roast fillet of lamb with wild mushrooms, or sauté calf's liver, while vegetarians could opt for aubergine, courgette and feta strudel. Desserts complete the picture impressively: armagnac parfait with Earl Grey syrup, and a near-perfect mousse brûlée, for example. The thoughtfully chosen wine list favours whites, and there are plenty of half-bottles; prices start at around £14. Café Rogano, in the basement of the building, is open throughout the day for a mixed bag of dishes ranging from dim-sum to Cumberland sausages with onion gravy.

CHEF: Derek Marshall PROPRIETOR: Alloa Pubs and Restaurants Ltd OPEN: all week 12 to 2.30, 6.30 to 10.30 (10 Sun) CLOSED: 25 and 26 Dec, 1 and 2 Jan MEALS: alc (main courses £12.50 to £28). Set L Sat and Sun £15, Mon to Fri £16.50 SERVICE: 10%, card slips closed CARDS: Access, Amex, Delta, Diners, Switch, Visa DETAILS: 50 seats. Private parties: 60 main room, 16 and 24 private rooms. Vegetarian meals. Children welcome. No smoking in dining-room until 2 L, 9 D. Wheelchair access. Music. Air-conditioned

Ubiquitous Chip £

12 Ashton Lane, Glasgow G12 8SJ — COOKING 2
TEL: 0141-334 5007 FAX: 0141-337 1302 — COST £13–£51

A combined restaurant and wine business, the Chip – in the *Guide* now for 23 consecutive editions – caters for a considerable throughput seven days a week, the dynamically bustling atmosphere pleasing many. Upstairs can get hot and smoky, but people seem not to mind. Downstairs is equally busy and offers a more expensive menu.

Ronald Clydesdale's cooking takes risks, and intended flavours may not always filter through or work perfectly, but it still makes the most of good Scottish ingredients, from creel-caught langoustines to Loch Fyne kippers to Aberdeen Angus fillet steak. The more contrived the dishes sound, almost inevitably the less successfully they turn out. What about a gigot of Renfrewshire mutton 'of nearly disintegrating tenderness' stuffed with mussels and sauced with a shellfish reduction? But a lot of people appreciate the Chip for its refreshingly unpompous approach and breezy style. It runs the gamut from simple squat lobsters with mayonnaise, through a plate of onion bread crostini with wild mushrooms and vanilla vinaigrette that must have fallen off the back of a bandwagon, to a rib-sticking suet pudding of lamb's kidney with rich madeira gravy. You have to admire all that brio and vitality.

While vegetarian haggis may be something of a culinary contradiction, the general run of things is gutsy enough. Desserts include a 'fragrant and delicious' cinnamon ice-cream on a mango coulis, and a 'very traditional' steamed fruit sponge with cold custard. 'We left with deep feelings of satisfaction and considered our money well spent,' reported one couple. Prices on a wine list of signal brilliance are as keen as mustard, even for the most illustrious items, and the range of wines offered by the glass alone is a treat. Poniatowski Vouvray, Bodegas Amezola Rioja and Piper's Brook Pinot Noir from Tasmania are among the gems. Wines upstairs at the Chip start from as little as £6.50.

CHEF/PROPRIETOR: Ronald Clydesdale OPEN: all week 12 to 2.30, 5.30 (6.30 Sun) to 11 CLOSED: 25 and 31 Dec, 1 Jan MEALS: alc (main courses upstairs £4 to £11, downstairs £11 to £15) SERVICE: not inc CARDS: Access, Amex, Diners, Visa DETAILS: 150 seats. 12 tables outside. Private parties: 80 main room, 25 and 45 private rooms. Vegetarian meals. Children's helpings. No pipes in dining-room. Wheelchair access (1 step; also WC). No music

Yes NEW ENTRY

22 West Nile Street, Glasgow G1 2PT — COOKING 1
TEL: 0141-221 8044 FAX: 0141-248 9159 — COST £19–£39

The name of Ferrier Richardson's latest venture gives a clue that it may be striving hard to become the trendiest place in town. Situated in the architect-driven business quarter, Yes consists of a long ground-floor bar and brasserie with a restaurant below. For a basement, the place is airy and spacious, with mirrored panels, clever lighting and lots and lots of purple. It is 'grande luxe in a Kenny Everett sort of way', mused one reporter. Staff are young, cheerful and well trained; and the menu is laid out like a piece of modern poetry (look to the end for the set price).

The style is what we have come to call 'eclectic' when we can find no other word to describe a combination of lime and dill butter, grilled aubergine provençale, beef teriyaki with rice, wasabi and pickled ginger, and a gâteau of haggis with whisky-butter sauce, neeps and tatties – the last presumably for the tourist trade. Ferrier Richardson's track record is impressive, although at inspection only one dish matched up to his capabilities: a ramekin-sized prawn and Gruyère soufflé, well risen and golden, with a pot of sauce to pour in. Desserts might be citrus ravioli with a minestrone of fresh fruit, passion-fruit crème brûlée, and peppermint and chocolate soufflé. Bread rolls (with olives or caraway seeds) come not with butter, but with olive oil for dunking. Three dozen straightforward wines kick off with house vin de pays at £8.95.

CHEFS: Ferrier Richardson and Derek Blair PROPRIETOR: Ferrier Richardson OPEN: Mon to Sat 12 to 2.30, 7 to 11 MEALS: Set L £9.95 (2 courses) to £12.95, Set D £17.95 (2 courses) to £24.95 SERVICE: not inc CARDS: Access, Amex, Visa DETAILS: 80 seats. Private parties: 100 main room, 16 private room. Vegetarian meals. Children welcome. Smart dress preferred. Music. Air-conditioned

GULLANE Lothian **map 11**

▲ *Greywalls*

Muirfield, Gullane EH31 2EG
TEL: (01620) 842144 FAX: (01620) 842241 **COOKING 3**
on A198, at W end of Gullane **COST £26–£51**

Greywalls overlooks the ninth and eighteenth greens of Muirfield golf course, one of Scotland's finest; the house was designed in 1901 by Lutyens, with a walled garden by Gertrude Jekyll, and the Weaver family has been here since 1948. It still feels like a large private holiday home, and doesn't stint on comfort either. 'There is no bogus *bonhomie*, but real fires, welcoming armchairs, bowls of flowers and a general air of reassurance and efficiency,' writes one visitor. The panelled library has a grand piano, and there are two dining-rooms, set with the best napery, cutlery, china and glass.

The four-course dinner menu changes daily to follow the market, and understandably leans towards fish and seafood: perhaps a casserole of mixed fish under puff pastry with a champagne and dill sauce, or scallops marinated in lemon juice and sea salt with a tomato and shallot compote. The style is accomplished and modern, taking in warm pigeon and artichoke salad, or a warm chicken mousseline with a morel mushroom sauce. Saucing is light, often using a splash of balsamic vinegar or a flavoured butter, and dishes commendably avoid excess: luxuries are not strewn about, and Paul Baron knows just how many different tastes a dish can stand.

The second course is a soup or sorbet, the fourth a selection of cheese, or else a pudding that sides with tradition but doesn't rely on heavy syrupy sponges: raspberry soufflé with vanilla sauce, for example, or Bakewell tart with almond custard, or a tangy lemon tart with blackcurrant sauce and a citrus sorbet. Sandwiches and light meals are offered at lunch-time. The backbone of the wine list is classic French, with short selections from the rest of Europe and the New World, and there is something to suit most pockets. House wine is £11.50.

CELLARMAN'S CHOICE: **Meursault 1991, Louis Latour, £30; Haut-Médoc, Ch. Cissac 1986, £23.**

CHEF: Paul Baron PROPRIETORS: Giles and Ros Weaver OPEN: all week 12.30 to 2, 7.30 to 9.15 CLOSED: Nov to Mar MEALS: alc L Mon to Sat (main courses £8.50 to £11). Set L Sun £20, Set D £33 SERVICE: not inc, card slips closed CARDS: Access, Amex, Diners, Switch, Visa DETAILS: 70 seats. Private parties: 50 main room, 20 private room. Car park. Children's helpings. Smart dress preferred. No smoking in dining-room. Wheelchair access (also WC). No music ACCOMMODATION: 22 rooms, all with bath/shower. TV. Phone. B&B £95 to £170. Deposit: £60. Rooms for disabled. Children welcome. Baby facilities. Pets by arrangement. Afternoon teas. Garden (*The Which? Hotel Guide*)

La Potinière

Main Street, Gullane EH31 2AA
TEL: (01620) 843214 COOKING **4**
on A198, 4m SW of North Berwick COST **£26–£45**

La Potinière has enjoyed the personal touch of the Browns since 1975 and a reporter felt that it was 'well worth the highest accolade for every aspect of cooking, atmosphere, wine, service, charm, good taste and judgement'. Once through the heavy lace curtains, all is as quietly French as can be including the menu, written in David Brown's elegant script and brown ink, which is passed around in a small baroque gilded frame, a 'silly but endearing' habit.

One value-for-money summer lunch consisted of cream of cep soup, sole au pistou with sauce vierge, leg of guinea-fowl stuffed with apricots, and then either Brie 'in first-class condition', or a chocolate cake with a firm outside and a soft centre. At dinner both cheese and pudding are included, to make up the five courses, and an 'innovative salad' appears at all meals after the main course: 'not a lollo rosso leaf in sight', and more likely to be made with 'finely chopped asparagus tips, mange-tout, podded peas and decent greenery, all lightly dressed'. The cooking is full of confidence, thanks to Hilary Brown's sure hand with balance, combinations and seasonings. Soups are homely and well reported, including a 'vivid orange-coloured purée of soothing carrots enlivened by apple and sweet-sharp apricot, with a hint of exotic spice: perfectly judged and totally delicious'. They come with splendidly rough wholemeal chunks of nut or raisin bread.

Fish has included a fillet of 'perfectly cooked' sole folded over a spoonful of pistou with a fuzzy topknot of crisp, shredded, deep-fried courgettes, surrounded by a sauce vierge based on excellent olive oil, a dish of 'vivid and well-balanced flavours'. The kitchen's sensitive handling of high-quality ingredients has also produced first-rate porc aux pruneaux: a thick tranche of tender and tasty pork with two huge prunes and a potato cake, and a 'superbly rich and fudgy sauce'.

David Brown welcomes, serves and advises. He is relaxed but correct, never pompous, and when it comes to wine he takes every question or suggestion seriously. His own recommendations are well worth following. This is not just a hugely good list, but a working cellar with wines waiting to appear on the list when they are ready, and removed when they start to decline. It ranges widely among the great and the good in claret and burgundy, harks back to mature vintages, and looks forward to new discoveries. South-west France is a strong section, and epitomises the approach: quality comes first, and low mark-ups ensure wonderful value. House wine is £9.75 a bottle.

CHEF: Hilary Brown PROPRIETORS: David and Hilary Brown OPEN: Mon, Tue, Thur and Sun L 1pm (one sitting), Fri and Sat D 8pm (one sitting) CLOSED: Oct, 25 Dec, 1 Jan, 1 week Jun MEALS: Set L Mon, Tue, Thur £18.75, Set L Sun £19.75, Set D £29.50 SERVICE: none CARDS: none DETAILS: 30 seats. Private parties: 30 main room. Car park. Children welcome. Smart dress preferred. No smoking in dining-room. Wheelchair access (1 step). No music

INVERNESS Highland map 11

▲ *Culloden House*

Inverness IV1 2NZ
TEL: (01463) 790461 FAX: (01463) 792181
take A96 from Inverness and turn right at Culloden signposted after 1m
COOKING 2
COST £23–£52

This grand piece of Scottish country housery squeezes the most out of location and expectation. You want Bonnie Prince Charlie? They got him. Slept here before his last battle. You want kilts? They got 'em. Ian McKenzie wears nothing else. The imposing Palladian mansion in 40 acres of grounds sports chandeliers, marble fireplaces and rooms the size of football pitches. You want venison, salmon, Scottish cheeses? They got 'em, although not necessarily all at once. The four-course dinner slips in a soup or sorbet before main courses of sirloin steak, breast of duck, or a roulade of trout fillets and sole mousse on a creamy leek sauce.

A vegetarian dish is always on the menu: sorrel and onion tart, perhaps, or a spinach strudel with goats' cheese and couscous. Yes, that was the Mediterranean you heard lapping beside the Moray Firth, although quenelles, terrines and timbales hint at a more general French influence. Sometimes the partnerships – guinea-fowl with an orange mousse and a port-flavoured sauce, or fillet of beef with blue cheese sauce and mushrooms – may be a touch ambitious. Posh clarets are tempered by affordable wines from around the world, with house wine from £2.50 a glass, or £9.25 a bottle.

CHEF: Michael Simpson PROPRIETORS: Ian and Marjory McKenzie OPEN: all week 12.30 to 2, 7 to 9 MEALS: Set L £12.99 (2 courses) to £16.50, Set D £35 SERVICE: not inc CARDS: Access, Amex, Diners, Switch, Visa DETAILS: 51 seats. Private parties: 51 main room, 34 private room. Car park. Vegetarian meals. No children under 10. Jacket and tie. No music ACCOMMODATION: 23 rooms, all with bath/shower. TV. Phone. B&B £120 to £220. Deposit: 100%. No children under 10. Afternoon teas. Garden

▲ *Dunain Park*

Inverness IV3 6JN
TEL: (01463) 230512 FAX: (01463) 224532
on A82, 1m out of Inverness
COOKING 1*
COST £24–£41

Six acres of gardens and woodland surround the Georgian house, two of them supplying the kitchen with vegetables, herbs and soft fruits. The dining-room has been completely refurbished this year, but the kitchen's output remains

Scottish with a French influence. Reporters have enjoyed first courses of a 'brilliant' warm salad of local chanterelle mushrooms, a courgette flower filled with a mousseline of chicken and served with a sabayon sauce, and a refreshing dish of dressed crab on a bed of leaves with a sweet vinaigrette. The style is contemporary, the flavours clear.

Ann Nicoll bakes her own bread, scones, shortbread and biscuits. She makes jams, cooks local venison and hare, bakes wild salmon in sea salt and serves it with a sauce of white port, lime and ginger, and makes a speciality of steaks from Highland cattle, 'the ones with the long coats and big horns', she explains helpfully. Loin of lamb is cooked 'perfectly pink'. Pan-frying the breasts of birds is a favourite: perhaps chicken in a madeira sauce, served with a filo pastry tartlet containing leek and bacon. Vegetables are steamed, sweets are from the buffet, with cheese or fresh fruit as an option. A wide-ranging list of carefully chosen wines is backed up by at least one single-malt whisky from every working distillery in Scotland that bottles its output. House wine is £10.

CHEF: Ann Nicoll PROPRIETORS: Ann and Edward Nicoll OPEN: all week 12 to 1.30, 7 to 9 CLOSED: 3 weeks Jan to Feb MEALS: alc D (main courses £13 to £15). Set L £16.50 SERVICE: not inc, card slips closed CARDS: Access, Amex, Diners, Switch, Visa DETAILS: 36 seats. Private parties: 12 main room. Car park. Vegetarian meals. Children's helpings. Smart dress preferred. No smoking in dining-room. Wheelchair access. No music ACCOMMODATION: 14 rooms, all with bath/shower. TV. Phone. B&B £35 to £150. Deposit: £50. Rooms for disabled. Children welcome. Baby facilities. Pets welcome in bedrooms only. Afternoon teas. Garden. Swimming-pool (*The Which? Hotel Guide*)

KENTALLEN Highland map 11

▲ *Ardsheal House* **NEW ENTRY**

Kentallen PA38 4BX
TEL: (01631) 740227 FAX: (01631) 740342 COOKING 2
on A828, 5m S of Ballachulish Bridge COST £24–£46

Ardsheal House has been bought back by Neil Sutherland, whose family home it was before the Taylors turned it into a hotel. It sits in 900 acres of privately owned hills, woods, gardens and shore-front. Despite the change of ownership, George Kelso remains at the stoves with Michelle Kelso as manager. 'Little has changed,' writes an old hand, 'except that there appear to be more staff and fewer dogs.' It is a convivial place that 'combines the warmth and informality of a friend's house with the care and comfort of a top-notch hotel'. There are still imposing views of Loch Linnhe and much heavy panelling, while the summer dining-room is a conservatory extension with geraniums, clematis and 'a pleasing feeling of light and space'.

Dinner, the main meal, is five courses, the second a set soup (mange-tout and ginger, for example), with a salad separating main course from pudding. Choice is limited to a couple of items at each stage, and the main-course options on a May menu were roast saddle of local venison with braised lentils, or pan-fried scallops with creamed spinach and red pepper sauce. Loch Linnhe prawns are a speciality, and might be poached with saffron risotto and spinach sauce. A spring reporter munched his way through warm quail tartlets with whole tender breasts of quail, snowy-white firm halibut with a red and green pepper sauce, and hot prune and armagnac soufflé. The standard of cooking generally holds its own, and niggles are minor: a 'sweet and heavy' tomato and fennel soup here, a 'cloying, fatty' ice-cream there. Service is 'professional without being stuffy, and friendly without being over-chatty'. The wide-ranging wine list is carefully chosen to balance quality and value, helped by ungreedy mark-ups and a fair spread of half-bottles. Four house wines are £11, or £2.50 a glass.

CHEF: George Kelso PROPRIETORS: Mr and Mrs Neil Sutherland OPEN: all week 12 to 1.45, 8.30 (one sitting) MEALS: Set L £18, Set D £32.50 SERVICE: none CARDS: Access, Amex, Switch, Visa DETAILS: 45 seats. Private parties: 30 main room. Car park. Children's helpings. Smart dress preferred. No smoking in dining-room. Wheelchair access. No music ACCOMMODATION: 13 rooms, all with bath/shower. Phone. D,B&B £85 to £180. Deposit: £100. Children welcome. Baby facilities. Pets welcome. Afternoon teas. Garden (*The Which? Hotel Guide*)

KILCHRENAN Strathclyde map 11

▲ *Taychreggan*

Kilchrenan, by Taynuilt PA35 1HQ
TEL: (01866) 833211 and 833366 COOKING 2
FAX: (01866) 833244 COST £17–£42

The edge of Loch Awe, a few miles south of Oban, is where to head for if you are in search of perfect tranquillity. 'It is so peaceful,' commented one reader, 'the silence is deafening.' Taychreggan is a seventeenth-century inn, once a pit-stop for cattle-drovers and now home to Euan and Annie Paul's highly rated country hotel. Their home-from-home approach seems readily appreciated, the attention 'friendly but not stifling'.

Chef Hugh Cocker is a busy man. When not baking bread or bottling conserves, he is out foraging for wild mushrooms. The exertions all come together in five-course set-price dinners that offer a pair of choices for each of the first two courses and none thereafter. The menu reads a little like a Scottish version of Lakeland cooking, with ambitious constructions being tried all the way through. In February a puff pastry pillow filled with asparagus, mushrooms and 'pencil leeks' on an orange sauce was followed by broccoli and almond soup, and went on to baked Shetland salmon with bacon and celeriac risotto, shiitakes and cherry tomatoes. Puddings, such as iced nougat glace with bitter chocolate sauce, precede the cheese selection. Sorbet, as an alternative to soup, may be based on anything from rhubarb to banana. The wine list offers plenty of choice below £20 across a broad spectrum. Some grand names are mobilised in the red Bordeaux section, and even the more expensive ones are not outrageously priced. House wines start with carafes of basic Côtes du Rhône at £6.75.

CHEF: Hugh Cocker PROPRIETORS: Dr and Mrs E.H.M. Paul OPEN: all week 12.30 to 2, 7.30 to 8.45 MEALS: alc L (main courses £5.50 to £11). Set D £28 SERVICE: not inc CARDS: Access, Amex, Delta, Switch, Visa DETAILS: 65 seats. 6 tables outside. Private parties: 30 main room. Car park. No children under 12. Smart dress preferred. No smoking in dining-room. Wheelchair access (also WC). Music ACCOMMODATION: 20 rooms, all with bath/shower. Phone. B&B £47 to £94. No children under 12. Pets welcome in bedrooms only. Afternoon teas. Garden. Fishing

KILLIECRANKIE Tayside map 11

▲ *Killiecrankie Hotel*

Killiecrankie, by Pitlochry PH16 5LG
TEL: (01796) 473220 FAX: (01796) 472451 COOKING 1*
off A9, 3m N of Pitlochry COST £35–£42

The hotel's four acres overlook the Pass of Killiecrankie and the lush wooded slopes where, in 1689, the first shots in the Jacobite rising rang out. Now roe deer graze unstartled by musket fire, and this 'solid stone manse' extends a welcome. The restaurant area resembles a baronial hunting lodge designed by Laura Ashley, thought one man, but the approach is refreshingly unpretentious.

John Ramsay cooks a fixed-price menu of four courses plus coffee, with cheeses offered after dessert. The style is recognisably country-house, mobilising good local ingredients in dishes that may end up quite complex but seem to succeed. A spring dinner began with 'baked cake' (more accurately a tart) of Isle of Gigha goats' cheese with crisp leaves and a pleasingly sharp balsamic dressing. Smoked salmon was given an appetising lift by being layered with gherkins, capers and a lime mayonnaise. Main courses always include a cold salad dish, often salmon but perhaps duck. Fish cookery is confident enough to garnish a meaty fish of grilled halibut with peppers, orange and ginger, the accompaniments finished with Scotch whisky. Guinea-fowl delivered good flavour contrast in the braising of a leg and steaming of smoked breast. Technique comes to the fore in desserts such as a flambé of fruits with Grand Marnier cream and properly crisped crème brûlée. Some fine Scottish cheeses are offered, and there are good home-made breads to go with them. The wine list covers most of the major regions, with small but well-chosen selections in each. Prices are pretty reasonable, and there is a commendably extensive page of halves. House Côtes de Gascogne is £8.80.

CHEF: John Ramsay PROPRIETORS: Colin and Carole Anderson OPEN: all week D only 7 to 8.30 CLOSED: Jan and Feb MEALS: Set D £27.50; alc bar L and D available SERVICE: not inc, card slips closed CARDS: Access, Delta, Switch, Visa DETAILS: 32 seats. Private parties: 16 main room. Car park. Children's helpings. No children under 5. Smart dress preferred. No smoking in dining-room. No music ACCOMMODATION: 10 rooms, all with bath/shower. TV. Phone. B&B £48 to £96. Deposit: £35. Children welcome. Baby facilities. Pets welcome. Afternoon teas. Garden (*The Which? Hotel Guide*)

KINCLAVEN Tayside map 11

▲ *Ballathie House*

Kinclaven, by Stanley PH1 4QN
TEL: (01250) 883268 FAX: (01250) 883396 COOKING 2
off B9099, take right fork 1m N of Stanley COST £20–£46

'The pleasure of visiting Ballathie begins as one turns in at the lodge to embark on the half-mile drive to the house through banks of rhododendrons, magnificent trees, strutting pheasants and well-tended lawns.' So wrote a traveller who appreciated the fact that 'good country living' and 'old-fashioned dignity' are alive and well in this baronial mansion on the banks of the River Tay. The hotel stands at the heart of a 1,500-acre sporting estate where visitors can enjoy all the pleasures and pursuits of the great outdoors. Reporters have marvelled at the views from the beautifully proportioned dining-rooms and have described the service as 'exceptional, with one or two deft touches but no fanfares or waving of serving-dishes'.

Fixed-price dinners (choose three or four courses) show off the quality of local produce, and the ingredients themselves tend to draw most effusive comments: Scottish asparagus with orange anglaise sauce, plump mussels, lamb 'beautifully done' with shallots and rosemary, and 'exquisite' squat lobsters with buttered noodles, for example. You can also choose from a handful of supplementary dishes, such as home-cured salmon with Arran mustard cream, oak-smoked beef with basil jelly, or medallions of Highland venison with baby poached pear and pickled walnut sauce. Vegetarians are well provided for by dishes such as tagliatelle with water-chestnuts and oyster mushrooms. 'Terrace lunches' focus on more straightforward offerings, including poached Tay salmon with lemon and dill butter sauce. The wine list spans the globe and plenty of half-bottles are on offer. A dozen house recommendations (all served by the glass) start at £9.50.

CHEF: Kevin MacGillivray PROPRIETOR: Ballathie House Hotel Ltd OPEN: all week 12.30 to 2, 7 to 9 MEALS: Set L £11 (2 courses) to £13.95, Set D £27.50 SERVICE: not inc CARDS: Access, Amex, Delta, Diners, Switch, Visa DETAILS: 70 seats. Private parties: 60 main room, 10 and 30 private rooms. Car park. Vegetarian meals. Children welcome. Smart dress preferred. No smoking in dining-room. Wheelchair access (also WC). Music ACCOMMODATION: 38 rooms, all with bath/shower. TV. Phone. D, B&B £77.50 to £210. Rooms for disabled. Children welcome. Baby facilities. Pets welcome. Afternoon teas. Garden. Fishing

---

KINGUSSIE Highland map 11

▲ *The Cross*

HIGHLAND 1996 GOOD DEAL

Tweed Mill Brae, Ardbroilach Road,
Kingussie PH21 1TC — COOKING 3*
TEL: (01540) 661166 FAX: (01540) 661080 — COST £45–£54

The nineteenth-century tweed mill is a couple of hundred yards up the hill from the traffic lights – there is only one set in Kingussie – then left down the drive. Conversion has been done kindly. The Cross is modern, and feels comfortable and spacious inside they-don't-make-them-like-that-any-more stone walls. But most of all its character derives from the unassuming proprietors, from Ruth Hadley's version of Scottish cooking and Tony Hadley's passion for wine. There is no attempt to hoodwink, with flavours or anything else; everything is all heart on sleeve and brimming with integrity.

The format of dinner is now standardised at five courses (the second one soup), and portions are small enough not to overpower. The cooking is mostly Scottish in style, using local game, mushrooms and west coast fish, plus, on occasion, that rarity pike, made into a sausage and served with a leek and lemon grass sauce. Neither Thai spicing nor the occasional French dish – ham and parsley terrine, for example – throws the food off its intended course. Ruth Hadley's approach often involves a gentle highlight of spice or heat or acidulation to point up the main item, and results in soups such as mushroom with coriander, in roast duck breast with a sauce of cranberries and ginger, or in fillet of venison with juniper and thyme. Reporters have enjoyed roast pigeon breast on green lentils with wild mushrooms, and salmon fish-cake, as well as old stagers like venison Francatelli and chocolate whisky laird.

There are no notes on the wine list; they are all in Tony Hadley's head. He and the list are as one. Just ask and he will measure you up, like a tailor, and pull out something to suit. If you want a bankable certainty, he has it in spades. If you want to try something new, no problem. The only gap is Italy. 'We used to stock some superb Italian wines, but nobody bought them.' Shame. There are over 30 bottles at £12.50 or less, and indeed prices throughout are amazingly generous, as is the tally of half bottles. There are no listed house wines sold by the glass, but 'there is always an interesting bottle I am about to open/have just opened'. CELLARMAN'S CHOICE: Buzet 'Cuvée Napoleon' 1985, Les Vignerons de Buzet, £14.75; Geoff Merrill Chardonnay 1986, McLaren Vale, S. Australia, £19.50.

CHEF: Ruth Hadley PROPRIETORS: Tony and Ruth Hadley OPEN: Wed to Mon D only 7 to 9 CLOSED: 1 to 26 Dec, 8 Jan to 28 Feb MEALS: Set D £35 SERVICE: not inc, card slips closed CARDS: Access, Delta, Switch, Visa DETAILS: 28 seats. Private parties: 28 main room. Car park. No children under 8. No smoking in dining-room. Wheelchair access (also WC). No music ACCOMMODATION: 9 rooms, all with bath/shower. Phone. DB&B £85 to £170. Deposit: £50. No children under 8. Garden

KINLOCHMOIDART Highland map 11

Kinacarra

Kinlochmoidart PH38 4ND
TEL: (01967) 431238 COOKING 2
on A861, at head of Loch Moidart COST £16–£34

The long stone cottage near Loch Moidart has been a school and a police station in its time. Pine tables have taken the place of desks, and people come here of their own free will nowadays, drawn by generous portions of locally produced venison, casseroled with red wine and peppers, and by fish and shellfish, from crab (in a roulade) to salmon served with an orange, rosemary and redcurrant sauce. Despite the appearance of a chicken breast baked with lime, honey and soy sauce, Frances MacLean's cooking is old-fashioned enough to take in French onion soup, fillet of sole véronique, and scallops in cheese and wine sauce.

What matters is that freshness makes itself felt, and the flavours are direct, with the garden supplying herbs for salads. Dinner is a choice from four first courses and half a dozen mains, one of them usually a nut roast, while puddings can be as rich as chocolate roulade with orange cream filling, or steamed ginger figgy pudding with Drambuie cream. The wine list is brief, helpfully annotated and fairly priced, with house wine at £8.75.

CHEF: Frances MacLean PROPRIETORS: Angus and Frances MacLean OPEN: Tue to Sun 12 to 2, 7 to 9 CLOSED: end Oct to Easter MEALS: alc (main courses £5 to £12) SERVICE: not inc DETAILS: 24 seats. 1 table outside. Private parties: 30 main room. Car park. Vegetarian meals. Children's helpings. Smart dress preferred. No smoking in dining-room. Wheelchair access (also WC). No music

KINLOCH RANNOCH Tayside map 11

▲ *Cuilmore Cottage* NEW ENTRY

Kinloch Rannoch PH16 5QB
TEL/FAX: (01882) 632218
first turning on left on southern loch road from Kinloch Rannoch
COOKING 1
COST £25–£30

A notice outside declares this to be 'the smallest hotel and restaurant in Scotland'. It is a tiled and whitewashed crofter's cottage, with a garden at the front, rows of vegetable beds to the side, and sheep and poultry at the back. 'A herd of red deer appeared in the field next door towards dusk'. A gleaming copper hot-water tank is the main feature of the dining-room, with pine panelling and family photographs hinting at the Scandinavian background of the Steffens, who hail from Denmark. 'There is no denying its smallness,' wrote one, as if he had tried to do so but failed. One square table seating eight people is pretty convincing evidence. On a good day, the other guests are fascinating conversationalists.

A reporter who telephoned on the day was told that dinner was at 7pm prompt, and that 'the main course was lamb, in case it helped me decide which wine to bring, as they have no licence'. On some evenings there may be a second sitting at 8.30, so check the situation first. 'There was no menu, written or announced, so we did not know what lay ahead.' In the event it was 'good honest food and lots of it', beginning with smoked salmon roulade and home-made bread, followed by 'rich, creamy broccoli and Stilton soup', and 'rather unexciting' lamb. Main courses on other occasions might be pigeon breast with shredded cabbage, beef with caramelised onions, or a grilling of whatever fish the market turns up. Steaming toffee pudding with caramel sauce on one occasion finished off both the meal and the reporter: 'After dinner we went for a brisk long walk as an antidote.'

CHEF: Anita Steffen PROPRIETORS: Jens and Anita Steffen OPEN: all week D only; non-residents must book at least 24 hours in advance to confirm time; residents 7 (one sitting) CLOSED: Nov to Jan MEALS: Set D £22.50. Unlicensed, but bring your own: no corkage SERVICE: not inc, card slips closed CARDS: Access, Visa DETAILS: 8 seats. Private parties: 10 main room. Car park. Vegetarian meals. Smart dress preferred. No smoking in dining-room. Music ACCOMMODATION: 2 rooms, both with bath/shower. D,B&B £45 to £90. Deposit: 50%. Pets welcome. Garden. Fishing

KYLESKU Highland map 11

▲ *Kylesku Hotel*

Kylesku IV27 4HW
TEL: (01971) 502231 FAX: (01971) 502313
on A894, at S side of old ferry crossing, by new bridge linking Ullapool and Kylestrome
COOKING 1*
COST £19–£37

The hamlet of Kylesku consists of 'the hotel, a couple of houses and two or three boats', reported one visitor. The view over Loch Glencoul from the hotel is 'breathtaking' and the building has been much extended over the years, but still 'cowers low to avoid the worst of the weather'. Fish is the thing here and can be seen being unloaded from the boats in the afternoon.

Marcel Klein's culinary approach is a robust one. Some reporters this year have felt that a little less elaboration would help, as in the unnecessary garnish of onion rings, capers and grated horseradish for a moist, light cured, smoked salmon. Mussels in puff pastry were described as 'delicious', while grilled plaice with potato cake was for one reporter 'like fish and chips in heaven'. If fish doesn't appeal, there could be carrot and red pepper soup, or home-made venison pâté, followed by duck breast with red cabbage and cherries, or chicken tikka. Tarts, pies and puddings, such as bread-and-butter, are laid out on a table for selection and can be served with home-made ice-cream or cream. Excellent breakfasts have been mentioned: a reporter especially enjoyed one that included 'lovingly cooked' field mushrooms. The welcome and service has been described as 'rather charmless' by one visitor, 'cheerful and generous' by another. The wine list fails to list producers, or even vintages in many cases. House French starts at £6.75.

CHEF/PROPRIETOR: Marcel Klein OPEN: all week 12 to 2.30, 6 to 9.45 CLOSED: Nov to Feb MEALS: alc (main courses £7 to £14). Set L and D £12 (2 courses) to £15.50 SERVICE: not inc, card slips closed CARDS: Access, Visa DETAILS: 28 seats. Private parties: 28 main room, 30 private room. Car park. Vegetarian meals. Children's helpings. Jacket and tie. No smoking in dining-room. Wheelchair access (also WC). Music ACCOMMODATION: 7 rooms, all with bath/shower. TV. B&B £25 to £48. Deposit: 10%. Rooms for disabled. Children welcome. Baby facilities. Small dogs welcome. Afternoon teas. Garden. Fishing

LINLITHGOW Lothian map 11

Champany Inn

Champany, Linlithgow EH49 7LU
TEL: (01506) 834532 and 834388
FAX: (01506) 834302 COOKING 3*
2m NE of Linlithgow at junction of A904 and A803 COST £29–£68

As we go to press the restaurant is being refurbished, and a new style of both menu and wine list is promised, but there are no plans to change the basic format that has made Champany Inn a focal point for some of the best steaks in Britain. The idea is simplicity itself, and it seems amazing that there is not a chain of little Champanies around the country. Aberdeen Angus beef is hung for three weeks in the Davidsons' own ionised chill-room, then cut to order, weighed and cooked. It comes on the bone, off the bone, from fillet or rib, indeed 'cut to your own specification', so the possibilities are endless. If you want a big piece, the meat is weighed and charged at about £1 an ounce. Some wonder about the cost, but the quality is uncompromising.

There are sauces, too, including an alcoholic Bonnie Prince Charlie, but simple chargrilling of such fine material demands the simplest accompaniment: classic béarnaise, perhaps, with potatoes, or wild mushrooms in season. Variety comes in the form of Loch Gruinart oysters, a whole lobster from the Champany's own sea-water pool, or grilled Shetland salmon. 'Light' lunches consist of a salad plus ribeye beef or grilled leg of lamb. So many red wines are suited to partner grilled beef that the list takes no chances and includes most of them, from *grand cru* burgundy downwards, from South African Pinotage upwards (the South African selection is exceptionally good), and from recent vintages back to the 1960s and 1970s. Mark-ups reflect the cost of keeping such a large stock, so it is not a place for bargains. The spirit list is a beaut. House wine is £10.50 and £12.50. CELLARMAN'S CHOICE: Thelema Mountain Vineyards Chardonnay 1993, Stellenbosch, S. Africa, £25; Rioja, Colección Personal Reserva 1988, Marqués de Griñon, £27.50.

CHEF: Clive Davidson PROPRIETORS: Clive and Anne Davidson OPEN: Mon to Fri L 12.30 to 2, Mon to Sat D 7 to 10 CLOSED: 25 and 26 Dec, 1 and 2 Jan MEALS: alc (main courses £14.50 to £25.50). Set L £13.75 (2 courses), Set D £27.50 to £35. Minimum £14.50 SERVICE: 10%, card slips closed CARDS: Access, Amex, Diners, Switch, Visa DETAILS: 50 seats. 10 tables outside. Private parties: 56 main room. Car park. Vegetarian meals. No children under 8. Smart dress preferred. Wheelchair access (1 step; also WC). No music

MILNGAVIE Strathclyde map 11

Gingerhill £

1 Hillhead Street, Milngavie G62 8AF
TEL: 0141-956 6515 COOKING 1
4m N of Glasgow, off A81 COST £8–£42

Size isn't everything, and what Gingerhill lacks in elbow-room it more than makes up for in *bonhomie*, thanks largely to the 'effervescent personality' of Carol Thomson. The business in this little first-floor room overlooking Milngavie shopping centre is predominantly fish, mostly prepared simply, sometimes slightly fancified but not to the point of pretension. Six 'absolutely fresh, top-grade' crayfish fried in butter with garlic might start you off in fine style, as might a seafood salad, a bowl of fish soup or deep-fried squid. An inspector thought the Oban mussels unusually small specimens, but a whole lemon sole on the bone was 'simple, fresh and delicious'. On the inventive side, monkfish thermidor came as 'excellent, firm, huge portions of fish in a memorably rich sauce'. Roast potatoes may seem odd with fish but they are nicely cooked, and salads are sharply dressed. Puddings, of the likes of lemon meringue pie, do not figure on the menu but are recited by the staff. Breads are a good selection and coffee is strong. There is no licence so bring your own and be sure that it's well chilled. The corkscrew's services come free.

CHEF: Heather Andrew PROPRIETOR: Carol Thomson OPEN: Mon to Sat L 11 to 3, Thur to Sat D 7.30 (one sitting) MEALS: alc (main courses £2.25 to £16.50). Unlicensed, but bring your own; no corkage SERVICE: not inc, card slips closed CARDS: Access, Visa DETAILS: 26 seats. 14 tables outside. Private parties: 16 main room, 10 and 16 private rooms. Vegetarian meals. Children's helpings. No smoking during D. Music

'We were pleasantly greeted by a well-spoken young man and an escaping baby black labrador.' (On eating in Kent)

MOFFAT Dumfries & Galloway map 11

▲ *Well View*

Ballplay Road, Moffat DG10 9JU
TEL: (01683) 220184

COOKING 1
COST £17–£33

This tall Victorian house surrounded by gardens is in an ordinary suburban street. At first sight there is little to distinguish it from others in the same mould, but Well View stands out from the crowd. The décor may be plain, but there is 'plenty of room between tables, blessedly no music, no smoking and unbelievable value' to be had. The pattern at dinner is five courses, one of them a mid-meal sorbet, preceded by appetisers in the lounge – perhaps mini-sausage-rolls or prawns on biscuits – then a haggis rissole once at table.

Choice is sensibly limited to four first courses and three mains, but the repertoire is wide-ranging and modestly inventive. Soups have included fennel with Pernod, and spiced broccoli with lentil, while smoked fish is a popular alternative. Chicken on one occasion was filled with a mousseline of guinea-fowl and served with a leek sauce, on another served with green curry, mango, lime and coconut, while fish has included sea bass with a dill and Chardonnay sauce. The menu recommends a white and a red wine, and a port and a dessert wine for the evening, culled from the enthuiastic list, which is being revised as we go to press. House French wine is £8.50 a bottle.

CHEF: Janet Schuckardt PROPRIETORS: Janet and John Schuckardt OPEN: Sun to Fri L 12.30 to 1.15, all week D 6.30 to 8.30 MEALS: Set L £13, Set D £23.50 SERVICE: none, card slips closed CARDS: Access, Amex, Visa DETAILS: 24 seats. Private parties: 12 main room, 6 private room. Car park. Children's helpings. No children under 5 D. Smart dress preferred. No smoking in dining-room. No music ACCOMMODATION: 6 rooms, all with bath/shower. TV. B&B £35 to £80. Deposit: £20. Children welcome. Baby facilities. Afternoon teas. Garden (*The Which? Hotel Guide*)

MUIR OF ORD Highland map 11

▲ *Dower House*

Highfield, Muir of Ord IV6 7XN
TEL/FAX: (01463) 870090
on A862, 1m N of Muir of Ord

COOKING 2*
COST £42–£50

The building which once headed the original estate was long ago destroyed by fire. 'Old photographs suggest this was no great loss,' thought a reporter, but the dower house itself is a pink, single-storeyed cottage of considerable charm, set amid ancient trees and real lawns where rabbits frisk. Inside, the feeling is unashamedly domestic, down to the numerous family photographs and the unstuffy approach of the Aitchisons. Robyn Aitchison cooks a daily-changing set menu of four courses plus coffee, with soup after the starter and a final alternative of pudding or Scottish cheeses. The switch to a no-choice format has evidently occasioned grumblings among the locals, but the style is gentle and uncontroversial enough for people not to feel apprehensive about what they might be given.

One inspection meal began well with a warm salad of John Dory spiked with basil and went on to courgette and rosemary soup, based on a deftly seasoned rich stock that imparted true depth of flavour. The main course was venison, seemingly long-marinated to attain great tenderness, and sauced with a bold but successful decoction of currants, pepper and juniper, and accompanied by potato rösti and aubergine. Baked peach with almonds and crème fraîche provided a light ending to an otherwise substantial meal. Other main courses have been langoustines in filo pastry (December), poached lemon sole with bacon in a chervil sauce (February) and darne of halibut in a herb and sesame coating with sorrel butter sauce (April). Coffee is served with home-made truffles. 'Service was leisurely, but deliberately timed to reflect the relaxed atmosphere of the house.' A resourceful and broad-minded wine list packs in plenty of treats. Those with money to spend should consult the impressive range of bin-ends. Prodigious quantities of half-bottles allow everybody to partake, though, and dessert wines are good. Four southern French house wines are £13.

CHEF: Robyn Aitchison PROPRIETORS: Mr and Mrs R.G. Aitchison OPEN: all week D only 7.30 to 9 CLOSED: Christmas, 1 week Mar, 1 week Oct MEALS: Set D £28 SERVICE: not inc, card slips closed CARDS: Access, Visa DETAILS: 20 seats. 2 tables outside. Private parties: 28 main room. Car park. Children's helpings. No children under 5. Smart dress preferred. No smoking in dining-room. Wheelchair access (also WC). No music ACCOMMODATION: 5 rooms, all with bath/shower. TV. Phone. B&B £45 to £75. Deposit: £35. Rooms for disabled. Children welcome. Baby facilities. Dogs by arrangement; £3 per dog per night. Garden

NAIRN Highland map 11

▲ *Clifton House*

Nairn IV12 4HW
TEL: (01667) 453119 FAX: (01667) 452836 COOKING 2
W of town roundabout on A96 COST £21–£38

J. Gordon Macintyre has lived in this Victorian house since 1931 and has run it as a hotel and restaurant since 1952. This is an ongoing family affair – son Charles has been at the stoves since 1990 – that retains a rare freshness as well as a past. Surroundings are stamped with a personal imprint. The art is real and original, the collections (one of porcelain dogs) have been put together by somebody who revels in them, not by somebody who has merely set out to decorate a restaurant. Relaxation and a total lack of pretence make this a most natural environment for the French provincial cooking that is the Macintyre style.

Dishes embrace set pieces, such as aubergine charlotte, rack of lamb à la Touraine, or entrecôte provençale, but often trade on simple butters – garlic-flavoured or beurre blanc, for instance – to help along a fillet of wild salmon or a plate of scallops. Otherwise, mayonnaise appears, served with crab or salmon, while fresh herbs add an extra lift to turbot or monkfish. The freshness can be astounding. Concessions to other traditions are few before the puddings, which might include poached peaches in vanilla syrup, mincemeat tart or sherry trifle. The considerable range of wines takes in very drinkable bottles under £10 as well as classics from almost every region. Judging by the vintages and prices, the claret must have been assembled gradually, much like the décor, over the

decades. A fair selection of wines by the glass (from £2) adds to the appeal of this high-quality but unsnooty list, as do the 50-plus malt whiskies.

CHEFS: J. Gordon Macintyre and Charles Macintyre PROPRIETOR: J. Gordon Macintyre OPEN: all week 12.30 to 1, 7 to 9.30 CLOSED: early Nov to end Mar MEALS: alc (main courses £7.50 to £14) SERVICE: none, card slips closed CARDS: Access, Amex, Diners, Visa DETAILS: 40 seats. Private parties: 20 main room, 12 private room. Car park. Vegetarian meals. Children's helpings. Smart dress preferred. No smoking in 1 dining-room. Music ACCOMMODATION: 12 rooms, all with bath/shower. B&B £50 to £104. Children welcome. Pets welcome. Afternoon teas. Garden (*The Which? Hotel Guide*)

OBAN Strathclyde map 11

▲ *Heatherfield House* NEW ENTRY

Albert Road, Oban PA34 5EJ
TEL/FAX: (01631) 562681

COOKING 2
COST £20–£44

Those who remember the Robertsons from their time at the Holly Tree Hotel in Kentallen, which was in the *Guide* from 1984 to 1989, will be pleased to hear of their return, albeit in a slightly different guise. They have re-surfaced as a small, family-run restaurant-with-rooms in this old grey-stone manse overlooking the distant bay, and are partway through refurbishment: the dining-room is complete, with pink walls and polished wooden floor, and so is the kitchen – the bedrooms are next. '"Larkinesque" is quite close to how we would like to be described,' write the Robertsons. Larkinesque it is, then.

Oban is well placed for fish – shellfish comes from Mull – and Alasdair Robertson cures his own hams, salamis and salmon, bakes a variety of daily breads, and makes his own jams, jellies and chutneys. Local honey, their own hens, and a nascent garden for fresh fruit, herbs and salad items shows how seriously they take the victualling. 'Brilliant handling of fish' is one of the attractions. At one May meal lightly poached sole 'really tasted of the sea', while a firm-textured escalope of salmon, 'grilled to perfection' and well matched with paprika, was the star turn. Results have sometimes been uneven, but sound techniques keep most of the cooking on course, including a terrine with 'a chunky and satisfying mix of game and pork', and a delicate, finely textured, pale pink salmon and sole mousseline of 'perfect consistency', served with a 'classic, bouncy' mayonnaise subtly spiked with ginger. The serviceable, wide-ranging 60-bin wine list includes six by the glass from £1.55, or £9.25 a bottle.

CHEF: Alasdair Robertson PROPRIETORS: Alasdair and Jane Robertson OPEN: Apr to Oct all week 12.30 to 2.30, 7 to 10; Nov to Mar Wed to Sat D bookings only CLOSED: 2 weeks Jan MEALS: alc (main courses £6.50 to £16.50). Set D £16.50. Minimum £5 D SERVICE: not inc, card slips closed CARDS: Access, Visa DETAILS: 30 seats. Private parties: 45 main room. Car park. Children's helpings. Smart dress preferred. No smoking in dining-room. Music ACCOMMODATION: 5 rooms 2 with bath/shower. TV. B&B £20 to £40. Deposit: £15. Children welcome. Small dogs welcome. Afternoon teas. Garden

All main entries are fully indexed at the back of the Guide.

▲ *Knipoch Hotel*

Knipoch, by Oban PA34 4QT
TEL: (01852) 316251 FAX: (01852) 316249 COOKING 1
on A816, 6m S of Oban COST £39–£60

The views are magnificent, though the décor is slightly underwhelming. The Craigs are busy people, smoking salmon, making ice-cream, baking bread and roasting coffee, so it comes as a surprise to some that the fixed-price menu offers no choice. A three-course dinner might begin with cock-a-leekie soup, followed by tasty fillet steak with béarnaise sauce, and finish with strawberry roulade. The same items, plus a fish course and cheese, become the 'gourmet menu' for the evening. The kitchen has produced good mushroom soup, smoked salmon, poached pear in a brandy-snap biscuit with vanilla ice-cream, and 'outstanding' crêpes suzette, though the price of dinner brings into question the value. There is no question about the quality of the wine list, which is as happy with a page of Bulgarians under £10 as with classed-growth claret from goodness-knows-how-many vintages. There is something for everybody, whatever the food, the mood or the pocket, plus a short recommended selection, and five vins de pays at £11.50 for those who like things simpler. CELLARMAN'S CHOICE: Stoneleigh Vineyards Sauvignon Blanc 1993, Marlborough, New Zealand, £11.70; Fronsac, Ch. Fontenac 1987, £15.20.

CHEFS: Jenny and Colin Craig PROPRIETORS: the Craig family OPEN: all week D only 7.30 to 9; L by arrangement CLOSED: mid-Nov to mid-Feb MEALS: Set D £29.50 to £39.50 SERVICE: not inc, card slips closed CARDS: Access, Amex, Delta, Diners, Switch, Visa DETAILS: 44 seats. Private parties: 24 main room, 12 private rooms. Car park. Children's helpings. Smart dress preferred. No smoking in dining-room. No music ACCOMMODATION: 17 rooms, all with bath/shower. TV. Phone. B&B £65 to £130. Children welcome. Baby facilities. Afternoon teas. Garden

PEAT INN Fife map 11

▲ *Peat Inn*

Peat Inn KY15 5LH
TEL: (01334) 840206 FAX: (01334) 840530 COOKING 4
at junction of B940 and B941, 6m SW of St Andrews COST £30–£66

One seasoned reporter who had not visited for two years found a marked improvement in the décor ('it was like a different place altogether'), the bright, fresh dining-room itself feeling even more relaxed and casual. The lounge where you sit for a drink before the meal (and coffee afterwards) smells of wood smoke even on the few days when the fire isn't lit.

The Wilsons' achievement over two decades has been to cook simply and well. That may not sound much, but it has involved placing local produce centre-stage, which has in turn meant seeking out and encouraging growers and producers to come up with their best on a regular basis. It has also meant divesting the food of unnecessary gesture, so that what appears on the plate reflects the food's origins. The result is an individual restaurant of high calibre that revels in the abundance of seafood – lobster might appear in a salad, or poached in a vegetable and herb broth – and game, such as roast saddle and braised shin of venison with flageolet beans. The set four-course lunch is rightly considered a bargain. The set dinner menu has no choice, but the à la carte offers a generous choice of around eight dishes per course. In addition, there is a 'tasting' menu (which has to be ordered by the whole table) consisting of small portions of specialities, which one reporter described as 'a logical progression of tastes and textures'.

The balancing act with flavours and textures, and the lightness of touch, are apparent in a rectangular box of light, buttery yet crisp puff pastry (among the best that an inspector had tasted) with a lattice lid, filled with field mushrooms and butter. Fish is skilfully treated, as in a simple, clean, fresh-tasting crab salad, brought up to date with a few shavings of Parmesan, or fillet of moist salmon – its skin encrusted with rock salt and seared to near blackness – sitting on a bed of colourful vegetables, with an acidulated basil butter sauce. Two trios of desserts – one of nuts, one of caramel – share the billing with a superbly presented feuilleté of wafer-thin chocolate biscuits with a scoop of white chocolate ice-cream in the centre, sitting on a circle of 'fantastic' rich dark chocolate sauce. Petits fours with coffee 'keep the quality running through to the end'.

The food's no-nonsense approach is reflected in the impeccably good wines and their unpompous service. David Wilson points to the hokum that surrounds wine service, particularly in grand establishments, and commendably has no truck with it. He assumes that customers have not come this far without being able to pour their own wine, and that not everybody is dying to spend as much money as possible, so despite some prestige bottles, mark-ups on the long list are designed to encourage us to drink well. CELLARMAN'S CHOICE: Auxey-Duresses 1992, Pascal, £24; Bourgogne Pinot Noir 1990, Dom. Courcel, £18.

CHEF: David Wilson PROPRIETORS: David and Patricia Wilson OPEN: Tue to Sat 12.30 for 1, 7 to 9.30 CLOSED: 25 Dec, 1 Jan MEALS: alc (main courses £16 to £19). Set L £18.50, Set D £28 SERVICE: none, card slips closed CARDS: Access, Amex, Diners, Switch, Visa DETAILS: 48 seats. Private parties: 24 main room, 12 private rooms. Car park. Vegetarian meals. Children's helpings. Smart dress preferred. No smoking in dining-room. Wheelchair access (also WC). No music ACCOMMODATION: 8 rooms, all with bath/shower. TV. Phone. B&B £75 to £140. Rooms for disabled. Children welcome. Pets welcome. Garden (*The Which? Hotel Guide*)

PEEBLES Borders map 11

▲ *Cringletie House*

Peebles EH45 8PL
TEL: (01721) 730233 FAX: (01721) 730244
on A703, 2½m N of Peebles

COOKING 2
COST £18–£38

A couple who have been visiting this Victorian sandstone mansion since 1971 have watched the Maguire family nurture and improve their business with unfailing enthusiasm. Evidence of Aileen Maguire's talents as an interior designer is everywhere; a conservatory 'shaped like a four-leaf clover' is a recent and very successful addition. The kitchen garden continues to flourish, and you may even be able to sample a new variety of purple Brussels sprout at the right time of year. The four-course fixed-price dinner menu is a regularly changing affair, and reporters have given the thumbs-up to a whole host of dishes. Soups, such as beetroot and orange, and 'delicate' sweetcorn and coriander, are consistently good, and there is plenty of support for well-tried favourites including roast duckling with apples and calvados, 'vibrantly fresh' lambs' liver with onion and grain mustard sauce, and medallions of beef with pink peppercorn sauce. Fish is often given up-to-the-minute treatment, as in rösti crab-cakes with sweetcorn salsa, baked salmon with couscous and saffron sauce, and grilled fillet of sole with a parsley crust and an 'interesting' onion and sun-dried tomato sauce. Highlights from the pudding list have included rich, intense butterscotch velvet with praline topping, and refreshing lemon posset. Light lunches are excellent value. The wine list has plenty of quality drinking to suit most palates and pockets, and around £10 will pay for something quite acceptable. House wine from Duboeuf is £11.50 a litre.

CHEFS: Aileen Maguire, Sheila McKellar and Paul Maguire PROPRIETORS: Stanley and Aileen Maguire OPEN: all week 1 to 1.45, 7.30 to 8.30 MEALS: alc L (main courses £6 to £7). Set L Sun £15, Set D £24.50 SERVICE: not inc, card slips closed CARDS: Access, Amex, Switch, Visa DETAILS: 56 seats. Private parties: 28 main room. Car park. Vegetarian meals. Children's helpings. No smoking in dining-room. No music ACCOMMODATION: 13 rooms, all with bath/shower. TV. Phone. B&B £52.50 to £104. Children welcome. Baby facilities. Afternoon teas. Garden (*The Which? Hotel Guide*)

PERTH Tayside map 11

Number Thirty Three

33 George Street, Perth PH1 5LA COOKING 1
TEL: (01738) 633771 COST £24–£42

Follow one reporter's advice and take a trip back in time: 'It is a delight to step from the bustling street of the old town of Perth into this 1930s fantasy of a horseshoe bar, Art Deco mirrors, pink walls, pink upholstery, pink tablecloths, and good decadent 1930s music to accompany it all. And a barman to match – for [owner] Gavin Billinghurst mixes a skilful Martini.' If you really want to get into the swing of things, you can lounge in comfort with a plate of oysters and a bottle of champagne as a prelude to your meal.

Scottish seafood is the main business of the day. Light dishes (starters and sweets only) are served in the Oyster Bar, where the high points might be 'first-rate' home-cured gravlax, shellfish platters and sticky toffee pudding. Restaurant main courses (on a separate 'white' menu) show that the kitchen knows its stuff: 'a fantastic parcel' of sea bass with prawns and mussels, or king scallops with an eye-catching saffron sauce, for example. Vegetables sent one reporter into a state of high excitement: 'sensational morsels' of perfectly cooked broccoli, pumpkin, courgette and more – each one 'an individual treat'. If you come here for something other than fish, you will probably have to settle for tagliatelle with smoked chicken, rack of lamb with rowan jelly or roast breast of duckling. Service is smooth and unobtrusive. House wine is £10.60.

CHEF: Mary Billinghurst PROPRIETORS: Gavin and Mary Billinghurst OPEN: Tue to Sat 12.30 to 2.30, 6.30 to 9.30 CLOSED: 25 and 26 Dec, last 2 weeks Jan SERVICE: not inc CARDS: Access, Amex, Visa DETAILS: 24 seats. Private parties: 24 main room. No children under 5. Smart dress preferred. No cigars in dining-room. Wheelchair access. Music

PORT APPIN Strathclyde map 11

▲ *Airds Hotel*

Port Appin PA38 4DF
TEL: (01631) 730236 FAX: (01631) 730535
2m off A828, on E shore of Loch Linnhe

COOKING 4
COST £47–£56

Stunning views are part and parcel of eating in western Scotland, but that does not diminish the impact of Loch Linnhe. The house, which used to be an inn serving travellers to Lismore island, is close to the shore and fulsomely decorated. If there is no overriding style, at least there is something for everybody, from worn Victorian prints of soulful dogs and horses, to tartan carpets and potted plants. *'C'est très curieux, le goût écossais'* was overheard at one table.

Prime Scottish produce underlies the operation, starting with 'simple and good Loch Linnhe prawns', crab in a light pastry tart with tomato coulis, or scallops served with shiitake mushrooms and a sweet-and-sour sauce. Since the larder doesn't change much, the menu doesn't either, although the slowly evolving cooking is modern enough to stay fresh. Some combinations stray close to the edge, as in roast guinea-fowl in a mild curry sauce with morels and onion marmalade, although most are as mainstream as smooth chicken liver parfait with redcurrant coulis and toasted brioche, and Aberdeen Angus beef surrounded by wild mushrooms, which provided 'a superb combination of flavours'.

'Consistently high quality' is the verdict of those who stay a few days, alternating light lunches of soup and sandwiches with full four-course dinners, the second of which is a soup. In case you were wondering what to do with a half-empty bottle of Sambuca – now that nobody throws coffee-beans in and sets fire to it – take a tip from Graeme Allen and splash a bit into a red pepper and fennel soup. Other alcohols turn up too: a madeira sauce for roast loin of stuffed rabbit, or champagne in a 'memorable' jelly of summer fruits. 'Agreeable ambience, delightful staff and faultless service' all contribute to the feeling that the hotel is 'first class in every respect', and that the outlay is 'money well spent.'

Wines convey a similar impression: completely unsnooty, kind to modest pockets, but ready with the special bottles just in case. You get the impression that if the wine list were a garden there wouldn't be a weed in sight. Everything is carefully chosen for quality at whatever level, and although the options may seem conservative they are utterly sound, backed up by generous half-bottles and good house wines from £11.

CHEF: Graeme Allen PROPRIETORS: Eric and Betty Allen and Graeme and Anne Allen OPEN: all week D only 8 (one sitting); light L available MEALS: Set D £35 SERVICE: not inc, card slips closed CARDS: Access, Amex, Visa DETAILS: 34 seats. Private parties: 40 main room. Car park. Children's helpings. Smart dress preferred. No smoking in dining-room. Wheelchair access. No music ACCOMMODATION: 12 rooms, all with bath/shower. TV. Phone. D,B&B £125 to £130. Deposit: £100. Rooms for disabled. Children welcome. Baby facilities. Afternoon teas. Garden (*The Which? Hotel Guide*)

▲ *Pierhouse*

Port Appin PA38 4DE
TEL: (01631) 730302 FAX: (01631) 730309
off A828, on E shore of Loch Linnhe, opposite Lismore ferry

COOKING 1
COST £17–£46

Port Appin is just off the Fort William to Oban road, and the whitewashed Pierhouse is by the edge of Loch Linnhe: a 170-year-old listed building that used to house the post office and piermaster. It now thrives on an informal approach appropriate to the pub-like rooms and the kitchen's straightforward handling of seafood. Loch Linnhe is a sea loch which provides all manner of fish and shellfish, which the MacLeods waste no time in harvesting. Lobsters, oysters, mussels and scallops, always available, are landed at the pier just a few yards from the kitchen, and prawns arrive twice daily. They could hardly be any fresher. Produce like this demands and gets the simplest treatment: garlic butter for the prawns and mussels, perhaps lemon butter for the scallops, with oysters served either cold or warm with Mornay sauce. Clam chowder is rich and creamy, salmon is locally smoked, and the Giant Platter (for two people) is a cold collation of most of the shellfish on offer. Apart from that there may be grilled salmon or halibut, and a steak or chicken dish for those who fancy a change. Choice at dinner is more generous than at lunch-time. The business is family run, and fronted by the tireless Callum MacLeod. Wines are on the ball, with a fair range of styles and prices starting at £9.50 (£1.70 a glass) for South African Sauvignon Blanc.

CHEF: Sheila MacLeod PROPRIETORS: the MacLeod family OPEN: all week 12 to 3, 6.30 to 9.30 MEALS: alc (main courses £6 to £17) SERVICE: not inc, card slips closed CARDS: Access, Switch, Visa DETAILS: 60 seats. 5 tables outside. Private parties: 20 main room, 20 private room. Car park. Children's helpings. Smart dress preferred. No smoking in 1 dining-room. Wheelchair access (3 steps; also WC). Music ACCOMMODATION: 11 rooms, all with bath/shower. TV. Phone. Air-conditioned. B&B £45 to £70. Deposit: 10%. Rooms for disabled. Children welcome. Baby facilities. Afternoon teas. Garden

PORTPATRICK Dumfries & Galloway map 11

▲ *Knockinaam Lodge*

Portpatrick DG9 9AD
TEL: (01776) 810471 FAX: (01776) 810435
off A77, 3m S of Portpatrick

COOKING 2
COST £34–£50

The name Portpatrick gives a clue that you could reach Ireland from here in a small boat (on a clear day you can see the coast easily enough), although there is no dock or quayside, just a small cove with a shingle beach. The house was built for summer entertaining in the nineteenth century, and is so remote that Churchill and Eisenhower used it for a secret meeting during the Second World War. Had they laid into the 80 malt whiskies now on offer in the panelled bar, the war might have taken a different turn. Knockinaam itself steers the same course as it did last year, despite new owners. Stuart Muir remains at the stoves.

The style is French-based, adapted and tweaked to modern requirements, and often perked up with a dash of something as cheerful as lime and coriander (for breast of chicken) or home-made chutney and balsamic vinaigrette (for scallops). Sometimes dishes are as simple as roast loin of lamb with a herb crust and rosemary jus, or steamed sea bass with noodles and sun-dried tomatoes; at other times they may be as unusual as a pineapple butter served with a feuilleté of mussels, or as involved as grilled salmon with braised lentils, together with Toulouse sausage if you please, and a tomato and chive sauce. British and French cheeses are an alternative to hot apple tart with calvados sauce, or raspberry crème brûlée served with warm shortbread. Wines are extensive and largely highfalutin, but 15 house wines are around £14, or £4 a glass.

CHEF: Stuart Muir PROPRIETORS: Michael Bricker and Pauline Ashworth OPEN: all week 12 to 2, 7 to 9.30 MEALS: Set L £25, Set D £32; bar L available SERVICE: not inc CARDS: Access, Amex, Diners, Visa DETAILS: 32 seats. Private parties: 32 main room. Car park. Children's helpings L; no children under 12 D. Smart dress preferred. No smoking in dining-room. Wheelchair access (1 step). Music ACCOMMODATION: 10 rooms, all with bath/shower. TV. Phone. B&B £70 to £140. Deposit: £100. Children welcome; high teas for under-12s. Baby facilities. Pets welcome in bedrooms only. Afternoon teas. Garden (*The Which? Hotel Guide*)

ST MARGARET'S HOPE Orkney map 11

▲ *The Creel*

Front Road, St Margaret's Hope,
South Ronaldsay KW17 2SL
TEL: (01856) 831311
off A961, 13m S of Kirkwall, on South Ronaldsay island

COOKING 3
COST £23–£49

Over 50 islands make up the Orcadian archipelago, but South Ronaldsay is easily reached by road from Kirkwall, along the A961 over the Churchill Barriers. The village is tiny, as is the plain grey-stone house on the sea-front, but the mix of locals and tourists generates a friendly atmosphere and a feeling of camaraderie. The menu doesn't change radically, which hardly matters for casual visitors, but those who stay can put in requests. A couple who did dined on soups of crab, smoked haddock and mixed fish, 'all thick and bursting with fresh flavour'. It would be surprising if fish did not feature, hence 'fat, juicy scallops with lentils and chervil', Grimbister mussels cooked with cider, tomatoes, leeks and garlic, or Scapa Bay prawns in garlic butter 'with an aroma that could make your mouth water at 50 paces'.

Those who associate Orkney with the Stone Age settlement Skara Brae may already know of beremeal bannock, 'a prehistoric type of barley now grown only on Orkney and a few fields in the north of Scotland,' explain the Craigies, from which they make a type of soda bread that, for one visitor, was 'a sensational new taste experience'. Alan Craigie also manages to lay his hands on some North Ronaldsay sheep in season: the ones that graze on the seashore on a diet rich in seaweed, producing a distinctive flavour in the meat. Orkney beef, meanwhile, is smoked over oak chips and served with rhubarb chutney, while fillet steak is 'the old-fashioned variety that is tender and has taste'.

Despite the drop of whisky or Drambuie that finds its way into a sauce, or a baby haggis that comes with chump of lamb, the food is not entirely dyed-in-the-wool. One evening, there was 'an inventive chickpea and fresh coriander stuffing for a chicken breast', which delighted a reporter. 'Alan Craigie is a superb chef who knows how to marry the best of Scottish produce with flavours from other cuisines.' Among puddings, however, pride of place goes to Orcadian Brides Cog pears, closely followed by strawberry shortcake. There is a good cheeseboard, and coffee comes with Orkney fudge. The wine list is barely more than a dozen bottles long, with house South African at £7.50, or £1.50 a glass.

CHEF: Alan Craigie PROPRIETORS: Alan and Joyce Craigie OPEN: May to end Sept all week D 7 to 9; Oct to Feb Fri to Sun D 7 to 9 (telephone first to check) CLOSED: Jan and sometimes during low season MEALS: alc (main courses £10.50 to £18.50) SERVICE: not inc, card slips closed CARDS: Access, Visa DETAILS: 38 seats. Private parties: 38 main room. Car park. Children's helpings. Smart dress preferred. Wheelchair access (2 steps; also WC). No music ACCOMMODATION: 3 rooms, all with bath/shower. TV. B&B £30 to £50. Deposit: £25. Children welcome. Baby facilities. Garden

STEIN Highland map 11

▲ *Loch Bay* £

1–2 Macleod Terrace, Stein, Waternish,
Isle of Skye IV55 8GA COOKING 1
TEL: (01470) 592235 COST £20–£44

'At the end of a walk on Skye and as near to paradise as a fish fanatic can get,' exclaimed a traveller who stumbled upon this gem. Stein is little more than an inn and a few dwellings. The restaurant is housed in two converted fishermen's cottages. Even on glorious summer days a fire burns in the grate, and visitors find the whole place delightful and the food excellent. The menu is devoted wholeheartedly to fresh seafood, and there's hardly a flash gesture or enveloping sauce to be seen. Oysters are served *au naturel* or grilled with garlic butter, wild salmon is poached, scallops are sauté, locally landed king prawns are served simply with a salad. Then there are cephalopods (squid, octopus and cuttlefish marinated in olive oil) and daily specials, depending on the catch. The star of the sweets is traditional clootie dumpling served warm with cream. Matching the fish is an admirable wine list dominated by some very drinkable whites. Also look for the three Highland wines brewed from silver birch sap, elderflowers and brambles. House French is £6.50.

CHEFS/PROPRIETORS: Margaret and Peter Greenhalgh OPEN: Sun to Fri 12 to 3, 6 to 9 CLOSED: Oct to Easter MEALS: alc (main courses £9 to £17) SERVICE: not inc, card slips closed CARDS: Access, Visa DETAILS: 26 seats. 2 tables outside. Private parties: 26 main room. Car park. Children's helpings. Smart dress preferred. No smoking in dining-room. Wheelchair access. Music ACCOMMODATION: 3 rooms, 1 with bath/shower. B&B £16 to £36. Children welcome. Baby facilities. Afternoon teas. Garden

indicates that smoking is either banned altogether or that a dining-room is maintained for non-smokers. The symbol does not apply to restaurants that simply have no-smoking areas.

STEWARTON Strathclyde map 11

▲ *Chapeltoun House*

Irvine Road, nr Stewarton KA3 3ED
TEL: (01560) 482696 FAX: (01560) 485100 COOKING 1
2m from Stewarton on B769 towards Irvine COST £23–£41

The house was built in 1900 as a family home for a Glasgow coal and shipping merchant and his family, and runs true to form with an oak-panelled hall and big, comfortable chairs in front of roaring fires. Table spacings are 'just about the most generous I can recall', according to a well-travelled reporter. The place 'oozes distinction and comfort' yet also manages to feel relaxing. Dinner is of two, three or four courses, and prices have come down a fraction since last year.

Fish from Ayr, Aberdeen Angus beef, local game, and Bonnet goats' cheese from Stewarton are among materials that pass through the kitchen, the last perhaps appearing on a herb brioche with a warm tomato chutney. Although Tom O'Donnell attempts some high-wire cooking, as in a pithiviers of monkfish in a cognac, grain-mustard and Swiss cheese sauce, he generally sticks to simpler dishes, such as smoked haddock and leek chowder, venison sausage with lentils, or a gratin of raspberries flavoured with kirsch. Service is friendly, not excessively formal, and the package is considered value for money. Wines are sensibly chosen with an eye for quality and value, and although the list lets rip at the top end, it is careful to consider those with £20 or less to spend. Twenty half-bottles and a dozen house recommendations are helpful. CELLARMAN'S CHOICE: Pata Negra Gran Reserva 1982, Cosecheros Abastecedores, £13.50; Bordeaux, Notre Dame de Landiras 1993, £13.50.

CHEF: Tom O'Donnell PROPRIETORS: Colin and Graeme McKenzie OPEN: all week 12 to 2, 7 to 9.15 CLOSED: first 2 weeks Jan MEALS: Set L £15.90, Set D £23.80 SERVICE: not inc, card slips closed CARDS: Access, Amex, Delta, Switch, Visa DETAILS: 50 seats. Private parties: 30 main room, 55 private room. Car park. Vegetarian meals. No children under 12. Smart dress preferred. No smoking in dining-room. Wheelchair access (2 steps). No music ACCOMMODATION: 8 rooms, all with bath/shower. TV. Phone. B&B £69 to £139. No children under 12. Pets by arrangement. Afternoon teas. Garden. Fishing (*The Which? Hotel Guide*)

STRONTIAN Highland map 11

▲ *Kilcamb Lodge*

Strontian PH36 4HY
TEL/FAX: (01967) 402257 COOKING 3
on A861, by N shore of Loch Sunart COST £29–£34

The Blakeway family's natural friendliness is one reason why visitors are attracted to this delightfully peaceful country lodge in 30 acres of grounds by the side of Loch Sunart. It is also a refreshingly unstuffy retreat: lively chatter rather than hushed whispering is the order of the day in the dining-room, and service is described as 'wonderful'.

The kitchen takes its cue from top-notch Scottish ingredients – squat lobsters hauled out of the loch, smoked produce from Glenuig, Highland beef, wild venison, indigenous cheeses – but it also looks further afield for Cumbrian air-dried ham and Welsh oatcakes. When it comes to guinea-fowl, the Blakeways' preference is for a born-and-bred English bird; they buy only free-range eggs and serve vegetables in abundance. Their cooking is lighter than before – according to one regular reporter – and cream levels have been drastically reduced (cucumber mousse with 'the correct wobble factor' now gains its richness from fromage frais). Presentation is also increasingly sophisticated, and the Blakeways are good at adding little flourishes that turn otherwise prosaic dishes into something rather special. Sweet, firm langoustines (caught just before they are prepared) need only a tiny salad, a dab of dill mayonnaise and some good bread to transform them into a memorable starter. The four-course dinner menu continues with soup, and this is invariably a winner: 'simply stunning' celery, almond and walnut vies for the laurels with cream of mushroom (an extravaganza of fresh and dried species). Among the main courses, roast saddle of venison, five slices arranged like a wigwam around a heap of crisp red cabbage and topped with a blob of juniper jelly, has been outstanding.

Desserts cater for 'the Billy Bunters among us': bread-and-butter pudding spiked with seriously alcoholic raisins, beautifully made lemon tart, and a dangerously intense chocolate crème brûlée – although there is light relief in the mixed fruit platter served with refreshing elderflower sorbet. Incidentals, such as appetising amuse-gueules, a good selection of herb teas and strong cafetière coffee, add to the overall pleasure. The wine list continues to develop and offers a good spread for most tastes and pockets. Six house wines start at £7.

CHEFS: Ann and Peter Blakeway PROPRIETORS: the Blakeway family OPEN: all week D only 7.30 (one sitting) CLOSED: mid-Nov to mid-Mar MEALS: Set D £25; light L available SERVICE: net prices, card slips closed CARDS: Access, Switch, Visa DETAILS: 26 seats. Private parties: 38 main room. Car park. Children's helpings. Smart dress preferred. No smoking in dining-room. Wheelchair access (also WC). No music ACCOMMODATION: 10 rooms, all with bath/shower. TV. B&B £42.50 to £85. Deposit: £35. Children welcome. Baby facilities. Pets welcome. Afternoon teas. Garden. Fishing (*The Which? Hotel Guide*)

SWINTON Borders map 11

▲ *Wheatsheaf Hotel, Four Seasons* £

Main Street, Swinton TD11 3JJ
TEL/FAX: (01890) 860257 COOKING 1
on A6112, Coldstream to Duns road COST £16–£39

This country inn close to the River Tweed tops up its local following with fishermen and tourists. Reasonable prices, comfortable rooms, good breakfasts and friendly, informal service are part of the appeal. Food is served in both lounge bar and informal dining-room, and is chosen from either a printed menu or a blackboard. Seafood (including Tweed salmon) and local game loom large, and the cooking is Franco-Scottish: deep-fried squid with pesto mayonnaise, or warm monkfish salad with lemon and herb dressing sit alongside smoked ham and haddie pancake, or herrings marinated with sloe gin, juniper and dill. Smoked salmon bisque tastes 'more of smoked salmon than the stuff itself does'. Alan Reid goes stalking with his butcher to stock up on red deer, which might turn up with a port and plum sauce. If some of the dishes hark back a decade or two, they are certainly cooked to reporters' liking. Vegetables are up to scratch, and puddings run to brown bread and Glayva ice-cream, or hot baked chocolate cheesecake with a warm coffee-bean sauce. A wide-ranging list of wines at friendly prices includes Louisvale Chardonnay and Hamilton-Russell Pinot Noir (both from South Africa) plus a page each of half-bottles and bin ends. Four house wines are £7.95 (£1.65 per glass).

CHEFS: Alan Reid and John Keir PROPRIETORS: Alan and Julie Reid OPEN: Tue to Sun 12 to 2.15, Tue to Sat 6 to 9.30 CLOSED: 2 weeks end Feb, 1 week end Oct MEALS: alc (main courses £4.50 to £14) SERVICE: not inc, card slips closed CARDS: Access, Visa DETAILS: 46 seats. 8 tables outside. Private parties: 28 main room, 18 and 28 private rooms. Car park. Vegetarian meals. Children's helpings. Smart dress preferred. No smoking in 1 dining-room. Wheelchair access (2 steps; also WC). No music ACCOMMODATION: 4 rooms, 3 with bath/shower. TV. B&B £42 to £65. Deposit: £25. Children welcome. Baby facilities. Pets welcome (by arrangement in bedrooms only). Garden

TROON Strathclyde map 11

▲ *Highgrove House* £

Old Loans Road, Troon KA10 7HL COOKING 1
TEL: (01292) 312511 FAX: (01292) 318228 COST £18–£40

'We were touched to be given what would have been a superb view over the Firth of Clyde, had it not been for the driving rain and sea mist.' But then it was February. Highgrove House is open all the time, and the choice of food is generous, to say the least, which may overstretch the kitchen (and service, come to that) at busy times. The *carte* offers a dozen or more main courses at both lunch and dinner, and although there is some overlap with the fixed-price menu there is still a lot for the kitchen to do: steaming local mussels, stuffing pancakes with Brie, pan-frying trout, grilling liver and dishing up warm apple and almond pudding with custard. Garnishes may be somewhat standardised – all sweets for one party came with spun sugar – but Highgrove's heart is in the right place, and meals have enough high points to convince reporters of its worth: well-flavoured, firm-textured fish terrine, for example, or warm salad of coarsely cut smoked salmon 'as different from the pallid see-through slices one gets south of the border as you could imagine'. The list of 60 varied wines starts with house French at £9.95.

CHEFS: William Costley and James Alison PROPRIETORS: William and Catherine Costley OPEN: all week 12 to 2.20, 6 to 9.30 MEALS: alc (main courses £6 to £14.50). Set L £14.95, Set D £22.50 SERVICE: not inc, card slips closed CARDS: Access, Amex, Delta, Switch, Visa DETAILS: 90 seats. 5 tables outside. Private parties: 80 main room, 20 private room. Car park. Vegetarian meals. Children's helpings. Smart dress preferred. No cigars/pipes in dining-room. Wheelchair access. Music ACCOMMODATION: 9 rooms, all with bath/shower. TV. Phone. B&B £58 to £95. Children welcome. Baby facilities. Afternoon teas. Garden

Report forms are at the back of the book; write a letter if you prefer; or if you are on the Internet, e-mail us at guidereports@which. co. uk.

▲ *Lochgreen House* NEW ENTRY

Monktonhill Road, Southwood, Troon KA10 7EN — COOKING 2*
TEL: (01292) 313343 FAX: (01292) 318661 — COST £21–£43

No puns need be made about this being a 'Costley' operation; indeed, it is considered a good-value twin for Bill and Catherine Costley's other Troon establishment, Highgrove House (see entry, above), but with 'more space and greater rural tranquillity'. The drive is lined with beeches, the lounge is oak-panelled and chintzy, and dinner is in the added-on conservatory, with impressive flower arrangements, stiff green curtains tweaked into prim white bows, and delightful garden views. Tables are spaced for privacy, and service is low-key.

Andrew Hamer makes his own pasta, is into polenta and coriander butter, and splashes a drop of alcohol in the sauces. The cooking has enjoyed mixed success, with some seasonings and flavourings rather muted, but among the highlights have been sweet chargrilled scallops with shiitake mushrooms tossed in oil, and a 'glittering salad' to accompany: 'the ingredients had been disposed with a practised eye yet apparently carefree abandon over the plate.' Goose liver parfait is unctuously rich, and the local butcher's crumbly-textured prize-winning haggis has been described as 'the best I have tasted' – and that from a Glaswegian inspector.

At its best, the cooking is accomplished, with sharp attention to detail, as in a generous portion of tender duck breast with good crisp skin, in a rich and well-judged madeira sauce, with a bright and tangy kumquat preserve to cut the richness. Desserts make more of fruits than is customary in Scotland, with brandy-snap baskets, pastry tarts, sabayon sauce and ice-cream woven in among them. The sensible list of wines has strength in the classic French regions but enough of interest for those who want to explore further afield. House wines are from £12.50.

CHEF: Andrew Hamer PROPRIETORS: Bill and Catherine Costley OPEN: all week 12 to 2, 7 to 9 MEALS: alc L (main courses £7 to £15). Set L Sun £16.95, Set D £25 SERVICE: not inc, card slips closed CARDS: Access, Amex, Switch, Visa DETAILS: 90 seats. Private parties: 45 main room, 18 to 30 private rooms. Car park. No children under 5 D. Smart dress preferred. No smoking in dining-room. Wheelchair access (also WC). Music ACCOMMODATION: 15 rooms, all with bath/shower. TV. Phone. B&B £90 to £110. Rooms for disabled. Children welcome. Afternoon teas. Garden

---

TURNBERRY Strathclyde — map 11

▲ *Turnberry Hotel*

Turnberry KA26 9LT — COOKING 2
TEL: (01655) 331000 FAX: (01655) 331706 — COST £32–£96

This grand hotel, overlooking two championship golf courses, was built 90 years ago. Its present Japanese owners have added a new spa and made it spick and span, yet it still retains an Edwardian clubhouse air. Just as important, it has a high standard of service to match: 'Our wishes were anticipated, and everything ran smoothly.' Like other hotels of this size, Turnberry keeps a variety of food outlets on the go: the Clubhouse for salads, roasts and sandwiches; the Bay for light meals of fish, meat, pasta and vegetables with some dishes low in fat and calories; and the showpiece Turnberry Restaurant itself.

The latter's style is a mixture of ancient and modern, with Beluga caviar, lobster thermidor and grilled Dover sole on the one hand, and warm forest mushroom and duck liver tartlet with lardons, Gruyère and a morel mushroom sauce on the other. Naturally seafood makes a splash, from west coast scampi, Turnberry Bay prawns and crab, to turbot poached in champagne and served in a crayfish sauce. Culinary cosseting is alive and well for those with the dosh to pay for it, but ingredients are good, and Stewart Cameron's cooking is well up to the demands of lobster bisque, Galloway beef with ceps and chanterelles, and roast Ayrshire lamb. In its favour, the food is commendably simple, impressing more by richness than elaboration, as in desserts of cognac and honey gâteau, or a harlequin of bitter chocolate and white chocolate mousse served with chocolate cream. The 100-bin list of expensive hotel wines has a few more additions from the New World this year. To demonstrate the point about the cost, house wine is £18.

CHEF: Stewart Cameron PROPRIETOR: Nitto World Co Ltd OPEN: Sun L 1 to 2.30, all week D 7.30 to 10; Mon to Sat lunches available in Bay and Clubhouse restaurants MEALS: alc (main courses £21 to £30). Set L £20.50, Set D £39.50 SERVICE: not inc, card slips closed CARDS: Access, Amex, Delta, Diners, Switch, Visa DETAILS: 180 seats. Private parties: 240 main room, 120 private room. Car park. Vegetarian meals. Children welcome. Jacket and tie. No pipes in dining-room. Wheelchair access (also WC). Music ACCOMMODATION: 132 rooms, all with bath/shower. TV. Phone. B&B £145 to £245. Rooms for disabled. Children welcome. Pets welcome in bedrooms only. Afternoon teas. Garden. Swimming pool (*The Which? Hotel Guide*)

UIG Western Isles map 11

▲ *Baile-na-Cille*

Timsgarry, Uig, Isle of Lewis PA86 9JD
TEL: (01851) 672242 FAX: (01851) 672241 COOKING 1*
B8011 to Uig, then right down track on to shore COST £28–£33

The tiny white-painted hotel – a converted manse and stables – is on the far side of the Outer Hebrides. 'Next stop America,' as Richard Gollin says, also pointing out that with a full house of two dozen guests, none of them need share a beach: there are 25 in the area, all of gleaming white sand, not to mention the full complement of hills, lochs and rivers for walking, fishing and generally getting away from it all. Just as important is the air of cheerfulness and good humour which pervades the entire operation. Lamb, venison and local seafood are among the items to which Jo Gollin turns to construct her set three-course dinners (plus cheese and fruit), which begin at 7.30pm. Likes and dislikes are discussed when booking. Vegetables are a forte, and home-baking is first-class. It is worth staying the night to enjoy the hearty breakfast, in which porridge and black pudding play starring roles, and anybody who cannot get through a full bottle of wine is invited to pay for half. The list is distinguished by having only two prices: £8.50 and £12.50.

CHEF: Joanna Gollin PROPRIETORS: Richard and Joanna Gollin OPEN: all week 7.30 (one sitting); L by arrangement CLOSED: 7 Oct to 15 Feb MEALS: Set D £21 SERVICE: not inc, card slips closed CARDS: Access, Visa DETAILS: 24 seats. Private parties: 24 main room. Car park. Vegetarian meals. Children's helpings. No smoking in dining-room. No music ACCOMMODATION: 12 rooms, 7 with bath/shower. B&B £19 to £60. Deposit: £50. Children welcome. Baby facilities. Pets welcome. Afternoon teas. Garden. Fishing (*The Which? Hotel Guide*)

ULLAPOOL Highland map 11

▲ *Altnaharrie Inn*

Ullapool IV26 2SS COOKING 5
TEL: (01854) 633230 COST £70–£84

'I had wanted to go to Altnaharrie Inn for a long time, and incredibly the food managed to surpass even the ridiculously high expectations I had,' began one typical report. One regular emphasised 'the consistently high standard of the cooking and the whole operation'. Another concluded that 'Altnaharrie is expensive but worth every penny'. Having to live up to all this is a terrible burden for anyone to bear, but Fred Brown and Gunn Eriksen manage it with deceptive ease. The feeling is that you are well looked after without being fussed over, and 'despite its reputation it is completely unstuffy'. One couple disrupted the smoothly oiled machine by setting out before breakfast to climb the An Teallach ridge. 'I did feel at the time as if we were treating one of the more important culinary establishments in Britain a bit like a glorified youth hostel, but we were given early coffee, toast and encouragement, plus a huge packed lunch. Our successful return ten hours later was celebrated.'

Altnaharrie is inaccessible by road, and anticipation is fuelled by the short boat-trip across the loch from Ullapool. There is no mains electricity either, but anyone hoping to find a run-down old shack with guttering candles will be disappointed. Gunn Eriksen's simple, clean, stylish taste pervades the house, and the generator is switched off as everybody goes to bed. The small scale, and the fact that everybody sits down at the same time for dinner, 'made it feel more like a house party than a restaurant' for one reporter. There is no choice before pudding on the five-course menu, but dislikes will already have been addressed when booking, and again on arrival. When return visitors find themselves eating a different menu from before, this is not by accident: a record is kept, so that each experience can be as fresh as the first; neighbouring tables may be tucking into different dishes.

The food is characterised by absolute freshness of ingredients, and by a clear sense of purpose. Fish and shellfish particularly benefit from this approach, as in a warm salad of scallops on a bed of spinach with lentils, morel mushrooms, and a champagne vinegar sauce. The second course is usually called 'soup', although the word may be inadequate to describe what appears: in one case lobster soup given edge by 'large quantities of chilli – this sounds disgusting, but the taste was exquisite'. The food is inventive, doesn't follow any particular 'school', but appears modern by virtue of its simplicity. Pasta – typically ravioli – is a useful device for packaging small surprises of this and that, either as a course in itself or as part of a main dish. At one meal it contained mushroom and grapes to accompany fillet of sika deer, which arrived on a bed of onions and green juniper berries. Banana baked in a pastry shell with an orange sauce, strawberries marinated in port and rosemary, and cloudberry ice-cream with spun sugar have been among dessert endorsements.

Service is 'faultless and friendly. Fred Brown runs everything smoothly in his own quiet way, and gives excellent advice about the gargantuan wine list.' 'We were very reluctant to take his advice to drink a light red wine with a dish of wild salmon with crab and ginger, but we did and it worked.' Burgundy has an edge over claret, but the all-round list has no real axe to grind, half-bottles are generous, and prices make other top-scoring restaurants look greedy.

CHEF: Gunn Eriksen PROPRIETORS: Fred Brown and Gunn Eriksen OPEN: all week D only 8 (one sitting) CLOSED: Nov to Easter MEALS: Set D £65 SERVICE: none, card slips closed CARDS: Access, Amex, Visa DETAILS: 18 seats. Private parties: 16 main room. Car park. No children under 8. Smart dress preferred. No smoking in dining-room. No music ACCOMMODATION: 8 rooms, all with bath/shower. D,B&B £135 to £340. Deposit: £100. No children under 8. Garden (*The Which? Hotel Guide*)

WALLS Shetland map 11

▲ *Burrastow House*

Walls ZE2 9PB
TEL: (01595) 809307 FAX: (01595) 809213
at Walls drive to top of hill, turn left, then follow road for 2m to Burrastow

COOKING 1
COST £19–£43

The house, dating from 1759, is at the end of a two-mile cul-de-sac. It is one of the most far-flung hotels in Britain – the *Guide*'s most northerly entry – and as remote as they come. Peat from surrounding acres burns in the welcoming open fire, comfort is a priority, and it feels pleasantly informal. 'A recent three-double-bedroomed extension, function room and conservatory now allow us to take disabled people and to run short courses,' writes Bo Simmons. There is nothing remote about the food (as up to date as crab rösti with salsa), which combines a wide European reach with a sound classical background, producing a salad of bacon, with sorrel and mussels, Hungarian mushroom soup, and warming casseroles such as venison with sloe-gin and juniper. Mediterranean flavours turn up in soupe au pistou, and butter sauces are customary with fish: flecked with saffron for a salmon steak, or speckled with chives for sea trout. Plum ice-cream, chocolate torte, and orange custard illustrate the range of puddings. Organic wines on the forty-strong list (most of which is under £20) include house wines at £8.50.

CHEF/PROPRIETOR: Bo Simmons OPEN: Tue to Sun 12.30 to 2.30, 7.30 to 9 CLOSED: Jan to Mar MEALS: alc L (main courses £6.50 to £9). Set D £28.50 SERVICE: not inc DETAILS: 35 seats. Private parties: 16 main room, 30 private room. Car park. Vegetarian meals. Children's helpings. No smoking in dining-room. Wheelchair access (also WC). No music ACCOMMODATION: 5 rooms, all with bath/shower. D,B&B £77 to £142. Deposit: 10%. Rooms for disabled. Children welcome. Baby facilities. Pets by arrangement. Afternoon teas. Garden. Fishing (*The Which? Hotel Guide*)

Wales

ABERAERON Dyfed map 4

Hive on the Quay £

Cadwgan Place, Aberaeron SA46 0BU — COOKING 1
TEL: (01545) 570445 — COST £12–£26

The harbour wall surrounds the courtyard of the old wharf where the Hive sits, and visitors call in on their way to and from the sea. Reasons for dropping by might be coffee and bara brith, a buffet lunch, a look at the honey-bee exhibition, an early dinner with the kids, or else an evening (high season only) pulling a crab to pieces, dipping it in mayonnaise and munching on salad and French bread. The Hive specialises in two things: honey, which finds its way into ice-creams, cakes, even children's sandwiches; and fish and shellfish from its own boats, which might end up in paella or fritto misto. Sewin, cockles and laverbread naturally feature, although not to the exclusion of steak and kidney pudding or oxtail stew. Cockle and bacon pie, grilled plaice with herb butter, or white and smoked fish layered with lasagne, are some of the ideas that keep the Hive busy. At lunch-times there is counter service only. Organic leanings are evident from flour (baking is the heart of the all-day menu) and from three organic wines on a minuscule list that also includes elderflower wine and Welsh mead from Llangollen at £1.50 a glass.

CHEFS: Sarah Holgate and Margaret Morgan PROPRIETORS: Margaret and Sarah Holgate OPEN: spring bank hol to mid-Sept all week L 12 to 2.30 and until 5 for teas, July and Aug D 6 to 9.30 CLOSED: mid-Sept to spring bank hol L, Sept to June D MEALS: alc (main courses L £2.50 to £10.50, D £7 to £12) SERVICE: not inc CARDS: Access, Visa DETAILS: 60 seats. 2 tables outside. Private parties: 15 main room. Vegetarian meals. Children's helpings. Wheelchair access. Music

ABERDOVEY Gwynedd map 7

▲ *Penhelig Arms Hotel*

Aberdovey LL35 0LT
TEL: (01654) 767215 FAX: (01654) 767690
on A493 Tywyn to Machynlleth road, opposite Penhelig station — COOKING 2
COST £17–£40

'It really is a gem of a place,' enthused a reporter of this black and white eighteenth-century inn by Penhelig harbour, in the vicinity of which wind-surfers brave the billows and rare birds breed undisturbed in their RSPB sanctuary. Lunches, except on Sundays (a three-course set meal), are served in the bar or the restaurant and offer soups such as broccoli and leek, as well as a range of generously filled sandwiches, fish pie, curries and casseroles. In the evenings, three-course fixed-price menus allow Jane Howkins to demonstrate her flair. Choice is formidably wide, the sauces alone an encyclopedic array, but she manages to bring most things off with aplomb, including a 'light and delicate' smoked chicken terrine, monkfish wrapped in bacon with a lemon hollandaise, and 'beautifully cooked' lamb cutlets. Vegetables usually have an interesting twist, as in lemon-zested French beans, and puddings such as lime soufflé with cardamom and ginger sauce keep the palate alert. Service covers a lot of ground in a session, but remains unflappable.

Robert Hughes has a passion for wine that spills out of the list on all sides, whether in traditional claret or among the Italian new wave. These are pedigree wines at prices that gladden the heart. He tells us that serving champagne at £3 a glass has increased sales dramatically. Well, it would, wouldn't it? A dozen and a half house recommendations under £15 get the list off to a good start. CELLARMAN'S CHOICE: Verdicchio Classico, Casal di Serra 1992, Umani Ronchi, £12.50; Martinborough Vineyard Pinot Noir 1993, New Zealand, £17.90.

CHEF: Jane Howkins PROPRIETORS: Robert and Sally Hughes OPEN: all week 12.15 to 2, 7 to 9.30 CLOSED: 25 and 26 Dec MEALS: alc (main courses £4.50 to £9). Set L Sun £12.50, Set D all week £18.50 SERVICE: not inc, card slips closed CARDS: Access, Delta, Switch, Visa DETAILS: 34 seats. Private parties: 20 main room, 20 private room. Car park. Children's helpings. Wheelchair access (1 step). No music ACCOMMODATION: 10 rooms, all with bath/shower. TV. Phone. B&B £39 to £78. Deposit: £40. Children welcome. Pets welcome. Afternoon teas (*The Which? Hotel Guide*)

ABERSOCH Gwynedd map 7

▲ *Porth Tocyn Hotel*

Abersoch LL53 7BU
TEL: (01758) 713303 FAX: (01758) 713538
on minor road 2m S of Abersoch through hamlets of Sarn Bach and Bwlchtocyn

COOKING 2
COST £23–£41

Porth Tocyn is an indefatigable institution that has graced the pages of the *Guide* for almost four decades, and visitors still adore it. The 1930s house may look unprepossessing in its pebble-dash coat, but the scenery is outstanding: the views stretch across Tremadog Bay to Snowdonia. No wonder the hotel casts a special magic. Getting the right mix of conviviality, 'light humour' and sound organisation is a good trick if you know how, and ebullient Nick Fletcher-Brewer has had years of practice. He is ably supported by his wife, who not only cooks but 'supervises serenely from the sidelines'. Dinner is set-price: choose just two courses or go the whole hog with five (including a 'magnificent' cheeseboard). Some ideas sound decidedly OTT (poached salmon fillets are served on pan-fried banana and topped with prawn and garlic yoghurt, for example), but the results seem impressive. One reporter wrote of an 'amazing' hazelnut roulade filled with pineapple and bacon; others have praised a 'truly Austrian' seafood strudel, lightly smoked salmon baked in a parcel, and mille-feuille of turkey escalopes with wild mushrooms, candied kumquats and a citrus coulis.

Finish with a 'free run' at the pudding list if you have the stamina: steamed sponge pudding soaked with treacle, and chocolate cheesecake discreetly spiked with sherry have been winners. Lunch is a simpler affair, with an extensive buffet stealing the show on Sundays. As befits a family-run hotel, Porth Tocyn treats children admirably: they are served 'proper food' in a separate room, and one of the owners' siblings generally eats with the youngsters – 'sure proof that the guests are not getting second best'. The wine list is a long read, and there are some eminently drinkable bottles tucked away among the French country wines and the New World section. House wines start at £10.50.

CHEF: Louise Fletcher-Brewer PROPRIETORS: the Fletcher-Brewer family OPEN: all week 12.30 to 2, 7.30 to 9.30 CLOSED: mid-Nov to week before Easter MEALS: Set L Sun £15.50, Set D £19 (2 courses) to £25.50; light lunch menu SERVICE: not inc, card slips closed CARDS: Access, Switch, Visa DETAILS: 50 seats. 10 tables outside. Private parties: 50 main room. Car park. Children's helpings. No children under 7 D. Smart dress preferred. Wheelchair access. No music ACCOMMODATION: 17 rooms, all with bath/shower. TV. Phone. B&B £41.50 to £99. Deposit: £40. Rooms for disabled. Children welcome. Baby facilities. Pets welcome in bedrooms only. Afternoon teas. Garden. Swimming-pool (*The Which? Hotel Guide*)

▲ *Riverside Hotel*

Abersoch LL53 7HW
TEL: (01758) 712419 FAX: (01758) 712671 COOKING 1*
on A499, 6m SW of Pwllheli COST £29–£36

This is a family-run seaside hotel overlooking the harbour, which puts two canoes and a rowing boat at guests' disposal, and arranges other activities from golf to bridge. One reporter who drives 50,000 miles a year and spends a large part of his time in hotels considers this 'a rare find, relaxing and restful', without the 'prissy pretension' of bigger hotels. But then the Bakewells have had 28 years here to get things right. Substantial five-course dinners (and lighter bar lunches) are the pattern, and the kitchen copes well with the mix of dishes from simple roast sirloin of Welsh beef to breast of chicken filled with asparagus and smoky bacon and served with an orange hollandaise.

Local fish and shellfish find their way easily enough on to the menu – in crab tartlet or fillet of sea bass en papillote – as do rabbit and hare. Vegetables to accompany main courses have included a bake of aubergine, courgette and tomato, and a stir-fried dish of broccoli and carrots in sesame oil. The second course is a soup (cream of carrot, orange and coriander at one meal), and cheese follows enterprising puddings of banana toffee meringues with butterscotch sauce, peppered strawberries with lemon honey thins, or chocolate Toblerone ice-cream. Forty-odd roving wines stay commendably below £20, with house wine around £10, and there is a short supplementary list from Adnams.

CHEFS/PROPRIETORS: John and Wendy Bakewell OPEN: all week D only 7.30 to 9 (8.15 low season); bar meals available L CLOSED: mid-Nov to end Feb MEALS: Set D £21 SERVICE: not inc, card slips closed CARDS: Access, Amex, Diners, Switch, Visa DETAILS: 32 seats. Private parties: 32 main room. Car park. No children under 5. Smart dress preferred. Music ACCOMMODATION: 12 rooms, all with bath/shower. TV. Phone. B&B £42 to £80. Deposit: £30. Children welcome. Baby facilities. Garden. Swimming pool. Fishing

BEAUMARIS Gwynedd map 7

▲ *Ye Olde Bulls Head Inn*

Castle Street, Beaumaris LL58 8AP COOKING 2*
TEL: (01248) 810329 FAX: (01248) 811294 COST £29–£43

The house dates back to 1472, which explains the wooden beams and crooked corridors. Although it has gathered antique weapons and a brass water clock over the centuries, it feels up to date, and four new bedrooms are being fashioned from former stabling as the *Guide* goes to press. According to Keith Rothwell and David Robertson, when they first opened a restaurant in the area 19 years ago, 'the availability of good produce was a total nightmare. Today things have swung the opposite way. With the exception of tropical fruit and vegetables, virtually all our produce comes from the immediate locality.' Among these local ingredients are smoked salmon, beef for bresaola, shellfish for bisque, and Dover sole, which might appear simply with a herb butter. Roast leg of lamb makes a frequent appearance (where does it not in Wales?), but the cooking is by no means backwoods.

'Our operation is evolving in parallel with the British palate rather then being at the cutting edge of it,' writes Keith Rothwell, in which guise it also collects a few Mediterranean treatments. The upshot is warm smoked salmon with fresh pasta in a chervil butter sauce, tartar of sea bass marinated with herbs and olive oil, and smoked duck with a mango and chilli salsa. One vegetarian was treated 'with special attention'. Puddings are not just run-of-the-mill either. Rhubarb and rosewater crumble, or an individual Anglesey strawberry Alaska on a white peach coulis, provides an upbeat finish. Bar lunches might include cold poached salmon with mayonnaise, hot bacon baguette, or a range of sandwiches. Wines are notable not just for their range and quality; they also home in on essentials, whether in France, Italy, Spain or New Zealand, and are offered at extremely reasonable prices. Five good house wines cost £12.50 a bottle, or £2.75 a glass. CELLARMAN'S CHOICE: Sancerre 'La Grande Côte' 1992, Cotat, £19.95; Bonny Doon 'Le Cigare Volant' 1990, £18.59.

CHEFS: Keith Rothwell and Soames Whittingham PROPRIETOR: Rothwell and Robertson Ltd OPEN: all week 12 to 1.30, 7.30 to 9.30 (9 Sun) CLOSED: 25 and 26 Dec, 1 Jan MEALS: alc (main courses £11.50 to £15). Set L £14.75, Set D £19.95 SERVICE: not inc CARDS: Access, Amex, Switch, Visa DETAILS: 70 seats. Private parties: 70 main room. Car park. Vegetarian meals. Children's helpings. No children under 7 D. Smart dress preferred. No smoking in dining-room. No music ACCOMMODATION: 15 rooms, all with bath/shower. TV. Phone. B&B £43 to £85. Children welcome (separate dining-room for under 7s D). Baby facilities (*The Which? Hotel Guide*)

Prices quoted in the Guide *are based on information supplied by restaurateurs. The prices quoted at the top of each entry represent a range, from the lowest meal price to the highest; the latter is inflated by 20 per cent to take account of likely price rises during the year of the* Guide.

BRECHFA Dyfed map 4

▲ *Tŷ Mawr*

Brechfa SA32 7RA
TEL: (01267) 202332 FAX: (01267) 202437 COOKING 2
on B4310, 6m N of A40 at Nantgaredig COST £29–£34

'Tŷ Mawr' is Welsh for 'large house', but Dick and Beryl Tudhope's hotel is no grand mansion. It is as cosy and intimate as an auberge transported to the peaceful heart of Welsh-speaking Wales. The garden of the sixteenth-century stone house is bounded on one side by the River Marlais. The interior is all bare walls, old beams and quarry-tiled floors, although the place isn't short on creature comforts. Beryl Tudhope's cooking is based soundly on carefully chosen local ingredients with occasional international flourishes: bread is baked in-house from organic flour, lamb and black beef are from a reliable butcher in Llandeilo, salmon and sewin are landed by coracle fishermen on the River Towy, and the carefully nurtured cheeses often include mature Teifi, Celtic Promise and Pencarreg.

The dinner menu is three courses plus coffee, with half a dozen options at each stage, and adopts what one reporter called a 'carefully measured' approach. As an alternative to one of Beryl's soups, try 'almost transparently thin' pancakes filled with Penclawdd cockles and laverbread or spicy filo triangles with an 'enticing' home-made chutney. Main courses might include noisettes of pink lamb with garlic and haricot bean sauce, game pot, or Chinese-style fillet of 'king trout' steamed with ginger and spring onions. Puddings are wholesome – spiced dried fruit compote with organic yoghurt – and can be chocolatey, as in a dark, intensely flavoured chocolate and almond slice with black cherry sauce. Details such as 'superior nibbles', well-handled vegetables and freshly brewed coffee with miniature shortbread biscuits get the thumbs-up. The wine list is a good, well-rounded collection of affordable bottles courtesy of Adnams and of Michael Anthony Wines of Haverfordwest. House wine is £8.95.

CHEF: Beryl Tudhope PROPRIETORS: Beryl and Dick Tudhope OPEN: Wed to Mon D only 7 to 9.30 CLOSED: last week Nov, last 2 weeks Jan MEALS: Set D £21.50 SERVICE: not inc, card slips closed CARDS: Access, Amex, Visa DETAILS: 35 seats. Private parties: 40 main room. Car park. Vegetarian meals. Children welcome. Smart dress preferred. No smoking in dining-room. No music ACCOMMODATION: 5 rooms, all with bath/shower. D,B&B £63 to £118. Deposit £10. Children welcome. Baby facilities. Pets welcome. Afternoon teas. Garden (*The Which? Hotel Guide*)

See inside the front cover for an explanation of the symbols used at the tops of entries.

'We placed our orders before 8.30pm but it was not until 9.30 that the first course made an appearance. By 10.15pm there was still no sign of the main courses; the nearest we got to food during this interval was when a waiter dropped a butter knife down the back of one of our party.' (On eating in Bedfordshire)

BROAD HAVEN Dyfed map 4

▲ *Druidstone* £

Druidstone Haven, Broad Haven,
nr Haverfordwest SA62 3NE
TEL: (01437) 781221 FAX: (01437) 781133
from B4341 at Broad Haven turn right at sea, after 1½m turn left to Druidstone Haven, hotel ¾m on right

COOKING 1
COST £15–£28

'There have been renovations in the past year,' observed a reporter, although the Druidstone still struck him as 'an unfinished symphony of a place'. The old stone house by the cliffs lives and breathes eccentricity. The Bells have been here since 1972 and nothing has dented their no-frills, laid-back approach to hospitality. An obstacle course of wellington boots and clutter is the first challenge as you go through the door; cats, dogs and children roam around; there is no standing on ceremony and no dress code (unless you count sweaters, T-shirts and jeans).

The dining-room is filled with books, paintings, an upright piano, bare pine tables and an ancient settee for worn-out youngsters. The original farmhouse kitchen with its Rayburn and refectory tables is now a friendly rendezvous for private parties, after-hours chats and reading the papers. Don't expect four-star comfort or showy cuisine here. Rod and Jane share most of the cooking: he produces the classic stuff, she majors in fish and vegetarian dishes with a homespun flavour. Soups, pâtés and roasts are firm favourites, but the menu also pulls in Creole chicken, baked sea bream with ginger and spring onion, Portuguese pot-roast lamb, and aubergine parmigiana. Organic breads and desserts, such as fresh fruit meringue or St Clement's soufflé, are Donna Banner's responsibility; cheeses are 'local and natural'. The wine list is short and suitably unostentatious. House wine is £6.50.

CHEFS: Rod and Jane Bell, and Donna Banner PROPRIETORS: Rod and Jane Bell OPEN: Sun L 1 to 2, Mon to Sat D 7.30 to 9.30 CLOSED: Mon to Wed 6 Nov to 13 Dec and 8 Jan to 14 Feb MEALS: alc (main courses £6 to £11) SERVICE: not inc, card slips closed CARDS: Access, Amex, Delta, Switch, Visa DETAILS: 40 seats. 6 tables outside. Private parties: 40 main room, 10 private room. Car park. Vegetarian meals. Children's helpings. Wheelchair access (also WC). Music ACCOMMODATION: 9 rooms and 5 cottages. B&B £25 to £60. Deposit: £20. Children welcome. Baby facilities. Pets welcome (exc in dining-room). Afternoon teas. Garden (*The Which? Hotel Guide*)

CAPEL COCH Gwynedd map 7

▲ *Tre-Ysgawen Hall*

Capel Coch, Llangefni, Anglesey LL77 7UR
TEL: (01248) 750750 FAX: (01248) 750035
on B5111, between Llangefni and Amlwch

COOKING 2
COST £21–£54

Restoration has made the most of the large, high-ceilinged rooms and correspondingly tall windows in this nineteenth-century manor house. The prosperous feel is matched by 'well-nigh perfect' service, which is personal and individual without being too familiar. Mark Colley's brand of British cooking rests on a classical French foundation, which means there are some smart twists and turns to the menu, as well as a degree of richness, weight and the occasional elaborate gesture. A modest quantity of alcohol trickles through the food, from port in the mushroom soup to an orange and Grand Marnier pancake soufflé. In true French fashion a simple butter sauce is a common accompaniment to grilled fish, with the addition of sorrel, perhaps, for fillet of coley, or chervil for sea bass – local fish is one of the strengths.

An openness to other influences brings variety in the form of ravioli filled with langoustines and lobster, flavoured with cardamom and ginger, or roast pigeon on a vanilla sauce with spicy black pudding. Sun-dried tomatoes make an appearance (with pan-fried loin of smoked Welsh pork), and other ideas range from a relatively straightforward dish of Cornish scallops pan-fried in olive oil with crispy leeks to a satisfying steamed sponge pudding with ice-cream and hot chocolate sauce. The far-flung list makes use of commercial and *négociant* wines to keep prices down but also includes more stylish fizz and claret. House Australian is £9.80, or £1.65 a glass.

CHEF: Mark Colley PROPRIETORS: Mr and Mrs Ray Craighead OPEN: all week 12 to 2.30, 7 to 9.30 MEALS: alc D (main courses £14 to £18). Set L £14, Set D £19.95 SERVICE: not inc CARDS: Access, Amex, Delta, Diners, Switch, Visa DETAILS: 64 seats. Private parties: 120 main room, 20 to 120 private rooms. Car park. Vegetarian meals. Children's helpings. Jacket and tie. Wheelchair access (2 steps; also WC). Music ACCOMMODATION: 20 rooms, all with bath/shower. TV. Phone. B&B £78.50 to £164. Deposit: 20%. Rooms for disabled. Children welcome. Baby facilities. Pets welcome by arrangement. Afternoon teas. Garden (*The Which? Hotel Guide*)

CARDIFF South Glamorgan map 4

Armless Dragon £

97 Wyeverne Road, Cathays, Cardiff CF2 4BG COOKING 1*
TEL: (01222) 382357 COST £15–£35

The Dragon's lair is a conversion of two terraced houses in the student quarter behind the university. David Richards has been running the show for some 12 years now, offering solid bistro cooking in surroundings that are decorated with greenery and prints for sale. The ambience is described as 'chummy'. A long list of daily specials carried around the room on a noticeboard and propped up on the chairs supplements the short menu of mainstays. Influences come from the Far East as well as Provence and most dishes make an impact, as an inspector discovered. Mussel and shrimp risotto was decently 'glutinous and pungent', while an octopus and grilled pepper salad brought fresh, crisp morsels of cephalopod together with sharply dressed accompaniments. Hake meunière was correctly cooked, the fish steak flaking moistly. Venison at the same meal was less successful, excepting its sauce: a rich port reduction full of 'hot surprises' from plenty of whole peppercorns. Puddings are particularly accomplished. Nut meringues with hot fudge sauce are agreeably sticky with good crunch factor; chocolate marquise is 'rich, thick and smooth' and used 'powerfully bitter' cocoa solids. There is a slight feeling these days of the kitchen running on automatic pilot, one of the consequences perhaps of keeping to a largely unchanging menu. Service has been, on occasion, 'lackadaisical' but is always cheery. A short but enterprising wine list is priced entirely under £20, save for champagnes. House French is £7.90.

CHEFS: David Richards and Debbie Coleman PROPRIETOR: David Richards OPEN: Tue to Fri L 12 to 2.15, Tue to Sat D 7 to 10.15 CLOSED: Christmas, bank hols MEALS: alc (main courses £8 to £14). Set L £7.90 (2 courses) to £9.90 SERVICE: not inc CARDS: Access, Amex, Delta, Diners, Switch, Visa DETAILS: 45 seats. Private parties: 50 main room. Vegetarian meals. Children's helpings. No cigars/pipes in dining-room. Wheelchair access. Music

La Brasserie

60 St Mary Street, Cardiff CF1 1FE COOKING 1
TEL: (01222) 372164 FAX: (01222) 668092 COST £15–£45

La Brasserie, along with its sisters Champers and Le Monde (all in the same block of buildings – see entries below), is part of the Benigno Martinez culinary empire, which now also includes the Caesar's Arms in Creigiau (see entry). The three informal cosmopolitan city-centre restaurants share a penchant for wooden tables and sawdust floors, but each has its own character, built on a wide variety of meat, fish and poultry cuts and preparations on display in cool cabinets. The whole complex has gradually expanded to embrace neighbouring properties, and La Brasserie is about to undergo major refurbishment: 'We will be extending the restaurant area all the way through to Mill Lane, effectively increasing the available seating to approximately 300 covers.' Opening times may change too, expanding to most of the day.

Make your choice at the counter, then help yourself from a range of salads. The menu is predictable and the cooking basic, but the food is fresh. La Brasserie aims to be French, although it doesn't quite hit the bull's-eye. It has a blackboard menu, loud pop rock Muzak, and you are handed a knife and fork wrapped in a paper serviette. The display includes juicy, meaty king prawns, chicken wings, dressed crab, spare ribs, fillet steak and grilled Scotch salmon, and the difference between first and main course is largely a matter of quantity. One reporter rates the £5 two-course lunch 'the best value in the city. Where else can you have either gravad lax or fresh grilled sardines, followed by pork kebab or fish of the day, for a fiver?' The help-yourself salad usually gets eaten while waiting for the order to be cooked. Sauces tend to be flour-based, and for no extra charge a waiter will happily grind pepper over your food. Desserts are limited: crêpes suzette or a selection of cheese. Wines are mostly French; house wine is £8.45 a bottle, or £1.45 and £2.85 per glass.

CHEFS: David Legg (Executive Chef), Kurt Fleming and Carmen Laventure PROPRIETOR: Benigno Martinez OPEN: Mon to Sat 12 to 2.30, 7 to 12.15 MEALS: alc (main courses £8.50 to £17). Set L £5 (2 courses) SERVICE: not inc, card slips closed CARDS: Access, Amex, Delta, Diners, Switch, Visa DETAILS: 80 seats. Children welcome. Smart dress preferred. Music

'I was particularly taken with the ladies' loo, which had a wonderful stained mirror, a marble topped dresser with a serious plant, and a sink in an old wooden surround with lots of big fluffy white towels. There was also a small fireplace with iron grate, dried flowers and a very desirable wooden advertising poster for cigarettes. Given a power shower, I could live in a bathroom like that.' (On eating in Wiltshire).

Le Cassoulet

5 Romilly Crescent, Canton, Cardiff CF1 9NP — COOKING 2*
TEL: (01222) 221905 — COST £28–£43

Another year, another chef at Le Cassoulet. Mark Freeman is the latest to take a turn, arriving in March 1995. His new home is a compact, thoroughly Gallic restaurant in one of Cardiff's more fashionable environs. Paintings and prints of an equine disposition are all around, tables are crowded close, and the culinary inspiration is south-west France. Service, too, is very French, and very friendly.

The reassuring message is that standards remain on track. If your whim is to try new aperitifs, go for the house cocktails, one of which is pousse-rapière: orange-flavoured armagnac topped up with sparkling wine. Starters may include a complicated but 'exquisite' dish of poached egg wrapped in smoked salmon and cucumber decorated with diamonds of red pepper sitting on a creamily dressed celeriac rösti. A main course of pot-roasted monkfish with a pepper ragoût and soya jus achieved 'excellent contrasts' and the fish itself was 'meaty, solid but juicy'. A 'generous and robust' cassoulet of duck confit, boudin blanc, pork, haricot beans and breadcrumbs was 'as good as any I have eaten outside its native region' for one reporter. Crème brûlée might be dolled up with ginger, coconut and banana, while another pudding may be a plate of no fewer than seven chocolate desserts (the white chocolate and vodka sorbet deserves full marks for bravery). Well-enjoyed French cheeses and tip-top coffee round things off nicely. Wines are exclusively French and mainly well chosen, although prices push hard in Bordeaux and Burgundy, and it is sad to see only two Alsace wines. Fittingly, the south-western selections seem to offer best value. House wines from the Ardèche are £9.50.

CHEF: Mark Freeman PROPRIETORS: Gilbert and Claire Viader OPEN: Tue to Fri L 12 to 2, Tue to Sat D 7 to 10 CLOSED: 2 weeks Christmas, Aug MEALS: Set L £16 (2 courses) to £19, Set D £20 (2 courses) to £26 SERVICE: not inc CARDS: Access, Amex, Delta, Diners, Switch, Visa DETAILS: 40 seats. Private parties: 40 main room. Vegetarian meals. Children's helpings. Smart dress preferred. No music

Champers £

61 St Mary Street, Cardiff CF1 1FE — COOKING 1
TEL: (01222) 373363 — COST £19–£46

Champers is the Spanish arm of the Benigno Martinez trio, and just as informal as La Brasserie (see entry, previous page). Expansion has not only brought more space and less intimacy, but has increased the range of tapas available: a laminated list of 30 ranging from garlic shrimps and potato omelette to excellent sweet-cured pata negra ham, or meatballs in a spicy sauce. 'You can just sit on stools at the long bar, sip Rioja, empty the bowl of plump green olives and then eat diced liver or bean stew, and leave happy; or you can sit at one of the old-fashioned wooden dining tables and eat juicy steaks, pork chops, lamb kebabs, or sizzling king prawns with a huge helping of hot drippy garlic bread and go home replete.'

Main courses are served on cast-iron grill plates set in a wooden base, and come with baked potato or French fries. The centrepiece – lightly cooked, firm monkfish, or chargrilled sirloin steak – is better than the sauce, while the simple salads, mostly with raw onion, are better than the dressing. An inspector's advice is to stick to tapas, which are more imaginative and varied. It is not difficult to make a meal of small quantities of anchovies marinated in oil and garlic, grilled quail, and tripe cooked with chickpeas and chorizo sausage. Spanish cheeses follow. Lobster is fresh on Wednesdays. Spanish house wines are £8.45 a bottle, or £1.45 and £2.85 per glass.

CHEFS: David Legg (Executive Chef), Denis Louis and Fernando Batista PROPRIETOR: Benigno Martinez OPEN: Mon to Sat L 12 to 2.30, all week D 7 to 12.15 MEALS: alc (main courses £4 to £17) SERVICE: not inc, card slips closed CARDS: Access, Amex, Delta, Diners, Visa DETAILS: 180 seats. Private parties: 25 main room. Children welcome. Smart dress preferred. Wheelchair access (also WC). Music

Le Monde £

62 St Mary Street, Cardiff CF1 1FE COOKING 1*
TEL: (01222) 387376 FAX: (01222) 668092 COST £19–£46

Bright, chromiumed, smoked-glassed, noisy and boisterous Le Monde is the flagship of the Martinez empire (see also Le Brasserie and Champers, Cardiff, above). Open-plan, with mock street lights for decoration, the restaurant occupies three different levels, with a huge display cabinet on the lowest. The welcome is friendly and, once you are seated – there is no booking so you may have to wait for a table – the well-organised service speeds things along. The same formula holds for Le Monde as for its sister establishments: good ingredients, simply and reliably cooked, with a good range of wines to match, except that here fish is the main business. The process of choosing can be a bit bewildering at first – the range is vast, with blackboards also offering specials, and black glass walls graffitied with wines – but people get the hang of it easily enough.

Fish is sold by weight and soon clocks up a high figure, although a medium-sized fish can do two people: sea bass is a speciality, baked in rock salt. The waiter removes the thick crust and fillets the fish, which is 'sea-fresh, with big fleshy flakes'. The quality of the buying is remarkably good, and results in queen scallops in a buttery herby broth, or three fat king prawns in the shell rapidly grilled and doused in garlic butter: 'meaty, tasty, pungent with freshness and garlic'. High-speed chefs and fast cooking times pile on the tempo and drama, as do rugby Saturdays. Spanish house wine is £8.45.

CHEFS: David Legg (Executive Chef), Tony Kocker PROPRIETOR: Benigno Martinez OPEN: Mon to Sat 12 to 2.30, 7 to 12 CLOSED: 25 and 26 Dec MEALS: alc (main courses £6 to £17) SERVICE: not inc, card slips closed CARDS: Access, Amex, Diners, Visa DETAILS: 180 seats. Private parties: 34 main room, 90 private room. Children welcome. Smart dress preferred. Music. Air-conditioned

The Guide *always appreciates hearing about changes of chef or owner.*

CHIRK Clwyd map 7

▲ *Starlings Castle* 🍷

Bronygarth, nr Chirk SY10 7NU
TEL/FAX: (01691) 718464
take Western Rhyn turn from A5 N of Oswestry to Selattyn, turn right through village, climb for 2½m, turn right at top of hill, then follow signs

COOKING 3
COST £27–£40

'Restaurant, bedrooms, pottery' is how Starlings Castle sums itself up in its colourful information sheet. It is less of a castle, more of a long, eighteenth-century farmhouse with low ceilings – very rural, quiet and relaxing. It is small-scale and personal: the Pitts do just about everything themselves. The 'refectory', as the dining-room styles itself, is light and white with decorative pottery everywhere, and the food creates a 'freshly made' impression. They don't bother about nibbles and petits fours, but the bread is home-made.

The traditional French provincial slant of the cooking is tempered with other ideas, such as Thai crab fish-balls with ginger, chilli and coriander, and grilled tuna with couscous and harissa. This is a kitchen in a state of evolution, and the result is a varied output in terms of both taste and technique, from cheese and leek tart to slow-cooked oxtail to a hot chocolate soufflé. Fish soup with rouille and croûtons is a long-standing Mediterranean favourite that now shares the billing with grilled goats' cheese with olive paste.

Antony Pitt deals in strong, clear tastes and is alive to textural qualities. He sharpens up the flavours with a coriander and chilli sauce for langoustines, an olive and caper vinaigrette for baked hake, and a paw-paw chutney with a terrine of pork, pigeon and pistachio. Damson vinegar, chilli salsa, aïoli, and a lime and garlic marinade for chicken help to brighten the whole tone of the cooking. An exotic note creeps into puddings too, as in a pineapple and papaya salad in rum, but mainstream ideas dominate, taking in poached pears with maple and walnut ice-cream, strawberry and white chocolate délices, and rhubarb and ginger tart. Coffee is served from a hand-thrown jug. A sure hand and an enquiring palate are evident in the 50-strong wide-ranging wine list, and mark-ups are not excessive. There are no half-bottles, but house wine is from £10.50, or £1.50 a glass. CELLARMAN'S CHOICE: Rioja Reserva Blanco 1988, Marques de Murrieta, £17.50; Ch. Musar 1987, Serge Hochar, £16.50.

CHEF: Antony Pitt PROPRIETORS: Antony and Jools Pitt OPEN: Sun L 12.30 to 2.30 (other days by arrangement), all week D 7.30 to 9.30 (10 Fri and Sat) MEALS: alc (main courses £10.50 to £14.50) SERVICE: not inc CARDS: Access, Amex, Diners, Visa DETAILS: 50 seats. 5 tables outside. Private parties: 50 main room, 20 and 50 private rooms. Car park. Children's helpings. No cigars/pipes in dining-room. Wheelchair access (also WC). Music ACCOMMODATION: 10 rooms, 3 with bath/shower. TV. D,B&B £41 to £94. Rooms for disabled. Children welcome. Baby facilities. Pets welcome in bedrooms only. Garden (*The Which? Hotel Guide*)

'Vegetables included fried potatoes cut in dice. They were tasty, but didn't really go with the ravioli unless, like me, you have fond memories of ravioli and chips constituting an introduction to sophisticated eating.' **(On eating in Suffolk)**

CLYTHA Gwent map 2

▲ *Clytha Arms*

Clytha NP7 9BW
TEL/FAX: (01873) 840206
off old Abergavenny to Raglan road, S of A40, 6m E of Abergavenny

COOKING 1*
COST £16–£38

Opinions differ about this converted dower house by the River Usk: some say it is a restaurant-with-rooms, others maintain it is still a country pub, complete with chapel pews in the bar, six real ales and superior food. Menus are chalked on blackboards. The highlight of the week for owners Andrew and Beverley Canning is Sunday lunch, when families fill the place and crowds tuck into 'copious' quantities of fish soup with 'excellent' bread, roasts with no fewer than eight different vegetables, and treacle pudding with custard. The repertoire is based resolutely on top-notch local produce. At times the results are classic French, although the balance is towards modern Welsh cooking with an exotic seam running through: roast duck with orange and turnip brûlée, spiced loin of lamb with lemon dhal, salmon in beer batter with capers and dill, for example. Visitors have spoken highly of 'outstandingly fresh' fish soup, smoked sewin with scrambled egg, and 'deliciously tender' venison chop with herb dumplings, but the undisputed star of the show must be wild mushroom and Caerphilly soufflé ('before it cooled it was three inches over the edge of the dish'). The cheeseboard is patriotically Welsh, while the line-up of puddings includes such things as ginger syllabub and a frothy dark chocolate mousse 'drenched in armagnac'. Service is casual and sometimes hard-pressed, but the young waitresses are never less than amiable. The short wine list offers some very creditable, reasonably priced wines, with house French and Australian £7.50.

CHEFS/PROPRIETORS: Andrew and Beverley Canning OPEN: Tue to Sun and bank hol Mons L 12.30 to 2.30, Tue to Sat D 7.30 to 9.30 MEALS: alc (main courses £8 to £15). Set L Sun £9.50 SERVICE: not inc, card slips closed CARDS: Access, Delta, Switch, Visa DETAILS: 66 seats. 10 tables outside. Private parties: 50 main room, 18 private room. Car park. Vegetarian meals. Children's helpings. Smart dress preferred. No smoking in dining-room. Wheelchair access (2 steps). No music ACCOMMODATION: 3 rooms, all with bath/shower. TV. B&B £40 to £65. Children welcome. Baby facilities. Garden

COLWYN BAY Clwyd map 7

Café Niçoise

124 Abergele Road, Colwyn Bay LL29 7PS
TEL: (01492) 531555

COOKING 2
COST £20–£43

This aims to be a transplanted provincial French restaurant, from its prints and Edith Piaf tapes right down to the roots of its 'menu touristique'. It is a welcoming place, and particularly good value, especially when a fixed-price, three-course meal can consist of tapénade and red pepper salad, salmon brochettes with a lemon and caper butter sauce, and profiteroles with a chocolate and nut sauce. The restaurant occupies three rooms, with dark pink, striped wallpaper and dark blue tablecloths. Service is 'friendly without being pally, professional without being snooty'. A blackboard of changing specials is removed from the wall, brought to table and read out. The food can be as simple as an assembly of ingredients for salade niçoise, or as straightforward as a sauté of mushrooms in garlic butter, but the produce is fresh and ambition is in line with what the kitchen can comfortably handle. Welsh lamb with winter vegetables, roast guinea-fowl with bacon and wild mushrooms, and crème brûlée with banana give an idea of what the *carte* offers. Seven house wines from £8.50 are also available by the glass at £1.75.

CHEF: Carl Swift PROPRIETORS: Lynne and Carl Swift OPEN: Thur to Sat L 12 to 2, Mon to Sat D 7 to 10 MEALS: alc (main courses £7 to £14.50). Set L and D £12.95. Minimum £5 SERVICE: not inc, card slips closed CARDS: Access, Amex, Switch, Visa DETAILS: 32 seats. Private parties: 30 main room. Vegetarian meals. Children's helpings. Smart dress preferred. Music

CREIGIAU Mid Glamorgan map 4

Caesar's Arms £

NEW ENTRY

Cardiff Road, Creigiau CF4 8NN
TEL: (01222) 890486 FAX: (01222) 892176 COOKING 1
2m N of M4, junction 33 COST £18–£43

Benigno Martinez, owner of La Brasserie, Champers and Le Monde (see entries, Cardiff), has extended this 1950s pub until the restaurant and its covered terrace are larger than the original building. But then food is the draw. This particular Martinez manifestation relies on the usual formula strengths of good-quality ingredients cooked simply and quickly, efficient service and decent wine at fair prices. All these factors are helped along by 'a pleasant atmosphere, bubbling conversations, and people obviously enjoying themselves'. It is a far cry from the uninspired mainstream of pub cooking.

Fish from hake to sewin, from sea bass to monkfish, is sold by weight; and steak, poultry and game are on show too. The routine is to 'go to the display cabinet, look at the fresh ingredients, read the blackboard for specials and wines, place an order', return to your table – laid with paper napkins, salt, pepper and vinegar – and await the food. The hearty style and lack of frills are appreciated. Skate cheeks (an item seen too rarely) are battered and deep-fried, king prawns come in garlic butter, lightly breadcrumbed lemon sole is 'supremely well cooked', and a whole small leg of lamb grilled with rosemary is 'astonishingly good'. Sticky toffee, pavlova and sachertorte ('a distant cousin of the Viennese original,' comments an inspector) are among the puddings. Service is laid back. Wines seesaw from *négociant* burgundy to Ch. Latour 1980, but with enough under £20 to suit the pub style. House wine is £7.95.

CHEF: Earl Smikle PROPRIETOR: Steadychance Ltd OPEN: all week L 12 to 2.30, Mon to Sat D 7 to 10.30 CLOSED: 25 Dec MEALS: alc (main courses £5 to £16.50) SERVICE: not inc, card slips closed CARDS: Access, Amex, Delta, Diners, Switch, Visa DETAILS: 150 seats. 12 tables outside. Private parties: 40 main room, 80 private room. Car park. Vegetarian meals. Children welcome. Smart dress preferred. Wheelchair access (also WC). Music

CRICKHOWELL Powys map 4

Nantyffin Cider Mill Inn £

Brecon Road, Crickhowell NP8 1SG
TEL/FAX: (01873) 810775 COOKING 1
1½m W of Crickhowell at junction of A40 and A479 COST £16–£36

The sixteenth-century mill on the River Usk, in the Brecon Beacons National Park, used to sell cider made on the premises, but the orchard is now a car park. The pink-washed stone building houses a couple of bars, which also serve food, and a converted barn that pairs exposed beams and stone walls with blue carpet tiles and conference-type stacking chairs; this is the canteen-like dining-room, on two levels. First-timers may need to specify whether they want to eat in the pub or restaurant, should keep an eye out for what is on the blackboards, and ask for the full wine list if they want to see it, since staff assume that everybody knows how the system works. Indeed, service is the weak point, but local support is strong for the package: a wide choice of dishes, all served in generous portions with lots of vegetables. Making an appearance might be steamed Chinese pork balls or lamb's liver with mashed potato, onion gravy and grilled bacon. Order roast duck or guinea-fowl and you get half the bird, the former with onion marmalade and an orange and Grand Marnier sauce, the latter with braised yellow peas and a garlic and thyme sauce. Puddings are not a high point, although decent coffee is served with mint crisps. Good-value wines from around the world, the vast majority under £20, are helpfully arranged by style. The fixed mark-up is customer-friendly, making the more expensive wines real bargains. Six house wines start at £8.75, and in the bar there is a list of ten inexpensive bottles, all also available by the glass.

CHEF: S. Gerrard PROPRIETORS: S. Gerrard and G. Bridgeman OPEN: Tue to Sun (and Mon Apr to Oct) 12 to 2.30, 6.45 to 10 CLOSED: 2 weeks Jan MEALS: alc (main courses £5 to £12.50). Set L Sun £10.70 SERVICE: not inc CARDS: Access, Delta, Switch, Visa DETAILS: 65 seats. 10 tables outside. Private parties: 70 main room. Car park. Vegetarian meals. Children's helpings. Smart dress preferred. No cigars/pipes in bar. Wheelchair access (also WC). Music

DOLGELLAU Gwynedd map 7

Dylanwad Da £

GWYNEDD 1996 BISTRO

2 Ffôs-y-Felin, Dolgellau LL40 1BS COOKING 1*
TEL: (01341) 422870 COST £19–£31

This 'friendly neighbourhood bistro' is as popular among English settlers as among Welsh people, not least because both languages are spoken. The dining-room is simply furnished with pine tables and chairs and paper tablecloths, and 'glows in a warm yellow tone'. Walls are decorated with paintings by local artists, the atmosphere is 'light and friendly', service is 'brisk and efficient', and prices are 'commendably reasonable'. The food can be slightly old-fashioned, but Dolgellau is perhaps not the place to try too many ultra-modern ideas. As it is, Dylan Rowlands steers a sensible course between extremes, which allows his monthly-changing menu to incorporate a smoked salmon and prawn timbale with mild horseradish sauce, and a casserole of Welsh lamb and roasted almonds.

Dishes may sound as ordinary as prawn vol-au-vent, but the pastry is good, the curry-flavoured cream sauce is delicate, and the prawns very fresh. What more could one ask of a prawn vol-au-vent? Flavours and seasonings are kept in check, and one reporter enjoyed a 'mild but spicy' plump herring soused in Muscadet, accompanied by an apple tartare sauce. At one meal, sticky toffee pudding 'seemed to be a slice of sponge loaf coated with a good toffee sauce', and was outshone by an 'intense and tangy tarte au citron with excellent pastry'. 'The vegetarian dishes are unusually attractive, and diners who are allergic to ingredients such as cheese, soya sauce and alcohol are well catered for.' Those who are not allergic to alcohol can choose from a short but lively list at prices which, outside Wales, would be considered suicidal for the restaurant. Yet Dylanwad Da survives. Would that more restaurants had the courage to follow this example. CELLARMAN'S CHOICE: Oyster Bay Chardonnay 1993, Marlborough, New Zealand, £11.95; Crozes-Hermitage 1992, Dom. Pochon, £10.95.

CHEF/PROPRIETOR: Dylan Rowlands OPEN: all week D only 7 to 9; L by arrangement CLOSED: Feb, Sun to Wed Oct to Jan and Mar to June (exc 1 week Easter, 1 week second bank hol in May) MEALS: alc (main courses £7 to £11.50) SERVICE: not inc CARDS: none DETAILS: 30 seats. Private parties: 30 main room. Vegetarian meals. Children's helpings. No smoking in dining-room. Wheelchair access (1 step). Music

EGLWYSFACH Powys map 7

▲ *Ynyshir Hall*

POWYS 1996 YOUNG TALENT

Eglwysfach, nr Machynlleth SY20 8TA
TEL: (01654) 781209 FAX: (01654) 781366 COOKING 3*
off A487, 6m SW of Machynlleth COST £27–£46

This white-painted hotel, backed by trees and tall shrubs, is bright and smart inside. The house is an elegant and colourful mix of floral print fabrics and paintings by owner Rob Reen, who also presides over the small, secluded bar. 'The food is as bold as the paintings on the wall,' claimed one (and that *is* bold) 'and decidedly brilliant'. Well-spaced tables stocked with 'unusually good paraphernalia' set the tone. Both food and paintings are modern, and owe at least some inspiration to southern Europe. A new broom has swept through the kitchen since last year, and instead of a single chef the Reens have appointed two young up-and-coming lads to share the role. They have been given free rein to call the shots and are proving worth their weight in Mediterranean vegetables.

Lunch is a light affair. Dinner is where the crackling energy is concentrated – in, for example, creamed smoked haddock with sauté potatoes and black pudding, or a dessert of glazed cinnamon risotto served with a miniature fruit compote. If you don't like the sound of clashing cultures, cover your ears now: fillet of sea bass is smeared with tapénade, placed on a bed of grilled sweet peppers and surrounded by a strongly flavoured Thai butter. 'Brilliant raw materials', in the words of one reporter, are the foundation. An inspector enjoyed a generous thick fillet of salmon in prime condition, briefly seared, on a bed of just-cooked vegetables with fondant potato: 'A dish bursting with flavour,' she concluded. There is nothing mean or apologetic about the food, it is as big-hearted as a fillet of Welsh black beef, cooked pink, sliced in three and topped with 'red onion jam'. A pithiviers of black pudding, and smooth vegetable purées – one each of leek and potato – accompanied. This is very self-assured cooking.

Cheeses in mint condition might include Cashel, Teifi with nettles, or Pencarreg; meals begin with first-rate little pastries; and bread is baked in-house. Wines from southern France, Italy and the New World add interest and value to the list, as does a dry Riesling Auslese, one of 12 house recommendations available by the glass. High quality is the norm, and the Reens keep their finger on the vinous pulse. House wine by the bottle starts at £11.

CHEFS: Christopher Dawson and Ian White PROPRIETORS: Joan and Rob Reen OPEN: all week 12.30 to 1.30, 7 to 8.45 MEALS: Set L £17.50, Set D £27.50 SERVICE: not inc, card slips closed CARDS: Access, Amex, Delta, Switch, Visa DETAILS: 40 seats. Private parties: 25 main room, 16 private room. Car park. No children under 9. Smart dress preferred. No smoking in dining-room. Music ACCOMMODATION: 8 rooms, all with bath/shower. TV. Phone. B&B £75 to £140. Deposit: 20%. No children under 9. Pets by prior arrangement. Afternoon teas. Garden (*The Which? Hotel Guide*)

FISHGUARD Dyfed map 4

▲ *Three Main Street*

DYFED 1996 ACHIEVER

3 Main Street, Fishguard SA65 9HG COOKING 2*
TEL: (01348) 874275 COST £17–£36

This Georgian town house is handy for the ferry terminal, where boats leave for Ireland. It goes in for stripped pine and styles itself a restaurant and coffee-house, serving morning coffee and light lunches of home-made focaccia filled with a mix of roasted peppers, aubergine, tomato and mozzarella, or mussel chowder, or a hot salad of duck confit. The informal candlelit restaurant comes into its own in the evening, when the *carte* offers a generous six or eight items per course.

There is admirable restraint about the interpretation of (mostly) British and French dishes, a sure sign of a confident cook. Marion Evans is at home with simple and direct flavours, and with light sauces, and is alive to textural contrast. 'How can something so simple achieve such a variety of tastes and textures?' was a question asked of a gratiné of strawberries and mascarpone cream, although it could equally well apply to several dishes. Tartlets, salads, pasta, soups and vegetables are all well judged, as is the timing of quickly cooked items, such as fish or sauté duck livers.

Despite the coastal location there is no undue emphasis on fish, though Cardigan Bay scallops, sea bass and sewin turn up. The menu is a balanced offering, refreshed daily, taking due account of the season where appropriate and drawing on local enterprise for as much as possible, including organic bread flour. Roast rack of Welsh lamb comes with bramble jelly, local Gressingham duck with Puy lentils, and grilled fillets of John Dory with citrus butter. Puddings avoid the pitfall of excess weight, cheeses include one or two from Wales, and wines pack a fair amount of interest into a short space. House French is £8.95.

CHEF: Marion Evans PROPRIETORS: Marion Evans and Inez Ford OPEN: Mon to Sat 12 to 2, 7 to 9.30 CLOSED: Feb, some Mons in winter MEALS: alc (main courses £5 to £13) SERVICE: not inc CARDS: none DETAILS: 36 seats. Private parties: 24 main room, 12 and 24 private rooms. Car park (residents only). Vegetarian meals. Children's helpings. No smoking in dining-room. Wheelchair access. No music ACCOMMODATION: 3 rooms, all with bath/shower. B&B £30 to £50. Deposit: £20 (*The Which? Hotel Guide*)

FORDEN Powys map 4

▲ *Edderton Hall*

Forden SY21 8RZ
TEL: (01938) 580339 FAX: (01938) 580452 COOKING 1
off A490, 4m S of Welshpool COST £20–£34

A white, bow-fronted Georgian house on top of the hill, Edderton Hall has stunning views over rolling countryside – and the town of Welshpool. A long track full of potholes leads up to it through unfenced pastures. Once you are there, the welcome is warm and genuine, and the comfortable, unpretentious restaurant-with-rooms feels homely and lived-in. 'We have no gymnasium, swimming-pool or squash court,' boast the Hawksleys. It is a place for simple, honest enjoyment rather than flounce.

Despite finding a few minor shortcomings, an inspector nevertheless praised the 'sound ingredients and unabashed home cooking' that produced a seafood gratin, tender leg of roast Welsh lamb, and a succulent fillet steak in a robust red wine sauce with shallots and morel mushrooms from the New Forest. Herbs from the garden help to power the saucing. Desserts might be apple and cinnamon tart or rhubarb jelly with angelica ice-cream and cinnamon shortbread. 'Since last year we have unblocked the chimney to the restaurant fireplace and now use it for cooking,' says Mrs Hawksley. 'As I run the place single-handedly for part of the time, especially out of season,' she adds (Warren Hawksley is an MP), 'I cannot cope with people just turning up. Please book.' The list of over 60 wines is supplied by Tanner's, with house wine at £8 a litre, £1.50 a glass.

CHEF: Evelyn Hawksley PROPRIETORS: Evelyn and Warren Hawksley OPEN: all week 1 to 2.30, 7.30 to 10 MEALS: Set L £12.95, Set D £22 SERVICE: not inc, card slips closed CARDS: Access, Amex, Diners, Visa DETAILS: 40 seats. 6 tables outside. Private parties: 20 main room, 12 and 45 private rooms. Car park. Children's helpings. Smart dress preferred. Wheelchair access (also WC). Music ACCOMMODATION: 8 rooms, all with bath/shower. TV. Phone. B&B £22 to £70. Children welcome. Pets welcome. Afternoon teas. Garden (*The Which? Hotel Guide*)

Restaurateurs justifiably resent no-shows. If you quote a credit card number when booking, you may be liable for the restaurant's lost profit margin if you don't turn up. Always phone to cancel.

FREYSTROP Dyfed map 4

Jemima's

Freystrop, nr Haverfordwest SA62 4HB
TEL: (01437) 891109 COOKING 2
on Burton road, 2m SW of Haverfordwest COST £16–£35

Jemima's is not a grand restaurant: 'unpretentious, warm and welcoming' is how one reporter described it. The bistro is used mainly at lunch-times, where a blackboard menu advertises soups, salads, pasta dishes, fresh fish or perhaps a meat casserole; while the restaurant – in an oblong shape with tables down both sides – comes into its own in the evening, when it offers a choice of five or six dishes per course. A seasoned reporter writes that Ann Owston 'does not try to impress but to produce what is available in the best possible manner' (which, of course, is what impresses). 'I am like a magpie,' she writes, 'and steal ideas from any style of cooking,' although she is more like a seagull when it comes to picking off what the boat brings in: monkfish, mussels and prawns for a simple seafood ragoût, fresh crab to be served with lime mayonnaise, or halibut, perhaps with a lentil and coriander sauce.

Salmon may be hot-smoked with a chive and cream sauce, or cold-smoked and partnered with marinated mackerel; and rabbit, duck, baked ham and venison also appear from time to time. The extent of the 'magpie's' territory can be gauged from roast Pembrokeshire lamb, oak-smoked chicken with red cabbage, Indonesian spiced fish with tomato salsa, seven-vegetables couscous, and wood-blewit mushrooms with cream in a pastry case. 'The food is simply served without any unnecessary garnish, thank goodness,' observed one satisfied customer. Sticky toffee pudding, crème caramel, and a well-stocked Welsh cheeseboard bring up the rear. Two dozen wines offer decent drinking for less than £15. House vin de pays is £8.50, or £2 a glass.

CHEF: Ann Owston PROPRIETORS: Ann Owston, Wendy Connelly and April Connelly OPEN: Tue to Sun L 12 to 2, Tue to Sat D 7 to 9 CLOSED: Tue and Wed in winter MEALS: alc (main courses £4.50 to £11). Set L Sun £10 SERVICE: not inc, card slips closed CARDS: Access, Amex, Delta, Visa DETAILS: 24 seats. Private parties: 16 main room. Car park. Vegetarian meals. Children's helpings. No smoking in dining-room. No music

HARLECH Gwynedd map 7

▲ *Castle Cottage*

Pen Llech, Harlech LL46 2YL COOKING 1*
TEL: (01766) 780479 COST £18–£30

Sheltering in the shadow of Harlech's Norman castle, close by the beach of northern Cardigan Bay, the Cottage is enviably sited. The weather may not always oblige, of course – horizontal sleet greeted one pair of March visitors – but the welcome within from chef-patron Glyn Roberts more than compensated.

The fixed-price dinner menus provide a good choice of sensibly straightforward dishes served in robust quantities. Fine duck confit impressed an inspector for its correct contrast of 'melting interior and crispy skin', and came with a salad of the (slightly overcooked) liver with segments of orange. A main course of grilled Anglesey rump steak was accompanied by a single vast flat mushroom and a cream sauce with two shades of peppercorn, green and pink. Rack of lamb was three large chops of succulent texture, garnished with pine-nut couscous and sauced with a 'deep and rich' decoction of red wine, shallots and garlic. Vegetables arrive mob-handed, good chunky dauphinois leading the pack. Cheese as a savoury finish is given a twist, warmed goats' cheese appearing with a sauce of leek, potato and bacon. A well-rendered crème brûlée flavoured with coffee had a 'fine brittle top' and a dice of kiwi, melon, pineapple and strawberry. Completing the picture were well-made petits fours and strong cafetière coffee. A decent spread of wines comes at scrupulously fair prices. The choices are not exactly state of the art, but the closing page of bin-ends is worth a peep. Wales is represented by Monnow Valley's crisp light white at £11.75. House French and California wines are £7.95.

CHEF: Glyn Roberts PROPRIETORS: Jacqueline and Glyn Roberts OPEN: Sun L 12.30 to 2, all week D 7 to 9.30 CLOSED: 3 weeks Feb MEALS: Set L Sun £12, Set D £16 (2 courses) to £18 SERVICE: not inc CARDS: Access, Amex, Delta, Switch, Visa DETAILS: 45 seats. Private parties: 45 main room. Vegetarian meals. Children's helpings. Smart dress preferred. No smoking in dining-room. Music ACCOMMODATION: 6 rooms, 4 with bath/shower. B&B £23 to £50. Deposit: £10. Children welcome. Baby facilities. Pets welcome in bedrooms only (*The Which? Hotel Guide*)

LAMPHEY Dyfed map 4

Dial Inn £

NEW ENTRY

The Ridgeway, Lamphey SA71 5NU
TEL/FAX: (01646) 672426 COOKING 1
just off A4139, Tenby to Pembroke road COST £13–£33

The Dower House of Lamphey Court was converted into a pub in the 1960s. An extraordinarily diverse display of pottery and china fills the often crowded bar (a brave move since the local rugby club drinks here), which serves Glamorgan cheese sausages with pickle, mussels in garlic butter, or falafel and hummus with Arab bread. Twin themes of robust country cooking, and a liking for fish and vegetable dishes enable the Parrys ('warm and friendly, much in evidence') to please a wide variety of tastes in both bar and dining-room, the latter due to be enlarged as the *Guide* comes out.

Among the more solid and familiar items are steak and kidney pie with oysters, and fillet of black beef (from Carmarthen) with peppercorn sauce. Pork, say the Parrys, is 'always from North Pembrokeshire. It's better up there.' A blackboard lists available fish, which might include skate wings, sewin with laverbread, or cracked crab claws. Reporters have enjoyed 'light and crisp' mushroom fritters with good mayonnaise, fillet steak 'which cut beautifully', and lamb casserole cooked with apricots, leeks and thyme. Main courses come with a good spread of vegetables, while puddings plough a predictable furrow of pavlova, apple pie or chocolate roulade, and there is always Welsh cheese. Around 20 wines stay mostly below £15, with house wine at £7.25 a bottle, or £1.20 a glass.

CHEF: Simon Periam PROPRIETORS: Francis and Jan Parry OPEN: all week 12 to 2, 7 to 9 CLOSED: 25 Dec MEALS: alc (main courses £5 to £12). Set L Sun £7.50 SERVICE: not inc, card slips closed CARDS: Access, Amex, Visa DETAILS: 30 seats. 5 tables outside. Private parties: 30 main room. Car park. Children's helpings. Smart dress preferred. No smoking in dining-room. Wheelchair access. Music

LLANBERIS Gwynedd map 7

Y Bistro

43–45 High Street, Llanberis LL55 4EU
TEL: (01286) 871278 COOKING 1
off A4086, at foot of Mount Snowdon COST £29–£38

This is walking country – Snowdon beckons – and the food is hearty enough to cater for walkers' appetites. It suits local tastes too, judging by the family groups. Opposite a plain lounge is a bar, where regulars tend to congregate; the dining-room is freshened by flowers and the reception is friendly. The simple bistro fare is not particularly ambitious, but it pleases. Salmon cakes come with lime mayonnaise, and a risotto is fashioned from smoked chicken and wild mushrooms. Locally landed brill or skate wing are grilled or pan-fried and served simply with, at most, a lemon butter. The occasional Mediterranean idea surfaces, as in roasted tomatoes with olive oil, olives, garlic, basil and mozzarella cheese, although anybody coming down off the mountain is more likely to be swayed by slices of leg of Welsh lamb, studded with rosemary and garlic then roasted on a bed of onions. This might be followed by old-fashioned warm syrup tart with whipped cream or spiced apple crumble. Wines are fairly priced and offer enough choice for the circumstances, with house wines at £8, or £1.60 a glass.

CHEF: Nerys Roberts PROPRIETORS: Danny and Nerys Roberts OPEN: Mon to Sat D only 7.30 to 9.45 MEALS: Set D £19 (2 courses) to £24.50 SERVICE: not inc, card slips closed CARDS: Access, Delta, Switch, Visa DETAILS: 60 seats. Private parties: 44 main room, 22 private room. Vegetarian meals. Children's helpings. Smart dress preferred. No smoking in dining-room. Wheelchair access (2 steps). Music

LLANDDEINIOLEN Gwynedd map 7

▲ *Ty'n Rhos*

Seion, Llanddeiniolen LL55 3AE
TEL: (01248) 670489 FAX: (01248) 670079
off B4366, 5m NE of Caernarfon on road signposted Seion COOKING 2
COST £25–£35

Ty'n Rhos started life as a farmhouse on the wide open plain between Snowdonia and the sea, before Lynda and Nigel Kettle transformed it into a country-house hotel. Over the years, Lynda's cooking has kept faith with its Welsh roots: she bakes her own bread rolls ('irresistible', according to one reporter), makes jams and preserves, harvests herbs and vegetables from the hotel's kitchen garden and buys her meat and fish from judicious local sources.

The results show up well in both the no-choice, four-course set dinner menu and the more extensive affair where prices depend on the main course. The cooking is an accessible blend of classics 'always with a twist of individuality', embellished with ideas drawn from near and far. Bresaola and gravlax are cured on the premises; otherwise, you might begin with a 'sculpted rose' of smoked salmon surrounded by slices of avocado. Chicken breast is stuffed with green herbs and cooked in a greaseproof paper bag that looks for all the world like 'an edible golden filo pastry pocket'; pork fillet is given the Malaysian treatment; fillets of lemon sole are enlivened with tomato and fennel compote. Desserts are always unusual: Christmas pudding ice-cream sounds like 'a particularly imaginative and satisfying way of using up the seasonal excesses in mid-January'. Or you might find anything from a little pot of chocolate cream with damson coulis to the evocatively entitled 'Theme on Orange' (clementines macerated in Cointreau and orange juice served with blood orange sorbet). Cheeses are ripe, Welsh and generous, coffee comes ad lib with home-made petits fours. The wine list is well spread, realistically priced and full of variety; halves show up well. 'Extremely drinkable' house wine is £8.

CHEFS: Lynda Kettle and Bill Ashton PROPRIETORS: Lynda and Nigel Kettle OPEN: Tue to Sat D only 7 to 8.30 MEALS: Set D £18.50 to £22.50 SERVICE: not inc, card slips closed CARDS: Access, Amex, Switch, Visa DETAILS: 32 seats. Private parties: 25 main room, 15 private room. Car park. Children's helpings. No children under 8. Smart dress preferred. No smoking in dining-room. No music ACCOMMODATION: 11 rooms, all with bath/shower. TV. Phone. B&B £35 to £80. Deposit: £20. Rooms for disabled. Children welcome. No children under 6. Afternoon teas. Garden (*The Which? Hotel Guide*)

LLANDEWI SKIRRID Gwent map 7

Walnut Tree Inn

Llandewi Skirrid NP7 8AW
TEL: (01873) 852797 COOKING 4
on B4521, 3m NE of Abergavenny COST £27–£59

The operation here has always been a highly personal one, devoid of a formulaic or standardised approach. Anybody expecting formal treatment in the grand-hotel manner will be severely disappointed. At one level, you will find the best pub food in Britain, and it comes as a revelation, sometimes a shock, to first-timers to realise that food of this quality does not need a flunkeyed greeter in a dinner jacket, tables with starched cloths or any of the ceremony with which posh restaurants often surround themselves. Such things are completely irrelevant to the enjoyment of good food, as the Walnut Tree, with its twice-daily queues, proves.

Tables in the restaurant usually need reserving well in advance, so the pressure is on the non-bookable bistro. 'On arrival at 6.55pm there were already about 20 people waiting for it to open.' Alternatively, it may be a good idea to arrive at around 9pm when the first wave is leaving. The bistro can be frenetic, even rowdy, but conviviality is the essence. 'We loved our lunch so much we went back for dinner next day.' A minority finds the cramped conditions off-putting, and the 25-yard dash to the outdoor lavatory a drag in wet weather, but everybody else is so charmed by the food that these drawbacks cease to matter. 'I am very much in favour of this restaurant and the values it espouses,' writes a supporter; 'so, despite the discomfort, I shall continue making pilgrimages there to have dishes like roasted pigeon on a bed of cabbage, surrounded by a ring of roasted garlic and chanterelles.'

The food may sound simple – crispy crab pancake, stuffed fried courgette flowers, Lady Llanover's salt-duck – but the ingredients needed to service a menu of 15 first and main courses, plus about 25 puddings, served to over 100 people a day are legion: squid, red mullet, gurnard, sun-dried tomatoes, coriander leaves, nam pla, porcini, ricotta, mozzarella, Parmesan, fresh figs, bilberries, gooseberry pickle, rowanberry jelly and so on. And still the kitchen finds time to introduce new dishes of pappardelle with scallops and pesto, or a plate of aubergine, fried artichoke, Piemontese peppers, courgettes, stuffed mushroom and polenta fritters, described by one reporter as 'vegetarian food for non-vegetarians'.

Far from being simple, this food takes experience, skill and flair to accomplish, but does not rely on fancy techniques, 'just an understanding of how to make tasty food'. The combination of a good idea, irreproachably fresh ingredients and perfect execution seems to do the trick. 'The intensity and balance of flavours is stunning', whether in the famed vincis grassi maceratese (pasta with porcini, truffles and Parma ham), or in the equally famed pudding – torte with three liqueurs – that presents amaretti biscuits and almonds with coffee, chocolate, liqueurs and thick cream. Owners and staff constitute 'one big happy family'. Bustle, efficiency and charm characterise the service, although for some it appears disorganised, even chaotic. French wines are classically tip-top, but the Italian section offers all that is necessary to accompany the food, with an endlessly fascinating range of flavours. A sense of adventure helps to get the best out of them. If the shortage of half-bottles is a problem, some compensation may be found in the choice of full bottles at less than £15. House Verdicchio and Rosso Piceno are £9.75 a litre.

CHEF: Franco Taruschio PROPRIETORS: Franco and Ann Taruschio OPEN: Tue to Sat 12.15 to 3.15, 7.15 to 10.15 CLOSED: 4 days Christmas, 2 weeks Feb MEALS: alc (main courses £10 to £16) SERVICE: not inc CARDS: none DETAILS: 108 seats. 8 tables outside. Private parties: 48 main room. Car park. Vegetarian meals. Children's helpings. Wheelchair access. No music. Air-conditioned

LLANDRILLO Clwyd map 7

▲ *Tyddyn Llan*

Llandrillo LL21 0ST
TEL: (01490) 440264 FAX: (01490) 440414 COOKING 2*
on B4401, 4½m S of Corwen COST £19–£40

This isolated hotel, built of rough grey stone, is on a B road that follows the River Dee as it skirts the Berwyn Mountains. Gradual upgrading has retained a high level of comfort throughout. 'Now that I know Peter Kindred designed sets for TV, I can see what has happened in the dining-room,' mused one. The décor is 'positively exciting', said another, pointing to the tall windows, french doors, classical pediments and cherubs, all enveloped in 'curtain fabrics, ruches, sashes and pelmets, the lot'. Despite set ideas about food and drink rituals, the extremely friendly service from the Kindreds adds to the homely feel.

The food is a mix of French (bourgeois and classical), British (ancient and modern) and some unusual exotic flavours. Rustic terrine with an onion and thyme marmalade shares the billing with a pasta dish of tagliatelle with wild mushrooms, olive oil, pesto and pecorino cheese, although how far it all adds up to an 'eclectic style' is a matter for debate. An inspector felt that some ingredients might have been better left out of dishes, and wondered if the undoubted effort and care that go into producing the food might benefit from tighter direction. An example was a warm salad of woodpigeon, rather overburdened with superfluous grapes and pistachio nuts.

However, there is much to praise, including a soup plate of fresh Welsh mussels with white wine and cream, which was 'simple and very good, unsophisticated, generous'. New-season Welsh lamb on the bone – excellent meat, with lots of texture and flavour, if unevenly cooked – came with powerfully garlicked, smoothly puréed flageolet beans. Portions are not large and vegetables do not vary, whatever the main course: gratin dauphinois heavy on the garlic, squeaky mange-tout, and stewed red cabbage. Good crème anglaise and quality ice-creams accompany puddings such as rhubarb and pear crumble. Wines are mostly young and include a good spread from humble to aristocratic, with fair prices. House recommendations below £15 include six available by the glass.

CHEFS: Dominic Gilbert and Wendy Phillips PROPRIETORS: Peter and Bridget Kindred OPEN: all week 12.30 to 2, 7 to 9.30 MEALS: Set L £10.75 (2 courses) to £12.75, Set D £21.50 to £23.50 SERVICE: not inc, card slips closed CARDS: Access, Amex, Diners, Switch, Visa DETAILS: 50 seats. Private parties: 35 main room, 35 private room. Car park. Vegetarian meals. Children's helpings. Smart dress preferred. No cigars/pipes in dining-room. Wheelchair access (also WC). Music ACCOMMODATION: 10 rooms, all with bath/shower. Phone. B&B £44 to £97. Deposit: £50. Children welcome. Baby facilities. Pets welcome (not in public areas). Afternoon teas. Garden. Fishing (*The Which? Hotel Guide*)

LLANDUDNO Gwynedd map 7

▲ *Bodysgallen Hall* 🍷

Llandudno LL30 1RS
TEL: (01492) 584466 FAX: (01492) 582519 COOKING 2
off A470, 2m SE of Llandudno COST £22–£50

A change in the kitchen guard took place at Bodysgallen Hall just as last year's *Guide* went to press. In came Michael Penny, previously sous-chef at Michael's Nook in Grasmere (see entry), unfazed by the transition from Lakeland cottage to Welsh baronial splendour. The Hall certainly imposes its scale on you: the gravel drive sweeps majestically on through vast grounds until a flight of stone steps ushers you straight into the lounge. A winter's worth of logs is piled on either side of the fireplace.

Set-price menus for lunch and dinner of three courses plus coffee form the backbone of the kitchen's operations, supplemented in the evenings by a 'gourmet' option that adds a soup and a sorbet. An inspection gourmet meal turned up some neat ideas and nifty execution such as a hollowed-out artichoke filled with vegetable dice accompanied by slices of the heart with blanched tomato and orange segments – a nice essay in textural and flavour contrasts. The mid-meal sorbet of pink grapefruit and champagne was 'divine'. Less cheering were a consommé of 'frankly tasteless' wild mushrooms with herb-stuffed ravioli, while a main course of tarragon-crusted beef fillet with a pepper ragoût scented with truffle oil was considered insufficiently truffly. A hot passion-fruit soufflé to finish was 'perfect, with a good citrusy tang and well risen', and was escorted by an 'excellent' biscuit basket of praline ice-cream. Welsh cheeses, such as Pencarreg and smoked Caerphilly, are well kept, and canapés and petits fours are on good form. Service is mostly 'formal but attentive'.

The wine list is as opulent as the surroundings, with French classics bolstered by canny selections from outside Europe. Prices throughout are very fair for the context, and the choice of half-bottles is abundant. Six French house wines open at £11.75. CELLARMAN'S CHOICE: Vin de pays de la Haute Vallée de l'Aude, Chardonnay 1993, £13; Minervois 1990, Ch. La Grave Rouge, £13.

CHEFS: Mike Penny and David Thompson PROPRIETOR: Historic House Hotels OPEN: all week 12.30 to 2, 7.30 to 9.45 MEALS: Set L £13.90 (2 courses) to £15.90, Set D £27.50 to £36 SERVICE: net prices, card slips closed CARDS: Access, Amex, Delta, Switch, Visa DETAILS: 55 seats. Private parties: 50 main room, 40 private room. Car park. Vegetarian meals. Children welcome. No children under 8. Jacket and tie. No smoking during meals. Music ACCOMMODATION: 29 rooms, all with bath/shower. TV. Phone. Room only £85 to £165. Rooms for disabled. Children welcome. No children under 8. Pets welcome in cottage suites. Afternoon teas. Garden (*The Which? Hotel Guide*)

Martin's

11 Mostyn Avenue, Craig-y-Don,
Llandudno LL30 1YS — COOKING 1*
TEL: (01492) 870070 — COST £22–£37

The two small and oddly decorated rooms may lack sophistication, but this is more than compensated for by food that is both pleasing and accomplished. Martin James changes some items on the menu daily, and has a well-stocked larder that might contain locally smoked salmon, truffle oil, quail's eggs, and foie gras which is made into a terrine and served with toasted brioche. He also makes fish terrines, and one of chicken, smoked bacon and duck liver, and is perfectly at home with straightforward but effective ideas such as warm pigeon breast salad, local scallops baked in their shell with fresh ginger, and roast loin of Welsh lamb filled with a mustard, garlic and herb butter. Vegetables are turned, a gesture doubtless picked up at Bodysgallen Hall (see entry above), where Martin James used to cook, but then he has also picked up along the way such things as sound pastrywork, which may show up in all three courses. Hot almond gâteau, hot lime tart, or passion-fruit soufflé feature among the puddings, and the chocolates that come with coffee are 'excellent'. Twenty wines are keenly priced, with house vin de pays at £7.50.

CHEF/PROPRIETOR: Martin James OPEN: Tue to Sat D only 7 to 9.30 CLOSED: first 2 weeks Jan MEALS: alc (main courses £8 to £12) SERVICE: not inc, card slips closed CARDS: Access, Amex, Delta, Visa DETAILS: 30 seats. Private parties: 30 main room. Vegetarian meals. Smart dress preferred. Wheelchair access (1 step). Music

Richard's

7 Church Walks, Llandudno LL30 2HD COOKING 1
TEL: (01492) 877924 and 875315 COST £20–£35

Located in a tall Victorian town house with log fires burning in winter, Richard Hendey's industrious bistro is open 365 evenings a year. Eating takes place on two floors, and bistro favourites such as garlic mushrooms, crab mayonnaise, and grilled sirloin with red wine, brandy and cream form the backbone of the long menus. There are inventive flourishes too. Black pudding comes with grapes, mushrooms, spiced apple and a barbecue sauce, while an exhaustive rollcall of Thai flavourings – coriander, lime leaves, coconut, ginger, pineapple, garlic, turmeric, chillies and lemon grass – spices up chargrilled chicken. Vegetables are praised for their variety, delicate cooking and the fact that they are 'not smothered in butter'. Puddings aim for maximum impact with the likes of coconut crème brûlée with banana and ginger sauce, apple crêpes with toffee sauce and ice-cream, and the melodious-sounding chocolate praline truffle terrine. This is a terrifically popular place ('on Friday night Richard was turning them away in droves'), so booking is advisable. Wines are helpfully grouped into sections of under and over £10, and few are over £20. The exceptions are a good range of champagnes and a slate of Alsace specialities that will enable regulars to conduct comparative tastings of Gewurztraminer to their hearts' content. Romanian house wines are £6.95.

CHEFS: Richard Hendey, Mark Roberts and John Crawford PROPRIETOR: Richard Hendey OPEN: all week D only 6 to 10.30 MEALS: alc (main courses £9 to £13) SERVICE: net prices, card slips closed CARDS: Access, Amex, Visa DETAILS: 50 seats. Private parties: 20 main room, 20 private room. Vegetarian meals. Children welcome. Smart dress preferred. Music

▲ *St Tudno Hotel*

Promenade, Llandudno LL30 2LP COOKING 2*
TEL: (01492) 874411 FAX: (01492) 860407 COST £22–£43

This Victorian seaside resort hotel, with a view on to Llandudno pier, is several cuts above most others of its genre. The Blands have been running it for over 20 years, and bring a formidable degree of self-assurance to the operation. Floral wallpaper and nineteenth-century prints establish a tone of quiet elegance, as does much of the cooking. The style is essentially modern British, using good Welsh produce, infused with some French techniques.

Dinner is a fixed-price affair of five courses with coffee, with a choice of soup, sorbet or salad for the second course. An inspection meal started with a classic combination of spanking-fresh queen scallops with crispy bacon strips on a carefully presented salad, followed by a poached fillet of plaice on a spaghetti of vegetables with a 'richly creamy' sauce containing whisky. Saddle of tender Welsh lamb was smartly dressed in a puff-pastry jacket and stuffed with aubergine and onion. Trelough duckling was 'pink and succulent' and intelligently balanced by basil pesto, puréed potato and caramelised shallots. Desserts which have been praised include a cold strawberry soufflé with a sablé biscuit, pineapple in a brandy-snap basket with chocolate-flecked ginger ice-cream, and a sharp sorbet of apple and calvados. A selection of Welsh farmhouse cheeses ends things with a patriotic flourish. The international wine list is mostly very keenly priced, and includes a delicate Welsh white wine from the Monnow Valley near Monmouth, as well as a strong set of house recommendations. House wines from the pays d'Oc are £9.50.

CHEFS: David Harding and Ian Watson PROPRIETORS: Martin and Janette Bland OPEN: all week 12.30 to 2, 7 to 9.30 (9 Sun) MEALS: Set L £15.50, Set D £27.50 SERVICE: not inc, card slips closed CARDS: Access, Amex, Diners, Switch, Visa DETAILS: 55 seats. Private parties: 30 main room. Car park. Vegetarian meals. No young children D. Smart dress preferred. No smoking in dining-room. Wheelchair access (3 steps). No music. Air-conditioned ACCOMMODATION: 21 rooms, all with bath/shower. TV. Phone. B&B £69 to £138. Deposit: £50. Children welcome. Baby facilities. Pets by arrangement only. Afternoon teas. Garden. Swimming-pool (*The Which? Hotel Guide*)

LLANFIHANGEL NANT MELAN Powys map 4

POWYS 1996 ENTHUSIAST

▲ *Red Lion Inn* £

Llanfihangel nant Melan, nr New Radnor LD8 2TN
TEL: (01544) 350220
on A44 Rhayader to Kington road, 3m W of New Radnor

COOKING 1
COST £12–£31

'We arrived in the dark: it was cold and foggy and the place seemed to be unoccupied. Not a bit of it! Gareth Johns met us with a hot drink and a place beside a roaring fire and the journey began to seem worth while.' So wrote a couple who stayed the night, and others have been equally enchanted by this old drovers' inn. Gareth Johns is a crusading supporter of local produce and Celtic cuisine; he is committed to the cause without being precious about it. Soups, such as spinach, leek and parsley, really do taste of their ingredients, and other dishes bristle with vivid accompaniments: damson relish is a foil for medallions of venison, home-pickled samphire appears with baked lake trout, and cardamom cream sauce spices up a vegetarian mille-feuille. Vegetables are many and varied: 'the first time for years that I've eaten mashed carrot and turnip like my mum does it, with lots of butter and pepper,' enthused one visitor. Puddings are rich confections along the lines of 'intense' chocolate terrine and tiramisù. Lunch is pub grub, pure and simple: braised local lamb, cod and chips, spiced salt-beef with parsley sauce. Mr Johns is currently researching traditional Welsh meads; otherwise, a handful of wines at rock-bottom prices do the trick for affordable quaffing. House wine is £4.95.

CHEF: Gareth Johns PROPRIETORS: Keith, Elizabeth and Gareth Johns OPEN: all week 12 to 2, 6.45 to 9 (9.30 Fri and Sat) CLOSED: Tue Nov to April MEALS: alc (main courses £4 to £11) SERVICE: not inc, card slips closed CARDS: Access, Delta, Visa DETAILS: 55 seats. 4 tables outside. Private parties: 20 main room, 20 private rooms. Car park. Vegetarian meals. Children's helpings. No smoking in 1 dining-room. No music ACCOMMODATION: 3 rooms, all with bath/shower. B&B £17.50 to £30. Children welcome. Pets by arrangement. Garden

LLANGAMMARCH WELLS Powys map 4

▲ *Lake Country House* 🍷 ✱

Llangammarch Wells LD4 4BS
TEL: (01591) 620202 FAX: (01591) 620457 COOKING 1*
off A483 at Garth, 6m W of Builth Wells COST £16–£38

The Edwardian country house is set in 50 acres of gardens and woodlands. Fishermen have access to a trout lake and four miles of river, while walkers have the hills on which to work up an appetite for dinner. Comfortable settees and casual chairs abound, and the vast luxurious lounge has a log fire for most of the year. The menu retains its long-established format of four courses, the first a soup, but there is now a little more choice – five first and five main courses – and the style has moved on to more vegetarian and organic options, including split-pea fritters with sauté spinach and plum tomatoes, or an artichoke and wild mushroom gâteau. A nearby organic farm supplies some of the meat, including lamb, but Richard Arnold is not shy of far-flung ingredients, serving breasts of pigeon and poussin with a passion-fruit and coriander jus.

Brecon venison, Cornish-landed turbot and Devon duckling put in an appearance, and there is generally a choice between lighter dishes, such as a salad of smoked tuna and scallops, and weightier first courses, like game and liver terrine with lentils, or honey-roast quail. Among the more adventurous puddings are orange and lemon-curd burnt creams, and a Tia Maria mousse layered between shortbread pastry biscuits on a white chocolate sauce. The wine list takes its claret very seriously, dividing up the growths and climbing the ladder to three-figure prices, but it also enjoys the bottom rungs and offers a wide selection at under £20 a bottle. Apart from Spain and perhaps Australia, countries outside France have more of a token presence. Two dozen half-bottles and a handful of house recommendations are welcome, including CELLARMAN'S CHOICE: Pinot Blanc 1991, Rolly-Gassmann, £18.75; Graves Rouge 1992, Cuvée Pierre Coste, £13.90.

CHEF: Richard Arnold PROPRIETORS: Jean-Pierre and Jan Mifsud OPEN: all week 12.15 to 2, 7.30 to 9 MEALS: alc L (main courses £4.50 to £6.50). Set L £15.50, Set D £24.50 SERVICE: net prices, card slips closed CARDS: Access, Amex, Delta, Diners, Switch, Visa DETAILS: 60 seats. Private parties: 60 main room, 20 private room. Car park. Vegetarian meals. Children's helpings. No children under 7 D. Smart dress preferred. No smoking in dining-room. Wheelchair access (also WC). Music ACCOMMODATION: 19 rooms, all with bath/shower. TV. Phone. B&B £70 to £135. Deposit: £40. Rooms for disabled. Children welcome. Baby facilities. Pets welcome. Afternoon teas. Garden. Fishing (*The Which? Hotel Guide*)

'The next table had an intriguing mix of people, including one who looked like the Dalai Lama. He launched into a plate of foie gras in a most un- Buddhist fashion and was a joy to watch. If he was the Dalai Lama, I'm converting to Buddhism next week. He was also the only man in the restaurant who was not required to wear a tie, which my husband thought most unfair.' (On eating in London)

LLANSANFFRAID GLAN CONWY Gwynedd **map 7**

▲ *Old Rectory*

Llanrwst Road, Llansanffraid Glan Conwy,
nr Conwy LL28 5LF
TEL: (01492) 580611 FAX: (01492) 584555 COOKING 3
on A470, ½m S of junction with A55 COST £39–£47

This small, elegant Georgian rectory with terraced garden is beautifully situated on a height overlooking Conwy castle and the tidal mouth of the river: a memorable view. It is a family-run country house – 'the home of an individual, with some class' – given to much wood panelling, antiques and a generous covering of drapes, pictures and rugs. Michael Vaughan runs front-of-house, and Wendy joins him from the kitchen at the end of the evening.

A strong Welsh identity pervades the food, with Black beef and mountain lamb taking pride of place among main courses: the lamb wrapped in leeks, perhaps, the beef served on a leek pancake. Meals are leisurely four-course affairs – one couple borrowed a board and managed three games of chess between courses – and there is no choice of either first or main dish. One autumn meal began with a generous steak of pink Atlantic char, firm and moist, on a bed of wild mushrooms and samphire with a mild tarragon sauce, and went on to a gamey breast of guinea-fowl, served with a cassoulet of its leg. The kitchen is not shy of effort, and sometimes builds up quite a few accompaniments on a plate, but it keeps important flavours centre-stage, helped by sharpenings of tomato vinaigrette with salmon and asparagus, or of balsamic vinegar sauce with fillet of beef.

An alternative to the plate of 'Welsh or Celtic' cheese is grilled goats' cheese or, for those who cannot eat cheese at all, either a sorbet (pink grapefruit and mint for one reporter) or a salad. The choice of puddings at one meal was between a light, pastry mille-feuille with 'plenty of plump strawberries and cream', and a crispy fruit-filled meringue in which blackberries dominated. The wine selection is intelligent and varied, with some choice of vintage where it matters, and stands out well for its pricing: many wines are well below £20 that, elsewhere, would be well above. Half-bottles are generous. CELLARMAN'S CHOICE: Franken, Casteller Hohnhart Silvaner Trocken 1991, Fürstlich Castell'sches Domänenamnt, £14.90; Crozes-Hermitage 'La Petite Roche' 1992, Chapoutier, £17.90.

CHEF: Wendy Vaughan PROPRIETORS: Michael and Wendy Vaughan OPEN: all week D only 7.30 for 8 (1 sitting, booking essential) MEALS: Set D £27.50 SERVICE: not inc, card slips closed CARDS: Access, Amex, Delta, Diners, Switch, Visa DETAILS: 16 seats. Private parties: 12 main room. Car park. Children's helpings; no children under 5. Smart dress preferred. No smoking in dining-room. No music ACCOMMODATION: 6 rooms, all with bath/shower. TV. Phone. DB&B £89.50 to £159. Deposit: £90. Children under 9 months and over 5 years welcome. Pets by arrangement. Garden (*The Which? Hotel Guide*)

CELLARMAN'S CHOICE: *Wines recommended by the restaurateur, normally more expensive than house wine.*

LLANWDDYN Powys map 7

▲ *Lake Vyrnwy Hotel*

Lake Vyrnwy, Llanwddyn SY10 0LY
TEL: (01691) 870692 FAX: (01691) 870259 COOKING 1*
on B4393, at SE end of Lake Vyrnwy COST £20–£36

Lake Vyrnwy is a good to place to get away from it all. The wonderful views and abundance of birds are mesmerising, and the estate that serves the reservoir covers 24,000 acres. The dam was built in the late nineteenth century to supply some of Liverpool's drinking water, and the hotel dates from the same period. Shooting, fishing, walking and bird-watching are not compulsory, but recommended, and fish and game naturally show up on the menu. Indeed, ingredients are impressive – their origins are usually credited – and there is much in-house activity: curing hams, smoking salmon, pickling herrings, preserving jams and baking bread, as well as picking wild mushrooms and soft fruits.

The food can be quite busy, too, as in a soufflé of Cornish crab, accompanied by a salad of crab and Colwyn Bay mussels with a lemon grass dressing, but it is generally purposeful. Roast sirloin of Welsh Black beef is served simply enough with Yorkshire pudding and gravy, and pan-fried breast of pheasant comes with creamed cabbage. Perhaps it is carping to complain about a glut of leeks in Wales, but one visitor felt that, in its finely shredded and deep-fried garnish form, it was rather overdone. Service is attentive but not stuffy, and the largely traditional wine list harbours some good bottles at fair prices: try Bordeaux, the Rhône, or Germany. House wine is £9.20.

CHEF: Andrew Wood PROPRIETOR: Market Glen Ltd OPEN: all week 12.30 to 1.45, 7.30 to 9.15 MEALS: Set L £13.95 to £14.95, Set D £22.50 SERVICE: not inc, card slips closed CARDS: Access, Amex, Delta, Diners, Switch, Visa DETAILS: 80 seats. Private parties: 80 main room, 100 private room. Car park. Vegetarian meals. Children's helpings. Smart dress preferred. No smoking in dining-room. Wheelchair access (also WC). No music ACCOMMODATION: 38 rooms, all with bath/shower. TV. Phone. B&B £60.50 to £127.50. Children welcome. Baby facilities. Pets welcome. Afternoon teas. Garden. Fishing (*The Which? Hotel Guide*)

LLANWRDA Dyfed map 4

Seguendo di Stagioni £

Harford, Pumpsaint, Llanwrda SA19 8DT
TEL/FAX: (01558) 650671
on A482 between Llanwrda and Lampeter, 1½m NW of Pumpsaint COOKING 1
COST £14–£33

This former transport café in deepest Wales is both a restaurant and a wine business. It is a difficult part of the country in which to run either, but the two together doubtless offer some cushioning against lean times. Booking is essential in case there's a wine tasting in progress. What stands out is the uncompromising commitment to Italian food and drink, and to 'tradition and culture'. This is no rural pizzeria, but a place that serves home-made ravioli filled with sweet pumpkin, braised beef in Barolo, and roasted peppers with the hot

Piemontese bagna cauda dressing of anchovies, garlic and olive oil. Live shellfish, spider crabs and locally smoked duck breast are among the treats.

Jennifer Taylor and Aldo Steccanella believe that healthy Italian food is not just an end in itself, but also a means to 'a more social and communicative attitude'. Along the lines, perhaps, of *Babette's Feast*, people tend to arrive early and leave late, having conversed happily with total strangers in between times, and in this sense the restaurant does indeed get close to the Italian view of eating and drinking as shared pleasures. Wines inevitably play their part in loosening tongues, and the selection includes excellent northern producers such as Allegrini, Deltetto, Puiatti and Mascarello, as well as some super Tuscans. House red and white from Veneto are £7.50. CELLARMAN'S CHOICE: Soave Classico 'La Rocca' 1993, Pieropan, £14.95; Chianti Rufina 'Villa di Vetrice' Riserva 1993, Grati, £14.95.

CHEF: Aldo Steccanella PROPRIETOR: Jennifer Taylor OPEN: Sun L 12 to 2.30, Wed to Sun D 7 to 10 MEALS: alc (main courses £9 to £14). Set L Sun £8.55 to £12.95, Set D £8.55 (Wed, Thur, Sun) to £14.95 SERVICE: not inc CARDS: none DETAILS: 40 seats. 4 tables outside. Private parties: 40 main room. Car park. Vegetarian meals. Children's helpings. No music

LLANWRTYD WELLS Powys map 4

▲ *Carlton House*

Dolycoed Road, Llanwrtyd Wells LD5 4SN COOKING 3*
TEL: (01591) 610248 COST £30–£41

This small, intimate Edwardian villa is 'really a town house kind of place', a restaurant-with-rooms. The building may not look much from outside, but once you're across the threshold, things improve rapidly. A small bar leads to a comfortable sitting-room, adjacent to a dining-room lined with bookshelves. A four-course dinner for £17.50 is good going, even for this rather remote part of Wales, and a spring menu offered rillettes of salmon, mushroom soup, then risotto of tomatoes or roast tenderloin of pork, and either chocolate and coffee mousse or Welsh cheese. The higher-priced 'Epicurean' menu brings more choice and a few more exotica, such as a seared salmon steak served Thai-style with lime, lemon grass, ginger, coriander and coconut cream.

The cooking is in touch with the current mood, in the form of shaved Parmesan and balsamic vinegar, and produces non-meat dishes such as roasted vegetable couscous, or pan-fried halloumi cheese with a lime and caper vinaigrette. At the same time it adopts the simple approach characteristic of so many 'amateur' cooks who follow their own nose. Rack of Welsh lamb, for instance, is all succulent pink meat with a simple lamb gravy, and comes with pink new potatoes, plain broccoli and carrots, 'all perfectly cooked'. The food quite properly makes its impact in terms of taste, which involves a combination of first-rate ingredients, a sound mastery of technique and fine judgement.

Pudding might be lemon posset with crushed raspberries, or spiced poached pear with cinnamon ice-cream and spiced syrup. A dish of baked goats' cheese and apple on a crisp, round croûton might turn up either as a first course or as a savoury at the end. Warm nibbles are first-rate, and home-made fudge comes with coffee. A good spread of wines at very reasonable prices adds to the pleasure and 'the excellent value for money'. House Australian is £9.

CHEF: Mary Ann Gilchrist PROPRIETORS: Alan and Mary Ann Gilchrist OPEN: Mon to Sat D only 7 to 8.30 CLOSED: Christmas to New Year MEALS: Set D £17.50 to £25 SERVICE: not inc, card slips closed CARDS: Access, Visa DETAILS: 12 seats. Private parties: 10 main room. Vegetarian meals. No children under 8 in dining-room. Smart dress preferred. No smoking in dining-room. Music ACCOMMODATION: 5 rooms, all with bath/shower. TV. B&B £35 to £59. Deposit: £30. Children welcome. Baby facilities. Pets welcome in bedrooms only (*The Which? Hotel Guide*)

LLYSWEN Powys map 4

▲ *Griffin Inn*

Llyswen LD3 0UR
TEL: (01874) 754241 FAX: (01874) 754592 COOKING 1
on A470 Builth Wells to Brecon road COST £16–£39

When the River Wye is in full flood, crashing outside not a dozen paces from the front door of this fifteenth-century inn, and the bar is packed with gamekeepers, there's little doubt that you are in sporting country. Richard and Di Stockton celebrated ten years in residence in 1994; their success is due to diligence, keenness and a hunger for new ideas. Hot off the press is the Griffin Tiffin – a great-value evening menu for two that is a bit like a Powys version of tapas. Every night, visitors can help along their drinking in the bar with a selection of bite-sized dishes, such as prawns with garlic and tarragon, or chicken with grapes, rosemary and mash.

Eileen Havard is a forthright cook who knows exactly how to handle all kinds of furred and feathered game: rabbit stew, pigeon pot-roasted with red wine, ragoût of venison cooked with lager. Otherwise, her menu is dotted with dishes that are big on flavour – oxtail braised in old ale, crab and laverbread tart, salmon risotto. Many vegetables, herbs and soft fruits are from the pub garden; cheeses are Welsh. Puddings are in the homespun mould of treacle tart, hot chocolate sponge, and pear and caramel roulade. The Griffin is a free house with real ales on draught, and a wine list that provides plenty of affordable drinking. A dozen or so house wines (starting at £7.50) are available by the glass.

CHEF: Eileen Havard PROPRIETORS: Richard and Di Stockton OPEN: all week L 12 to 2, Mon to Sat D 7 to 9 CLOSED: 25 and 26 Dec MEALS: alc (main courses £5 to £13). Set L Sun £12.50 SERVICE: not inc, card slips closed CARDS: Access, Amex, Delta, Diners, Switch, Visa DETAILS: 40 seats. 4 tables outside. Private parties: 40 main room, 14 private room. Car park. Vegetarian meals. Children's helpings. Smart dress preferred. No smoking in dining-room. Wheelchair access (also WC). No music ACCOMMODATION: 8 rooms, 7 with bath/shower. Phone. B&B £28.50 to £60. Deposit: £10. Children welcome. Baby facilities. Pets welcome. Garden. Fishing

'The only positive impression that all four savoury courses left me with was that they are good at buying smoked salmon.' **(On eating in Hereford & Worcester)**

▲ *Llangoed Hall* **NEW ENTRY**

Llyswen LD3 0YP
TEL: (01874) 754525 FAX: (01874) 754545 COOKING 2
on A470, 1m NW of Llyswen COST £28–£66

This luxury country-house hotel is set in ten acres of beautiful gardens and parkland in equally beautiful countryside. The original castle was restored and re-designed in 1912 by Clough Williams-Ellis of Portmeirion fame, though many of the Jacobean features, including the impressive stone façade and porchway, were retained. Today 'it oozes gracious living', from the stately lounge (overlooking the croquet lawn), where aperitifs and canapés are served, to the Edwardian dining-room with its thick carpets, heavy curtains and large round candlelit tables laid with expensive linen: 'a truly delightful place to have dinner'. Twenty-seven-year-old Ben Davies began cooking here in February 1995. He has spent a year in Provence, which explains some of the lightness and sunshine in the menu, and has also cooked at Calcot Manor, Tetbury, and Hambleton Hall, Hambleton (see entries), among others; he is therefore no stranger to country-house cooking.

Davies makes a point of using local produce, from organic vegetables to honey from the next village, Welsh lamb killed by a local butcher, venison from Brecon, Glamorgan sausage and laverbread. Fish seems a strong suit, and among successes have been a small fillet of sea bass with roasted peppers in a light, smooth and intensely flavoured tomato sauce, and an escalope of salmon with small pieces of fennel, baby beetroot and a balsamic dressing. An inspector, however, found the overall execution patchy, as in roast guinea-fowl with 'bullet-hard flageolet beans that should never have been let out of the kitchen', and felt that there was a desire to impress with over-complicated dishes. He was impressed, none the less, with a 'delicate' chocolate soufflé that was enhanced by a caramel ice-cream in a sablé basket wrapped in a cage of spun sugar. The menu advises that there will be a short pause between courses; or as one reporter put it 'long periods when not a lot happened'. The 300-bin country-house wine list is big on classic wines at country-house prices. It makes a speciality of Ch. Gruaud-Larose, but not of wines under £20; and £4.50 for a glass of house wine seems almost to defeat the object.

CHEF: Ben Davies PROPRIETOR: Sir Bernard Ashley OPEN: all week 12 to 2, 7.15 to 9.30 MEALS: alc (main courses £13.50 to £19.50). Set L Sun £16.75, Set L Mon to Sat £13 (2 courses) to £16, Set D £29.50 SERVICE: not inc, card slips closed CARDS: Access, Amex, Delta, Diners, Switch, Visa DETAILS: 40 seats. 4 tables outside. Private parties: 30 main room, 14 and 50 private rooms. Car park. Vegetarian meals. No children under 8. Smart dress preferred. No smoking in dining-room. Wheelchair access (1 step; also WC). Music ACCOMMODATION: 23 rooms, all with bath/shower. TV. Phone. B&B £95 to £195. Deposit: £50. No children under 8. Dogs welcome in kennels. Afternoon teas. Garden. Fishing (*The Which? Hotel Guide*)

If a restaurant is new to the Guide *this year (did not appear as a main entry in the last edition),* NEW ENTRY *appears opposite its name.*

MATHRY Dyfed map 4

Ann FitzGerald's Farmhouse Kitchen

Mabws Fawr, Mathry SA62 5JB
TEL: (01348) 831347
off A487, 6m SW of Fishguard

COOKING 2
COST £16–£42

'Every year the *Guide* has something to say about our pot-holed drive and decaying farm buildings,' notes Lionel FitzGerald. Concessions to urban notions of convenience have lately been creeping in, however: 'We now have tarmac. Not only that, renovation of the buildings is under way, there is now a car park and I wouldn't be surprised if we had street lights next.' This, as you might have guessed, is south-west Wales at its most ruggedly unembellished. Once inside, you may be caught unawares by the tastefully decorated dining-room, in which informality reigns.

Anglo-French might just about describe the cooking, but there are excursions into oriental modes too, and it is all built on a solid foundation of good local materials. Menus are quite extensive for the scale of the place, and the broadly based *carte* is joined by fixed-price lunch and dinner menus. Classic bistro starters like moules marinière and garlic-buttered snails are offset by more recherché dishes such as a deep-fried filo roll of curried crabmeat and bamboo shoots served with rice noodles cooked in sesame oil and soy. Main courses offer the likes of salmon braised in Crémant de Bourgogne and finished with cream and dill, or a painstaking preparation of rabbit, in which the saddle is stuffed with black pudding and apple, wrapped in bacon and roasted, and the leg braised in red wine and port with mushrooms and grain mustard. That touch of flash continues into puddings that utilise a fair amount of alcohol. Bananas are flamed in rum before being wrapped in a crêpe, bread pudding comes with a whisky sauce, and strawberries are marinated in Grand Marnier. Fine Welsh and other cheeses are kept in good condition. Both the FitzGeralds are practised hosts, and make you feel very welcome.

France takes up most of the cellar, but the 15-bottle Italian section is stunningly good. Prices are extremely considerate and almost make up for the absence of half-bottles and the token presence of some countries. House wines from Languedoc, Sicily and Bulgaria are £9 a bottle, or £2.20 a glass.

CHEFS/PROPRIETORS: Ann and Lionel FitzGerald OPEN: all week 12 to 2, 7 to 9 CLOSED: L Christmas to Easter (exc bookings) MEALS: Set L £10, Set L Sun £14, Set D £17 to £21.50 SERVICE: not inc, card slips closed CARDS: Access, Visa DETAILS: 35 seats. 3 tables outside. Private parties: 40 main room. Car park. Vegetarian meals. Children's helpings. No smoking in 1 dining-room. Wheelchair access (also WC). Music

indicates that smoking is either banned altogether or that a dining-room is maintained for non-smokers. The symbol does not apply to restaurants that simply have no-smoking areas.

NANTGAREDIG Dyfed map 4

▲ *Four Seasons*

Cwmtwrch Farm Hotel, Nantgaredig SA32 7NY
TEL: (01267) 290238 FAX: (01267) 290808 COOKING 1
on B4310, 1m N of Nantgaredig COST £20–£40

The restaurant forms part of a burgeoning leisure complex housed in a converted farmhouse and its outbuildings in the lush Towy Valley. Stripped pine and cream walls in the conservatory dining-room impart a pleasantly relaxed atmosphere, and a display of dozens of keys hanging from a beam is among the visual distractions.

Good use is made by the kitchen of locally sourced ingredients, such as Brechfa smoked salmon, sewin from the Towy, Carmarthen ham and Welsh goats' cheese. Spring vegetable soup is a 'tasty, thick and creamy' liquidised version, while a salad of smoked venison and Parmesan offers lightly smoked, rich, rather dry meat with plenty of good cheese and olives. 'One of the best pieces of fish eaten in a long time' was the verdict of one who tried sewin with a lemon butter sauce. Fillet of sea bass redolent of dill and fennel is baked and sauced with white wine. A vegetarian option might be a tasty three-cheese and spinach pancake in tomato sauce. Traditional puddings of the likes of 'rich and fruity' sherry trifle and 'excellent, light creamy' crème caramel are followed by robust espresso. 'Friendly and informal' service keeps everybody happy.

The operation also includes a wine business that supplies the restaurant. Selections on the list are imaginative, and the value increases as the more illustrious byways are explored. House wines are £8.50.

CHEFS: Maryann Wright and Charlotte Pasetti PROPRIETORS: Maryann and Simon Wright, and Charlotte Pasetti OPEN: Mon to Fri L; 12.30 to 2.30, Mon to Sat D 7.15 to 9 MEALS: alc L (main courses £6.50 to £14). Set D £17.50 SERVICE: not inc DETAILS: 50 seats. Private parties: 50 main room. Car park. Vegetarian meals. Children's helpings. Wheelchair access. Music ACCOMMODATION: 6 rooms, all with bath/shower. TV. B&B £36 to £46. Deposit: 10%. Rooms for disabled. Children welcome. Pets welcome. Garden. Swimming-pool

NEWPORT Dyfed map 4

▲ *Cnapan*

East Street, Newport SA42 0SY COOKING 1*
TEL: (01239) 820575 FAX: (01239) 820878 COST £13–£34

A family atmosphere prevails at this snug Georgian house – three generations of family, to be precise – with grandchildren helping during school holidays. Imposing domestic solidity pervades the dining-room, where the Welsh dressers are packed with ornaments that include a fireman's brass helmet. Judith Cooper and Eluned Lloyd cook some enterprising food, with the latter – herself a vegetarian – offering non-meat-eaters their own menu. The style is at once homely and imaginative. Soups pile on the flavours, as in cauliflower, apple and celery seasoned with cumin and served with hot garlic soda bread. Seafood likewise is boldly treated, either as a starter of crab and prawn pancake flashed under the grill, or in a main course of layered cod fillet and smoked salmon with a cheese, coriander and breadcrumb topping. Fruity accompaniments with meat are a theme, so expect mango and orange with guinea-fowl perhaps, or cranberries in a port sauce with soy- and honey-flavoured duck. Vegetables come in profusion. Rich puddings take in mincemeat, apricot and ginger tart, and 'sticky-tacky' chocolate roll filled with chocolate mousse and served with raspberries and cream. There are also some good local cheeses. A reader who found the service at full stretch and not quite coping one evening none the less pointed out that 'the food is original and good'. Breakfasts, too, are enjoyed by those who stay.

Within its limited compass, the wine list displays knowledgeable choice, with a £20 limit reining in everything except champagne. House French and German are £7.45.

CHEFS: Eluned Lloyd and Judith Cooper PROPRIETORS: Eluned and John Lloyd, Michael and Judith Cooper OPEN: Wed to Mon L 12 to 2, Mon and Wed to Sat D 7 to 9 (Sun D bookings only) CLOSED: 25 and 26 Dec, Feb MEALS: alc (main courses £4 to £12.50). Set L Sun £8.95 SERVICE: not inc, card slips closed CARDS: Access, Visa DETAILS: 35 seats. 6 tables outside. Private parties: 35 main room. Car park. Vegetarian meals. Children's helpings. Smart dress preferred. No smoking in dining-room. Wheelchair access (2 steps). Music ACCOMMODATION: 5 rooms, all with bath/shower. TV. B&B £23 to £46. Deposit: £30. Children welcome. Baby facilities. Garden (*The Which? Hotel Guide*)

NORTHOP Clwyd map 7

▲ *Soughton Hall*

Northop CH7 6AB
TEL: (01352) 840811 FAX: (01352) 840382 COOKING 2
off A5119, 1m S of Northop COST £27–£68

The opulence of the eighteenth-century bishop's palace, with its tapestries, fireplaces and ornate ceilings, is tempered by warmth and real beauty. Corporate visitors keep it going on weekdays, and families at weekends, although some have felt elbowed-out by the wedding trade. There have also been changes in the organisation. Fixed-price menus have gone, leaving two *cartes* operating in tandem: a simple 'house dinner' and a more elaborate 'gourmet dinner', both also available at lunch-time. The house menu hops between prawn and pineapple cocktail on the one hand, and a warm breakfast-type salad of crispy bacon, spicy sausage, black pudding and a poached egg on the other. Roasting and chargrilling are the commendably simple techniques applied to chump of Welsh lamb with bubble and squeak, baby chicken with tarragon, and well-hung steaks.

Those are the new developments, prompted by customer demand, but the more heavily wrought gourmet menu stays with ravioli filled with chicken and pistachio mousseline, surrounded by fried livers and a shallot and red wine jus, or a terrine of salmon, lobster and monkfish wrapped in smoked salmon, served with tapénade and a caviare and chervil vinaigrette. Reports suggest that, as a rule, plain and simple dishes done well impress more than complex ones, especially when the price difference is taken into account, but the flexibility here is welcome, and doubtless if 'market forces' display a strong preference for either school the balance may shift. When it comes to puddings, the struggle may be more even, with strawberry cheesecake and gooseberry fool ranged against lemon tart with raspberry coulis, or a selection of home-bottled fruits. Good-value New World wines stand up well to pedigree French ones on a list that includes Welsh Monnow Valley and five house wines from £10.95.

CHEF: Christopher Plummer PROPRIETORS: John and Rosemary Rodenhurst OPEN: Mon to Sat L 12 to 2, all week D 7 to 10 MEALS: alc (main courses £9.50 to £20) SERVICE: not inc, card slips closed CARDS: Access, Amex, Visa DETAILS: 50 seats. Private parties: 60 main room, 22 to 114 private rooms. Car park. Vegetarian meals. Jacket and tie. No smoking in dining-room. Music ACCOMMODATION: 14 rooms, all with bath/shower. TV. Phone. B&B £70 to £119. Deposit: 25%. Children welcome. Afternoon teas. Garden (*The Which? Hotel Guide*)

PENMAENPOOL Gwynedd map 7

▲ *Penmaenuchaf Hall*

Penmaenpool LL40 1YB
TEL/FAX: (01341) 422129 NEW CHEF
off A493, 2m W of Dolgellau COST £27–£43

The 'truly fabulous' Victorian mansion is five miles from the sea above the Mawddach estuary, with 13 miles of fishing at its disposal, and set in 21 acres of gardens amidst a small forest of rhododendrons. It has been lavishly refurbished and turned from a private house (built for a Bolton cotton magnate) into a country house hotel by Mark Watson and Lorraine Fielding. Drapes, oak panelling, a big fireplace, lots of flowers, comfortable armchairs and books by the yard may be the standard props of such places, but are no less welcome for being so. If they are designed to impress, they work.

As we went to press, we learned that Sue Kesseck from Shoes, High Ongar, has taken over in the kitchen. The format remains more or less as before, with both à la carte and set-price menus at lunch and dinner, but as a result, we have had insufficient time to gather the feedback we need to award a mark for cooking this year.

Wines are well chosen across the board, and although the six hours' notice requested for decanting fine claret and old burgundy could mean dinner at two o'clock in the morning, it is a minor inconvenience for Ch. Langoa-Barton 1978, and allows a reasonable interval to fill with other goodies from the Rhône to Mexico. Nine house wines begin at £9.95, or £1.95 per glass. CELLARMAN'S CHOICE: Pinot Blanc 1991, Rolly-Gassmann, £18.55; Petite Sirah 1992, L.A. Cetto, Mexico, £10.90.

CHEF: Sue Kesseck PROPRIETORS: Mark Watson and Lorraine Fielding OPEN: all week 12 to 2.30, 7 to 9.30 (9 Sun) MEALS: alc L (main courses £7 to £16). Set L £12.95 to £14.95, Set D £23 SERVICE: not inc, card slips closed CARDS: Access, Amex, Delta, Diners, Switch, Visa DETAILS: 30 seats. Private parties: 70 main room, 18 private room. Car park. Vegetarian meals. No children under 10 after 8pm. Smart dress preferred. No smoking in dining-room. Wheelchair access (also WC). Music ACCOMMODATION: 14 rooms, all with bath/shower. TV. Phone. B&B £50 to £150. Deposit: £15. Children welcome. Baby facilities. Pets welcome (to stay in gun room only). Afternoon teas. Garden. Fishing (*The Which? Hotel Guide*)

PONTFAEN Dyfed map 4

▲ *Tregynon Country Farmhouse Hotel*

Gwaun Valley, Pontfaen SA65 9TU
TEL: (01239) 820531 FAX: (01239) 820808
at junction of B4313 and B4329, take B4313 towards Fishguard, then take first right, and first right again

COOKING 1
COST £22–£33

Peter and Jane Heard are geared to guests who stay a fortnight, and they never repeat the same dish in those two weeks – nor, supplies permitting, cook a vegetable (including potato) the same way – thus producing a revolving menu, as the brochure says, 'like a cartwheel with fourteen spokes'. The sixteenth-century stone farmhouse is, by the proprietors' own admission, 'in an isolated spot in the middle of nowhere'. Dinner is three courses, the first meat-free, and the main course needs to be settled in advance, by telephone for non-residents. The Heards rely on local free-range eggs, fish and organic cheeses, smoke their own bacon and gammon, are careful about artificial additives and preservatives, and give vegetarians a much fairer deal than usual. 'We pride ourselves on being able to cater for most special diets.' Dressings and sauces tend to sweetness, as in chicken cooked with tropical fruits and white wine, or beef cooked with tomatoes, honey and Moscatel wine, and non-vegetarians have remarked on the general lack of flavour. Puddings might include whisky oatmeal syllabub layered with strawberries, or bread-and-butter pudding with the addition of marmalade and rum. Around 40 wide-ranging wines are extensively annotated and stay commendably under £20. House French is £8.95.

CHEFS: Peter and Jane Heard, and Siân Philips PROPRIETORS: Peter and Jane Heard OPEN: all week D only 7.30 to 8.45 MEALS: Set D £15.50 SERVICE: not inc, card slips closed CARDS: Access, Visa (3% surcharge on payments by credit card) DETAILS: 30 seats. Private parties: 16 main room, 14 private room. Car park. Vegetarian meals. No children under 8. Smart dress preferred. No smoking in dining-room. Music ACCOMMODATION: 8 rooms, all with bath/shower. TV. Phone. B&B £46 to £65 (double rooms). Deposit: 25%. Rooms for disabled. Children welcome. Baby facilities. Afternoon teas. Garden (*The Which? Hotel Guide*)

PORTHGAIN Dyfed map 4

Harbour Lights

Porthgain, nr St David's SA62 5BL
TEL: (01348) 831549
off A487 at Croesgoch, 4m W of Mathry

COOKING 2*
COST £25–£33

Intrepid people walking along this precipitous stretch of the Pembrokeshire coastal path will come across Harbour Lights. The restaurant occupies an old stone cottage in a narrow inlet where the surrounding countryside is a riot of wild flowers and gorse in spring, making the outside tables a temptation on a fine day. Anne Marie Davies does the cooking, and is supported ably by family members who run the front-of-house. The Davieses have been here over a decade, and the formula has attracted growing support.

A light lunch menu is available at midday, but in the evening the stops are pulled out for a three-course, set-price dinner. The menu changes every two or three days and makes versatile use of local resources for dishes like Pembrokeshire mussels cooked with white wine, shallots, garlic and cream; laverbread and smoked bacon gratinated with Welsh cheese; and local sirloin steak with herb butter sauce. A May crab salad served as a starter was 'easily large enough for a main course'. Sewin cooked in a filo parcel, accompanied by cabbage with tarragon and potatoes with a sprinkling of lovage, was also 'exceptional'. Substantial puddings like sticky toffee with banana, toasted nuts and cream, or a hot compote of apple, rhubarb and ginger in a crêpe, are particularly recommended. An agreeable miscellany of wines at sensible prices is offered, and a selection is also available by the glass. House French is £8.50.

CHEF/PROPRIETOR: Anne Marie Davies OPEN: Tue to Sat 12 to 2, 6.30 to 9 (telephone to check in winter) CLOSED: Dec and Jan MEALS: Set D £16.50 to £19.50; light lunch menu SERVICE: not inc, card slips closed CARDS: Access, Delta, Switch, Visa DETAILS: 32 seats. 10 tables outside. Private parties: 20 main room. Vegetarian meals. Children welcome. No cigars/pipes in dining-room. Music

PORTMEIRION Gwynedd map 7

▲ *Hotel Portmeirion*

Portmeirion LL48 6ET
TEL: (01766) 770228 FAX: (01766) 771331 COOKING 2
off A487, signposted from Minffordd COST £20–£39

'The Italianate village is like a fairy-tale' and the sense of seclusion from the outside world – in a cleft of hillside above the Traeth Bach estuary – adds to the feeling of unreality. The village and grounds are owned by a charitable foundation and, when the day-trippers have gone home, residents can stroll quietly through Sir Clough Williams-Ellis's architectural extravaganza at leisure, 'which adds to the magic'. The dining-room of the hotel is equally theatrical, whether looking out on the changing tide or into the semicircular room with its tripartite mural. Craig Hindley's food is 'contemporary British' and takes advantage of Welsh produce, including locally caught fish and game, and vegetables, fruits and cheeses from local farms. 'Outstanding raw materials,' summed up an inspector.

The food makes an impression of lightness, particularly in dishes such as roast salmon with creamed leeks and a tomato butter sauce. Pasta might appear in the form of a single UFO-shaped raviolo, filled with smoked chicken and lobster, on strips of carrot with an anchovy and port sauce. Flavour combinations can work well, as in a terrine-type slice of pressed spiced beef cut in rough chunks and set in an excellent aspic jelly – tasting 'soft and sensuous, subtly yet clearly spiced with cloves' – and in a 'terrific' warm plum and almond flan with a five-spice vanilla custard. Incidentals, such as bread and pre-meal nibbles, might be improved, but the restaurant manager is 'wonderful' and the staff treat 'absolutely everyone as if they were flavour-of-the-month'. The hotel operates a bilingual policy, and it struck one English reporter as 'odd that there should be a Welsh word for burgundy'. Bwrgwyn, like most other sections of the wine list, is high on quality, and the house selection helpfully picks out three dozen good wines under £13.50. It is a most unstuffy list with some real gems and a very fair pricing policy. House French is £9.50. CELLARMAN'S CHOICE: Cyfuniad Sych

Pant Teg 1994, De Morgannwg, Llysfaen, £12.50; Châteauneuf-du-Pape 1992, Celliers de Marrenon, £13.50.

CHEF: Craig Hindley PROPRIETOR: Portmeirion Ltd OPEN: Tue to Sun L 12.30 to 2, all week D 7 to 9.30 CLOSED: 7 Jan to 2 Feb MEALS: Set L £10.50 (2 courses) to £13.50, Set L Sun £16, Set D £20 (2 courses) to £25 SERVICE: not inc, card slips closed CARDS: Access, Amex, Delta, Diners, Switch, Visa DETAILS: 100 seats. 3 tables outside. Private parties: 100 main room, 14 and 35 private rooms. Car park. Vegetarian meals. Children's helpings. Smart dress preferred. No smoking in dining-room. Wheelchair access (3 steps; also WC). No music ACCOMMODATION: 37 rooms, all with bath/shower. TV. Phone. B&B £56.50 to £167. Rooms for disabled. Children welcome. Baby facilities. Garden. Swimming-pool (*The Which? Hotel Guide*)

PWLLHELI Gwynedd map 7

▲ *Plas Bodegroes*

Nefyn Road, Pwllheli LL53 5TH
TEL: (01758) 612363 FAX: (01758) 701247 COOKING 4
on A497, 1m W of Pwllheli COST £39–£46

For a time this Georgian manor house was on the market, but Christopher Chown changed his mind and still runs it in tandem with the Hole in the Wall (see entry, Bath). The difficulty of keeping two balls in the air is partially solved by having such good stand-ins as Adrian Walton (in Bath) and Andrew Price here. The house, small and gracious, looks out on to an avenue of tall and ancient beech trees, and there is a quiet air of comfort about the place. 'We like the cool, civilised atmosphere,' noted one, while another called it 'subdued'. A collection of paintings by Welsh artists adds colour to the elegant and tastefully furnished dining-room.

Five-course dinners are of 'manageable proportions' ('meagre' to one appetite), but with coffee thrown in, and all for £30, 'it must have few critics'. Menus revolve slowly round a core repertoire of well-tried dishes, particular treatments varying with the season and occasion, giving the food both continuity and variety. One couple recalled similar dishes on their last visit three years previously, while another couple who stayed two nights found that half the menu had changed by the second evening. The pattern is four or five courses per course, with some imaginative ideas such as hotpot of shellfish and asparagus with lemon grass and chilli.

Given the proximity to Cardigan Bay, fish is a natural, appearing as fillet of sea-trout wrapped in Carmarthen ham with leeks and mustard sauce, or perhaps a sumptuous fillet of turbot baked beneath a fennel and herb crust. At one meal, samphire gave a dish of mussels and monkfish in puff pastry 'that seashore and sea breezes taste'. What appeals is that 'natural tastes shine through', be it from an intense blackcurrant sauce served with dark, juicy, meaty duck, or roast breast of guinea-fowl with girolles. Lack of ostentation endears the cooking to reporters, as well as 'splendid use of local materials, and many home-made offerings'. Saucing is particularly light, and vegetables arrive as part of the main dish.

Puddings avoid stodgy clichés, offering gratin of peaches with pistachio and kumquat ice-cream, or summer pudding with elderflower custard. Cheese is five pieces served on a plate 'with no choice and no explanation of their origin', or there is grilled goats' cheese. Ordinary bread and amuse-gueules, and meat cooked well instead of rare, took the shine off it all for one reporter, but generally the relaxed and efficient service smoothes things along. Wines are enthusiastically chosen for character and personality, rather than formal credentials, although there is pedigree claret and burgundy for those who want it. Alsace seems to be a hobby, and although most countries don't field a large number of wines, there is ample variety. Prices are not at all greedy, and the house selection of around 15 wines, mostly under £20, makes a good starting point. CELLARMAN'S CHOICE: Meursault 1989, François Jobard, £37; Côte Rôtie 1986, Guigal, £29.

CHEFS: Christopher Chown and Andrew Price PROPRIETORS: Plas Bodegroes Ltd OPEN: Tue to Sun D only 7 to 9.30 CLOSED: Nov to Feb MEALS: Set D £30 SERVICE: not inc, card slips closed CARDS: Access, Amex, Switch, Visa DETAILS: 40 seats. Private parties: 40 main room, 16 private room. Car park. No smoking in dining-room. Wheelchair access (1 step; also WC). Music ACCOMMODATION: 8 rooms, all with bath/shower. TV. Phone. D,B&B £65 to £160. Deposit: £50. Pets welcome in bedrooms by arrangement only. Garden

REYNOLDSTON West Glamorgan map 4

▲ *Fairyhill* 🍷

Reynoldston SA3 1BS COOKING 2
TEL: (01792) 390139 FAX: (01792) 391358 COST £21–£39

This attractive, secluded eighteenth-century square stone mansion is set in 24 acres of grounds in the heart of the Gower Peninsula. Seven well-spaced tables in the green and yellow dining-room have views of the gardens and parkland. Two January visitors arrived 'to a pleasant welcome and a blazing fire'. Others, too, have found the warm and friendly atmosphere much to their liking, and the service 'unobtrusive but very friendly'. It is 'a particularly civilised place in which to spend an evening'.

Local produce figures strongly. A market gardener two miles away grows vegetables (including pink fir potatoes), venison comes from Bwlch, and Penclawdd yields not only cockles and laverbread but also pré-salé lamb, while Swansea market, 20 minutes away, supplies the fish. Clarity and a sense of purpose define the food, which flies the modern Welsh flag in, for example, a dish of scrambled eggs with cockles and roasted peppers, or fillet of Welsh lamb with a 'properly made and cooked' sausage of lamb and rosemary, on a crisp celeriac pancake. Fish and shellfish are moist and full of flavour, whether scallops with black fettucini in an aromatic saffron sauce lightly spiked with lemon, or poached fillet of local sewin with samphire and hollandaise sauce.

Bresaola 'Taruschio' pays homage to the Walnut Tree Inn: it is a large portion of thinly cut, dark red, lean and well-marinated topside. Nor does the pace slacken towards the end. Dinner offers a generous choice of nine items per course, ending at one meal with a light pudding of shortcrust pastry filled with frangipane sponge and prunes, served with an armagnac cream, and a soft, smooth, rich crème brûlée with a hot, crisp, caramelised topping of sliced banana. Lunch is simpler but looks a bargain. Wines go to the trouble of offering all ten Beaujolais crus, half a dozen vintages of Chateaux Cissac and Latour, a page of Coche-Dury Burgundy, five Welsh wines, and more. Prices are very fair.

House vin de pays d'Oc is £9.50. CELLARMAN'S CHOICE: Rully 1992, Olivier Leflaive, £17; Côtes du Rhône Villages 1992, Ch. de Grand Moulas, £14.50.

CHEF: Paul Davies PROPRIETORS: Paul Davies, Jane and Peter Camm, and Andrew Hetherington OPEN: all week 12.30 to 2.15, 7.30 to 9.15 CLOSED: 3 days after Christmas, Sun D winter MEALS: Set L £10.95 (2 courses) to £13.95, Set D £19.50 (2 courses) to £24.50 SERVICE: not inc, card slips closed CARDS: Access, Amex, Delta, Switch, Visa DETAILS: 68 seats. 4 tables outside. Private parties: 45 main room, 45 private room. Car park. Vegetarian meals. Children's helpings. No children under 8 D. No cigars/pipes in dining-room. Wheelchair access (1 step; also WC). Music ACCOMMODATION: 8 rooms, all with bath/shower. TV. Phone. B&B £65 to £120. No children under 8. Pets welcome in bedrooms only. Garden (*The Which? Hotel Guide*)

ROSEBUSH Dyfed map 4

Tate's at Tafarn Newydd

Rosebush, nr Clynderwen SA66 7RA
TEL: (01437) 532542
on B4313, 8m SE of Fishguard

COOKING 2
COST £14–£36

Diana Richards hit the road last December, bidding a fond farewell to Goodwick, where Tate's once was, and pitching up at the Tafarn Newydd, or New Inn, 'on a crossroads in the middle of nowhere'. The new venue still looks like a pub from the outside, but the Tate's format is preserved within. Bistro-style eating from a blackboard menu is on offer in the bar; there is also a large dining-room, its walls rag-rolled in deep blue-green, with oil burners on the tables, for more formal eating.

Continuity has been preserved in a cooking style which, in the modern idiom, tries its hand at whatever sounds interesting, wherever it comes from. So the ragoos and possets of *ancien régime* Britain sit alongside Vietnamese chicken and Italian agrodolce duck. Wales gets a look-in too, in a gratin of laverbread, cockles and bacon tried at an inspection meal, when another starter of a generous quantity of chicken livers found themselves forced into an 'unsubtle' marriage with walnuts and nothing else; some leaves would have helped. Walnuts are used again in a sauce with yoghurt to make a 'perfect foil' for firm, fresh sea bass – 'an imaginative combination'. Noisettes of lamb with a 'salty crust' are cooked to a perfect pink. Puddings can be the best part of a meal: lemon posset spiked with zest and served in a glass with a sablé biscuit is 'rich, tangy and excellent', for example, while Basque cherry gâteau is a 'sweet cakey pastry' encasing a good fruit filling. Bread may be a home-baked ciabatta flecked with olives and sprinkled with salt. The bare floor and walls can make for a bit of a hubbub, and front-of-house staff may be unfamiliar with what is being served, but on the whole the transition to new premises has been negotiated well. House wine is £7.95 a bottle.

CHEF/PROPRIETOR: Diana Richards OPEN: all week L 12 to 2.30, Tue to Sun D 7 to 9.30 MEALS: alc (main courses £4.50 to £13.50). Set L Sun £6.50 to £8.95 SERVICE: not inc, card slips closed CARDS: Access, Delta, Visa DETAILS: 20 seats. 6 tables outside. Private parties: 50 main room, 50 private room. Vegetarian meals. No smoking in dining-room. Wheelchair access (1 step). Music

ROSSETT Clwyd map 7

Churtons £

Machine House, Chester Road, Rossett LL12 0HW
TEL: (01244) 570163 FAX: (01244) 570099 COOKING 1
on B5445, off A483, between Chester and Wrexham COST £20–£39

Once upon a time in Liverpool there was a family of wine merchants called Churton who were so successful that they even had their own brand of whisky. Eventually they moved to Wales, converted a barn in the village of Rossett and never looked back. Over the years the building has continued to develop, into a pleasantly informal food and wine bar on two levels with panelled walls, wooden floors and a hotch-potch of wooden furniture. The blackboard menu promises bistro food to suit all tastes: soups, pâtés and salads loom large, but the repertoire is shot through with eclectic ideas that could encompass tapénade, Morecambe Bay shrimps with garlic, and lamb and cashew nuts with a 'perfect' couscous. Vegetarians are not ignored: watercress pancakes with oyster mushrooms in paprika sauce delighted one reporter. Desserts range from bread-and-butter pudding to lemon and lime mousse. Churtons' wine list is carefully chosen and reasonably priced; bottles and cases can be ordered to take away. Seven house wines (all served by the glass) start at £7.90.

A second branch at Tarporley in Cheshire is run along similar lines: 55 High Street, Tarporley CW6 0DP, (01829) 732483.

CHEFS: Ade Garratt, Jackie Lloyd, Louise MacDougall and Marie Baddeley PROPRIETORS: Nicholas Churton and James Churton OPEN: Mon to Fri L 12 to 2.15, Mon to Sat D 7 to 10 CLOSED: 24 Dec to 3 Jan, bank hol Mons MEALS: alc (main courses £7 to £14) SERVICE: not inc CARDS: Access, Amex, Visa DETAILS: 55 seats. 4 tables outside. Private parties: 20 main room, 12 private room. Car park. Vegetarian meals. No children under 12. Smart dress preferred. Wheelchair access (1 step). Music. Air-conditioned

ST DAVID'S Dyfed map 4

Morgan's Brasserie NEW ENTRY

20 Nun Street, St David's SA62 6NT COOKING 1
TEL: (01437) 720508 COST £24–£34

This 'smartish', small brasserie, is family-run – Ceri and Simon are brothers – and opened its doors in 1993. The menu is strongly fish-based, reflecting St David's position at the end of the Pembroke peninsula, surrounded by sea on three sides. The catch is landed at Milford Haven, and some of it appears – either on the standard menu or on the blackboard – as fillet of plaice, baked monkfish, or grilled blue-fin shark steak.

A pair of reporters enjoyed a 'delicious, deeply fishy, golden brown soup' in which were piled mussels, chunks of salmon, halibut, crab's legs and prawns: 'a meal on its own'. Simply cooked fish such as salmon or halibut are highlights, perhaps with laverbread sauce, or a sauce of smoked salmon and shrimp. Steaks are from Welsh Black beef, and might be served chargrilled or flamed in brandy with green peppercorn sauce. Cheeses – along the lines of St David's Cheddar, St Illtyd and Cashel blue – are kept in good condition, and puddings might include 'satisfyingly rich' chocolate truffle cake, or poached pears with shortbread pastry and crème pâtissière. Around 30 wines stay mostly under £15, whites coded for sweetness, reds for body. House wine is £7.25, or £1.50 a glass.

CHEF: Simon Morgan PROPRIETORS: Ceri and Elaine Morgan OPEN: Mon to Sat D only 6.30 to 9 CLOSED: Jan and Feb, Mon and Tue Oct to Dec MEALS: alc (main courses £11 to £12.50) SERVICE: not inc CARDS: Access, Delta, Visa DETAILS: 36 seats. Private parties: 36 main room. Vegetarian meals. Children's helpings. Smart dress preferred. No cigars/pipes in dining-room. Wheelchair access. Music

SWANSEA West Glamorgan map 4

L'Amuse **NEW ENTRY**

2 Woodville Road, Mumbles, Swansea SA3 4AD COOKING 1*
TEL: (01792) 366006 COST £19–£33

A new star has illuminated the Swansea scene, or the Mumbles scene, to be precise. Kate Cole, who is well-known hereabouts – she used to cook at Fairyhill (see entry, Reynoldston) – has taken over a corner site in the back streets of this seaside village, and painted it a difficult-to-miss white and vivid pillar-box red. 'A cheerful, stylish French-Mediterranean feel, put together on a budget', is how one reporter saw the L-shaped room of ten tables with busy cloths and poster-covered walls.

Naturally, meals begin with an amuse-gueule: a moist, meaty help-yourself terrine of pork and chicken livers, and a bowl of gherkins: 'a meal on its own unless you exercise self-control'. French country cooking is the basis, from Mediterranean fish soup with aïoli, through *oeuf plat* on spinach with lightly cooked smoked salmon, to a dish of gizzards with sauté potatoes on salad leaves, dressed in a sweet-and-sour oily balsamic dressing. But roast sirloin of beef with Yorkshire pudding and horseradish cream (for two people) shows the kitchen is not hidebound French. Cooking keeps both meat and fish – including a boned skate wing with saffron sauce – moist and tender, and if results sometimes appear no more than the sum of their parts, then such straightforwardness is welcome. 'Perfectly cooked' vegetables match the rest of the output, cheeses include Tête de Moine shaved into a frilly mound, and puddings are serviceable rather than exciting. Friendly service from white-aproned students might be more informed. 'No ashtrays provided. The place was full and no one smoked. Hooray!' Three dozen well-chosen wines are mostly French and fairly priced. House wine is £7.50.

CHEF/PROPRIETOR: Kate Cole OPEN: Tue to Sun; 12 to 2.15, 7 to 9 MEALS: Set L £8.55 (2 courses) to £11.95, Set D £16.50 SERVICE: not inc, card slips closed CARDS: Access, Amex, Delta, Visa DETAILS: 35 seats. Private parties: 50 main room. Children welcome. No music

'Spring chicken may have been on the menu, but there were none among the clientele.' (On eating in Cumbria)

La Braseria

28 Wind Street, Swansea SA1 1DZ — COOKING 1*
TEL: (01792) 469683 — COST £17–£34

Opened in 1987 as a phoenix rising from the ashes of the Builders' Arms pub, La Braseria is a catering success story. The idea – generated by Benigno Martinez in Cardiff (see entries La Brasserie, Champers, Le Monde) – was to provide the locals with whacking, self-selected, freshly grilled steaks and salads that they could pile as high as they dared. Most people think that the place resembles a converted Spanish barn, with battered wine barrels everywhere, old timbers, terracotta pots and sawdust on the floor. Rioja flows freely and 'bouncy flamenco-type Muzak' keeps everyone in the mood. This is a 'classless institution', where shoppers looking for juicy burgers rub shoulders in the queue with people eager to splash out on Dover sole or lobster. Stay on the ground floor if you want meat, go upstairs for fish.

The formula remains the same: what you see is what you get. Select your chosen cut (keep your eyes peeled for novelties such as ostrich), decide whether you want it chargrilled, fried or baked, then help yourself from the salad bar; the only other accompaniments are 'perfect' jacket potatoes and 'crispy' French fries. Start with gravlax, escargots or spare ribs and finish off with cheese or a wedge of creamy gâteau. Service keeps the place running in top gear: it needs to, because there is a turnover of around 400 covers at weekends and crowds pack in for the unbeatable-value lunches. Best bets on the wine list are the Riojas, but there are also some serious vintage clarets on show. Siglo Saco house wine is £8.25.

CHEF: Manuel Tercero PROPRIETOR: Iceimp Ltd OPEN: Mon to Sat 12 to 2.30, 7 to 11.30 CLOSED: 25 and 26 Dec MEALS: alc (main courses £6 to £12). Set L £6 (2 courses) SERVICE: not inc, card slips closed CARDS: Access, Amex, Delta, Diners, Switch, Visa DETAILS: 192 seats. Private parties: 20 main room. Children welcome. Smart dress preferred. Wheelchair access (1 step; also WC). Music

Number One Wind Street

1 Wind Street, Swansea SA1 1DE — COOKING 2
TEL: (01792) 456996 — COST £19–£35

The street name doesn't refer to gusty weather: it apparently derives from '*winde*', meaning a road with lots of little alleys running off it. Much of central Swansea – particularly near the old castle ruins and the new marina – is currently undergoing renewal, and this 'spick-and-span haven' is ideally placed for business lunchers, shoppers and a mixed crowd in the evening. The interior is 'elegant bistro', a spruce assortment of colourful paintings on the magnolia and blue walls, fresh flowers and modern light oak tables. Staff are genuinely friendly and happily converse on first-name terms with many of the regulars. Kate Taylor reigns in the kitchen, and she continues to develop a repertoire of French provincial dishes with a modern Welsh accent based on local produce. Fish is in good supply ('it was brought in fresh from the market while we were at the table,' observed one couple), so you can expect dishes of skate with black butter, monkfish provençale, sea bass with laverbread sauce or baked fillet of hake with a herb crust. Reporters have also singled out 'unadulterated' watercress soup, 'rough-textured' rillettes of duck, and a genuine version of cassoulet redolent of Languedoc. Rounding things off are 'thick, creamy, munchy' bread-and-butter pudding 'straight out of the grand-mère school of cookery', plum and apple tart, or raspberry vacherin. Set-price lunches are a bargain, and the shortish evening *carte* is equally good value. Similarly, the wine list is an affordable selection of intelligently chosen bottles (mostly from France) with sensible descriptions. House wine is £7.25.

CHEFS: Kate Taylor and Alan Johns PROPRIETORS: Kate Taylor and Peter Gillen OPEN: Mon to Sat L 12 to 2.30, Wed to Sat D 7 to 9.30 CLOSED: bank hols MEALS: alc (main courses £9 to £13). Set L £9.50 (2 courses) to £11.95 SERVICE: not inc CARDS: Access, Amex, Delta, Visa DETAILS: 40 seats. Private parties: 40 main room. Vegetarian meals. Children welcome. Wheelchair access. Music

TALSARNAU Gwynedd map 7

▲ *Maes-y-Neuadd* $*

Talsarnau LL47 6YA
TEL: (01766) 780200 FAX: (01766) 780211 COOKING 2
off B4573, 1m S of Talsarnau COST £18–£43

'One of the most beautiful settings it is possible to imagine,' enthused a visitor from Berkshire. Maes-y-Neuadd – a granite and slate manor house with fourteenth-century origins and more recent additions – stands in eight acres of gardens, orchards and grounds against the mountainous backdrop of Snowdonia National Park. It is maintained and personally run by two families, 'who do it with every possible enthusiasm, courtesy and competence', and even find time to produce oils, vinegars and preserves as a commercial sideline. Dinner is served in a gracious Georgian room with views across the gardens to Tremadoc Bay.

The daily menu is fixed-price and you can choose three, four or five courses at dinner, and up to three courses at lunch-time. Welsh lamb is a permanent feature; otherwise, Peter Jackson draws on a rich seam of home-grown and local produce for a feast that might run as follows: warm pigeon salad with quail's eggs and madeira jus, then mushroom consommé with asparagus and a filo parcel, followed by salmon dumplings with mussels and cockles. The centrepiece could be pot-roast guinea-fowl with kumquats, shallots and garlic or loin of pork with 'a laverbread waistcoat'. The 'Grand Finale' is a plate of desserts and home-made ice-creams, plus Welsh cheeses served with home-baked carrot and herb bread. Coffee and sweetmeats bring up the rear. The up-to-date list of around 100 wines has its centre of gravity in France, with a good spread of clarets and some pedigree burgundy. Quality is high, Spain gets more than a token presence, and if prices are slightly high for Wales, that makes them fair by most other standards. House wine is £8.90, Welsh wine is £14.95. CELLARMAN'S CHOICE: Bonny Doon Malvasia Bianca, Ca' del Solo 1992, California, £18.05; Côtes du Rhône Villages, Ch. du Grand Moulas 1994, £13.80.

CHEF: Peter Jackson PROPRIETORS: Michael and June Slatter, and Malcolm and Olive Horsfall OPEN: all week 12 to 1.45, 7 to 9 MEALS: Set L £9.75 (2 courses) to £11.75, Set L Sun £14.25, Set D £22 to £28 SERVICE: not inc, card slips closed CARDS: Access, Amex, Delta, Diners, Switch, Visa DETAILS: 50 seats. Private parties: 40 main room, 12 and 14 private rooms. Car park. Vegetarian meals. Children's helpings. No children under 8 D. Smart dress preferred. No smoking in dining-room. Wheelchair access (1 step; also WC). Music ACCOMMODATION: 16 rooms, all with bath/shower. TV. Phone. B&B £51 to £159. Deposit: £25 per person. Rooms for disabled. Children welcome. Baby facilities. Pets by arrangement. Afternoon teas. Garden (*The Which? Hotel Guide*)

TALYLLYN Gwynedd map 7

▲ *Minffordd Hotel*

Talyllyn LL36 9AJ
TEL: (01654) 761665 FAX: (01654) 761517 COOKING 1
at junction of A487 and B4405, 8m SW of Dolgellau COST £21–£26

Mary McQuillan and Mark Warner took over this former coaching-inn during 1994 and are treading the same path as their predecessors. The change-over has been almost imperceptible, and even those who have taken the Minffordd to their hearts over the years have been hard-pressed to spot the join. The backdrop of Cader Idris and Snowdonia remains awesome, azaleas and rhododendrons bloom outside, and the atmosphere is as personable as ever. 'It is rather like going home to a warm and welcoming family,' notes one reporter. The daily-changing dinner menu runs to four courses – four starters, a choice of meat or fish as the centrepiece, followed by assorted puddings and an 'excellent' Anglo-Welsh cheeseboard. This is robust, uncomplicated cooking dictated by good ingredients. One visitor enjoyed an attractively constructed salmon and prawn roulade, breast of chicken with creamy blue cheese sauce, and an exceedingly rich brown bread and armagnac ice-cream. Another opted for cream of celery soup, thickly sliced Welsh lamb with port and redcurrant sauce, then a refreshingly unfussy fresh fruit salad. The wine list, from Tanners, is a sensibly priced and well-spread selection of around three dozen bottles. House wine is £7.65.

CHEF: Mark Warner PROPRIETORS: Mary McQuillan and Mark Warner OPEN: all week D only 8 (one sitting) CLOSED: Jan and Feb MEALS: Set D £17.50 SERVICE: none, card slips closed CARDS: Access, Visa DETAILS: 24 seats. Private parties: 24 main room. Car park. No children under 5. Smart dress preferred. No smoking in dining-room. No music ACCOMMODATION: 6 rooms, all with bath/shower. Phone. B&B £29 to £70. Deposit: 10%. No children under 5. Afternoon teas. Garden. Fishing (*The Which? Hotel Guide*)

indicates a change of chef since last year's Guide.

Report forms are at the back of the book; write a letter if you prefer; or if you are on the Internet, e-mail us at guidereports@which. co. uk.

THREE COCKS Powys map 4

▲ *Three Cocks Hotel*

Three Cocks LD3 0SL
TEL/FAX: (01497) 847215 COOKING 2
on A438, between Brecon and Hay-on-Wye COST £27–£44

The hamlet of Three Cocks consists of little more than two inns facing each other across the through road. The eponymous one is a slate-roofed stone building smothered in creepers that has been run by the Winstones as a hotel for the past decade. 'Idiosyncratic' is the best description of the interior styling, which takes in a death-mask of Beethoven glaring from the lounge fireplace and some reproduction wall-hangings, though the dining-room affords 'nice green views' of the garden.

Best value lies with the four-course set meal. The first course offers a pair of soup choices, one of which will very likely use shellfish. Fish is the main business of the next – eminently fresh skate with black butter or mussels baked with garlic, perhaps – but smoked ham from the Ardennes is always present as a testament to Michael Winstone's time in Belgium. Main courses feature fine meats such as thinly sliced duck breast with well-roasted skin in a sauce of honey and sherry vinegar, or – even better – loin of Welsh lamb of 'excellent texture, beautifully timed', served with a 'cake' of finely chopped courgettes of 'clear and strong' flavour. Desserts of bland apple mousse and a chocolate marquise have disappointed, though chocolate and nougat terrine, and the savoury alternative of grilled goats' cheese with honey sauce have prompted praise. Coffee comes with truffles and waffles. The Three Cocks continues to draw enthusiastic support from readers, who also remark on service that is 'friendly, courteous and willing to chat'. The short, predominantly French wine list has some good bottles, though prices are weighted towards the top end. House French is £8. Belgian beers on offer include cherry-flavoured Kriek and Trappist Chimay.

CHEF: Michael Winstone PROPRIETORS: Mr and Mrs Michael Winstone OPEN: Mon and Wed to Sat L 12 to 1.30, Mon and Wed to Sun D 7 to 9 CLOSED: Dec and Jan, first 10 days Feb MEALS: alc (main courses £14.50 to £17). Set L and D £24 SERVICE: net prices, card slips closed CARDS: Access, Visa DETAILS: 30 seats. Private parties: 30 main room. Car park. Children's helpings. Smart dress preferred. Music ACCOMMODATION: 7 rooms, all with bath/shower. B&B £62 (double room). Children welcome. Baby facilities. Garden (*The Which? Hotel Guide*)

TREFRIW Gwynedd map 7

Chandler's £✱

Trefriw LL27 0JH
TEL: (01492) 640991 COOKING 1*
off B5106, NW of Llanrwst COST £22–£37

Supporters of this informal restaurant heap praise on the friendly and welcoming partners, on the food and on the value for money. An open fire, 'pleasing décor' and school-bench seating set the tone, while the food ranges from onion bhajia through roast rack of Welsh lamb with a mustard glaze to polenta cake with aubergine, tomato and Gorgonzola. Fish varies with the market – steamed grey mullet, perhaps, or wild salmon with Cajun spices – although prawns with garlic mayonnaise are a regular item, as is a steak of some sort. Despite the variety, the cooking does not make excessive use of exotic flavours, just enough to provide interest, as in a blackened chicken breast with paprika, lemon and soy sauce, for instance. 'Delicious rolls' are baked in-house, vegetarians have a choice of two main courses, although advance warning is required to prepare vegan meals. Afterwards, there may be queen of puddings, tarte au citron or a popular trio of yoghurt ice-creams that leave 'a lovely clean palate at the end of a meal'. A short but zippy list of wines at drink-me-quick prices adds enomously to the value.

CHEFS/PROPRIETORS: Adam and Penny Rattenbury, and Tim Kirton OPEN: Tue to Sat, D only 7 to 10 (Thur to Sat only Nov to Easter) CLOSED: 3 weeks Sept to Oct, Christmas to New Year, 1 week end Jan, 2 weeks mid-Feb MEALS: alc (main courses £8.50 to £13.50) SERVICE: not inc, card slips closed CARDS: Access, Delta, Visa DETAILS: 36 seats. Private parties: 30 main room. Car park. Vegetarian meals. Children welcome. No smoking in dining-room. Wheelchair access (2 steps). Music

WELSH HOOK Dyfed map 4

▲ *Stone Hall*

Welsh Hook, Wolf's Castle SA62 5NS
TEL: (01348) 840212 FAX: (01348) 840815
1½m off A40, between Letterston and Wolf's Castle, W of Welsh Hook

COOKING 1
COST £22–£36

The dining-room is in the oldest part of this 600-year-old manor house, with slate-flagged floors, massive oak beams and a huge inglenook fireplace. French furniture is not the only thing that gives a clue as to the style of cooking. 'As our bedroom was over the kitchen, we can testify that there were voluble conversations in French during preparations for dinner, and at breakfast the following morning.' Martine Watson is assisted by a succession of French associates, and there is the stamp of authenticity on a staple south-western soup of vegetables and cured duck (garbure), fillet of beef bordelaise, and tarte Tatin. The Watsons bake bread, smoke their own fish and meat and serve up rustic dishes of snails in garlic butter, or moules marinière, with only minor modification for local tastes. The set four-course dinner menu changes daily and looks a steal. One evening it began with garbure followed by lemon sole mousse, then pork with mustard, then chocolate pithivier. Four dozen predominantly French wines keep prices well within reason, with house Gamay and Sauvignon Blanc from Touraine at £9.50.

CHEFS: Martine Watson and Jean-Yves Poujade PROPRIETORS: Alan and Martine Watson OPEN: all week D only 7 to 9.30 CLOSED: 2 weeks late Jan MEALS: alc (main courses £11 to £12). Set D £15.50 SERVICE: not inc CARDS: Access, Amex, Diners, Visa DETAILS: 34 seats. Private parties: 45 main room, 20 private room. Car park. Children's helpings. Smart dress preferred. No cigars/pipes in dining-room. Wheelchair access (1 step; also WC). No music ACCOMMODATION: 5 rooms, all with bath/shower. TV. B&B £46 to £63. Deposit: £20. Children welcome. Baby facilities. Afternoon teas. Garden (*The Which? Hotel Guide*)

WHITEBROOK Gwent map 2

▲ *The Crown at Whitebrook* 🍷

Whitebrook NP5 4TX
TEL: (01600) 860254 FAX: (01600) 860607
5m S of Monmouth, on unclassified road between A466 and B4293

COOKING 3
COST £24–£44

The Crown is an ancient alehouse, now run as a restaurant-with-rooms by Roger and Sandra Bates. She cooks, he serves, in an 'easy and relaxed' ambience. Menu descriptions appear first in French (whether the style of the dish is French or not), and the food turns out to be hearteningly good. A croustade of wild mushrooms displays the 'separate and distinct tastes' of the respective varieties encased within, and comes with an appealingly rich sauce of tarragon, parsley and cream. Another classic dish partners local black pudding with smoked bacon and caramelised apple in a calvados sauce that neatly counterpoints the sweetness of the sliced fruit. A veal dish was pronounced 'thoroughly enjoyable' in whatever language: lightly cooked slices of English veal layered with 'tissue-thin pasta' given strength with Parmesan and tarragon. Best end of Welsh lamb is roasted in a herb crust and served with a 'particularly imaginative' mousse of spinach and laverbread. Vegetables come in a protean array, supplemented by a little green salad with pine-nuts and a vinaigrette. Apple charlotte works well, its crisp outer casing containing soft apple slices rather than a purée, with cinnamon ice-cream alongside. A chocolate trio of great panache consists of a strongly flavoured sponge pudding, 'deliciously soft' ice-cream in a brandy-snap, and a white chocolate confection on a base of crumbled dark chocolate. Good coffee and petits fours are taken in a lounge buzzing with post-prandial happiness.

A prodigious list of wines is offered. Quality has been painstakingly sought in every region, not just of France but of Germany, Spain and Italy and outside Europe too. Mark-ups are not particularly fiendish, with prices steadfastly in proportion to the overall sense of value. Halves are dotted throughout, and there is a fine selection of ports. House wines are £8.50. CELLARMAN'S CHOICE: Lenton Brae Cabernet Sauvignon 1991, Margaret River, W. Australia, £13.95; Margaux Private Reserve 1989, Schröder et Schÿler, £16.95.

CHEF: Sandra Bates PROPRIETORS: Roger and Sandra Bates OPEN: Tue to Sun L 12 to 1.45, Mon to Sat D 7 to 9.30 (Sun D residents only) CLOSED: 2 weeks Jan, 2 weeks July MEALS: Set L £15.95, Set D £25.95; bar lunch available SERVICE: not inc, card slips closed CARDS: Access, Amex, Delta, Diners, Switch, Visa DETAILS: 36 seats. 5 tables outside. Private parties: 34 main room, 8 and 12 private rooms. Car park. Vegetarian meals. Children's helpings. Smart dress preferred. No cigars/pipes in dining-room. No music ACCOMMODATION: 12 rooms, all with bath/shower. TV. Phone. B&B £35 to £80. Children welcome. Pets welcome by arrangement. Garden (*The Which? Hotel Guide*)

🍾 denotes an outstanding wine cellar; 🍷 denotes a good wine list, worth travelling for.

Isle of Man

BALLASALLA Isle of Man map 8

Rosa's Place

Main Road, Ballasalla IM9 2DA COOKING 1*
TEL: (01624) 822940 FAX: (01624) 822702 COST £21–£37

For many years this was La Rosette, but the new name heralds a radical rethink and a more informal approach to running this popular neighbourhood restaurant. Robert and Rosa Phillips have altered the layout of their delightfully intimate dining-room, re-arranged the seating and put up wall-sized mirrors to create the illusion of space. They have also re-structured their menus. Excellent-value lunches are priced according to the number of courses eaten, dinner is fixed-priced for three courses. Local fish is grilled or baked with garlic, meat and poultry are given rich sauces, and vegetarians are looked after. A mixed platter of seafood with pâté, avocado and Parma ham makes an attractive starter, while fillet steak might appear with mango and sweet-and-sour sauce, or 'butterflied' and filled with scallops, or else served with a sauce of herbs, red wine and port. Desserts are attractive concoctions such as lemon terrine draped with lime sauce, or orange and Grand Marnier pudding. The Phillipses still have a full licence and sell a range of 'table wines' for £9.50 (customers can also bring their own bottle).

CHEFS/PROPRIETORS: Robert and Rosa Phillips OPEN: Mon to Sat 12 to 3, 7.30 to 10 MEALS: Set L £9 (2 courses) to £12.50, Set D £22. Minimum £6. Licensed, but bring your own: no corkage SERVICE: not inc CARDS: Access DETAILS: 50 seats. Private parties: 20 main room, 10 to 20 private rooms. Vegetarian meals. Children's helpings. No cigars/pipes in dining-room. No music

DOUGLAS Isle of Man map 8

▲ *Boncompte's*

Admiral House, Loch Promenade, Douglas IM1 2LX COOKING 2
TEL: (01624) 629551 FAX: (01624) 675021 COST £18–£45

The smartly appointed dining-room with well-spaced tables has an impressive view over the bay. Meals begin in the elegant lounge with a drink, home-produced crisps, and a copy of the hand-written menu. Much of the cooking is as timeless as steak and kidney pie or mixed grill, and some of it is as old-fashioned as deep-fried Brie, and some as up to date as beef carpaccio with Parma ham. Fish is a strong suit, from freshly caught local Dover sole grilled on the bone, to queenies with bacon and garlic, while smoking is applied to salmon (served with asparagus or avocado) and to boar, which comes with Cumberland sauce. A 'one-person joint' of roast suckling pig sounds a comparative rarity. Local produce includes Manx lamb, perhaps boned and stuffed with leeks and mushrooms, and the cooking is generally well handled. Puddings (usually from the trolley) might include crème brûlée or sherry trifle. Smugglers, in the basement, is the place for chargrills. The list of around 70 wines is rather short on detail, but much of it is under £20, beginning with house French at £9.50.

CHEF: Michael Ashe PROPRIETORS: Jaime and Jill Boncompte-Amoros OPEN: Mon to Fri L 12.30 to 2, Mon to Sat D 7.30 to 10 CLOSED: 25 and 26 Dec, Easter Mon MEALS: alc (main courses £11.50 to £16.50). Set L £11.50, Set D £16.95 SERVICE: not inc, card slips closed CARDS: Access, Amex, Diners, Switch, Visa DETAILS: 80 seats. Private parties: 85 main room, 28 private room. Vegetarian meals. Children's helpings. Smart dress preferred. No cigars/pipes in dining-room. Wheelchair access (also WC). Music. Air-conditioned ACCOMMODATION: 12 rooms, all with bath/shower. TV. Phone. B&B £50 to £110. Rooms for disabled. Children welcome. Baby facilities

L'Expérience NEW ENTRY

Summerhill, Douglas IM2 4PL
TEL: (01624) 623103 FAX: (01624) 626214
at the northern end of promenade, at the bottom of Summerhill

COOKING 1
COST £11–£35

The name on the menu is printed in blue, white and red – in case anyone doubted the Frenchness of this particular experience. Tony and Jill Quirk's restaurant stands at the end of the promenade overlooking the broad sweep of Douglas Bay. The tricolour flies high above the entrance, waitresses in Breton jerseys do their stuff in a dark dining-room plastered wall to ceiling with posters, and an accordionist plays on Saturday night. It is 'probably as French as one would hope to get without crossing the Channel', said one local reporter.

Dinner involves choosing one of three fixed-price menus, and the style is dependably provincial. Mussels, frogs' legs, snails, onion soup – all the classics are here – but the kitchen also flirts with roast duck breast stuffed with apricots, and salmon baked in filo pastry with basil and fromage frais. Seafood is cooked to telling effect, local queenies in Pernod, and scallops in a sauce of mustard, brandy, cheese and cream. An extensive vegetarian menu is also offered. Desserts are, mostly, creamy little morsels of the chocolate mousse and crème caramel variety. The all-French wine list is short and reliable and features bottles of Jenlain country beer too. House wine is £8.50.

CHEF: Tony Quirk PROPRIETORS: Tony and Jill Quirk OPEN: Mon and Wed to Sat 12 to 2, 7 to 11 (also Tue and Sun D late July to early Sept) CLOSED: 3 weeks late Oct to mid-Nov MEALS: alc L (main courses £5 to £6). Set D £14.95 to £21.95 SERVICE: not inc CARDS: Access, Amex, Diners, Switch, Visa DETAILS: 65 seats. 2 tables outside. Private parties: 65 main room. Vegetarian meals. Children welcome. Wheelchair access. Music. Air-conditioned

Channel Islands

ST PETERS Guernsey map 1

Café du Moulin

Rue du Quanteraine, St Peters GY7 9DP COOKING 1
TEL: (01481) 65944 FAX: (01481) 66468 COST £19–£37

The setting is 'breathtaking', exclaimed a Londoner who loved everything about David and Gina Mann's converted granary in a remote spot on the island. Meals are served in a pleasant warm room with simple furnishings, and staff are agreeably attentive. The Manns continue to build up their network of local suppliers and are moving over to free-range and organic produce, having become increasingly disenchanted with what 'conventional' butchers have to offer. Even so, they look to the Shetlands for salmon, which they cure on the premises and serve with dill vinaigrette. David Mann says that his holiday in Thailand has only added to his existing liking for ethnic food, so you can expect dishes such as sesame chicken parcels with hoisin dip, and spiced chickpea croquettes, lining up alongside fresh tuna with roasted pepper salad, bourride, loin of lamb with pesto, and Hindle Wakes (a seventeenth-century Lancashire recipe for chicken breast stuffed with prunes and herbs). A separate vegetarian menu ensures that carnivores do not have it all their own way. Bringing up the rear are home-made ice-creams, lemon tart made with a 'light hand', and old-fashioned trifle. The short wine list brings together some classy names from individual vineyards, particularly in France and Australia. House wines start at £7.50.

CHEFS: David Mann and Guy Moignan PROPRIETORS: David and Gina Mann OPEN: Tue to Sun L 12 to 1.30, Tue to Sat D 7 to 9.30; open all week July, Aug, and Sept MEALS: alc (main courses £13). Set L £10.95 (2 courses) to £13.95, Set D £15.95 SERVICE: not inc CARDS: Access, Switch, Visa DETAILS: 46 seats. 11 tables outside. Private parties: 40 main room. Car park. Vegetarian meals. Children's helpings; no children under 7 D. Smart dress preferred. No smoking while others eat. Wheelchair access (also WC). Music

ST SAVIOUR Jersey map 1

▲ *Longueville Manor*

St Saviour JE2 7SA COOKING 2*
TEL: (01534) 25501 COST £24–£68

Longueville occupies its own wooded valley overlooking a lake where jet-black swans glide serenely. Eating goes on in two areas, one a pleasant modern

extension looking on to a courtyard garden, the other a more distinctive room with original panelling in intensely dark oak relieved by 'high-backed chairs in peachy-pink'. Chef Andrew Baird offers a variety of dinner menus: a set-price affair of four courses including coffee and petits fours (the second course a sorbet), an extensive *carte* and an eight-course *menu dégustation*. Vegetarians have their own fixed-price menu with plenty of choice. The style is as country-house as you would expect. Paupiette of sole filled with spinach and langoustines, pot-roasted squab with prune compote and glazed pears, and calves' sweetbreads and kidney with potato galette and roast shallots are all mere starters. Main courses such as guinea-fowl pot-roasted à la grand-mère in a rich reduction arrive beneath a silver dome. If puddings such as a white chocolate flower filled with lemon mousse don't tempt, then have the farmhouse cheeses. Service is 'not at all obsequious or too speedy but always attentive'. The wine list is a rather old-fashioned sort. The regions of Bordeaux are respectfully anatomised, while Burgundy relies heavily on négociants. Outside France, the selections are a touch perfunctory, and the mark-ups are stiff. House burgundy is £12.50.

CHEF: Andrew Baird PROPRIETORS: the Lewis and Dufty families OPEN: all week L 12.30 to 2, D 7.30 to 9.30 MEALS: alc D (main courses £18 to £19.50). Set L £18, Set D £28.50 and £50 SERVICE: net prices, card slips closed CARDS: Access, Amex, Delta, Diners, Switch, Visa DETAILS: 65 seats. 25 tables outside. Private parties: 65 main room, 16 and 20 private rooms. Car park. Vegetarian meals. Children's helpings. Smart dress preferred. No smoking in 1 dining-room. Wheelchair access. No music. Air-conditioned ACCOMMODATION: 32 rooms, all with bath/shower. TV. Phone. B&B £115 to £215. Deposit: £75. Rooms for disabled. Children welcome. Pets welcome in bedrooms only. Afternoon teas. Garden. Swimming-pool (*The Which? Hotel Guide*)

Northern Ireland

BALLYCLARE Co Antrim map 16

Ginger Tree

29 Ballyrobert Road, Ballyclare BB9 9RY — COOKING 1
TEL: (01232) 848176 — COST £13–£42

The décor is minimalist at this converted farmhouse that serves authentic Japanese food. To make things easy for first-timers, there are several set menus built around tempura, sukiyaki and yakinikufu (slices of sirloin cooked in saké, garlic, ginger and shoyu). A cut-price také menu is also available Monday to Friday. The *carte* includes everything from soups and sashimi to tonkatsu (deep-fried loin of pork in breadcrumbs) and tori teriyaki. Tea and saké are appropriate drinks, although there is also a mainly European wine list. House wine is £8.95.

CHEFS/PROPRIETORS: Shotaro Obana and Elizabeth English OPEN: Mon to Fri L 12 to 2.30, Mon to Sat D 7 to 9 (9.30 Sat) CLOSED: 24 to 26 Dec, 12 and 13 July MEALS: alc (main courses £7 to £11.50). Set L £6.80 to £10.25, Set D £12.95 to £26.50 SERVICE: not inc CARDS: Access, Amex, Delta, Diners, Visa DETAILS: 60 seats. Private parties: 80 main room, 25 private room. Car park. Vegetarian meals. Children's helpings. Smart dress preferred. Wheelchair access (also WC). Music. Air-conditioned

BELFAST Co Antrim map 16

La Belle Epoque

61–63 Dublin Road, Belfast BT2 7RS — COOKING 2
TEL: (01232) 323244 FAX: (01232) 240040 — COST £15–£35

The cooking is as French as the name at this well-established city restaurant, and the chef works to a classic repertoire that encompasses eveything from fillet of beef Café de Paris to suprême of chicken with tarragon cream sauce. Duck might be served with plum and ginger sauce or with raspberries, while salmon is grilled and served with béarnaise sauce. A choice of hot and cold starters is balanced by an equal assortment of desserts ranging from crêpes suzette to iced apricot and almond bombe. Service has been described as 'impeccable'. The well-spread wine list also comes in for praise: reporters particularly approve of the extensive choice of half-bottles. House wines start at £8.

CHEF: A. Rousse PROPRIETORS: G. Sanchez, A. Rousse, C. Fitzgerald and J. Delbart OPEN: Mon to Fri L 12 to 5.30, Mon to Sat D 6 to 11 MEALS: alc (main courses £4.50 to £11.50). Set L £5 to £10 (both 2 courses), Set D Mon to Thur £15 SERVICE: not inc CARDS: Access, Amex, Diners, Visa DETAILS: 83 seats. Private parties: 30 main room. Vegetarian meals. Children welcome. Wheelchair access (also WC). Music

Nick's Warehouse

35–39 Hill Street, Belfast BT1 2LB COOKING 1*
TEL: (01232) 439690 COST £13–£33

The warehouse in question was once the bonded store for Bushmills whiskey, and some of today's patrons once carried wicker-bound flagons down Hill Street. The Prices converted it in 1988 into an up-to-date wine bar and restaurant that now turns out some vivid, fashionable food drawing on North America, southern Europe and everybody's grandma.

Spinach and pea soup with crusty bread, black pudding with lentils in garlic cream, and lamb chops with a black-bean salsa demonstrate the range. The Thai chicken salad eaten by an inspector was 'a light, sharp starter' dressed in chilli and salt with tomato concasse – 'a wonderful combination' – while a fine piece of sirloin had a strong oyster mushroom and stout sauce made from a top-notch stock. Duck breast comes with sweet accompaniments: blackcurrants, perhaps, or honey and ginger. Marsala pot au crème, a kind of crème caramel with raisins soaked in Marsala, has been a shade too light on the bottle to be really thrilling, but chocolate squidgy log with an orange compote might satisfy, and there are Irish cheeses. Breads and olives are of exceptionally high quality, and staff are 'relaxed and laid back' in the best sense. The jolly wine list is full of exclamation marks and has some very drinkable stuff at fair prices. Six house wines start at £6.50.

CHEFS: Nick Price and Simon Toye PROPRIETORS: Nick and Kathy Price OPEN: Mon to Fri L 12 to 2.30 (3 wine bar), Tue to Sat D 6 to 9 CLOSED: 25 and 26 Dec, Easter Mon, 12 July MEALS: alc L (main courses wine bar £4 to £5, restaurant £7 to £12). Set D wine bar and restaurant £13.95 (2 courses) to £16.95. Minimum £7.50 L in restaurant SERVICE: not inc, card slips closed; 10% for parties of 6 or more CARDS: Access, Amex, Diners, Visa DETAILS: wine bar 45 seats, restaurant 45 seats. Private parties: 50 main room. Vegetarian meals. Children's helpings in restaurant. Wheelchair access (1 step; also WC). Music. Air-conditioned

Roscoff 🍷

7 Lesley House, Shaftesbury Square, Belfast BT2 7DB COOKING 4
TEL: (01232) 331532 FAX: (01232) 312093 COST £23–£47

Roscoff – its glass frontage looking into a cool arena of steel and light wood – occupies pride of place in Belfast's restaurant heartland. One used to softer lines thought it looked 'possibly a little too like a dentist's surgery', but there is considerably greater jollity to be had here. Paul Rankin exudes an unequivocal passion for food, the kind of commitment that wants to celebrate flavours by letting them speak for themselves as far as possible, gradually over the years paring away many of the frills that a classical training induces. Here the Mediterranean idiom has been embraced, not because it is this decade's 'thing', but because it is about minimal intervention. This can produce some exciting results. Slice some salmon very fine à la carpaccio, add a salad of leaves and flowers, sharpen it all up with leaf coriander and pickled ginger, and the verdict elicits rhapsodies: 'The combination was so well balanced and matched so perfectly that one flavour never exceeded another – all mingled brilliantly.' The same can happen when chanterelles, mousserons, shiitakes and garlic shoots are added to tagliatelle, or when peas, smoked salmon and a poached egg are stuffed into an artichoke heart.

A simple twist can lift a dish considerably, as when croûtons of polenta are strewn over a salad of duck confit. Monkfish is roasted, accompanied by aubergine (brittle from the oven), chopped sun-dried tomatoes and a puddle of oil pungent with garlic and chilli. More chilli goes into a sauce for top-quality beef fillet with mushrooms and tiny rosemary-flavoured potatoes. Crème brûlée has a texture like pannacotta, while white chocolate cheesecake with macerated cherries, and peach and raspberry crêpes make the most of seasonal fruits. Real espresso ensures meals end with a bang. The largely 'charming' service would do well to let people pour their own wine if that's what suits them. A broadly based spread of house wines is available by the glass (from £2) or bottle (from £10.50).

CHEFS/PROPRIETORS: Paul and Jeanne Rankin OPEN: Mon to Fri L 12.30 to 2.15, Mon to Sat D 6.30 to 10.15 CLOSED: 25 and 26 Dec, Easter Mon MEALS: Set L £15.50, Set D £23.50 SERVICE: not inc; 10% on parties of 6 or more CARDS: Access, Amex, Diners, Visa DETAILS: 75 seats. Private parties: 75 main room. Vegetarian meals. Children's helpings. Smart dress preferred. Wheelchair access (also WC). Music. Air-conditioned

Strand £

12 Stranmillis Road, Belfast BT9 5AA — COOKING 1
TEL: (01232) 682266 FAX: (01232) 663189 — COST £15–£30

A favourite with business people, students and lecturers from nearby Queen's University, Anne Turkington's bistro-cum-wine-bar thrives on good value and all-day opening. Nip in for a quick lunch or linger through the evening. The menu promises generous platefuls of baked cod with herb crust and provençale sauce, stir-fried beef with oyster mushrooms and noodles, vegetable curry with 'nutty rice' and all the trimmings, and stuffed duck breast with madeira, bacon and olives. You might start with smoked chicken salad or sauté tiger prawns with lemon and chilli and finish off with 'delicious' banoffi pie. Service is bistro friendly. House wine is £5.95.

CHEF: Michael McAuley PROPRIETOR: Anne Turkington OPEN: all week 12 to 11 CLOSED: 25 and 26 Dec MEALS: alc (main courses £4 to £9) SERVICE: not inc CARDS: Access, Amex, Delta, Diners, Switch, Visa DETAILS: 85 seats. Private parties: 25 main room, 25 private room. Vegetarian meals. Children's helpings. Smart dress preferred. Music. Air-conditioned

Not inc *in the details at the end of an entry indicates that no service charge is made and any tipping is at the discretion of the customer.*

BELLANALECK Co Fermanagh map 16

Sheelin £

Main Street, Bellanaleck, nr Enniskillen BT92 2BA
TEL: (0365) 348232 NEW CHEF
on A509, 4m S of Enniskillen COST £12–£30

As we went to press, new members of the Cathcart family took over the running of this flower-garlanded thatched house. Malcolm Cathcart's brother-in-law is now at the stove, and he has introduced a few innovative dishes to augment the restaurant's well-tried traditional repertoire. Evening visitors now have a chance to sample couscous and mafe (beef in peanut sauce with vegetables) alongside garlic mushrooms, pan-fried lamb chops, and poached salmon steaks stuffed with parsley and garlic. Lunches and high teas are as homespun as ever. House wine is £6.50.

CHEF: Ababacar Diouf PROPRIETORS: Mr and Mrs Malcolm Cathcart OPEN: all week 12 to 2.30, 7 to 9.30 MEALS: alc (main courses L £3.50 to £4.50, D £7.50 to £11) SERVICE: not inc CARDS: Access, Visa DETAILS: 40 seats. Private parties: 20 main room, 20, 20 private room. Car park. Vegetarian meals. Children's helpings. Wheelchair access (also WC). Music

LONDONDERRY Co Londonderry map 16

▲ *Beech Hill Country House*

32 Ardmore Road, Londonderry BT47 1QL
TEL: (01504) 49279 FAX: (01504) 45366
off A6 Londonderry to Belfast road at Faughan Bridge, COOKING 2
opposite Ardmore Chapel COST £19–£43

In more than 30 acres of grounds a couple of miles from the town centre, this early-eighteenth-century house is a boon to the area. Dinner is served in the elegant Ardmore restaurant overlooking the gardens, with their ponds and waterfalls. There is plenty of flair and elaboration here, as well as a fondness for fruity accompaniments: witness ballottine of chicken en crépinette filled with spiced black pudding and served with kumquat marmalade, and fillet of venison with sloe-gin and bramble sauce garnished with raspberry chutney. Vegetarians have their own menu featuring dishes such as filo of wild mushrooms with sweet potato and garlic mash. Everything, from bread and pasta to petits fours, is made on the premises. Fifty wines provide plenty of creditable drinking from the Old and New Worlds. House wine is £8.95.

CHEF: Noel McMeel PROPRIETOR: Seamus Donnelly OPEN: all week 12.30 to 2.30, 7 to 9.30 CLOSED: 24 and 25 Dec MEALS: alc (main courses £10 to £14.50). Set L £12.95, Set D £18.95 SERVICE: not inc CARDS: Access, Amex, Visa DETAILS: 40 seats. Private parties: 15 to 80 private rooms. Car park. Vegetarian meals. Children's helpings. Smart dress preferred. No smoking in dining-room. Music ACCOMMODATION: 17 rooms, all with bath/shower. TV. Phone. B&B £52.50 to £80. Rooms for disabled. Children welcome. Baby facilities. Afternoon teas. Garden

PORTRUSH Co Antrim map 16

Ramore

The Harbour, Portrush BT56 8BN COOKING 2
TEL: (01265) 824313 COST £21–£38

Its location by the harbour, and crazed-stone cladding on the ground floor gave Ramore the air of a yacht club for one reporter. The atmosphere within is certainly jaunty, in both the ground-floor wine bar and upstairs restaurant: furniture is high-tech, staff are smartly attired, and ingredients and culinary influences from all over are mixed and matched with happy disregard for tradition. Langoustine lasagne with mushrooms and white truffle oil has been a thought-provoking starter, and main courses follow in grand style: Irish salmon with a champagne and chive sauce, filet mignon sauced with lobster, and duck confit in an amalgam of bitter chocolate and raspberry vinegar. A trio of sorbets – grapefruit, pear and chocolate – comes in a pastry case with a compote of rhubarb. The wine list takes its business seriously, sourcing good-value bottles from around the world and keeping a tight rein on prices. House wines from Australia's Nottage Hill are £7.50.

CHEF: George McAlpin PROPRIETORS: George and Jane McAlpin OPEN: Tue to Sat D only 6.30 to 10.30 MEALS: alc (main courses £8 to £11) SERVICE: not inc CARDS: Access, Visa DETAILS: 85 seats. Private parties: 85 main room. Car park. Vegetarian meals. Children welcome. No smoking in 1 dining-room. Music. Air-conditioned

Republic of Ireland

We have not given marks for cooking for the Republic of Ireland entries because of a shortage of reports; please do give us feedback should you visit. To telephone the Republic from mainland Britain, dial 00 353 followed by the number listed, but dropping the initial 0. Prices are quoted in Irish punts.

ADARE Co Limerick map 16

Adare Manor

Adare
TEL: (061) 396566 FAX: (061) 396124 COST £37–£75

The Manor is a majestic edifice in high-Gothic style, with a two-tiered dining-room looking over formal gardens. Gerard Costelloe cooks with a sense of brio and with an eye to modern trends. Dinner may take in seafood feuilleté with champagne and chervil cream, potato and oyster soup, herb-crusted lamb cutlets with garlic and shallot confit, and baked coffee soufflé on a sauce of Jameson's whiskey. The expansive wine list includes plenty of halves. House wines are £18.

CHEF: Gerard Costelloe PROPRIETORS: Tom and Judy Kane OPEN: all week 12.30 to 2.30, 7 to 10 MEALS: alc (main courses £12 to £21). Set D £32 SERVICE: 15%, card slips closed CARDS: Access, Amex, Diners, Visa DETAILS: 70 seats. Private parties: 30 and 190 private rooms. Car park. Vegetarian meals. Children's helpings. Jacket and tie. Wheelchair access (also WC). Music ACCOMMODATION: 64 rooms, all with bath/shower. TV. Phone. B&B £195 to £220. Rooms for disabled. Children welcome. Pets welcome. Afternoon teas. Garden. Swimming-pool. Fishing

AHAKISTA Co Cork map 16

Shiro

Ahakista
TEL: (027) 67030 FAX: (027) 67206
on coast road from Durrus toward Sheep's Head COST £46–£55

The prospect of eating sashimi in a former priest's dwelling should be enough to send curious gastronomes to the southern tip of County Cork. Kei Pilz's dinner menu couldn't be simpler: start with zen-zai appetisers, move on to sunomono soup, then choose between tempura, teriyaki, Japanese curry or haru-maki (pastry pockets of chopped pork and vegetables with a cheese centre). If you need refreshing, there is home-made ice-cream to finish. An adapted menu is offered to vegetarians. Tea and saké suit the food, and Shiro has a modest wine list with prices starting at £12. You can also take your own wine (corkage £3).

CHEF: Kei Pilz PROPRIETORS: Kei and Werner Pilz OPEN: all week D only 7 to 9 MEALS: Set D £33 SERVICE: 10% (optional), card slips closed CARDS: Access, Amex, Diners, Visa; 5% surcharge on credit card transactions DETAILS: 16 seats. Private parties: 5 main room. Car park. Vegetarian meals. No children under 12. Smart dress preferred. No smoking in 1 dining-room. Wheelchair access. No music. Air-conditioned

BALLINA Co Mayo map 16

▲ *Mount Falcon Castle*

Ballina
TEL: (096) 70811 FAX: (096) 71517
on N57 between Foxford and Ballina COST £27–£33

Baked Moy salmon with mustard sauce is the house speciality at this Victorian-Gothic mansion set in 100 acres. A typical five-course dinner menu might run as follows: salmon pâté, vegetable soup, lamb cutlets with white wine and tarragon sauce, then Boodles orange fool and Irish cheeses, rounded off with coffee or tea. Much of the produce, from vegetables to free-range eggs, comes from the hotel's farm and garden. The wine list features a few vintage clarets but concentrates on everyday drinking. House wine is £9.50.

CHEF: Denise Moyles PROPRIETOR: Constance Aldridge OPEN: all week D only 8 (one sitting) CLOSED: Christmas, Feb and Mar MEALS: Set D £20 SERVICE: not inc, card slips closed CARDS: Access, Amex, Diners, Visa DETAILS: 28 seats. Private parties: 28 main room, 6 private room. Car park. Children's helpings. Smart dress preferred. Wheelchair access (2 steps; also WC). No music ACCOMMODATION: 10 rooms, all with bath/shower. Phone. B&B £45 to £98. Deposit: 10%. Children welcome. Baby facilities. Pets welcome. Garden. Fishing

BALLYDEHOB Co Cork map 16

Annie's

Main Street, Ballydehob
TEL: (028) 37292 COST £26–£33

Local fish and well-hung meat are the mainstays at Annie's, and the kitchen delivers anything from brill and sole stuffed with crab to poached monkfish, from sweet-and-sour pork to chicken Kiev. Start with the likes of crab and avocado, and finish with raspberry mousse. In summer Annie's is also open during the day as a coffee-shop. The wine list is sound, with house wines starting at £11.

CHEFS/PROPRIETORS: Dano and Anne Barry OPEN: Tue to Sat D only 6.30 to 9.30 (times may vary in winter) MEALS: alc (main courses £12 to £14). Set D £22 SERVICE: not inc CARDS: Access, Visa DETAILS: 24 seats. Private parties: 24 main room. Children's helpings. No cigars/pipes in dining-room. Wheelchair access. Music

BALLYLICKEY Co Cork map 16

▲ *Ballylickey Manor*

NEW ENTRY

Ballylickey, Bantry Bay
TEL: (027) 50071 FAX: (027) 50124 COST £35–£63

Three-hundred-year-old Ballylickey Manor is tucked among the rugged inlets of Bantry Bay, with wonderful sea views and a backdrop of mountains. There is a small dining-room in the house itself, but most meals are eaten in the colourful summery atmosphere of the pool-side restaurant. Choose from dishes such as sorrel soup, paupiettes of sole with langoustines, veal with port sauce, and apple tart. The house speciality (for two people at £20.50 per person) is home-made duck foie gras with a bottle of Beaumes-de-Venise to share. The French wine list is not cheap, but does seems to suit the food and setting. House wine is £16.

CHEF: Gilles Eynaud PROPRIETORS: Mr and Mrs Graves OPEN: all week 12.30 to 2.15, 7 to 9.30 CLOSED: mid-Nov to mid-Mar MEALS: alc (main courses £10 to £18). Set D £25 to £29 SERVICE: 10%, card slips closed CARDS: Access, Amex, Visa DETAILS: 40 seats. 4 tables outside. Private parties: 10 main room. Car park. Children's helpings. Jacket and tie. No smoking in dining-room. No music ACCOMMODATION: 11 rooms, all with bath/shower. TV. Phone. B&B £90 (double room) to £165. Children welcome. Garden. Swimming-pool. Fishing

BALLYVAUGHAN Co Clare map 16

▲ *Gregans Castle*

Ballyvaughan
TEL: (065) 77005 FAX: (065) 77111
on N67, 3½m S of Ballyvaughan COST £19–£68

The hotel peers loftily over Galway Bay, whence comes much of the seafood that goes into dishes such as soup with a rouille of roast peppers, garlic and saffron, or a pot of mussels with tomato concassé. Goats' cheese from Inagh comes on garlic bread with black olives and tomatoes. Flavours build up in meat dishes, such as pork noisette with gingered apples and a honey cream sauce. An enterprising wine list casts its net wide. House French and Italian are £11.95.

CHEF: Paul Cosgrove PROPRIETORS: the Haden family OPEN: all week 12 to 3, 7 to 8.30 CLOSED: end Oct to late Mar MEALS: alc (main courses £4.50 to £28). Set D £27 SERVICE: 15%, card slips closed CARDS: Access, Visa DETAILS: 50 seats. Private parties: 80 main room. Car park. Vegetarian meals. Children's helpings. No smoking in 1 dining-room. Wheelchair access (also WC). No music ACCOMMODATION: 22 rooms, all with bath/shower. Phone. B&B £76 to £200. Rooms for disabled. Children welcome. Baby facilities. Afternoon teas. Garden

BRAY Co Wicklow map 16

Tree of Idleness

Sea-front, Bray
TEL: (01) 2863498 COST £24–£50

Susan Courtellas's restaurant near Dun Laoghaire continues to impress for the vibrancy of its cooking. The ethnic provenance is Greek-Cypriot, against a more general Mediterranean background, utilising good Irish produce. Tomatoes are baked with a stuffing of bacon, mushrooms and herbs, lambs' liver is fried with sage and orange, and crabmeat is baked with cheese and herbs for starters. Chicken Kyrenia brings together a breast of the bird with veal fillet and Dublin Bay prawns in a sauce of herbs and cream. Desserts come on a trolley. The wine list is deeply classical, offering many mature French vintages. House wines start at £10.

CHEF: Ismail Basaran PROPRIETOR: Susan Courtellas OPEN: Tue to Sun D only 7.30 to 11 (10 Sun) CLOSED: 25 Dec, first 2 weeks Sept MEALS: alc (main courses £10 to £16.50). Set D Sun to Fri £15.50 to £19 SERVICE: 10%, card slips closed CARDS: Access, Amex, Diners, Visa DETAILS: 50 seats. Private parties: 20 main room. Vegetarian meals. No children under 12. Smart dress preferred. Wheelchair access. Music

CASHEL Co Tipperary map 16

Chez Hans

Rockside, Cashel
TEL: (062) 61177 COST £30–£47

Hans's place is a former Methodist church below the Rock of Cashel. Among rich sauces you will also now find some lighter touches, inspired by the Mediterranean and California. The kitchen makes profitable use of fish, including Rossmore oysters, mussels and scallops, as well as lobsters from Kinsale. Poultry is free-range: turkey breast is served with lemon balm sauce, duck is dressed up with honey and thyme, while chicken is accompanied by a sabayon of leeks and Cashel Blue cheese. Around 70 wines provide plenty of fair drinking from reliable sources. House wines (including a couple of Rieslings from the Matthiä family's own vineyard) start at £10.50.

CHEF/PROPRIETOR: Hans-Peter Matthiä OPEN: Tue to Sat D only 6.30 to 10 CLOSED: first 3 weeks Jan MEALS: alc (main courses £14 to £19.50) SERVICE: not inc, card slips closed CARDS: Access, Visa DETAILS: 60 seats. Private parties: 80 main room. Car park. Children's helpings. Smart dress preferred. No cigars/pipes in dining-room. Wheelchair access (also WC). Music. Air-conditioned

CASTLEBALDWIN Co Sligo map 16

▲ *Cromleach Lodge* $✱

Ballindoon, Castlebaldwin
TEL: (071) 65155 FAX: (071) 65455 COST £40–£48

The Lodge, a country-house hotel in the modern idiom, stands on a hillside overlooking Lough Arrow. It makes an impressive setting for Moira Tighe's cooking, which is based around a daily-changing dinner menu running to six courses. Fish always shows up well, and organic produce is used whenever possible. House Bordeaux is £13.

CHEF: Moira Tighe PROPRIETORS: Christy and Moira Tighe OPEN: all week D only 6.30 to 9 (8 Sun) CLOSED: Nov to Jan MEALS: Set D £30 SERVICE: not inc, card slips closed CARDS: Access, Amex, Diners, Visa DETAILS: 50 seats. Private parties: 25 main room, 4 to 25 private rooms. Car park. No children under 10 after 7pm. Smart dress preferred. No smoking in dining-room. Wheelchair access (2 steps). Music ACCOMMODATION: 10 rooms, all with bath/shower. TV. Phone. B&B £53 to £130. Rooms for disabled. Children welcome. Garden. Fishing

---

CLIFDEN Co Galway map 16

O'Grady's

Market Street, Clifden
TEL: (095) 21450 FAX: (095) 21994 COST £17–£41

The setting is a village in the western reaches of Connemara, but this is no outpost of culinary insularity. O'Grady's has access to some of the best seafood in the area and the kitchen is capable of transforming it into dishes such as baked stuffed mussels with pesto, monkfish with blackened scallops on a coriander duxelles, and fillets of brill with fennel and tomato. This global approach spills over into the remainder of the repertoire: warm salad of smoked chicken with soy and hazelnut vinaigrette, or home-made black pudding with a compote of sweet apple and oysters, for example. The wine list spreads its net far and wide; house wines are £10.50.

CHEF: P.J. Heffernan PROPRIETOR: Michael O'Grady OPEN: all week 12.30 to 2.30, 6.30 to 9.45 CLOSED: Nov to 10 Mar, Sun mid-Mar to 1 Jun MEALS: alc (main courses £11 to £15). Set L £9.95. Minimum £10.95. Licensed, but bring your own: corkage £4 SERVICE: not inc, card slips closed CARDS: Access, Amex, Visa DETAILS: 65 seats. Private parties: 21 main room, 13 private room. Vegetarian meals. No children under 6. Smart dress preferred. Music ACCOMMODATION: 8 rooms, all with bath/shower. TV. Phone. Air-conditioned. B&B £25 to £46. Deposit: 20%. Rooms for disabled. No children under 7. Garden. Swimming pool. Fishing

---

CLONAKILTY Co Cork map 16

Dunworley Cottage

Butlerstown, Clonakilty
TEL: (023) 40314
signposted from Timoleague, S of Bandon COST £22–£46

Dunworley takes healthy eating seriously enough to flag items on its menus according to their gluten or cholesterol levels. Organic produce and fresh fish are the order of the day. Marinated herrings, smoked mussels in vinaigrette, and cured wild salmon with crème fraîche appear among the starters. Swedish meatballs were once only on the children's menu, but a grown-up-sized portion is now offered 'by popular demand'. Other main courses of chicken with white wine, mushrooms and cream, or fillet steak with green peppercorn sauce may be followed by the house ice-cream gâteau, mint mousse or Apfelstrudel. The wine list provides a solid international choice, with house French £10.25.

CHEF: Åsa Helmersson PROPRIETOR: Katherine Norén OPEN: Wed to Sun 1 to 3, 6.30 to 9 (L in summer only) CLOSED: Nov, Jan to mid-Mar MEALS: alc (main courses £6 to £14). Set D £20 to £22 SERVICE: 10% CARDS: Access, Amex, Diners, Visa DETAILS: 60 seats. Private parties: 30 main room, 30 private room. Car park. Vegetarian meals. Children's helpings. No children after 7.30. No smoking in 1 dining-room. Wheelchair access. Music

CORK Co Cork map 16

Arbutus Lodge

Montenotte, Cork
TEL: (021) 501237 FAX: (021) 502893 COST £22–£52

A rare arbutus tree grows in the garden of this elegant eighteenth-century town house that has been home to the Ryan family since 1961. Some feel that the interior has echoes of faded grandeur, with fine Irish paintings and antiques in the lounge, and pseudo-classical columns, chandeliers and flower arrangements gracing the formal dining-room: 'the suburban equivalent of a country house,' in fact. The cooking is an amalgam of French and Irish, and the kitchen knows how to treat good raw materials in a straightforward, unfussy way. Soups, such as cream of mushroom, are absolutely spot-on and reporters speak with one voice about the virtues of mussels in a creamy sauce laced with garlic, Pernod and almonds. Also reaping praise have been a delicate salad of crab and mango, a sauté of veal kidneys in a featherlight puff pastry, grilled black sole, and 'succulent' chicken covered with wild mushrooms (that tasted as if they had come straight from the forest) on a purée of swede with madeira sauce. Rack of lamb is 'fairly classically done'. An 'extremely classy' slate of desserts promises everything from home-made ice-creams and astringent lemon balm sorbet to pear and almond tart; the Irish cheeseboard is also well worth exploring. The much-lauded wine list is a hefty, leather-bound tome with a solid French base and a magnificent run of vintages ('with prices to match'). Even the house wines, starting at £10.15, are first-class.

CHEFS: David McCann and Declan Ryan PROPRIETORS: the Ryan family OPEN: Mon to Sat 1 to 2, 7 to 9.30 CLOSED: 24 to 28 Dec MEALS: alc (main courses £12.50 to £15.50). Set L £14.50, Set D £22.50 SERVICE: not inc CARDS: Access, Amex, Diners, Visa DETAILS: 60 seats. Private parties: 8 main room, 24 to 150 private rooms. Car park. Vegetarian meals. Children's helpings. No cigars/pipes in dining-room. No music. Air-conditioned ACCOMMODATION: 20 rooms, all with bath/shower. TV. Phone. B&B £35 to £150. Deposit: £20. Children welcome. Baby facilities. Garden

Clifford's

18 Dyke Parade, Cork
TEL: (021) 275333 COST £21–£47

'Tastefully sophisticated' is how one reporter describes the converted Georgian building with its Irish linen napery, top-class tableware and eye-catching paintings. Service is mainly Gallic formal, without a hint of 'crustiness'. Michael Clifford has unquestionably made his mark in the Mardyke district of Cork, and the considered view is that he is producing some of the most accomplished food in the city. In his hands, 'oaty' Clonakilty black pudding is fashioned into a revelatory gâteau with layers of thin glazed potatoes and a purée of apple, mushrooms and garlic. His ragoût of wood pigeon comes with a rich nettle sauce and a sprinkling of pearl barley. The loyalty to Irish produce extends to locally smoked fish, terrine of chicken and leeks with Milleens cheese, and gratiné of Castletownbere prawns with scallops. Energy and enthusiasm extend right to the end of the fixed-price menu: warm plums poached in red wine with a blob of vanilla ice-cream is a great favourite, while farmhouse cheeses from near and far are accompanied by home-baked biscuits. The backbone of the wine list is a contingent of classic, middle-of-the-road French wines, and a dozen house wines start at £12. Michael has now opened a less formal and less expensive bistro next door.

CHEF/PROPRIETOR: Michael Clifford OPEN: Tue to Fri L 12.30 to 2.30, Tue to Sat D 7.30 to 10.30 CLOSED: 1 week Christmas, last 2 weeks Aug MEALS: Set L £13.50, Set D £29.50 SERVICE: not inc CARDS: Access, Amex, Delta, Diners, Visa DETAILS: 45 seats. Private parties: 30 private room. Children's helpings. Smart dress preferred. No smoking in 1 dining-room. No music. Air-conditioned

Crawford Gallery Café £

Emmett Place, Cork
TEL: (021) 274415 COST £18–£26

Owned and run by the team from Ballymaloe House (see entry, Shanagarry), this café is festooned with pictures from the gallery. Fish comes in each day from Ballycotton Pier, and the kitchen turns out everything from bread, scones and cakes to ice-creams. Breakfast is served, and you can also come in for afternoon tea. At lunch-time the menu takes on a Mediterranean flavour: a warm salad of crispy bacon and potatoes with sun-dried tomatoes and Parmesan, Italian beef stew served with champ, and glazed loin of bacon with peperonata, whiskey sauce and bananas. Open sandwiches are also on offer. House Duboeuf is £10.

CHEFS: Paddy Cullinane and Rory O'Connell PROPRIETOR: Shanagarry Café Ltd OPEN: Mon to Sat daytime only 9 (10 Sat) to 5 CLOSED: 25 Dec to 4 Jan, bank hols MEALS: alc (main courses £7) SERVICE: not inc CARDS: Access, Visa DETAILS: 70 seats. Private parties: 100 main room, 250 private room. Vegetarian meals. Children's helpings. No cigars/pipes in dining-room. Wheelchair access (also WC). Music. Air-conditioned

Ivory Tower NEW ENTRY

Exchange Buildings, 35 Princes Street, Cork
TEL: (021) 274665 FAX: (021) 277750 COST £16–£49

Exchange Buildings are near the old English Market. A couple hurtling back to the airport stumbled across the Ivory Tower and considered they had made a great discovery. Fine prawn bisque and a warm salmon salad left them well satisfied, but fancies may be tickled by the oddball theme nights, such as the Taurean Gourmet evening or the Menu in White. That latter consisted of vichyssoise, sea bream cooked in duck fat with anise sauce, rabbit with a peach and vanilla glaze, and white chocolate parfait. Otherwise, the range extends from pissaladière to Moroccan smoked chicken stir-fry. A good, broadly based wine list is realistically priced, with house wines £11.

CHEF/PROPRIETOR: Seamus O'Connell OPEN: Tue to Sun L 12 to 2.45, Tue to Sat D 5 to 10.30 CLOSED: 3 days Christmas MEALS: alc (main courses £4 to £18). Set D Tue to Thur £15 to £30 SERVICE: 10% on credit card transactions (optional), not included otherwise, card slips closed CARDS: Access, Visa DETAILS: 40 seats. Private parties: 40 main room. Vegetarian meals. Children's helpings. No cigars in dining-room. Music. Air-conditioned

DINGLE Co Kerry map 16

▲ *Doyle's*

John Street, Dingle
TEL: (066) 51174 FAX: (066) 51816 COST £22–£43

The Doyles continue to excel, serving fresh seafood with a minimum of fuss to the seasonal population of this holiday town. Local fishermen and other suppliers maintain a regular flow of top-notch raw materials for the kitchen. Twice-baked cheese soufflé is a recommended starter, or you might choose oysters or a warm salad of red pepper with tomato and basil. Fish naturally dominates the main courses (baked lemon sole with lobster sauce, and halibut in tomato sauce have both been good), and there is roast rack of lamb for meat-eaters. Desserts have included chocolate cheesecake in addition to home-made ice-creams. The wine list goes for whites in a big way, and the German section is notably impressive. House wine is £10.80.

CHEF: Stella Doyle PROPRIETORS: John and Stella Doyle OPEN: Mon to Sat D only 6 to 9.30 CLOSED: mid-Nov to mid-Mar MEALS: alc (main courses £11 to £16). Set D 6 to 7 £13.95 SERVICE: 10%, card slips closed CARDS: Access, Diners, Visa DETAILS: 50 seats. Private parties: 20 main room. Children's helpings. No smoking in 1 dining-room. Wheelchair access (1 step). No music ACCOMMODATION: 8 rooms, all with bath/shower. TV. Phone. B&B £40 to £60. Deposit: 1 night's stay. Rooms for disabled. Children welcome

▲ *Half Door*

John Street, Dingle
TEL: (066) 51600 FAX: (066) 51297 COST £17–£53

The O'Connors' homely seafood restaurant, with its eponymous stable door and rough-stone walls, is deservedly popular. Seafood platters of prawns, oysters, mussels, lobster and crab with marie-rose dip will satisfy the true devotee. Main courses include salmon fillet with leeks, sole rolled around smoked salmon mousse, and lobster thermidor. The meat-minded might opt for citrus-sauced duck or a steak. Finish with rich chocolate cake or a puff pastry creation with bananas and cream. The extensive wine list takes in some quite serious French bottles. House selections start at £11.

▲ *This symbol means accommodation is available.*

CHEF: Denis O'Connor PROPRIETORS: Denis and Teresa O'Connor OPEN: Wed to Mon 12.30 to 2.30, 6 to 10 CLOSED: 10 Jan to Easter MEALS: alc (main courses £4.50 to £24) SERVICE: not inc CARDS: Access, Amex, Diners, Visa DETAILS: 56 seats. Private parties: 20 main room. No children after 8pm. Smart dress preferred. No smoking in 1 dining-room. Wheelchair access. Music. Air-conditioned. ACCOMMODATION: 7 rooms, all with bath/shower. TV. B&B £25 to £40. Rooms for disabled. Children welcome. Baby facilities. Garden

DOUGLAS Co Cork map 16

Lovetts

Churchyard Lane, Well Road, Douglas
TEL: (021) 294909 and 293604 FAX: (021) 508568 COST £23–£47

After more than 17 years in business, Dermod and Margaret Lovett recently opened an evening brasserie offering chargrilled local fish and steaks for customers wanting a casual alternative to their formal restaurant. The Lovetts are keen supporters of what they call 'artisan food producers' and stock their larder with consignments of Clonakilty black pudding, locally reared meat and specialist farmhouse cheeses. You can expect anything from warm salad of crispy duck, and chicken with wild mushroom crostini to chargrilled squid with garlic and spicy salsa, grilled black sole on the bone, and pan-fried medallions of monkfish. Desserts are mostly based on home-made ice-cream. The wine list is a catholic selection with plenty of choice across the board. House wine is £11.

CHEF: Marie Harding PROPRIETORS: Dermod and Margaret Lovett OPEN: Mon to Fri L 12.30 to 2, Mon to Sat D 7 to 9.30 CLOSED: 1 week Christmas, bank hols MEALS: alc D (main courses £9 to £16). Set L £14.50, Set D £24 SERVICE: 12.5% (optional), card slips closed CARDS: Access, Amex, Diners, Visa DETAILS: 35 seats. Private parties: 40 main room, 25 private room. Car park. Vegetarian meals. Children's helpings. Smart dress preferred. Wheelchair access (also WC). Music

DUBLIN Co Dublin map 16

Commons

Newman House, 85–86 St Stephen's Green, Dublin 2
TEL: (01) 4752597 and 4780530 FAX: (01) 4780551 COST £29–£72

Sip an aperitif on the terrace before moving into this swish restaurant housed in one of Dublin's most elegant Georgian buildings. Chef Michael Bolster takes his cue from the setting and offers a luxurious menu of modern dishes based around local produce. Slices of duck foie gras are pan-fried and served with grilled Clonakilty black pudding and a pear and hazelnut dressing, roast fillet of Irish beef is laid on a polenta croûton and dressed with a jus of madeira and ceps, while grilled turbot is accompanied by a confit of garden peas and smoked bacon and a sauce of Beluga caviare. Desserts are in similar vein: parfait of figs and prunes with marinated fruits, or warm apple tart with honey ice-cream. Prices are by no means cheap, particularly if you decide to plunder the upper-crust wine list. House wine is £14.

CHEF: Michael Bolster PROPRIETOR: Michael Fitzgerald OPEN: Mon to Fri L 12.30 to 2.15, Mon to Sat D 7 to 10.15 CLOSED: 2 week Christmas, bank hols MEALS: alc (main courses £17.50 to £20). Set L £18 SERVICE: 15% CARDS: Access, Amex, Delta, Diners, Switch, Visa DETAILS: 60 seats. Private parties: 12 main room, 20 and 50 private rooms. Vegetarian meals. Children welcome. Smart dress preferred. Music. Air-conditioned

Le Coq Hardi

35 Pembroke Rd, Ballsbridge, Dublin 4
TEL: (01) 6689070 and 6684130 FAX: (01) 6689887 COST £39–£78

This end-of-terrace Georgian house might be mistaken for a gentlemen's club, with its antique furniture, wood panelling and brass. John Howard makes the best of plentiful Irish produce for a repertoire that veers between the luxurious (terrine of foie gras, pot-roast snipe with chicory, steamed Howth lobster) and the earthily traditional (black and white pudding with potato cake, braised lamb shank). The restaurant is also renowned for its 30-page wine list. If you haven't time to browse, consider the daily selection of around 20 wines. House wine is £16.

CHEFS: John Howard and James O'Sullivan PROPRIETORS: John and Catherine Howard OPEN: Mon to Fri L 12.30 to 2.30, Mon to Sat D 7 to 11 CLOSED: 2 weeks Christmas, 2 weeks Aug, bank hols MEALS: alc (main courses £16 to £21). Set L £18, Set D £30 SERVICE: 12½%, card slips closed CARDS: Access, Amex, Diners, Visa DETAILS: 70 seats. Private parties: 50 main room, 10 to 30 private rooms. Car park. Vegetarian meals. Children welcome. Smart dress preferred. No smoking in 1 dining-room. Music

Eastern Tandoori

34–35 South William Street, Dublin 2
TEL: (01) 6710428 and 6710506 FAX: (01) 6779232 COST £15–£43

'When you pass through the door you leave Ireland and enter the heart of India,' claims the owner of this tandoori. The oven is used for everything from quail to crab claws, and the menu treads a familiar path, taking in lamb pasanda, chicken jalfrezi, sag gosht and prawn bhuna. House wine is £11.50. There is a branch at Old Parish Hall, Kill Lane, Deansgrange, Blackrock; TEL: (01) 2892856.

CHEFS: Hendry Paul, Olli Ulla, Iqbal Ahmend and Shah Alam PROPRIETORS: Mr and Mrs Feroze Khan OPEN: Mon to Sat L 12 to 2.30, all week D 6 to 11.30 CLOSED: 25 and 26 Dec, Good Fri MEALS: alc (main courses £7 to £14). Set L £7.50, Set D £14.95 to £19.50. Minimum £9.50 D SERVICE: 12.5%, card slips closed CARDS: Access, Amex, Diners, Visa DETAILS: 64 seats. Private parties: 100 main room. Vegetarian meals. Children's helpings. Smart dress preferred. No smoking in 1 dining-room. Wheelchair access. Music. Air-conditioned

Ernie's NEW ENTRY

Mulberry Gardens, Dublin 4
TEL: (01) 2693300 FAX: (01) 2693260 COST £23–£57

Ernie's is in a stone-built corner house, with a patio garden and fountain floodlit at night. Oil paintings dominate the walls in a pleasantly decorated

dining-room. Sandra Earl's cooking is squarely in the modern urban mould, delivering dishes like a tian of crab on a bed of celeriac and hazelnuts with lemon mayonnaise, or strips of pigeon in a salad dressed with sesame oil and balsamic vinegar. Wicklow lamb is 'beautiful meat, with a lovely natural taste', roasted pink and served with lentils and wild mushrooms. Finish with chocolate marquise, or apple and apricot crumble on a shortbread pastry base. An expansive list of French classics at high prices is supplemented by briefer selections from here and there. House French starts at £12.95.

CHEF: Sandra Earl PROPRIETORS: the Evans family OPEN: Tue to Fri L 12.30 to 2.30, Tue to Sat D 7.30 to 10.30 CLOSED: 1 week Christmas MEALS: alc D (main courses £13 to £17). Set L £13.95, Set D £25 SERVICE: 12.5% CARDS: Access, Amex, Diners, Visa DETAILS: 60 seats. Private parties: 60 main room. Vegetarian meals. No children under 12. Smart dress preferred. Wheelchair access (2 steps). No music. Air-conditioned

Les Frères Jacques

74 Dame Street, Dublin 2
TEL: (01) 6794555 FAX: (01) 6794725 COST £22–£53

'First-class Irish produce with a modern French touch,' promise the owners, and a shorthand dispatch from a reporter suggests that their aim is fulfilled: 'hot oysters superb, as was sole, very friendly French staff'. The menus show some interesting ideas, such as a starter of carpaccio of Connemara salmon with avocado and shallot cream, and main courses of trout fillet wrapped in Bayonne ham with a red wine sauce, or spiced saddle of lamb with a red pepper fumet and green tomato chutney. Desserts neatly sidestep the obvious in creations such as summer fruit clafoutis with star-anise ice-cream. France is the main preoccupation of the wine list, which has some fine wines at not outrageous prices. House wines are £10.50.

CHEFS: Brian Porteus and Marc Moissard PROPRIETORS: Jean-Jacques and Suzy Caillabet OPEN: Mon to Fri L 12.30 to 2.30, Mon to Sat D 7.30 to 10.30 (11 Fri and Sat) CLOSED: 25 to 30 Dec, bank hols MEALS: alc D (main courses £16 to £18.50). Set L £13, Set D £20 SERVICE: 12½% (optional) CARDS: Access, Amex, Visa DETAILS: 65 seats. Private parties: 40 main room, 20 and 40 private rooms. Wheelchair access (1 step). Music

Kapriol

45 Lower Camden Street, Dublin 2
TEL: (01) 4751235 and 2985496 COST £28–£55

Kapriol is an Italian restaurant of great comfort and charm. Pasta dishes include rigatoni with mushrooms, cream and Parmesan, and tortelloni of spinach and ricotta, and there is also bruschetta with Parma ham, salami and olives. Prawns, brandy and cream are marshalled into service to sauce more than one fish dish, while meats are favourites like veal saltimbocca and beef fillet in the Rossini manner. The wine list needs subheadings for easier use, but at least credits all the producers' names and specifies the years. House wines from Abruzzo are £10.80 for a carafe holding just under a litre.

CHEF: Egidia Peruzzi PROPRIETORS: Egidia and Giuseppe Peruzzi OPEN: Mon to Sat D only 7.30 to 12 CLOSED: 3 weeks Aug MEALS: alc (main courses £8.50 to £17) SERVICE: 12½% CARDS: Access, Amex, Diners, Visa DETAILS: 30 seats. Private parties: 30 main room. Vegetarian meals. Children's helpings. Smart dress preferred. Wheelchair access (1 step). Music

Locks

1 Windsor Terrace, Portobello, Dublin 8
TEL: (01) 4543391 and 4538352 FAX: (01) 4538352 COST £22–£53

Five minutes out of the city centre, on the banks of the Grand Canal, Locks offers sound modern cooking. Characteristic dishes include seafood sausage on black tagliatelle; monkfish with prawns and spring onions sauced with orange, mustard and chilli; and lamb fillet stuffed with apricots, pine-nuts and ginger. Chef Brian Buckley uses as much organic produce as he can get his hands on. A comprehensive wine list contains much of sound pedigree, but the prices match the quality. House Duboeuf is £10.95.

CHEF: Brian Buckley PROPRIETOR: Claire Douglas OPEN: Mon to Fri L 12.30 to 2, Mon to Sat D 7.15 to 11 CLOSED: 1 week after Christmas, 2 weeks July to Aug MEALS: alc (main courses £14 to £18). Set L £13.95, Set D £22 SERVICE: 12.5%, card slips closed CARDS: Access, Amex, Diners, Visa DETAILS: 50 seats. Private parties: 65 main room, 40 private room. Children's helpings. Smart dress preferred. No smoking in 1 dining-room. Wheelchair access. No music

Patrick Guilbaud

46 James Place, Dublin 2
TEL: (01) 6764192 FAX: (01) 6601546 COST £29–£65

'Still the best food in Dublin!' says a supporter of this purpose-built restaurant in the heart of the city's business centre. 'French and pricey, stylish and flamboyant,' comments another devotee. The whole set-up lives and breathes modern elegance. Service is professional French, with much dramatic lifting of cloches, but there's also a touch of Irish softness beneath all the formality.

Chef Guillaume Lebrun delivers cuisine of a very high order, and luxury ingredients loom large: warm foie gras is paired daringly with Irish smoked salmon, or transformed into a galette with Sauternes and green peppercorns. But all is not show and lavishness: crubeens (pickled pig's trotters) find their way into ravioli and are also served with a mushroom pudding. Spectacle for its own sake reaches a peak with desserts such as passion-fruit sorbet and ginger-flavoured nougatine floating in 'a sea' of passion-fruit coulis. Cheeses are from one of the best French suppliers. The mainly French wine list is 'distinguished – if a little predictable', observes one who knows about these things. 'Le Petit Cave' holds a clutch of house wines starting at £14.

All main entries are fully indexed at the back of the Guide.

CHEF: Guillaume Lebrun PROPRIETOR: Patrick Guilbaud OPEN: Tue to Sat 12.30 to 2, 7.30 to 10.15 CLOSED: 17 Mar MEALS: alc (main courses £18 to £19). Set L £18.50, Set D £30 to £45 SERVICE: 15% CARDS: Access, Amex, Diners, Visa DETAILS: 80 seats. Private parties: 80 main room, 30 private room. Car park. Children's helpings. welcome. Smart dress preferred. No music. Air-conditioned

Roly's Bistro

NEW ENTRY

7 Ballsbridge Terrace, Dublin 4
TEL: (01) 6682611 FAX: (01) 6608535 COST £15–£36

This hyperactive 3-year-old is opposite the American Embassy. An enthusiastic supporter writes: 'it has become my favourite spot in Dublin.' Ponder the likes of salmon, sole and smoked haddock terrine with horseradish cream, or pigeon breast with red onions and gingered oranges to start, and main courses of monkfish medallions with pesto and couscous, or honey-glazed pork with lemon and mint risotto. This is up-to-the-minute metropolitan food. Finish with Paris-Brest gâteau, or rhubarb and raisin pudding. As if that weren't joy enough, 'the staff are brilliant'. The concise wine list keeps prices sensible. Eleven house selections come at £9.50 the bottle, with basic house French at £8.50.

CHEF: Colin O'Daly PROPRIETORS: Roly Saul, John O'Sullivan, John Mulcahy and Colin O'Daly OPEN: all week 12 to 2.45, 6 to 10 CLOSED: 25 and 26 Dec, Good Fri MEALS: alc D (main courses £7 to £13). Set L £9.50 SERVICE: 10%, card slips closed CARDS: Access, Amex, Diners, Visa DETAILS: 150 seats. Private parties: 10 main room. Vegetarian meals. Children welcome. Wheelchair access (also WC). Music. Air-conditioned

La Stampa

35 Dawson Street, Dublin 1
TEL: (01) 6778611 FAX: (01) 6773336 COST £18–£45

Paul Flynn's cooking receives rave reviews. Sliced rare beef in a salad dressed with truffle oil followed by roast lamb on a croûton with mashed potato added up to 'a fantastic experience' for one diner. Otherwise expect baby squid on saffron risotto, chicken and cashew-nut filo tart, turbot in a potato coat with leek velouté, or honey-roast duck with hash browns. Chocolate marquise for dessert comes with a mint sorbet. This is top-flight stuff. Service is hailed as 'superb, attentive but not pushy'. The wine list is disappointingly pricey. Look to Italy or South Africa for relief, or the house selection of half a dozen, which come at £12 a bottle or £2.50 a glass.

CHEFS: Paul Flynn and Martin Lynch PROPRIETOR: Louis Murray OPEN: Mon to Fri L 12.30 to 2.30, all week D 6.30 to 11.15 (11.45 Fri and Sat) CLOSED: 25 Dec, St Stephen's Day, Good Fri MEALS: alc D (main courses £10 to £16). Set L £10.50 SERVICE: not inc; 10% for parties of 6 or more CARDS: Access, Amex, Diners, Visa DETAILS: 200 seats. Private parties: 160 main room, 60 private room. Vegetarian meals. Children welcome. No pipes in dining-room. Music. Air-conditioned

The Guide *is totally independent, accepts no free hospitality, and survives on the number of copies sold each year.*

DUN LAOGHAIRE Co Dublin map 16

Restaurant na Mara

1 Harbour Road, Dun Laoghaire
TEL: (01) 2806767 and 2800509 FAX: (01) 2844649 COST £21–£61

The converted booking hall of still-functioning Dun Laoghaire station is the setting: a high-ceilinged, columned space of early-Victorian splendour. Formally attired waiters have a touch of the undertaker, thought one man, but Derek Dunne's food matches the general sense of grandeur. Seared foie gras with an apple blini, guinea-fowl on cabbage with a morel cream sauce, and pistachio and poppy-seed parfait with jellied fruits are typical dishes from the *carte*. A reporter who thought some of the food good-looking but pallid none the less finished with the best-ever bread-and-butter pudding 'of perfect sweetness with a hint of cinnamon'. The wine list is a mini-encyclopedia, but prices are high.

CHEF: Derek Dunne PROPRIETORS: Irish Rail Catering Services OPEN: Mon to Sat 12.30 to 2.30, 7 to 10.30 CLOSED: Christmas, bank hols MEALS: alc D (main courses £16 to £23). Set L £11 (2 courses) to £13.50, Set D £23 SERVICE: 15%, card slips closed CARDS: Access, Amex, Diners, Visa DETAILS: 75 seats. Private parties: 75 main room, 36 private room. Vegetarian meals. Children's helpings. Smart dress preferred. No smoking in 1 dining-room. Music

DURRUS Co Cork map 16

Blairs Cove House

Durrus, nr Bantry
TEL: (027) 61127
1m out of Durrus on Barleycove to Goleen road COST £35–£42

Converted from outbuildings attached to a Georgian mansion, this restaurant works to the simplest of formulas. Start by helping yourself to something from the vast buffet of pâtés, cold cuts and seafood, then proceed to the main courses. Grills feature prominently, but you can also get confit of Ballydehob duck or herb-crusted fillet of salmon. Puddings may include carrot cake and tiramisù, and there are farmhouse cheeses. House wine is £11.

CHEFS/PROPRIETORS: Philippe and Sabine De Mey OPEN: Tue to Sat (and Mon July and Aug) D only 7.30 to 9.30 CLOSED: Nov to Feb MEALS: Set D £25 SERVICE: 10%, card slips closed CARDS: Access, Visa DETAILS: 70 seats. Private parties: 35 main room. Car park. Children's helpings. Smart dress preferred. No cigars in dining-room. Music

GOREY Co Wexford map 16

Eugenes NEW ENTRY

Ballyedmond, Gorey, Co Wexford
TEL: (054) 89288
on R741, 9m S of Gorey COST £16–£26

This extremely promising restaurant is in the unlikely setting of the yellow-painted extension to Harney's pub, with a chippy sandwiched between the two. Eugene Callaghan – formerly Paul Rankin's right-hand man at Roscoff (see entry, Belfast) – does an admirable job in providing food for the bar, fish and chips for the take-away and 'superior fare' for travellers in search of a formal meal. His wife hosts the front-of-house with a certain degree of reticence. The classically founded cooking has produced lambs' kidneys in puff pastry, seared fillet of cod with a delicate ginger and saffron sauce, and a thoroughly old-fashioned rhubarb and almond crumble. Soda bread is baked in-house, buttered mashed potato is hard to beat, and there are herb teas as well as coffee to round things off. The carefully chosen wine list is an adequate selection of around 40 bins that rarely strays outside France. Prices start at £9.95.

CHEF: Eugene Callaghan PROPRIETORS: Eugene and Elizabeth Callaghan OPEN: Wed to Mon 12.30 to 2, 7 to 9.30 CLOSED: 1 week before Easter, 2 weeks Sept MEALS: Set L £9.50, Set D £14.50 SERVICE: not inc CARDS: Access, Amex, Diners, Visa DETAILS: 30 seats. Private parties: 32 main room. Car park. Children's helpings. Smart dress preferred. No cigars/pipes in dining-room. Wheelchair access (3 steps). Music

▲ *Marlfield House*

Courtown Road, Gorey
TEL: (055) 21124 FAX: (055) 21572
1m outside Gorey COST £27–£48

This lavishly appointed hotel is designed to impress. The sylvan décor in the dining-room that gave one man the feel of being in a 'tropical jungle' turns into the real thing in the conservatory extension. Kevin Arundel took over the stoves in 1994, and his menus offer an appealing breadth of choice. The carefully conceived dishes include a terrine of crab, sole and smoked salmon wrapped in leeks with a fennel and lemon dressing, turbot roasted with thyme and served with an orange butter sauce, and beef fillet on creamed celeriac with roasted garlic and salsify and a red wine sauce. An 'open sandwich' of strawberries with lemon cream and a passion-fruit coulis makes a good dessert. France leads the wine list, with claret better represented than burgundy, and there are short selections from elsewhere. Seven house wines are each £13.

CHEF: Kevin Arundel PROPRIETORS: the Bowe family OPEN: all week 12.45 to 1.45, 7.30 to 9 CLOSED: mid-Dec to mid-Jan MEALS: Set L £18, Set D £30 SERVICE: 10%, card slips closed CARDS: Access, Amex, Diners, Visa DETAILS: 60 seats. Private parties: 25 main room, 25 and 30 private rooms. Car park. Vegetarian meals. No children in dining-room D. Jacket and tie. Wheelchair access (also WC). No music ACCOMMODATION: 19 rooms, all with bath/shower. TV. Phone. B&B £50 to £455. Deposit: 1 night's stay. Rooms for disabled. Children welcome. Baby facilities. Pets by arrangement. Afternoon teas. Garden

HOWTH Co Dublin map 16

King Sitric $*

East Pier, Howth
TEL: (01) 8325235 and 8326729 FAX: (01) 8392442 COST £31–£61

The monarch in question was a Norse king. History aside, this green-painted restaurant is in what was once the harbour-master's house, so it should come as no surprise that fish is the thing here. The quality of the raw materials shines through in dishes such as a plainly poached fillet of brill or ragoût of mixed seafood with wild mushrooms and home-made tagliatelle. Chicken is free-range, vegetables are organically grown where possible, and cheeses are Irish. The wine list has real class, with a contingent of pedigree French bottles stealing most of the limelight. House wine is £11.50.

CHEF: Aidan MacManus PROPRIETORS: Aidan and Joan MacManus OPEN: Mon to Sat D only 6.30 to 11 CLOSED: 1 week Jan, week before Easter, bank hols MEALS: alc (main courses £7.50 to £22.50). Set D £23; light L available in sea food bar in summer SERVICE: not inc, card slips closed CARDS: Access, Amex, Diners, Visa DETAILS: 75 seats. Private parties: 45 main room, 22 private room. Children's helpings. Smart dress preferred. No smoking in 1 dining-room. Wheelchair access (also WC). Music

KANTURK Co Cork map 16

▲ *Assolas Country House*

Kanturk
TEL: (029) 50015 FAX: (029) 50795
signposted from N72, NE of Kanturk, 8m W of Mallow COST £35–£42

Assolas is all creeper-clad dignity, its handsome grounds kept well in trim, and a river ambles past nearby. Hazel Bourke's seasonal menus represent palpable value. Expect the likes of Kenmare mussels in brioche, duck confit with a potato galette, Blackwater salmon with beurre blanc, and venison sauced with red wine and juniper berries. A spread of pedigree French wines may offer more attractions than the rather perfunctory showing from elsewhere. Guigal's Côtes du Rhône in red and white is the house wine at £14.

CHEF: Hazel Bourke PROPRIETORS: the Bourke family OPEN: all week D only 7 to 8.30 CLOSED: 1 Nov to 1 Apr MEALS: Set D £28 SERVICE: none, card slips closed CARDS: Access, Visa DETAILS: 30 seats. Private parties: 18 main room, 18 private room. Car park. Children's helpings. Smart dress preferred. No cigars in dining-room. No music ACCOMMODATION: 9 rooms, all with bath/shower. Phone. B&B £55 to £150. Deposit: 100%. Children welcome. Baby facilities. Garden. Fishing

KENMARE Co Kerry map 16

▲ *Park Hotel Kenmare*

Kenmare
TEL: (064) 41200 FAX: (064) 41402 COST £29–£88

The hotel looks like a Victorian château surrounded by acres of woodland overlooking Kenmare Bay and describes its cooking as 'progressive Irish with a Pacific Rim flavour'. Warm salad of squab pigeon with brunoise of foie gras, cumin, apple and lavender vinaigrette is a typically daring starter, while main courses could include fillet of salmon with a compote of red peppers and leeks, or grilled fillet of beef with a chartreuse of oxtail and a truffle and port demi-glaze. Desserts come in for the same elaborate treatment: a parfait of coconut and Malibu in a pastry basket with vanilla-flavoured rice and a cherry compote. The wine list is a global heavyweight by any standards. House wine is £16.

CHEF: Bruno Schmidt PROPRIETOR: Francis Brennan OPEN: all week 1 to 1.45, 7 to 8.45 CLOSED: 6 Nov to 23 Dec, 2 Jan to 5 Apr MEALS: alc D (main courses £20 to £30). Set L £18.50, Set D £37 SERVICE: not inc CARDS: Access, Amex, Diners, Visa DETAILS: 80 seats. Private parties: 30 main room, 15 private room. Car park. Vegetarian meals. No children under 4 D. Smart dress preferred. No smoking in 1 dining-room. Wheelchair access (also WC). Music ACCOMMODATION: 50 rooms, 45 with bath/shower. TV. Phone. B&B £112 to £167. Rooms for disabled. Children welcome. Baby facilities. Afternoon teas. Garden

▲ *Sheen Falls Lodge, La Cascade*

Kenmare
TEL: (064) 41600 FAX: (064) 41386 COST £29–£61

This hotel is one of the more dramatic recent conversions. A seventeenth-century country retreat with all mod cons, it is set in spacious grounds. The glint of ambition may be read in dishes such as crabmeat with spring onion, ginger, apple and coconut milk, or globe artichoke with quail's eggs and lobster on a saffron aïoli. Main courses run from sesame-crusted John Dory with salsa verde to loin of veal with dried tomato, sage and caponata. Chocolate and hazelnut frangipane with caramel cream ends things on a high note, and there are good Irish cheeses. The wine list – 1950s clarets, a run of Hermitage La Chapelle, the best of the New World – is what you would expect in the context. House wines are £17.50 (white) and £18.50 (red).

CHEF: Fergus Moore PROPRIETOR: Bent Hoyer OPEN: Sun L 1 to 2, all week D 7.30 to 9.30 CLOSED: early Jan to early Feb MEALS: set L £17.50, Set D £37.50 SERVICE: not inc, card slips closed CARDS: Access, Amex, Diners, Visa DETAILS: 120 seats. Private parties: 120 main room, 80 private room. Car park. Vegetarian meals. No children under 3. Smart dress preferred. Wheelchair access (2 steps; also WC). Music ACCOMMODATION: 40 rooms, all with bath/shower. TV. Phone. B&B £175 to £230. Deposit: £100. Rooms for disabled. Children welcome. Pets welcome. Afternoon teas. Garden. Fishing

KILKENNY Co Kilkenny map 16

▲ *Lacken House*

Dublin Road, Kilkenny
TEL: (056) 61085 FAX: (056) 62435 COST £31–£50

Eugene and Breda McSweeney's family-run guesthouse wears its Irishness on its sleeve, and Eugene's kitchen is well endowed with the fruits of local enterprise. He serves roast Callan bacon with whole-grain mustard sauce, smokes his own salmon, trout and chicken, includes Kilkenny Rooster potatoes among his dishes of organic vegetables, and loads his cheeseboard with such names as Lavistown and Abbey Blue Brie. Fish also appears in the shape of baked crab gâteau, seafood chowder, and salmon fillet with warm tomato vinaigrette. The wine list is a good one, with house wine £12.

CHEF: Eugene McSweeney PROPRIETORS: Eugene and Breda McSweeney OPEN: Tue to Sat D only 6.30 to 10.30 CLOSED: 1 week Christmas MEALS: alc (main courses £13.50 to £17.50). Set D £22 SERVICE: not inc, card slips closed CARDS: Access, Amex, Diners, Visa DETAILS: 30 seats. Private parties: 40 main room, 12 private room. Car park. Vegetarian meals. Children's helpings. Smart dress preferred. Music. Air-conditioned ACCOMMODATION: 8 rooms, all with bath/shower. TV. Phone. B&B £31 to £60. Deposit: 10%. Children welcome. Baby facilities. Garden

KINSALE Co Cork map 16

▲ *Blue Haven*

3 Pearse Street, Kinsale, Co Cork
TEL: (021) 772209 COST £27–£47

Kinsale bills itself as 'the gourmet capital of Ireland', a town that has its own 'food trail' and plays host to lofty international forums. At the centre of things is the Blue Haven, appropriately decked out in shades of blue and yellow. The evening restaurant menu goes for elaboration in a big way (filo parcels of crab with caviare sauce, roulade of pork with champagne and oyster mushrooms) but a slimmed-down (cheaper) version can be eaten in the wood-panelled bar and conservatory. Reports suggest that bar meals are robust rather than refined: curried parsnip soup with soda bread, hot wood-smoked salmon with lemon butter sauce, and gratin of monkfish tinged with Pernod show what the kitchen has to offer. The wine list is notable for its extensive 'house selections', averaging around £11 a bottle.

CHEF: Richard Madden PROPRIETORS: Brian and Anne Cronin OPEN: bar all week 12.30 to 3, 7 to 10.30, restaurant all week D only 7 to 10.30 CLOSED: 25 Dec, 2 weeks Jan SERVICE: 10% restaurant, not inc bar CARDS: Access, Amex, Diners, Visa DETAILS: restaurant 85 seats, bar 112 seats. 10 tables outside. Private parties: 50 main room. Vegetarian meals. No smoking area. Wheelchair access (also WC). Music. Air-conditioned ACCOMMODATION: 19 rooms, all with bath/shower. TV. Phone. B&B £45 to £130. Deposit: 1 night. Room for disabled. Children welcome. Baby facilities. Afternoon teas. Garden

LETTERFRACK Co Galway map 16

▲ *Rosleague Manor*

Letterfrack
TEL: (095) 41101 FAX: (095) 41168
on N59 to Westport, 7m NW of Clifden COST £20–£48

This Regency manor-house overlooks a sheltered bay, with mountains and forests huddling round. Nigel Rush's inventive cooking is another plus-point. Diners alarmed to be offered 'six of the best' will be reassured to find they are local oysters. Other dishes may include spiced duck blinis with cucumber and spring onion, celery and lovage soup, brill poached in vermouth, and guinea-fowl with raisins. Desserts tend to be squishy: profiteroles with butterscotch sauce, or chocolate mousse. The wine list is mostly reasonably priced, with house vin de pays d'Oc £11.

CHEF: Nigel Rush PROPRIETORS: Anne and Patrick Foyle OPEN: all week 12.30 to 2.30, 8 to 9.30 CLOSED: Nov to Easter MEALS: alc (main courses £5 to £15). Set D £25 SERVICE: not inc, card slips closed CARDS: Access, Amex, Visa DETAILS: 65 seats. Private parties: 25 main room. Car park. Children's helpings. Smart dress preferred. No smoking in dining-room. Music ACCOMMODATION: 20 rooms, all with bath/shower. Phone. B&B £40 to £140. Rooms for disabled. Children welcome. Pets welcome in bedrooms only. Afternoon teas. Garden

MALLOW Co Cork map 16

▲ *Longueville House*

Mallow
TEL: (022) 47156 FAX: (022) 47459
3m W of Mallow on N72 Killarney road COST £25–£55

Not only does this grand Georgian mansion have the requisite walled garden for growing vegetables and herbs, but it also maintains a farm (where sheep and pigs are reared for the table) and boasts its own vineyard. Evening meals are served in the high-ceilinged Presidents' Room where portraits of famous faces from Ireland's past look down on the assembled company. William O'Callaghan's ambitious repertoire might include pan-fried smoked fillet of beef with horseradish and Guinness sauce, noisettes of milk-fed Longueville lamb with tarragon sauce, and fillets of black sole with a crab parcel and lime sauce. France and Spain are the most interesting contenders on the reasonably priced wine list. House wine is £13.

CHEF: William O'Callaghan PROPRIETORS: Michael and Jane O'Callaghan OPEN: Sun L 12.30 to 1.45, all week D 7 to 9 CLOSED: Christmas and New Year MEALS: alc D (main courses £17 to £19). Set L Sun £16, Set D £27. Minimum £27 D; bar L available SERVICE: not inc, card slips closed CARDS: Access, Amex, Diners, Visa DETAILS: 50 seats. Private parties: 30 main room, 30 private room. Car park. Vegetarian meals. Children's helpings. Smart dress preferred. No smoking in dining-room. Wheelchair access (also WC). No music ACCOMMODATION: 21 rooms, all with bath/shower. TV. Phone. B&B £53 to £158. Deposit: 50%. Children welcome. Baby facilities. Afternoon teas. Garden. Fishing

MIDLETON Co Cork map 16

Farmgate

Coolbawn, Midleton
TEL: (021) 632771 COST £15–£37

Máróg O'Brien keeps things simple in her lively local enterprise, which means encouraging informality and avidly supporting regional producers. Shellfish and free-range poultry are specialities and her menu is full of good things: Rossmore oysters with a herbed hollandaise, tartlet of black pudding and apple in a red pepper coulis, and casserole of beef in Murphy's stout are typical offerings. Máróg describes her wine list as 'limited'. House wine is £9.50. The Farmgate Café, English Market, Princes Street, Cork, (021)278134 is a related set-up.

CHEFS: Máróg O'Brien and Angela Collins PROPRIETOR: Máróg O'Brien OPEN: Mon to Sat L 12 to 4, Fri and Sat D 7.30 to 9.45 CLOSED: 3 days Christmas MEALS: alc (main courses L £4 to £10, D £8 to £14) SERVICE: not inc CARDS: Access, Visa DETAILS: 70 seats. 4 tables outside. Private parties: 60 main room, 25 private room. Vegetarian meals. Children's helpings. No pipes in dining-room. Wheelchair access (1 step; also WC). Music. Air-conditioned

MOYCULLEN Co Galway **map 16**

Drimcong House

Moycullen
TEL: (091) 85115 and 85585 COST £26–£49

'Upstanding!' is how Gerry Galvin describes his business. He goes out of his way to lay his hands on 'great' lamb, Atlantic fish, organic vegetables, wild duck, and cheeses from Irish farms. A typical meal from one of his weekly dinner menus might run along the lines of pan-fried oyster-cakes with chilli cream, then a soup or sorbet before a joint of Drimcong pork or poached chicken breast with smoked salmon and spinach. Desserts range from home-made ice-creams to plum and almond tart. House white wine is £9.50 a bottle.

CHEF: Gerry Galvin PROPRIETORS: Gerry and Marie Galvin OPEN: Tue to Sat D only 6.30 to 10.30 CLOSED: Christmas to Mar MEALS: alc (main courses £15 to £16.50) Set D £16.95 SERVICE: 10% CARDS: Access, Amex, Diners, Visa DETAILS: 50 seats. Private parties: 50 main room, 10 to 30 private rooms. Car park. Vegetarian meals. Children's helpings. Smart dress preferred. Wheelchair access (3 steps; also WC). Music

NEWPORT Co Mayo **map 16**

▲ *Newport House* ⁕

Newport
TEL: (098) 41222 FAX: (098) 41613 COST £36–£51

Kieran and Thelma Thompson's Georgian house has a great deal going for it. The setting, overlooking the estuary, is delightful and the owners have private salmon fishing rights in the bay. They smoke some of the catch themselves and grow vegetables in a walled kitchen garden. Their daily-changing five-course dinner menu always provides plenty of choice at each stage: start, perhaps, with crab salad and tomato mayonnaise, then move on to cold summer fruit soup, before tackling a main course such as chargrilled veal steak with mustard seed sauce. Irish cheeses come next, possibly followed by poached pears with walnut ice-cream or a dish of fresh loganberries. The wine list is a big, beefy slate with a serious French presence and plenty of good stuff from around the world. House wines start at £10.

CHEF: John Gavin PROPRIETORS: Kieran and Thelma Thompson OPEN: all week D only 7.30 to 9.30; light L available CLOSED: 1 Oct to 19 Mar MEALS: Set D £28 SERVICE: not inc, card slips closed CARDS: Access, Amex, Diners, Visa DETAILS: 38 seats. Private parties: 14 main room. Car park. Children's helpings. Smart dress preferred. No smoking in dining-room. No music ACCOMMODATION: 18 rooms, all with bath/shower. Phone. B&B £58 to £120. Rooms for disabled. Children welcome. Baby facilities. Pets welcome in courtyard rooms only. Afternoon teas. Garden. Fishing

OUGHTERARD Co Galway map 16

▲ *Currarevagh House*

Oughterard, Connemara
TEL: (091) 82312 and 82313 FAX: (091) 82731
4m NW of Oughterard on Hill of Doon Lakeshore road COST £25–£30

A Victorian grey-stone building in tranquil Connemara, Currarevagh House seems to radiate homeliness. Fixed-price, no-choice dinner menus are the business. Dishes have included duck liver terrine with tomato coulis, black sole with lemon butter, pork roulade with calvados sauce, and rack of lamb cooked in honey and Guinness. Simple desserts make use of standbys like brandy-snaps and chocolate, and Irish cheeses are always served. The serious wine list is intelligently annotated and offers a good choice. House wines start at £8.50.

CHEF: June Hodgson PROPRIETORS: Harry and June Hodgson OPEN: all week D only 8 (one sitting) CLOSED: Nov to Mar MEALS: Set D £18.75 SERVICE: 10% CARDS: none DETAILS: 30 seats. Private parties: 12 main room. Car park. Children by arrangement. Smart dress preferred. No smoking in dining-room. No music ACCOMMODATION: 15 rooms, all with bath/shower. B&B £44 to £96. Children by arrangement. Pets welcome. Garden. Fishing

SHANAGARRY Co Cork map 16

▲ *Ballymaloe House*

Shanagarry, nr Midleton
TEL: (021) 652531 FAX: (021) 652021
2m outside Cloyne on Ballycotton road COST £25–£53

The Allen family has worked hard to maintain standards over 30 years of running Ballymaloe, both within the hotel and on the farm that provides much of the top-quality produce used in the kitchens. A couple long familiar with this place wrote in praise of a dinner that included a timbale of grated carrot and apple with a honeyed vinaigrette, salmon en papillote with autumn herbs, chicken with diced cucumber braised in Chardonnay, and a bacon chop sauced with Irish whiskey. Raspberry frangipane tart, or praline ice-cream provide good, simple finishing touches. House Duboeuf is £13.

CHEFS: Myrtle Allen and Rory O'Connell PROPRIETORS: the Allen family OPEN: all week 1 to 2, 7 to 9.30 CLOSED: 24 to 26 Dec MEALS: Set L £16, Set D £30 SERVICE: not inc, card slips closed CARDS: Access, Amex, Diners, Visa DETAILS: 100 seats. Private parties: 70 main room, 15 and 25 private rooms. Car park. Vegetarian meals. No children under 6 D. Smart dress preferred. No smoking in 1 dining-room. Wheelchair access (also WC). No music ACCOMMODATION: 33 rooms, all with bath/shower. Phone. B&B £67 to £130. Deposit: £50. Rooms for disabled. Children welcome. Baby facilities. Garden. Swimming-pool

indicates that smoking is either banned altogether or that a dining-room is maintained for non-smokers. The symbol does not apply to restaurants that simply have no-smoking areas.

WATERFORD Co Waterford map 16

Dwyers $*

8 Mary Street, Waterford
TEL: (051) 77478 COST £21–£38

The Dwyers' small, unpretentious restaurant near the water-front inspires with cooking that may take in a herbed chicken and pistachio sausage with sorrel and apple relish, hake bordelaise with aïoli, and walnut-crusted rack of lamb. Desserts end meals on a grand note with strawberries Romanoff or brown bread ice-cream with a caramel and whiskey sauce. The fixed-price menu represents very good value. The wine list is compact and conservative, though it does find room for a Swiss white. Prices open at £10.20.

CHEF: Martin Dwyer PROPRIETORS: Martin and Sile Dwyer OPEN: Mon to Sat D only 6 to 10 CLOSED: 4 days Christmas, 2 weeks July MEALS: alc (main courses £10.50 to £14). Set D 6 to 7.30 £14 SERVICE: not inc CARDS: Access, Amex, Diners, Visa DETAILS: 32 seats. Private parties: 32 main room, 8 private room. Children's helpings. No smoking in 1 dining-room. Wheelchair access (also WC). Music

WEXFORD Co Wexford map 16

Granary

Westgate, Wexford
TEL: (053) 23935 COST £23–£37

The building the Hattons' restaurant occupies was once used for storing grain. Things are a lot livelier now, as is evidenced in the pre-opera dinners, where service goes into a dextrous whirl. One man began with mussels that were 'juicy and fat with lots of flavour' and baked with garlic, tarragon and olive oil. The famous black and white puddings of Clonakilty are served in a warm salad, and another favourite starter is a piece of treacle bread with Cashel Blue cheese melted over it. Chicken Selskar turns out to be the breast baked under a Parmesan and almond crust and sauced with orange. A serviceable wine list keeps prices within bounds. House Duboeuf is £9.95.

CHEFS: Mary Hatton and Vincent Whitmore PROPRIETORS: Paddy and Mary Hatton OPEN: Mon to Sat D only 6 to 10 (plus Suns before bank hols and during Wexford Festival) CLOSED: 3 days Christmas MEALS: alc (main courses £11 to £13). Set D 6 to 7.30 (7 Fri and Sat) £12.95 to £15.95, Set D £18.95 SERVICE: not inc CARDS: Access, Amex, Diners, Visa DETAILS: 45 seats. Private parties: 20 main room, 15 private room. Vegetarian meals. Children's helpings 6 to 7pm. Wheelchair access. Music

WICKLOW Co Wicklow map 16

▲ *Old Rectory* $*

Wicklow
TEL: (0404) 67048 FAX: (0404) 69181 COST £32–£46

If you don't fancy your asparagus crêpe bedecked with marigold petals and borage flowers, there are more conventional dishes. Well-made stuffings are a strong point, as in a wild mushroom, bacon, red onion and thyme assemblage that goes into a brace of roasted quail, while paupiettes of black sole are filled with crabmeat and given a light lobster sauce. Desserts may include a two-tone chocolate and Cointreau mousse in a chocolate cup with brandied clementines. Spain and France head up the authoritative wine list. Prices open at £11.

CHEF: Linda Saunders PROPRIETORS: Paul and Linda Saunders OPEN: all week D only 8 (one sitting; 7.30 to 9 Fri and Sat) CLOSED: Nov to Mar MEALS: alc (main courses £16 to £18). Set D £26 SERVICE: net prices, card slips closed CARDS: Access, Amex, Diners, Visa DETAILS: 20 seats. Private parties: 20 main room. Car park. Vegetarian meals. Children's helpings. Smart dress preferred. No smoking in dining-room. Wheelchair access (3 steps). Music ACCOMMODATION: 5 rooms, all with bath/shower. TV. Phone. B&B £67 to £90. Deposit: £30. Children welcome. Baby facilities. Garden

YOUGHAL Co Cork map 16

▲ *Aherne's* NEW ENTRY

163 North Main Street, Youghal
TEL: (024) 92424 FAX: (024) 93633 COST £21–£37

Once a pub, now a restaurant-with-rooms, Aherne's is capable of turning out some above-average cooking, principally of seafood. Choose from a *carte* or set-price menu for food that mixes and matches the simple (mussels in garlic butter, seafood chowder, fillet steak with red wine sauce) with the more ambitious (brill wrapped around crabmeat with a lobster sauce, or scallops in a sauce made of the corals with prawns and monkfish). Cheesecake is flavoured with Bailey's and comes with an orange coulis, and dark bread contains treacle. Staff 'epitomise Irish hospitality'. The wine list does the rounds at prices that aren't excessive, the house selection starting at £11.50.

CHEF: David Fitzgibbon PROPRIETORS: the Fitzgibbon family OPEN: all week 12.30 to 2.15, 6.30 to 9.30 (bar 11 to 10.30) CLOSED: 6 days Christmas MEALS: Set L £13.50, Set D £22.50; bar meals available SERVICE: 10%, card slips closed CARDS: Access, Amex, Diners, Visa DETAILS: 60 seats. 3 tables outside. Private parties: 60 main room, 20 private room. Car park. Vegetarian meals. Children's helpings. Smart dress preferred. Wheelchair access (1 step). Music ACCOMMODATION: 10 rooms, all with bath/shower. TV. Phone. B&B £55 to £70. Deposit: 30%. Rooms for disabled. Children welcome. Afternoon teas

Round-ups

Looking for a suitable place to eat at can be a lottery, especially if you are travelling around the country with no set plans in mind. The round-up section is intended to provide some interesting gastronomic possibilities, whether you find yourself in the West Country or the northern outposts of Scotland. Pubs are becoming increasingly valuable as sources of high-quality food, but the listings also include modest family-run enterprises in country towns, racy café/bars and ethnic restaurants in big cities, and a sprinkling of hotel dining-rooms in all parts of the land. Dip into this section and you are almost bound to find somewhere that suits your needs and your pocket. Entries are based on readers' recommendations supported by inspectors' reports. Sometimes a restaurant appears in the round-up section instead of the main entries because there are changes in the air or because positive feedback has been thin on the ground. Reports on these places are especially welcome, as they help to broaden our coverage of good eating places in Britain. Round-up entries (outside London) are arranged alphabetically by location within England, Scotland, Wales, the Channel Islands and Northern Ireland.

England

• **ALFRISTON** (East Sussex)
Moonrakers High Street, (01323) 870472. Two fifteenth-century cottages converted into a local restaurant offering the likes of carrot and coriander soup, suprême of guinea-fowl and 'superb' banoffi pie. Service is friendly and there is a good wine list.

• **ALTRINCHAM** (Greater Manchester)
Franc's 2 Goose Green, 0161-941 3954. A useful address providing good-value French bistro food, decent bread, salads and crêpes. The coffee is pleasant, too. Sundays are geared towards families.

• **AMBLESIDE** (Cumbria)
Sheila's Cottage The Slack, (015394) 33079. Part 'country tea-room', part restaurant, and a valued asset for Lakeland tourists. Snacks, cakes, and lunch dishes such as duck with green lentil salad are bolstered by more ambitious suppers. A promising new kitchen team was finding its feet as we went to press.

• **AMERSHAM** (Buckinghamshire)
Gilbey's 1 Market Square, Old Amersham (01494) 727242. Wine at shop prices is the big selling-point at this colourfully decorated restaurant. Monthly menus are also good value: for warm salad of oyster mushrooms and French beans, and grilled sea bream with polenta. Desserts are a strong point.

• **ASHFORD** (Derbyshire)
Riverside Country House Hotel Fennel Street, (01629) 814275. Invitingly situated Georgian mansion with gardens running down to the banks of the Wye. Restaurant menus feature the likes of poached egg in brioche with wild mushrooms, and roast fillet of pork with apple and apricot chutney. All-day brasserie dishes and afternoon teas are served in the Buttery Bar.

• **ATHERSTONE** (Warwickshire)
Chapel House Friar's Gate, (01827) 718949. Converted eighteenth-century dower house with walled gardens and decent accommodation. Fixed-price dinners encompass everything from halibut and mussel feuilleté to steak and kidney pie. Excellent puddings. Helpful, friendly service.

• **BAKEWELL** (Derbyshire)
Renaissance Bath Street, (01629) 812687. Promising new venue opposite Bath Gardens. Menus change every three weeks and the cooking is classic French:

fish mousse with watercress sauce, roast rack of lamb with thyme, and strawberry shortbread have been recommended.

• **BARHAM** (Kent)

Old Coach House Dover Road, (01227) 831218. Personally run hotel recommended for its warmth, cosiness and tolerant attitude to youngsters, not to mention its food. Reporters have enjoyed stuffed mussels, salmon with capers, and liver and bacon with a vast array of crunchy vegetables.

• **BARNARD CASTLE** (Co Durham)

Market Place Teashop 29 Market Place, (01833) 690110. Generous homecooking and unbeatable value in old-fashioned surroundings. The kitchen produces everything from tea and cakes to robust lunches with a strong vegetarian bias. A useful daytime bolt hole for families and walkers off the moors.

• **BASLOW** (Derbyshire)

Cavendish Hotel Baslow, (01246) 582311. Grand stone edifice that makes much of its setting on the Chatsworth Estate and its proximity to the Peak District. Eat in the enormous restaurant or the all-day Garden Room, where the menu ranges from sushi to home-made bangers.

• **BATH** (Avon)

Beaujolais 5 Chapel Row, Queens Square, (01225) 423417. 'The oldest French restaurant in Bath' is handy for the Theatre Royal and a godsend for families. Lunch attracts the business crowd, while dinner offers sound bistro cooking along the lines of snails in puff pastry and duck with pears and port.

Priory Hotel Weston Road, (01225) 331922. Imposing Georgian country house, one mile from the centre of Bath. The setting exudes English elegance, the cooking is modern French. Chef Michael Collom remains, but new owners have initiated extensive refurbishment. More reports, please.

• **BERWICK-UPON-TWEED** (Northumberland)

Rob Roy Dock Road, Tweedmouth, (01289) 306428. Freehouse, B&B and restaurant on the south bank of the River Tweed. Seafood is the name of the game – be it Lindisfarne oysters, wild salmon, sea trout or lobsters. Border steaks, lamb and game form the principal back-up.

• **BEVERLEY** (Humberside)

Cerutti 2 Beverley Station, (01482) 866700. Good for rail travellers and those who appreciate arty décor. The mood is congenial and the menu has a plentiful showing of East Coast fish.

• **BIRMINGHAM** (West Midlands)

Henrys 27 St Pauls Square, 0121-200 1136. Away from Chinatown, in the impressively gentrified 'Jewellery Quarter' of the city, this mainly Cantonese place caters for those who like sizzling dishes, plenty of duck, and seafood in edible baskets.

Punjab Paradise 377 Ladypool Road, 0121-449 4110. One of the most consistent balti houses among the scores of cafés and restaurants in the Sparkhill district of the city. Prices are no longer the cheapest around, but the quality is high. Open evenings and Sunday lunch.

San Carlo 4 Temple Street, 0121-633 0251. Deservedly popular, modern place providing a creditable choice of Italian food just off the main city-centre shopping area. Pasta is reliable, focaccia is enormous, and the blackboard of fish specials is worth exploring.

Taipan 2A Wrottesley Street, 0121-622 3883. Upstairs restaurant in the Chinese quarter offering a polyglot version of oriental cooking. DIY Korean barbecues are the best bets, but customers can also choose between Cantonese 'steam bowls', Peking duck, Thai cuisine and seafood.

• **BLACKMORE END** (Essex)

Bull Blackmore End, nr Braintree, (01371) 851037. The Bruce family has turned this country pub into a much-sought-after Essex eating-place. Expect plenty of pub favourites as well as more ambitious offerings such as saddle of venison with pickled walnuts and madeira sauce.

• **BLEWBURY** (Oxfordshire)

Blewbury Inn London Road, (01235) 850496. Nettle and duck soup, rump of lamb with pearl barley, and ginger cake with rhubarb compote are typical of Paul Lane's cooking in this no-frills Cotswold pub. Real ales are on draught, wines are dependable and the inn has three bedrooms.

• **Bootle** (Merseyside)

Rui's 13 Aintree Road, 0151-922 1212. Lively trattoria serving good pasta, pizzas and continental stalwarts ranging from calamares to beef Stroganov and grilled lemon sole. 'Amazing-value' weekday lunches and 'early-diner' menus.

• **Bradford** (West Yorkshire)

Symposium 7 Albion Street, Idle, (01274) 616587. Converted Victorian pharmacy three miles from the city centre, now thriving as a 'food and wine bar'. Stuart Nunn did a stint at Brasserie Forty Four (see main entry, Leeds) and his cooking is in the fashionable mould of warm salad of black pudding with poached egg, pork fillet with pesto mash, and monkfish bouillabaise. More reports, please.

• **Braunston** (Leicestershire)

Blue Ball Inn Ceder Street, (01577) 722135. Ancient shires inn transformed into an eminently civilised pub with echoes of a French auberge. The kitchen aims high and the set-up is clearly modelled on its sister establishment, the Peacock Inn, Redmile (see round-up entry).

• **Brighton** (East Sussex)

Browns 3–4 Duke Street, (01273) 323501. This is the south-coast offshoot of a chain of bar/restaurants founded in Oxford. Large windows open up the frontage in fine weather. Specials could range from meat balls with spaghetti to cod in Guinness batter with mushy pea fritters.

Topps Hotel 17 Regency Square, (01273) 729334. The hotel is Topps, the restaurant is Bottoms. Locals and residents drop in for dinner, when the menu promises such things as scampi in a sauce of pepper purée, stuffed quail, and 'substantial' veal chop topped with garlic breadcrumbs.

• **Brightwell Baldwin** (Oxfordshire)

Lord Nelson Inn Brightwell Baldwin, nr Watlington (01491) 612497. A resplendent flower-filled patio is the great summertime attraction at this 'quaint' sixteenth-century pub. Bar food and restaurant meals are of equal standard and you can expect dishes such as smoked haddock with curry sauce, and roast guinea-fowl with cider.

• **Bristol** (Avon)

Bistro Twenty One 21 Cotham Road South, 0117-942 1744. Greatly enlarged, windowless bistro with 'sepulchral lighting', but a dependable French menu based on first-class ingredients. Simplicity reigns in the shape of fish soup, sweetbreads, turbot with saffron sauce, and pear sablé.

Browns 38 Queens Road, 0117-929 3601. One of a mini-chain of lively all-day bar/restaurants. Added attractions here include three terraces for al fresco eating and a jazz pianist most evenings. Browns offers eclectic food and is children-friendly.

• **Broadstairs** (Kent)

Marchesi's 18 Albion Street, (01843) 862481. A godsend for Kent holidaymakers looking for a buzzy atmosphere and old favourites such as fish soup, peppered duck breast, or roast rack of lamb with flageolet beans. Set-lunches are good value and the long wine list includes plenty from the New World.

• **Brockton** (Shropshire)

Feathers Brockton, (01746) 785202. Wildly eccentric décor and a lively bistro menu are the outstanding features of this impressively re-styled roadside pub. On the blackboard you might find mozzarella and tomato salad, teriyaki duck, grilled brochettes of monkfish, and hot vanilla pudding.

• **Broughton In Furness** (Cumbria)

Beswicks Langholm House, The Square, (01229) 716285. Family-run restaurant holding pride of place in Broughton's Georgian square. Local produce shows up well and the vegetarian menu gets plenty of votes. Desserts are in the Lakeland tradition of date and ginger pudding, and Westmorland tart.

• **BURFORD** (Oxfordshire)
Lamb Inn Sheep Street, (01993) 823155. Enticing fifteenth-century Costwold inn bedecked with creepers and full of antiques. Cottagey accommodation, creditable bar lunches and Anglo-French evening meals in the formal dining-room.

• **BURGH LE MARSH** (Lincolnshire)
Windmill 46 High Street, (01754) 810281. Bread is baked with flour from the mill and the kitchen is firmly committed to local produce. Fresh asparagus soup, rack of new season's lamb, seafood gougère and 'perfect' crème brûlée found favour in May. Pleasant, music-free surroundings.

• **BURY ST EDMUNDS** (Suffolk)
Ravenwood Hall Rougham, (01359) 70345. Tranquil country house with historical connections set in woodland three miles from Bury. Home-made preserves and smoked produce show up on the menu, which ranges from roast pork or beef suet pudding to chicken breast filled with ginger-scented vegetables.

• **BYTHORN** (Cambridgeshire)
White Hart, Bennett's Bythorn, (01832) 710226. The Bennetts used to run the Pheasant, Keyston (see main entry) before moving to this pleasant old pub down the road. Good game, imaginative sauces and star-rated desserts have been highpoints of meals in the conservatory restaurant.

• **CAMBRIDGE** (Cambridgeshire)
Browns 23 Trumpington Street, (01223) 461655. 'Busy, bustling and bright' all-day bar/restaurant serving breakfast, tea, hot sandwiches, chargrills, salads and daily specials ranging from honey-glazed ham hock with mash to field mushroom Stroganov. Brilliant for families.

• **CANTERBURY** (Kent)
Pierre Victoire 12 Best Lane, (01227) 788300. One of the more recent additions to this chain, but dedicated to the same principles of modern food at low prices. The kitchen feeds all comers and the pace is fast. Set lunches are unbeatable value; pre-theatre dinners are a close second.

• **CARTMEL** (Cumbria)
Aynsome Manor Cartmel, (01539) 536653. Delightful family-run hotel just outside one of South Lakeland's oldest villages. Fixed-price dinners could feature locally smoked venison, baked trout with leeks and tomato sauce, and roast duckling with peach and brandy sauce.

• **CHELTENHAM** (Gloucestershire)
Beaujolais 15 Rotunda Terrace, (01242) 525230. Pleasing French food in charming surroundings overlooking one of Cheltenham's elegant streets. The table d'hôte menu offers outstanding value for dishes such as caramelised onion tart, fillet of beef with oyster mushroom sauce, and hot pear and sticky toffee pudding.

• **CHESTER** (Cheshire)
Franc's 14 Cuppin Street, (01244) 317952. Brisk, lively brasserie with French posters on the walls, 'Continental' opening times and good children's facilities. Dishes are in the classic mould of salade niçoise, steak frites and pork dijonnaise. Seasonal food festivals are also organised.

• **CHICHESTER** (West Sussex)
38–39 Little London 38-39 Little London, (01243) 537550. Colourful Mediterranean-style venue on two levels with a terrace for barbecues. Expect good-value dishes such as soupe au pistou, brioche of wild mushrooms, casseroled rabbit with prunes, and alcoholic crêpes.

• **CHITTLEHAMHOLT** (Devon)
Highbullen Chittlehamholt, (01769) 540561. The Neil family's Victorian-Gothic mansion has unforgettable views and is a sporting enthusiast's dream, but it's also a relaxed venue for dependable food. Expect unflashy home cooking, with well-sauced meat and fish, decent vegetables and 'irresistibly rich' puddings.

• **CLACTON-ON-SEA** (Essex)
Wendle's 3 Rosemary Road, (01255) 426316. A lively 'oasis in a desert' specialising in fish cooked to order, but also serving steaks, game and vegetarian dishes. Tapas and sangria are available Tuesday to Friday (7 to 9pm), and theme nights are popular.

• **Coggeshall** (Essex)
White Hart Market End, (01376) 561654. Historic Essex coaching-inn, parts of which date back to the fifteenth century. Italian owners, predominantly old-fashioned Italian food and a useful wine list to match. Bedrooms are smart and well equipped.

• **Corbridge** (Northumberland)
Valley Old Station House, (01434) 633434/633923. Lively Indian set in an old station-house and offering a novel 'passage to India' service that brings visitors from Newcastle by train. The cooking is generally a cut above the curry-house average; starters and vegetables stand out.

• **Cotebrook** (Cheshire)
Alvanley Arms Forest Road, (01829) 760200. This converted farmhouse north-east of Tarporley is locally renowned for its high-quality pub food. Robust hotpots and pies share the billing with more ambitious specials such as pork in mushroom and cider sauce.

• **Cumnor** (Oxfordshire)
Vine Inn 11 Abingdon Road, (01865) 862567. Vine-covered, eighteenth-century inn that woos the crowds with a vast blackboard menu. Expect lots of fish, plus pasta, grills and stir-fries. Bonuses are the play area in the garden and the non-smoking conservatory.

• **Darley Abbey** (Derbyshire)
Darleys Darley Abbey Mills, (01332) 364987. A great setting in a converted mill canteen overlooking the Derwent rapids, north of Derby. Daily deliveries of fresh produce are used for a menu that might feature Caesar salad, a trio of fish with lobster sauce, roast loin of pork and some homely desserts.

• **Dartington** (Devon)
Cott Inn Dartington, (01803) 863777. Showpiece medieval inn famous for its eye-catching thatched roof. Lunch is a buffet, evening meals revolve around local produce: breast of duck with rhubarb and ginger, chargrilled salmon and Normandy-style rabbit are typical.

• **Dartmouth** (Devon)
The Exchange 5 Higher Street, (01803) 832022. 'A little gem' in an ancient building known as the Tudor House. The menu has a strong American accent: black-bean cakes, chicken breast coated in pecan nuts, and chargrilled lobster with banana and chilli salsa are typical. Open all week except Tuesdays. More reports, please.

• **Deddington** (Oxfordshire)
Dexter's Market Place, (01869) 338813. Neighbourhood restaurant in a pretty village square offering a varied menu with modern overtones. Wild mushrooms on olive toast, Thai scallop soup, beef fillet with roasted vegetables, and hot passion-fruit soufflé have been enjoyed. 'Well-chosen, interesting' wines.

• **Denshaw** (Greater Manchester)
Rams Head Ripponden Road, (01457) 874802. Serious pub food is now the attraction at this old stone farmhouse not far from the M62. Peter Midwood pulls out all the stops for a menu that might list game soup, sauté smoked chicken with pineapple or bread-and-butter pudding.

• **Dent** (Cumbria)
Stone Close Main Street, (0153 96) 25231. Dales tea-shop in two converted cottages that provides daytime sustenance for famished walkers and tourists. Robust food is served in a setting of beams and flagstone floors, and the place also has three homely bedrooms.

• **Derby** (Derbyshire)
Le Dijon 115 London Road, (01332) 205050. Students from the Tertiary College at Wilmorton flex their culinary muscles in the kitchen here, but all comers are welcome to enjoy the fruits of their labours. Lunches have a gastronomic 'theme', while fixed-price dinners are French. Open only from Tuesday to Friday.

• **Diss** (Norfolk)
Diss Coffee House and Sing Tong Thai St Nicholas Street, (01379) 651580. By day this cottagey, pine-furnished place serves coffee and cakes, plus a few English and Thai dishes. In the evening it fulfils its role as East Anglia's longest-running Thai restaurant, with straightforward but emphatic home-cooking.

• **DODDINGTON** (Lincolnshire)
Littlehouse Restaurant Doddington Hall, (01522) 690980. Rustic eating place providing eclectic food for travellers and visitors to Doddington Hall. Dinners are served from Thursday to Saturday; light lunches and afternoon teas on Wednesday and Sunday (May to September). Don't miss the home-made ice-creams.

• **DODDISCOMBSLEIGH** (Devon)
Nobody Inn Doddiscombsleigh, (01647) 252394. A prodigious wine list plus a staggering choice of West Country cheeses are the star turns in this out-of-the-way village inn. Choose between traditional bar food or more elaborate restaurant dishes such as braised lambs' sweetbreads.

• **DULVERTON** (Somerset)
Ashwick House (01398) 323868. Charming, if slightly 'eccentric', Edwardian country-house overlooking the Barle Valley. Chef/proprietor Richard Sherwood works to a daily handwritten dinner menu: soups, pastry-work and puddings have been singled out for praise. Also open for Sunday lunch, and accommodation is available.

• **ELSTOW** (Bedfordshire)
St Helena High Street, (01234) 344848. Highly popular Bedfordshire restaurant with a strong local following. Set menus and specials cater for all tastes, which means anything from sole and steaks to turbot with chive butter sauce, and haggis on corned beef hash with a poached egg.

• **ELTON** (Cambridgeshire)
Loch Fyne Oyster Bar The Old Dairy, (01832) 280298. Loch Fyne oysters and smoked fish are the things to eat in this casual outpost of the empire based in Cairndow (see main entry, Scotland), a short drive from Peterborough. Cooked dishes are also available, although these draw a mixed response.

• **EPPING** (Essex)
Neil's 142 High Street, (01992) 576767. Fungi and game from Epping Forest are augmented by fresh fish for a modern menu that ranges from Cajun crab bake to best end of lamb with red onion confit. Hot soufflés, farmhouse cheeses, single malts and wines form the back-up.

• **FARNHAM** (Surrey)
Chesa Bowling Alley, Crondall, (01252) 850328 Modern, custom-built restaurant in a hamlet just outside Farnham. Peter Hughes works to a menu of French-inspired dishes such as Roquefort quiche with chilli compote, brill with curry and watercress sauce, and lemon tart. Intimate surroundings and informal service.

• **FAWLEY** (Buckinghamshire)
Walnut Tree Fawley, (01491) 638360. Civilised Chiltern country inn with excellent views and a conservatory dining-room. Accomplished cooking along the lines of asparagus with hollandaise, calf's liver with black pudding, and medallions of venison with two sauces. Brakspear ales, good wines, 'first-class' service.

• **FIRLE** (East Sussex)
Ram Inn Firle, (01273) 858222. Exemplary country pub in a 'glorious Downland village'. The Wooller family makes use of local, free-range produce for a homespun menu that covers everything from ploughman's and pies to salads and fruit crumbles. **£**

• **FLETCHING** (East Sussex)
Griffin Inn Fletching, (01825) 722890. Log fires, a tiered garden and highly rated bar food are a winning combination in this beamed sixteenth-century hostelry. Restaurant meals are based on local produce; Thursday night is fish night. Well-kept ales and a sound wine list. Accommodation is available.

• **FOTHERINGHAY** (Northamptonshire)
Falcon Inn Fotheringhay, (01832) 226254. 'Good country pub food, good beer and good wine' sum up this popular inn standing in the shadow of Fotheringhay's awesome church. Home-made soups, pâtés, roasts and casseroles are backed up by some splendid puddings.

• **FOULSHAM** (Norfolk)
The Gamp Claypit Lane, (01362) 684114. Pleasant country restaurant with a recently added garden room. A sound

choice for English-inspired dishes such as roast duckling with plum and sloe-gin compote, and 'superb' fruit crumbles. Sunday lunch is a winner.

• **FRISTON** (Suffolk)

Old Chequers Aldeburgh Road, (01728) 688270. Pleasing village pub with a warm atmosphere and a good line in food. Lunch is a hot-and-cold buffet. Evening meals follow an eclectic path, taking in dim-sum, seafood chowder and stuffed pheasant breast with chestnuts and cranberries.

• **GLOOSTON** (Leicestershire)

Old Barn Inn Andrews Lane, (01858) 545215. Sixteenth-century stone inn with a civilised atmosphere, three bedrooms and daily menus advertising 'serious' pub food. Expect anything from hot roast beef sandwiches to salmon Wellington with dill and vermouth. Tip-top real ales.

• **GOOSNARGH** (Lancashire)

Bushell's Arms Church Lane, (01772) 865235. Regional foods, local recipes and ideas plucked from the world larder make up the repertoire in this industriously run North Country pub. Set lunches are exceptional value and the place also boasts a commendable wine list.

Solo Goosnargh Lane, (01772) 865206. Relaxed, welcoming venue that reminded one reporter of her grandmother's parlour. Dinner menus have an international flavour: gnocchi, smoked salmon with lime vinaigrette, or duck with orange sauce. The sweet trolley is a winner.

• **GOSFIELD** (Essex)

Green Man The Street, (01787) 472746. Extremely busy Greene King pub a few miles from Braintree. The cooking is a mixture of traditional English pies, casseroles and roasts, backed up by more ambitious stuff such as turbot with lobster sauce. Lunch is a splendid buffet.

• **GRAMPOUND** (Cornwall)

Eastern Promise 1 Moor View, (01726) 883033. Family-run Chinese restaurant (Mrs Tse cooks) quirkily located in a historic Cornish village. The décor has echoes of a genuine tea-house and the cooking is a mix of Peking/Szechuan classics, plus a few personal inventions.

• **GRANGE IN BORROWDALE** (Cumbria)

Borrowdale Gates Hotel Grange-in-Borrowdale, (01768) 777204. Family-run Victorian house set against the impressive backdrop of the Borrowdale Valley. Four-course dinners have an international flavour (cod florentine, fillet of lamb en croûte); light lunches are served in the lounge.

• **GREAT YARMOUTH** (Norfolk)

Seafood Restaurant 85 North Quay, (01493) 856009. Fresh fish from Lowestoft and 'first-class dry martinis' are the stars of the show at the Kikis family's popular restaurant on the quay. Steaks and Stroganov are carnivorous alternatives to oysters, lobster and sole.

• **GUISELEY** (West Yorkshire)

Harry Ramsden's White Cross, (01943) 874641. The prospect of eating battered haddock in a setting of crystal chandeliers, panelling and stained glass is the reason why visitors are lured to Harry Ramsden's – 'the largest fish-and-chip restaurant in the world'.

• **GWEEK** (Cornwall)

Mellanoweth Gweek, nr Helston, (01326) 22271. A pleasant cottage restaurant-with-rooms, divided up into a charming dining-area and a lunchtime bistro/crêperie located in an outhouse. Friendly service, excellent value for money.

• **HALIFAX** (West Yorkshire)

Holdsworth House Holdsworth, (01422) 240024. Built in 1633, the house is 'a splendid example of a Calder Valley yeoman's hall'. The dining-room is all panelling and antiquity, while the menu inhabits the up-to-the-minute world of scallops with chargrilled vegetables, and guinea-fowl with cabbage and lentils.

• **HARROGATE** (North Yorkshire)

Bettys 1 Parliament Street, (01423) 502746. The original branch of a mini-chain of North Country tea-rooms opened by Frederick Belmont in 1919. Morning coffee and afternoon tea are 'a real gastronomic experience', all the more fun if the trio is playing. Tailor-made for families.

• **Hatch Beauchamp** (Somerset)
Nightingales Bath House Farm, (01823) 480806. After a sabbatical, the Barlows are back in residence at this modest country restaurant not far from Taunton. Opening times are very restricted (ring for details), but the atmosphere is pleasantly rustic and the cooking yields fair results.

• **Hawkshead** (Cumbria)
Room with a View First Floor, Laburnum House, The Square, (01539) 436751. The Grahams offer a valuable service by providing vegetarian sustenance for tourists on the Beatrix Potter trail. Their international menu takes in anything from Californian cassoulet to Mediterranean vegetable plait, and Mexican dishes.

• **Hemel Hempstead** (Hertfordshire)
Gallery Restaurant Old Town Hall Arts Centre, (01442) 232416. Admirable restaurant in a bare-boarded room above the Old Town Hall, offering some of the best value food in the area. The menu features modern salads, pasta, snacks and dishes ranging from twice-baked soufflé to chicken in turmeric and yoghurt.

• **Heybridge** (Essex)
Chigborough Lodge Chigborough Road, (01621) 853590. Vine-encrusted barn transformed into a tiny restaurant close to the River Blackwater. Expect reliable Anglo-French dishes such as grilled mushrooms with goats' cheese, salmon fillet with Pernod, and strawberry shortcake.

• **Hockley Heath** (West Midlands)
Nuthurst Grange Nuthurst Grange Lane, (01564) 783972. Close to Birmingham's urban sprawl, but in a secluded setting complete with landscaped gardens. Dishes are prettily presented, and recent successes have included tomato and mozzarella tart, oxtail in burgundy and thyme sauce, and chocolate roulade.

• **Hope** (Shropshire)
Stables Drury Lane, Hopesgate, (01743) 891344. Archetypal Shropshire country pub way off the beaten track overlooking Long Mountain. Wonderful views, seriously good beers, 'tremendously cheap' wines and creditable home-cooking. Fish and vegetables are strikingly fresh.

• **Hopton Wafers** (Shropshire)
Crown Inn Hopton Wafers, nr Cleobury Mortimer, (01299) 270372. Immaculate sixteenth-century country inn with cottagey accommodation and lawns running down to a stream. Formal meals are served with courtesy in the restaurant, where dishes range from Herefordshire steaks to monkfish with lemon butter. Bar food is of a similar standard.

• **Hove** (East Sussex)
Quentin's 42 Western Road, (01273) 822734. Industrious home production and an eclectic viewpoint set the tone in this rather swish place. Salmon with lime and chilli, whisky-flamed venison, and apple pie with lavender ice-cream are typical of Quentin Fitch's monthly menus.

• **Hoxne** (Suffolk)
Swan Low Street, (01379) 668275. A classy pub wine list is one reason why this historic Suffolk inn stands out from the crowd. Another is its menu of daily specials, which might include Jerusalem artichoke soup; duck, bacon and walnut salad; and monkfish with fennel and tomato.

• **Ilkley** (West Yorkshire)
Bettys 32–34 The Grove, (01943) 608029. Offshoot of a mini-chain of tearooms with several branches across Yorkshire. Breads and cakes are unmissable, afternoon tea is a delight, light meals add a more cosmopolitan note. Superb children's facilities.

• **Ivy Hatch** (Kent)
Plough Coach Road, (01732) 810268. The setting is a tile-hung Kentish pub, but the food has high aspirations and a French accent. Reserve a table in the bar or conservatory and choose from a menu that embraces duck pâté, skate meunière, and guinea-fowl forestière.

• **Keighley** (West Yorkshire)
Headley's 396–398 Skipton Road, (01535) 607375. Great family place, although the décor is Yorkshire traditional and the lights are low. Expect generous casseroles and toad-in-the-hole, as well as more showy offerings. Separate bowls of steaming hot vegetables are greatly appreciated.

• **Keswick** (Cumbria)
Brundholme Hotel Brundholme Road, (01768) 774495. Tranquil retreat for Wordsworth devotees, high above the River Greta. Ian Charlton cooks some stylish dishes – shellfish cassoulet with black tagliatelle, Herdwick lamb with sauté parsnips, for example – and grows his own vegetables.

• **Kingsteignton** (Devon)
Old Rydon Inn Rydon Road, (01626) 54626. Impressively restored 300-year-old farmhouse where visitors can sample imaginative pub food in a converted cider loft, or settle for a full meal in the conservatory. Look for fish and game specials on the blackboard.

• **Knapp** (Somerset)
Rising Sun Knapp, nr North Curry, (01823) 490436. A dazzling array of fish from near and far is the reason why travellers set a course for this fifteenth-century Somerset longhouse. Prices are by no means cheap, but the quality is seldom in doubt. Sunday lunch is a good bet for those who favour red meat.

• **Knowstone** (Devon)
Masons Arms Inn Knowstone, nr South Molton, (01398) 341231/341582. This medieval thatched cottage is an impressive all-rounder in the first division of traditional country inns. The kitchen delivers genuine pub food of the best kind, backed up by first-rate beers and decent wines.

• **Knutsford** (Cheshire)
Brasserie Belle Epoque 60 King Street, (01565) 633060. Flamboyant Edwardian showpiece that has moved with the times (and changed its name). The atmosphere is lively, and the eclectic brasserie menu globetrots from tripe or black pudding to chargrilled fish, risottos and trendy salads.

• **Lacock** (Wiltshire)
At the Sign of the Angel 6 Church Street, (01249) 730230. Owned by the Levis family since 1944 and still a thoroughly English retreat in the heart of a National Trust village. Food ranges from cottage pie and smoked haddock fish-cakes to monkfish in mustard sauce. Accommodation is in character.

• **Lancaster** (Lancashire)
Pierre Victoire 27A St Georges Quay, (01524) 843199 A recent addition to Pierre Levicky's growing empire of cut-price eating-houses. The setting is a 'stark' warehouse conversion by the banks of the Lune and the food is in the mould of cucumber soup, casseroled chicken, and pear and kiwi tart.

• **Lechlade** (Gloucestershire)
Rieunier's 6 Oak Street, (01367) 252587. 'A small but lovingly thought-out restaurant' in a Cotswold terrace, with a less expensive bistro at the back. Home-made sausages and fresh ravioli add a twist to René Rieunier's mainstream French menu. Good fish and puddings.

• **Leeds** (West Yorkshire)
La Grillade 31–33 East Parade, 0113-2459707. Long-serving brasserie recommended for simply prepared grills, baskets of chips, Gallic stalwarts such as coq au vin, plus good coffee and cheese. Breakfast is served from 8am and the show closes at 11pm.
Olive Tree Oaklands, 55 Rodley Lane, 0113-256 9283. Friendly Greek restaurant on the outskirts of the city, run with great enthusiasm by the Psarias family. Meze are good value, and the place caters admirably for adults and children alike. Tuesday night is bouzouki night.

• **Leicester** (Leicestershire)
Heath's 169 Evington Road, 0116-273 3343. Seafood bar/restaurant opened by one of Leicester's leading fish-merchants. Freshness is the key and the menu spans everything from cod and chips to turbot with oyster mushrooms. Have a plate of oysters or a full meal. Wines from Eldridge Pope, Trappist beers, friendly service. More reports, please.

• **Lewes** (East Sussex)
Twenty 20 Fisher Street, (01273) 487568. Enthusiastically run bistro offering a limited menu of French-style dishes, with fish as the major suit; the achievable aim is to keep the bill below £10. Chocolate nut cream is the best-selling dessert.

• **Lichfield** (Staffordshire)
Swinfen Hall Hotel Swinfen, (01543) 481494. Sumptuously decorated Georgian mansion with a 'wondrous' entrance hall, minstrels' gallery and an abundance of carved woodwork. Chef Chris Morrall works hard, set menus are reasonably priced and staff are keen to please.

• **Little Bedwyn** (Wiltshire)
Harrow Inn Little Bedwyn, nr Marlborough, (01672) 870871. Run by a village co-operative since 1991, this Victorian inn is a pub success story. The food has up-to-the-minute overtones – duck with lentils and pancetta, grilled tuna with tomato and horseradish – and there is also good drinking to be had.

• **Little Hampden** (Buckinghamshire)
Rising Sun Little Hampden, (01494) 488393/488360. Stylish Chiltern inn offering an up-market menu that embraces everything from baked avocado with crabmeat to apple-smoked rabbit with mustard sauce, and sea bass with tempura prawns. The Woodman's Lunch is a good bet for daytime refuelling.

• **Liverpool** (Merseyside)
Café Retro 20 Mathew Street, 0151-236 4123. Occupying the original premises of the Armadillo restaurant, this laid-back café/bar trades in salads, sandwiches and chargrills, backed up by a few sweets. Excellent home-baked bread, decent coffee.

• **Long Melford** (Suffolk)
Chimneys Hall Street, (01787) 379806. Well-liked country restaurant in an archetypal sixteenth-century, half-timbered house. Jason Shroeder offers dishes such as grilled halibut with mustard, and casseroled rabbit with fennel and saffron. Fish nights are a feature.

• **Lower Oddington** (Gloucestershire)
Fox Inn Lower Oddington, nr Stow-on-the-Wold, (01451) 870888/570555. Stylishly revamped Cotswold pub with a flagstoned bar, several discreet eating areas and a walled garden. Salmon fish-cakes and warm chicken and avocado salad are fixtures on the bistro-style menu. Tip-top draught beers and even better wines.

• **Ludlow** (Shropshire)
Dinham Hall Ludlow, (01584) 876464. Converted Georgian house a stone's throw from the gates of Ludlow Castle. Bread is baked in-house and the kitchen has delivered acceptable pea and mint soup, duck breast with Grand Marnier, beef and venison pie, and tarte Tatin. Service is disarmingly attentive.

• **Lynmouth** (Devon)
Rising Sun Hotel Harbourside, (01598) 753223. An enviable harbourside setting, impeccable service and careful cooking are the scoring points of this fourteenth-century smugglers' inn. Reporters have praised smoked venison, fillet of turbot with raspberry sauce, and apple fritters with clotted cream.

• **Madingley** (Cambridgeshire)
Three Horseshoes High Street, (01954) 210221. The two-mile drive out of Cambridge to this premier-league pub/restaurant is well worth while. The menu is modern brasserie with a strong Italian accent (Tuscan bread soup, ricotta and pepper soufflé, chargrilled tuna with beans) and outstanding Italian wines to match. More reports, please.

• **Malmesbury** (Wiltshire)
Old Bell Abbey Row, (01666) 822344. Founded in 1220 and ranked as one of England's oldest 'hostelries'. The cooking shows its English roots with home-cured fish, roasts, and stuffed pig's trotter with black pudding, but also zooms off for grilled halibut with red onion and herb crust. Bar meals and cream teas are available.

• **Manchester** (Greater Manchester)
Café Alto 9–11 Wilmslow Road, Rusholme, 0161-225 7108. Trendy

modern venue on the fringe of Manchester's 'curry alley'. Caesar salad, black pudding with mango, and Thai fish with couscous are typical of the kitchen's global repertoire. Excellent-value early evening menus.

Café Istanbul 79–81 Bridge Street, 0161-833 9942. Authentic Turkish café with glass-topped tables, decorative tiles and plates on the walls. Excellent-value meze, high-protein kebabs and casseroles backed up by gutsy Turkish and French wines. Handy for the Opera House.

Gaylord Amethyst House, Spring Gardens, 0161-832 4866. The international face of Indian cuisine in central Manchester, providing competent, consistent food. Sedate décor sets the tone and the menu runs from tandooris to well-handled vegetarian dishes.

Granada Hotel, El-Meson 404 Wilmslow Road, Withington, 0161-434 3480. Spanish tapas bar and restaurant in the basement of the Granada Hotel. Tortillas, meatballs, squid and spicy sausages are helped along by some gusty Spanish wines. Great atmosphere, great value for money.

Market Restaurant Edge Street/104 High Street, 0161-834 3743. Opposite the city's former produce market, this highly individual bistro gets full marks for its terrific atmosphere and service. Monthly menus range far and wide for bobotie, caponata, herb-crusted chicken breast, and champagne rhubarb fool. Belgian beers, good wines.

Sanam 145-153 Wilmslow Road, Rusholme, 0161-224 8824/1008. One of Manchester's 'old-stagers' offering consistent, jazzily spiced Indian food at prices that are eminently affordable. No frills, long opening hours, unlicensed (drink lassi or a milkshake instead).

Tai Pan Brunswick House, 81-97 Upper Brook Street, 0161-273 2798. Stylish Cantonese place about 15 minutes' walk from Chinatown. Relax in the vast dining-room, order dim-sum at lunch-time or explore the full menu for dinner. Cold roast duck, prawn-cake with vegetables, and stuffed aubergine with black-bean sauce have been enjoyed.

• **MARTINHOE** (Devon)

Old Rectory Martinhoe, nr Barnstaple, (01598) 763368. Secluded family-run hotel in three acres of grounds surrounded by Exmoor National Park. Suzanne Bradbury's dinner menu has country overtones: smoked quail with sloe jelly, leg of lamb with juniper berries, and casseroled beef with horseradish are typical examples.

• **MELLOR** (Greater Manchester)

Devonshire Arms Longhurst Lane, 0161-427 2563. A classic example of a traditional northern pub. What lifts it out of the ordinary is the landlord's cordial presence and the cook's tour of a menu that spans everything from home-cured gravlax and French onion soup to apple pie.

• **MIDDLEHAM** (North Yorkshire)

Waterford House Kirkgate, (01969) 622090. A monumental list of more than 800 wines attracts connoisseurs to this stone guest-house on the edge of the Dales National Park. Daily menus are built on sound ingredients including wild Tay salmon, Yorkshire lamb and free-range chicken.

• **MILNROW** (Greater Manchester)

Meme's 22 Dale Street, (01706) 353651. 'No smoking' is one of the selling points in this pleasant local restaurant; another is the home-made fig and pecan bread. Potato cakes with tomato chutney, chicken with tarragon and mustard sauce, and chocolate rum pots have also been praised.

• **MONKTON COMBE** (Avon)

Combe Grove Manor Brassknocker Hill, (01225) 834644. Historic Georgian house and country club in a magnificent setting overlooking Limpley Stoke Valley. Choose between formal meals in the Georgian restaurant or lighter food in the casual atmosphere of the Vaults.

• **MORETONHAMPSTEAD** (Devon)

Reverend Woodforde 11A Cross Street, (01647) 440691. 'A great little family restaurant' offering a distinct version of English country cooking based on

Dartmoor game, naturally reared meat and local fish – although chanterelles and other wild fungi are the owners' passion. Open for dinner only from Monday to Saturday.

• **MORPETH** (Northumberland)
La Brasserie 59 Bridge Street, (01670) 516200. Run by the Wilkinson family since 1975, this North Country bistro continues to deliver sound cooking in casual surroundings. Dishes range from confit of duck to chargrilled tuna with asparagus and spinach. Eminently affordable wines.

• **NANCENOY** (Cornwall)
Trengilly Wartha Inn Nancenoy, nr Falmouth, (01326) 340332. Seriously difficult to find, but worth the effort. Take in the views from the conservatory, enjoy imaginative food and tip-top real ales in the bar or opt for the fixed-price menu in the restaurant. The wine list is good too.

• **NEWCASTLE UPON TYNE** (Tyne & Wear)
Café Procope 35 The Side, 0191-232 3848. Hip, alternative café in a trendy part of the city, serving a wildly eclectic assortment of dishes with strong vegetarian overtones. Fish-cakes with oyster sauce, satay with tempeh, and Lithuanian potatoes are typical examples.

• **NEW HAW** (Surrey)
L'Ecluse 10 Woodham Lane, (01932) 858709. A useful neighbourhood address if you are looking for fair bistro cooking in the Weybridge area. Choose from the short *carte* or the list of blackboard specials. The simplest dishes tend to be the most successful.

• **NEWNHAM** (Kent)
George Inn 44 The Street, nr Sittingbourne, (01795) 890237. Impeccably rustic brick and tile-hung Kentish pub with 'museum displays' of birds and butterflies. Some imaginative daily specials include salmon koulibiac with samphire sauce, mixed liver risotto and elderflower fritters.

• **NIDD** (North Yorkshire)
Nidd Hall Nidd, nr Harrogate, (01423) 771598. Vaulted cellars, marble columns and ornate fireplaces are among the sumptuous assets at this Georgian-style mansion north of Harrogate. Prices are high, but the cooking generally succeeds in fusing past and present in grand style.

• **NORTHALLERTON** (North Yorkshire)
Bettys 188 High Street, (01609) 775154. Expect queues at all branches of Bettys. Enjoy freshly baked rolls and Sam Smith's lager before embarking on soup and summer sundaes. Coffee comes in 'the biggest breakfast cups' you can imagine.

• **NORTH BOVEY** (Devon)
Blackaller Hotel North Bovey, (01647) 440322. Converted seventeenth-century woollen mill on the banks of the River Bovey. Fixed-price dinners (bookings only) offer 'creative' modern British cooking based around local ingredients. Professional service and 'impressive' accommodation.

• **NORTON** (Shropshire)
Hundred House Hotel Bridgnorth Road, Norton, nr Shifnal, (01952) 730353. Idiosyncratic Georgian coaching-inn with extraordinary décor and spectacular herb gardens. Promising menus with eclectic brasserie overtones, well-kept real ales and some intriguing wines. Improvements are in the air; more reports, please.

• **NORWICH** (Norfolk)
Tatlers 21 Tombland, (01603) 621822. Four-square Georgian-style house in a cobbled enclave hard by the arched gateway leading to the cathedral. The mood is informal and the kitchen produces wild mushroom and fennel soup, 'outstanding' gravlax and venison casserole.

Thailand 9 Ring Road, (01603) 700444. Custom-built restaurant on the outskirts of the city, run by Richard Kidd and his Thai wife. She cooks to a short menu of satays, soups, curries and stir-fries, backed up by a fair choice for vegetarians.

• **NOTTINGHAM** (Nottinghamshire)
Higoi 57 Lenton Boulevard, 0115-942 3379. One of few creditable Japanese restaurants in the Midlands. Makoto Kato's menu is an affordable introduction to the cuisine, and he provides bento lunch-boxes to take away. Kaiseki

banquets are formal midweek events. More reports, please.

Hotel des Clos Old Lenton Lane, (0115) 986 6566. 'A small resting-place' tucked away in converted farm buildings on the banks of the Trent. Chef/proprietor John Abbey delivers 'beautifully presented' dishes in modern hotel-style; fish has been favourably endorsed. The 300-strong wine list is big on Chablis.

● **OLDBURY** (West Midlands)

Jonathans 16 Wolverhampton Road, 0121-429 3757. Extraordinary Midlands hotel/restaurant (and much more besides) with 'a quirky Victorian atmosphere'. The best value is in the bistro: successes have included 'moules et frites', terrine with apricot chutney, and butterscotch ice-cream.

● **ORFORD** (Suffolk)

Butley-Orford Oysterage Market Hill, (01394) 450277. Lively, no-frills place with a near-legendary reputation for local oysters, mussels and home-smoked fish; the salmon is top-class. A favourite with the Aldeburgh Festival crowd; open all week in summer, but limited opening times during winter.

● **OVER STRATTON** (Somerset)

New Farm Over Stratton, nr South Petherton, (01460) 240584. Innovative food and B&B in a converted hamstone barn close to the A303. Monthly menus could feature such things as skate with elderflower and gooseberries, and chicken with mascarpone and rosemary. 'Sublime' puddings and good British cheeses.

● **OXFORD** (Oxfordshire)

Bangkok House 42A Hythe Bridge Street, (01865) 200705. Well-supported Thai restaurant where the food is 'full of delightful flavours and interesting textures'. Dishes are deftly served by helpful waitresses. Drink Singha Thai beer or non-alcoholic fruit punch.

Browns 5–11 Woodstock Road, (01865) 511995. Jeremy Mogford's original has spawned branches in Brighton, Bristol and Cambridge, but the principles remain the same: all-day opening, no-frills, and real food for palates young and old, including a children's menu. Expect anything from ribs with home-made chips to linguine with walnuts and pesto. Jazz pianist early evening.

Ma Cuisine 21 Cowley Road, (01865) 201316. Peaceful French restaurant set among the ethnic culinary contingent on Cowley Road. André Chavagnon delivers creditable versions of classics such as timbale of mussels, and duck with apples and calvados. Excellent-value light lunches.

Munchy Munchy 6 Park End Street, (01865) 245710. Highly idiosyncratic café delivering a fast version of South East Asian home cooking conjured up from herbs, spices and fresh ingredients in unexpected combinations. Very short daily menu, strong flavours, low prices. Excellent teas, oriental beers and a handful of wines.

Opium Den 79 George Street, (01865) 248680. Long-running Chinese restaurant offering an accessible assortment of mainly Peking and Szechuan dishes running from crispy aromatic duck and sizzlers to braised lobster three-ways and Singapore noodles. Good for vegetarians.

● **PENKRIDGE** (Staffordshire)

William Harding's House Mill Street, (01785) 712955. The setting is rural, but this restaurant in a 400-year-old listed building draws much of its trade from the nearby motorway network. Watercress and pear soup, ragoût of monkfish, and chilled lemon soufflé are examples from the dinner menu.

● **PETERSTOW** (Hereford & Worcester)

Peterstow Country House Peterstow, nr Ross-on-Wye, (01989) 562826. Converted rectory in a prime site close to the Forest of Dean and the River Wye. Choose between the *carte* and the table d'hôte, which offers dishes such as fillet of red mullet with home-made pasta, crépinettes of oxtail, and tarte Tatin.

● **PINNER** (Greater London)

La Giralda 66–68 Pinner Green, 0181-868 3429. Long-standing suburban venue for reliable Continental cooking with strong Spanish overtones, backed up by a notable Spanish wine list. Gazpacho and paella share the bill with steaks and honey-roast rack of lamb.

• **Plymouth** (Devon)
Ocean Palace 30A Western Approach, (01752) 660170. Recently opened Chinese on the site of the sadly missed Yang Cheng. First impressions are that the menu has veered towards Peking and the cooking remains competent. Pork dumplings and scallops with Chinese greens have been fine.

• **Portsmouth** (Hampshire)
Seagull 13 Broad Street, (01705) 824866. Intimate seafood place in the heart of the Old Town by the fish markets. Christopher Trim is a 'charming' host, his wife cooks. Daily menus might include spicy chicken salad, fillet of brill provençale and monkfish with mustard sauce.

• **Powerstock** (Dorset)
Three Horseshoes Powerstock, nr Bridport, (01308) 485328. One of Dorset's most favoured country inns, rebuilt in 'Victorian-railway style' using local stone and tiles. Apart from the setting, fish from the Weymouth day boats is the main attraction.

• **Redmile** (Leicestershire)
Peacock Inn Main Street, Church Corner, (01949) 842554. Highly rated village pub hidden away in the Vale of Belvoir. Eat French, bistro-style food and drink beer in the deliberately rustic bar; otherwise go for the fixed-price restaurant menu. Accommodation – and other changes – are in the pipeline. More reports, please.

• **Redruth** (Cornwall)
Tabb's Tregea Terrace, (01209) 842488. Cosy restaurant in a converted granite forge run by a friendly young couple. Menus change seasonally and the kitchen is hot on chargrilling, stir-fries and searing. Fish is a speciality, home-made sweets are greatly liked.

• **Reeth** (North Yorkshire)
Burgoyne Hotel On the Green, (01748) 884292. A 'wonderful setting' in the heart of Swaledale is one of the attractions of this comfortably appointed 'Georgian-style' hotel. Ingredients are freshly procured; the kitchen is especially strong on traditional roasts and puddings.

• **Reigate** (Surrey)
La Barbe 71 Bell Street, (01737) 241966. Good neighbourhood bistro serving old-school, patriotically French dishes along the lines of escargots bourgogne, salade paysanne, entrecôte béarnaise and carré d'agneau. Excellent French cheeseboard.

• **Richmond** (Surrey)
Burnt Chair 5 Duke Street, 0181-940 9488. The in-place for pre- and post-theatre meals in Richmond. Conditions are cramped, but service is friendly and the food is serious. Warm assiette of seafood, confit of duck, lamb with tabbouleh, and ginger ice-cream have been appreciated.

• **Rochdale** (Greater Manchester)
After Eight Hurst Hill Hotel, 2 Edenfield Road, (01706) 46432. In a beautiful Georgian house with a walled garden, this is a relaxed spot for capable cooking along the lines of seafood mille-feuilles, venison with elderberry and cherry brandy sauce, and pineapple brandy-snap. Full vegetarian menu.

• **Rochford** (Essex)
Renouf's Bradley Way, (01702) 541334. Renouf's continues to serve south Essex well by providing modern accommodation and consistent old-school French food. Lobster and crab terrine, bouillabaise, beef Wellington and coq au Chambertin are the kind of dishes you can expect.

• **Rockbeare** (Devon)
Jack in the Green London Road, (01404) 822240. Right on the A30, this stylishly refurbished roadhouse has a menu featuring the likes of tempura king prawns, Cajun chicken with peanut dressing, and duck breast with lime, ginger and chilli. Good beers and wines.

• **Roydhouse** (West Yorkshire)
Three Acres Inn Roydhouse, Shelley, (01484) 602606. Revamped coaching-inn (with accommodation) in the Pennine foothills between the M1 and the M62. Food ranges from bar snacks to restaurant

meals with a modern flavour (carpaccio of beef, scallop risotto, vegetable tempura, etc.).

• **Saffron Walden** (Essex)
Old Hoops 15 King Street, (01799) 522813. Outstanding-value set meals (Tuesday to Friday) are the best bets in this oak-beamed restaurant. Well-tried bistro-style dishes, heaps of vegetables and good sweets are backed up by a sound wine list. Excellent service.

• **St Martin's** (Isles of Scilly)
St Martin's Lowertown, (01720) 422092. A glorious base from which to explore the Scilly Isles. Modern hotel comforts, leisure facilities, memorable sunsets and 'beautiful food'. Service is reckoned to be 'first-class'. Accommodation is available and children are welcome.

• **Salisbury** (Wiltshire)
Harpers 6–7 Ox Row, Market Square, (01722) 333118. A godsend for Salisbury shoppers, who crowd into the upstairs dining-room for bargain-price lunches ranging from roast joints, bangers with chips and butter-bean bobotie. Evening meals are a shade more ambitious, but equally good value.

• **Scarborough** (North Yorkshire)
Lanterna 33 Queen Street, (01723) 363616. Long-established trattoria popular with tourists and the Scarborough 'old guard' who go for 'those you have loved' favourites such as spaghetti carbonara, steak with Barolo, chicken pizzaiola and creamy desserts. Adequate wines, brisk service.

• **Seaview** (Isle of Wight)
Seaview Hotel High Street, (01983) 612711. Family-run hotel holding centre-stage in an unassuming seaside resort. Local produce, from lobsters to asparagus and garlic, dominates the menu in the elegant dining-room. Decent bar meals and real ales are also available.

• **Sheffield** (South Yorkshire)
Mediterranean 271 Sharrowvale Road, 0114 266 1069. Daytime tapas are a treat in this pleasant converted shop, while the restaurant lives up to its name with a repertoire featuring fish soup, baked whole sea bass, and loin of lamb in pastry with red wine sauce. More reports, please.

• **Sherborne** (Dorset)
Pheasants 24 Greenhill, (01935) 815252. 'Superb hospitality and service' have impressed visitors to this friendly restaurant-with-rooms. The menu caters for all tastes, globetrotting from gazpacho and warm salads to Chinese-style pork and sea bass with oysters.

• **Shere** (Surrey)
Kinghams Gomshall Lane, (01483) 202168. Originally an 'antique' cottage, now a charmingly informal restaurant complete with an outdoor pool and gardens for special occasions. The cooking is mixed, but fish is a good bet and the wine list is reasonably priced.

• **Sheringham** (Norfolk)
Arthur Browne's 23–29 Wyndham Street, (01263) 822242. Named after a famous citizen of Sheringham, this no-smoking restaurant is a potential crowd-pleaser. Pizzas with modern toppings are the backbone; otherwise the choice ranges from salad of grilled king prawns to fillet steak with oyster mushrooms.

• **Shipton-under-Wychwood** (Oxfordshire)
Lamb Inn High Street, (01993) 830465. Centuries-old Cotswold stone inn offering unfussy bar food, a lunchtime buffet and real ales in a stoically traditional setting. Fixed-price dinners are based soundly on local produce. The accommodation has been recommended.

• **Slaugham** (West Sussex)
Chequers Slaugham, nr Handcross, (01444) 400239. Fish and four-poster beds attract visitors to this 'hotel, restaurant and seafood bar' within reach of Gatwick Airport. Eat in the bar or the conservatory restaurant and choose from a menu that ranges from marinated anchovies and salmon en croûte to curries and kleftiko.

• **Speen** (Buckinghamshire)
Old Plow Inn Flowers Bottom Lane, (01494) 488300. Delightful old inn deep in the Chiltern beechwoods that now bills itself as a restaurant and bistro. The food

is in keeping: smoked duck and mango salad, grilled rump of lamb with potato dumplings, salmon with Japanese pickled ginger, iced lemon parfait.

• **Stockland** (Devon)
King's Arms Inn Stockland, (01404) 881361. Huge eighteenth-century thatched pub with a mass of bars, a dining-room and affordable B&B. Food is taken seriously and the blackboard menu spans everything from spinach soup and curries to 'superb' salmis of duck. Lunchtime snacks, real ales and well-chosen wines.

• **Stocksfield** (Northumberland)
Branches Branch House, Branch End Terrace, (01661) 844264. Reliable and reasonably priced, this popular restaurant is noted for classic dishes such as home-cured gravlax, breast of duckling with green peppercorns, and smoked local venison with leek and chestnut timbale.

• **Stoke-on-Trent** (Staffordshire)
Ria 61–67 Piccadilly, Hanley, (01782) 264411. Accessible Thai cooking from a long menu that embraces 'excellent' soups, fiery salads, curries, noodles and curiosities such as deep-fried minced pork and herbs on bread, and salmon with palm sugar and tamarind. Bookings only at lunch-time.

• **Stratford-upon-Avon** (Warwickshire)
Opposition 13 Sheep Street, (01789) 269980. A sound bet for bistro food near the theatre. Service is speedy and the waitresses 'often sing while serving'. Expect good-value salads, filled croissants, chilli, and dishes ranging from potted salmon to chargrilled steaks.

• **Stretton** (Leicestershire)
Ram Jam Inn Great North Road, (01780) 410776. Revamped roadside inn that shows motorway motels how things should be done. Refuelling platefuls are served all day in the open-plan eating area, more serious dishes in the formal restaurant. Good accommodation is a bonus for A1 travellers.

• **Sutton Gault** (Cambridgeshire)
Anchor Inn Sutton Gault, (01353) 778537. A superbly evocative setting by the Ouse Washes. Impressive wines, fine cheeses, and cooking which makes the best of good ingredients are sufficiently good reasons for seeking out this ancient ferry inn. Accommodation is now available. More reports, please.

• **Tarrant Monkton** (Dorset)
Langton Arms Tarrant Monkton, nr Blandford Forum, (01258) 830225. The Davisons (ex-La Belle Alliance, Blandford Forum, see main entry) are now in residence at this family-friendly 300-year-old thatched pub. Food is served in the bar and bistro, and the place is also noted for its excellent range of beers and wines.

• **Taunton** (Somerset)
Capriccio 41 Bridge Street, (01823) 335711. Echoes of the Mediterranean make this bright-and-breezy place a favourite Taunton haunt. Furnishings are genuine Italian and the cooking is a notch above trattoria basic, promising such things as vitello tonnata and ravioli stuffed with venison. Pasta and ice-cream are made on the premises.

• **Tewkesbury** (Gloucestershire)
Le Bistrot André 78 Church Street, (01684) 290357. 'Unpretentious' sums up this old-style bistro, where French music plays and the blackboard lists such things as rack of lamb and sea bass with fennel. Onion soup is a perennial favourite. Service is 'extrovert'. Open evenings only from Monday to Saturday.
New World 61 High Street, (01684) 292225. Vietnamese cooking comes to the Cotswolds in the shape of this comfortable restaurant. The menu is a mixed bag with lots of Chinese and Indonesian influences, while New World wines show up on the list. Lunch by prior arrangement; take-aways available.

• **Tideford** (Cornwall)
Heskyn Mill Tideford, nr Saltash, (01752) 851481. Local produce shows up well in this converted eighteenth-century watermill. Menus cover everything from scallops with leeks and bacon to wild boar with cider sauce. Apple-pie with clotted cream makes an old-fashioned finale.

• **Topsham** (Devon)
Drake's Fore Street, (01392) 875172. Billed as a 'wine and ale house', this venture is starting to win friends. Downstairs is the bar, upstairs is the gallery where you can eat from an eclectic menu that takes in salmon tartare, Thai-style chicken, lamb with lentils, and coffee-poached pear.

• **Torquay** (Devon)
Burley's 43 Babbacombe Downs Road, Babbacombe, (01803) 316661. Up-market restaurant in an enclave of genteel guest houses and private hotels overlooking Torbay. The cooking is ambitious and results are fair: chicken liver parfait, poached John Dory with basil sauce, and Amaretto ice-cream have been recommended.

• **Treburley** (Cornwall)
Springer Spaniel Treburley, nr Launceston, (01579) 370424. A one-time run-of-the-mill watering-hole transformed into a high-profile food pub by a couple of Bristol restaurateurs. Blackboard menus advertise a mixed bag of dishes from venison terrine and Caesar salad to Singapore laksa and halibut en croûte.

• **Tresco** (Isles of Scilly)
Island Hotel (01720) 422883. An enchanting setting on the Island of Flowers. The 'beautifully designed' dining-room has glorious sea views, and the kitchen puts great store by local fish: scallops with asparagus, chargrilled monkfish, and tuna with deep-fried vegetables have all found favour. Puddings are good, too.

• **Tuckenhay** (Devon)
Floyd's Inn (Sometimes) Bow Creek, Tuckenhay, nr Totnes, (01803) 732350. Caviare on the menu, well-appointed bedrooms and a teddy bear called George presiding over the dining-room are typical features of Keith Floyd's idiosyncratic pub. The waterside setting is a delight and there are some fine wines to sip while watching the boats. Not cheap.

• **Wansford** (Cambridgeshire)
Haycock Hotel Wansford, nr Peterborough, (01780) 782223. Gem of a seventeenth-century coaching-inn, with an impeccable pedigree and splendid gardens along the banks of the Nene. Eat formally in one of the restaurants, or have something light in the Orchard Room. Excellent wine list.

• **Wantage** (Oxfordshire)
Foxes 8 Newbury Street, (01235) 760568. Cottagey restaurant off the market-place, providing a warm welcome and some enterprising food along the lines of salad of Mediterranean vegetables, monkfish with lime and coconut milk, and almond mousse with strawberries.

• **Warwick** (Warwickshire)
Fanshawe's 22 Market Place, (01926) 410590. Value for money and ample portions are the scoring points in the Fanshawes' town-centre restaurant. Menus are fixed-priced, and recommended dishes have included salmon and prawn mousse, pork with Dijon mustard and blackcurrant bavarois.
Findons 7 Old Square, (01926) 411755. Up-and-coming town-centre restaurant on the ground floor of a listed Georgian house. Moules marinière, pigeon with wild mushrooms, venison with kumquats and walnuts, and crème brûlée have been recommended. Ten good-value house wines.

• **Watton-at-Stone** (Hertfordshire)
George & Dragon High Street, (01920) 830285. Civilised, well-liked village pub with an all-round menu that spans everything from filled pancakes or fillet steak in a bun to baked salmon with whisky and lemon juice. Greene King real ales; drinkable wines.

• **Westcliff On Sea** (Essex)
Paris 719 London Road, (01702) 344077. 'An oasis' in a gastronomically bereft area of south Essex by the seaside. The kitchen delivers creditable renditions of salad of pigeon breast with sherry vinegar, beef fillet with red wine sauce, and skate with asparagus.

• **West Kirby** (Merseyside)
Banks Bistro 95 Banks Road, 0151-625 6767. Enterprising set-up with bags of atmosphere, friendly service and lively

food. Free-range produce is used for a creative menu that leapfrogs from England to South East Asia. Good home-made puddings and decent wines. Another branch is at 5 Rose Mount, Oxton, 0151-670 0446.

• **Weymouth** (Dorset)
Perry's 4 Trinity Road, (01305) 785799. Neat harbourside restaurant with marble-topped tables and pleasing views. All kinds of seafood served in all kinds of ways, but carnivores and vegetarians are also accommodated. Lunch is a fixed-price menu. Drinkable wines.

• **Whitewell** (Lancashire)
Inn at Whitewell Whitewell, Forest of Bowland, (01200) 448222. The inn *is* Whitewell. Its setting in the Forest of Bowland is splendidly isolated, and the place now operates as a fully fledged complex complete with a wine merchant's and art gallery. Accommodation has been praised and the kitchen delivers reliable food based on top-quality ingredients.

• **Whittlesford** (Cambridgeshire)
Tickell Arms Whittlesford, (01223) 833128. Rather hard to find (off A505 or M11 junction 10, south of Cambridge). The house rules are strict (smart dress, no children, no cigarettes), but this country pub is a quirky gem. Delightful gardens are one of its attractions and the food is sound. Bread, salads and game are high points.

• **Winchester** (Hampshire)
Nine The Square 9 Great Minster Street, (01962) 864004. 'The table in our bay window is the most popular in Winchester,' say the owners of this wine bar/restaurant hard by the cathedral. Expect a menu that encompasses everything from bresaola and brodetto to Thai-style black bream. Home-made pasta is a strong point, and the value for money is commendable.

• **Windermere** (Cumbria)
Holbeck Ghyll Holbeck Lane, (01539) 432375. Converted Victorian hunting-lodge, now a caringly maintained country-house hotel with glorious views from its grand panelled dining-room. Pan-fried monkfish with garlic and tarragon butter, and loin of Cumbrian lamb with green lentils are typical dishes.

• **Winforton** (Hereford & Worcester)
Sun Inn Winforton, (01544) 327677. Exemplary pub food in a cosy, rough-stone inn close to the River Wye. Ploughman's come with brilliant farmhouse cheeses, and Wendy Hibbard's cooking is a catholic mix of traditional English and far-flung exotic. First-rate real ales and better-than-average wines. Affordable accommodation.

• **Witham** (Essex)
Lian High House, 5 Newland Street, (01376) 510684. Ornately decorated Chinese restaurant in a converted private house with a porticoed entrance. Crispy roast duck is a favourite, but the menu spans everything from Peking ravioli and Szechuan double-cooked pork to Hunanese lamb. Not cheap.

• **Woodbridge** (Suffolk)
Wine Bar 17 Thoroughfare, (01394) 382557. 'Infectiously casual intimacy' sums up the mood in this jazzily decorated first-floor wine bar. Call in for a glass of interesting wine – plus superb olives, bread and tapénade – or choose from the imaginative blackboard menu.

• **Woodford Green** (Essex)
Pizzeria Bel-Sit 439 High Road, 0181-504 1164. Expect to queue for at least 20 minutes for oustanding pizzas in this highly popular Essex venue. Toppings are dazzlingly good and the crisp garlic bread is oozingly garlicky. Have a bottle of Peroni beer while you are waiting in line.

• **Woodseaves** (Staffordshire)
Old Parsonage High Offley, (01785) 284446. Set in open countryside off the A519, this restaurant-with-rooms also boasts a conservatory with great views. Keenly priced four-course menus with a modern flavour are bolstered by a serious British cheeseboard. Sunday lunch is recommended.

• **York** (North Yorkshire)
Bettys 6–8 St Helen's Square, (01904) 659142. Archetypal tea-rooms devoted to the tourist trade (cakes and menus can be purchased as souvenirs). Superb

pâtisserie, modern salads, classic afternoon teas, and hot dishes ranging from rösti to Masham sausages. Impressive children's facilities. Good Alsatian wines.

Grange Hotel, Ivy Restaurant, 1 Clifton, (01904) 644744. Change is in the air at this converted Regency town house within walking distance of the Minster. Eat in the formal restaurant or opt for something more casual in the basement brasserie. A seafood bar was planned as we went to press. More reports, please.

Scotland

• **ABERLOUR** (Grampian)
Archiestown Hotel by Aberlour, (01340) 810218. Charming old stone-built hotel highly popular with anglers and golfers. Judith Bulger's fixed-price dinner menus feature praiseworthy fish, abundant vegetables and 'delicious' puddings. Michael Bulger keeps 'a good cellar'.

• **ALLOA** (Central)
Gean House Gean Park, (01259) 219275. Luxurious, Lutyens'-style house with a 'compelling atmosphere' surrounded by a beautifully landscaped park. A short, modern menu is backed up by an equally sensibly priced wine list. Accommodation is available.

• **ARDUAINE** (Strathclyde)
Loch Melfort Hotel Arduaine, (01852) 200233. Glorious views across the bay to the Sound of Jura are one of the assets at this imposing hotel next to Arduaine Gardens. Bar lunches, afternoon teas and formal dinners make it a useful pit-stop for tourists and travellers.

• **AYR** (Strathclyde)
Fouters 2A Academy Street, (01292) 261391. Lively, good-value bistro in the vaulted basement of an old bank building. Fish is the strong suit on the *carte* and 'bistro menu': lobster lunches are a summer attraction. The wine list is a decent slate from local merchants, Whighams.

• **BALLATER** (Grampian)
Craigendarroch Hotel The Oaks, (01339) 755858. Prestigious hotel and country club complex with 'exciting' views of the River Dee and the mountains beyond. Ambitious fixed-price dinners are presented in a 'modern fashion' and the service is excellent.

• **BALQUHIDDER** (Central)
Monachyle Mhor Balquhidder, (01877) 384622. 'A real joy' of a farmhouse hotel set in 2,000 acres of grounds overlooking Lochs Voile and Doine. Fish is the star turn: look for squat lobsters, pin-head hake, red mullet, scallops and much more. Breakfast is a mammoth Scottish affair.

• **BIGGAR** (Strathclyde)
Culter Mill Coulter Village, (01899) 20950. Attractively converted grain mill (complete with grinding stones and a ghost) that now houses a good-value bistro as well as a restaurant. Mussels in cream sauce, rabbit with honey and mustard, and cloutie dumpling have found favour.

• **CROMARTY** (Highland)
Thistles 20 Church Street, (01381) 600471 Unpretentious venue providing wholesome food for tourists. Vegetarians do well with lentil and lemon soup, or bulgar, tahini and red pepper bake; others feast on haggis, or lemon sole stuffed with hazelnuts. Friendly service, down-to-earth prices.

• **DALRY** (Strathclyde)
Braidwoods Drumastle Mill Cottage, (01294) 833544. Promising newcomer in a pair of old stone cottages down a remote track (ring for directions). A delightful atmosphere is backed up by sharp cooking: Finnan haddock and pepper soup, guinea-fowl with oyster mushrooms and capers, and a 'very fine' lemon tart are typical dishes. More reports, please.

• **EDINBURGH** (Lothian)

Ann Purna 45 St Patrick's Square, 0131-662 1807. Family-run vegetarian restaurant offering excellent-value South Indian and Gujarati food in smoke-free surroundings. Flavours are challenging, there is Indian rice beer to drink and service is sincere. Handy for the Festival Theatre.

Montpeliers 159–161 Bruntsfield Place, 0131-229 3115. 'A wonderfully useful place', open all day and serving everything from 'brilliant' bacon butties to breast of guinea-fowl with lentils and thyme, and 'uncannily good' banoffi pie. Loud music, buzzy cheerful atmosphere.

Pepito's 24A Stafford Street, 0131-225 9575. Modest little Mexican place in Edinburgh's West End. The menu is sensibly short, but there's plenty of variation and dishes have a 'distinctive quality'. Nachos, frijoles, burritos, tacos, chimichangas and pecan pie are the things to expect.

Pierre Victoire 10 Victoria Street, 0131-225 1721. The original branch of Pierre Levicky's ever-growing list of cut-price eating-houses. Value-for-money is the main attraction, with a legendary set lunch. Another branch is at 6–8 Union Street, 0131-557 8451.

Suruchi 14A Nicholson Street, 0131-556 6583. Culture and cuisine share the limelight in this Indian restaurant where music and dancing, art exhibitions and food festivals are part of the show. The menu spans India, with plenty of options for meat-eaters and vegetarians alike.

Waterfront Wine Bar 1C Dock Place, Leith, 0131-554 7427. Go for the waterfront setting, a blackboard menu of fish (sardines), grills (ribeye steak) and salads (Mexican three-bean), and the wine. This relaxed dockside venue peddles an ever-changing enthusiast's list, big names are avoided and prices are commendably low. Best tables are in the conservatory.

• **FAIRLIE** (Strathclyde)

Fins Fencefoot Farm, (01475) 568989. Originally the farm stables, but now a tasteful, professionally run restaurant specialising in the freshest of local seafood. Sea bass with lemon-butter sauce has been outstanding, and vegetables are cooked to perfection.

• **GLASGOW** (Strathclyde)

Amber Regent 50 West Regent Street, 0141 331-1655. A sound bet for reliable Cantonese cooking in the heart of Glasgow. Classy décor – with prices to match – and a menu that offers seafood aplenty, sizzling satays, duck every-which-way, and specials such as aromatic crispy chicken.

Cabin 996 Dumbarton Road, Whiteinch, 0141-954 7102. Serious cooking, singing, and dancing on the tables are the heady mix in this venue. Daily menus follow the market and fish has been praised. Licensed, but you can also bring your own wine (£2 corkage).

Fire Station 33 Ingram Street, 0141-552 2929. The ladders and hoses are long gone, but this marble-walled ex-fire station now does duty as a cheerful eating-place manned by amazingly helpful young staff. Pizzas, pasta and burgers are served in a variety of ways, and the wine is worth drinking.

• **KELSO** (Borders)

Sunlaws House Hotel Heiton, (01573) 450331. History looms large at this baronial Borders mansion, and the kitchen flies the flag with a patriotic mix of steaks, lamb and game, plus lobster and salmon for good measure. Consistent results, but by no means cheap.

• **KILBERRY** (Strathclyde)

Kilberry Inn Kilberry-by-Tarbert, (01880) 770223. Jan and Kath Leadbeaters' pub with rooms is about as remote as they come (follow winding, single-track B8024), but visitors make the trek for the good-humoured atmosphere, cottagey comfort and exemplary country cooking.

• **KINBUCK** (Central)

Cromlix House Kinbuck, by Dunblane, (01786) 822125. Evocative Victorian sand-stone edifice with its own chapel, set in a 3,000-acre estate. Major pluses are the sophisticated approach to local produce, plus a classy vegetarian menu and a heavyweight wine list. Not cheap.

• **Kinross** (Tayside)
Grouse & Claret Heatheryford, (01577) 864212. Part of the Heatheryford Country Centre, which also includes an art gallery and accommodation, as well as opportunities for walking and fishing. David Futong uses local produce for a repertoire that ranges from game terrine to grilled salmon with braised fennel.

• **Markinch** (Fife)
Balbirnie House Balbirnie Park, by Glenrothes, (01592) 610066. Country-house hotels don't come much grander than this peach of a Georgian mansion set in a 400-acre landscaped park complete with golf course. The arrival of a new chef as we went to press promises great things. More reports, please.

• **Newton Stewart** (Dumfries & Galloway)
Kirroughtree Hotel (01671) 402141. Gloriously situated eighteenth-century mansion in eight acres of grounds overlooking the Galloway countryside. Elaborate modern hotel cooking with fish as the star; luxury ingredients, 'outstanding' sauces and Scottish cheeses. More reports, please.

• **Scarista** (Western Isles)
Scarista House Scarista, Isle of Harris, (01859) 550238. 'A wonderful place to stay' in remote surroundings. Spanking-fresh fish, thoughtfully prepared vegetables, green salads from the garden and farmhouse cheese are the things people remember. Breakfasts are brilliant, too.

• **Shieldaig** (Highland)
Tigh an Eilean Shieldaig, by Strathcarron, (01520) 755251. Spectacularly situated hotel among the Torridon Hills with views of the Isle of Pines. The cooking is restrained and classical; fish shows up well in dishes such as moules marinière and poached wild salmon hollandaise.

Wales

• **Cardiff** (South Glamorgan)
Chikako's 10–11 Mill Lane, (01222) 665279. Cardiff's only authentic Japanese restaurant, run by ever-present Chikako Cameron. The menu divides equally between dishes produced in the kitchen (teriyaki, tempura) and those prepared at the table (teppanyaki, shabu-shabu).
De Courcey's Tyla Morris Ave, (01222) 892232. A popular spot for Sunday lunch. At other times fixed-price menus provide the best deal, with dishes such as curried parsnip soup, sea bream with beurre blanc, and strawberry charlotte. Bread is home-baked, cheeses are Welsh.
Quayles 6–8 Romilly Crescent, (01222) 341264. Good value and bags of enthusiasm in the suburbs of Cardiff. Early-bird menus, a short *carte*, fish specials and gourmet evenings are part of the package. Home-baked breads, home-grown organic vegetables and ice-creams have been singled out.

• **Clydach** (Gwent)
Drum and Monkey Blackrock, (01873) 831980. Sixteenth-century two-storey building that doubles as bar and restaurant. Fish specials augment a menu that might include leek and potato soup, confit of duck, and coconut parfait. Friendly atmosphere and knowledgeable service. A new chef is in residence, so more reports, please.

• **Crickhowell** (Powys)
Bear Hotel Crickhowell, (01873) 810408. High-class coaching-inn valued for its traditional virtues. Bar food and restaurant meals are based on local produce, but ideas are global. Japanese prawns, venison with pink peppercorns, and turbot with avocado have been recommended. Excellent wines, too. More reports, please.

• **Glanwydden** (Gwynedd)
Queen's Head Glanwydden, (01492) 5146570. Still a favourite with travellers from both sides of the border, this spruce pub scores with its homely atmosphere and wide-ranging menu – although quantity sometimes comes before quality. Most praise is reserved for the puddings and the 'splendid' wine list.

• **Llanaber** (Gwynedd)
Llwyndu Farmhouse Llwyndu, nr Barmouth, (01341) 280144. Farmhouse B&B formerly providing dinner for residents only, but now catering for all comers (providing tables are available). Meals are served in a handsome dining-room and the kitchen delivers straightforward stuff such as leek and potato soup, and salmon and prawn tagliatelle.

• **Llanfyllin** (Powys)
Seeds 5 Penybryn Cottages, (01691) 648604. Mark and Felicity Seagers' pleasant country restaurant is a useful address in the little known backwaters of Powys. Lamb and cheeses are Welsh, fish might be baked cod with cockles and vermouth, and puddings are 'worthwhile'. Snacks are laid on as extras for day-time visitors.

• **Llangollen** (Clwyd)
Gales 18 Bridge Street, (01978) 860089. A wine-and-beer bar where people come to chat, meet friends, have a drink and eat a quick snack. Pan-fried flavourful steak with a jacket potato is the recommendation, plus a bottle of almost anything from the interesting and very sympathetically priced list; even the fine wines are good value.

• **Porthkerry** (South Glamorgan)
Egerton Grey Porthkerry, nr Rhoose, (01446) 711666. Restored Edwardian rectory in a peaceful wooded valley within reach of Cardiff airport. Elaborately constructed dishes are served in a mahogany- panelled dining-room to the accompaniment of classical music. Service is silky smooth.

• **Swansea** (West Glamorgan)
Annie's 56 St Helen's Road, (01792) 655603. Ann Gwilym's spruce converted schoolhouse remains a favourite with Swansea locals, who appreciate the fair prices and cheery atmosphere. Her fixed-price dinner menus might feature such dishes as onion tart, cassoulet, and hake with Gruyère and spinach crust.
Barrows 42 Newton Road, (01792) 361443. Chris Keenan has re-surfaced at this wine-bar-cum-restaurant not far from Oystermouth Castle. Blackboard menus promise a bit of everything, from Thai curry and pork steak with sweet-and-sour sauce to salmon risotto. Wines are a good match for the food. More reports please.

• **Trefriw** (Gwynedd)
Hafod House Trefriw, (01492) 640029. Spectacular views of the Conwy Valley are one of the attractions at this personally run hotel. Another is Norman Barker's cooking, which jumps from Welsh faggots or braised lamb with bubble and squeak, to warm salad of duck with wild mushrooms.

• **Welshpool** (Powys)
Golfa Hall Llanfair Road, (01938) 553399. Once a farmhouse on the Powis Castle Estate, Golfa Hall is now a spacious hotel set in eight acres of grounds. The kitchen works in tandem with top-drawer local suppliers, and it is great value for money.

Channel Islands

• **Gorey** (Jersey)
Jersey Pottery Restaurant Gorey, (01534) 851119. The Jones family has run this pottery for three generations and their Garden Restaurant provides fine lunches with seafood as the main theme. Up-to-the-minute starters (such as crab-cakes with chilli) precede salads and grills.

• **St Brelade** (Jersey)
Sea Crest Hotel Petit Port, (01534) 46353. Intimate seaside hotel in a secluded bay overlooking the conservation area of La Pulente Headland. The kitchen delivers creditable Anglo-French cooking with the emphasis on local fish, backed up by warm salads and flambés.

• **St Peter Port** (Guernsey)
La Frégate Les Cotils, St Peter Port, (01481) 724624. Take in the 'magical' views of the harbour and the castle before considering the menu in this long-standing Guernsey hotel. The cooking is French, fish has attracted good reports and the espresso coffee is hard to beat. Sunday lunch is also a good bet.

Le Nautique Quay Steps, (01481) 721714. A spectacular quayside setting and reliable fish cookery are the attractions in this converted wine cellar, bedecked with nautical bric-à-brac. There is also praise for the 'intelligent' wine list. Prices are inclusive of service.

Northern Ireland

• **Belfast** (Co Antrim)
Saints and Scholars 3 University Street, (01232) 325137. A cross between school dinners and a modern fast-food outlet. The waitresses wear uniforms, while the menu straddles everything from Chinese duck to Louisiana chicken. Great fun, high turnover, fair prices.

• **Helen's Bay** (Co Down)
Deanes on the Square 7 Station Square, 01247 852841. Idiosyncratic eating-place housed in a Scottish baronial folly on the platform beside the Belfast to Bangor line. It makes an unexpected setting for Mediterranean vegetables with goats' cheese and pesto, pork fillet in truffle and nut-oil sauce, and roast cod with Asian ratatouille.

New Entries

These restaurants are new to the *Guide* this year, although some may have appeared in previous years, or in the round-ups last year.

London

Alfred, WC2
Atelier, W1
Atlantic Bar and Grill, W1
Brown's Hotel, W1
Café dell'Ugo, SE1
Le Café du Jardin, WC2
Caffé Italia, SE3
Charco's, SW3
Chez Bruce, SW17
Chiaroscuro, WC1
Chiswick, W4
Como Lario, SW1
The Cow, W2
Harbour City, W1
Interlude de Chavot, W1
Jones Restaurant and Bar, WC2
Mantanah, SE25
Mon Plaisir, WC2
Moshi Moshi Sushi, EC2
Nicole's, W1
Le Palais du Jardin, WC2
People's Palace, SE1
Rasa, N16
St George's Hotel, The Heights, W1
St John, EC1
Stepping Stone, SW8
Tabac, W10
Tamarind, W1
Tate Gallery Restaurant, SW1
Union Café, W1
Wilsons, W14

England

Aldeburgh, Lighthouse
Alvechurch, The Mill
Arncliffe, Amerdale House
Beckington, Woolpack
Bilbrough, Bilbrough Manor
Boston Spa, Café Provence
Brighton, Terre à Terre
Buckland, Lamb Inn
Cheesden, French Connection
Chelsworth, Peacock Inn
Coln St Aldwyns, New Inn
Colston Bassett, Martins Arms
Corscombe, Fox Inn
Crosthwaite, Punchbowl Inn
Cumnor, Bear & Ragged Staff
Dorchester, George Hotel
East Witton, Blue Lion
Halifax, Design House
Haslemere, Fleur de Sel
Kenilworth, Simpson's
Leeds, Pool Court
Lidgate, Star Inn
Liversedge, Healds Hall Hotel, Harringtons
Ludlow, Merchant House
Manchester, Chiang Rai
Marsden, Olive Branch
Oxford, Gee's
Padstow, Bistro Margot Thomas
Painswick, Country Elephant
Pitton, Silver Plough
Ponteland, Café 21
Preston, Heathcote's Brasserie
Southall, Brilliant
Stanton, Leaping Hare Café
Sudbury, Red Onion Bistro
Trusham, Cridford Inn
Wilmington, Crossways
Winchester, Hotel du Vin & Bistro
Winchester, Old Chesil Rectory
Wolterton, Saracen's Head
Yarm, D.P. Chadwick's
Yattendon, Royal Oak
York, Middlethorpe Hall

Scotland

Auchterarder, Auchterarder House
Ballater, Balgonie Country House
Dervaig, Druimard Country House
Edinburgh, Crannog
Glasgow, Crannog
Glasgow, Yes
Kentallen, Ardsheal House
Kinloch Rannoch, Cuilmore Cottage
Oban, Heatherfield House
Troon, Lochgreen House

Wales

Creigiau, Caesar's Arms
Lamphey, Dial Inn
Llyswen, Llangoed Hall
St David's, Morgan's Brasserie
Swansea, L'Amuse

Isle of Man

Douglas, L'Expérience

Republic of Ireland

Ballylickey, Ballylickey Manor
Cork, Ivory Tower
Dublin, Ernie's
Dublin, Roly's Bistro
Gorey, Eugenes
Youghal, Aherne's

Closures

Whatever happened to that restaurant? Those listed below have closed since the last edition of the *Guide*, though one or two have re-opened under a different name.

London

Argyll, SW3
La Gaulette, W1
Harveys, SW17

England

Peano, Barnsley
Cobbett's, Botley
Hunters Lodge, Broadway
Morels, Haslemere
Shoes, High Ongar
Hedgehog Hall, Kelsale
Randells, Launceston
Pool Court, Pool in Wharfedale
Yang Cheng, Plymouth
Blue Goose, Settle
Brown's, Southampton
Sir Toby's, Stratford-upon-Avon
Chez Max, Surbiton
Poston Mill, Vowchurch
Well House, Watlington
London House, Winkleigh

The Good Food Club 1995

Many thanks to all the following people who contributed to this year's *Guide* . . .

N. Abercrombie
Dr Sidney Abrahams
Sir John Acland
D.E. Adam
Miss Beverley Adams
Martin Adams
Mr and Mrs R.W.G. Adams
Robert Adams
Peter Adcock
John Aird
Mr and Mrs Aldersey-Williams
Ms Carol Aldridge
Ms Anastasia Alexander
David Alexander
Minda and Stanley Alexander
S. Alexander
Mrs Valerie Alexander
B.D. Allen
Francis Allen
Mr and Mrs G. Allen
J.R. Allen
Malcolm Allen
Martin Allen
W.J. Allen
Sir Anthony Alment
David Ander
Ms F. Anderson
Mr and Mrs E.I Andrews
Gwen and Peter Andrews
Mr and Mrs Kurt Angelrath
Mr and Mrs R.L. Annesley
Mrs E.C. Appleby
Ms Lucy Appleby
T. Appleton
Mrs Cynthia Archer
P.F. Arden
David Arditti
Mrs Y. Aris
Brian Ashby
Dr Robert Asher
L. Ashmore
Mervyn Asquith
Mr and Mrs C.D. Atkins
W. Atkinson
Mrs L. Audemard
Ms Kate Austin
Andrew Averill
Mrs C.S. Avery Jones
Ms Jill Avery
Michael Awty
Ms Wendy Backhouse
Mrs J. Bacon
Mr and Mrs R. Baggallay
Richard Bailey
Ms Jill Baines
Mr and Mrs J. Baird
A.A. Baker
D.A. Baker
Mr and Mrs Paul Baker
Mr and Mrs I. Balaam
Mr and Mrs S.K. Ball
J. Bancroft
David Banford
Miss W.E. Bangs
Ms Diana Bannister
Mr and Mrs Bannister
Mr and Mrs Bill Barber
H.F.H. Barclay
Mrs Stella Barclay
John Barker
Lt Col K.A.S. Barker
Nicolas Barker
Antony Barnes
Ms Erica Barnett
Ms Joyce Barney
Geoff Barratt
B.J. Barry
Dr A.J. Barson
Mr and Mrs J. Bartholomew
J.N. Bartlett
Matthew Bartlett
Miss Holly Barton
Mrs E.A. Barwood
Stanley Bates
Mrs I.P. Bateson
Mrs M.G. Bateson
Jeremy Bath
Mrs S. Batty
C.H. Baylis
Conrad Bayliss
Andrew Bean
Tim Beaumont
Mrs J. Beaumont-Nesbitt
Peter Becconsall
Mr and Mrs H.H.E. Beck
Christopher Beckett
F.R. Beckett
Mr and Mrs R. Beckett
S. Bedford
Mr and Mrs Simon Bedwell
Adam Bee
A.J. Beer
Mrs A. Bell
R.P. Bellamy
Mrs A. Bellerby
Kevin Bence
J.P. Bennett
Norman Bennett
A.J. Bentley
H.R. Bentley
Roy Bentley
Mr and Mrs M. Benton
William Bentsen
Bill Beresford
Stephen Beresford
Mrs Gabriele Berneck
Miss C. Berry
David Berry
Mr and Mrs E. Berry
Mrs Mary Beseke
Dr R.K. Bhatt
Mrs J.D. Bidwell
Mr and Mrs Hew Billson
Mr and Mrs Chris Birch
E.R. Birch
Michael Bird
R.G. Birt
Ms Jasmine Birtles
Michael Black
Ms Anne Blackburn
Roger Blackburn
Mrs V. Blackburn
Michael Blair
Mrs J.L. Blake
Mrs J.A. Blanks
Edward Blincoe
Mr and Mrs S. Bliss
Col and Mrs P.A.D. Boden
Mr and Mrs Ken Bogas
K.W. Bogle
Julian Boles
Mrs Elizabeth Bolgar
J. Bolt
Mrs Julia Bolwell
Mr and Mrs Alan Bond
Yvonne and Kevin Bond
N.J. Bonham-Carter
A. Bonnett
Mrs Elizabeth Bonython
Ms Margaret Booth
Mr and Mrs N. Bore
Ms Catherine Bott
R.S. Bourne
Robin Bourne
J.J. Bowden
J. Bowlby
E. Bowyer
Ms Nicola Boyne
Ms Gill Bracey
Mr and Mrs K.G. Bracey
Dr J.M. Bradbury
The Earl of Bradford
Anthony Bradshaw
Mr and Mrs J.G. Bradshaw
M. Brady

Mrs M. Brady
Ms Nicola Braidwood
Nial Brannigan
Major J.M. Bray
N.P. Bray
Mrs Anne Brearley
Ms Ruth Breddal
Ms Roisin Bresnihan
M.J. Brett
Edwin Brew
Robert Brian
Ms Clare Bridgman
Mrs Angela Bridle
Mr and Mrs John Brierley
Mrs J. Briggs
Ms Clare Brigstocke
Dominic Brisby
Roy Bromell
Dr I.G. Bronks
Prof Charles Brook
Dr Oliver Brooke
C.L. Brookes
Fred Brookes
Prof Michael Brookes
J.D. Brooks
Mr and Mrs Tony Brooks
Mr and Mrs T.A. Broster
Mrs A.M. Brown
Mrs Alison Brown
Ms C.H. Brown
Mrs Clement Brown
David Brown
G. Brown
Mrs J.A. Brown
Ms Jane Brown
John Brown
Ms Kaye Brown
Mrs P. Brown
Dr William Brown
Col and Mrs E. Browne
B. Browning
Eric Bruce
Sir Gordon Brunton
Mr and Mrs John Bryant
Ms F. Bryson
P.M.A. Buckman
Richard Bull
B.J. Bullen
Mrs Daphne Bullock
Sir Michael Bunbury
Mrs Daphne Burgess
Mrs Henrietta Burlison
A.P. Burnett
Mr and Mrs Peter Burnstone
M.H. Burr
Ian Burrell
S. Keith Burrell
Ms S. Burton
Khan Busby
M. Busby
Mrs K.B. Bushen
Jane Butler
Mr and Mrs Paul Butler
Stephen Butler
P. Byers
Mr and Mrs Martin Byrom
Peter Byworth
Nicholas Caiger
D.J. Calder
David Calder
Mrs M.W. Calderon
Robert Caldicott
Stuart Cameron
Mr and Mrs Mark Cannon
Mr and Mrs I. Capel
Mrs Diana Capey
B.D. Capp
Mrs G. Carlile
W.P.B. Carlin
Mr and Mrs Gordon Carling
Mr and Mrs P.H. Carlisle
Mrs Helen Carlton
Mr and Mrs G.W. Carr
Mrs J.J. Carr
Ms M. Carr
Mrs Patricia Carr
Peter Carr
Roger Carr
Dr John Carroll
Dennis Carswell
Mrs K. Carter
P.E. Carter
Kim Cartledge
Mrs S. Cartlidge
David Cartwright
J.A.H. Cartwright
Robert Carty
Richard Cashmore
Mrs Maureen Casket
John Cass
R.E. Catlow
Leslie Caul
Mr and Mrs Tom Caulcott
Patrick Cavendish
George Cernoch
Keith Chadwick
Robert Chandler
Ronald Chapman
Mrs Joy Chapple
J.A. Chard
Mr and Mrs Barry Charles
Ms Peggy Chath
W.J. Chesneau
S.W. Chinn
Dr H.B.J. Chishick
Guy-André Chomette
Miss M.E. Clamp
Ms Lesley Clare
M.C.E. Clark
Mrs Patricia Clark
Mrs M. Clarke
R.R.S. Clarke
M.F. Clayton
D. Cleaver
Mrs Jennifer Clegg
Mr and Mrs N. Cleveland
E. Clifford White
Simon Clifton
Doug and Avrille Close
Adam Cochrane
Mrs Wendy Cocup
Ms Muriel Cohen
Mrs Rosemary Coia
Ian Cole
Ms Celia Coleman
Mr and Mrs G.G. Coleman
Ms Jennifer Collard
Mrs Janet Collett
Prof Leslie Collier
C.A. Collishaw
Simon Collison
Mrs Gillian Collymore
Mrs Hannah Colton
M. Comninos
Sean Connolly
Peter Constable
A. Cooper
Ms Beverley Cooper
Derek Cooper
Richard Cooper
Dr and Mrs J.C.W. Cope
Mr and Mrs M.B. Corbett
J. Corbluth
Mr and Mrs Robin Cornah
Ms Amanda Cornick
Mrs K. Corrales
Anthony Cosson
Graham Cotton
Mark Coupe
B. Cousins
A. Cowell
A.P. Cox
J.L. Cox
Mrs J.R. Cox
Michael Cox
Richard Coxon
R.D. Cramond
Ms Louise Crane
Mr and Mrs Peter Crane
Jock Craven
Dr K.W.E. Craven
Miss L.N. Craxford
Ms Florence Creavin
Mrs Helen Crisp
George Critchley
Mrs Paula Critchley
Mr and Mrs J.H. Critchlow
T.E. Crompton
J.D. Crosland
A. Cross
Mrs Mary Cross
Rodney Cross
N.P. Crowe
Simon Crutchley
Geoffrey Cullinan
Prof and Mrs C.F. Cullis
Frank Cummins
John Cunningham
Prof James S. Curl
A.M.T. Currie
Dr Margaret Currie
Mrs Jenny Cutte
Roger Dadd
Theo Dampney
Mrs P. Dando
M. Daneshvar
Dr and Mrs S.R.D. da Prato
Mr and Mrs L. Darby
Mrs Brenda Dargue
David Davey
Mr and Mrs P. Davey
Prof T.J. David
Mrs A. Davidson
G.S.M. Davidson
W.H. Davidson
C.V. Davies
Mrs Carol Davies
Graham Davies

Ms Helen Davies
Miss Martina Davies
P. Davies
Prof and Mrs R.J. Davies
Roger Davies
Andrew Davis
Brian Davis
M.S. Davis
Michael Davis
Bill Davy
Dr and Mrs R.P.R. Dawber
Mr and Mrs D. Dawkins
Mr and Mrs Keith Dawson
Peter Dawson
Ms Jill Day-Lewis
G. Deadman
N.C. Dee
Mr and Mrs A.E. Demby
Mr and Mrs J. Denby
Mrs Dennes
Peter Denney
Kenneth Derrick
C. Devereux
I.C. Dewey
Ms Fiona Dick
Ms Sarah Dixon
Colin Divall
George Dobbie
Mrs A. Dobney
Mrs Dorothy Dockery
B.E. Dodd
J.I. Dodd
G. Dodds
Mrs Joan Dodson
Christopher Doel
Mr and Mrs Ian Donaldson
Patrick Donnelly
Mrs Dianne Doubtfire
Mr and Mrs James Douglas
R.H. Downs
Mrs P.J. Doyle
Aubrey Drapkin
Ms Amanda Drew
Mrs Judith Drew
Ms Annabelle Drinkell
Derek Drummie
Mr and Mrs S. Drury
John Ducker
Mr and Mrs Ben Dudden
Richard Duggleby
Mr and Mrs J.E. Dulley
Mrs Anne Duncan
J.E. Dunford
Hugh Durell
Denis Durno
Clive Dutson
P.F. Dutton
Mrs Wendy Dutton
Richard Dyson
Mrs C. Eades
Mr and Mrs W.A. Eaglesham
Mrs Judith Earl
Mr and Mrs Colin EastaughMr and Mrs N.L. Easton
Dr S. Eden
Dr Philip Edmondson
A. Edwards
Mrs Aileen Edwards
Anton Edwards
Guy Edwards
P.G. Edwards
Mr and Mrs Philip Egerton
John Elder
Steven Elief
John Ellinger
John Elliott
Mrs Lynn Elliott
Mrs M. Ellis
John Elvidge
Mr and Mrs D.D. Embury
Prof and Mrs C.E. Engel
Ms Caroline England
Mr and Mrs R. Ennals
Mr and Mrs E.J. Epstein
Michael Erben
David Erskine
Maurice Escow
Mr and Mrs Marc Eskenazi
Dr Elizabeth Esteve-Coll
Mrs H. Etherington
C.D. Evans
J.S. Evans
Peter Evans
Philip Evans
R.A. Evans
Ms S.F. Evans
Ms Susan Evans
Mr and Mrs Edward Everest
John Fahy
James Fair
Ms Helen Fairley
Jed Falby
Mrs Elisabeth Fanstone
A.G. Farkas
David Farrall
W.T. Farrington
Mr and Mrs D.R. Farthing
Ian Fasham
S. Fazackerly
Roger Feakins
G.D. Fearnehough
T.M. Feeney
W.P.Q. Feiner
P. Fells
G.A. Fenn
K.L. Fenner
A.B.X. Fenwick
Dr P.E. Fewings
Dr and Mrs E. Fishburn
Mrs C.E. Fisher
L.I. Fisher
Mrs S.E. Fisher
Mr and Mrs Gordon Fishwick
Mr and Mrs Nicholas Fiske
J. Flatau
Kenneth Fletcher
M.J. Fletcher
Dr Ron Fletcher
G.F. Flint
C. Foden
Ms Linda Foley
Mr and Mrs Colin Forbes
C. Ford
G. Ford
Christopher Forman
Michael Forrest
Peter Forrest
Mr and Mrs Roger Forward
John Foster
R.J.N. Fowler
Peter Fraenkel
Mrs A.W. Frame
Dr Richard France
Mrs P. Francis
P. Francis
R. Frankenburg
Andrew Frankl
R. Frankland
Gordon Franklin
Sir Michael Franklin
Ms Fiona Fraser
Mrs Jane Fraser
M.R. Freeman
C.W. Freyer
David Frise
Malcolm Fyfe
K.F. Gabbertas
Dr and Mrs R. Gadsby
Simon Gardner
Mrs P.J. Garvey
Ms C.A. Gavin
Mr and Mrs D.M. Gavin
Dr Ian Gavin
P.R. Gawn
D.M. Gaythwaite
J. Gazdak
Mrs Ann Geen
Mr and Mrs David Gerrie
Hunter Gholson
J.W. Gibbon
Peter Gibbon
Mr and Mrs Austin Gibbons
Richard Gibson
D.S. Gidda
Mrs Mary A. Gilchrist
David Giles
Phillip Gill
Dr F.J. Gilmurray
Dr Alan Gilston
Ms Nanette Glaisyer
Mr and Mrs Bud Glickman
Roger Glover
Mr and Mrs Jim Godfrey
Ms Maria Goldberg
Joy and Raymond Goldman
Mark Golinsky
Tom Gondris
Steve Goodacre
Mr and Mrs David Goodall
Mrs Susan Goodchild
Mrs Jan Goodenough
D. Goodger
Mrs Pamela Goodman
Tom Gordon
M. Gordon-Russell
Frank Gorman
Dr John Gosden

Mr and Mrs A. Gough
Mrs J.B. Gould
P. Gould
A.R. Gowers
Alan Graham
D. Graham
R.L. Grant
Simon Grant
Stephen Grant
Mr and Mrs Brian Green
Ms Kate Green
C. Greenhow
Stephen Greensted
N.D.A. Greenstone
J. Greenwood
Mr and Mrs K. Greenwood
Conal Gregory
Professor K.J. Gregory
P.L.F. Gregory-Hood
R.F. Grieve
Ms Sandra Griffiths
J.E. Grimditch
Mr and Mrs Jim Grimes
N.M. Grimwood
Don Grisbrook
Dr R.N. Gruneberg
Ms Helen Guiver
M.R. Gulek
Ms Melanie Gulliver
Ms Rosalind Gunning
Mr and Mrs I. Gunstone
Anish Gupta
R.J. Hackett
Mr and Mrs P. Haigh
Dr Bryan Hall
C.J. Hall
Ivor Hall
Dr Janet Hall
Mr and Mrs P.J. Hall
J.H. Hallam
W.J. Hallett
Mrs B. Hallows
Mr and Mrs Michael Hallsworth
D. Hamilton
R.J.A. Hamilton-Peters
F.A. Hammond
G.B.T. Hammond
Mrs M. Hampson-Moores
F.J.T. Hancock
Peter Handley
P.L. Hands
Philip Hanna
R.F. Hannay
Mr and Mrs J. Hannon
John C. Harding
P.H. Harding
P.J. Harding
R. Harding
Alan Hardwick
M.J. Harkin
David Harkness
Christopher Harlowe
Robert Harper
Tim Harper
Raymond Harris
K.T. Harrison
Eric Hart
L.L. Hart
R.M. Hartley
Mr and Mrs Benedict Hartman
Dr Harvey
E. Hastings
D. Hattersley Smith
Frank Hawkins
Mrs Brenda Haydon
A.A. Hayes
P.J. Haynes
Donald Haywood
Mrs Clare Heath
Mrs G. Heath
Canon Neil Heavisides
Andrew Hendrie
Alex Henshaw
N.F. Henshaw
Mr and Mrs Frank Henson
Mr and Mrs G. Herel
J. Hermans
Lord Herschell
Andrew Herxheimer
Gad Heuman
James Hewlett
Mr and Mrs Stephen Hey
Rupert Higgins
M.A. Highwood
F.R. Hilborne
A.C. Hill
Mr and Mrs James Hill
Mr and Mrs M. Hill
Wendy Hillary
Mr and Mrs D.W. Hills
E. Hinds
Mr and Mrs R. Hinds
Ms Claire Hird
Ms Penelope Hoare
Dr Stephen Hoars
A.H. Hobson
Dr P.R. Hobson
Martyn Hocking
Malcolm Hodgson
Mr and Mrs D.E. Hogan
Desmond Hogan
A.F. Hohler
David Holbrook
Roger Hole
Nick Hollis
Derek Holmes
Mr and Mrs R. Holmes
P.E. Holt
Ruth & David Honour
John Hood
Sir Arthur Hoole
J. Hooper
Dr James Hooper
Ms Jenny Hooper
Derek Hopes
Ralph Hopton
Mr and Mrs R.H. Horncastle
Mr and Mrs Ray Horrocks
A.D.J. Horsler
John Hoskins
Dr Keith Hotten
N. Hounsome
David House
William Houseley
Capt Vincent Howard
D.P. Howell
N.G. Howell
Mrs Dianne Howlett
David Hoyle
Mr and Mrs Peter Hudson
Ms Philippa Hudson
Gwilym Hughes
Jon Hughes
Mrs Darwin Hunt
P.J. Hunt
Dr Tim Hunt
William Hunter
J.D.W. Hurd
Mr and Mrs B.C. Hurley
J.M. Hurrell
Mrs D.M. Hutchinson
Mr and Mrs David Hyman
H.J. Hyman
T.J. Hypher
Mrs Rosemary Inge
Dr and Mrs D.H. Isaac
Jeff Isaacs
Ms Judith Isherwood
Dr Christopher Isles
Mrs Lydia Jack
Mrs J.J. Jackson
James McG. Jackson
Mrs M.B. Jackson
Robert Jackson
Ms Wendy Jacob
Eric Jaffé
Mrs Beverley James
Geoffrey James
Mrs Jan James
Martin Janson
K.M. Janton
Ms Caroline Jarrett
Mr and Mrs F.W. Jary
Prof Barrie Jay
Mrs Brenda Jeeves
Mr and Mrs P. Jeffery
Dr E.H. Jellinek
C. Jenkins
David Jenkins
Mrs E.A. Jenner
David Jervois
Mr and Mrs Brian Jobson
B.M. Joce
Dr Norman Johnson
Miss R.I. Johnson
Richard Johnson
Dr I.H.D. Johnston
Ms S. Johnston
Mrs Audrey Jones
Ms Clare Jones
Colin Jones
Derek Jones
Ian Jones
J.C. Jones
Lesley Jones
Mrs Majorie Jones
R.A. Jones
Timothy Jones
Ms Loraine de Jong
Mr and Mrs S.C. Jordan

N.A. Joseph
Mr and Mrs M. Joyce
M.R Judd
R. Judt
A.D. Kahan
Ms Sukhrinder Kalsi
Dr Leon Kaufman
J.G. Kavanagh
Mrs M. Kealey
Ms Georgiana Keane
Ms Sheila Keene
A. Kellett-Long
Dr Catriona Kelly
Roger Kenber
Ms Susan Kennedy
Ms L. Kenworthy
Mr and Mrs W. Kerr
Rev Peter Kettle
Ms Elizabeth Key
Mrs K.A. Keyser
J.H. Kilby
Ms Carol King
Stuart King
James Kingston-Stewart
J.M. Kirker
Ms Janet Kite
C. Kone
Dr and Mrs Lionel Kreeger
I. Laidlaw-Dickson
Stephen Lambert
Gordon Lammie
W. Lampkin
John Lancaster
K.M. Landsberg
Mrs P. Lane
P. Lane
P.M. Lane
Mr and Mrs J.C.V. Lang
Tony and Christine Langrick
Mrs D. Langton
Mrs Sarah Large
Mr and Mrs Sam Larmour
Mrs R. Latham
R.K. Latham
John Lawrence
Mrs M.E. Lawrence
Rod Lawson
Mrs Jean Lawton
Mrs Angela Layton
J.L.R. Leach
Ms Susan Leach
Dr A.D. Leading
B.T. Leak
Anthony Lee
D.S. Lee
M.I. Leese
Cdr J.M. Lefeaux
David Leonard
P.L. Leonard
Ms Jane Leslie
D.J. Lethem
Lionel Leventhal
Mrs Joanna Levine
A.S. Levitt
M. Lewis
Roland Lewis
Mrs Anne Lewis-Smith
Joseph Lewy
Mr and Mrs Nigel Lickley
David Lidderdale
Ms L. Lim
Gordon Lindsay
Ms Jenny Linford
Dr and Mrs J.R. Ling
D.R. and A.J. LinnellJ.W. Little
Martin Llewellyn
David Lloyd
Dr David Lloyd
Ms Jane L. Francis
J.W. Lloyd
Ms Christine Lloyd Jones
Mr and Mrs Julian Lloyd
Mrs Brigitta Lock
S.J. Lock
Patrick Locke
Ms Janet Lockett
Ms Victoria Logue
T. Lomas
David Long
R.C. Loombe
Ms Valerie Loveland
Ms V. Low
Mr and Mrs P.A. Lowater
S.J. Lowings
J.N. Lunn
Mrs Susan Lushman
Alan Lynch
I.J. Lyons
J.A. Lyons
Mr and Mrs D.C. Mace
Prof Graham Macgregor
A.J. Macintosh
Mrs S.A. Mackenzie
Mr and Mrs L.M. Mackinnon
Dr and Mrs M.D. Mackinnon
Mr and Mrs Brian & Christine Mackness
Prof H. Maclean
John Macleod
Norman Macleod
Mr and Mrs R.P.S. Macnutt
Ms Caroline Macomber
Mr and Mrs M. Magee
Geoffrey Magnay
Peter Mahaffey
Ms Helen Maher
George Maidment
L. Mainwaring
George Mair
Peter Mair
James Malcomson
Mr and Mrs David Malyon
Ms Carol Mann
Mr and Mrs David Margetts
Eddie Marler
Mr and Mrs Noel Marriott
Mrs C. Marris
Roger Marsh
Dr and Mrs Rosemary Marsh
Mrs S. Marsh
D.S. Marshall
Mr and Mrs Derek Marshall
Ms Janette Marshall
R.O. Marshall
Mr and Mrs T.F. Marshall
A.S. Martin
Dr D.J.R. Martin
Mrs Joan Martin
Mr and Mrs Robin Martin
Tony and Heather Martin
Vincent Martin
John Martyn
Prof and Mrs H.T. Mason
Andrew Mate
Adam Mather
K.G. Mather
Paul Mather
D.P.L. Matthews
Mr and Mrs M.R.A. Matthews
Mrs S.M. Matthews
P. Matthison
Mr and Mrs Michael Maudsley
Chris Maurer
Ms E. May
Ian May
Mr and Mrs Kenneth May
P.G.L. May
Peter Mayo
Edward Mayor
Mr and Mrs D.G. McAdam
Andrew McAlpine
Jean McConnell
Dr and Mrs G. McDade
J.A. McDade
Ms Catriona Mcdonald
Kate McDowall
Donald McEwan
Y.S. McEwan
Prof and Dr I.D. McFarlane
Charles McFeeters
Dr Ian McGill
Mr and Mrs G.T. McGinn
Mrs D. McHale
Mr and Mrs Maurice McKee
Colin McKerrow
J.A. McKinnell
Ian McLaren
Lady Rose McLaren
Peter McLeod
Mike McMaster
Paul Meader
P.R. Meadows
Mrs Patricia Meadows
Mr and Mrs Mark Medcalf
A. Meekings
Ms Angela Megson
Mrs A. Melley
Ms Carole Mellis
Lucy Melrose
Mr and Mrs Malcolm Menzies
Ms Diane Mercer
Ms Hilary Meth
Michael Meyer
Ms Josephine Michalec
Paul Milican
Ms Ruth Millan
Ms Nancy de Mille
H.J. Miller
Ms Karen Miller

Dr and Mrs U. Miller
T.W. Miller-Jones
Ms Angela Milligan
H.G. Millward
Mrs S.B. Milne
Mrs Ann Milner
George Milner
Mr and Mrs Stephen Milner
Miss D.F. Milroy
Alan Milton
Ms Anthea Minchom
Mr and Mrs Paul Miron
Mr and Mrs R.E. Mitchell
Ms Susan Mitchell
S. Mitra
Robert Moates
Miss R.C. Moles
Dr J. Mollon
C. Moncreiffe
Mrs C. Money
Dr Barry Monk
Mrs Sue Montague
Ms Kathryn Montgomery
Swapna Mookerjee
Prof Eric Moonman
Anthony Moore
Mrs E.A. Moore
Mrs Penelope Moores
Mr and Mrs A.R. Moreton
Mrs D.O. Morgan
R.C. Morgan
Seamus Morley
Mrs Margaret Morris
V.G.F. Morris
Mrs Jean Morrison
John Morrison
Mrs Maureen Morrison
W.O.A. Morton
Mr and Mrs Aryeh Moss
Brian Moss
Mr and Mrs David Moulton
Mr and Mrs W.A. Moxon
Mr and Mrs Matt Mulcahy
John Mullarkey
Michael Mullen
W. Mullins
Paul Munday
Neil Munro
David Murdoch
Mr and Mrs A.M. Murphy
G.R. Murray
Patrick Murrin
Mr and Mrs B. Natton
Dr Malcolm Nattrass
C.H. Naylor
Anthony Neale
Thomas Neate
Mrs Anne Needham
David Needham
Mr and Mrs John Neilson
R.H. Nelson
C.J. Netting
Michael Neve
Dr Richard Neville
N.R. Newport-Black
D.M. Newrick
Mark Newson-Smith
P.N. Nicholas
Dudley Nicholls
Dr T. Nicholson-Lailey
Ann Nicoll
Mrs J.W. Nightingale
Mrs K. Nixon
Dr Gerd Nonneman
Ms Julia Norman
Mrs L. Norman
Mr and Mrs P. Norman-Smith
J.G. Norris
Mrs Shelagh Norton
Graham Norwood
D.W.J. O'Brien
Ms Mary O'Connor
Noel O'Gregan
Mrs P.M. O'Toole
G.E. Oatley
John Oddey
A. Offer
Dr C. Offord
R.A.L. Ogston
Dr Brendan Olding
Andrew Orange
O.R. Orlinski
Count Christopher Orssich
Mrs Patricia Orwell
Mr and Mrs R.E. Osborne
Tom Osborne
Ms Jill Otley
Mrs Jennifer Owen
G. Packham
Mrs M.C. Packman
Paula Paino
Mr and Mrs T. Palmer
Dr Richard Parish
Martin Park
Mrs Susan Park
Barbara and George Parker
Dr D. Parker
J.J. Parker
J.R. Parker
M.R. Parker
Dr R.B. Parker
John Parkes
Chris Parkin
Ms Jennifer P. Jenkins
Mrs H. Parsons
R.M.S. Parsons
Miss E. Passon
Mrs C. Payne
Mr and Mrs A. Peace
Simon Pearce
Mrs B. Pearson
Mr and Mrs Gerry Pearson
Mr and Mrs Oliver Peck
Yves Pecquet
Mr and Mrs G. Penfold
Mr and Mrs C.S. Perkins
John Perkins
Denis Perry
Robert Peters
B.W.B. Pettifer
Ms Karen Pheasant
Cyril Philips
Mrs Alicia Phillips
Eric Phillips
J.C. Phillips
R.A. Phillips
Dr S. Pinkerton
Ms Geraldine Pipping
Ms Elspeth Pirie
Michael Pitel
Giles Pitman
Hugh Pitt
R.N. Pittman
Roger Plant
Mrs J. Plante-Cleall
Simon Pollentime
B.E. Polley
Ms Lucy Portch
Vincent Porter
B.C.B. Portman
S. Potter
Ms Sue Potts
Miss M. Powell
Prof and Mrs G. Pratt
D.B. Prell
J.W. Price
Mr and Mrs D.R. Pritchard
Mr and Mrs M.J. Procter
Mrs S.A. Procter
Drs J.R. Pryse
Keith Puddy
Chris Purchase
Christopher and Barbara Purser
Howard Pursey
C. Purslow
Robert G. Quevedo
P.J. Quirk
E.F. Raine
Mrs Joan Rainey
Dr and Mrs D.S. Rampton
A. Randall
P.R. Ranft
Dr A.M. Rankin
Mrs M. Rankine
Dr M.S. Raschid
Dr and Mrs Len Ratoff
Peter Ratzer
Dr D.C. Rawlins
Dr and Mrs E.C. Raybould
P.F. Raymond-Cox
Ms Ann Rayner
Philip Rayner
Chris Rea
A.C. Read
Mr and Mrs M. Redfern
Mr and Mrs A.E. Reed
Alan Reeve
Mrs J. Reeve
Mr and Mrs Andrew Reeves
Duncan Reeves
Dr T.A. Reilly
Dr and Mrs W. Reith
E.E. Reumel
Mr and Mrs I.J. Reynolds
Mr and Mrs M.S. Reynolds
R.V. Reynolds
Mr and Mrs M. Rhael Davies
Mr and Mrs P.J. Rich

Mr and Mrs M.W.C. Richards
C.J. Richardson
David Richardson
Michael Richfield
Carol Riddick
John Riddleston
Lloyd Ridgwell
Gordon Ringrose
Mrs S. Rivers
Ms Charlotte Rix
Alan Roberts
Bruce Roberts
Mrs Ruth Roberts
Mrs Sally Roberts
Dr Elizabeth Robertson
Ms Felicity Robertson
Alan Robinson
Ms Joanna Robinson
J. Rochelle
Frank Rogers
C.A.J. Rollason
Mrs Sylvia Rondel
Dr T.J. Roper
Mrs B.S. Rose
Dr and Mrs Bernard Rose
Dr Eric Rose
M.K. Rose
Mr and Mrs Peter Rosengard
Christopher Ross
M.S. Roth
Mrs Virginia Routh
Mrs Jill Rowley
I.J. Roxburgh
Mrs Angela Royle
Mrs Jacqueline Rubens
J.S. Rutter
W. Ruxton
Ms Ilse Ryder
L. Saffron
Andrew St. John
Mrs P.M. Salt
Philip Sanders
Mr and Mrs B. Sandham
Mrs Catherine Sands
Dr N. Sankarayya
Ms Kate Santon
Miss Louise Sargent
P.R. Sargent
Richard Saunders
Ms Anne Savage
R. Savage
Canon Michael Saward
David de Saxe
P.D. Sayer
Ms Carol Sayers
Mrs Eithne Scallan
Derek Scantlebury
Tony Schneider
Mrs C.B. Schoeb
Michael Schofield
Dr Gunter Scholz
N.E.A. Schoon
R. Schwarz
Ms Louise Schweitzer
Dr G.L. Scott
J.G. Scott
Julian Scott
Marc Seale
Philip Seaman
Mrs G.K. Sears
Peter Seglow
A. de Segundo
J.P. Selby
Mrs Alison Sennett
Ms Christine Seward-Byld
H. Sewell
Dr E.S Shaffer
J.P. Sharp
Ms Priscilla Sharp
Mrs D. Sharpe
John Sharpe
Dr J.T.R. Sharrock
Ian Shaw
Ms Irene Shaw
Mrs Elspeth Shepherd
Mrs Louise Sheppard
Kaori Shimmyo
Mr and Mrs Christopher Shorley
Ms Angie Short
Mr and Mrs G. Short
Peter Shotts
Mr and Mrs S. Shragg
K.W. Siddall
Mr and Mrs J. Siderfin
Ian Sier
M. Simonow
Ms Faye Simpson-White
Mrs Ann Sinclair
B.G. Sinclair
C. Sinclair-Stevenson
R. Sinclair-Taylor
Dr Alan Singleton
C.D. Skeet
Peter Skinnard
D.A. Slade
Mr and Mrs R.F. Slade
J.C. Slaughter
Malcolm Slocombe
Mr and Mrs K. Smales
Brian Small
Simon Small
Alan Smallman
N.S.L. Smart
Mrs B.J. Smith
Dr Derek Smith
Ms F.M.K. Smith
Miss J. Smith
Dr John Smith
Mr and Mrs N.L.V. Smith
Neil Smith
P. Smith
R.C.F. Smith
Robin Smith
William Smith
F. Smithies
Mrs F. Smyth
Dr D. Snashall
Mr and Mrs Chuck Snider
Len Snow
David Soley
Mr and Mrs W.A. Somers
Wg Cdr R.M. Sparkes
M.L. Spector
Alan Spedding
Ms Wendy Speight
Ms L. Squire
Mrs Karen Squire
Mr and Mrs Clive Stadler
Ms Gertrude Stafford
Harry Stainton
Mrs Charlotte Standing
T.J. Stanford
Ms Annie Stanley
J. Stanley-Smith
Mrs Jill Stansfield
Mrs L. Stanton
Andrew Stead
Mrs J.D. Stearn
Gordon Steel
Mrs G.M. Stein
F.M. Steiner
Dr and Mrs C.J. Stephens
Prof James S. Curl
G.V. Stevens
Mrs Alexander Stevenson
Capt and Mrs J.S. Stewart
Dr R.H.M. Stewart
P.J. Stock
Lord Stodart of Leaston
Mr and Mrs Richard Stone
C.M.R. Stoneham
Dr D.W. Stooke
Mrs C.A. Stratford
Hilary and Malcolm Strong
Michael Sutcliffe
Mrs E. Sutherland
Peter Sutton
Mrs P. Swallow
Mrs C.A. Swingler
Mrs I. Switzman
Ms Brenda Symes
Z.W Szymanski
Mr and Mrs W.H. Tannahill
David Tanner
Dr and Mrs J. Tanner
J.A. Tarrant
D.W. Tate
Mr and Mrs M. Tate
Mark Tattersall
Ms Moyra Tawse
Mrs A. Taylor
Mrs A.C. Taylor
A.R. Taylor
Mr and Mrs A.S. Taylor
Mrs A.C. Taylor
Chris Taylor
David Taylor
Ms Elsa Taylor
George Taylor
Mrs J. Taylor
Mr and Mrs John Taylor
Mr and Mrs K.W. Taylor
S. Taylor
Mr and Mrs Steven Taylor
T.W.S. Taylor
Mrs Wendy Taylor
Mrs M.E. Thacker
John Theakstone
Mrs E. Thin
Alan Thomas
O.G. Thomas
T.B. Thomas
Tom Thomas
Tudor Thomas
A. Thompson

Ms Andrea Thompson
Miss Thompson-Smith
Colin Thomson
H. Thomson Jones
Ms Judith Thomson
Dr A.G. Thornton
D. Thornton
Mr and Mrs G.N. Thornton
John Thorogood
Mr and Mrs C. Thorp
Howard Thrift
Peter Throssell
Graham Thwaites
Richard Tickell
David Tidmarsh
W.A. Timbs
J.E.C. Timlin
Anthony Tinsley
H. Tint
Julian Tobin
Mrs Jan Todd
Mrs P. Todd
Ms T.J.M. Tomkinson
Michael Tomlinson
Chris T.C. Wan
Dr C.M. Tonks
C.G. Toomer
J.P.S. Tottman
Richard Totty
Michael Townson
Mr and Mrs N.J. Train
Ms Jane Travers
Ms Sylvia Trench
L. Trerress
Prof Michael Trimble
Ms Victoria Trombetta
Mr and Mrs D. Troughton
Mr and Mrs J. Truscott
Mrs D. Turjak
B.W.B. Turner
Grenville Turner
S. Turner
Ms Siobhan Turner
Stuart Turner
J.S. Turpin
Curzon Tussaud
Ms Jane Twelves
Ms Debbie Tyler
Douglas Tyler
Mr and Mrs M. Tyler
Mrs Vicky Umbers
Nicholas Underhill
Adrian Underwood
Dr G. Undrill
P.G. Urben
John Urquhart
I.D. Usher
Ms Patricia Valentine
Edward Vandyk
Mr and Mrs Dick Vardy
Ms Gloria Varley
Mr and Mrs R. Vaughan
G. Verbickas
A.C. Verdie
Gerald Vinestock
Dr M.H.G. Waddington
Frank Wade
Simon Wade
Alan Wadley
Mark Waghorn
Mrs Loraine Waites
Ms M. Wakagi
Ms Jane Wakefield
Tom Wakeford
Mrs A.M. Walden
C. Walker
Mrs M.J. Walker
P.J. Wallace
Dr M.V. Wallbank
Mr and Mrs R. Wallbridge
D.J. Wallington
Barry Wallwork
P.K. Walsh
Capt P.J. Walsh
Miles Walton
Mr and Mrs David Ward
K.P. Ward
Ms Tessa Ward
Mr and Mrs T.E. Ward-Hall
A.J. Wardrop
Ms Rachel Ware
Sir Brian Warren
Major E.M. Warrick
Mrs P.M. Warrington
R.A. Wartnaby
Michael Warvill
Toshio Watanabe
J.S. and F. Waters
Denis and Juliet Watkins
Paul Watkins
Ms Sarah Watkinson
Mrs Anna Watson
Mr and Mrs G.S. Watson
Mr and Mrs E.K. Watts
David Wavre
J. Webb
Ronald Webb
H.G. Webster
M.K. Webster
Ms Luisa Welch
Michael Wellby
Ms Barbara Wensworth
L. Wernick
Bernard Wesson
I.E. West
J.F.M. West
M.J. West
John Weston
Ms Sarah Weston
Mrs M. Weston-Smith
Mrs Barbara Westwell
P.H.S. Wettern
Mrs S.E. Wharton
B.G. Wheatley
Ben Whitaker
Dr G.T. Whitaker
Mrs Janet Whitcut
Mr and Mrs Bob White
Mrs Julia White
N.H. White
Robert White
Mrs S. White
John Whitehead
R.J. Whitelam
John Whiting
Paul Whittaker
Paul Whittard
Mr and Mrs Stephen Whittle
D.N. Whyte
H.B. Wienand
Mr and Mrs I.B. Wigglesworth
Lord Wigoder
Tom Wild
E.J. Wilde
Paul Wilkins
A.E.R. Wilkinson
Roger Wilkinson
Elske Willenborg
P. Willer
Graham Willey
Ms Katherine William-Powlett
Mrs Alma Williams
Donald Williams
Gareth Williams
Geo Williams
Mrs J.B. Williams
J.R. Williams
Mrs M. Williams
R.B. Williams
Mrs V.M. Williamson
Dr Elma Willocks
Mr and Mrs I. Wilson
Ms Lesley Wilson
Prof P.N. Wilson
Mr and Mrs Peter Wilson
Ralph Wilson
T. Wilson
T.M. Wilson
Prof J. Wilson-Barnett
Ms Jenny Wilson-Jones
E.P. Wiltshire
K. Winckles
G. Wiseman
Mr and Mrs T. Withers
D.E. Witts
W.R. Wombell
K.K. Wong
Ms Clare Wood
Les Wood
Robert Wood
Miss Jane Woodall
M.B. Woodgate
C. Woodhead
E.R. Woodhead
David Woods
Barbara Wooldridge
R.C. Woolgrove
Alan Worsdale
Mrs Kay Worsley-Cox
A.C. Wright
Dr B.E.M. Wright
Mrs C. Wright
Mr and Mrs G.L. Wright
Dr Harold Wright
Mrs Olive Wright
Mrs V. Wright
Mr and Mrs John Wyatt
R.J. Wyndham
Ms Suzanne Wynn
J. Yardley
Mr and Mrs Richard Yarrow
Mr and Mrs Roger Young
Prof J.S. Yudkin
Dr Peter Zacharias

Index of main entries

Report Form

To the Editor *The Good Food Guide*
FREEPOST, 2 Marylebone Road, London NW1 1YN

Or send your report by electronic mail to: *guidereports@which.co.uk*

From my personal experience the following establishment should/should not be included in the *Guide*.

____

____

Telephone____________________

I had lunch/dinner/stayed there on ____________________ 19____

I would rate this establishment _____ out of five.

please continue overleaf

My meal for ____ people cost £ ______________ *attach bill where possible*

☐ Please tick if you would like more report forms

Reports received up to **June 1996** will be used in the research of the 1997 edition.

I am not connected in any way with management or proprietors.
Name and address (BLOCK CAPITALS)

____

____

Signed ____

Report Form

To the Editor *The Good Food Guide*
FREEPOST, 2 Marylebone Road, London NW1 1YN

Or send your report by electronic mail to: *guidereports@which.co.uk*

From my personal experience the following establishment should/should not be included in the *Guide*.

Telephone_______________

I had lunch/dinner/stayed there on _______________ 19____

I would rate this establishment _____ out of five.

please continue overleaf

My meal for ____ people cost £ ______________ *attach bill where possible*

☐ Please tick if you would like more report forms

Reports received up to **June 1996** will be used in the research of the 1997 edition.

I am not connected in any way with management or proprietors.
Name and address (BLOCK CAPITALS)

____

____

Signed ______________________________